A-Level Year 2

Pure Mathematics

Exam Board: Edexcel

Year 2 of Edexcel A-Level Maths is no picnic. In fact, it's the opposite of a picnic. It's like a formal dinner where they serve algebra and calculus instead of dessert.

Fortunately, this CGP Student Book makes the Pure Maths topics easier to digest. It's packed with brilliant study notes, tips, examples and an *enormous* helping of questions — including a practice exam at the end.

But that's not all... there are fully worked answers for every question at the back, <u>and</u> a free Online Edition to enjoy. It's as irresistible as an after-dinner mint.

CGP

How to get your free Online Edition

Go to **cgpbooks.co.uk/extras** and enter this code...

1453 0324 6085 7042

Contents

Published by CGP

Editors:
Sarah George, Samuel Mann, Caroline Purvis, Rosa Roberts, Ben Train, Ruth Wilbourne, Dawn Wright.

Contributors:
Katharine Brown, Vijesh Chauhan, Jane Chow, Mick Coe, Claire Creasor, Margaret Darlington, Anna Gainey, Stephen Green, Dave Harding, Barbara Mascetti, James Nicholson, Charlotte O'Brien, Andy Pierson, Lauren Reynolds, Rosemary Rogers, Andy Smith, Mike Smith, Simon Thornhill

ISBN: 978 1 78908 363 7

Cover design concept by emc design ltd.

With thanks to Glenn Rogers and David Ryan for the proofreading.
With thanks to Emily Smith for the copyright research.

Printed by Elanders Ltd, Newcastle upon Tyne.
Clipart from Corel®

About this Book

In this book you'll find...

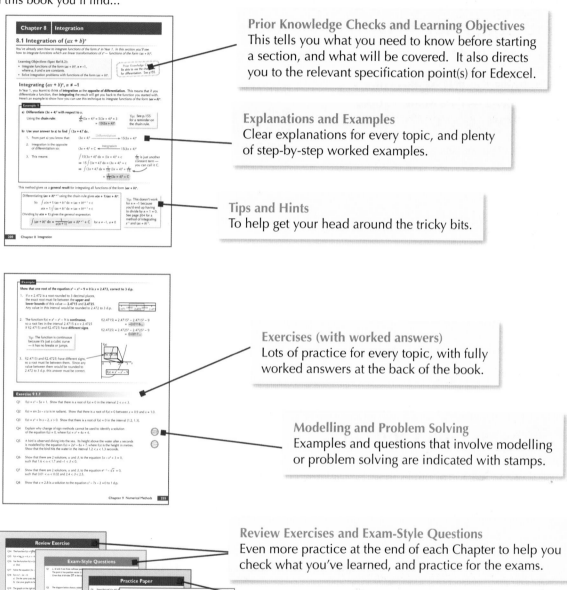

Prior Knowledge Checks and Learning Objectives
This tells you what you need to know before starting a section, and what will be covered. It also directs you to the relevant specification point(s) for Edexcel.

Explanations and Examples
Clear explanations for every topic, and plenty of step-by-step worked examples.

Tips and Hints
To help get your head around the tricky bits.

Exercises (with worked answers)
Lots of practice for every topic, with fully worked answers at the back of the book.

Modelling and Problem Solving
Examples and questions that involve modelling or problem solving are indicated with stamps.

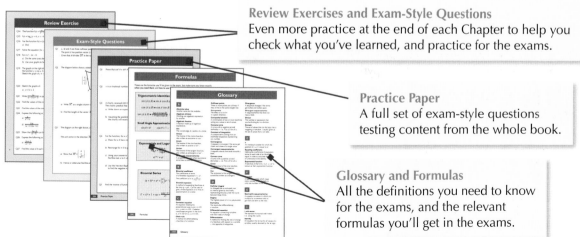

Review Exercises and Exam-Style Questions
Even more practice at the end of each Chapter to help you check what you've learned, and practice for the exams.

Practice Paper
A full set of exam-style questions testing content from the whole book.

Glossary and Formulas
All the definitions you need to know for the exams, and the relevant formulas you'll get in the exams.

This book covers the Pure Mathematics content in A-level Maths that's not in AS

The Edexcel **A-level** Mathematics course has **three** exam papers:

Paper 1 — Pure Mathematics 1
Paper 2 — Pure Mathematics 2

- 2 hours each
- 100 marks each
- 33.33% of your A-level each

Both of these papers test the same material.

Start off with the material covered in the **Pure Mathematics — Year 1/AS Student Book**, then move on to **this book**.

This paper tests the material in the **Statistics & Mechanics — Year 1/AS Student Book** and the **Statistics & Mechanics — Year 2 Student Book**.

There may be some questions in Paper 3 that also use the Pure maths covered in the **Pure Mathematics — Year 1/AS Student Book** and **this book**.

Paper 3 — Statistics and Mechanics

- 2 hours
- 100 marks — split into Sections A: Statistics (50 marks) and B: Mechanics (50 marks)
- 33.33% of your A-level

Formulas, Tables and Large Data Set

With each exam paper you'll have a **formula booklet** which contains **formulas** and **statistical tables** that you might need to use.

The relevant ones for the material in this book are on p.396-397.

You'll also be working with a **large data set** throughout your course. This will only be used in Paper 3. More information and practice on using the data set can be found in the **Statistics & Mechanics — Year 1/AS Student Book**.

Tip: Although you don't have to learn these formulas off by heart, it's important that you practise using them, and also know which formulas are **not** given to you.

1.1 Proof by Contradiction

There's only one type of proof you didn't see in Year 1 to learn here, and that's proof by contradiction.

Learning Objective (Spec Ref 1.1):
- Use proof by contradiction to show that statements are true.

Prior Knowledge Check:
You should be familiar
with proof from Year 1.

Types of proof

Proof in mathematics is all about using logical arguments to show that a statement is true or false. So far, you've learned three main types of proof:

Proof by deduction: using known facts and logic to show that the statement must be true.

Proof by exhaustion: breaking a statement down into two or more cases that cover all possible situations, then showing that the statement is true for all of them.

Disproof by counter-example: giving one example that shows that the statement is not true.

The other method that you need to know is **proof by contradiction**.

Proof by contradiction

To prove a statement by **contradiction**, you start by saying "assume the statement **is not true**...". You then show that this would mean that something **impossible** would have to be true, which means that the initial assumption has to be wrong, so the original statement must be true.

Example 1

Prove the following statement: *"If x^2 is even, then x must be even."*

You can prove this statement by contradiction.

1. Assume the statement is **not true**.   Then there must be an **odd number** x for which x^2 is even.

2. If x is odd, then you can write x as **$2k + 1$**, where k is an integer, and find x^2 in terms of k.

    $x^2 = (2k + 1)^2 = 4k^2 + 4k + 1$
    $4k^2 + 4k = 2(2k^2 + 2k)$ is **even** because it is 2 × an integer
    $\Rightarrow 4k^2 + 4k + 1$ is **odd**.

3. But this **isn't possible** if the statement that x^2 is even is true. You've **contradicted** the assumption that there is an odd number x for which x^2 is even.

    So if x^2 is **even**, then x must be **even**, hence the original statement is **true**.

Example 2

Prove that $\sqrt{2}$ is irrational.

1. Start by assuming that the statement is not true, i.e. that $\sqrt{2}$ can be written as $\frac{a}{b}$ with a and b both non-zero integers. You can also assume that a and b do not have any common factors (otherwise they'd cancel down to a different a and b).   If $\sqrt{2} = \frac{a}{b}$, then $\sqrt{2}b = a$

2. Square both sides: $2b^2 = a^2$ — so a^2 is an **even** number.

3. You saw in the previous example that if a^2 is **even**, then a must be **even** as well. So replace a with $2k$ for some integer k:

   $2b^2 = (2k)^2 = 4k^2 \Rightarrow b^2 = 2k^2$

4. Like before, this tells you that b must be **even** (since b^2 is even). However, you assumed at the start that a and b had **no common factors**, so you have **contradicted** your initial assumption.

Therefore $\sqrt{2}$ **cannot** be written as a fraction $\frac{a}{b}$, so it is **irrational**.

You can use the same method to prove the irrationality of any surd, although you need to prove the statement *"If x^2 is a multiple of a prime number p, then x must also be a multiple of p"*, which is a bit trickier than the proof in Example 1.

This next example uses proof by contradiction to prove that there is no 'largest number' of a certain type. You assume that there is one, then you can simply add to it to get a bigger number of the same type, which contradicts your initial assumption. You can use this trick in quite a few proofs.

Example 3

Prove by contradiction that there are infinitely many prime numbers.

1. Assume that there are a **finite** number of primes (say n), and list them all:

   $p_1 = 2, p_2 = 3, p_3 = 5, \dots , p_{n-1}, p_n$

2. Now **multiply** all of these together:

   $p_1 p_2 p_3 \cdots p_{n-1} p_n$ — call this number, which is a multiple of every prime number, P.

3. Now think about $P + 1$ — if you **divide** $P + 1$ by p_1, you get:

   $(P + 1) \div p_1 = (p_1 p_2 p_3 \cdots p_{n-1} p_n + 1) \div p_1$
   $= p_2 p_3 \cdots p_{n-1} p_n$ remainder 1

4. In fact, dividing $(P + 1)$ by any prime number gives a **remainder** of **1**.

   Tip: Some proofs use $P = p_1 p_2 \cdots p_n + 1$ — but the method is the same.

5. So $(P + 1)$ **isn't divisible** by **any** of the prime numbers in the list, so either it is **also** a prime number or it is a **product** of some other prime numbers that **aren't** in the list. Either way, there is at least one prime number that is **not** on the list, which **contradicts** the assumption that the list contained **all** of them. So there must be **infinitely many** prime numbers.

Exercise 1.1.1

Q1 Prove, by contradiction, that there is no largest multiple of 3.

Q2 Prove that if x^2 is odd, then x must be odd.

Q3 a) Prove that the product of a non-zero rational number and an irrational number is always irrational.

   b) Disprove the statement that the product of an irrational number and an irrational number is always irrational.

Q3-5 Hint: Remember that every rational number can be written as a fraction $\frac{a}{b}$ where a and b are integers.

Q4 Prove that there is no smallest positive rational number.

Q5 Prove that $1 + \sqrt{2}$ is irrational.

Exam-Style Questions

Q1 Prove that if x^3 is odd, then x must be odd.

[2 marks]

Q2 Prove, by contradiction, that there is no largest odd integer.

[2 marks]

Q3 Prove that if $x^2 + 3$ is odd, then x must be even.

[2 marks]

Q4 a) Prove that the sum of a rational number and an irrational number is always irrational.

[3 marks]

b) Hence prove that there is no largest irrational number.

[2 marks]

Q5 a) Suppose x is an integer.
Prove by exhaustion that if x^2 is a multiple of 3, then x must be a multiple of 3.

[3 marks]

b) Hence prove that $\sqrt{3}$ is irrational.

[3 marks]

Q6 a) Prove that the difference between a rational number and an irrational number is always irrational.

[4 marks]

b) Hence or otherwise disprove the statement:
"The sum of an irrational number and an irrational number is always irrational."

[2 marks]

Q7 Prove that $\sqrt[3]{5}$ is irrational.
(You may assume that if x^3 is a multiple of 5, then x must be a multiple of 5.)

[3 marks]

2.1 Simplifying Expressions

This chapter involves a lot of algebraic fractions. You have to factorise, cancel, multiply, divide, add and subtract them. This will come in handy in other parts of maths, so it's a pretty important skill.

Learning Objectives (Spec Ref 2.6):

- Simplify rational expressions (i.e. algebraic fractions with linear or quadratic denominators) by factorising and cancelling.
- Simplify rational expressions by adding, subtracting, multiplying and dividing algebraic fractions.
- Simplify algebraic fractions with linear denominators by using algebraic division.

Prior Knowledge Check:
Be able to simplify and factorise polynomials — covered in Year 1 of this course.

Simplifying algebraic fractions

Algebraic fractions are a lot like normal fractions — and you can treat them in the same way, whether you're adding, subtracting, multiplying or dividing them. All fractions are much easier to deal with when they're in their **simplest form**, so the first thing to do with algebraic fractions is to simplify them as much as possible.

Look for **common factors** in the numerator and denominator — **factorise** top and bottom and see if there's anything you can **cancel**.

If there's a **fraction** in the numerator or denominator (e.g. $\frac{1}{x}$), **multiply** the whole algebraic fraction (i.e. top and bottom) by the same factor to get rid of it (for $\frac{1}{x}$, you'd multiply through by x).

Examples

Simplify the following:

a) $\dfrac{x-1}{x^2+3x-4}$

Try factorising the denominator first.

There's an $(x-1)$ on the top and bottom which will cancel:

$$\frac{x-1}{x^2+3x-4}$$
$$=\frac{\cancel{x-1}}{\cancel{(x-1)}(x+4)}=\boxed{\frac{1}{x+4}}$$

b) $\dfrac{3x+6}{x^2-4}$

Both the numerator and the denominator will factorise.

The denominator is the difference of two squares:

$$\frac{3x+6}{x^2-4}$$
$$=\frac{3\cancel{(x+2)}}{\cancel{(x+2)}(x-2)}=\boxed{\frac{3}{x-2}}$$

c) $\dfrac{x^3-1}{2x^2+5x-7}$

Factorise top and bottom again — the coefficients sum to 0 in each case so $(x-1)$ is a factor.

The quadratic won't factorise any further.

$$\frac{x^3-1}{2x^2+5x-7}$$
$$=\frac{\cancel{(x-1)}(x^2+x+1)}{(2x+7)\cancel{(x-1)}}=\boxed{\frac{x^2+x+1}{2x+7}}$$

d) $\dfrac{2 + \dfrac{1}{2x}}{4x^2 + x}$ Factorise the denominator.

$\dfrac{2 + \dfrac{1}{2x}}{4x^2 + x}$

Get rid of this fraction by multiplying the top and bottom by $2x$.

$= \dfrac{2 + \dfrac{1}{2x}}{x(4x + 1)}$

Tip: Take your time with messy expressions and work things out in separate steps.

$= \dfrac{\left(2 + \dfrac{1}{2x}\right) \times 2x}{x(4x + 1) \times 2x} = \dfrac{4x + 1}{2x^2(4x + 1)} = \dfrac{1}{2x^2}$

Exercise 2.1.1

Simplify the following:

Q1 $\dfrac{4}{2x + 10}$

Q2 $\dfrac{5x}{x^2 + 2x}$

Q3 $\dfrac{6x^2 - 3x}{3x^2}$

Q4 $\dfrac{4x^3}{x^3 + 3x^2}$

Q5 $\dfrac{3x + 6}{x^2 + 3x + 2}$

Q6 $\dfrac{x^2 + 3x}{x^2 + x - 6}$

Q7 $\dfrac{2x - 6}{x^2 - 9}$

Q8 $\dfrac{5x^2 - 20x}{2x^2 - 5x - 12}$

Q9 $\dfrac{3x^2 - 7x - 6}{2x^2 - x - 15}$

Q10 $\dfrac{x^3 - 4x^2 - 19x - 14}{x^2 - 6x - 7}$

Q11 $\dfrac{x^3 - 2x^2}{x^3 - 4x}$

Q12 $\dfrac{1 + \dfrac{1}{x}}{x + 1}$

Q14 Hint: You need to multiply the top and bottom by the same term to get rid of the fractions. Don't just multiply the top by $2x$ and the bottom by x.

Q13 $\dfrac{3 + \dfrac{1}{x}}{2 + \dfrac{1}{x}}$

Q14 $\dfrac{1 + \dfrac{1}{2x}}{2 + \dfrac{1}{x}}$

Q15 $\dfrac{\dfrac{1}{3x} - 1}{3x^2 - x}$

Q16 $\dfrac{2 + \dfrac{1}{x}}{6x^2 + 3x}$

Q17 $\dfrac{\dfrac{3x}{x + 2}}{\dfrac{x}{x + 2} + \dfrac{1}{x + 2}}$

Q18 $\dfrac{2 + \dfrac{1}{x + 1}}{3 + \dfrac{1}{x + 1}}$

Q20 Hint: Multiplying each term by x^2 will get rid of all the fractions.

Q19 $\dfrac{1 - \dfrac{2}{x + 3}}{x + 2}$

Q20 $\dfrac{4 - \dfrac{1}{x^2}}{2 - \dfrac{1}{x} - \dfrac{1}{x^2}}$

Q21 $\dfrac{\dfrac{4}{x} + \dfrac{x}{4} + 2}{\dfrac{4}{x} + 1}$

Q22 $\dfrac{x^3 + 6x^2 - x - 6}{x^3 + 7x^2 + 4x - 12}$

Adding and subtracting algebraic fractions

You'll have come across adding and subtracting fractions before, so here's a little reminder of how to do it:

1. Find the common denominator

Take all the individual 'bits' from the bottom lines and **multiply** them together.

Only use each bit **once** unless something on the bottom line is raised to a **power**.

> **Tip:** The common denominator should be the lowest common multiple (LCM) of all the denominators.

2. Put each fraction over the common denominator

Multiply both top and bottom of each fraction by the same factor — whichever factor will turn the denominator into the **common denominator**.

3. Combine into one fraction

Once everything's over the common denominator you can just **add** (or **subtract**) the **numerators**.

Examples

a) Simplify: $\dfrac{2}{x-1} - \dfrac{3}{3x+2}$

1. Multiply the denominators to get the **common denominator**:

$$(x-1)(3x+2)$$

2. Multiply the top and bottom lines of each fraction by whichever factor changes the denominator into the common denominator:

$$\frac{2 \times (3x+2)}{(x-1) \times (3x+2)} - \frac{3 \times (x-1)}{(3x+2) \times (x-1)}$$

3. All the denominators are the same — so you can just subtract the numerators:

$$\frac{2(3x+2) - 3(x-1)}{(3x+2)(x-1)} = \frac{6x+4-3x+3}{(3x+2)(x-1)}$$

(Your final answer needs to be **fully simplified** to get all the marks in an exam, so always check if there's any more that can be done at the end.)

$$= \frac{3x+7}{(3x+2)(x-1)}$$

b) Simplify: $\dfrac{2y}{x(x+3)} + \dfrac{1}{y^2(x+3)} - \dfrac{x}{y}$

1. The individual 'bits' here are x, $(x+3)$ and y, but you need to use y^2 because there's a y^2 in the denominator of the second fraction. So the common denominator is $xy^2(x+3)$

2. Multiply the top and bottom lines of each fraction by whichever factor changes the denominator into the common denominator:

$$\frac{2y \times y^2}{x(x+3) \times y^2} + \frac{1 \times x}{y^2(x+3) \times x} - \frac{x \times xy(x+3)}{y \times xy(x+3)}$$

3. All the denominators are the same — so you can just add the numerators:

$$\frac{2y^3 + x - x^2y(x+3)}{xy^2(x+3)}$$

$$= \frac{2y^3 + x - x^3y - 3x^2y}{xy^2(x+3)}$$

Simplify the following:

Q1 $\dfrac{2x}{3} + \dfrac{x}{5}$

Q2 $\dfrac{2}{3x} - \dfrac{1}{5x}$

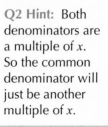
Q2 Hint: Both denominators are a multiple of x. So the common denominator will just be another multiple of x.

Q3 $\dfrac{3}{x^2} + \dfrac{2}{x}$

Q4 $\dfrac{x+1}{3} + \dfrac{x+2}{4}$

Q5 $\dfrac{2x}{3} + \dfrac{x-1}{7x}$

Q6 $\dfrac{3x}{4} - \dfrac{2x-1}{5x}$

Q7 $\dfrac{2}{x-1} + \dfrac{3}{x}$

Q8 $\dfrac{3}{x+1} + \dfrac{2}{x+2}$

Q9 $\dfrac{4}{x-3} - \dfrac{1}{x+4}$

Q10 $\dfrac{6}{x+2} + \dfrac{6}{x-2}$

Q11 $\dfrac{3}{x-2} - \dfrac{5}{2x+3}$

Q12 $\dfrac{3}{x+2} + \dfrac{x}{x+1}$

Q13 $\dfrac{5x}{(x+1)^2} - \dfrac{3}{x+1}$

Q14 $\dfrac{5}{x(x+3)} + \dfrac{3}{x+2}$

Q15 $\dfrac{x}{x^2-4} - \dfrac{1}{x+2}$

Q16 $\dfrac{3}{x+1} + \dfrac{6}{2x^2+x-1}$

Q17 $\dfrac{2}{x} + \dfrac{3}{x+1} + \dfrac{4}{x+2}$

Q18 $\dfrac{3}{x+4} - \dfrac{2}{x+1} + \dfrac{1}{x-2}$

Q19 $2 - \dfrac{3}{x+1} + \dfrac{4}{(x+1)^2}$

Q20 $\dfrac{2x^2-x-3}{x^2-1} + \dfrac{1}{x(x-1)}$

Multiplying and dividing algebraic fractions

Multiplying algebraic fractions

You **multiply** algebraic fractions in exactly the same way that you multiply normal fractions — multiply the numerators together, then multiply the denominators. Try to **factorise** and **cancel** any **common factors** before multiplying.

Example 1

Simplify the following:

a) $\dfrac{x^3}{2y} \times \dfrac{8y^2}{3}$

Cancel all common factors:

$\dfrac{x^3}{{}_1 2y} \times \dfrac{8y^2\,{}^{4y}}{3}$

Then multiply top by top and bottom by bottom:

$= \dfrac{x^3 \times 4y}{1 \times 3} = \dfrac{4x^3 y}{3}$

b) $\dfrac{x^2-2x-15}{2x+8} \times \dfrac{x^2-16}{x^2+3x}$

Factorise the expressions in both fractions and cancel:

$\dfrac{(x+3)(x-5)}{2(x+4)} \times \dfrac{(x+4)(x-4)}{x(x+3)}$

Then just multiply as before:

$= \dfrac{(x-5)(x-4)}{2x} \left(= \dfrac{x^2-9x+20}{2x} \right)$

Dividing algebraic fractions

To **divide** by an algebraic fraction, you just **multiply** by its reciprocal (as you would for normal fractions). The reciprocal is 1 ÷ the original thing — for fractions you just turn the fraction upside down.

Example 2

Simplify the following:

a) $\dfrac{8}{5x} \div \dfrac{12}{x^3}$ Turn the second fraction upside down... $\dfrac{8}{5x} \times \dfrac{x^3}{12}$

...then cancel all common factors: $= \dfrac{^2\!8}{5x} \times \dfrac{x^3\, x^2}{\cancel{12}_3}$

Now multiply. ⟶ $= \dfrac{2 \times x^2}{5 \times 3} = \dfrac{2x^2}{15}$

b) $\dfrac{3x}{5} \div \dfrac{3x^2 - 9x}{20}$ Turn the second fraction upside down, and then cancel. Note that the $3x^2 - 9x$ has been factorised first. $\dfrac{3x}{5} \times \dfrac{20^{\,4}}{3x(x-3)} = \dfrac{4}{x-3}$

Exercise 2.1.3

Simplify the following:

Q1 a) $\dfrac{2x}{3} \times \dfrac{5x}{4}$ b) $\dfrac{6x^3}{7} \times \dfrac{2}{x^2}$

Q1 Hint: Remember — cancelling **before** you multiply will make things a whole lot simpler.

c) $\dfrac{8x^2}{3y^2} \times \dfrac{x^3}{4y}$ d) $\dfrac{8x^4}{3y} \times \dfrac{6y^2}{5x}$

Q2 a) $\dfrac{x}{3} \div \dfrac{3}{x}$ b) $\dfrac{4x^3}{3} \div \dfrac{x}{2}$

c) $\dfrac{3}{2x} \div \dfrac{6}{x^3}$ d) $\dfrac{2x^3}{3y} \div \dfrac{4x}{y^2}$

Q3 $\dfrac{x+2}{4} \times \dfrac{x}{3x+6}$ Q4 $\dfrac{4x}{5} \div \dfrac{4x^2+8x}{15}$

Q5 $\dfrac{2x^2-2}{x} \times \dfrac{5x}{3x-3}$ Q6 $\dfrac{2x^2+8x}{x^2-2x} \times \dfrac{x-1}{x+4}$

Q7 $\dfrac{x^2-4}{9} \div \dfrac{x-2}{3}$ Q8 $\dfrac{2}{x^2+4x} \div \dfrac{1}{x+4}$

Q9 $\dfrac{x^2-1}{3} \div \dfrac{x^2+x}{6}$ Q10 $\dfrac{2x^2-2x-24}{x^2+7x+12} \div \dfrac{2}{x+4}$

Q18 Hint: Work from left to right.

Q11 $\dfrac{x^2+4x+3}{x^2+5x+6} \times \dfrac{x^2+2x}{x+1}$ Q12 $\dfrac{x^2+5x+6}{x^2-2x-3} \times \dfrac{3x+3}{x^2+2x}$

Q13 $\dfrac{x^2-4}{6x-3} \times \dfrac{2x^2+5x-3}{x^2+2x}$ Q14 $\dfrac{x^2+7x+6}{4x-4} \div \dfrac{x^2+8x+12}{x^2-x}$

Q15 $\dfrac{x^2+4x+4}{x^2-4x+3} \times \dfrac{x^2-2x-3}{2x^2-2x} \times \dfrac{4x-4}{x^2+2x}$ Q16 $\dfrac{x}{6x+12} \div \dfrac{x^2-x}{x+2} \times \dfrac{3x-3}{x+1}$

Q17 $\dfrac{x^2+5x}{2x^2+7x+3} \times \dfrac{2x+1}{x^3-x^2} \div \dfrac{x+5}{x^2+x-6}$ Q18 $\dfrac{3x}{x+2} \div \dfrac{x-2}{x-3} \div \dfrac{x^2-3x}{x^2-4}$

Algebraic division

Important terms

Certain terms come up a lot in algebraic division, so make sure you know what they all mean.

> **Polynomial** — an algebraic expression made up of the sum of constant terms and variables raised to **positive integer** powers. For example, $x^3 - 2x + \frac{1}{2}$ is a polynomial, but $x^{-3} - 2x^{\frac{3}{2}}$ is **not** as it has a negative power and a fractional power of x.
>
> **Degree** — the highest power of x in the polynomial. For example, the degree of $4x^5 + 6x^2 - 3x - 1$ is 5.
>
> **Divisor** — this is the thing you're dividing by. For example, if you divide $x^2 + 4x - 3$ by $x + 2$, the divisor is $x + 2$.
>
> **Quotient** — the bit that you get when you divide by the divisor (not including the **remainder** — see below).

Method 1 — using the formula

There's a handy **formula** you can use to do algebraic division:

> A polynomial f(x) can be written in the form:
>
> $$\mathbf{f}(x) \equiv \mathbf{q}(x)\mathbf{d}(x) + \mathbf{r}(x)$$
>
> where: q(x) is the quotient,
> d(x) is the divisor,
> and r(x) is the remainder.

Tip: The $\equiv$ symbol means it's an identity.

For example:

$$4x^5 - 7x^2 + 3x - 9 \div x^2 - 5x + 8.$$

This bit is f(x). ↗
It has a degree of 5.

↖ This bit is d(x), the divisor.
It has a degree of 2.

In the exam, you'll only have to divide by a linear factor (i.e. with a degree of 1). Here's a step-by-step guide to using the formula:

- First, you have to work out the **degree** of the **quotient**, which will depend on the degree of the polynomial f(x): **deg q(x) = deg f(x) − 1**. The **remainder** will have degree **0**.

- Write out the division using the formula, but replace q(x) and r(x) with **general polynomials**. For example, a general polynomial of degree 2 is $Ax^2 + Bx + C$, where A, B and C are constants to be found. A general polynomial of degree 0 is just a constant, e.g. D.

- The next step is to work out the values of the **constants** (A, B, etc.). You do this by substituting in values for x to make bits disappear, and by **equating coefficients** (i.e. compare the coefficients of each power of x on either side of the identity).

- It's best to start with the **constant term** and work **backwards** from there.

- Finally, write out the division again, replacing A, B, C, etc. with the values you've found.

When you're using this method, you might have to use **simultaneous equations** to work out some of the coefficients (have a look back at your Year 1 notes for a reminder of how to do this if you need to). The method looks a bit tricky, but follow through the examples below to see how it works.

Example 1

Divide $x^4 - 3x^3 - 3x^2 + 10x + 5$ by $x - 2$.

1. First, work out the **degrees** of the **quotient** and **remainder**:

   $f(x)$ has degree 4, so the quotient $q(x)$ has degree $4 - 1 = 3$. The remainder $r(x)$ has degree 0.

2. Write out the division in the form $f(x) \equiv q(x)d(x) + r(x)$, replacing $q(x)$ and $r(x)$ with general polynomials of degree 3 and 0:

   $x^4 - 3x^3 - 3x^2 + 10x + 5 \equiv (Ax^3 + Bx^2 + Cx + D)(x - 2) + E$

3. Substitute $x = 2$ into the identity to make the $q(x)d(x)$ bit disappear:

   $16 - 3(8) - 3(4) + 10(2) + 5 = 0 + E$
   $16 - 24 - 12 + 20 + 5 = E \Rightarrow \boxed{E = 5}$

   So now the identity looks like this:

   $x^4 - 3x^3 - 3x^2 + 10x + 5 \equiv (Ax^3 + Bx^2 + Cx + D)(x - 2) + 5$

4. Substitute $x = 0$ into the identity:

   when $x = 0$, $5 = -2D + 5 \Rightarrow \boxed{D = 0}$

   So now you have:

   $x^4 - 3x^3 - 3x^2 + 10x + 5 \equiv (Ax^3 + Bx^2 + Cx)(x - 2) + 5$

5. For the remaining terms, **equate the coefficients** on both sides. Expanding the brackets on the RHS and collecting terms gives:

   $x^4 - 3x^3 - 3x^2 + 10x + 5$
   $\equiv Ax^4 + (B - 2A)x^3 + (C - 2B)x^2 - 2Cx + 5$

6. The coefficient of x^4 is A on the RHS and 1 on the LHS $\Rightarrow \boxed{A = 1}$
   Similarly, comparing the coefficients of x^3 gives: $B - 2A = -3 \Rightarrow \boxed{B = -1}$
   Comparing the coefficients of x gives: $-2C = 10 \Rightarrow \boxed{C = -5}$

   So the identity looks like this:

   $\boxed{x^4 - 3x^3 - 3x^2 + 10x + 5 \equiv (x^3 - x^2 - 5x)(x - 2) + 5}$

Example 2

Divide $x^3 + 5x^2 - 18x - 18$ by $x - 3$.

1. $f(x)$ has degree 3, so $q(x)$ has degree $3 - 1 = 2$

2. Write out the division in the form $f(x) \equiv q(x)d(x) + r(x)$:

   $x^3 + 5x^2 - 18x - 18 \equiv (Ax^2 + Bx + C)(x - 3) + D$

3. Substituting in $x = 3$ gives $\boxed{D = 0}$, so:

   $x^3 + 5x^2 - 18x - 18 \equiv (Ax^2 + Bx + C)(x - 3)$

4. Now, setting $x = 0$ gives $-18 = -3C \Rightarrow \boxed{C = 6}$: $x^3 + 5x^2 - 18x - 18 \equiv (Ax^2 + Bx + 6)(x - 3)$

5. Equating the coefficients of x^3 and x^2 gives $\boxed{A = 1}$ and $B - 3A = 5 \Rightarrow \boxed{B = 8}$. So: $\boxed{x^3 + 5x^2 - 18x - 18 \equiv (x^2 + 8x + 6)(x - 3)}$

Simply stating the identity at the end doesn't always answer the question. If you're asked to divide one thing by another, then you might need to state the **quotient** and the **remainder** which you've worked out using the formula.

So for Example 1 on the previous page: $(x^4 - 3x^3 - 3x^2 + 10x + 5) \div (x - 2) = x^3 - x^2 - 5x$ **remainder 5**.
For Example 2: $(x^3 + 5x^2 - 18x - 18) \div (x - 3) = x^2 + 8x + 6$ (i.e. remainder 0).

Method 2 — algebraic long division

You can also use **long division** to divide two algebraic expressions (using the same method you'd use for numbers).

> **Tip:** You might have come across this method in Year 1.

Example 3

Divide $(2x^3 - 7x^2 - 16x + 11)$ by $(x - 5)$.

1. Start by dividing the first term in the polynomial by the first term of the divisor: $2x^3 \div x = 2x^2$. Write this answer above the polynomial.

$$\begin{array}{r} 2x^2 \\ x-5\overline{)2x^3-7x^2-16x+11} \end{array}$$

2. Multiply the divisor $(x - 5)$ by this answer $(2x^2)$ to get $2x^3 - 10x^2$.

$$\begin{array}{r} 2x^2 \\ x-5\overline{)2x^3-7x^2-16x+11} \\ 2x^3-10x^2 \end{array}$$

3. Subtract this from the main expression to get $3x^2$. Bring down the $-16x$ term just to make things clearer for the next subtraction.

$$\begin{array}{r} 2x^2 \\ x-5\overline{)2x^3-7x^2-16x+11} \\ -\ (2x^3-10x^2) \\ \hline 3x^2-16x \end{array}$$

4. Now divide the first term of the remaining polynomial $(3x^2)$ by the first term of the divisor (x) to get $3x$ (the second term in the answer).

$$\begin{array}{r} 2x^2+3x \\ x-5\overline{)2x^3-7x^2-16x+11} \\ -\ (2x^3-10x^2) \\ \hline 3x^2-16x \end{array}$$

5. Multiply $(x - 5)$ by $3x$ to get $3x^2 - 15x$, then subtract again and bring down the $+11$ term.

$$\begin{array}{r} 2x^2+3x \\ x-5\overline{)2x^3-7x^2-16x+11} \\ -\ (2x^3-10x^2) \\ \hline 3x^2-16x \\ -\ (3x^2-15x) \\ \hline -x+11 \end{array}$$

6. Divide $-x$ by x to get -1 (the third term in the answer). Then multiply $(x - 5)$ by -1 to get $-x + 5$.

$$\begin{array}{r} 2x^2+3x-1 \\ x-5\overline{)2x^3-7x^2-16x+11} \\ -\ (2x^3-10x^2) \\ \hline 3x^2-16x \\ -\ (3x^2-15x) \\ \hline -x+11 \\ -\ (-x+5) \\ \hline 6 \end{array}$$

7. After subtracting, this term (6) has a degree that's **less** than the degree of the divisor, $(x - 5)$, so it can't be divided. This is the **remainder**.

8. So: $(2x^3 - 7x^2 - 16x + 11) \div (x - 5) = 2x^2 + 3x - 1$ remainder 6.

9. This could also be written as: $\dfrac{2x^3 - 7x^2 - 16x + 11}{x - 5} = 2x^2 + 3x - 1 + \dfrac{6}{x - 5}$

Exercise 2.1.4

Q1 Use the formula $f(x) \equiv q(x)d(x) + r(x)$ to divide the following expressions. In each case, state the quotient and remainder.

a) $(x^3 - 14x^2 + 6x + 11) \div (x + 1)$

b) $(2x^3 + 5x^2 - 8x - 17) \div (x - 2)$

c) $(6x^3 + x^2 - 11x - 5) \div (2x + 1)$

Q1 Hint: If you're told which method to use make sure you show all your working clearly to prove that you know how to use the method.

Q2 Write $3x^4 - 8x^3 - 6x - 4$ in the form $(Ax^3 + Bx^2 + Cx + D)(x - 3) + E$, and hence state the result when $3x^4 - 8x^3 - 6x - 4$ is divided by $x - 3$.

Q3 Use long division to divide the following expressions. In each case, state the quotient and remainder. (You will have done some of these before in Q1, but using a different method.)

a) $(x^3 - 14x^2 + 6x + 11) \div (x + 1)$

b) $(x^3 + 10x^2 + 15x - 13) \div (x + 3)$

c) $(2x^3 + 5x^2 - 8x - 17) \div (x - 2)$

d) $(3x^3 - 78x + 9) \div (x + 5)$

e) $(x^4 - 1) \div (x - 1)$

f) $(8x^3 - 6x^2 + x + 10) \div (2x - 3)$

Q3d) Hint: Add in a $0x^2$ term to make sure you don't miss any terms when dividing.

In the following questions you can choose which method to use.

Q4 Divide $10x^3 + 7x^2 - 5x + 21$ by $2x + 1$, stating the quotient and remainder.

Q5 Divide $3x^3 - 8x^2 + 15x - 12$ by $x - 2$, stating the quotient and remainder.

Q6 Divide $16x^4$ by $2x - 3$, stating the quotient and remainder.

Q7 Divide $2x^3 - 5x^2 - 21x + 36$ by $2x - 3$, and hence solve $2x^3 - 5x^2 - 21x + 36 = 0$.

Q8 Divide $x^4 + 3x^3 + x^2 + 1$ by $x + 1$, and hence give one solution to $x^4 + 3x^3 + x^2 = -1$.

Q9 Divide $3x^4 + x^3 - 5x^2 - 4x + 4$ by $3x - 2$.

Q10 Divide $3x^4 + 7x^3 - 22x^2 - 8x$ by $x - 2$, and hence solve the equation $3x^4 + 7x^3 - 22x^2 - 8x = 0$.

Q11 Using algebraic division, solve the equation $2x^4 - 5x^3 - 50x^2 - 85x - 42 = 0$.

2.2 Mappings and Functions

A mapping is just a set of instructions that tells you how to get from one value to another, and a function is a special kind of mapping.

Learning Objectives (Spec Ref 2.8):

- Understand the definitions of mappings and functions and be able to deduce whether a given mapping is a function.
- Use function notation.
- Identify the domain and range of a given function.
- Restrict the domain of a mapping to make it a function.
- Identify whether a function is one-to-one or many-to-one for a given domain.

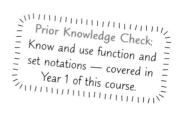

Prior Knowledge Check:
Know and use function and set notations — covered in Year 1 of this course.

Mappings and functions

Mappings

A **mapping** is an operation that takes one number and transforms it into another. For example, 'multiply by 5', 'square root' and 'divide by 7' are all mappings. The set of numbers you start with is called the **domain**, and the set of numbers they become is called the **range**.

Mappings can be drawn as **mapping diagrams**, like the one shown here for 'multiply by 5 and add 1' acting on the domain {−1, 0, 1, 2}:

Use the notation {1, 2, ...} for the domain and range if they are a **discrete** list of values. If they can take **any value** above or below a limit, use e.g. $x \geq 0$.

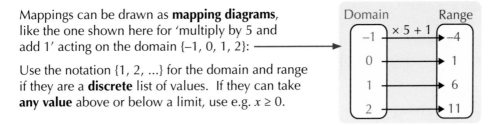

The domain and/or range will often be the set of **real numbers**, $\mathbb{R}$. A real number is any positive or negative number (or 0) — including fractions, decimals, integers and surds. If x can take any real value, it's usually written as $x \in \mathbb{R}$ ($\in$ means 'belongs to'). Other sets of numbers include $\mathbb{Z}$, the set of **integers**, and $\mathbb{N}$, the set of **natural numbers** (positive integers, not including 0).

You might have to work out the range of a mapping from the domain you're given. For example, $y = x^2$, $x \in \mathbb{R}$ has the range $y \geq 0$, as the squares of all real numbers are positive (or zero).

Functions

Some mappings take every number in the domain to exactly **one** number in the range. These mappings are called **functions**. Functions are written using the following notation:

$$f(x) = 5x + 1 \quad \text{or} \quad f : x \rightarrow 5x + 1$$

You've probably seen at least the f(x) notation before, but you need to be able to understand and use both.

You can substitute values for x into a function to find the value of the function at that point, as shown in Example 1 at the top of the next page.

Example 1

a) Give the value of f(–2) for the function f(x) = x² – 1.

Just replace each x in the function with –2 and calculate the answer:

$$f(-2) = (-2)^2 - 1 = 4 - 1 = \boxed{3}$$

b) Find the value of x for which f(x) = 12 for the function f : x → 2x – 3.

Solve this like a normal equation:

$$2x - 3 = 12 \implies 2x = 15 \implies x = \boxed{7.5}$$

Functions can also be given in **several parts** (known as '**piecewise**' functions). Each part of the function will act over a different domain. For example:

$$f(x) = \begin{cases} 2x + 3 & x \le 0 \\ x^2 & x > 0 \end{cases}$$

So f(2) is $2^2 = 4$ (because $x > 0$), but f(–2) is $2(-2) + 3 = -1$ (because $x \le 0$).

> **Tip:** You'll see different letters used for functions over the next few pages, not just 'f'.

If a mapping takes a number from the domain to **more than one** number in the range (or if it isn't mapped to any number in the range), it's **not** a function.

Example 2

The mapping shown here **is a function**, because any value of x in the domain maps to **only one** value in the range.

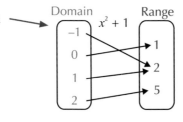

> **Tip:** Although each value in the domain only maps to one value in the range, the reverse is not true. This means it's a 'many to one' function — there's more about these on p.19.

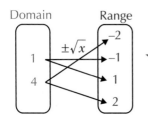

The mapping shown here is **not a function**, because a value of x in the domain can map to **more than one** value in the range.

Exercise 2.2.1

Q1 Draw a mapping diagram for the map "multiply by 6" acting on the domain {1, 2, 3, 4}.

Q2 $y = x + 4$ is a map with domain $\{x : x \in \mathbb{N}, x \le 7\}$. Draw the mapping diagram.

Q3 Complete the mapping diagrams below:

a)

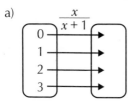

b)

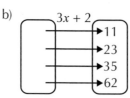

> **Q4 Hint:** 'Evaluate' is just another way of asking you to 'find the value of'.

Q4 For the function $g : x \to \dfrac{1}{2x + 1}$, $x > -\dfrac{1}{2}$, evaluate g(0) and g(2).

Q5 f defines a function $f : x \rightarrow \dfrac{1}{2 + \log_{10}x}$ for the domain $x > 0.01$. Evaluate f(1) and f(100).

Q6 a) Find the range of the function $h(x) = \sin x$, $0° \le x \le 180°$.

b) Find the range of $j(x) = \cos x$ on the same domain.

Q7 Hint: To find the largest possible domain, think about what values of x need to be excluded to make the function valid.

Q7 State the largest possible domain and range of each function:

a) $f(x) = 3^x - 1$

b) $g(x) = (\ln x)^2$

Q8 State whether or not each of the mapping diagrams below shows a function, and if not, explain why.

a)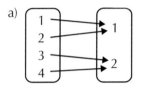

b)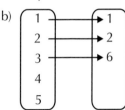

c)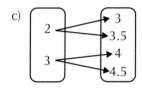

Graphs of functions

Mappings and functions with a **continuous** domain (such as $x \in \mathbb{R}$, i.e. not a discrete set of values) can be drawn as **graphs**. Drawing a graph of, say, $f(x) = x^2$ is exactly the same as drawing a graph of $y = x^2$.

For each value of x in the **domain** (which goes along the horizontal x-axis) you can plot the corresponding value of $f(x)$ in the **range** (up the vertical y-axis):

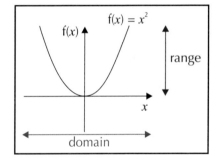

Drawing graphs can make it easier to **identify functions**, as shown below.

Example 1

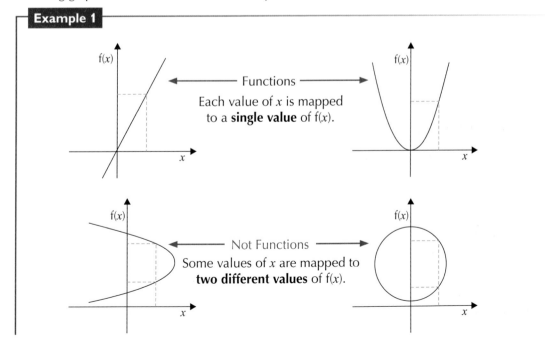

Functions — Each value of x is mapped to a **single value** of $f(x)$.

Not Functions — Some values of x are mapped to **two different values** of $f(x)$.

The graph on the right isn't a function for $x \in \mathbb{R}$ because $f(x)$ is **not defined** for $x < 0$.

This just means that when x is negative there is no real value that $f(x)$ can take.

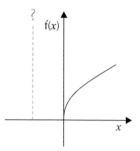

Tip: This could be turned into a function by restricting the domain to $x \geq 0$ — see the next page.

Finding ranges and domains using graphs

Sketching a graph can also be really useful when trying to find limits for the domain and range of a function.

Example 2

a) **State the range for the function $f(x) = x^2 - 5$, $x \in \mathbb{R}$.**

1. The smallest possible value of x^2 is 0.

2. So the smallest possible value of $x^2 - 5$ must be -5.

3. So the range is $f(x) \geq -5$.

4. This can be shown clearly by sketching a graph of $y = f(x)$:

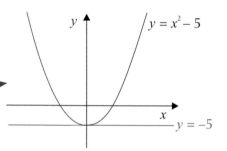

b) **State the domain for $f(x) = \sqrt{(x-4)}$, giving your answer in set notation.**

1. There are no **real** solutions for the square root of a negative number.

2. This means there is a limit on the domain so that $x - 4 \geq 0$.

3. This gives a domain of $x \geq 4$ — in set notation, this is $\{x : x \geq 4\}$

4. Again, this can be demonstrated by sketching a graph of $y = f(x)$:

Tip: Remember, the : means "such that", so this is the set of x, such that x is greater than or equal to 4. The range for this function, in set notation, is $\{f(x) : f(x) \geq 0\}$.

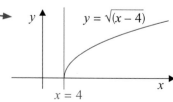

Turning mappings into functions

Some mappings that aren't functions can be turned into functions by **restricting their domain**.

For example, consider the graph
of the mapping $y = \dfrac{1}{x-1}$ for $x \in \mathbb{R}$: ────

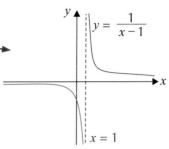

The mapping $y = \dfrac{1}{x-1}$ for $x \in \mathbb{R}$
is **not** a function, because it's not defined at $x = 1$.

(You will often see asymptotes on a graph when
a mapping is undefined at a certain value.)

But if you change the domain to $x > 1$,
the mapping is now a **function**, as shown: ────────

You could also restrict the domain by
giving values that x can't be equal to,
e.g. $x \in \mathbb{R}$, $x \neq 1$. In this case the graph
would be in two parts like in the first
diagram.

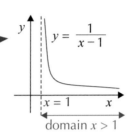

Exercise 2.2.2

Q1 State whether or not each of the graphs below shows a function, and if not, explain why.

a)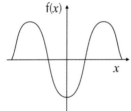

b)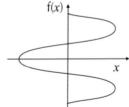

Q2 For each of the following functions, sketch the graph of the function for the given domain,
marking relevant points on the axes, and state the range.

a) $f(x) = 3x + 1$ $x \geq -1$

b) $f(x) = x^2 + 2$ $-3 \leq x \leq 3$

c) $f(x) = \cos x$ $0° \leq x \leq 360°$

d) $f(x) = \begin{cases} 5 - x & 0 \leq x < 5 \\ x - 5 & 5 \leq x \leq 10 \end{cases}$

Q3 State the domain and range for the following functions,
giving your answers in set notation:

a)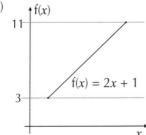

b)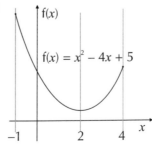

> **Q3 Hint:** Use the
> given functions
> to work out the
> domain from the
> given range, or
> the range from
> the given domain.

Q4 The graph below shows the function $f(x) = \dfrac{x+2}{x+1}$,

defined for the domain $x \geq 0$. State the range.

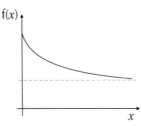

Q4-5 Hint: Use the functions to work out where the asymptotes lie. The range (or domain) will lie on one side of the asymptote.

Q5 The diagram shows the function $f(x) = \dfrac{1}{x-2}$

drawn over the domain $x > a$. State the value of a.

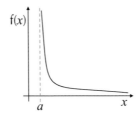

Q6 The diagram shows the function $f(x) = \sqrt{9-x^2}$ for $x \in \mathbb{R}$,
$a \leq x \leq b$. State the values of a and b.

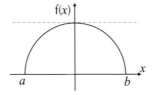

Q6 Hint: $9 - x^2$ cannot be negative, as you can't take the square root of a negative number, so work out the values of x for which $9 - x^2 \geq 0$ and use these as the domain.

Q7 $h(x) = \sqrt{x+1}$, $x \in \mathbb{R}$. Using set notation, give a restricted domain so that h is a function.

Q8 $k : x \rightarrow \tan x$, $x \in \mathbb{R}$. Give an example of a domain which would make k a function.

Q7-8 Hint: Sketch a graph of each one first and identify where any asymptotes might be.

Q9 $m(x) = \dfrac{1}{x^2-4}$. What is the largest continuous domain which would make m(x) a function?

Q10 The diagram on the right shows the graph of $y = f(x)$.

 a) Explain why f is not a function on the domain $x \in \mathbb{R}$.

 b) State the largest possible domain that would make f a function.

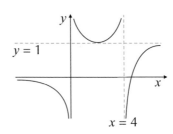

Types of function

One-to-one functions

> A function is **one-to-one** if each value in the **range**
> corresponds to **exactly one** value in the **domain**.

Sketching a graph is a good way to help you identify the type of function.

Example 1

The function $f : x \rightarrow 2x$, $x \in \mathbb{R}$ is one-to-one, as only one value of x
in the domain is mapped to each value in the range (the range is also $\mathbb{R}$).
You can see this clearly on a sketch of the function:

Only 3 in the domain is
mapped to 6 in the range.

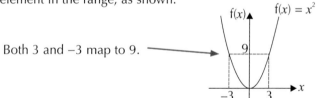

Many-to-one functions

> A function is **many-to-one** if some values in the **range**
> correspond to **more than one (many)** values in the **domain**.

Remember that no element in the domain can map to more than one element
in the range, otherwise it wouldn't be a function.

Example 2

The function $f(x) = x^2$, $x \in \mathbb{R}$ is a many-to-one function, as two elements
in the domain map to the same element in the range, as shown:

Both 3 and −3 map to 9.

Exercise 2.2.3

Q1   State whether each function below is one-to-one or many-to-one.

   a) $f(x) = x^3$ $x \in \mathbb{R}$

   b) $f : x \rightarrow \sin 2x$ $-180° < x \leq 180°$

   c) $f(x) = \log_{10} x$ $x > 0$

   d) $f(x) = \begin{cases} x + 2 & -2 \leq x < 0 \\ 2 - x & 0 \leq x \leq 2 \end{cases}$

   e) $f(x) = \begin{cases} 2^x & x \geq 0 \\ 1 & x < 0 \end{cases}$

2.3 Composite Functions

When one function is applied to another it makes a different function.
This is known as a composite function.

Learning Objectives (Spec Ref 2.8):
- Combine two or more functions into one composite function.
- Know that fg means 'do g first, then f'.
- Solve equations involving composite functions.

Composite functions

- If you have two functions f and g, you can combine them (do one followed by the other) to make a new function. This is called a **composite function**.

- Composite functions are written **fg(x)**. This means 'do g **first**, then f'. If it helps, put brackets in until you get used to it, so fg(x) = f(g(x)).

- The **order** is really important — usually fg(x) ≠ gf(x). If you get a composite function that's written f²(x), it means ff(x). This just means you have to do f **twice**.

- Composite functions made up of three or more functions work in exactly the same way — just make sure you get the order right.

Example 1

If f(x) = x − 2 and g(x) = 3x, then find:

a) fg(6):

First substitute 6 into g(x). Then substitute the value that comes out into f(x):

$$6 \xrightarrow{\quad g(6) \quad} \boxed{3 \times 6} \longrightarrow 18 \xrightarrow{\quad f(18) \quad} \boxed{18 - 2} \longrightarrow 16 \qquad \text{So } \boxed{fg(6) = 16}$$

b) gf(6):

This time substitute 6 into f(x) first. Then substitute the value that comes out into g(x):

$$6 \xrightarrow{\quad f(6) \quad} \boxed{6 - 2} \longrightarrow 4 \xrightarrow{\quad g(4) \quad} \boxed{3 \times 4} \longrightarrow 12 \qquad \text{So } \boxed{gf(6) = 12}$$

c) fg(x):

This time leave everything in terms of x. Do g first, then f:

$$x \xrightarrow{\quad g(x) \quad} \boxed{3x} \longrightarrow 3x \xrightarrow{\quad f(3x) \quad} \boxed{(3x) - 2} \longrightarrow 3x - 2 \qquad \text{So } \boxed{fg(x) = 3x - 2}$$

> **Tip:** Comparing the answers to a) and b) you can see that fg(x) ≠ gf(x).

d) gf(x):

$$x \xrightarrow{\quad f(x) \quad} \boxed{x - 2} \longrightarrow x - 2 \xrightarrow{\quad g(x - 2) \quad} \boxed{3(x - 2)} \longrightarrow \begin{array}{c} 3(x - 2) \\ \text{or} \\ 3x - 6 \end{array} \qquad \text{So } \boxed{gf(x) = 3x - 6}$$

The key to composite functions is to work things out in steps. Set out your working for composite functions as shown in the examples below.

Example 2

For the functions $f : x \to 2x^3$, $x \in \mathbb{R}$ and $g : x \to x - 3$, $x \in \mathbb{R}$, find:

a) **fg(4)**   b) **fg(0)**   c) **gf(0)**   d) **fg(x)**   e) **gf(x)**   f) **$f^2(x)$**.

a) $fg(4) = f(g(4)) = f(4 - 3) = f(1) = 2 \times 1^3 = \boxed{2}$

b) $fg(0) = f(g(0)) = f(0 - 3) = f(-3) = 2 \times (-3)^3 = 2 \times -27 = \boxed{-54}$

c) $gf(0) = g(f(0)) = g(2 \times 0^3) = g(0) = 0 - 3 = \boxed{-3}$

d) $fg(x) = f(g(x)) = f(x - 3) = \boxed{2(x - 3)^3}$

e) $gf(x) = g(f(x)) = g(2x^3) = \boxed{2x^3 - 3}$

f) $f^2(x) = f(f(x)) = f(2x^3) = 2(2x^3)^3 = \boxed{16x^9}$

> **Tip:** Don't forget the 2^3 when expanding $(2x^3)^3$ in part f).

Domain and range of composite functions

Two functions with given domains and ranges may form a composite function with a **different** domain and range.

> **Tip:** Working out the domains and ranges of composite functions can be tricky — but sketching a graph always helps.

Example 3

Give the domain and range of the composite function fg(x), where:

$f(x) = 2x^2 + 1$, domain $x \in \mathbb{R}$, range $f(x) \geq 1$ and $g(x) = \dfrac{1}{x + 3}$, domain $x > -3$, range $g(x) > 0$

1. First work out the composite function in terms of x:

$$fg(x) = f(g(x))$$
$$= f\left(\frac{1}{x + 3}\right) = 2\left(\frac{1}{x + 3}\right)^2 + 1$$

2. Next, consider the graph of the composite function over the domain and range of the original functions:

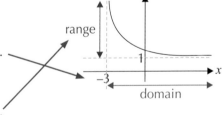

As $g(x)$ is restricted to $x > -3$, the domain of $fg(x)$ is also restricted to $x > -3$.

Since $\dfrac{1}{x + 3}$ is always > 0 for the domain $x > -3$, $2\left(\dfrac{1}{x + 3}\right)^2 + 1$ must be > 1.

So fg(x) has a domain of $\boxed{x > -3}$ and a range of $\boxed{fg(x) > 1}$.

For a composite function fg(x), the domain can also be found by putting the **range** of **g(x)** into **f(x)**. If the domain of f(x) does not fully include the range of g(x) then the domain of g(x) will have to be **restricted further**. See Example 4 on the next page.

Example 4

Find the domain of fg(x), where f(x) = $\sqrt{x}$, x ≥ 0, and g(x) = x + 5, x ∈ ℝ

1. The range of g(x) is g(x) ∈ ℝ. This is bigger than the domain of f(x), so the domain of g(x) will need to be restricted.

2. The input into f needs to be ≥ 0.
   Since for fg(x) the input into f is g(x) (i.e. x + 5): $x + 5 ≥ 0 \Rightarrow x ≥ -5$

   So the largest possible
   domain for fg(x) is $x ≥ -5$.

In the example above, if the domain was not restricted, then fg(x) would be undefined in places — e.g. fg(–6) = f(–6 + 5) = f(–1) = $\sqrt{-1}$ (which is undefined).

Exercise 2.3.1

Q1 $f : x \rightarrow x^2$, x ∈ ℝ and g : x → 2x + 1, x ∈ ℝ. Find the values of:

   a) fg(3)   b) gf(3)   c) f²(5)   d) g²(2)

Q2 f(x) = sin x for {x : x ∈ ℝ} and g(x) = 2x for {x : x ∈ ℝ}. Evaluate fg(90°) and gf(90°).

Q3 $f : x \rightarrow \dfrac{3}{x + 2}$, x > –2 and g : x → 2x, x ∈ ℝ.

   a) Find the values of gf(1), fg(1) and f²(4)

   b) Explain why fg(–1) is undefined.

   Q3b) Hint: Try to find the value of fg(–1), or consider the domains and ranges of f(x) and g(x).

Q4 f(x) = cos x, x ∈ ℝ and g(x) = 2x, x ∈ ℝ. Find the functions:

   a) fg(x)   b) gf(x)

Q5 f(x) = 2x – 1, x ∈ ℝ and g(x) = 2ˣ, x ∈ ℝ. Find the functions:

   a) fg(x)   b) gf(x)   c) f²(x)

Q6 f(x) = $\dfrac{2}{x - 1}$ for {x : x > 1} and g(x) = x + 4 for {x : x ∈ ℝ}.

   Find the functions fg(x) and gf(x), writing them as single fractions in their simplest forms.

Q7 f(x) = $\dfrac{x}{1 - x}$ for {x : x ∈ ℝ, x ≠ 1} and g(x) = x² for {x : x ∈ ℝ}.
   Find f²(x) and gfg(x).

Q8 f(x) = x² with domain x ∈ ℝ, and g(x) = 2x – 3 also with domain x ∈ ℝ.

   a) Find fg(x) and write down its range.

   b) Find gf(x) and write down its range.

   Q8-9 Hint: Sketching the graphs of the composite functions will help you find the ranges and domains.

Q9 f(x) = $\dfrac{1}{x}$ and g(x) = ln (x + 1), both with domain {x : x > 0}.

   a) Find gf(x) and write down its range and largest possible domain.

   b) Find fg(x) and write down its range and largest possible domain.

Q10 Given that f(x) = 3x + 2, g(x) = 5x – 1, and h(x) = x² + 1 (all with domain {x : x ∈ ℝ}), find fgh(x).

Solving composite function equations

If you're asked to **solve** an equation such as fg(x) = 8, the best way to do it is to work out what fg(x) is, then **rearrange** fg(x) = 8 to make **x** the subject.

Example 1

For the functions $f : x \to \sqrt{x}$ with domain $\{x : x \geq 0\}$ and $g : x \to \dfrac{1}{x-1}$ with domain $\{x : x > 1\}$, solve the equation fg(x) = $\dfrac{1}{2}$ and state the range of fg(x).

1. First, find fg(x):

$$fg(x) = f\left(\frac{1}{x-1}\right) = \sqrt{\frac{1}{x-1}} = \frac{1}{\sqrt{x-1}}$$

$$\Rightarrow \frac{1}{\sqrt{x-1}} = \frac{1}{2}$$

2. Rearrange to find x:

$$\Rightarrow \sqrt{x-1} = 2 \Rightarrow x - 1 = 4 \Rightarrow \boxed{x = 5}$$

3. To find the range, draw the graph of fg(x):

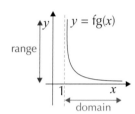

You can see that the domain of fg(x) is $\{x : x > 1\}$ and the range is $\boxed{\{fg(x) : fg(x) > 0\}}$.

Tip: Be careful with the domains and ranges of composite functions. Have a look back at pages 21-22 for more on how to find them.

Example 2

For the functions $f : x \to 2x + 1, x \in \mathbb{R}$ and $g : x \to x^2, x \in \mathbb{R}$, solve gf(x) = 16.

1. Find gf(x):

$$gf(x) = g(2x+1) = (2x+1)^2$$

2. Solve gf(x) = 16: $(2x+1)^2 = 16 \Rightarrow (2x+1) = 4 \text{ or } -4 \Rightarrow 2x = 3 \text{ or } -5 \Rightarrow \boxed{x = \frac{3}{2} \text{ or } x = -\frac{5}{2}}$

Exercise 2.3.2

Q1 For the following functions, solve the given equations:

    a) $f(x) = 2x + 1, x \in \mathbb{R}$ $g(x) = 3x - 4, x \in \mathbb{R}$ fg(x) = 23

    b) $f(x) = \dfrac{1}{x}$ for $\{x : x \neq 0\}$ $g(x) = 2x + 5$ for $\{x : x \in \mathbb{R}\}$ gf(x) = 6

    c) $f(x) = x^2$ for $\{x : x \in \mathbb{R}\}$ $g(x) = \dfrac{x}{x-3}$ for $\{x : x \neq 3\}$ gf(x) = 4

    d) $f(x) = x^2 + 1, x \in \mathbb{R}$ $g(x) = 3x - 2, x \in \mathbb{R}$ fg(x) = 50

    e) $f(x) = 2x + 1, x \in \mathbb{R}$ $g(x) = \sqrt{x}, x \geq 0$ fg(x) = 17

    f) $f(x) = \log_{10} x, x > 0$ $g(x) = 3 - x, x \in \mathbb{R}$ fg(x) = 0

    g) $f(x) = 2^x$ for $\{x : x \in \mathbb{R}\}$ $g(x) = x^2 + 2x$ for $\{x : x \in \mathbb{R}\}$ fg(x) = 8

    h) $f(x) = \dfrac{x}{x+1}, x \neq -1$ $g(x) = 2x - 1, x \in \mathbb{R}$ fg(x) = gf(x)

Q2 $f : x \to x^2 + b, x \in \mathbb{R}$ and $g : x \to b - 3x, x \in \mathbb{R}$ (b is a constant).

    a)   Find fg and gf and give the range of each in terms of b.

    b)   Given that gf(2) = –8, find the value of fg(2).

2.4 Inverse Functions

Inverse functions 'undo' functions. So if a function tells you to do a certain thing to x, the inverse of that function tells you how to get back to the start.

> **Learning Objectives (Spec Ref 2.8):**
> - Understand which functions will have inverses.
> - Know that $f^{-1}f(x) = ff^{-1}(x) = x$.
> - Find the inverse of a function, and find its domain and range.
> - Draw and interpret graphs of functions and their inverses.

Prior Knowledge Check:
Be able to sketch and transform graphs, and solve equations involving exponentials and logs — covered in Year 1 of this course.

Inverse functions and their graphs

- An **inverse function** does the **opposite** to the function. So if the function was '+ 1', the inverse would be '– 1', if the function was '× 2', the inverse would be '÷ 2' etc.

- The inverse for a function f(x) is written **f⁻¹(x)**.

- An inverse function maps an element in the **range** to an element in the **domain** — the opposite of a function. This means that only **one-to-one** functions have inverses, as the inverse of a many-to-one function would be one-to-many, which isn't a function. (See page 19 for more on the different types of functions.)

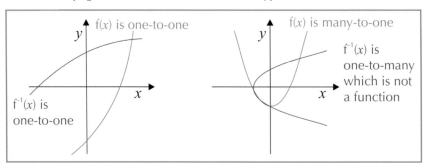

For any inverse $f^{-1}(x)$:

$$f^{-1}f(x) = x = ff^{-1}(x)$$

Doing the function and then the inverse...   ...is the same as doing the inverse then doing the function — both just give you x.

> **Tip:** $f^{-1}f(x)$ is a composite function (p.20). It just means 'do f then f⁻¹'.

The **domain** of the inverse is the **range** of the function, and the **range** of the inverse is the **domain** of the function.

> ## Example 1
>
> **A function f(x) = x + 7 has domain x ≥ 0 and range f(x) ≥ 7. State whether the function has an inverse. If so, find the inverse, and give its domain and range.**
>
> The function f(x) = x + 7 is one-to-one, so it does have an inverse.
>
> The inverse of +7 is –7, so $f^{-1}(x) = x - 7$.
>
> f⁻¹(x) has domain $x \geq 7$ (the range of f(x)), and range $f^{-1}(x) \geq 0$ (the domain of f(x)).

For simple functions (e.g. in the example above), it's easy to work out what the inverse is by looking at it. But for more complex functions, you need to **rearrange** the original function to **change the subject**.

Finding the inverse of a function

Here's a general method for finding the inverse of a given function:

- Replace f(x) with y to get an equation for **y in terms of x**.
- **Rearrange** the equation to make x the subject.
- Replace x with $f^{-1}(x)$ and y with x — this is the **inverse function**.
- **Swap** round the **domain** and **range** of the function.

Tip: It's easier to work with y than f(x).

Example 2

Find the inverse of the function $f(x) = \sqrt{2x - 1}$, with domain $x \geq \frac{1}{2}$ and range $f(x) \geq 0$. State the domain and the range of the inverse.

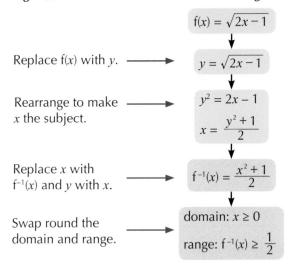

Replace f(x) with y. ⟶

Rearrange to make ⟶
x the subject.

Replace x with
$f^{-1}(x)$ and y with x. ⟶

Swap round the ⟶
domain and range.

$$f(x) = \sqrt{2x - 1}$$

$$y = \sqrt{2x - 1}$$

$$y^2 = 2x - 1$$

$$x = \frac{y^2 + 1}{2}$$

$$f^{-1}(x) = \frac{x^2 + 1}{2}$$

domain: $x \geq 0$

range: $f^{-1}(x) \geq \frac{1}{2}$

Tip: Breaking it into steps like this means you're less likely to go wrong. It's worth doing it this way even for easier functions.

Example 3

Find the inverse of the function $f(x) = 2^x + 1$ with domain $\{x : x \geq 0\}$, and state its domain and range.

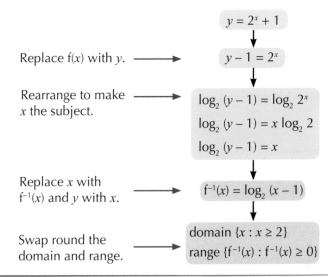

Replace f(x) with y. ⟶

Rearrange to make ⟶
x the subject.

Replace x with
$f^{-1}(x)$ and y with x. ⟶

Swap round the ⟶
domain and range.

$$y = 2^x + 1$$

$$y - 1 = 2^x$$

$$\log_2 (y - 1) = \log_2 2^x$$
$$\log_2 (y - 1) = x \log_2 2$$
$$\log_2 (y - 1) = x$$

$$f^{-1}(x) = \log_2 (x - 1)$$

domain $\{x : x \geq 2\}$
range $\{f^{-1}(x) : f^{-1}(x) \geq 0\}$

Tip: If you're not given the domain and / or the range of the function you'll need to work it out. In this example, x is always at least 0, so f(x) must always be at least $2^0 + 1 = 2$.

Graphs of inverse functions

The inverse of a function is its **reflection** in the line $y = x$.

Example 4

Sketch the graph of the inverse of the function $f(x) = x^2 - 8$ with domain $x \geq 0$.

Step 1: Draw f(x).

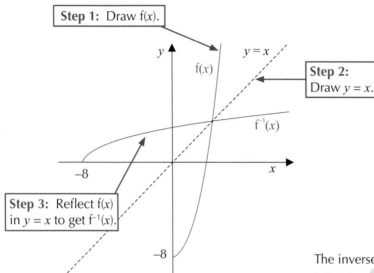

Step 2: Draw $y = x$.

Step 3: Reflect f(x) in $y = x$ to get $f^{-1}(x)$.

Tip: Only sketch the function over the given domain and range. Otherwise you won't be able to see the correct domain and range for the graph of the inverse when you do the reflection.

The inverse function is $f^{-1}(x) = \sqrt{x + 8}$.

It's easy to see what the domains and ranges are from the graph —
$f(x)$ has domain $x \geq 0$ and range $f(x) \geq -8$, and $f^{-1}(x)$ has domain $x \geq -8$ and range $f^{-1}(x) \geq 0$.

Exercise 2.4.1

Q1 Do the functions shown in the diagrams below have inverses? Justify your answers.

a)

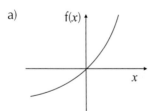

b)

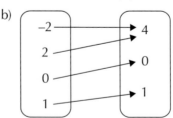

Q2 For the following functions, explain whether or not an inverse f^{-1} exists:

a) $f(x) = \sin x$, $x \in \mathbb{R}$

b) $f(x) = x^2 + 3$, $x \in \mathbb{R}$

c) $f(x) = (x - 4)^2$ for $\{x : x \geq 4\}$

Q2-6 Hint: If in doubt, sketch a graph of the function to check domains and ranges.

Q3 Find the inverse of each of the following functions, stating the domain and range:

a) $f(x) = 3x + 4$, $x \in \mathbb{R}$

b) $f(x) = 5(x - 2)$, $x \in \mathbb{R}$

c) $f(x) = \dfrac{1}{x + 2}$, $x > -2$

d) $f(x) = x^2 + 3$ for $\{x : x > 0\}$

Q4 $f(x) = \dfrac{3x}{x+1}$, $x > -1$.

a) Find $f^{-1}(x)$, stating the domain and range.

b) Evaluate $f^{-1}(2)$.

c) Evaluate $f^{-1}\left(\dfrac{1}{2}\right)$.

> **Q4-5 Hint:** The range of f(x) is quite tricky to find — you might find it helpful to think about what happens to f(x) as $x \to \infty$ and sketch the graph.

Q5 $f(x) = \dfrac{x-4}{x+3}$ for $\{x : x > -3\}$.

a) Find $f^{-1}(x)$, stating the domain and range.

b) Evaluate $f^{-1}(0)$.

c) Evaluate $f^{-1}\left(-\dfrac{2}{5}\right)$.

Q6   Find the domain and range of $f^{-1}(x)$ for the following functions:

a) $f(x) = \log_{10}(x-3)$, $x > 3$

b) $f(x) = 4x - 2$, $1 \leq x \leq 7$

c) $f(x) = \dfrac{x}{x-2}$ for $\{x : x < 2\}$

d) $f(x) = 3^{x-1}$ for $\{x : x \geq 2\}$

e) $f(x) = \tan x$, $0° \leq x < 90°$

f) $f(x) = \ln(x^2)$ for $\{x : 3 \leq x \leq 4\}$

Q7   Find the inverse $f^{-1}(x)$ for the following functions, giving the domain and range:

a) $f(x) = e^{x+1}$, $x \in \mathbb{R}$

b) $f(x) = x^3$, $x < 0$

c) $f(x) = 2 - \log_2(x)$, $x \geq 1$

d) $f(x) = \dfrac{1}{x-2}$ for $\{x : x \neq 2\}$

e) $f(x) = \dfrac{1}{e^x}$, $x \in \mathbb{R}$

f) $f(x) = \log_{10} e^x$, $x \in \mathbb{R}$

Q8 $f(x) = 2x + 3$, $x \in \mathbb{R}$. Sketch $y = f(x)$ and $y = f^{-1}(x)$ on the same set of axes, marking the points where the functions cross the axes.

Q9 $f(x) = x^2 + 3$, $x > 0$.

a) Sketch the graphs of $f(x)$ and $f^{-1}(x)$ on the same set of axes.

b) State the domain and range of $f^{-1}(x)$.

Q10 $f(x) = \dfrac{1}{x+1}$ for $\{x : x > -1\}$.

a) Sketch the graphs of $f(x)$ and $f^{-1}(x)$ on the same set of axes.

b) Explain how your diagram shows that there is just one solution to the equation $f(x) = f^{-1}(x)$.

Q11 $f(x) = \dfrac{1}{x-3}$, $x > 3$.

a) Find $f^{-1}(x)$ and state its domain and range.

b) Sketch $f(x)$ and $f^{-1}(x)$ on the same set of axes.

c) How many solutions are there to the equation $f(x) = f^{-1}(x)$?

d) Solve $f(x) = f^{-1}(x)$.

Q12 $f(x) = \dfrac{3x+6}{x^2-2x-8}$, $x < 4$.

a) Find $f^{-1}(x)$ and state its domain and range.

b) Show that there is one solution to $f^2(x) = f^{-1}(x)$ within the domain of $f^{-1}(x)$.

2.5 Modulus

Sometimes in maths you want to work with numbers or functions without having to deal with negative values. The modulus function lets you do this.

Learning Objectives (Spec Ref 2.7 & 2.9):
- Understand the meaning of the modulus, including modulus notation.
- Write the modulus of a number or function.
- Sketch the graph of $y = |ax + b|$.
- Sketch the graphs of $y = |f(x)|$ and $y = |f(-x)|$, given the graph of $y = f(x)$.
- Solve equations and inequalities involving the modulus.

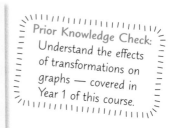

Prior Knowledge Check:
Understand the effects of transformations on graphs — covered in Year 1 of this course.

The modulus function

Modulus of a number

The **modulus** of a number is its **size** — it doesn't matter if it's positive or negative. So for a positive number, the modulus is just the same as the number itself, but for a negative number, the modulus is its numerical value without the minus sign. The modulus is sometimes called the **absolute value**.

> The modulus of a number, x, is written $|x|$.
>
> In general terms, for $x \geq 0$, $|x| = x$ and for $x < 0$, $|x| = -x$.

For example, the modulus of 8 is 8, and the modulus of −8 is also 8. This is written $|8| = |-8| = 8$.

Modulus of a function

Functions can have a modulus too — the modulus of a function $f(x)$ is just $f(x)$ but with any negative values that it can take turned positive. Suppose $f(x) = -6$, then $|f(x)| = 6$. In general terms:

> $|f(x)| = f(x)$ when $f(x) \geq 0$ and $|f(x)| = -f(x)$ when $f(x) < 0$.

If the modulus is inside the brackets in the form $f(|x|)$, then you make the x-value positive **before** applying the function. So $f(|-2|) = f(2)$.

Modulus graphs

$y = |f(x)|$

- For the graph of $y = |f(x)|$, any **negative** values of $f(x)$ are made **positive** by **reflecting** them in the **x-axis**.

- This **restricts** the **range** of the modulus function to $|f(x)| \geq 0$ (or some subset within $|f(x)| \geq 0$, e.g. $|f(x)| \geq 1$).

- The easiest way to draw a graph of $y = |f(x)|$ is to initially draw $y = f(x)$, then **reflect** the negative part in the **x-axis**.

$y = f(|x|)$

- For the graph of $y = f(|x|)$, the **negative** x-values produce the same result as the corresponding **positive** x-values. So the graph of $f(x)$ for $x \geq 0$ is **reflected** in the **y-axis** for the negative x-values.

- The range of $f(|x|)$ will be the **same** as the range of $f(x)$ for values of $x \geq 0$.

- To draw a graph of $y = f(|x|)$, first draw the graph of $y = f(x)$ for **positive** values of x, then **reflect** this in the **y-axis** to form the rest of the graph.

For the graph of $y = |f(-x)|$, you reflect the entire graph in the y-axis first and then reflect the negative part in the x-axis.

Example 1

Draw the graphs of $y = |f(x)|$ and $y = f(|x|)$ for $f(x) = 5x - 5$. State the range of each.

$y = |f(x)|$:

1. Draw the graph of $y = 5x - 5$.

2. Where the graph goes below the x-axis (i.e. for negative y-values), draw it as a dotted line.

3. Reflect the negative (dotted) part of the line in the x-axis.

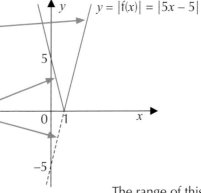

$y = |f(x)| = |5x - 5|$

The range of this is $|f(x)| \geq 0$

$y = f(|x|)$:

1. Draw the graph of $y = 5x - 5$ as before.

2. For negative x-values, reflect the part of the line where x is positive in the y-axis.

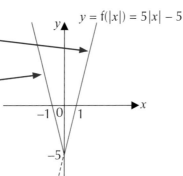

$y = f(|x|) = 5|x| - 5$

Tip: For $y = |f(x)|$ graphs you reflect the **dotted** line in the **x-axis**, but for these $y = f(|x|)$ graphs you reflect the **solid** line in the **y-axis**.

The range of this is $f(|x|) \geq -5$

Example 2

To the right is the graph of $f(x) = x^2 - 4x$.
Use this to sketch the graph of $y = |f(-x)|$.

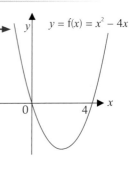

$y = f(x) = x^2 - 4x$

1. Reflect the entire graph of $y = x^2 - 4x$ in the y-axis to give $f(-x)$.

2. Where the graph goes below the x-axis (i.e. for negative y-values), draw it as a dotted line.

3. Reflect the negative (dotted) part of the line in the x-axis.

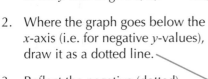

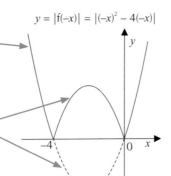

$y = |f(-x)| = |(-x)^2 - 4(-x)|$

Q1 Sketch the following graphs, labelling any axis intercepts, and state the range of each:

a) $y = |x + 3|$

b) $y = |5 - x|$

c) $y = |3x - 1|$

d) $y = |x| - 9$

e) $y = 2|x| + 5$

f) $y = 3|x| - 11$

Q2 For each of the following functions, sketch the graph of $y = |f(x)|$, labelling any axis intercepts:

a) $f(x) = 2x + 3$

b) $f(x) = 4 - 3x$

c) $f(x) = -4x$

d) $f(x) = 7 - \frac{1}{2}x$

e) $f(x) = -(x + 2)$

f) $f(x) = -1 - 5x$

Q3 Match up each graph (1-4) with its correct equation (a-d):

a) $y = |x| + 4$

b) $y = |2x - 10|$

c) $y = |x + 1|$

d) $y = |2x| - 2$

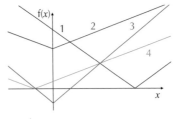

Q3 Hint: Try sketching the graphs from the given functions to see what shape they should be, then compare them in terms of where they cross the x and y axes.

Q4 a) For each of the graphs below, sketch the graph of $y = |f(x)|$:

(i)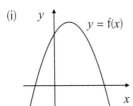

(ii)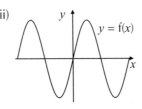

(iii)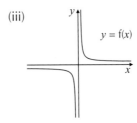

b) For part (i) above, sketch the graph of $y = |f(-x)|$.

Q5 Draw the graph of the function $f(x) = \begin{cases} |2x + 4| & x < 0 \\ |x - 4| & x \geq 0 \end{cases}$

Q6 For the function $f(x) = 3x - 5$:

a) Draw, on the same axes, the graphs of $y = f(x)$ and $y = |f(x)|$.

b) How many solutions are there to the equation $|3x - 5| = 2$?

Q6b) Hint: Read across from 2 on the y-axis to find the number of values of x for which $|3x - 5| = 2$.

Q7 For the function $f(x) = 4x + 1$:

a) Draw accurately the graph of $y = |f(-x)|$.

b) Use your graph to solve the equation $|f(-x)| = 3$.

Q8 The diagram on the right shows the graph of $f(x) = 2 - x$:

a) Let $g(x) = f(|x|)$. Draw accurately the graph of $y = g(x)$.

b) Let $h(x) = |g(x)|$. On separate axes, draw the graph of $y = h(x)$.

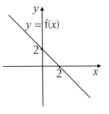

Solving modulus equations and inequalities

You might be asked to substitute a modulus value into an expression to find the possible values that the expression could take.

Example 1

a) **If $|x| = 2$, what are the possible values of $5x - 3$?**

If $|x| = 2$, then either $x = 2$ or $x = -2$. So substitute these two values into the expression.

$x = 2 \Rightarrow 5x - 3 = 5(2) - 3 = 10 - 3 = \boxed{7}$

$x = -2 \Rightarrow 5x - 3 = 5(-2) - 3 = -10 - 3 = \boxed{-13}$

b) **Find all of the possible values of $|3x - 4|$ when $|x| = 6$.**

$|x| = 6$ means $x = 6$ or $x = -6$:

$x = 6 \Rightarrow |3(6) - 4| = |18 - 4| = |14| = \boxed{14}$

$x = -6 \Rightarrow |3(-6) - 4| = |-18 - 4| = |-22| = \boxed{22}$

$|f(x)| = n$ and $|f(x)| = g(x)$

The method for solving equations of the form $|f(x)| = n$ is shown below.
Solving $|f(x)| = g(x)$ is exactly the same — just replace n with $g(x)$.

> **Step 1:** Sketch the functions $y = |f(x)|$ and $y = n$ on the same axes. The solutions you're trying to find are where they **intersect**.
>
> **Step 2:** From the graph, work out the ranges of x for which $f(x) \geq 0$ and $f(x) < 0$: e.g. $f(x) \geq 0$ for $x \leq a$ or $x \geq b$ and $f(x) < 0$ for $a < x < b$. These ranges should 'fit together' to cover **all** possible x-values.
>
> **Step 3:** Use this to write **two new equations**, one true for each range of x:
>
> $\quad$ ① $f(x) = n \quad$ for $x \leq a$ or $x \geq b$
>
> $\quad$ ② $-f(x) = n \quad$ for $a < x < b$
>
> **Step 4:** Solve each equation and check that any solutions are **valid**. Get rid of any solutions outside the range of x you have for that equation.
>
> **Step 5:** Look at the graph and **check** that your solutions look right.

Sketching the graphs will show you where the solutions should be — it's easy to accidentally find solutions of $f(x) = g(x)$ that **don't** satisfy $|f(x)| = g(x)$ if you don't draw the graphs first.

Example 2

Solve $|2x - 4| = 5 - x$.

This question is an example of $|f(x)| = g(x)$, where $f(x) = 2x - 4$ and $g(x) = 5 - x$.

1. Sketch $y = |2x - 4|$ and $y = 5 - x$.
   The graphs cross twice:

$2x - 4 < 0$ when $x < 2$

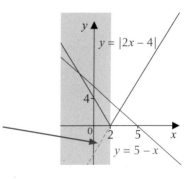

---

2. Looking at where $f(x) \geq 0$
   and where $f(x) < 0$ gives:

      ① $2x - 4 = 5 - x$ for $x \geq 2$

      ② $-(2x - 4) = 5 - x$ for $x < 2$

3. Solving these gives:

      ① $3x = 9 \Rightarrow x = \boxed{3}$
        (valid because $x \geq 2$)

      ② $-x = 1 \Rightarrow x = \boxed{-1}$
        (valid because $x < 2$)

   Tip: Make sure that you check whether your solutions are within the valid range for each equation.

4. Checking against the graph, there are two solutions and they're where we expected.

$|f(x)| = |g(x)|$

When using **graphs** to solve functions of the form $|f(x)| = |g(x)|$ you have to do a bit more work at the start to identify the different areas of the graph. There could be regions where:

- $f(x)$ and $g(x)$ are **both** positive or **both** negative — for solutions in these regions you need to solve the equation **f(x) = g(x)**.

- One function is **positive** and the other is **negative** — for solutions in these regions you need to solve the equation **–f(x) = g(x)**.

(Solving $-f(x) = -g(x)$ is the same as solving $f(x) = g(x)$,
and solving $f(x) = -g(x)$ is the same as solving $-f(x) = g(x)$.)

There is also an **algebraic** method for solving equations of this type:

> If $|a| = |b|$ then $a^2 = b^2$.
> So if $|f(x)| = |g(x)|$ then $[f(x)]^2 = [g(x)]^2$.

Tip: The squaring method works for solving $|f(x)| = n$ as well — write $[f(x)]^2 = n^2$, then rearrange and solve.

This is true because squaring gives the **same answer** whether the value is **positive** or **negative**. You'll usually be left with a **quadratic** to solve, but in some cases this might be easier than using a graphical method.

The following example shows how you could use either method to solve the same equation.

Example 3

Solve $|x - 2| = |3x + 4|$.

1. Square both sides and rearrange:

   $|x - 2| = |3x + 4|$
   $\Rightarrow (x - 2)^2 = (3x + 4)^2$
   $\Rightarrow x^2 - 4x + 4 = 9x^2 + 24x + 16$
   $\Rightarrow 8x^2 + 28x + 12 = 0$
   $\Rightarrow 2x^2 + 7x + 3 = 0$

   Tip: For this example the algebraic method involves less work than using graphs.

2. Factorise and solve:

   $\Rightarrow (2x + 1)(x + 3) = 0$

   $x = \boxed{-\dfrac{1}{2}}$ and $x = \boxed{-3}$

   Tip: You can use the quadratic formula to solve it if it won't easily factorise.

3. You can check these solutions by sketching the graphs:

4. There are two intersections — one where f(x) is negative but g(x) is positive (shaded grey) and the other where f(x) and g(x) are both negative (i.e. where $x < -1\frac{1}{3}$).

These correspond to the two solutions $x = -\frac{1}{2}$ and -3.

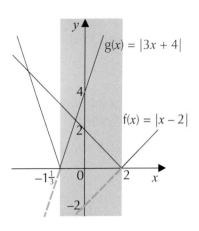

$g(x) = |3x + 4|$

$f(x) = |x - 2|$

Solving inequalities

Inequalities with a modulus can be a bit nasty to solve. Just remember that $|x| < 5$ means that $x < 5$ and $-x < 5$ (which is the same as $x > -5$). So $|x| < 5 \Rightarrow -5 < x < 5$. Similarly, if $|x| > 5$, you'd end up with $x > 5$ and $x < -5$. In general, for $a > 0$:

$$|x| < a \Rightarrow -a < x < a$$

$$|x| > a \Rightarrow x > a \text{ or } x < -a$$

Using this, you can **rearrange** more complicated inequalities like $|x - a| \leq b$. From the method above, this means that $-b \leq x - a \leq b$, so **adding** a to **each bit** of the inequality gives $a - b \leq x \leq a + b$.

Example 4

Solve $|x - 4| < 7$

1. Using the theory above: $\qquad\qquad |x - 4| < 7 \Rightarrow -7 < x - 4 < 7$

2. Now add 4 to each bit: $\qquad\qquad -7 + 4 < x < 7 + 4$, so $-3 < x < 11$

For more complicated modulus inequalities, it's often helpful to draw the graph — take a look at this next example:

Example 5

Solve $|2x - 4| > 5 - x$.

1. Sketch the graphs of $y = |2x - 4|$ and $y = 5 - x$ (if you're thinking that this looks familiar, you're dead right — this is the graph you drew on p.31).

2. You solved the equation $|2x - 4| = 5 - x$ on p.31, so you know that the graphs cross at $x = 3$ and $x = -1$.

3. Now highlight the areas where the graph of $|2x - 4|$ (the red line) is above the graph of $5 - x$ (the blue line):

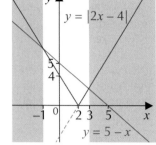

4. You can see that there are two regions that satisfy the inequality — the region to the left of $x = -1$ and the region to the right of $x = 3$.

5. So the solutions of the inequality are:

$$x < -1 \text{ or } x > 3$$

In set notation, the answer would be: $\{x : x < -1\} \cup \{x : x > 3\}$

Exercise 2.5.2

Q1 Solve the following equations:

a) $|x - 2| = 6$

b) $|4x + 2| = 10$

c) $2 - |3x - 4| = 1$

d) $9 - |x + 3| = 0$

e) $|2x + 3| = 1$

f) $|2 - x| = 4$

Q2 If $|x| = 5$, find the possible values of $|3x + 2|$

Q3 If $|x| - 2 = -1$, find the possible values of $|7x - 1|$

Q4 If $|x| = 3$, find the possible values of $|-2x + 1|$

Q5 a) On the same axes sketch the graphs of $|f(x)|$ and $g(x)$, where:
$f(x) = 2x + 3$ and $g(x) = x - 1$

b) Hence find any solutions of the equation $|f(x)| = g(x)$.

Q6 a) On the same axes sketch the graphs of $|f(x)|$ and $|g(x)|$, where:
$f(x) = 5x + 10$ and $g(x) = x + 1$

b) Hence find any solutions of the equation $|f(x)| = |g(x)|$.

Q7 Solve, either graphically or otherwise:

a) $|x + 2| = |2x|$

b) $|4x - 1| = |2x + 3|$

c) $|3x - 6| = |10 - 5x|$

Q8 If $|4x + 1| = 3$, find the possible values of $2|x - 1| + 3$

Q9 Solve the following inequalities:

a) $|x| < 8$

b) $|x| \geq 5$

c) $|2x| > 12$

d) $|4x + 2| \leq 6$

e) $3 \geq |3x - 3|$

f) $6 - 2|x + 4| < 0$

g) $3x + 8 < |x|$

h) $2|x - 4| \geq x$

i) $|x - 3| \geq |2x + 3|$

Q10 Give the solutions of $x + 6 \leq |3x + 2|$ in set notation.

Q11 Find the possible values of $|5x + 4|$, given that $|1 + 2x| \leq 3$.

2.6 Transformations of Graphs

You should be familiar with the basic graph transformations. Now you have to know how to put them all together to form combinations of transformations.

Learning Objectives (Spec Ref 2.9):

- Sketch graphs when $y = f(x)$ has been affected by a combination of these transformations:
  $y = f(x + a)$, $y = f(x) + a$, $y = af(x)$, $y = f(ax)$.
- Interpret transformed graphs, including finding coordinates of points.

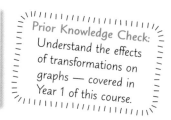

Prior Knowledge Check:
Understand the effects of transformations on graphs — covered in Year 1 of this course.

Transformations of graphs

The four transformations

The transformations you've met before are translations (a vertical or horizontal shift), stretches (either vertical or horizontal) and reflections in the *x*- or *y*- axis. Here's a quick reminder of what each one does:

$y = f(x + a)$

For $a > 0$: $f(x + a)$ is $f(x)$ translated a **left**,
   $f(x - a)$ is $f(x)$ translated a **right**.

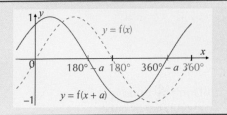

$y = f(x) + a$

For $a > 0$: $f(x) + a$ is $f(x)$ translated a **up**,

   $f(x) - a$ is $f(x)$ translated a **down**.

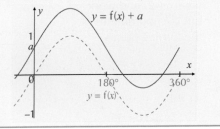

$y = af(x)$

The graph of $af(x)$ is $f(x)$ **stretched** parallel to the **y-axis** (i.e. vertically) by a factor of a.

And if $a < 0$, the graph is also **reflected** in the **x-axis**.

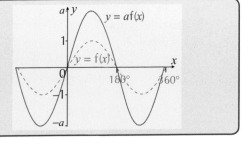

$y = f(ax)$

The graph of $f(ax)$ is $f(x)$ **stretched** parallel to the **x-axis** (i.e. horizontally) by a factor of $\frac{1}{a}$.

And if $a < 0$, the graph is also **reflected** in the **y-axis**.

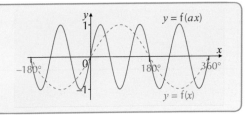

Combinations of transformations

Combinations of transformations can look a bit tricky, but if you take them one step at a time they're not too bad. Don't try and do all the transformations at once — break it up into the separate bits shown on the previous page and draw a graph for each stage.

Example 1

The graph below shows the function $y = f(x)$. Draw the graph of $y = 3f(x + 2)$, showing the coordinates of the turning points.

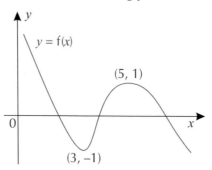

Tip: Make sure you do the transformations the right way round — you should do the bit in the brackets first.

1. Don't try to do everything at once. First draw the graph of $y = f(x + 2)$ and work out the coordinates of the turning points:

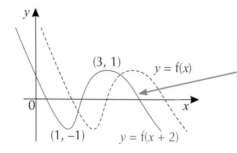

The graph is translated **left** by **2 units**, so **subtract 2** from the *x*-coordinates.

2. Now use your graph of $y = f(x + 2)$ to draw the graph of $y = 3f(x + 2)$:

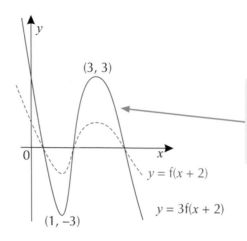

This is a **stretch** in the direction of the *y*-axis with scale factor **3**, so **multiply the y-coordinates by 3.**

Example 2

The graph on the right shows the function f(x) = |x|.

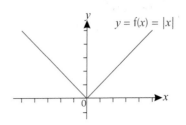

a) **Draw the graph of f(x) after a translation by $\begin{pmatrix} -1 \\ 4 \end{pmatrix}$ and give its equation.**

1. You need to do a **horizontal translation left** by **1**...

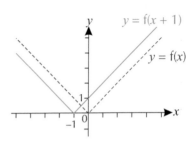

2. ...followed by a **vertical translation** of **4 upwards**:

3. The equation of the new graph is: $y = f(x + 1) + 4$

4. Replace f(x) with the original function |x|: $y = |x + 1| + 4$

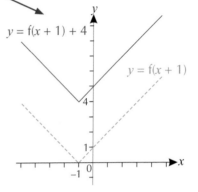

> **Tip:** If you're not sure whether your graph is correct, try putting some numbers into the function and checking them against coordinates on the graph.

b) **The function g(x) shown on the right is a translation of f(x). Give the translation vector for this transformation, and the equation of g(x).**

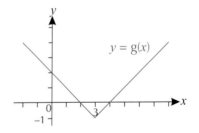

1. The transformation is a **horizontal** translation of 3 to the **right**, and a **vertical** translation of 1 **downwards**.   So the translation vector is $\begin{pmatrix} 3 \\ -1 \end{pmatrix}$

2. To find the equation of g(x), use the equations for each translation:

    Horizontal translation of 3 to the right = f(x − 3)

    Vertical translation of 1 downwards = f(x − 3) − 1

3. Now replace f with the actual function given above: $g(x) = f(x − 3) − 1$

    $\Rightarrow g(x) = |x − 3| − 1$

Example 3

**The graph to the right shows
the function $y = \sin x$, $0° \leq x \leq 360°$.
Draw the graph of $y = 2 - \sin 2x$, $0° \leq x \leq 360°$.**

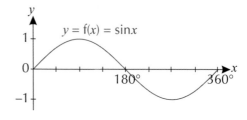

The turning points are at $(90°, 1)$ and $(270°, -1)$,
and the y-intercept is $(0, 0)$.

1. Rearranging to $y = -\sin 2x + 2$ gives a
function in the form $y = -f(2x) + 2$.
So describe this as a series of transformations.

- a **horizontal stretch** by a factor of $\frac{1}{2}$,
- a **vertical stretch** by a factor of **–1**,
- and a **vertical translation** by **2 up**
(in the positive y-direction).

2. Draw the graph of $y = \sin 2x$, by
squashing the graph horizontally by a
factor of 2 (i.e. a stretch by a factor of $\frac{1}{2}$). ——→

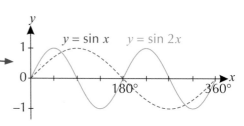

The turning points have been squashed up in the
x-direction, so halve the x-coordinates:

$(45°, 1)$ and $(135°, -1)$

There are also now an extra two within the domain,
each one occurring a further $90°$ along the x-axis:

$(225°, 1)$ and $(315°, -1)$

3. A stretch with a factor of –1 doesn't change the size
of the graph, you just have to reflect in the x-axis.
So draw $y = -\sin 2x$, by reflecting in the x-axis.

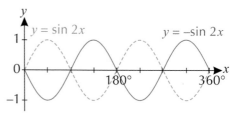

This transformation flips the turning points,
so multiply the y-coordinates by –1. ——→ They're now at $(45°, -1)$, $(135°, 1)$,
$(225°, -1)$ and $(315°, 1)$.

4. Finally, translate the graph of $y = -\sin 2x$ up by 2 to
get the graph of $y = -\sin 2x + 2$ (or $y = 2 - \sin 2x$).

Add 2 to the y-coordinates of the turning points to
give $(45°, 1)$, $(135°, 3)$, $(225°, 1)$ and $(315°, 3)$.

The y-intercept is also translated up by 2: it's at $(0, 2)$.

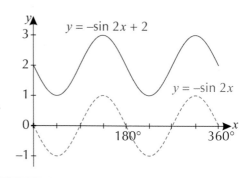

Q1 Given that $f(x) = x^2$, sketch the following graphs on the same axes:

a) $y = f(x)$ b) $y = f(x) + 3$ c) $y = f(x - 2)$ d) $y = f(x + 4) - 1$

In each case, write down the coordinates of the turning point, and in parts b)-d), give the translation as a column vector.

Q2 The graph of $f(x) = x^3$ is translated to form the graph of $g(x) = f(x - 1) + 4$.

a) Sketch the graphs of $y = f(x)$ and $y = g(x)$.

b) Give this translation as a column vector.

c) What is the equation of $g(x)$?

Q3 Given that $f(x) = |x|$, sketch the following graphs on the same axes:

a) $y = f(x)$ b) $y = f(x) + 2$ c) $y = f(x - 4)$ d) $y = 2f(x + 1)$

In parts b)-d) describe the transformation from $y = f(x)$ in words.

Q4 Let $f(x) = |2x - 6|$. On the same axes sketch the graphs of:

a) $y = f(x)$ b) $y = f(-x)$ c) $y = f(-x) + 2$

Q5 Let $f(x) = \dfrac{1}{x}$. On the same axes sketch the graphs of:

a) $y = f(x)$ b) $y = -f(x)$ c) $y = -f(x) - 3$

Q6 Let $f(x) = e^x$. On the same axes sketch the graphs of:

a) $y = f(x)$ b) $y = f(3x - 2)$ c) $y = f(2x + 1) - 1$

Q7 a) Let $f(x) = \cos x$. Sketch the graph $y = f(x)$ for $0° \le x \le 360°$.

b) On the same axes sketch the graph of $y = f(2x)$.

c) On the same axes sketch the graph of $y = 1 + f(2x)$.

d) State the coordinates of the minimum point(s) of $y = \cos 2x + 1$, in the interval $0° \le x \le 360°$.

Q8 Complete the following table for the function $f(x) = \sin x$ ($0° \le x \le 360°$).

Transformed function	New equation	Maximum value of transformed function	Minimum value of transformed function
$f(x) + 2$			
$f(x - 90°)$			
$f(3x)$			
$4f(x)$			

Q9 Complete the following table for the function $f(x) = x^3$:

Transformed function	New equation	Coordinates of point of inflection
$f(x) + 1$		
$f(x - 2)$		
$-f(x) - 3$		
$f(-x) + 4$		

Q10 $y = \cos x$ is translated by the vector $\begin{pmatrix} 90° \\ 0 \end{pmatrix}$ and stretched by scale factor $\frac{1}{2}$ parallel to the y-axis.

    a) Sketch the new graph for $0 \le x \le 360°$.

    b) Write down its equation.

Q11 a) Sketch the graph of $y = f(x)$ where $f(x) = \frac{1}{x}$.

    b) Write down the sequence of transformations needed to map $f(x)$ on to $g(x) = 3 - \frac{1}{x}$.

    c) Sketch the graph of $y = g(x)$.

Q12 Complete the following table:

Original graph	New graph	Sequence of transformations
$y = x^3$	$y = (x - 4)^3 + 5$	
$y = 4^x$	$y = 4^{3x} - 1$	
$y = \|x + 1\|$	$y = 1 - \|2x + 1\|$	
$y = \sin x$	$y = -3\sin 2x + 1$	

Q13 a) Write $y = 2x^2 - 4x + 6$ in the form $y = a[(x + b)^2 + c]$.

    b) Hence list the sequence of transformations that will map $y = x^2$ on to $y = 2x^2 - 4x + 6$.

    c) Sketch the graph of $y = 2x^2 - 4x + 6$.

    d) Write down the coordinates of the minimum point of the graph.

Q14 Starting with the curve $y = \cos x$, state the sequence of transformations which could be used to sketch the following curves:

    a) $y = 4 \cos 3x$ b) $y = 4 - \cos 2x$ c) $y = 2 \cos(x - 60°)$

Q15 The diagram to the right shows $y = f(x)$ with a minimum point, P, at $(2, -3)$. Copy the diagram and sketch each of the following graphs. In each case state the new coordinates of the point P.

    a) $y = f(x) + 5$

    b) $y = f(x + 4)$

    c) $y = -f(x)$

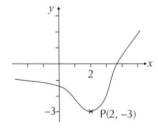

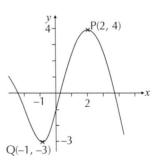

Q16 The diagram shows $y = f(x)$ with a minimum point, Q, at $(-1, -3)$ and a maximum point, P, at $(2, 4)$.

Copy the diagram and sketch each of the following graphs. In each case state the new coordinates of the points P and Q.

    a) $y = f(x - 1) + 3$

    b) $y = -f(2x)$

    c) $y = |f(x + 2)|$

Q17 If $f^{-1}(x + 1) = \ln x$, find $f(x)$. Describe the transformation that maps $y = f(x)$ on to $y = f^{-1}(x + 1)$.

2.7 Partial Fractions

Sometimes an algebraic fraction can be split into a sum of simpler fractions. Here you'll see a couple of methods you can use to do this, depending on what type of denominator you have.

Learning Objective (Spec Ref 2.10):

- Write algebraic fractions with linear or constant numerators as partial fractions, including fractions with denominators of the form $(ax + b)(cx + d)(ex + f)$ and $(ax + b)(cx + d)^2$.

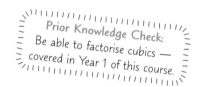

Prior Knowledge Check:
Be able to factorise cubics — covered in Year 1 of this course.

Expressing in partial fractions

You can split a fraction with **more than one linear factor** in the denominator into **partial fractions**.

This means writing it as a **sum** of two or more **simpler fractions**.

The **denominators** of these simpler fractions will be **factors** of the denominator of the original fraction.

This is useful in lots of areas of maths, such as **integration** (see p.239-240) and **binomial expansions** (p.146-147).

Example 1

- $\dfrac{7x - 7}{(2x + 1)(x - 3)}$ can be written as partial fractions of the form $\dfrac{A}{(2x + 1)} + \dfrac{B}{(x - 3)}$

- $\dfrac{7x - 1}{(x - 3)(x - 1)(x + 2)}$ can be written as partial fractions of the form $\dfrac{A}{(x - 3)} + \dfrac{B}{(x - 1)} + \dfrac{C}{(x + 2)}$

- $\dfrac{21x - 2}{9x^2 - 4}$ can be written as partial fractions of the form $\dfrac{A}{(3x - 2)} + \dfrac{B}{(3x + 2)}$

If you're asked to write an algebraic fraction as partial fractions, start by writing the partial fractions out with A, B and C as numerators as shown above. You might have to factorise the denominator first, like in the last example.

The tricky bit is **working out** what A, B and C are. Follow this method:

- **Write out** the expression as an identity, e.g. $\dfrac{7x - 7}{(2x + 1)(x - 3)} \equiv \dfrac{A}{(2x + 1)} + \dfrac{B}{(x - 3)}$

- **Add** the partial fractions together, i.e. write them over a **common denominator**.

- **Cancel** the denominators from both sides (they'll be the same).

- This will give you an **identity** for A and B, for example: $7x - 7 \equiv A(x - 3) + B(2x + 1)$

- Use the Substitution method or the Equating Coefficients method:

Substitution	Equating Coefficients
Substitute a number for x to leave you with just one constant on the right hand side.	Equate the constant terms, coefficients of x and coefficients of x^2, then solve the equations simultaneously.

Example 2

Express $\dfrac{7x-1}{(x-3)(x-1)(x+2)}$ in partial fractions.

1. Write it out as an **identity**:

$$\frac{7x-1}{(x-3)(x-1)(x+2)} \equiv \frac{A}{(x-3)} + \frac{B}{(x-1)} + \frac{C}{(x+2)}$$

2. **Add** the partial fractions — this means writing them over a **common denominator**:

$$\frac{A}{(x-3)} + \frac{B}{(x-1)} + \frac{C}{(x+2)} \equiv$$

$$\frac{A(x-1)(x+2) + B(x-3)(x+2) + C(x-3)(x-1)}{(x-3)(x-1)(x+2)}$$

This adding step can be a bit fiddly, so you should check that each term will cancel to produce the original fraction.

3. **Cancel** the denominators from both sides of the original identity, so the numerators are **equal**: $\quad 7x - 1 \equiv A(x-1)(x+2) + B(x-3)(x+2) + C(x-3)(x-1)$

Substitution Method

Substitute values of x which make one of the expressions in brackets equal zero to get rid of all but one of A, B and C.

- Substituting $x = 3$ gets rid of B and C:

  $21 - 1 = A(3-1)(3+2) + 0 + 0$
  $20 = 10A \qquad\qquad \Rightarrow A = 2$

- Substituting $x = 1$ gets rid of A and C:

  $7 - 1 = 0 + B(1-3)(1+2) + 0$
  $6 = -6B \qquad\qquad \Rightarrow \mathbf{B = -1}$

- Substituting $x = -2$ gets rid of A and B:

  $-14 - 1 = 0 + 0 + C(-2-3)(-2-1)$
  $-15 = 15C \qquad\qquad \Rightarrow C = -1$

Equating Coefficients Method

- Compare coefficients in the numerators:

  $7x - 1 \equiv A(x-1)(x+2) + B(x-3)(x+2) + C(x-3)(x-1)$
  $\equiv A(x^2 + x - 2) + B(x^2 - x - 6) + C(x^2 - 4x + 3)$
  $\equiv (A + B + C)x^2 + (A - B - 4C)x + (-2A - 6B + 3C)$

- Equating x^2 coefficients: $\quad 0 = A + B + C$

- Equating x coefficients: $\quad 7 = A - B - 4C$

- Equating constant terms: $\quad -1 = -2A - 6B + 3C$

- Solving these equations simultaneously gives $A = 2$, $B = -1$ and $C = -1$ (the same as the substitution method)

Generally it's easier to try the **substitution** method first. Here, it's actually quite tricky to solve the simultaneous equations that you get by equating coefficients.

4. Finally, **replace** A, B and C in the original identity:

$$\frac{7x-1}{(x-3)(x-1)(x+2)} \equiv \frac{2}{(x-3)} - \frac{1}{(x-1)} - \frac{1}{(x+2)}$$

Tip: Don't forget to write out your solution like this once you've done all the working.

Example 3

Express $\dfrac{3-x}{x^2+x}$ in partial fractions.

1. First you need to **factorise** the denominator:

$$\frac{3-x}{x^2+x} \equiv \frac{3-x}{x(x+1)}.$$

2. Now write as an **identity** with partial fractions:

$$\frac{3-x}{x(x+1)} \equiv \frac{A}{x} + \frac{B}{x+1}.$$

3. **Add** the partial fractions and **cancel** the denominators from both sides:

$$\frac{3-x}{x(x+1)} \equiv \frac{A(x+1)+Bx}{x(x+1)}$$

$$\Rightarrow \quad 3-x \equiv A(x+1)+Bx$$

Here it's easier to **equate coefficients** because A is the only letter that appears in the constant term.

- **Compare coefficients:** Equating constant terms: $3 = A$

  Equating x coefficients: $-1 = A + B \Rightarrow -1 = 3 + B \Rightarrow \boldsymbol{B = -4}$

- **Replace** A and B in the identity:

$$\frac{3-x}{x^2+x} \equiv \frac{3}{x} - \frac{4}{(x+1)}$$

Exercise 2.7.1

Q1 Express $\dfrac{3x+3}{(x-1)(x-4)}$ in the form $\dfrac{A}{x-1} + \dfrac{B}{x-4}$.

Q2 Express $\dfrac{5x-1}{x(2x+1)}$ in the form $\dfrac{A}{x} + \dfrac{B}{2x+1}$.

Q3 Find the values of the constants A and B in the identity $\dfrac{3x-2}{x^2+x-12} \equiv \dfrac{A}{x+4} + \dfrac{B}{x-3}$.

Q4 Write $\dfrac{2}{x^2-16}$ in partial fractions.

Q5 Factorise $x^2 - x - 6$ and hence express $\dfrac{5}{x^2-x-6}$ in partial fractions.

Q6 Write $\dfrac{11x}{2x^2+5x-12}$ in partial fractions.

Q7 a) Factorise $x^3 - 9x$ fully.

   b) Hence write $\dfrac{12x+18}{x^3-9x}$ in partial fractions.

Q8 Write $\dfrac{3x+9}{x^3-36x}$ in the form $\dfrac{A}{x} + \dfrac{B}{x+6} + \dfrac{C}{x-6}$.

Q9 a) Use the Factor Theorem to fully factorise $x^3 - 7x - 6$.

   b) Hence write $\dfrac{6x+2}{x^3-7x-6}$ in partial fractions.

Q10 Express the following in partial fractions:

a) $\dfrac{6x+4}{(x+4)(x-1)(x+1)}$

b) $\dfrac{15x-27}{x^3-6x^2+3x+10}$

c) $\dfrac{2x+7}{x^3-2x^2-5x+6}$

d) $\dfrac{162}{x^3-81x}$

e) $\dfrac{6-x}{2x^3-7x^2+7x-2}$

f) $\dfrac{x+4}{15x^3-x^2-2x}$

Repeated factors

If the denominator of an algebraic fraction has **repeated linear factors** the partial fractions will take a slightly **different form**, as shown in the examples below.

- The **power** of the repeated factor tells you **how many** times that factor should appear in the partial fractions.

  $$\frac{7x-3}{(x+1)^2(x-4)} \text{ is written as } \frac{A}{(x+1)} + \frac{B}{(x+1)^2} + \frac{C}{(x-4)}$$

- A factor that's **squared** in the original denominator will appear in the denominator of **two** of your partial fractions — once squared and once just as it is.

  $$\frac{32x-14}{x^2(2x+7)} \text{ is written as } \frac{A}{x} + \frac{B}{x^2} + \frac{C}{(2x+7)}$$

Tip: A factor that's **cubed** will appear **three** times — once cubed, once squared and once just as it is.

Example 1

Express $\dfrac{5x+12}{x^2(x-3)}$ **in partial fractions.**

1. x is a **repeated factor** so the answer will be of the form $\dfrac{A}{x} + \dfrac{B}{x^2} + \dfrac{C}{(x-3)}$.

2. Write it out as an **identity**:

   $$\frac{5x+12}{x^2(x-3)} \equiv \frac{A}{x} + \frac{B}{x^2} + \frac{C}{(x-3)}$$

3. **Add** the partial fractions:

   $$\frac{5x+12}{x^2(x-3)} \equiv \frac{Ax(x-3) + B(x-3) + Cx^2}{x^2(x-3)}$$

4. **Cancel** the denominators from both sides, so that the numerators are **equal**:

   $$5x+12 \equiv Ax(x-3) + B(x-3) + Cx^2$$

5. **Substitute** $x = 3$ to get rid of A and B:

   $$15 + 12 = 0 + 0 + C(3^2)$$
   $$\Rightarrow 27 = 9C \Rightarrow \mathbf{C = 3}$$

6. **Substitute** $x = 0$ to get rid of A and C:

   $$0 + 12 = 0 + B(0-3) + 0$$
   $$\Rightarrow 12 = -3B \Rightarrow \mathbf{B = -4}$$

7. There's no value of x you can substitute to get rid of B and C and just leave A, so **equate coefficients** of x^2:

   Coefficients of x^2 are: $\quad 0 = A + C$
   You know $C = 3$, so: $\quad 0 = A + 3 \Rightarrow \mathbf{A = -3}$

8. **Replace** A, B and C in the identity:

   $$\frac{5x+12}{x^2(x-3)} \equiv -\frac{3}{x} - \frac{4}{x^2} + \frac{3}{(x-3)}$$

Example 2

Express $\dfrac{4x+15}{(x+2)^2(3x-1)}$ **in partial fractions.**

1. Write the **identity**:

   $$\frac{4x+15}{(x+2)^2(3x-1)} \equiv \frac{A}{(x+2)} + \frac{B}{(x+2)^2} + \frac{C}{(3x-1)}$$

2. **Add** the partial fractions:

$$\frac{A}{(x+2)} + \frac{B}{(x+2)^2} + \frac{C}{(3x-1)} \equiv$$

$$\frac{A(x+2)(3x-1) + B(3x-1) + C(x+2)^2}{(x+2)^2(3x-1)}$$

3. **Cancel** the denominators from both sides: $4x + 15 \equiv A(x+2)(3x-1) + B(3x-1) + C(x+2)^2$

4. **Substitute** $x = -2$ to get rid of A and C:

$-8 + 15 = 0 + B(-6-1) + 0$

$\Rightarrow 7 = -7B \qquad \Rightarrow \boldsymbol{B = -1}$

5. **Substitute** $x = \frac{1}{3}$ to get rid of A and B:

$\frac{4}{3} + 15 = 0 + 0 + C\left(\frac{1}{3}+2\right)^2$

$\Rightarrow \frac{49}{3} = \frac{49}{9}C \Rightarrow \boldsymbol{C = 3}$

6. There's no value of x you can substitute to get rid of B and C to just leave A, so try **equating coefficients** instead:

Equate coefficients of x^2: $0 = 3A + C$
You know $C = 3$, so: $\qquad -3 = 3A \Rightarrow \boldsymbol{A = -1}$

(There is another method you could have used here — when there's no value of x which will get rid of B and C, you can substitute in any simple value of x (e.g. $x = 0$ or 1) and the values that you have calculated for B and C. From this you can find A.)

7. **Replace** A, B and C in the original identity:

$$\frac{4x+15}{(x+2)^2(3x-1)} \equiv -\frac{1}{(x+2)} - \frac{1}{(x+2)^2} + \frac{3}{(3x-1)}$$

Exercise 2.7.2

Q1 Express $\dfrac{3x}{(x+5)^2}$ in the form $\dfrac{A}{(x+5)} + \dfrac{B}{(x+5)^2}$.

Q2 Write $\dfrac{5x+2}{x^2(x+1)}$ in the form $\dfrac{A}{x} + \dfrac{B}{x^2} + \dfrac{C}{(x+1)}$.

Q3 Write the following in partial fractions.

a) $\dfrac{2x-7}{(x-3)^2}$
b) $\dfrac{6x+7}{(2x+3)^2}$
c) $\dfrac{7x}{(x+4)^2(x-3)}$
d) $\dfrac{11x-10}{x(x-5)^2}$

Q4 Express $\dfrac{5x+10}{x^3-10x^2+25x}$ in partial fractions.

Q5 Express $\dfrac{3x+2}{(x-2)(x^2-4)}$ in partial fractions.

Q6 Express $\dfrac{7x+3}{x^2(3-2x)}$ in partial fractions.

Q7 Find the value of c such that $\dfrac{x+17}{(x+1)(x+c)^2} = \dfrac{1}{x+1} - \dfrac{1}{x+c} + \dfrac{5}{(x+c)^2}$

Q8 a) Show that $2x^3 + 7x^2 + 4x - 4$ can be factorised as $(x+2)(ax+b)(cx+d)$, where a, b, c and d are integers to be found.

b) Hence, express $\dfrac{x-13}{2x^3+7x^2+4x-4}$ in partial fractions.

Review Exercise

Q1 Simplify the following:

a) $\dfrac{4x^2 - 25}{6x - 15}$

b) $\dfrac{2x + 3}{x - 2} \times \dfrac{4x - 8}{2x^2 - 3x - 9}$

c) $\dfrac{x^2 - 3x}{x + 1} \div \dfrac{x}{2}$

Q2 Write the following as a single fraction:

a) $\dfrac{x}{2x + 1} + \dfrac{3}{x^2} + \dfrac{1}{x}$

b) $\dfrac{2}{x^2 - 1} - \dfrac{3x}{x - 1} + \dfrac{x}{x + 1}$

c) $\dfrac{2}{(x + 1)^2} - \dfrac{x}{x + 1} + \dfrac{1}{3x}$

Q3 Write $2x^3 + 8x^2 + 7x + 8$ in the form $(Ax^2 + Bx + C)(x + 3) + D$.
Using your answer, state the result when $2x^3 + 8x^2 + 7x + 8$ is divided by $(x + 3)$.

Q4 Divide $x^4 + x^3 - 5x^2 - 7x - 2$ by $x + 1$, hence find a solution to $x^4 + x^3 - 5x^2 - 7x = 2$.

Q5 For the following mappings, state the range and say whether or not the mapping is a function.
If not, explain why, and if so, say whether the function is one-to-one or many-to-one.

a) $f(x) = x^2 - 16, \ x \geq 0$

b) $f : x \rightarrow x^2 - 7x + 10, \ x \in \mathbb{R}$

c) $f(x) = \sqrt{x}, \ x \in \mathbb{R}$

Q6 $f(x) = \dfrac{5}{2x + 1}$ defines a mapping.

a) Evaluate $f(0)$ and $f(\tfrac{1}{2})$.

b) Draw the mapping diagram for the domain $x \in \mathbb{N}, \ x < 6$ and list the range.

c) Is the mapping a function for the domain $x \in \mathbb{Z}$? If not, explain why not.

d) Is the mapping a function for the domain $x \in \mathbb{R}$? If not, explain why not.

Q7 a) Sketch the graph of the function $f(x) = \begin{cases} x^2 - 2 & -2 < x < 2 \\ 2 & \text{otherwise} \end{cases}$

b) State the range of the function.

Q8 For each pair of functions f and g, find $fg(2)$, $gf(1)$ and $fg(x)$.

a) $f(x) = \dfrac{3}{x}, \ x > 0$ and $g(x) = 2x + 3, \ x \in \mathbb{R}$

b) $f(x) = 3x^2, \ x \geq 0$ and $g(x) = x + 4, \ x \in \mathbb{R}$

Q9 $f(x) = \log_{10} x$ and $g(x) = 10^{x+1}$.

a) Find the values of $fg(1)$, $gf(1)$, $f^2(10)$ and $g^2(-1)$. b) Explain why $f^2(1)$ is undefined.

Q10 $f(x) = 3x$ and $g(x) = x + 7$, both with domain $x \in \mathbb{R}$.
Find the composite functions $fg(x)$, $gf(x)$ and $g^2(x)$.

Q11 A one-to-one function f has domain $x \in \mathbb{R}$ and range $f(x) \geq 3$.
Does this function have an inverse? If so, state its domain and range.

Q12 Using algebra, find the inverse of the function $f(x) = \sqrt{2x - 4}, \ x \geq 2$.
State the domain and range of the inverse.

Q13 $f(x) = \cos x, \ 0 \leq x \leq \dfrac{\pi}{2}$. Does the inverse function $f^{-1}(x)$ exist? Justify your answer.

Review Exercise

Q14 The function $f(x) = \dfrac{x}{x-1}$, $x < 1$. Show that $f(x) = f^{-1}(x)$, hence find $f^2(x)$.

Q15 $f(x) = \log_{10}(x + 4)$, $x > -4$. Find $f^{-1}(x)$.

Q16 For the function $f(x) = 2x - 1$, $x \in \mathbb{R}$, sketch the graphs of:

    a) $|f(x)|$ b) $f(|x|)$

Q17 Solve the equation $|3x - 1| = |4 - x|$.

Q18 $f(x) = x^2 - 2x - 8$.

    a) On the same axes sketch the graphs of $|f(x)|$ and $f(|x|)$.

    b) Use your graphs to help you solve the equation $f(|x|) = -5$.

Q19 The graph on the right shows
the function $y = \cos x$, $0 \le x \le 360°$.
Sketch the graph of $y = -\cos 2x + 1$.

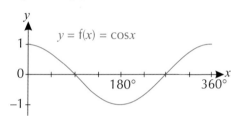

Q20 Sketch the graphs of:

    a) $y = 3x + 2$ b) $y = |3x + 2|$ c) $y = -|3x + 2|$

Q21 Write $\dfrac{2x}{(x-5)(x+5)}$ as partial fractions in the form $\dfrac{A}{(x-5)} + \dfrac{B}{(x+5)}$.

Q22 Find the values of the constants A and B in the identity $\dfrac{2-x}{(3x+2)(x+1)} \equiv \dfrac{A}{(3x+2)} + \dfrac{B}{(x+1)}$.

Q23 Find the values of the constants A and B in the identity $\dfrac{x-3}{x^2+3x+2} \equiv \dfrac{A}{(x+1)} + \dfrac{B}{(x+2)}$.

Q24 Express the following as partial fractions:

    a) $\dfrac{4}{x^2+x}$ b) $\dfrac{4x+5}{(x+4)(2x-3)}$ c) $\dfrac{5x}{x^2+x-6}$

    d) $\dfrac{10x}{(x+3)(2x+4)}$ e) $\dfrac{6x+10}{(2x+1)(2-3x)}$ f) $\dfrac{2x+1}{x^2+3x}$

Q25 Show that $\dfrac{2x-5}{(x-5)^2}$ can be written in the form $\dfrac{A}{(x-5)} + \dfrac{B}{(x-5)^2}$.

Q26 Express the following as partial fractions.

    a) $\dfrac{2x+2}{(x+3)^2}$ b) $\dfrac{-18x+14}{(2x-1)^2(x+2)}$ c) $\dfrac{x-5}{x^3-x^2}$

Q27 Find the value of b such that $\dfrac{bx+7}{(x+1)^2(x+2)} = \dfrac{3}{x+1} + \dfrac{2}{(x+1)^2} - \dfrac{3}{x+2}$.

Exam-Style Questions

Q1 $f(x) = \dfrac{1}{x} - \dfrac{2x}{x+1}$

    a) Rewrite $f(x)$ as the quotient $f(x) = \dfrac{g(x)}{h(x)}$, where $g(x)$ and $h(x)$ are
        both fully factorised quadratic functions to be found.

                                                                     [3 marks]

    b) The graph $y = f(x)$ is plotted.
        What are the equations of the vertical asymptotes of this graph?

                                                                     [2 marks]

Q2   The diagram below shows a sketch of the curve $y = f(x)$, $-12 \le x \le 12$.

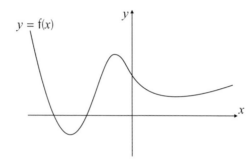

    The curve intersects the axes at $x = -9$, $x = -5$ and $y = 4$, and has a minimum at point $(-7, -2)$.

    a) For each of the following equations in the given intervals, state all the solutions that can
        be found with the information provided, and state the number of unknown solutions:

        (i) $f(x) = -f(x)$, $-12 \le x \le 12$

        (ii) $f(x) = f(|x|)$, $-12 \le x \le 0$

        (iii) $f(x) = f^{-1}(x)$, $-12 \le x \le 12$

                                                                   [6 marks]

    b) On a separate set of axes, sketch the curve for $y = f(4x) + 2$.
        Clearly label any axis-intercepts and the interval for which it is valid.

                                                                      [4 marks]

Q3 $g(x) = x^3 + x^2 - x - 1$

    a) Given that $(x - 1)$ is a factor of $g(x)$, fully factorise $g(x)$.

                                                                     [3 marks]

    b) Hence, express $\dfrac{x-5}{x^3 + x^2 - x - 1}$ in partial fractions.

                                                                     [4 marks]

Exam-Style Questions

Q4   Given that $r(x) = 2x^3 + 9x^2 - 5x - 39$, solve $r(x) = x + 1$.

[6 marks]

Q5   a) For the functions
$$f(x) = 2x - 3, \ x \in \mathbb{R} \quad , \quad g(x) = \frac{1}{x}, \ x > 0$$
find the following composite functions, along with the range and domain of each.

(i) fg(x)

(ii) gf(x)

[4 marks]

b) f(x) is combined with a third function, h(x), to form the composite function hf(x), where h(x) and hf(x) are both linear. This is shown in the diagram below.

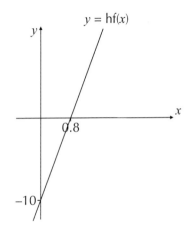

Use the information given in the diagram to find an expression for h(x).

[4 marks]

Q6   a) $f(x) = |2x - 5|$ and $g(x) = 3|x| + 4$.
On the same set of axes, sketch the following, clearly labelling any axis-intercepts:

(i) $y = f(x)$

(ii) $y = g(x)$

[4 marks]

b) Hence or otherwise solve the inequality $f(x) > g(x)$.

[3 marks]

c) The inequality $f(x) > g(x) + k$, where k is a real number, has no real solutions.
Find the smallest possible value of k.

[1 mark]

3.1 Arcs and Sectors

You'll be familiar with angles being measured in degrees. Radians are another unit of measurement for angles. They can be easier to use than degrees when measuring things like the arc length of a sector of a circle or its area, and they come up a lot in trigonometry and throughout the course.

Learning Objectives (Spec Ref 5.1):
- Use radians as the measure for the size of an angle.
- Use the formula $s = r\theta$ to work out the arc length of a sector of a circle.
- Use the formula $A = \frac{1}{2}r^2\theta$ to work out the area of a sector.

Radians

A **radian** (rad) is just another unit of measurement for an angle.

1 radian is the angle formed in a **sector** that has an **arc length** that is the same as the **radius**.

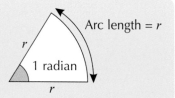

Tip: Radians are sometimes shown by 'rad' after the number, or a '^{c}' (e.g. $4\pi^c$), but most of the time angles in radians are given without a symbol.

In other words, if you have a **sector** with an angle of **1 radian**, then the **length** of the **arc** will be exactly the **same length** as the **radius** r.

It's important to know how **radians relate to degrees**:
- 360 degrees (a complete circle) = 2π radians
- 180 degrees = π radians
- 1 radian is about 57 degrees

You also need to know how to **convert** between the two units. The table below shows you how:

Converting angles	
Radians to degrees: Divide by π, multiply by 180.	**Degrees to radians:** Divide by 180, multiply by π.

Here's a table of some of the **common angles** you're going to need, in degrees and radians:

Degrees	0	30	45	60	90	120	180	270	360
Radians	0	$\frac{\pi}{6}$	$\frac{\pi}{4}$	$\frac{\pi}{3}$	$\frac{\pi}{2}$	$\frac{2\pi}{3}$	π	$\frac{3\pi}{2}$	2π

It's a good idea to learn these common angles — they come up a lot.

Examples

a) Convert $\frac{\pi}{15}$ into degrees.

   1. To convert from radians
      to degrees, divide by π...

$$\frac{\pi}{15} \div \pi = \frac{1}{15}$$

   2. ... then multiply by 180.

$$\frac{1}{15} \times 180 = \boxed{12°}$$

> **Tip:** Notice how the angle was given without a symbol — if this happens, you can just assume it's in radians.

b) Convert 120 degrees into radians.

To convert from degrees to radians, divide by 180 and then multiply by π:

$$\frac{120}{180} \times \pi = \frac{2\pi}{3}$$

← This one's in the table on the previous page.

c) Convert 297 degrees into radians.

Divide by 180 and then multiply by π:

$$\frac{297}{180} \times \pi = \boxed{1.65\pi \text{ or } 5.18 \text{ rad (3 s.f.)}}$$

Exercise 3.1.1

Q1 Convert the angles below into radians. Give your answers in terms of π.

   a) 180°   b) 135°   c) 270°

   d) 70°   e) 150°   f) 75°

Q2 Convert the angles below into degrees.

   a) $\frac{\pi}{4}$ b) $\frac{\pi}{2}$ c) $\frac{\pi}{3}$

   d) $\frac{5\pi}{2}$ e) $\frac{3\pi}{4}$ f) $\frac{7\pi}{3}$

Arc length and sector area

A **sector** is part of a circle formed by **two radii** and part of the **circumference**. The **arc** of a sector is the **curved** edge of the sector. You can work out the **length** of the arc, or the **area** of the sector — as long as you know the **angle** at the **centre** (θ) and the **length** of the **radius** (r).

When working out arc length and sector area, you **always** work in radians.

Arc length

For a circle with **radius** r, a sector with **angle** θ (measured in **radians**) has **arc length** s, given by: $\boxed{s = r\theta}$

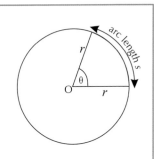

- If you put $\theta = 2\pi$ in this formula (and so make the sector equal to the whole circle), you find that the distance all the way round the outside of the circle is $s = 2\pi r$.

- This is just the normal **circumference** formula.

Sector area

For a circle with **radius** r, a sector with **angle** θ (measured in **radians**) has **area** A, given by: $\boxed{A = \frac{1}{2}r^2\theta}$

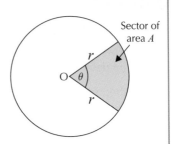

- Again, if you put $\theta = 2\pi$ in the formula, you find that the area of the whole circle is $A = \frac{1}{2}r^2 \times 2\pi = \pi r^2$.

- This is just the normal '**area of a circle**' formula.

Example 1

Find the exact length L and area A in the diagram to the right.

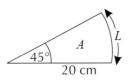

1. It's asking for an arc length and sector area, so you need the angle in **radians**:

$$45° = \frac{45 \times \pi}{180} = \frac{\pi}{4} \text{ radians}$$

2. Now put everything in your formulas:

$$L = r\theta = 20 \times \frac{\pi}{4} = \boxed{5\pi \text{ cm}}$$

$$A = \frac{1}{2}r^2\theta = \frac{1}{2} \times 20^2 \times \frac{\pi}{4} = \boxed{50\pi \text{ cm}^2}$$

Example 2

Find the area of the shaded part of the symbol.

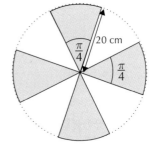

1. Use the area formula to find the area of one 'leaf'.

$$\frac{1}{2} \times 20^2 \times \frac{\pi}{4} = 50\pi \text{ cm}^2$$

2. Multiply by 4 to find the total area.

$$4 \times 50\pi = \boxed{200\pi \text{ cm}^2}$$

Tip: You could have also worked this out in one step using the total angle of all the shaded sectors (π).

Example 3

Find the exact value of θ in the diagram to the right.

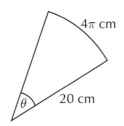

Use the formula for the arc length:

$$s = r\theta \implies 4\pi = 20\theta$$

$$\implies \theta = \frac{4\pi}{20} = \boxed{\frac{\pi}{5} \text{ radians}}$$

Example 4

The sector shown has an area of 6π cm². Find the arc length, s.

1. First, get the angle in radians: $60° = \dfrac{60 \times \pi}{180} = \dfrac{\pi}{3}$ radians

2. Use the area formula to work out the radius.

   $A = \dfrac{1}{2}r^2\theta \Rightarrow 6\pi = \dfrac{1}{2} \times r^2 \times \dfrac{\pi}{3}$

   $\Rightarrow 36 = r^2$

   $\Rightarrow r = 6$

   Tip: $\dfrac{\pi}{3}$ is one of the common angles from the table on p.50 — it's definitely worth learning them.

3. Substitute this value of r into the equation for arc length: $s = r\theta = 6 \times \dfrac{\pi}{3} = \boxed{2\pi \text{ cm}}$

Exercise 3.1.2

Q1 The diagram below shows a sector OAB. The centre is at O and the radius is 6 cm. The angle AOB is 2 radians. Find the arc length and area of this sector.

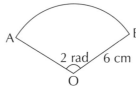

Q2 The diagram on the right shows a sector OAB. The centre is at O and the radius is 8 cm. The angle AOB is 46°. Find the arc length and area of this sector to 1 d.p.

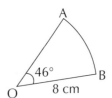

Q3 A sector of a circle of radius 4 cm has an area of 6π cm². Find the exact value of the angle θ.

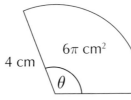

Q4 The diagram on the right shows a sector of a circle with a centre O and radius r cm. The angle AOB shown is θ.

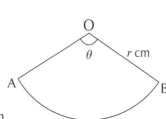

For each of the following values of θ and r, give the arc length and the area of the sector. Where appropriate, give your answers to 3 s.f.

a) $\theta = 1.2$ radians, $r = 5$ cm   b) $\theta = 0.6$ radians, $r = 4$ cm

c) $\theta = 80°$, $r = 9$ cm   d) $\theta = \dfrac{5\pi}{12}$, $r = 4$ cm

Q5   The diagram below shows a sector ABC of a circle, where the angle BAC is 0.9 radians. Given that the area of the sector is 16.2 cm², find the arc length *s*.

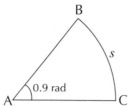

Q6   A circle C has a radius of length 3 cm with centre O. A sector of this circle is given by angle AOB which is 20°. Find the length of the arc AB and the area of the sector. Give your answer in terms of π.

Q7   The sector below has an arc length of 7 cm. The angle BAC is 1.4 rad. Find the area of the sector.

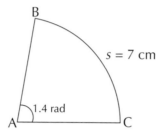

Q8   The sector ABC below is part of a circle, where the angle BAC is 50°. Given that the area of the sector is 20π cm², find the arc length BC. Give your answer in terms of π.

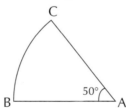

Q9   A circle of radius *r* contains a sector of area 80π cm². Given that the arc length of the sector is 16π cm, find the angle of the sector (θ) and the value of *r*, giving your answers to 3 s.f.

Q10   The diagram below shows a semicircle of radius 2 cm, with a smaller sector of radius 1 cm removed. Given that the area of the sector A and the area of B are equal, find the exact value of θ.

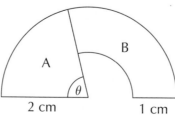

3.2 Small Angle Approximations

When you're working in radians, there are some very handy approximations for the sin, cos and tan values of a really small angle. They're not perfect, and they become less accurate with larger angles, but they're important for finding the derivatives of the trig functions (which you'll see in Chapter 7).

Learning Objectives (Spec Ref 5.2):
- Use the small angle approximations for $\sin \theta$, $\cos \theta$ and $\tan \theta$.
- Use a combination of these to approximate functions for small θ.

The small angle approximations

When θ (measured in radians) is very small, you can approximate the value of $\sin \theta$, $\cos \theta$ and $\tan \theta$ using the **small angle approximations**:

$$\sin \theta \approx \theta \qquad \cos \theta \approx 1 - \frac{1}{2}\theta^2 \qquad \tan \theta \approx \theta$$

You don't need to know where they come from, but it might help you to understand why they work. Sin θ, cos θ and tan θ can each be written as an **infinite series** (a sum of terms — see Chapter 5 for more on series and summation notation) known as the **Maclaurin series**:

$$\sin \theta = \theta - \frac{1}{6}\theta^3 + \frac{1}{120}\theta^5 - \dots = \sum_{n=0}^{\infty}(-1)^n\frac{\theta^{2n+1}}{(2n+1)!}$$

$$\cos \theta = 1 - \frac{1}{2}\theta^2 + \frac{1}{24}\theta^4 - \dots = \sum_{n=0}^{\infty}(-1)^n\frac{\theta^{2n}}{(2n)!}$$

$$\tan \theta = \theta + \frac{1}{3}\theta^3 + \frac{2}{15}\theta^5 - \dots$$

Tip: The Maclaurin series for tan θ is a bit messy in sum notation, so it's been left out here.

When θ is small ($\theta < 1$), θ^n gets smaller and smaller as n increases, so most of the terms in each series will be tiny (almost 0). Choosing to ignore all of the terms with θ^3 or a higher power leaves you with something close to the actual answer — so $\sin \theta \approx \theta$, $\cos \theta \approx 1 - \frac{1}{2}\theta^2$ and $\tan \theta \approx \theta$.

Note that these approximations only work when $\theta < 1$ — above that, the θ^n terms get bigger instead of smaller, so you can't ignore them.

Remember, θ must be in radians for these to work, not in degrees — you may have to convert before you use the approximations.

Example 1

Give an approximation for cos 0.2.

1. Write down the small angle approximation for cos. $\cos \theta \approx 1 - \frac{1}{2}\theta^2$

2. Then substitute in $\theta = 0.2$: $\cos 0.2 \approx 1 - \frac{1}{2}(0.2)^2$

   $\approx 1 - 0.02 = \boxed{0.98}$

The actual value of cos 0.2 is 0.980067 (to 6 d.p.), so this approximation is pretty accurate.

Approximating functions

These approximations are most useful for approximating more **complicated functions**, which could involve sin, cos and tan of **multiples** of θ (when θ is small, you can assume that multiples of θ are also small). Make sure that you apply the approximation to **everything** inside the trig function.

For example: $\tan 4\theta \approx 4\theta$ $\qquad \sin \frac{1}{2}\theta \approx \frac{1}{2}\theta$ $\qquad \cos 3\theta \approx 1 - \frac{1}{2}(3\theta)^2$

You might have to use more than one formula in a question.

Example 2

Find an approximation for $f(\theta) = 4 \cos \theta \tan 3\theta$ when θ is small.

Replace cos and tan with the small angle approximations.

$f(\theta) \approx 4 \times (1 - \frac{1}{2}\theta^2) \times 3\theta \quad \leftarrow \approx \cos \theta$, $\approx \tan 3\theta$
$= (4 - 2\theta^2) \times 3\theta$
$= \boxed{12\theta - 6\theta^3}$ (or $6\theta(2 - \theta^2)$)

Example 3

Show that $\dfrac{2\theta \sin 2\theta}{1 - \cos 5\theta} \approx \dfrac{8}{25}$ when θ is small.

Use the small angle approximations for each trig function.

$f(\theta) = \dfrac{2\theta \sin 2\theta}{1 - \cos 5\theta} \approx \dfrac{2\theta(2\theta)}{1 - \left(1 - \frac{1}{2}(5\theta)^2\right)}$

$= \dfrac{4\theta^2}{\frac{25}{2}\theta^2} = \boxed{\dfrac{8}{25}}$ as required

---

Exercise 3.2.1

Q1 Use the small angle approximations to estimate the following values, then find the actual values on a calculator:

a) sin 0.23   b) cos 0.01   c) tan 0.18

Q2 For the values of θ below, use the small angle approximations to estimate the value of $f(\theta) = \sin \theta + \cos \theta$, then use a calculator to find the actual answer:

a) $\theta = 0.3$ b) $\theta = 0.5$ c) $\theta = 0.25$ d) $\theta = 0.01$

Q3 Find an approximation for the following expressions when θ is small:

a) $\sin \theta \cos \theta$ b) $\theta \tan 5\theta \sin \theta$ c) $\dfrac{\sin 4\theta \cos 3\theta}{2\theta}$

d) $3 \tan \theta + \cos 2\theta$ e) $\sin \frac{1}{2}\theta - \cos \theta$ f) $\dfrac{\cos \theta - \cos 2\theta}{1 - (\cos 3\theta + 3 \sin \theta \tan \theta)}$

Q4 A pendulum of length 6 cm follows the arc of a circle. Its straight-line displacement as a vector is given by: $\mathbf{d} = 6 \sin \theta\, \mathbf{i} + 6(1 - \cos \theta)\mathbf{j}$.

a) Show that the magnitude of the displacement is $6\sqrt{2(1 - \cos \theta)}$.

b) Show that, when θ is small, the magnitude of the displacement can be approximated by the arc length s.

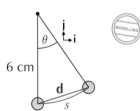

3.3 Inverse Trig Functions

In Chapter 2 you saw that some functions have inverses, which reverse the effect of the function. The trig functions have inverses too.

Learning Objectives (Spec Ref 5.4):

- Know that the inverse of the trig functions sin, cos and tan are arcsin, arccos and arctan.
- Recognise and sketch the graphs of arcsin, arccos and arctan, including their restricted domains and ranges.
- Evaluate the inverse trig functions.

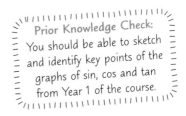

Prior Knowledge Check:
You should be able to sketch and identify key points of the graphs of sin, cos and tan from Year 1 of the course.

Arcsin, arccos and arctan

The inverse trig functions

> Arcsin is the inverse of **sin**. You might see it written as arcsine or sin⁻¹.
>
> Arccos is the inverse of **cos**. You might see it written as arccosine or cos⁻¹.
>
> Arctan is the inverse of **tan**. You might see it written as arctangent or tan⁻¹.

The inverse trig functions **reverse** the effect of sin, cos and tan — e.g. sin 30° = 0.5, so arcsin 0.5 = 30°. You should have buttons for doing arcsin, arccos and arctan on your calculator — they'll probably be labelled sin⁻¹, cos⁻¹ and tan⁻¹.

Graphs of the inverse trig functions

The functions sine, cosine and tangent **aren't one-to-one** mappings (see p.19). This means that more than one value of x gives the same value for sin x, cos x or tan x. For example: cos 0 = cos 2π = cos 4π = 1, and tan 0 = tan π = tan 2π = 0.

If you want the inverses to be **functions**, you have to **restrict the domains** of the trigonometric functions to make them **one-to-one**.

The graphs of the inverse functions are the **reflections** of the sin, cos and tan graphs in the line $y = x$.

Arcsin

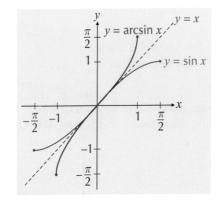

- For arcsin, limit the **domain** of sin x to $-\frac{\pi}{2} \leq x \leq \frac{\pi}{2}$ (the range of sin x is still **–1 ≤ sin x ≤ 1**).

- So the **domain** of arcsin x is **–1 ≤ x ≤ 1**.

- The **range** of arcsin x is $-\frac{\pi}{2} \leq$ **arcsin** $x \leq \frac{\pi}{2}$.

- The graph of **y = arcsin x** goes through the **origin**.

- The coordinates of its **endpoints** are $\left(-1, -\frac{\pi}{2}\right)$ and $\left(1, \frac{\pi}{2}\right)$.

Arccos

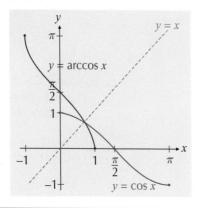

- For arccos, limit the **domain** of cos x to $0 \leq x \leq \pi$ (the range of cos x is still $-1 \leq \cos x \leq 1$.)

- So the **domain** of arccos x is $-1 \leq x \leq 1$.

- The **range** of arccos x is $0 \leq \arccos x \leq \pi$.

- The graph of $y = \arccos x$ crosses the **y-axis** at $\left(0, \frac{\pi}{2}\right)$.

- The coordinates of its **endpoints** are $(-1, \pi)$ and $(1, 0)$.

Arctan

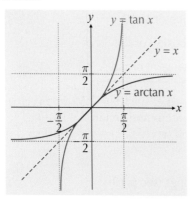

- For arctan, limit the **domain** of tan x to $-\frac{\pi}{2} < x < \frac{\pi}{2}$ (this **doesn't limit** the range of tan x.)

- This means that the **domain** of arctan x **isn't** limited (it's $x \in \mathbb{R}$) — note that there are no endpoints marked on the graph.

- The **range** of arctan x is $-\frac{\pi}{2} < \arctan x < \frac{\pi}{2}$.

- The graph of $y = \arctan x$ goes through the **origin**.

- It has **asymptotes** at $y = \frac{\pi}{2}$ and $y = -\frac{\pi}{2}$.

Learn the **key features** of these inverse trig graphs — you might be asked to **transform** them in different ways. There's more on **transformations of graphs** on pages 35-38.

Evaluating arcsin, arccos and arctan

If a is an angle within the interval $-\frac{\pi}{2} \leq a \leq \frac{\pi}{2}$ (or $-90° \leq a \leq 90°$) such that **sin $a = x$**, then **arcsin $x = a$**. So to evaluate **arcsin x** you need to find the angle a in this interval such that **sin $a = x$**. Using a calculator, this will be the answer you get when you enter "**$\sin^{-1} x$**" (for a given value of x).

Similarly, to find **arccos x**, you need to find the angle a within the interval $0 \leq a \leq \pi$ (or $0° \leq a \leq 180°$) such that **cos $a = x$**, and **arctan x** is the angle a in the interval $-\frac{\pi}{2} < a < \frac{\pi}{2}$ (or $-90° < a < 90°$) such that **tan $a = x$**.

When evaluating inverse trig functions, it's helpful know the **sine**, **cosine** and **tangent** of some **common angles**. Here's a quick recap of the method of drawing triangles — and **SOH CAH TOA**.

Remember: SOH CAH TOA...

$$\sin x = \frac{\text{opp}}{\text{hyp}} \qquad \cos x = \frac{\text{adj}}{\text{hyp}} \qquad \tan x = \frac{\text{opp}}{\text{adj}}$$

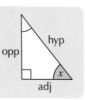

The sin, cos and tan of 30°, 45° and 60° can be found by drawing the following triangles and using **SOH CAH TOA**.

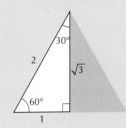

Draw an equilateral triangle with 60° angles and sides of 2 and split it to make a right-angled triangle.

Use Pythagoras to work out the length of the third side.

Draw a right-angled triangle where the edges adjacent to the right angle have length 1.

Use Pythagoras to work out the length of the third side.

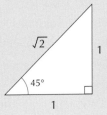

You should already know the sin, cos and tan of 90° and 180°, so you can work out all the values in this table:

$x°$	x (rad)	$\sin x$	$\cos x$	$\tan x$
0	0	0	1	0
30	$\dfrac{\pi}{6}$	$\dfrac{1}{2}$	$\dfrac{\sqrt{3}}{2}$	$\dfrac{1}{\sqrt{3}}$
45	$\dfrac{\pi}{4}$	$\dfrac{1}{\sqrt{2}}$	$\dfrac{1}{\sqrt{2}}$	1
60	$\dfrac{\pi}{3}$	$\dfrac{\sqrt{3}}{2}$	$\dfrac{1}{2}$	$\sqrt{3}$
90	$\dfrac{\pi}{2}$	1	0	—
180	π	0	−1	0

Be careful though — the first solution you find might **not** lie within the appropriate domain for the inverse function (see the graphs on pages 57-58). To find a solution that **does** lie in the correct domain, you need to use the **graphs** of the functions, or the **CAST diagram** that was introduced in the first year of this course (you might find it useful to look back at your Year 1 notes on solving trig equations in a given interval). The following examples show how to use these methods.

Examples

a) **Evaluate, without using a calculator, arccos 0.5. Give your answer in degrees.**

1. First, work out the angle a for which cos $a = 0.5$ using a right-angled triangle:

$0.5 = \dfrac{1}{2}$ which is either sin 30° (if using $\dfrac{\text{opp}}{\text{hyp}}$ on the triangle) or cos 60° (if using $\dfrac{\text{adj}}{\text{hyp}}$).

We are looking for the inverse of cos, so $a = 60°$.

2. Check that this answer lies in the appropriate limited domain for cos.

For cos, $0 \leq \alpha \leq \pi$ in radians, which is $0° \leq \alpha \leq 180°$.

60° lies within this domain, so $\boxed{\text{arccos } 0.5 = 60°}$.

b) **Evaluate, without using a calculator, arctan (−1). Give your answer in radians.**

1. You need to find the angle for which tan $a = -1$, over $-\dfrac{\pi}{2} < a < \dfrac{\pi}{2}$.
First use the triangles to find the value of a for when tan $a = 1$.

Using this triangle, you can see that tan $\dfrac{\pi}{4} = 1$.

2. But you need to look at the symmetry of the tan x graph to find the solution for tan $a = -1$.

The graph shows that if tan $\frac{\pi}{4} = 1$, then tan $-\frac{\pi}{4} = -1$.

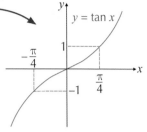

3. Check that this answer lies in the appropriate domain for tan.

The domain of tan is limited to $-\frac{\pi}{2} < a < \frac{\pi}{2}$. $-\frac{\pi}{4}$ is in this interval, so $\boxed{\text{arctan} (-1) = -\frac{\pi}{4}}$.

c) **Evaluate arcsin $\left(-\frac{1}{\sqrt{2}}\right)$ without using your calculator. Give your answer in radians.**

1. Use the triangle from the previous example:

$$\sin \frac{\pi}{4} = \frac{1}{\sqrt{2}}$$

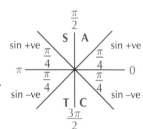

2. To find the angle a such that $\sin a = -\frac{1}{\sqrt{2}}$, look at the CAST diagram.

Positive solutions for sin x are found in the 'S' and 'A' quadrants.

So sin x is negative in the 'T' and 'C' quadrants, which means:

$$a = \pi + \frac{\pi}{4} = \frac{5\pi}{4}, \text{ or } 0 - \frac{\pi}{4} = -\frac{\pi}{4}.$$

3. Find the answer that lies in the appropriate domain for sin.

Only the second of these answers lies within the domain $-\frac{\pi}{2} \leq a \leq \frac{\pi}{2}$, so $\boxed{\text{arcsin} \left(-\frac{1}{\sqrt{2}}\right) = -\frac{\pi}{4}}$.

Exercise 3.3.1

Q1 Evaluate the following, giving your answer in radians.

    a) arccos 1   b) arcsin $\frac{\sqrt{3}}{2}$ c) arctan $\sqrt{3}$ d) arccos $\frac{1}{\sqrt{2}}$

Q2 a) Sketch the graph of $y = 2$ arccos x for $-1 \leq x \leq 1$.

    b) Sketch the graph of $y = \frac{1}{2}$ arctan x and state the range.

Q3 By drawing the graphs of $y = \frac{x}{2}$ and $y = \cos^{-1} x$, determine the number of real roots of the equation $\cos^{-1} x = \frac{x}{2}$.

> **Q3 Hint:** Remember $\cos^{-1} x$ is just another name for arccos x.

Q4 Evaluate the following, giving your answers in radians:

    a) $\sin^{-1} (-1)$ b) $\cos^{-1} \left(-\frac{\sqrt{3}}{2}\right)$ c) $\tan^{-1} \left(-\frac{1}{\sqrt{3}}\right)$ d) $\sin^{-1} \left(-\frac{1}{2}\right)$

Q5 Evaluate the following:

    a) $\tan \left(\text{arcsin} \frac{1}{2}\right)$ b) $\cos^{-1} \left(\cos \frac{2\pi}{3}\right)$ c) $\cos \left(\text{arcsin} \frac{1}{2}\right)$

Q6 $f(x) = 1 + \sin 2x$. Find an expression for $f^{-1}(x)$.

3.4 Cosec, Sec and Cot

There are a few more trig functions to learn— the reciprocals of sin, cos and tan: cosec, sec and cot.

Learning Objectives (Spec Ref 5.4 & 5.7):

- Know that the reciprocals of sin, cos and tan are cosec, sec and cot.
- Recognise and sketch the graphs of cosec, sec and cot.
- Evaluate the reciprocal trig functions.
- Simplify expressions involving the reciprocal trig functions.
- Solve equations involving the reciprocal trig functions.

> **Prior Knowledge Check:**
> Be able to transform
> graphs. See p.35.

Graphs of cosec, sec and cot

When you take the **reciprocal** of the three main trig functions, sin, cos and tan, you get three new trig functions — **cosecant** (or **cosec**), **secant** (or **sec**) and **cotangent** (or **cot**).

> **Tip:** $\tan\theta \equiv \dfrac{\sin\theta}{\cos\theta}$, so you can also think of $\cot\theta$ as being $\dfrac{\cos\theta}{\sin\theta}$.

$$\operatorname{cosec}\theta \equiv \frac{1}{\sin\theta} \qquad \sec\theta \equiv \frac{1}{\cos\theta} \qquad \cot\theta \equiv \frac{1}{\tan\theta}$$

Examples

Write the following in terms of sin and cos only:

a) **cosec 20°**

$$\operatorname{cosec} 20° = \frac{1}{\sin 20°}$$

b) **sec π**

$$\sec\pi = \frac{1}{\cos\pi}$$

c) **cot $\dfrac{\pi}{6}$**

$$\cot\frac{\pi}{6} = \frac{1}{\tan\frac{\pi}{6}} = \frac{\cos\frac{\pi}{6}}{\sin\frac{\pi}{6}}$$

> **Tip:** The trick for remembering which is which is to look at the third letter — cosec (1/sin), sec (1/cos) and cot (1/tan).

Graph of cosec

This is the graph of **y = cosec x**:

> **Tip:** The x-coordinates of the turning points for cosec x are the same as for sin x, but a maximum on sin x becomes a minimum on cosec x, and vice versa.

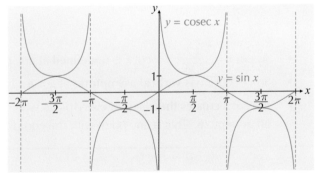

- Since $\operatorname{cosec} x = \dfrac{1}{\sin x}$, $y = \operatorname{cosec} x$ is **undefined** at any point where $\sin x = 0$.

- So $y = \operatorname{cosec} x$ has **vertical asymptotes** at $x = n\pi$ (where n is any integer).

- The graph $y = \operatorname{cosec} x$ has **minimum** points at $x = ..., -\dfrac{3\pi}{2}, \dfrac{\pi}{2}, \dfrac{5\pi}{2}, ...$ At these points, $y = 1$.

- It has **maximum** points at $x = ..., -\dfrac{\pi}{2}, \dfrac{3\pi}{2}, \dfrac{7\pi}{2}, ...$ At these points, $y = -1$.

Graph of sec

This is the graph of $y = \sec x$:

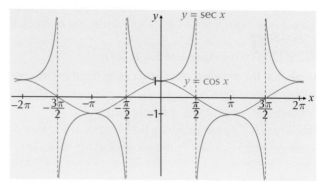

- As $\sec x = \dfrac{1}{\cos x}$, $y = \sec x$ is **undefined** at any point where $\cos x = 0$.
- So $y = \sec x$ has vertical asymptotes at $x = n\pi + \dfrac{\pi}{2}$ (where n is any integer).
- The graph of $y = \sec x$ has **minimum** points at $x = 0, \pm2\pi, \pm4\pi, \ldots$
  (wherever the graph of $y = \cos x$ has a **maximum**). At these points, $y = 1$.
- It has **maximum** points at $x = \pm\pi, \pm3\pi, \ldots$
  (wherever the graph of $y = \cos x$ has a **minimum**). At these points, $y = -1$.

Graph of cot

This is the graph of $y = \cot x$:

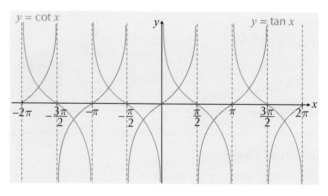

- As $\cot x = \dfrac{1}{\tan x}$, $y = \cot x$ is **undefined** at any point where $\tan x = 0$.
- So $y = \cot x$ has **vertical asymptotes** at $x = n\pi$ (where n is any integer).
- $y = \cot x$ **crosses the x-axis** at every place where the graph of $\tan x$ has an asymptote. This is any point with the coordinates $\left(\left(n\pi + \dfrac{\pi}{2}\right), 0\right)$.

Just like the graphs of $\sin x$ and $\cos x$, the graphs of $\operatorname{cosec} x$ and $\sec x$ have a **period** of 2π **radians** — this just means they **repeat themselves** every 2π (or $360°$).

The graphs of $\tan x$ and $\cot x$ both have a **period** of π **radians**.

Transformations of cosec, sec and cot

The graphs of the cosec, sec and cot functions can be **transformed** in the same way as other functions.

Examples

a) **Sketch the graph of $y = \cot 2x$ over the interval $-\pi \leq x \leq \pi$.**

If $f(x) = \cot x$, then $y = f(2x)$.

This transformation is a **horizontal stretch** by a factor of $\frac{1}{2}$ (i.e. the graph is squashed up in the x-direction by a factor of 2).

> **Tip:** Look back at pages 35-38 for more on transformations of graphs.

The x-coordinates of the asymptotes for $y = \cot 2x$ are **half** of those for $y = \cot x$.

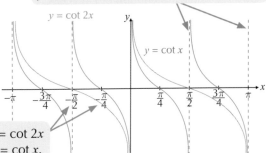

The x-intercepts for $y = \cot 2x$ are **half** of those for $y = \cot x$.

The period of the graph is also halved: $y = \cot 2x$ repeats itself every $\frac{\pi}{2}$ radians.

b) **Give the coordinates of the maximum point on the graph of $y = \sec(x - 30°) + 1$, between 0° and 360°.**

1. Identify the transformation of the graph of $f(x) = \sec x$:

Let $f(x) = \sec x$, then $y = f(x - 30°) + 1$ — this transformation is a **horizontal translation right** by **30°**, followed by a **vertical translation up** by **1**.

2. Translate the maximum point of $f(x)$:

The graph of $f(x) = \sec x$ has a maximum point at **(180°, −1)**.

Under the transformation, the x-coordinate will be **increased by 30°** and the y-coordinate will be **increased by 1**, so the coordinates of the maximum point on the transformed graph will be: **(210°, 0)** .

c) **Describe the position of the asymptotes on the graph of $y = \operatorname{cosec}\left(x + \frac{\pi}{3}\right)$.**

1. Identify the transformation of the graph of $f(x) = \operatorname{cosec} x$:

Let $f(x) = \operatorname{cosec} x$, then $y = f\left(x + \frac{\pi}{3}\right)$ — this transformation is a **horizontal translation left** by $\frac{\pi}{3}$.

2. Translate the asymptotes of $f(x)$:

The graph of $f(x) = \operatorname{cosec} x$ has asymptotes at $x = n\pi$ (where n is any integer).

Each asymptote will be translated left by $\frac{\pi}{3}$, so there will be asymptotes at

$x = n\pi - \frac{\pi}{3}$ (where n is any integer).

Q1 a) Sketch the graph of $y = \sec x$ for $-2\pi \le x \le 2\pi$.

b) Give the coordinates of the minimum points within this interval.

c) Give the coordinates of the maximum points within this interval.

d) State the range of $y = \sec x$.

Q1d) Hint: Think about which values are **not** included in the range.

Q2 a) Sketch the graph of $y = \operatorname{cosec} x$ for $0 < x < 2\pi$.

b) Give the coordinates of any maximum and minimum points within this interval.

c) State the domain and range of $y = \operatorname{cosec} x$.

Q3 Describe the transformation that maps $y = \sec x$ onto $y = \operatorname{cosec} x$.

Q3 Hint: Compare the graphs you've drawn for Q1 and Q2.

Q4 a) Describe the transformation that maps $y = \cot x$ onto $y = \cot \frac{x}{4}$.

b) What is the period, in degrees, of the graph $y = \cot \frac{x}{4}$?

c) Sketch the graph of $y = \cot \frac{x}{4}$ for $0° \le x \le 360°$.

Q5 a) Sketch the graph of $y = 2 + \sec x$ for $-2\pi \le x \le 2\pi$.

b) Give the coordinates of any maximum and minimum points within this interval.

c) State the domain and range of $y = 2 + \sec x$.

Q6 a) Sketch the graph of $y = 2 \operatorname{cosec} 2x$ for $0° \le x \le 360°$.

b) Give the coordinates of the minimum points within this interval.

c) Give the coordinates of the maximum points within this interval.

d) For what values of x in this interval is $y = 2 \operatorname{cosec} 2x$ undefined?

Q7 a) Describe the position of the asymptotes on the graph of $y = 2 + 3 \operatorname{cosec} x$.

b) What is the period, in degrees, of the graph $y = 2 + 3 \operatorname{cosec} x$?

c) Sketch the graph of $y = 2 + 3 \operatorname{cosec} x$ for $-180° < x < 180°$.

d) State the range of $y = 2 + 3 \operatorname{cosec} x$.

Evaluating cosec, sec and cot

To **evaluate** cosec, sec or cot of a number, first evaluate sin, cos or tan, then work out the **reciprocal** of the answer.

Examples

a) Evaluate 2 sec(–20°) + 5, giving your answer to 3 significant figures.

1. Write out the expression in terms of sin, cos or tan.

$$\sec x = \frac{1}{\cos x}, \text{ so } 2 \sec(-20°) + 5 = \frac{2}{\cos(-20°)} + 5$$

2. Use a calculator to find the answer.

$$\frac{2}{\cos(-20°)} + 5 = \frac{2}{0.93969...} + 5 = \boxed{7.13 \text{ to 3 s.f.}}$$

b) Evaluate cosec $\frac{\pi}{4}$ without a calculator. Give your answer in surd form.

1. Use cosec $x = \frac{1}{\sin x}$.

$$\operatorname{cosec} \frac{\pi}{4} = \frac{1}{\sin \frac{\pi}{4}}$$

2. Use the right-angled triangle on the right to find $\sin \frac{\pi}{4}$.

$$\sin \frac{\pi}{4} = \frac{1}{\sqrt{2}}$$

3. Evaluate cosec $\frac{\pi}{4}$.

$$\operatorname{cosec} \frac{\pi}{4} = \frac{1}{\left(\frac{1}{\sqrt{2}}\right)} = \sqrt{2}$$

c) Find the exact value of $\cot\left(-\frac{\pi}{6}\right)$.

1. Use $\cot x = \frac{1}{\tan x}$.

$$\cot\left(-\frac{\pi}{6}\right) = \frac{1}{\tan\left(-\frac{\pi}{6}\right)}$$

2. Evaluate $\tan\left(-\frac{\pi}{6}\right)$.

$$\tan \frac{\pi}{6} = \frac{1}{\sqrt{3}}$$

The graph of $y = \tan x$ shows that if $\tan \frac{\pi}{6} = \frac{1}{\sqrt{3}}$, then $\tan\left(-\frac{\pi}{6}\right) = -\frac{1}{\sqrt{3}}$.

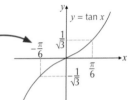

3. Evaluate $\cot\left(-\frac{\pi}{6}\right)$.

$$\cot\left(-\frac{\pi}{6}\right) = \frac{1}{\left(-\frac{1}{\sqrt{3}}\right)} = -\sqrt{3}$$

d) Find cosec 300° without using a calculator.

1. Use cosec $x = \frac{1}{\sin x}$.

$$\operatorname{cosec} 300° = \frac{1}{\sin 300°} = \frac{1}{\sin(360° - 60°)}.$$

2. Use a CAST diagram to find sin 300°.

The CAST diagram shows that sin 300° is the same size as sin 60°, but it lies in a quadrant where sin is negative.

So $\sin 300° = -\sin 60° = -\frac{\sqrt{3}}{2}$.

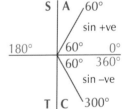

3. Evaluate cosec 300°.

So $\operatorname{cosec} 300° = \frac{1}{\left(-\frac{\sqrt{3}}{2}\right)} = -\frac{2}{\sqrt{3}}$

Exercise 3.4.2

Q1 Evaluate the following, giving your answers to 2 decimal places:

a) cosec 80°

b) sec 75°

c) cot 30°

d) sec(−70°)

e) 3 − cot 250°

f) 2 cosec 25°

Q2 Evaluate the following, giving your answers to 3 significant figures:

a) $\sec 3$ b) $\cot 0.6$ c) $\operatorname{cosec} 1.8$ d) $\sec(-1)$

e) $\operatorname{cosec} \dfrac{\pi}{8}$ f) $8 + \cot \dfrac{\pi}{8}$ g) $\dfrac{1}{1 + \sec \dfrac{\pi}{10}}$ h) $\dfrac{1}{6 + \cot \dfrac{\pi}{5}}$

Q3 Using the table of common angles on p.59, find the exact values of:

a) $\sec 60°$ b) $\operatorname{cosec} 30°$ c) $\cot 45°$

d) $\operatorname{cosec} \dfrac{\pi}{3}$ e) $\sec(-180°)$ f) $\operatorname{cosec} 135°$

g) $\cot 330°$ h) $\sec \dfrac{5\pi}{4}$ i) $\operatorname{cosec} \dfrac{5\pi}{3}$

j) $\operatorname{cosec} \dfrac{2\pi}{3}$ k) $3 - \cot \dfrac{3\pi}{4}$ l) $\dfrac{\sqrt{3}}{\cot \dfrac{\pi}{6}}$

Q4 Find, without a calculator, the exact values of:

a) $\dfrac{1}{1 + \sec 60°}$ b) $\dfrac{2}{6 + \cot 315°}$ c) $\dfrac{1}{\sqrt{3} - \sec 30°}$

d) $1 + \cot 420°$ e) $\dfrac{2}{7 + \sqrt{3}\cot 150°}$ f) $\dfrac{2}{1 - \operatorname{cosec} 330°}$

Simplifying expressions and solving equations

Simplifying expressions

You can use the cosec, sec and cot relationships to **simplify expressions**.
This can make it a lot easier to **solve** trig equations.

Examples

a) **Simplify $\cot^2 x \tan x$.**

Use $\cot x = \dfrac{1}{\tan x}$. $\cot^2 x \tan x = \left(\dfrac{1}{\tan^2 x}\right)\tan x = \dfrac{1}{\tan x} = \boxed{\cot x}$

b) **Show that $\dfrac{\cot x \sec x}{\operatorname{cosec}^2 x} \equiv \sin x$.**

Use all three relationships: $\dfrac{\cot x \sec x}{\operatorname{cosec}^2 x} \equiv \dfrac{\left(\dfrac{\cos x}{\sin x}\right)\left(\dfrac{1}{\cos x}\right)}{\left(\dfrac{1}{\sin^2 x}\right)} \equiv \dfrac{\left(\dfrac{1}{\sin x}\right)}{\left(\dfrac{1}{\sin^2 x}\right)} \equiv \boxed{\sin x}$ as required

c) **Write the expression $(\operatorname{cosec} x + 1)(\sin x - 1)$ as a single fraction in terms of $\sin x$ only.**

1. Expand the brackets. $(\operatorname{cosec} x + 1)(\sin x - 1) = \operatorname{cosec} x \sin x + \sin x - \operatorname{cosec} x - 1$

2. Use $\operatorname{cosec} x = \dfrac{1}{\sin x}$. $\operatorname{cosec} x \sin x + \sin x - \operatorname{cosec} x - 1$

$= \left(\dfrac{1}{\sin x}\right)\sin x + \sin x - \left(\dfrac{1}{\sin x}\right) - 1 = 1 + \sin x - \left(\dfrac{1}{\sin x}\right) - 1$

$= \sin x - \dfrac{1}{\sin x} = \boxed{\dfrac{\sin^2 x - 1}{\sin x}}$

Solving equations

You can **solve** equations involving cosec, sec and cot by **rewriting** them in terms of sin, cos or tan and solving as usual (often you'll need to get them all in terms of the same trig function, e.g. all sin). You may also need to use the **CAST diagram** (or the graph of the trig function) to find all the solutions in a given interval.

Examples

a) Solve sec $x = \sqrt{2}$ in the interval $0 \leq x \leq 2\pi$.

1. Write in terms of cos x by giving the reciprocal.

   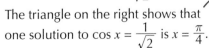 sec $x = \sqrt{2}$, so cos $x = \dfrac{1}{\sqrt{2}}$

2. Find one solution to the equation.

   The triangle on the right shows that one solution to cos $x = \dfrac{1}{\sqrt{2}}$ is $x = \dfrac{\pi}{4}$.

3. Use the CAST diagram to find the other solution in the interval.

   The other positive solution is in the fourth quadrant, where $x = 2\pi - \dfrac{\pi}{4} = \dfrac{7\pi}{4}$.

   So the two solutions are

   $$x = \dfrac{\pi}{4} \text{ and } x = \dfrac{7\pi}{4}.$$

   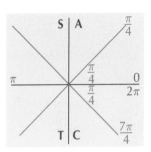

b) Solve $\operatorname{cosec}^2 x - 3\operatorname{cosec} x + 2 = 0$ in the interval $-180° \leq x \leq 180°$.

1. This is a quadratic equation in cosec x which can be factorised.

   $(\operatorname{cosec} x - 1)(\operatorname{cosec} x - 2) = 0$

2. This gives two equations to solve.

$\operatorname{cosec} x - 1 = 0$	$\operatorname{cosec} x - 2 = 0$
$\Rightarrow \operatorname{cosec} x = 1$	$\Rightarrow \operatorname{cosec} x = 2$
$\Rightarrow \sin x = 1$	$\Rightarrow \sin x = \dfrac{1}{2}$
One solution to this is $x = 90°$.	One solution to this is $x = 30°$.

3. Use the graph of $y = \sin x$ to find other solutions in the interval $-180° \leq x \leq 180°$.

   sin $x = 1$ only has one solution in this interval.

   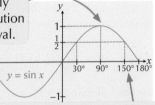

   The symmetry of the graph means there is another solution to sin $x = \dfrac{1}{2}$ at $x = 180° - 30° = 150°$.

   So the solutions are: $x = 30°$, $x = 90°$ and $x = 150°$.

Q1 Simplify the following expressions:

a) $\sec x + \dfrac{1}{\cos x}$

b) $(\operatorname{cosec}^2 x)(\sin^2 x)$

c) $2\cot x + \dfrac{1}{\tan x}$

d) $\dfrac{\sec x}{\operatorname{cosec} x}$

e) $(\cos x)(\operatorname{cosec} x)$

f) $\dfrac{\operatorname{cosec}^2 x}{\cot x}$

g) $5\cot x - \dfrac{\operatorname{cosec} x}{\sec x}$

h) $\dfrac{1}{\sec^2 x} + \dfrac{1}{\operatorname{cosec}^2 x}$

Q2 Show that:

a) $\sin x \cot x \equiv \cos x$

b) $\sec x - \cos x \equiv \tan x \sin x$

c) $\dfrac{\sec x}{\cot x} \equiv \sin x \sec^2 x$

d) $\tan x \operatorname{cosec} x \equiv \sec x$

e) $\dfrac{(\tan^2 x)(\operatorname{cosec} x)}{\sin x} \equiv \sec^2 x$

f) $\operatorname{cosec} x\,(\sin x + \cos x) \equiv 1 + \cot x$

Q3 Solve these equations for $0° \le x \le 360°$. Give your answers in degrees to 1 decimal place.

a) $\sec x = 1.9$

b) $\cot x = 2.4$

c) $\operatorname{cosec} x = -2$

d) $\sec x = -1.3$

e) $\cot x = -2.4$

f) $\dfrac{1}{2}\operatorname{cosec} x = 0.7$

g) $4\sec 2x = -7$

h) $5\cot 3x = 4$

> **Q3 Hint:** Use a calculator to find one solution, but then look at the graph or the CAST diagram to find any other solutions in the interval.

Q4 Solve these equations for $0 \le x \le 2\pi$, giving your answers in radians in terms of π.

a) $\sec x = 2$

b) $\operatorname{cosec} x = -2$

c) $\cot 2x = 1$

d) $\sec 5x = -1$

e) $\operatorname{cosec} 3x = -\sqrt{2}$

f) $\cot 4x = \dfrac{1}{\sqrt{3}}$

Q5 Solve the equation $\cot 2x - 4 = -5$ in the interval $0 \le x \le 2\pi$. Give your answers in terms of π.

Q6 Solve for $0° \le x \le 360°$, $2\operatorname{cosec} 2x = 3$. Give your answers to 1 decimal place.

Q7 Find, for $0 \le x \le 2\pi$, all the solutions of the equation $-2\sec x = 4$. Give your answers in terms of π.

Q8 Solve $\sqrt{3}\operatorname{cosec} 3x = 2$ for $0 \le x \le 2\pi$. Give your answers in terms of π.

Q9 Solve the following for $0° \le x \le 180°$, giving your answers to 1 d.p. where appropriate:

a) $\sec^2 x - 2\sqrt{2}\sec x + 2 = 0$

b) $2\cot^2 x + 3\cot x - 2 = 0$

Q10 Solve the equation $(\operatorname{cosec} x - 3)(2\tan x + 1) = 0$ for $0° \le x \le 360°$. Give your answers to 1 decimal place.

3.5 Identities Involving Cosec, Sec and Cot

An identity is an equation that's true for all values of a variable. You've met some trig identities — you can build on these to include cosec, sec and cot.

Learning Objective (Spec Ref 5.5):

- Know and use the following identities:
  $\sec^2 \theta \equiv 1 + \tan^2 \theta$ and $\operatorname{cosec}^2 \theta \equiv 1 + \cot^2 \theta$

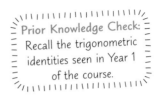

Prior Knowledge Check:
Recall the trigonometric identities seen in Year 1 of the course.

Deriving the identities

By now you should be familiar with the following **trig identities**:

$$\cos^2 \theta + \sin^2 \theta \equiv 1 \qquad \tan \theta \equiv \frac{\sin \theta}{\cos \theta}$$

Tip: The $\equiv$ sign tells you that this is true for all values of θ, rather than just certain values.

You can use them to produce a couple of other identities:

$$\sec^2 \theta \equiv 1 + \tan^2 \theta \qquad \operatorname{cosec}^2 \theta \equiv 1 + \cot^2 \theta$$

You need to know how to **derive** these identities from the ones you already know.

Deriving $\sec^2 \theta \equiv 1 + \tan^2 \theta$

Start with the identity $\cos^2 \theta + \sin^2 \theta \equiv 1$ and divide through by $\cos^2 \theta$.

$$\frac{\cos^2 \theta}{\cos^2 \theta} + \frac{\sin^2 \theta}{\cos^2 \theta} \equiv \frac{1}{\cos^2 \theta}$$

$$\tan \theta \equiv \frac{\sin \theta}{\cos \theta}, \text{ so } \frac{\sin^2 \theta}{\cos^2 \theta} = \tan^2 \theta$$

$$1 + \tan^2 \theta \equiv \frac{1}{\cos^2 \theta}$$

The definition of $\sec \theta = \dfrac{1}{\cos \theta}$, so replace $\dfrac{1}{\cos^2 \theta}$ with $\sec^2 \theta$.

$$1 + \tan^2 \theta \equiv \sec^2 \theta$$

Rearrange slightly... $\qquad \sec^2 \theta \equiv 1 + \tan^2 \theta$

Tip: These are examples of proof by deduction, where known facts are used to prove that other relationships are true.

Deriving $\operatorname{cosec}^2 \theta \equiv 1 + \cot^2 \theta$

Start again with $\cos^2 \theta + \sin^2 \theta \equiv 1$ but this time divide through by $\sin^2 \theta$.

$$\frac{\cos^2 \theta}{\sin^2 \theta} + \frac{\sin^2 \theta}{\sin^2 \theta} \equiv \frac{1}{\sin^2 \theta}$$

$$\tan \theta \equiv \frac{\sin \theta}{\cos \theta}, \text{ so } \frac{\cos^2 \theta}{\sin^2 \theta} = \frac{1}{\tan^2 \theta}$$

$$\frac{1}{\tan^2 \theta} + 1 \equiv \frac{1}{\sin^2 \theta}$$

The definition of **cot** $\theta = \dfrac{1}{\tan \theta}$, so replace $\dfrac{1}{\tan^2 \theta}$ with $\cot^2 \theta$.

$$\cot^2 \theta + 1 \equiv \frac{1}{\sin^2 \theta}$$

The definition of **cosec** $\theta = \dfrac{1}{\sin \theta}$, so replace $\dfrac{1}{\sin^2 \theta}$ with $\cosec^2 \theta$.

$$\cot^2 \theta + 1 \equiv \cosec^2 \theta$$

Rearrange slightly... **$\cosec^2 \theta \equiv 1 + \cot^2 \theta$**

Using the identities

You can use identities to get rid of any trig functions that are making an equation difficult to solve.

Example 1

Simplify the expression $3 \tan x + \sec^2 x + 1$.

1. Use $\sec^2 \equiv 1 + \tan^2 \theta$ to swap $\sec^2 x$ for $1 + \tan^2 x$: $\qquad$ $3 \tan x + 1 + \tan^2 x + 1$

2. Now rearrange: $\qquad$ $\tan^2 x + 3 \tan x + 2$

3. This is a quadratic in $\tan x$ which will factorise: $\qquad$ $(\tan x + 1)(\tan x + 2)$

Example 2

Solve the equation $\cot^2 x + 5 = 4 \cosec x$ in the interval $0° \leq x \leq 360°$.

1. Use **$\cosec^2 \theta \equiv 1 + \cot^2 \theta$** to swap $\cot^2 x$ for $\cosec^2 x - 1$.

   $\cosec^2 x - 1 + 5 = 4 \cosec x$
   $\cosec^2 x + 4 = 4 \cosec x$
   $\cosec^2 x - 4 \cosec x + 4 = 0$

2. Factorise the quadratic in $\cosec x$.

   $(\cosec x - 2)(\cosec x - 2) = 0$

3. Solve the quadratic for $\cosec x$.

   $(\cosec x - 2) = 0 \implies \cosec x = 2$

4. Convert this into $\sin x$ and solve.

   $\dfrac{1}{\sin x} = 2 \implies \sin x = \dfrac{1}{2} \implies x = 30°$

5. To find the other values of x, draw a quick sketch of the sine curve.

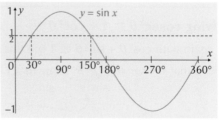

From the graph, $\sin x$ takes the value of $\dfrac{1}{2}$ **twice** in the given interval, so the solutions are $x = \boxed{30°}$ and $x = 180 - 30 = \boxed{150°}$.

Example 3

Given that $\cot x = \sqrt{8}$**, where** $0° \leq x \leq 180°$**, show how you can use the identity** $\text{cosec}^2\,\theta \equiv 1 + \cot^2\,\theta$ **to find the exact value of** $\sin x$**. Use Pythagoras' Theorem to confirm the result.**

1. Use the value for $\cot x$ and the identity $\text{cosec}^2\,\theta \equiv 1 + \cot^2\,\theta$ to find $\text{cosec}\,x$:

   $\cot x = \sqrt{8}$, so $\cot^2 x = 8$

   $\text{cosec}^2\,x \equiv 1 + \cot^2 x$
   $\text{cosec}^2\,x = 1 + 8 = 9$
   $\Rightarrow \text{cosec}\,x = \pm 3$

2. Solve the equation using $\text{cosec}\,x = \dfrac{1}{\sin x}$:

   $\dfrac{1}{\sin x} = \pm 3 \Rightarrow \sin x = \pm\dfrac{1}{3}$

   $0° \leq x \leq 180°$, and $\sin x$ is positive over this interval,

   so: $\boxed{\sin x = \dfrac{1}{3}}$

To confirm this using Pythagoras' Theorem:

1. Use $\cot x = \sqrt{8}$ to draw a right-angled triangle:

   $\cot x = \sqrt{8} \Rightarrow \tan x = \dfrac{1}{\cot x} = \dfrac{1}{\sqrt{8}}.$

   (i.e. the opposite has a length of 1 and the adjacent has a length of $\sqrt{8}$)

   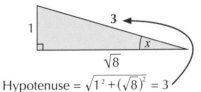

2. Use Pythagoras' Theorem to find the length of the hypotenuse:

   Hypotenuse $= \sqrt{1^2 + (\sqrt{8})^2} = 3$

3. Use the triangle to find $\sin x$:

   So $\boxed{\sin x = \dfrac{\text{opp}}{\text{hyp}} = \dfrac{1}{3}}$ as required

---

Exercise 3.5.1

Q1 Express $\text{cosec}^2 x + 2\cot^2 x$ in terms of $\text{cosec}\,x$ only.

Q2 Simplify the following expression: $\tan^2 x - \dfrac{1}{\cos^2 x}$.

Q3 Given that $x = \sec\theta + \tan\theta$, show that $x + \dfrac{1}{x} = 2\sec\theta$.

Q4 a) Show that the equation $\tan^2 x = 2\sec x + 2$ can be written as $\sec^2 x - 2\sec x - 3 = 0$.

    b) Hence solve $\tan^2 x = 2\sec x + 2$ over the interval $0° \leq x \leq 360°$, giving your answers in degrees to 1 decimal place.

> **Q4 Hint:** The 'hence' in part b) means you should use the result of part a) and solve $\sec^2 x - 2\sec x - 3 = 0$, as a quadratic in $\sec x$.

Q5 a) Show that the equation $2 \operatorname{cosec}^2 x = 5 - 5 \cot x$ can be written as $2 \cot^2 x + 5 \cot x - 3 = 0$.

   b) Hence solve $2 \operatorname{cosec}^2 x = 5 - 5 \cot x$ over the interval $-\pi \le x \le \pi$, giving your answers in radians to 2 decimal places.

Q6 a) Show that the equation $2 \cot^2 A + 5 \operatorname{cosec} A = 10$ can be written as $2 \operatorname{cosec}^2 A + 5 \operatorname{cosec} A - 12 = 0$.

   b) Hence solve $2 \cot^2 A + 5 \operatorname{cosec} A = 10$ over the interval $0° \le x \le 360°$, giving your answers in degrees to 1 decimal place.

Q7 Solve the equation $\sec^2 x + \tan x = 1$ for $0 \le x \le 2\pi$, giving exact answers.

> **Q7 Hint:**
> First write out the equation in terms of $\tan x$ only.

Q8 a) Given that $\operatorname{cosec}^2 \theta + 2 \cot^2 \theta = 2$, find the possible values of $\sin \theta$.

   b) Hence solve the equation $\operatorname{cosec}^2 \theta + 2 \cot^2 \theta = 2$ in the interval $0° \le \theta \le 180°$.

Q9 Solve the equation $\sec^2 x = 3 + \tan x$ in the interval $0° \le x \le 360°$, giving your answers to 1 d.p.

Q10 Solve the equation $\cot^2 x + \operatorname{cosec}^2 x = 7$, giving all the solutions in the interval $0 \le x \le 2\pi$ in terms of π.

Q11 Solve the equation $\tan^2 x + 5 \sec x + 7 = 0$, giving all the solutions in the interval $0 \le x \le 2\pi$ to 2 decimal places.

Q12 Given that $\tan \theta = \frac{60}{11}$, and $180° \le \theta \le 270°$, find the exact value of:

   a) $\sin \theta$ b) $\sec \theta$ c) $\operatorname{cosec} \theta$

Q13 Given that $\operatorname{cosec} \theta = -\frac{17}{15}$, and $180° \le \theta \le 270°$, find the exact value of:

   a) $\cos \theta$ b) $\sec \theta$ c) $\cot \theta$

Q14 Given that $\cos x = \frac{1}{6}$, use the identity $\sec^2 \theta = 1 + \tan^2 \theta$ to find the two possible exact values of $\tan x$.

Proving other identities

You can also use identities to prove that two trig expressions are the same, as shown in the examples below and on the next page. You just need to take one side of the identity and play about with it until you get what's on the other side.

> **Examples**
>
> a) **Show that** $\dfrac{\tan^2 x}{\sec x} \equiv \sec x - \cos x$.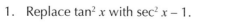
>
> Looking at the **left-hand side** of the identity:
>
> 1. Replace $\tan^2 x$ with $\sec^2 x - 1$.
>
> $$\frac{\tan^2 x}{\sec x} \equiv \frac{\sec^2 x - 1}{\sec x}$$
>
> 2. Rearrange to get the right-hand side of the identity.
>
> $$\equiv \frac{\sec^2 x}{\sec x} - \frac{1}{\sec x} \equiv \sec x - \cos x$$

b) Prove the identity $\dfrac{\tan^2 x}{\sec x + 1} \equiv \sec x - \cos^2 x - \sin^2 x.$

1. Starting with the left-hand side, replace $\tan^2 x$ with $\sec^2 x - 1$.

2. Factorise the $\sec^2 x - 1$ — it's the difference of two squares.

3. Cancel and then use $\cos^2 x + \sin^2 x \equiv 1$ to replace the '1'. This gives you the right-hand side.

$$\dfrac{\tan^2 x}{\sec x + 1} \equiv \dfrac{\sec^2 x - 1}{\sec x + 1}$$

$$\equiv \dfrac{(\sec x + 1)(\sec x - 1)}{\sec x + 1}$$

$$\equiv \sec x - 1$$

$$\equiv \sec x - (\cos^2 x + \sin^2 x)$$

$$\equiv \sec x - \cos^2 x - \sin^2 x$$

When proving identities, keep checking that you're **getting closer** to the other side of the identity. As well as using the **known identities**, there are lots of little tricks you can use, such as looking for the 'difference of two squares', and multiplying the top and bottom of a fraction by the **same expression**.

Exercise 3.5.2

PROBLEM SOLVING

Q1 a) Show that $\sec^2 \theta - \mathrm{cosec}^2 \theta \equiv \tan^2 \theta - \cot^2 \theta.$

b) Hence prove that $(\sec \theta + \mathrm{cosec}\,\theta)(\sec \theta - \mathrm{cosec}\,\theta) \equiv (\tan \theta + \cot \theta)(\tan \theta - \cot \theta).$

Q2 Prove that $\mathrm{cosec}\,x - \sin x = \cos x \cot x.$

Q3 Prove the identity $(\tan x + \cot x)^2 \equiv \sec^2 x + \mathrm{cosec}^2 x.$

Q4 Prove that $\dfrac{1 - \sec x}{\tan x} \equiv \cot x - \mathrm{cosec}\,x.$

Q5 Prove the identity $\tan^2 x + \cos^2 x \equiv (\sec x + \sin x)(\sec x - \sin x).$

Q6 Prove that $(\sec x + \cot x)(\sec x - \cot x) \equiv \tan^2 x - \mathrm{cosec}^2 x + 2.$

Q7 Prove the identity $\sec^2 \theta \, \mathrm{cosec}^2 \theta \equiv 2 + \cot^2 \theta + \tan^2 \theta.$

Q8 Prove that $\dfrac{\sec^2 x + 1}{\tan^2 x} \equiv \dfrac{\sec^4 x - 1}{\tan^4 x}.$

Q9 Prove that $\dfrac{\cos \theta}{\sin \theta} + \dfrac{\sin \theta}{\cos \theta} \equiv \mathrm{cosec}\,\theta \sec \theta.$

Q10 Prove the identity $\dfrac{(\sec x - \tan x)(\tan x + \sec x)}{\mathrm{cosec}\,x - \cot x} \equiv \cot x + \mathrm{cosec}\,x.$

Q11 Prove that $\dfrac{\cot x}{1 + \mathrm{cosec}\,x} + \dfrac{1 + \mathrm{cosec}\,x}{\cot x} \equiv 2 \sec x.$

Q12 Prove the identity $\dfrac{\mathrm{cosec}\,x + 1}{\mathrm{cosec}\,x - 1} \equiv 2 \sec^2 x + 2 \tan x \sec x - 1.$

3.6 The Addition Formulas

The addition formulas are a special set of trig identities that can be used to simplify trig expressions where there are two different angles, or where there is a sum of angles.

Learning Objectives (Spec Ref 5.6-5.8):
- Know and use the formulas for sin ($A \pm B$), cos ($A \pm B$) and tan ($A \pm B$).
- Understand the geometric proof of the addition formulas.

Finding exact values

The identities shown below are known as the **addition formulas**.

You can use the addition formulas to find the **sin**, **cos** or **tan** of the **sum** or **difference** of two angles, and to 'expand the brackets' in expressions such as sin ($x + 60°$) or $\cos \left(n - \frac{\pi}{2} \right)$.

$$\sin (A \pm B) \equiv \sin A \cos B \pm \cos A \sin B$$

$$\cos (A \pm B) \equiv \cos A \cos B \mp \sin A \sin B$$

$$\tan (A \pm B) \equiv \frac{\tan A \pm \tan B}{1 \mp \tan A \tan B}$$

Watch out for the $\pm$ and $\mp$ signs in the formulas — especially for cos and tan. If you use the sign on the **top** on the **left-hand side** of the identity, you have to use the sign on the **top** on the **right-hand side** too — so cos($A + B$) = cos A cos B – sin A sin B.

Proving the addition formulas

You need to understand the **geometric proof** of these formulas, and although it looks rather complicated, it only uses basic trigonometry.

Step 1:

- Start with a right-angled triangle with a hypotenuse of 1, where one of the angles is $A + B$.

- This is a right-angled triangle, so sin ($A + B$) = $\frac{\text{opp}}{\text{hyp}}$ and cos ($A + B$) = $\frac{\text{adj}}{\text{hyp}}$, and since the hypotenuse is 1, you can write down the lengths of each side: opp = sin ($A + B$) and adj = cos ($A + B$).

- Add these labels to the diagram as shown.

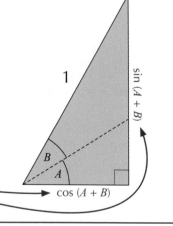

Step 2:

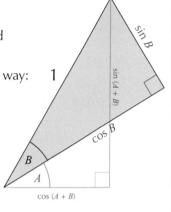

- If you extend the dotted line, you can form another right-angled triangle with a hypotenuse of 1. This time, the angle is B.

- You can find the lengths of the sides of this triangle in the same way: write out $\sin B = \dfrac{\text{opp}}{\text{hyp}}$ and $\cos B = \dfrac{\text{adj}}{\text{hyp}}$, then use the fact that the hypotenuse is 1 to get opp $= \sin B$ and adj $= \cos B$.

- Then add these to the diagram as well.

Step 3:

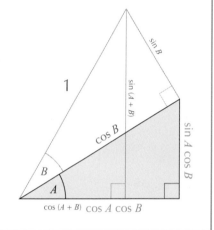

- Now form another right-angled triangle using angle A as shown. This one has a hypotenuse with length $\cos B$.

- So this time, when you rearrange the equations $\sin A = \dfrac{\text{opp}}{\text{hyp}}$ and $\cos A = \dfrac{\text{adj}}{\text{hyp}}$, use hyp $= \cos B$, which gives opp $= \sin A \cos B$ and adj $= \cos A \cos B$.

- Label these sides, and make sure it's clear which length is $\cos (A + B)$ and which is $\cos A \cos B$.

Step 4:

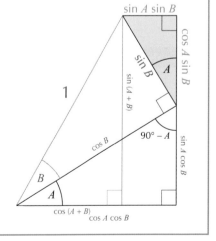

- The last triangle you need to draw has a hypotenuse of $\sin B$ and an angle of A. If you're not sure where this angle comes from, have a look at the diagram.

- So $\sin A = \dfrac{\text{opp}}{\text{hyp}}$ and $\cos A = \dfrac{\text{adj}}{\text{hyp}}$, and since hyp $= \sin B$, opp $= \sin A \sin B$ and adj $= \cos A \sin B$.

- Label these sides on the diagram.

Step 5:

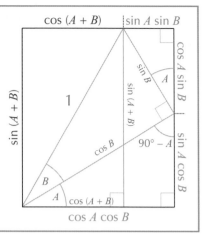

- You've now labelled enough sides to prove the formulas — here's the diagram again, with the labels for sin (A + B) and cos (A + B) moved to make things a bit clearer.

- Using the height of the diagram, you can see that:

  sin (A + B) = sin A cos B + cos A sin B

- The width of the diagram shows you that:

  cos A cos B = cos (A + B) + sin A sin B

  $\Rightarrow$ **cos (A + B) = cos A cos B − sin A sin B**

This is the proof of the **sin** and **cos** formulas — see p.79 for a proof of the **tan** formula.

You can work out the subtraction formulas from the addition ones, by using the fact that **sin −B = −sin B** and **cos −B = cos B** — you can see these are true by looking at the graphs of y = sin x and y = cos x.

sin (A − B) = sin A cos (−B) + cos A sin (−B) = **sin A cos B − cos A sin B**

cos (A − B) = cos A cos (−B) − sin A sin (−B) = **cos A cos B + sin A sin B**

You can also prove them geometrically using a similar method as for sin(A + B) and cos(A + B). You'll end up with the diagram below — work through it yourself to make sure you know where the labels come from.

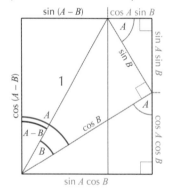

> **Tip:** Start with the triangle with angle A − B and hypotenuse 1, and then add on the triangle with angle B below it.

Example 1

a) Find the exact value of sin 18° cos 12° + cos 18° sin 12°.

Use the **sin** addition formula, where A = 18° and B = 12°.

sin A cos B + cos A sin B ≡ sin (A + B)

sin 18° cos 12° + cos 18° sin 12° = sin (18° + 12°)

$$= \sin 30° = \frac{1}{2}$$

b) Write $\dfrac{\tan 5x - \tan 2x}{1 + \tan 5x \tan 2x}$ **as a single trigonometric ratio.**

Use the **tan** addition formula, with A = 5x and B = 2x.

$$\frac{\tan 5x - \tan 2x}{1 + \tan 5x \tan 2x} = \tan (5x - 2x) = \boxed{\tan 3x}$$

---

c) **Given both x and y are acute, find the exact value of cos $(x + y)$ if $\sin x = \frac{4}{5}$ and $\sin y = \frac{15}{17}$.**

1. You know x and y are acute, so you can find cos x and cos y by drawing triangles and using SOH CAH TOA and Pythagoras.

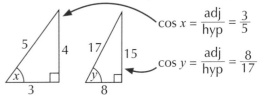

$$\cos x = \frac{\text{adj}}{\text{hyp}} = \frac{3}{5}$$

$$\cos y = \frac{\text{adj}}{\text{hyp}} = \frac{8}{17}$$

2. Then use the cos addition rule.

$$\cos (x + y) = \cos x \cos y - \sin x \sin y$$
$$= \left(\frac{3}{5} \times \frac{8}{17}\right) - \left(\frac{4}{5} \times \frac{15}{17}\right) = -\frac{36}{85}$$

You should know the value of sin, cos and tan for **common angles**, in degrees and radians (see p.59). You can use your knowledge of these angles, along with the addition formulas, to find the **exact value** of sin, cos or tan for **other** angles.

Find a **pair** of common angles which **add or subtract** to give the angle you're after, then plug them into the addition formula, and work it through.

Example 2

Using the addition formula for tangent, show that tan 15° = 2 − $\sqrt{3}$.

1. Pick two angles that add or subtract to give 15°. It's easiest to use tan 60° and tan 45°, since neither of them are fractions.

$$\tan 15° = \tan (60° - 45°)$$

2. Put them into the tan addition formula.

$$= \frac{\tan 60° - \tan 45°}{1 + \tan 60° \tan 45°}$$

3. Substitute the values for tan 60° ($= \sqrt{3}$) and tan 45° ($= 1$) into the equation.

$$= \frac{\sqrt{3} - 1}{1 + (\sqrt{3} \times 1)} = \frac{\sqrt{3} - 1}{\sqrt{3} + 1}$$

4. Now rationalise the denominator of the fraction to get rid of the $\sqrt{3}$.

$$= \frac{\sqrt{3} - 1}{\sqrt{3} + 1} \times \frac{\sqrt{3} - 1}{\sqrt{3} - 1} = \frac{3 - 2\sqrt{3} + 1}{3 - \sqrt{3} + \sqrt{3} - 1}$$

5. Then simplify the expression.

$$= \frac{4 - 2\sqrt{3}}{2} = 2 - \sqrt{3} \text{ as required}$$

Exercise 3.6.1

Q1 Use the addition formulas to find the exact values of the following:

a) $\cos 72° \cos 12° + \sin 72° \sin 12°$

b) $\cos 13° \cos 17° - \sin 13° \sin 17°$

c) $\dfrac{\tan 12° + \tan 18°}{1 - \tan 12° \tan 18°}$

d) $\dfrac{\tan 500° - \tan 140°}{1 + \tan 500° \tan 140°}$

e) $\sin 35° \cos 10° + \cos 35° \sin 10°$

f) $\sin 69° \cos 9° - \cos 69° \sin 9°$

Q2 Use the addition formulas to find the exact values of the following:

a) $\sin \dfrac{2\pi}{3} \cos \dfrac{\pi}{2} - \cos \dfrac{2\pi}{3} \sin \dfrac{\pi}{2}$

b) $\cos 4\pi \cos 3\pi + \sin 4\pi \sin 3\pi$

c) $\dfrac{\tan \dfrac{5\pi}{12} + \tan \dfrac{5\pi}{4}}{1 - \tan \dfrac{5\pi}{12} \tan \dfrac{5\pi}{4}}$

d) $\cos \dfrac{\pi}{9} \cos \dfrac{5\pi}{9} - \sin \dfrac{\pi}{9} \sin \dfrac{5\pi}{9}$

Q3 Write the following expressions as a single trigonometric ratio:

a) $\sin 5x \cos 2x - \cos 5x \sin 2x$

b) $\cos 4x \cos 6x - \sin 4x \sin 6x$

c) $\dfrac{\tan 7x + \tan 3x}{1 - \tan 7x \tan 3x}$

d) $5 \sin 2x \cos 3x + 5 \cos 2x \sin 3x$

e) $8 \cos 7x \cos 5x + 8 \sin 7x \sin 5x$

f) $\dfrac{\tan 8x - \tan 5x}{1 + \tan 8x \tan 5x}$

Q4 $\sin x = \dfrac{5}{13}$ and $\cos y = \dfrac{24}{25}$, where x and y are both acute angles. Calculate the exact value of:

a) $\sin (x - y)$

b) $\cos (x + y)$

c) $\cos (x - y)$

d) $\tan (x + y)$

> **Q4-5 Hint:** You'll need to work out $\cos x$ and $\sin y$ before you can answer parts a)-d). You can use the triangle method or the identity $\cos^2 \theta + \sin^2 \theta \equiv 1$ to work them out.

Q5 $\sin x = \dfrac{3}{4}$ and $\cos y = \dfrac{3}{\sqrt{10}}$, where x and y are both acute angles. Calculate the exact value of:

a) $\sin (x + y)$

b) $\cos (x - y)$

c) $\operatorname{cosec} (x + y)$

d) $\sec (x - y)$

Q6 Using the addition formula for cos, show that $\cos \dfrac{\pi}{12} = \dfrac{\sqrt{6} + \sqrt{2}}{4}$.

Q7 Using the addition formula for sin, show that $\sin 75° = \dfrac{\sqrt{6} + \sqrt{2}}{4}$.

Q8 Using the addition formula for tan, show that $\tan 75° = \dfrac{\sqrt{3} + 1}{\sqrt{3} - 1}$.

Simplifying, solving equations and proving identities

You might be asked to use the addition formulas to **prove an identity**. All you need to do is put the numbers and variables from the left-hand side into the addition formulas and simplify until you get the expression you're after.

Example 1

Prove that $\cos (a + 60°) + \sin (a + 30°) \equiv \cos a$.

1. Put the numbers from the question into the addition formulas.

$\cos(a + 60°) + \sin(a + 30°)$
$\equiv (\cos a \cos 60° - \sin a \sin 60°) + (\sin a \cos 30° + \cos a \sin 30°)$

2. Substitute in any sin and cos values that you know — be careful with the + and − signs here.

$= \dfrac{1}{2} \cos a - \dfrac{\sqrt{3}}{2} \sin a + \dfrac{\sqrt{3}}{2} \sin a + \dfrac{1}{2} \cos a$

$\cos 60° \qquad \sin 60° \qquad \cos 30° \qquad \sin 30°$

3. Simplify the expression.

$= \dfrac{1}{2} \cos a + \dfrac{1}{2} \cos a = \boxed{\cos a}$ as required

---

Example 2

Use the sine and cosine addition formulas to prove that $\tan(A + B) \equiv \dfrac{\tan A + \tan B}{1 - \tan A \tan B}$.

1. Start with the identity $\tan\theta \equiv \dfrac{\sin\theta}{\cos\theta}$.

   $$\tan(A + B) \equiv \frac{\sin(A + B)}{\cos(A + B)}$$

2. Replace $\sin(A + B)$ and $\cos(A + B)$ with the addition formulas for each.

   $$\equiv \frac{\sin A \cos B + \cos A \sin B}{\cos A \cos B - \sin A \sin B}$$

3. Divide each part of the fraction by $\cos A \cos B$ and cancel where possible.

   $$\equiv \frac{\dfrac{\sin A \cos B}{\cos A \cos B} + \dfrac{\cos A \sin B}{\cos A \cos B}}{\dfrac{\cos A \cos B}{\cos A \cos B} - \dfrac{\sin A \sin B}{\cos A \cos B}}$$

   Tip: The first term on the denominator needs to be '1' — divide through by this term to get the 1 in the right place.

   $$\equiv \frac{\dfrac{\sin A}{\cos A} + \dfrac{\sin B}{\cos B}}{1 - \left(\dfrac{\sin A}{\cos A}\right)\left(\dfrac{\sin B}{\cos B}\right)} \equiv \frac{\tan A + \tan B}{1 - \tan A \tan B}$$

Example 3

Use the addition formulas to show that $\cos A + \cos B \equiv 2\cos\left(\dfrac{A + B}{2}\right)\cos\left(\dfrac{A - B}{2}\right)$.

1. Start with the cos addition formulas:

   $$\cos(x + y) \equiv \cos x \cos y - \sin x \sin y$$
   $$\cos(x - y) \equiv \cos x \cos y + \sin x \sin y$$

2. Add the two expressions together:

   $$\cos(x + y) + \cos(x - y)$$
   $$\equiv \cos x \cos y - \sin x \sin y + \cos x \cos y + \sin x \sin y$$
   $$\equiv 2\cos x \cos y$$

3. Substitute in $A = x + y$ and $B = x - y$.

   Subtracting these gives:
   $$A - B = x + y - (x - y) = 2y, \text{ so } y = \frac{A - B}{2}$$

   Adding gives:
   $$A + B = x + y + (x - y) = 2x, \text{ so } x = \frac{A + B}{2}$$

   Tip: This is one of the factor formulas. The others are given in the formula booklet — see p.396.

   So $\cos A + \cos B \equiv 2\cos\left(\dfrac{A + B}{2}\right)\cos\left(\dfrac{A - B}{2}\right)$

You can also use the addition formulas to **solve** complicated trig equations.

Example 4

Solve $\sin\left(x + \dfrac{\pi}{2}\right) = \sin x$ in the interval $0 \le x \le 2\pi$.

1. Replace $\sin\left(x + \dfrac{\pi}{2}\right)$ using the sin addition formula — using the table of common values on page 59, $\cos\dfrac{\pi}{2} = 0$ and $\sin\dfrac{\pi}{2} = 1$.

   $$\sin x \cos\frac{\pi}{2} + \cos x \sin\frac{\pi}{2} = \sin x$$
   $$\Rightarrow 0 + \cos x = \sin x$$

2. Divide through by $\cos x$:

   $$\frac{\cos x}{\cos x} = \frac{\sin x}{\cos x}$$

3. Replace $\dfrac{\sin x}{\cos x}$ with $\tan x$:

   $$\frac{\cos x}{\cos x} = \tan x \Rightarrow \tan x = 1$$

4. Solve for $0 \le x \le 2\pi$:

   $$x = \frac{\pi}{4} \text{ and } \frac{5\pi}{4}$$

Q1 Use the sine and cosine addition formulas to prove
that $\tan(A - B) \equiv \dfrac{\tan A - \tan B}{1 + \tan A \tan B}$.

Q1 Hint: Look at the proof of $\tan(A + B)$ on the previous page.

Q2 Prove the following identities:

a) $\dfrac{\cos(A - B) - \cos(A + B)}{\cos A \sin B} \equiv 2 \tan A$

b) $\frac{1}{2}[\cos(A - B) - \cos(A + B)] \equiv \sin A \sin B$

c) $\sin(x + 90°) \equiv \cos x$

d) $\cos(x + 180°) \equiv -\cos x$

Q3 Solve $4 \sin\left(x - \dfrac{\pi}{3}\right) = \cos x$ in the interval $-\pi \le x \le \pi$.
Give your answers in radians to 2 decimal places.

Q4 a) Show that $\tan\left(-\dfrac{\pi}{12}\right) = \sqrt{3} - 2$.

b) Use your answer to a) to solve the equation $\cos x = \cos\left(x + \dfrac{\pi}{6}\right)$
in the interval $0 \le x \le \pi$. Give your answer in terms of π.

Q5 Show that $2 \sin(x + 30°) \equiv \sqrt{3} \sin x + \cos x$.

Q6 a) Show that $\sin(\theta - 45°) \equiv \dfrac{1}{\sqrt{2}}(\sin\theta - \cos\theta)$.

b) Use your answer to part a) to solve $4 \sin(\theta - 45°) = \sqrt{2} \cos\theta$
in the interval $0 \le \theta \le 360°$. Give your answers to 3 significant figures.

Q7 Write an expression for $\tan\left(\dfrac{\pi}{3} - x\right)$ in terms of $\tan x$ only.

Q8 $\tan A = \dfrac{3}{8}$ and $\tan(A + B) = \dfrac{1}{4}$. Find the exact value of $\tan B$.

Q9 Show that $\sin A + \sin B \equiv 2 \sin\left(\dfrac{A + B}{2}\right)\cos\left(\dfrac{A - B}{2}\right)$.

Q10 a) Given that $\sin(x + y) = 4 \cos(x - y)$, write an expression for $\tan x$ in terms of $\tan y$.

b) Use your answer to a) to solve $\sin\left(x + \dfrac{\pi}{4}\right) = 4 \cos\left(x - \dfrac{\pi}{4}\right)$ in the interval $0 \le x \le 2\pi$.

Q11 Solve the following equations in the given interval.
Give your answers to 2 decimal places.

a) $\sqrt{2} \sin(\theta + 45°) = 3 \cos\theta$, $0° \le \theta \le 360°$

b) $2 \cos\left(\theta - \dfrac{2\pi}{3}\right) - 5 \sin\theta = 0$, $0 \le \theta \le 2\pi$

c) $\sin(\theta - 30°) - \cos(\theta + 60°) = 0$, $0° \le \theta \le 360°$

Q12 Use the sin addition formula to show that $\sin\left(x + \dfrac{\pi}{6}\right) \approx \dfrac{1}{2} + \dfrac{\sqrt{3}}{2}x - \dfrac{1}{4}x^2$ when x is small.

3.7 The Double Angle Formulas

You can use the addition formulas to get the double angle formulas —
you'll find them really handy throughout the course.

Learning Objective (Spec Ref 5.6-5.8):

- Know and be able to use the double angle formulas for sin $2A$, cos $2A$ and tan $2A$.

Deriving the double angle formulas

Double angle formulas are a special case of the addition formulas, using $(A + A)$ instead of $(A + B)$. They're called "double angle" formulas because they take an expression with a $2x$ term (a double angle) inside a trig function, and change it into an expression with only single x's inside the trig functions.

You need to know the double angle formulas for **sin**, **cos** and **tan**. Their derivations are given below. You can also prove these **geometrically** in the same way as on pages 74-76 — just replace B with A.

---

sin $2A \equiv 2$ sin A cos A

- Start with the **sin addition formula** (see p.74), but replace 'B' with 'A':
  $$\sin (A + A) \equiv \sin A \cos A + \cos A \sin A$$

- $\sin (A + A)$ can be written as sin $2A$, and so:
  $$\sin 2A \equiv \sin A \cos A + \cos A \sin A \equiv \boxed{2 \sin A \cos A}$$

---

cos $2A \equiv \cos^2 A - \sin^2 A$

- Start with the **cos addition formula**, but again replace 'B' with 'A':
  $$\cos (A + A) \equiv \cos A \cos A - \sin A \sin A$$
  $$\Rightarrow \boxed{\cos 2A \equiv \cos^2 A - \sin^2 A}$$

- You can then use $\cos^2 A + \sin^2 A \equiv 1$ to get:
  $$\cos 2A \equiv \cos^2 A - (1 - \cos^2 A) \text{ and } \cos 2A \equiv (1 - \sin^2 A) - \sin^2 A$$

  $$\boxed{\cos 2A \equiv 2 \cos^2 A - 1} \qquad \boxed{\cos 2A \equiv 1 - 2 \sin^2 A}$$

> **Tip:** The double angle formula for cos has three different forms which are all very useful.

---

tan $2A \equiv \dfrac{2 \tan A}{1 - \tan^2 A}$

- Start with the **tan addition formula**, and again replace 'B' with 'A':
  $$\tan (A + A) \equiv \frac{\tan A + \tan A}{1 - \tan A \tan A}$$

- Simplifying this gives:
  $$\boxed{\tan 2A \equiv \frac{2 \tan A}{1 - \tan^2 A}}$$

Using the double angle formulas

Like the other trig identities covered in this chapter, the double angle formulas are useful when you need to find an **exact value**. You won't usually be told which identity to use, so work on being able to spot the clues — if you're asked for an 'exact value', you should think of your **common angles**. 15° is half of a common angle, so this should get you thinking about double angle formulas.

Example 1

a) Use a double angle formula to work out the exact value of sin 15° cos 15°.

1. This looks the most like the sin double angle formula, $\sin 2A \equiv 2 \sin A \cos A$, but it needs to be rearranged slightly.

$$\sin 2A \equiv 2 \sin A \cos A$$
$$\Rightarrow \sin A \cos A \equiv \tfrac{1}{2} \sin 2A$$

2. Now put in the numbers from the question:

$$\sin 15° \cos 15° = \tfrac{1}{2} \sin 30° = \tfrac{1}{2} \times \tfrac{1}{2} = \boxed{\tfrac{1}{4}}$$

b) $\sin x = \frac{2}{3}$, where x is acute. Find the exact value of cos 2x and sin 2x.

1. For cos 2x, use the cos double angle formula in terms of sin.

$$\cos 2A \equiv 1 - 2 \sin^2 A$$
$$\Rightarrow \cos 2x = 1 - 2\left(\tfrac{2}{3}\right)^2 = \boxed{\tfrac{1}{9}}$$

2. For sin 2x, use the sin double angle formula.

$$\sin 2A \equiv 2 \sin A \cos A$$

3. To use this, first work out cos x from sin x using the triangle method.

$$\cos x = \frac{\text{adj}}{\text{hyp}} = \frac{\sqrt{5}}{3}$$

4. Now put the values into the sin double angle formula as usual.

$$\sin 2x = 2 \sin x \cos x$$
$$= 2 \times \frac{2}{3} \times \frac{\sqrt{5}}{3} = \boxed{\frac{4\sqrt{5}}{9}}$$

The double angle formulas are also handy for **simplifying expressions** in order to solve equations.

Example 2

Write $1 - 2 \sin^2 \left(\frac{3x}{2}\right)$ as a single trigonometric ratio.

1. Look for an identity that is similar to this expression, containing a 'sin²'. The cos double angle formula (in terms of sin) looks best.

$$\cos 2A \equiv 1 - 2 \sin^2 A$$

2. Compare the expression with the right-hand side of the identity.

$$1 - 2 \sin^2 \left(\frac{3x}{2}\right)$$
$$\text{So } A = \frac{3x}{2} \Rightarrow 2A = 3x$$

3. Put this into the identity to get the expression in a single cos term.

$$\boxed{1 - 2 \sin^2 \frac{3x}{2} \equiv \cos 3x}$$

Q1 Use the double angle formulas to write down the exact values of:

a) $4 \sin \frac{\pi}{12} \cos \frac{\pi}{12}$

b) $\cos \frac{2\pi}{3}$

c) $\frac{\sin 120°}{2}$

d) $\frac{\tan 15°}{2 - 2 \tan^2 15°}$

e) $2 \sin^2 15° - 1$

f) $\tan^2 \frac{\pi}{3}$

> **Q1 Hint:** For some of these there are other ways to find the answer, but if you've been asked to use a certain method then show your working using that method.

Q2 An acute angle x has $\sin x = \frac{1}{6}$. Find the exact values of:

a) $\cos 2x$

b) $\sin 2x$

c) $\tan 2x$

d) $\sec 2x$

e) $\operatorname{cosec} 2x$

f) $\cot 2x$

Q3 Angle x has $\sin x = -\frac{1}{4}$, and $\pi \le x \le \frac{3\pi}{2}$.
Find the exact values of:

a) $\cos 2x$

b) $\sin 2x$

c) $\tan 2x$

d) $\sec 2x$

e) $\operatorname{cosec} 2x$

f) $\cot 2x$

> **Q3 Hint:** Angle x lies in the 3rd quadrant of the CAST diagram, so $\sin x$ and $\cos x$ are negative but $\tan x$ is positive.

Q4 Write the following expressions as a single trigonometric ratio:

a) $\frac{\sin 3\theta \cos 3\theta}{3}$

b) $\sin^2 \left(\frac{2y}{3}\right) - \cos^2 \left(\frac{2y}{3}\right)$

c) $\frac{1 - \tan^2 \left(\frac{x}{2}\right)}{2 \tan \left(\frac{x}{2}\right)}$

Solving equations and proving identities

If an equation has a **mixture** of $\sin x$ and $\sin 2x$ terms in it, there's not much that you can do with it in that state. But you can use one of the **double angle formulas** to simplify it, and then solve it.

Example 1

Solve the equation $\cos 2x - 5 \cos x = 2$ in the interval $0 \le x \le 2\pi$.

1. First use the cos double angle formula to get rid of $\cos 2x$ (this version of the formula will stop you ending up with a mix of sin and cos terms).

$$\cos 2A \equiv 2 \cos^2 A - 1$$
$$\Rightarrow 2 \cos^2 x - 1 - 5 \cos x = 2$$

2. Simplify so you have zero on one side.

$$2 \cos^2 x - 5 \cos x - 3 = 0$$

3. Factorise and solve the quadratic — let $y = \cos x$ and write as a quadratic in y if it helps.

$$(2 \cos x + 1)(\cos x - 3) = 0$$
$$\Rightarrow (2 \cos x + 1) = 0 \text{ or } (\cos x - 3) = 0$$

$x - 3 = 0 \Rightarrow \cos x = 3$, which has **no solutions**, since $-1 \le \cos x \le 1$.
So the only solutions are when $2\cos x + 1 = 0$.

---

4. Find all the solutions in the given interval.

$2 \cos x + 1 = 0 \implies \cos x = -\frac{1}{2}$

Tip: You can either sketch the graph of cos x to find all values of x in the given interval, or use a CAST diagram.

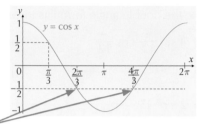

$\cos x = -\frac{1}{2}$ for two values in the interval — once at $\frac{2\pi}{3}$ and again at $2\pi - \frac{2\pi}{3} = \frac{4\pi}{3}$.

$\cos x = \frac{1}{2}$ for $x = \frac{\pi}{3}$, so using the symmetry of the graph above,

$x = \frac{2\pi}{3}$ or $x = \frac{4\pi}{3}$.

The following examples show how the double angle formulas can be used to **prove** other identities.

Example 2

Prove that $2 \cot \frac{x}{2}\left(1 - \cos^2 \frac{x}{2}\right) \equiv \sin x$.

1. Use the identity $\sin^2 \theta \equiv 1 - \cos^2 \theta$ to replace the $1 - \cos^2 \frac{x}{2}$ on the left-hand side.

Left-hand side: $2 \cot \frac{x}{2} \sin^2 \frac{x}{2}$

2. Now use $\cot \theta = \frac{\cos \theta}{\sin \theta}$.

$\dfrac{2 \cos \frac{x}{2} \sin^2 \frac{x}{2}}{\sin \frac{x}{2}} \equiv 2 \cos \frac{x}{2} \sin \frac{x}{2}$

3. Use the sin double angle formula with $A = \frac{x}{2}$.

$2 \cos \frac{x}{2} \sin \frac{x}{2} \equiv \sin x$ as required

---

Clever tricks like splitting up the angle so you can use the addition formulas can really help if you're stuck on a trig identity question.

Example 3

Show that $\cos 3\theta \equiv 4 \cos^3 \theta - 3 \cos \theta$.

1. Split up 3θ and then use the cos addition formula.

$\cos 3\theta \equiv \cos(2\theta + \theta)$
$\equiv \cos 2\theta \cos \theta - \sin 2\theta \sin \theta$

2. Now you've got terms that involve 2θ, you can use the cos and sin double angle formulas.

$\equiv (2 \cos^2 \theta - 1) \cos \theta - (2 \sin \theta \cos \theta) \sin \theta$

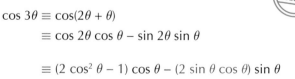

cos double angle formula   sin double angle formula

---

3. Tidy this up by expanding the brackets and using $\sin^2 \theta \equiv 1 - \cos^2 \theta$.

$\equiv 2 \cos^3 \theta - \cos \theta - 2 \sin^2 \theta \cos \theta$

$\equiv 2 \cos^3 \theta - \cos \theta - 2(1 - \cos^2 \theta)\cos \theta$

$\equiv 2 \cos^3 \theta - \cos \theta - 2 \cos \theta + 2 \cos^3 \theta$

$\equiv \boxed{4 \cos^3 \theta - 3 \cos \theta}$ as required

Tip: You can use a similar method to show that $\sin 3\theta \equiv 3 \sin \theta - 4 \sin^3 \theta$.

The half angle formulas

The double angle formulas for cos can be **rearranged** to give another three useful identities known as the **half angle formulas**.

The following examples show how you can derive them — you don't need to know these derivations for your exam, but they're good examples of using identities.

Example 4

a) Show that $\cos^2 \left(\frac{\theta}{2}\right) \equiv \frac{1}{2}(1 + \cos \theta)$.

1. Start with the double angle formula for cos:

$$\cos 2A \equiv 2 \cos^2 A - 1$$

2. Replace A with $\frac{\theta}{2}$:

$$\cos \theta \equiv 2 \cos^2 \left(\frac{\theta}{2}\right) - 1$$

3. Rearrange to get the half angle formula for cos:

$$\boxed{\cos^2 \left(\frac{\theta}{2}\right) \equiv \frac{1}{2}(1 + \cos \theta)}$$

b) Show that $\sin^2 \left(\frac{\theta}{2}\right) \equiv \frac{1}{2}(1 - \cos \theta)$.

1. Start with the double angle formula for cos that contains sin:

$$\cos 2A \equiv 1 - 2\sin^2 A$$

2. Again, replace A with $\frac{\theta}{2}$:

$$\cos \theta \equiv 1 - 2\sin^2 \left(\frac{\theta}{2}\right)$$

3. Rearrange to get the half angle formula for sin:

$$\boxed{\sin^2 \left(\frac{\theta}{2}\right) \equiv \frac{1}{2}(1 - \cos \theta)}$$

c) Hence show that $\tan^2 \left(\frac{\theta}{2}\right) \equiv \frac{1 - \cos \theta}{1 + \cos \theta}$.

1. Start with the identity $\tan x \equiv \frac{\sin x}{\cos x}$:

$$\tan \left(\frac{\theta}{2}\right) \equiv \frac{\sin\left(\frac{\theta}{2}\right)}{\cos\left(\frac{\theta}{2}\right)}$$

2. Square both sides:

$$\tan^2 \left(\frac{\theta}{2}\right) \equiv \frac{\sin^2\left(\frac{\theta}{2}\right)}{\cos^2\left(\frac{\theta}{2}\right)}$$

3. Replace $\sin^2 \left(\frac{\theta}{2}\right)$ and $\cos^2 \left(\frac{\theta}{2}\right)$ with their half angle formulas from examples a) and b).

$$\tan^2 \left(\frac{\theta}{2}\right) \equiv \frac{\frac{1}{2}(1 - \cos \theta)}{\frac{1}{2}(1 + \cos \theta)}$$

4. Simplify to get the half angle formula for tan:

$$\boxed{\tan^2 \left(\frac{\theta}{2}\right) \equiv \frac{1 - \cos \theta}{1 + \cos \theta}}$$ as required

Q1 Solve the equations below in the interval $0 \le x \le 360°$. Give your answers to 1 decimal place.

    a) $4 \cos 2x = 14 \sin x$

    b) $5 \cos 2x + 9 \cos x = -7$

    c) $4 \cot 2x + \cot x = 5$

    d) $\tan x - 5 \sin 2x = 0$

> **Q1d) Hint:** There should be 7 solutions in the given interval, but two of them are easy to miss...

Q2 Solve the equations below in the interval $0 \le x \le 2\pi$. Give your answers to 3 significant figures.

    a) $4 \cos 2x - 10 \cos x + 1 = 0$
    b) $\dfrac{\cos 2x - 3}{2 \sin^2 x - 1} = 3$

    c) $2 \sin x \cos x = 4 \cos^2 x - 4 \sin^2 x$
    d) $2 \cos 4x + \sin 2x = -1$

Q3 Solve the equations below in the interval $0 \le x \le 2\pi$. Give your answers in terms of π.

> **Q3b) Hint:** Try writing $\sin x$ as $\sin 2\left(\frac{x}{2}\right)$ and using the sin double angle formula.

    a) $\cos 2x + 7 \cos x = -4$
    b) $\sin x + \cos \frac{x}{2} = 0$

    c) $\sin x - \cos 2x = 0$
    d) $\cos x = 7 \cos \frac{x}{2} + 3$

Q4 Use the double angle formulas to prove each of the identities below.

    a) $\sin 2x \sec^2 x \equiv 2 \tan x$
    b) $\dfrac{2}{1 + \cos 2x} \equiv \sec^2 x$

    c) $\cot x - 2 \cot 2x \equiv \tan x$
    d) $\tan 2x + \cot 2x \equiv 2 \operatorname{cosec} 4x$

> **Q4d) Hint:** Write the left-hand side in terms of sin and cos first.

Q5 a) Show that $\dfrac{1 + \cos 2x}{\sin 2x} \equiv \cot x$.

    b) Use your answer to part a) to solve $\dfrac{1 + \cos 4\theta}{\sin 4\theta} = 7$
    in the interval $0 \le \theta \le 360°$. Give your answers to 1 d.p.

Q6 a) Show that $\dfrac{\cot^2 x + 1}{\cot^2 x - 1} \equiv \sec 2x$.

    b) Use your answer to part a) to solve $\dfrac{\cot^2 2\alpha + 1}{\cot^2 2\alpha - 1} = -3$
    in the interval $-\pi \le \alpha \le \pi$, giving your answers to 3 s.f.

Q7 Solve the equation $\cot x = \tan \frac{x}{2}$ in the interval $0 \le x \le 2\pi$, giving your answer in radians in terms of π.

> **Q7 Hint:** Write $\cot x$ as $\dfrac{1}{\tan x}$, then use $\tan x = \tan 2\left(\frac{x}{2}\right)$.

Q8 a) Show that $\operatorname{cosec} x - \cot \frac{x}{2} \equiv -\cot x$.

    b) Use your answer to a) to solve $\operatorname{cosec} y = \cot \frac{y}{2} - 2$
    in the interval $-\pi \le y \le \pi$. Give your answers to 3 s.f.

Q9 a) Given that $\sin \theta = \frac{5}{13}$, and that θ is acute, find: (i) $\cos\left(\frac{\theta}{2}\right)$,   (ii) $\sin\left(\frac{\theta}{2}\right)$.

    b) Hence find $\tan\left(\frac{\theta}{2}\right)$.

3.8 The R Addition Formulas

The R addition formulas are used to help solve equations which contain a mix of cos and sin terms.

Learning Objective (Spec Ref 5.6-5.8):
- Know and use expressions for $a \cos \theta + b \sin \theta$ in the equivalent forms of $R \cos (\theta \pm \alpha)$ or $R \sin (\theta \pm \alpha)$.

Expressions of the form $a \cos \theta + b \sin \theta$

If you're solving an equation that contains both $\sin \theta$ and $\cos \theta$ terms, e.g. $3 \sin \theta + 4 \cos \theta = 1$, you need to rewrite it so that it only contains one trig function.

The formulas that you use to do that are known as the **R formulas**:

One set for **sine**:
$$a \sin \theta \pm b \cos \theta \equiv R \sin (\theta \pm \alpha)$$

And one set for **cosine**:
$$a \cos \theta \pm b \sin \theta \equiv R \cos (\theta \mp \alpha)$$

where a, b and R are **positive**, and α is **acute**.

You need to be careful with the + and − signs in the cosine formula.
If you have $a \cos \theta + b \sin \theta$ then use $R \cos (\theta - \alpha)$.

Using the R formulas

- You'll start with an identity like $2 \sin x + 5 \cos x \equiv R \sin (x + \alpha)$, where R and α need to be found.

- First, **expand** the right hand side using the **addition formulas** (see p.74):
$$2 \sin x + 5 \cos x \equiv R \sin x \cos \alpha + R \cos x \sin \alpha$$

- **Equate the coefficients** of $\sin x$ and $\cos x$. You'll get two equations:
  - ① $R \cos \alpha = 2$ and ② $R \sin \alpha = 5$

- To find α, **divide** equation ② by equation ①, (because $\frac{R \sin \alpha}{R \cos \alpha} = \tan \alpha$) then take **tan⁻¹** of the result.

- To find R, **square** equations ① and ② and **add** them together, then take the **square root** of the answer. This works because:
$$(R \sin \alpha)^2 + (R \cos \alpha)^2 \equiv R^2 (\sin^2 \alpha + \cos^2 \alpha) \equiv R^2$$
  (using the identity $\sin^2 \alpha + \cos^2 \alpha \equiv 1$)

This method looks a bit scary, but follow through the next example and it should make more sense.

Example 1

Express 4 cos x + 5 sin x in the form R cos $(x \pm \alpha)$.

1. Find the correct R formula to use — the expression is in the form $a \cos \theta + b \sin \theta$ and you want the answer in terms of cos.

    $a \cos \theta + b \sin \theta \equiv R \cos (\theta \pm \alpha)$

    $4 \cos x + 5 \sin x \equiv R \cos (x - \alpha)$

2. Expand the right hand side using the cos addition formula.

    $4 \cos x + 5 \sin x \equiv R \cos x \cos \alpha + R \sin x \sin \alpha.$

3. Equate the coefficients of sin x and cos x to find α and R:

    ① $R \cos \alpha = 4$ and ② $R \sin \alpha = 5$

4. Divide ② by ① to find α.

    $\tan \alpha = \frac{5}{4} \Rightarrow \alpha = 51.3°$ (1 d.p.)

5. Square ① and ② and add to find R.

    ①² : $R^2 \cos^2 \alpha = 16$

    ②² : $R^2 \sin^2 \alpha = 25$

    ①² + ②²: $R^2 \cos^2 \alpha + R^2 \sin^2 \alpha = 16 + 25$

    $\Rightarrow R^2 (\cos^2 \alpha + \sin^2 \alpha) = 41$

    $\Rightarrow R^2 = 41$

    $\Rightarrow R = \sqrt{41}$

    Tip: R is always positive (so take the positive root) and α is always acute (so take the angle in the first quadrant of the CAST diagram when solving).

6. Put the values for α and R back into the identity to get the answer.

    $4 \cos x + 5 \sin x \equiv \boxed{\sqrt{41} \cos (x - 51.3°)}$

Example 2

a) Show that $5 \sin x - 5\sqrt{3} \cos x \equiv 10 \sin \left(x - \frac{\pi}{3}\right)$.

1. Find the correct R formula to use — the expression is in the form $a \sin \theta - b \cos \theta$ and you want the answer in terms of sin.

    $a \sin \theta + b \cos \theta \equiv R \sin (\theta \pm \alpha)$

    $5 \sin x - 5\sqrt{3} \cos x \equiv R \sin (x - \alpha)$

2. Expand the right hand side using the sin addition formula.

    $5 \sin x - 5\sqrt{3} \cos x \equiv R \sin x \cos \alpha - R \cos x \sin \alpha$

3. Equate the coefficients of sin x and cos x to find α and R:

    ① $R \cos \alpha = 5$ and ② $R \sin \alpha = 5\sqrt{3}$

4. Divide ② by ① to find α.

    ② ÷ ①: $\frac{R \sin \alpha}{R \cos \alpha} = \tan \alpha = \frac{5\sqrt{3}}{5} = \sqrt{3}$

    $\Rightarrow \alpha = \frac{\pi}{3}$

5. Square ① and ② and add to find R.

    ①² + ②²: $R^2 \cos^2 \alpha + R^2 \sin^2 \alpha = 5^2 + (5\sqrt{3})^2$

    $\Rightarrow R^2(1) = 100$

    $\Rightarrow R = 10$

6. Then put the values for α and R back into the identity.

    $5 \sin x - 5\sqrt{3} \cos x \equiv \boxed{10 \sin \left(x - \frac{\pi}{3}\right)}$ as required

b) Hence sketch the graph of $y = 5 \sin x - 5\sqrt{3} \cos x$ in the interval $-\pi \le x \le \pi$.

Write $y = 5 \sin x - 5\sqrt{3} \cos x$
as $y = 10 \sin\left(x - \frac{\pi}{3}\right)$ and transform
the graph of $y = \sin x$ as appropriate:

> **Tip:** Look back at pages 35-38 for a reminder about transformations of graphs.

This transformation is a translation of the graph of $y = \sin x$ horizontally right by $\frac{\pi}{3}$ followed by a stretch vertically by a scale factor of 10.

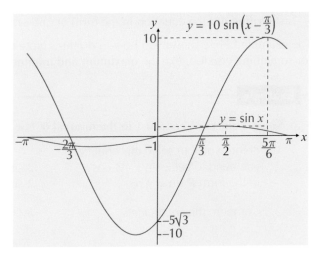

You can transform the maximum and minimum points of the graph in the same way —
the maximum on $y = \sin x$ at $\left(\frac{\pi}{2}, 1\right)$ gets translated right by $\frac{\pi}{3}$ (so add $\frac{\pi}{3}$ to the x-coordinate)
and stretched vertically by 10 (so multiply the y-coordinate by 10), to become $\left(\frac{5\pi}{6}, 10\right)$.

Exercise 3.8.1

Q1 Express $3 \sin x - 2 \cos x$ in the form $R \sin (x - \alpha)$.
Give R in surd form and α in degrees to 1 decimal place.

Q2 Express $6 \cos x - 5 \sin x$ in the form $R \cos (x + \alpha)$.
Give R in surd form and α in degrees to 1 decimal place.

Q3 Express $\sin x + \sqrt{7} \cos x$ in the form $R \sin (x + \alpha)$.
Give R in the form $m\sqrt{2}$ and α in radians to 3 significant figures.

Q4 Write $5 \sin \theta - 6 \cos \theta$ in the form $R \sin (\theta - \alpha)$, where $R > 0$ and $0 \le \alpha \le 90°$.

Q5 Show that $\sqrt{2} \sin x - \cos x \equiv \sqrt{3} \sin (x - \alpha)$, where $\tan \alpha = \dfrac{1}{\sqrt{2}}$.

Q6 Show that $3 \cos 2x + 5 \sin 2x \equiv \sqrt{34} \cos (2x - \alpha)$, where $\tan \alpha = \dfrac{5}{3}$.

> **Q6 Hint:** Treat the $2x$ just the same as an x.

Q7 a) Express $\sqrt{3} \sin x + \cos x$ in the form $R \sin (x + \alpha)$.
Give R and α as exact answers and α in radians in terms of π.

b) Hence sketch the graph of $y = \sqrt{3} \sin x + \cos x$ in the interval $-\pi \le x \le \pi$.

c) State the coordinates of any maximum and minimum points and intersections with the axes of the graph in b).

> **Q7c) Hint:** Write down their coordinates on the graph of $y = \sin x$ first, then apply the transformations to them.

Applying the R addition formulas

To solve equations of the form $a \sin \theta + b \cos \theta = c$, it's best to work things out in different **stages** — first **writing out** the equation in the form of one of the **R formulas**, then **solving** it.

The example below shows you how to do this. Note that you might be asked for something else too, like the **maximum and minimum values** of the function.

Example

a) Solve $2 \sin x - 3 \cos x = 1$ in the interval $0° \le x \le 360°$.

1. Before you can solve this equation, you need to get $2 \sin x - 3 \cos x$ in the form $R \sin (x - \alpha)$.

   $2 \sin x - 3 \cos x \equiv R \sin (x - \alpha)$
   $2 \sin x - 3 \cos x \equiv R \sin x \cos \alpha - R \cos x \sin \alpha$

2. Compare the coefficients.

   $R \cos \alpha = 2$ and $R \sin \alpha = 3$

3. Solve for α.

   $\dfrac{R \sin \alpha}{R \cos \alpha} = \tan \alpha = \dfrac{3}{2}$

   $\Rightarrow \alpha = \tan^{-1} 1.5 = 56.31°$ (2 d.p.)

4. Solve for R.

   $R^2 \cos^2 \alpha + R^2 \sin^2 \alpha = 2^2 + 3^2$

   $\Rightarrow R^2 = 13 \Rightarrow R = \sqrt{13}$

   So $2 \sin x - 3 \cos x = \sqrt{13} \sin (x - 56.31°)$

5. Now solve the equation.

   $2 \sin x - 3 \cos x = 1 \Rightarrow \sqrt{13} \sin (x - 56.31°) = 1$

   $\Rightarrow \sin (x - 56.31°) = \dfrac{1}{\sqrt{13}}$

6. Since $0° \le x \le 360°$, look for solutions in the interval $-56.31° \le (x - 56.31°) \le 303.69°$ (just take 56.31° away from the original interval).

   $x - 56.31° = \sin^{-1}\left(\dfrac{1}{\sqrt{13}}\right) = 16.10°$,

   or $180 - 16.10 = 163.90°$ (2 d.p.)

   There are no solutions in the range $-56.31° \le (x - 56.31°) \le 0°$ since $\sin x$ is negative in the range $-90° \le x \le 0°$.

   So $x = 16.10 + 56.31 = \boxed{72.4°}$ (1 d.p.)

   or $x = 163.90 + 56.31 = \boxed{220.2°}$ (1 d.p.)

b) What are the maximum and minimum values of $2 \sin x - 3 \cos x$?

Use the properties of the sin function to find the maximum and minimum.

The maximum and minimum values of the **sin** function are ± 1, so the maximum and minimum values of $R \sin (x - \alpha)$ are $\pm R$.

$2 \sin x - 3 \cos x = \sqrt{13} \sin (x - 56.31°) \Rightarrow R = \sqrt{13}$

So the maximum and minimum values are $\boxed{\pm\sqrt{13}}$.

Q1 a) Express $5 \cos \theta - 12 \sin \theta$ in the form $R \cos (\theta + \alpha)$,
where $R > 0$ and α is an acute angle in degrees (to 1 d.p.).

b) Hence solve $5 \cos \theta - 12 \sin \theta = 4$ in the interval $0° \le \theta \le 360°$.

c) State the maximum and minimum values of $5 \cos \theta - 12 \sin \theta$.

Q2 a) Express $2 \sin 2\theta + 3 \cos 2\theta$ in the form $R \sin (2\theta + \alpha)$,
where $R > 0$ (given in surd form) and $0 < \alpha < \frac{\pi}{2}$ (to 3 s.f.).

> **Q2b) Hint:** Take care with the interval here to make sure you get all the correct solutions for θ.

b) Hence solve $2 \sin 2\theta + 3 \cos 2\theta = 1$ in the interval $0 \le \theta \le 2\pi$.

Q3 a) Express $3 \sin \theta - 2\sqrt{5} \cos \theta$ in the form $R \sin (\theta - \alpha)$.
Give R in surd form and α in degrees to 1 d.p.

b) Hence solve $3 \sin \theta - 2\sqrt{5} \cos \theta = 5$ in the interval $0° \le \theta \le 360°$.

c) Find the maximum value of $f(x) = 3 \sin x - 2\sqrt{5} \cos x$
and the smallest positive value of x at which it occurs.

Q4 a) Express $f(x) = 3 \sin x + \cos x$ in the form $R \sin (x + \alpha)$.
where $R > 0$ (given in surd form) and $0° < \alpha < 90°$ (to 1 d.p.).

b) Hence solve the equation $f(x) = 2$ in the interval $0° \le x \le 360°$.

c) State the maximum and minimum values of $f(x)$.

Q5 a) Express $4 \sin x + \cos x$ in the form $R \sin (x + \alpha)$,
where $R > 0$ (given in surd form) and $0 < \alpha < \frac{\pi}{2}$ (to 3 s.f.).

b) Hence find the greatest value of $(4 \sin x + \cos x)^4$.

c) Solve the equation $4 \sin x + \cos x = 1$ for values of x in the interval $0 \le x \le \pi$.

Q6 a) Write $f(x) = 8 \cos x + 15 \sin x$ in the form $R \cos(x - \alpha)$, where $R > 0$ and $0 < \alpha < \frac{\pi}{2}$.

b) Solve the equation $f(x) = 5$ in the interval $0 \le x \le 2\pi$.

c) Find the minimum value of $g(x) = (8 \cos x + 15 \sin x)^2$
and the smallest positive value of x at which it occurs.

> **Q6c) Hint:** Think about what happens to the negative values when you square a function.

Q7 The function g is given by $g(x) = 2 \cos x + \sin x, \ x \in \mathbb{R}$.
$g(x)$ can be written as $R \cos (x - \alpha)$, where $R > 0$ and $0° < \alpha < 90°$.

a) Show that $R = \sqrt{5}$, and find the value of α (to 3 s.f.).

b) Hence state the range of $g(x)$.

> **Q7b) Hint:** This is just another way of asking for the maximum and minimum values of the function.

Q8 Express $3 \sin \theta - \frac{3}{2} \cos \theta$ in the form $R \sin (\theta - \alpha)$,
where $R > 0$ and $0 < \alpha < \frac{\pi}{2}$, and hence solve the equation
$3 \sin \theta - \frac{3}{2} \cos \theta = 3$ for values of θ in the interval $0 \le \theta \le 2\pi$.

Q9 Solve the equation $4 \sin 2\theta + 3 \cos 2\theta = 2$ for values of θ in the interval $0 \le \theta \le \pi$.

3.9 Modelling with Trig Functions

Physicists and engineers use trig functions a lot — the fact that they repeat every 2π makes them really useful for modelling situations where motion repeats periodically, such as bouncing or swinging. You'll need to use all the trigonometry you've learned so far.

Learning Objective (Spec Ref 5.9):
- Use trigonometry to model real-life problems.

Trigonometry in modelling

Trigonometric functions show up a lot in modelling problems. Things that happen in a cycle, like the motion of a child on a swing, or tidal patterns, could be modelled with sin and cos.

When tackling these questions, remember to check whether you should be working in degrees or radians. Make sure that you give your answers to a suitable degree of accuracy (3 s.f. is usually fine).

Example 1

The height of an object bouncing on a spring is modelled by the equation $h = 5 + 2 \sin \left(5t + \frac{\pi}{3}\right)$ where t is the time in seconds and h is the height in cm. Find the first time at which $h = 4$ cm.

1. Set $h = 4$ in the equation and solve.

    Tip: If you see π in a question it means it's in radians.

$$5 + 2 \sin \left(5t + \frac{\pi}{3}\right) = 4$$
$$2 \sin \left(5t + \frac{\pi}{3}\right) = -1$$
$$\sin \left(5t + \frac{\pi}{3}\right) = -\frac{1}{2}$$
$$\left(5t + \frac{\pi}{3}\right) = \sin^{-1}\left(-\frac{1}{2}\right) = -\frac{\pi}{6}, \frac{7\pi}{6}, \frac{11\pi}{6}, \dots \text{ etc}$$

2. Use the fact that time cannot be negative to find the valid solutions:

    Tip: Be careful when using inverse trig functions to solve equations — you usually get multiple solutions so you need to decide which one(s) to use.

$t \geq 0$, which means that $5t + \frac{\pi}{3} \geq \frac{\pi}{3}$.

The first solution to satisfy this inequality is $\frac{7\pi}{6}$:
$$5t + \frac{\pi}{3} = \frac{7\pi}{6} \Rightarrow 5t = \frac{5\pi}{6} \Rightarrow t = \frac{\pi}{6}$$

So the first time it has a height of 4 cm is at $t = \frac{\pi}{6} = $ **0.524 s (3 s.f.)**

Example 2

Two sound waves are modelled by the functions f(θ) and g(θ), where f(θ) = 12 sin θ and g(θ) = $4\sqrt{3}$ cos θ. The two waves combine to produce a new wave given by h(θ) = f(θ) + g(θ).

a) Write the equation for this new wave in the form $R \sin (\theta + \alpha)$, where α is measured in radians, giving your answers as exact values.

1. Set h(θ) equal to $R \sin (\theta + \alpha)$.

    h(θ) = 12 sin θ + $4\sqrt{3}$ cos θ = $R \sin (\theta + \alpha)$

2. Expand $R \sin (\theta + \alpha)$ using the sin addition formula and equate the coefficients.

    $R \sin (\theta + \alpha) = R \sin \theta \cos \alpha + R \cos \theta \sin \alpha$
    $\Rightarrow R \cos \alpha = 12$ and $R \sin \alpha = 4\sqrt{3}$

3. Now solve for R and α:

$$R = \sqrt{12^2 + (4\sqrt{3})^2} = \sqrt{144 + 48} = \sqrt{192} = 8\sqrt{3}$$

$$\tan \alpha = \frac{4\sqrt{3}}{12} = \frac{\sqrt{3}}{3} = \frac{1}{\sqrt{3}} \Rightarrow \alpha = \frac{\pi}{6}$$

So $\quad h(\theta) = 8\sqrt{3}\ \sin\left(\theta + \frac{\pi}{6}\right)$

b) The amplitude, a, of a sound wave is equivalent to half the distance between the maximum and minimum values of the wave (as shown). Find the amplitude of $h(\theta)$.

1. Write down the minimum and maximum points of the sin function.

    $\sin\theta$ has a maximum of 1 and a minimum of -1.

2. Find the transformation of $\sin\theta$ to $h(\theta)$:

    $\sin\theta$ is translated horizontally by $-\frac{\pi}{6}$, and stretched vertically by a scale factor of $8\sqrt{3}$.

3. Find the amplitude of $h(\theta)$:

    The maximum and minimum values of $h(\theta)$ are $\pm R$ — i.e. $8\sqrt{3}$ and $-8\sqrt{3}$, so its amplitude is $\frac{1}{2}(8\sqrt{3} - (-8\sqrt{3})) = 8\sqrt{3}$

Exercise 3.9.1

MODELLING

Q1 A circular plot of land with a radius of 20 m is separated into three gardens. Each garden is a sector of the circle, with angles of 120°, 144° and 96° respectively. Calculate the area and perimeter of each garden (to 3 s.f.).

Q2 Adam wants to form a function to model the hours of daylight in his town throughout the year. He knows that the function should be of the form $f(t) = A + B \cos t$, where A and B are positive constants and the time, t, is in radians.

   a) The daylight hours vary from 7 to 17. Find the values of A and B.

   b) He now wants to adjust the model so that t is measured in months. He rewrites his function as $g(t) = A + B \cos (Ct + D)$. Find the values of C and D, such that the longest day of the year occurs at $t = 0$ and the shortest day of the year occurs at $t = 6$.

Q3 The height of a buoy floating in a harbour, measured in metres, is modelled by the function $h(t) = 14 + 5 (\sin t + \cos t)$, where t is time in hours. By writing $h(t)$ in the form $14 + R \cos (t - \alpha)$, find the maximum and minimum height of the buoy (to 1 d.p.).

Q4 Antonia goes on a fairground ride. She is strapped into a small spinning disc, which is attached to a large rotating wheel.

   a) The height, in metres, of the centre of the disc above the ground after t seconds is given by $H = 10 + \frac{7}{2}(\sin t - \sqrt{3} \cos t)$. Write this in the form $H = 10 + R \sin (t - \alpha)$, where $R > 0$ and $0 < \alpha \leq \frac{\pi}{2}$.

   b) Antonia's height above the ground, h, is given by $h = H - \cos 2(t - \alpha)$. Use the double angle formulas to show that $h = A + R \sin (t - \alpha) + B \sin^2 (t - \alpha)$, and give the values of A and B. It could help to set $(t - \alpha) = x$.

   c) Hence find the first time when Antonia is 13 m above the ground.

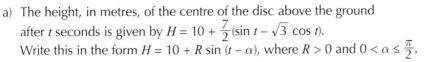

Review Exercise

Q1 a) Convert these angles into radians, giving your answers in terms of π:

      (i) 15°   (ii) 50°   (iii) 330°   (iv) 225°

    b) Convert these angles into degrees:

      (i) $\dfrac{7\pi}{12}$ (ii) $\dfrac{7\pi}{6}$ (iii) $\dfrac{5\pi}{3}$ (iv) $\dfrac{13\pi}{12}$

Q2 The diagram on the right shows a sector ABC of a circle, with centre A and a radius of 10 cm. The angle BAC is 0.7 radians. Find the arc length BC and area of this sector.

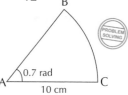

Q3 Use the small angle approximations to estimate $\tan\theta - \cos\theta$ for:

    a) $\theta = 0.13$ b) $\theta = 0.07$ c) $\theta = 0.26$

Q4 When θ is small, find an approximation for the expressions below:

    a) $\sin 3\theta \tan 4\theta$ b) $\cos 4\theta + \cos 8\theta$ c) $\dfrac{2\theta^3}{\sin 2\theta \cos\theta}$

Q5 Using trig values for common angles, evaluate the following in radians, between 0 and $\dfrac{\pi}{2}$:

    a) $\sin^{-1}\dfrac{1}{\sqrt{2}}$ b) $\cos^{-1}\dfrac{1}{2}$ c) $\tan^{-1}\dfrac{1}{\sqrt{3}}$

Q6 Sketch the graphs of arcsin, arccos and arctan showing their domains and ranges.

Q7 The diagram on the right shows the curve $y = \dfrac{1}{1 + \cos x}$ for $0 \le x \le \dfrac{\pi}{2}$:

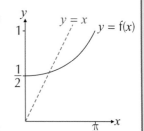

    a) If $y = f(x)$, show that $f^{-1}(x) = \arccos\left(\dfrac{1}{x} - 1\right)$.

    b) State the domain and range of this inverse function.

    c) Sketch $y = f^{-1}(x)$ on the same axes as $y = f(x)$.

Q8 Given that $f(x) = \sin^{-1} x + \cos^{-1} x + \tan^{-1} x$, find the value, in radians, of:

    a) $f(1)$ b) $f(-1)$

Q9 For $\theta = 30°$, find the exact values of:

    a) $\operatorname{cosec}\theta$ b) $\sec\theta$ c) $\cot\theta$

Q10 Sketch the graphs of cosecant, secant and cotangent for $-2\pi \le x \le 2\pi$.

Q11 a) Describe the transformation that maps $y = \sec x$ onto $y = \sec 4x$.

    b) What is the period, in radians, of the graph $y = \sec 4x$?

    c) Sketch the graph of $y = \sec 4x$ for $0 \le x \le \pi$.

    d) For what values of x in this interval is $\sec 4x$ undefined?

Review Exercise

Q12 Given that $x = \operatorname{cosec} \theta$ and $y = \cot^2 \theta$, show that $y = x^2 - 1$.

Q13 If $x = \sec \theta$ and $y = 2 \tan \theta$, express y in terms of x only.

Q14 a) Show that the equation $\operatorname{cosec}^2 x = \dfrac{3 \cot x + 4}{2}$ can be written as $2 \cot^2 x - 3 \cot x - 2 = 0$.

b) Hence solve the equation $\operatorname{cosec}^2 x = \dfrac{3 \cot x + 4}{2}$.
Give all the values of x in the interval $0 \le x \le 2\pi$ in radians to 2 decimal places.

Q15 Given that θ is acute and $\cos \theta = \dfrac{1}{2}$:

a) Give the exact value of $\sec \theta$.

b) Use Pythagoras' Theorem to find the value of $\tan \theta$.

c) Use the identity $\sec^2 \theta \equiv 1 + \tan^2 \theta$ to find the value of $\tan \theta$ and confirm that it is the same as in part b).

d) Give the exact value of $\cot \theta$.

e) Using the identity $\operatorname{cosec}^2 \theta \equiv 1 + \cot^2 \theta$, give the exact value of $\sin \theta$.

Q16 Express the following as a single trig function:

a) $\sin 2x \cos 9x + \cos 2x \sin 9x$

b) $3 \cos 5x \cos 7x - 3 \sin 5x \sin 7x$

c) $\dfrac{\tan 12x - \tan 8x}{1 + \tan 12x \tan 8x}$

d) $12 \sin \dfrac{7x}{2} \cos \dfrac{3x}{2} - 12 \cos \dfrac{7x}{2} \sin \dfrac{3x}{2}$

Q17 Using the addition formula for cos, find the exact value of $\cos \dfrac{7\pi}{12}$.

Q18 Find $\sin (A + B)$, given that $\sin A = \dfrac{4}{5}$ and $\sin B = \dfrac{7}{25}$ and that both A and B are acute angles.

Q19 Use the double angle formula to solve the equation $\sin 2\theta = -\sqrt{3} \sin \theta$ for $0° \le \theta \le 360°$.

Q20 Solve the equations below in the interval $0 \le x \le 2\pi$, giving your answers to 3 s.f. where necessary.

a) $4 \sin x = \sin \dfrac{x}{2}$

b) $\tan \dfrac{x}{2} \tan x = 2$

Q21 Solve the equations below in the interval $0 \le x \le 2\pi$. Give your answers in radians in terms of π.

a) $2 \tan 2x = \tan x$

b) $\sin 6x - \cos 3x = 0$

Q22 a) Write $3 \cos \theta - 8 \sin \theta$ in the form $R \cos (\theta + \alpha)$, where $R > 0$ and $0 \le \alpha \le 90°$.

b) Hence solve $3 \cos \theta - 8 \sin \theta = 1.2$ in the interval $0° \le \theta \le 360°$.

Q23 The height above the ground, h m, of a rider on a pirate ship at a theme park is modelled by the function: $h = 5 \sin t + 3 \cos t + 2$, where t is the time in seconds. Find the maximum height above the ground that the rider reaches. Give your answer to 2 decimal places.

Q1   The graph of $y = \cos^{-1} x$ is shown on the right.

Given that A and C are the end points of the graph, state the coordinates of points A, B and C in radians.

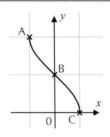

[3 marks]

Q2   a) Show that $\tan \dfrac{5\pi}{12} = 2 + \sqrt{3}$.

[3 marks]

b) Hence, or otherwise, find the exact value of $\cot \dfrac{5\pi}{12}$. Your answer should be given in the form $a + \sqrt{b}$, where a and b are constants to be found.

[1 mark]

Q3   Find the solutions of $2 \sin 2\theta - \cos \theta = 0$ in the interval $0 \le \theta \le 2\pi$. Give your answers in radians to 3 s.f.

[5 marks]

Q4   A discus must be thrown so that it lands within a bounded sector of angle 40°. The curved edge of the sector is 100 m away, as shown in the diagram below.

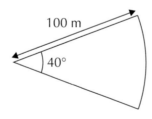

a) Find the area of the region in which the discus could land and lie within the bounds. Give your answer to 3 significant figures.

[3 marks]

b) Find the length of the boundary of the region to 3 significant figures.

[2 marks]

Q5   a) Approximate $\tan 5°$ using an appropriate small angle approximation.

[2 marks]

b) State the percentage error (to 3 s.f.) when using the small angle approximation.

[2 marks]

Exam-Style Questions

Q6 a) Write $7 \cos x - 11 \sin x$ in the form $R \cos (x + \alpha)$, where $R > 0$ and $0° < \alpha < 90°$.

[3 marks]

   b) Describe the transformations that map the graph of $y = \cos x$
   to the graph of $y = 7 \cos x - 11 \sin x$.

[2 marks]

   c) State the maximum value of $y = 7 \cos x - 11 \sin x$
   and a value of x for which this maximum occurs.

[2 marks]

   d) Solve $7 \cos x - 11 \sin x = 3$ in the interval $0 \leq x \leq 360°$,
   giving your answers to 1 d.p.

[4 marks]

Q7 Solve $\operatorname{cosec}^2 x = 4 + 2 \cot x$ in the interval $0 \leq x \leq 2\pi$, giving your answers to 3 s.f.

[7 marks]

Q8 a) Show that $\cot \theta + \tan \theta \equiv 2 \operatorname{cosec} 2\theta$.

[3 marks]

   b) Hence, solve $\cot 2\theta + \tan 2\theta = \frac{7}{2}$ in the interval $0 \leq \theta \leq \pi$,
   giving your answers to 3 s.f.

[5 marks]

Q9 In a beach town, the height of the tide in feet can be modelled by the function
$h(t) = a + b \sin \left(\frac{1}{2}(t - \pi) \right)$, where t is the time in hours.

   a) Given that the height of the tide is 9 feet at low tide
   and 17 feet at high tide, find the values of a and b.

[3 marks]

   b) How many hours after low tide does the tide first reach 11 feet in this model?

[5 marks]

Q10 Prove that $\tan x (\operatorname{cosec} 2x + \cot 2x) \equiv 1$.

[5 marks]

4.1 Parametric Equations of Curves

Parametric equations have x and y in separate equations, both defined in terms of another variable. It sounds complicated, but it can often make things a lot easier, as you'll see in this chapter.

Learning Objectives (Spec Ref 3.3 & 3.4):
- Calculate Cartesian coordinates for a curve given in parametric form.
- Find the coordinates of intersection points between a parametric curve and other lines.

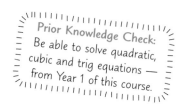

Prior Knowledge Check:
Be able to solve quadratic, cubic and trig equations — from Year 1 of this course.

Finding coordinates from parametric equations

Normally, graphs in the (x, y) plane are described using a **Cartesian equation** — a single equation linking x and y. Sometimes, particularly for more complicated graphs, it's easier to have two linked equations, called **parametric equations**.

In parametric equations, x and y are each defined separately in terms of a **third variable**, called a **parameter**. The parameter is usually either t or θ.

Parametric equations are often used to model the path of a moving particle, where its **position** (given by x and y) depends on time, t. You'll use them in kinematics, in the Applied part of this course.

Example 1

Sketch the graph given by the parametric equations $y = t^3 - 1$ and $x = t + 1$.

1. Start by making a table of coordinates. Choose some values for t and calculate x and y at these values:

t	-2	-1	0	1	2
x	-1	0	1	2	3
y	-9	-2	-1	0	7

$x = -2 + 1 = -1$,
and $y = (-2)^3 - 1 = -9$.

$x = 1 + 1 = 2$,
and $y = 1^3 - 1 = 0$.

2. Now plot the Cartesian (x, y) coordinates on a set of axes as usual:

Tip: You won't necessarily be expected to sketch a curve from its parametric equations in the exam — but finding the Cartesian coordinates like this can make it easier to picture the graph.

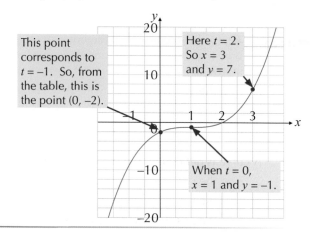

This point corresponds to $t = -1$. So, from the table, this is the point $(0, -2)$.

Here $t = 2$. So $x = 3$ and $y = 7$.

When $t = 0$, $x = 1$ and $y = -1$.

Example 2

Sketch the graph given by $x = \cos\theta$ and $y = \sin\theta + 1$.

1. Make a table as before with values for θ over a suitable interval (such as $0 \le \theta \le 2\pi$).

2. Plot the points — you should spot that they lie on a circle with centre $(0, 1)$ and radius 1. ($x = a + r\cos\theta$, $y = b + r\sin\theta$ are the general parametric equations for a circle with centre (a, b).)

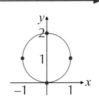

θ	x	y
0	1	1
$\dfrac{\pi}{2}$	0	2
π	-1	1
$\dfrac{3\pi}{2}$	0	0
2π	1	1

You can use the parametric equations to find **x-y values** at a given value of the parameter, and to find the value of the **parameter** for given x- or y-coordinates. There's often a limit on the **domain** of the parameter like the one in Example 3 below — see pages 13-17 for more about domains of functions. For example, the parameter can't take a value that would set the denominator of any fraction to zero.

Example 3

A flying disc is thrown from the point $(0, 0)$. After t seconds, it has travelled x m horizontally and y m vertically, modelled by the parametric equations $x = t^2 + 2t$ and $y = 6t - t^2$ $(0 \le t \le 6)$.

a) Find the x- and y- values of the position of the disc after 2.5 seconds.

Just substitute $t = 2.5$ into the equations for x and y.

When $t = 2.5$: $x = 2.5^2 + 2 \times 2.5 = 6.25 + 5 = \boxed{11.25}$

$y = 6 \times 2.5 - 2.5^2 = 15 - 6.25 = \boxed{8.75}$

b) After how many seconds does the disc reach a height of 5 metres?

Now you want the value of t when $y = 5$.

$5 = 6t - t^2 \Rightarrow t^2 - 6t + 5 = 0 \Rightarrow (t - 1)(t - 5) = 0$

$\Rightarrow \boxed{t = 1\text{ s}}$ and $\boxed{t = 5\text{ s}}$

c) What is the value of y when the disc reaches the point $x = 24$ m?

1. Use the equation for x to find t first.

$24 = t^2 + 2t \Rightarrow t^2 + 2t - 24 = 0 \Rightarrow (t + 6)(t - 4) = 0$

$\Rightarrow t = -6$ or $t = 4$, but t is restricted to $0 \le t \le 6$, so $t = 4$ s

2. Then use it in the other equation to find y.

$y = 6 \times 4 - 4^2 = 24 - 16 = \boxed{8}$

Exercise 4.1.1

Q1 A curve is defined by the parametric equations $x = 3t$, $y = t^2$.

a) Find the coordinates of the point where $t = 5$.

b) Find the value of t at the point where $x = 18$.

c) Find the possible values of x at the point where $y = 36$.

Q2 A curve is defined by the parametric equations $x = 2t - 1$, $y = 4 - t^2$.

a) Find the coordinates of the point where $t = 7$.

b) Find the value of t at the point where $x = 15$.

c) Find the possible values of x at the point where $y = -5$.

Q3 A curve has parametric equations $x = 2 + \sin\theta$, $y = -3 + \cos\theta$.

a) Find the coordinates of the point where $\theta = \frac{\pi}{4}$.

b) Find the acute value of θ at the point where $x = \frac{4 + \sqrt{3}}{2}$.

c) Find the obtuse value of θ at the point where $y = -\frac{7}{2}$.

> **Q3b) & c) Hint:** There is only one acute value of θ possible in b), and only one obtuse value of θ possible in c).

Q4 For the curve defined by the parametric equations $x = t^2 + 5t$, $y = 6 + 3t^2$:

a) Find the possible values of t when $y = 33$.

b) Find the possible values of y when $x = 6$.

Q5 Complete the table below, and hence sketch the curve represented by the parametric equations:
$x = 5t$, $y = \frac{2}{t}$, for $t \neq 0$.

t	-5	-4	-3	-2	-1	1	2	3	4	5
x										
y										

Q6 Sketch the curve represented by the parametric equations
$x = 1 + \sin\theta$, $y = 2 + \cos\theta$ for the values $0 \le \theta \le 2\pi$.
Use the table below to help you, and give your answers to 2 d.p.

> **Q6 Hint:** Make sure your calculator's set to radians.

θ	0	$\frac{\pi}{4}$	$\frac{\pi}{3}$	$\frac{\pi}{2}$	$\frac{2\pi}{3}$	$\frac{3\pi}{4}$	π	$\frac{4\pi}{3}$	$\frac{3\pi}{2}$	$\frac{5\pi}{3}$	2π
x											
y											

Q7 The curve C is defined by the parametric equations $y = 10 - t^2$, $x = 2t^2 - 7t$.

a) Find the value of a if $(a, 1)$ is a point on the curve and $a > 1$.

b) Show that the point $(-6, 4)$ does not lie on curve C.

Q8 The orbit of a comet around the Sun is modelled by the parametric equations
$x = 3 \sin\theta$, $y = 7 + 9 \cos\theta$, for $0 \le \theta \le 2\pi$, where the point $(0, 0)$ represents the Sun, and where 1 unit on the x- and y-axes represents 1 astronomical unit (AU, 1 AU $\approx$ 150 million km).

How far, in AU, is the comet from the Sun when:

> **Q8b) Hint:** You'll need to use Pythagoras.

a) $\theta = 0$,   b) $\theta = \frac{\pi}{2}$?

Q9 The path of a toy plane thrown from a tower is modelled by the parametric equations
$x = t^2 + 4t$, $y = 25 - t^2$ for $0 \le t \le 5$, where t is the time taken in seconds, and x and y are the horizontal and vertical distances in metres to the plane from the point at ground level at the foot of the tower.

a) How far does the plane travel in the horizontal direction in the first 2 seconds?

b) Sonia is standing 21 m from the base of the tower, in line with the path of the plane. At what height above the ground does the toy plane pass over Sonia's head?

Finding intersections

A lot of parametric equations questions involve identifying points on the curve defined by the equations. You'll often be given the parametric equations of a curve, and asked to find the coordinates of the **points of intersection** of this curve with another line (such as the x- or y-axis).

Use the information in the question to **solve for t** at the intersection point(s). Then **substitute the value(s) of t** into the parametric equations to work out the **x and y values** (i.e. the **coordinates**) at the intersection point(s). The example below shows how to tackle a question like this.

Example

The curve shown has the parametric equations $y = t^3 - t$ and $x = 4t^2 - 1$.
Find the coordinates of the points where the graph crosses:
a) the x-axis,   b) the y-axis,   and c) the line $8y = 3x + 3$.

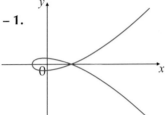

a) On the x-axis, $y = 0$.

1. Use the parametric equation for y to find the values of t where the graph crosses the x-axis. You need to factorise and solve the cubic.

    $0 = t^3 - t \Rightarrow t(t^2 - 1) = 0 \Rightarrow t(t + 1)(t - 1) = 0$
    $\Rightarrow t = 0, t = -1, t = 1$

2. Now use those values of t to find the x-coordinates.

    When $t = 0$: $x = 4(0)^2 - 1 = -1$
    When $t = -1$: $x = 4(-1)^2 - 1 = 3$
    When $t = 1$: $x = 4(1)^2 - 1 = 3$

    $t = -1$ and $t = 1$ give the same coordinates — that's where the curve crosses over itself.

    So the graph crosses the x-axis at (−1, 0) and (3, 0).

b) On the y-axis, $x = 0$.

This time, use the parametric equation for x to find the values of t, then use those values to find the y-coordinates.

$0 = 4t^2 - 1 \Rightarrow t^2 = \frac{1}{4} \Rightarrow t = \pm\frac{1}{2}$

When $t = \frac{1}{2}$: $y = \left(\frac{1}{2}\right)^3 - \frac{1}{2} = -\frac{3}{8}$

When $t = -\frac{1}{2}$ $y = \left(-\frac{1}{2}\right)^3 - \left(-\frac{1}{2}\right) = \frac{3}{8}$

Tip: The sketch shows there are two points where the graph crosses each axis.

So the graph crosses the y-axis at $\left(0, -\frac{3}{8}\right)$ and $\left(0, \frac{3}{8}\right)$.

c) Part c) is just a little trickier.

1. First, substitute the parametric equations into $8y = 3x + 3$.

    $8y = 3x + 3 \Rightarrow 8(t^3 - t) = 3(4t^2 - 1) + 3$

2. Rearrange and factorise to find the values of t you need.

    $8t^3 - 8t = 12t^2 \Rightarrow 8t^3 - 12t^2 - 8t = 0$
    $\Rightarrow t(2t + 1)(t - 2) = 0 \Rightarrow t = 0, t = -\frac{1}{2}, t = 2$

3. Go back to the parametric equations to find the x- and y-coordinates.

    When $t = 0$: $x = -1, y = 0$

    When $t = -\frac{1}{2}$: $x = 4\left(\frac{1}{4}\right) - 1 = 0, y = \left(-\frac{1}{2}\right)^3 + \frac{1}{2} = \frac{3}{8}$

    When $t = 2$: $x = 4(4) - 1 = 15, y = 2^3 - 2 = 6$

    So the graph crosses the line $8y = 3x + 3$ at:

Tip: Check the answers by sticking these values back into $8y = 3x + 3$.

$(-1, 0), \left(0, \frac{3}{8}\right), (15, 6)$

Q1 The curve with parametric equations $x = 3 + t$, $y = -2 + t$ meets the x-axis at the point A and the y-axis at the point B. Find the coordinates of A and B.

Q1 Hint: A lies on the x-axis and B lies on the y-axis, so in each case you know one of the coordinates.

Q2 The curve C has parametric equations $x = 2t^2 - 50$, $y = 3t^3 - 24$.

   a) Find the value of t where the curve meets the x-axis.

   b) Find the values of t where the curve meets the y-axis.

Q3 The curve with parametric equations $x = 64 - t^3$, $y = \frac{1}{t}$, for $t \neq 0$, meets the y-axis at the point P. Find the coordinates of the point P.

Q4 Find the coordinates of the point of intersection, P, of the line $y = x - 3$ and the curve with parametric equations $x = 2t + 1$, $y = 4t$.

Q4 Hint: Replace the x and y in the Cartesian equation with the parametric equations.

Q5 Find the coordinates of the point(s) of intersection of the curve $y = x^2 + 32$ and the curve with parametric equations $x = 2t$, $y = 6t^2$.

Q6 Find the points of intersection of the circle $x^2 + y^2 = 32$ and the curve with parametric equations $x = t^2$, $y = 2t$.

Q7 The curve with parametric equations $x = a(t - 2)$, $y = 2at^2 + 3$ $(a \neq 0)$, meets the y-axis at $(0, 4)$.

   a) Find the value of the constant a.

   b) Hence determine whether the curve meets the x-axis.

Q8 A curve has parametric equations $x = \frac{2}{t}$, $y = t^2 - 9$, for $t \neq 0$.

   a) Find the point(s) at which the curve crosses the x-axis.

   b) Does the curve meet the y-axis? Explain your answer.

   c) Find the coordinates of the point(s) at which this curve meets the curve $y = \frac{10}{x} - 3$.

Q9 A curve has parametric equations $x = 3 \sin t$, $y = 5 \cos t$ and is defined for the domain $0 \leq t \leq 2\pi$.

   a) Determine the coordinates at which this curve meets the x- and y-axes.

   b) Find the points where the curve meets the line $y = \left(\frac{5\sqrt{3}}{9}\right)x$.

Q10 A simulation models the paths of two ships using parametric equations. The ships are modelled as points, with no width or length. The path taken by the first ship is given by $x_1 = 24 - t$, $y_1 = 10 + 3t$. The path taken by the second ship is given by $x_2 = t + 10$, $y_2 = 12 + 2t - 0.1t^2$. For both sets of equations, $0 \leq t \leq 30$, where t is the time in hours since the start of the simulation, and x and y are measured in miles East and North respectively. According to the simulation, will the two ships collide?

4.2 Parametric and Cartesian Equations

As well as finding Cartesian coordinates for a curve given in parametric form, you can also work out the Cartesian equation from the parametric equations.

Learning Objectives (Spec Ref 3.3):
- Convert parametric equations into Cartesian form.

Prior Knowledge Check:
Trig identities — from Year 1 and pages 69, 74 and 81.

Converting parametric equations to Cartesian equations

Some parametric equations can be **converted** into **Cartesian equations**. There are two main ways to do this:

- **Rearrange** one of the equations to make the **parameter** the subject, then **substitute** the result into the **other** equation.

- If your equations involve **trig functions**, use **trig identities** to **eliminate** the parameter.

The examples below show how the first method works.

Example 1

Give the Cartesian equations, in the form $y = f(x)$, of the curves represented by the following pairs of parametric equations:

Tip: The equations in part a) are the same as in the example on p.98.

a) $y = t^3 - 1$ and $x = t + 1$,

   1. You want the answer in the form $y = f(x)$, so leave y alone for now, and rearrange the equation for x to make t the subject: $x = t + 1 \implies t = x - 1$

   2. Now you can eliminate t from the equation for y:

$$y = t^3 - 1$$

Tip: Just replace every 't' in the equation for y with '$x - 1$'. You could use the binomial theorem or Pascal's triangle to find the coefficients in the expansion of $(x - 1)^3$.

$$\implies y = (x - 1)^3 - 1 = (x - 1)(x^2 - 2x + 1) - 1$$
$$\implies y = x^3 - 2x^2 + x - x^2 + 2x - 1 - 1$$
$$\implies y = x^3 - 3x^2 + 3x - 2$$

So the Cartesian equation is $\boxed{y = x^3 - 3x^2 + 3x - 2}$.

b) $y = \dfrac{1}{3t}$ and $x = 2t - 3$, $t \neq 0$.

  Use the same method as above:

$$x = 2t - 3 \implies t = \frac{x + 3}{2}$$

$$\text{So } y = \frac{1}{3t} \implies y = \frac{1}{3\left(\dfrac{x + 3}{2}\right)}$$

$$\implies y = \frac{1}{\left(\dfrac{3(x + 3)}{2}\right)} \implies \boxed{y = \frac{2}{3x + 9}}$$

Trigonometric functions

Things get a little trickier when the likes of sin and cos decide to put in an appearance. For trig functions you need to use **trig identities**.

Example 2

A curve has parametric equations $x = 1 + \sin \theta$, $y = 1 - \cos 2\theta$. Give the Cartesian equation of the curve in the form $y = f(x)$.

Tip: If one of the equations includes $\cos 2\theta$ or $\sin 2\theta$, you'll probably need to use one of the **double angle formulas** from p.81 to get it in terms of $\sin \theta$ or $\cos \theta$.

1. If you try to make θ the subject of these equations, things will get messy. Find a way to get both x and y in terms of the **same trig function**. You can get $\sin \theta$ into the equation for y using the identity $\cos 2\theta \equiv 1 - 2\sin^2 \theta$:

    $y = 1 - \cos 2\theta = 1 - (1 - 2\sin^2 \theta) = 2\sin^2 \theta$

2. Rearrange the equation for x:

    $\sin \theta = x - 1$

3. Replace '$\sin \theta$' in the equation for y with '$x - 1$' to get y in terms of x:

    $y = 2\sin^2 \theta \implies y = 2(x - 1)^2 = 2x^2 - 4x + 2$

    So the Cartesian equation is $\boxed{y = 2x^2 - 4x + 2.}$

Example 3

A curve is defined parametrically by $x = 4 \sec \theta$, $y = 4 \tan \theta$. Give the equation of the curve in the form $y^2 = f(x)$, and hence determine whether the curve intersects the line $y + 3x = 4$.

Tip: Note that you're asked for the equation in the form $y^2 = f(x)$ not $y = f(x)$.

1. Start by rearranging each equation to make the trig function the subject:

    $x = 4 \sec \theta \implies \sec \theta = \dfrac{x}{4}$ and $y = 4 \tan \theta \implies \tan \theta = \dfrac{y}{4}$

2. Find an identity that contains both $\sec \theta$ and $\tan \theta$:

    $\sec^2 \theta \equiv 1 + \tan^2 \theta$

3. Substitute the trig functions with the x and y terms:

    $\left(\dfrac{x}{4}\right)^2 = 1 + \left(\dfrac{y}{4}\right)^2$

4. Rearrange to get an equation in the right form:

    $x^2 = 16 + y^2 \implies \boxed{y^2 = x^2 - 16}$

5. To see whether the curve intersects $y + 3x = 4$, rearrange and substitute for y in the equation of the curve:

    $y + 3x = 4 \implies y = 4 - 3x$
    $\implies (4 - 3x)^2 = x^2 - 16$
    $\implies 16 - 24x + 9x^2 = x^2 - 16$
    $\implies 8x^2 - 24x + 32 = 0$
    $\implies x^2 - 3x + 4 = 0$

    Tip: The last bit comes from the quadratic formula. For a quadratic $ax^2 + bx + c = 0$, there are only real solutions when $b^2 - 4ac \geq 0$, because of the $\sqrt{b^2 - 4ac}$ bit in the formula.

    There are no real roots to this equation ($b^2 - 4ac < 0$), so the line and the curve do not intersect.

Q1 For each of the following parametrically-defined curves,
find the Cartesian equation of the curve in an appropriate form.

a) $x = t + 3, y = t^2$

b) $x = 3t, y = \dfrac{6}{t}, t \neq 0$

c) $x = 2t^3, y = t^2$

d) $x = t + 7, y = 12 - 2t$

e) $x = t + 4, y = t^2 - 9$

f) $x = \dfrac{t+2}{3}, y = t^2 - t$

g) $x = t^2 - \dfrac{t}{2}, y = 5 - 8t$

h) $x = \sin \theta, y = \cos \theta$

i) $x = \sin \theta, y = \cos 2\theta$

j) $x = 1 + \sin \theta, y = 2 + \cos \theta$

k) $x = \cos \theta, y = \cos 2\theta$

l) $x = \cos \theta - 5, y = \cos 2\theta$

Q2 By eliminating the parameter θ, express the curve defined by the parametric equations
$x = \tan \theta, y = \sec \theta$ in the form $y^2 = f(x)$.

Q3 Write the curve $x = 2 \cot \theta, y = 3 \operatorname{cosec} \theta$ in the form $y^2 = f(x)$.

Q4 A circle is defined by the parametric equations $x = 5 + \sin \theta, y = -3 + \cos \theta$.

a) Find the coordinates of the centre of the circle, and the radius of the circle.

b) Write the equation of the curve in Cartesian form.

Q5 A curve has parametric equations $x = \dfrac{1 + 2t}{t}, y = \dfrac{3 + t}{t^2}, t \neq 0$.

a) Express t in terms of x.

b) Hence show that the Cartesian equation of the curve is: $y = (3x - 5)(x - 2)$.

c) Sketch the curve.

Q6 Express $x = \dfrac{2 - 3t}{1 + t}, y = \dfrac{5 - t}{4t + 1}$ ($t \neq -1, t \neq -0.25$), in Cartesian form.

Q7 Find the Cartesian equation of the curve defined by the parametric equations
$x = 5 \sin^2 \theta, y = \cos \theta$. Express your answer in the form $y^2 = f(x)$.

Q8 a) Express $x = a \sin \theta, y = b \cos \theta$ in Cartesian form.

b) Use your answer to a) to sketch the curve.

c) What type of curve has the form $x = a \sin \theta, y = b \cos \theta$?

> **Q8b) Hint:** Find the x-
> and y-intercepts first —
> it will give you an idea
> of the graph's shape.

Q9 A curve has parametric equations $x = 3t^2, y = 2t - 1$.

a) Show that the Cartesian equation of the curve is $x = \dfrac{3}{4}(y + 1)^2$.

b) Hence find the point(s) of intersection of this curve with the line $y = 4x - 3$.

Q10 Find the Cartesian equation of the curve $x = 7t + 2, y = \dfrac{5}{t}, t \neq 0$,
in the form $y = f(x)$ and hence sketch the curve, labelling any
asymptotes and points of intersection with the axes clearly.

> **Q10 Hint:** It's much
> easier to sketch if you
> can transform a standard
> curve shape — see pages
> 35-38 for a recap.

Review Exercise

Q1 A curve is defined by the parametric equations $x = \frac{1}{t}$, $y = \frac{2}{t^2}$ $(t \neq 0)$.

    a) Find the value of t when $x = \frac{1}{4}$ and hence find the corresponding y-coordinate.

    b) Find the possible values of t when $y = \frac{1}{50}$.

Q2 A curve is defined by the parametric equations $x = t^3 + t^2 - 6t$, $y = 4t - 5$.
Find the coordinates of the points where this curve crosses the y-axis.

Q3 A curve is defined by the parametric equations $y = 2t^2 + t + 4$ and $x = \frac{6-t}{2}$.

    a) Find the values of x and y when $t = 0$, 1, 2 and 3.

    b) What are the values of t when: (i) $x = -7$ (ii) $y = 19$?

    c) Find the Cartesian equation of the curve, in the form $y = f(x)$.

Q4 Find the coordinates of the points where the line $y = 10x - 8$ crosses
the curve defined by the parametric equations $x = \frac{t+3}{5}$ and $y = t^2 - t$.

Q5 The parametric equations of a curve are $x = 2 \sin \theta$ and $y = \cos^2 \theta + 4$, $-\frac{\pi}{2} \leq \theta \leq \frac{\pi}{2}$.

    a) What are the coordinates of the points where: (i) $\theta = \frac{\pi}{4}$ (ii) $\theta = \frac{\pi}{6}$?

    b) What is the Cartesian equation of the curve?

    c) What restrictions are there on the values of x for this curve?

Q6 The curve C is defined by the parametric equations $x = \frac{\sin \theta}{3}$ and $y = 3 + 2 \cos 2\theta$.
Find the Cartesian equation of C.

Q7 A curve has parametric equations $y = 4 + \frac{3}{t}$ and $x = t^2 - 1$ $(t \neq 0)$.
What are the coordinates of the points where this curve crosses:

    a) the y-axis,   b) the line $x + 2y = 14$?

Q8 The parametric equations describing curve K are $x = 4 - \cos 2\theta$, $y = \sin^4 \theta - \frac{1}{2}$, $0 \leq \theta \leq \pi$.

    a) Find the coordinates of the point on curve K where $\theta = \frac{\pi}{3}$.

    b) Explain why curve K does not cross the y-axis.

    c) Find the Cartesian equation of curve K, in the form $y = f(x)$.

Q9 The movement of a particle is modelled by the parametric
equations $x = -e^t \sin 2t$, $y = e^t \cos 2t$, for $0 \leq t \leq 2\pi$.

    a) Find the exact value of x at each point where $y = 0$.

    b) If d is the distance of the particle from the origin $(0, 0)$:

        (i) Find an equation for d in terms of t.

        (ii) Find the exact coordinates of the point where $d = e^{\frac{\pi}{8}}$.

Exam-Style Questions

Q1 A curve has parametric equations:
$$x = \frac{2t - 3}{t} \quad \text{and} \quad y = 2t + 6, \qquad 1 < t \le 6$$

a) Find the points where the curve crosses the coordinate axes.

[3 marks]

b) Find the Cartesian equation of the curve in the form $y = f(x)$.

[3 marks]

c) Find the range of f(x).

[2 marks]

Q2 The curve C has parametric equations:
$$x = 2t \quad \text{and} \quad y = t(at + 6), \qquad t \in \mathbb{R}$$

a) If the line $y = ax - 4$ is a tangent to the curve, find the possible values for a.

[4 marks]

b) Sketch the possible curves for C on the same set of axes,
showing where they cross the coordinate axes and each other.

[4 marks]

Q3 A curve C has parametric equations:
$$x = 2\cos t \quad \text{and} \quad y = 5\cos 3t, \qquad -\pi < t < \pi$$

a) Show that a Cartesian equation for C can be written in the form $y = Ax(x^2 - B)$,
where A and B are constants to be found, and give the domain of the function.

[6 marks]

b) Explain why the line $y = 6$ does not cross C.

[1 mark]

c) The line $y = kx$ crosses C exactly 3 times, where k is a positive constant.
Find the range of possible values for k.

[4 marks]

Q4 A curve C has parametric equations:
$$x = 2t^2 + 3t \quad \text{and} \quad y = 2t^2 - 3t, \qquad t \in \mathbb{R}$$

a) Show that there are no values of t within the given domain
where both x and y take negative values.

[3 marks]

b) Show that a Cartesian equation for C can be written in the form
$0 = x^2 + y^2 + Axy + B(x + y)$ where A and B are constants to be found.

[5 marks]

5.1 Sequences

A sequence is a list of numbers that follow a certain pattern — e.g. 2, 4, 6, 8..., or 1, 4, 9, 16...
There are two main ways of describing sequences — n^{th} term formulas and recurrence relations.

Learning Objectives (Spec Ref 4.2):
- Use an nth term formula to generate terms in a sequence, or find the position of a term with a given value.
- Show that a sequence is increasing, decreasing or neither.
- Write recurrence relations and use them to generate sequences.

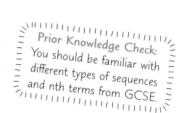

Prior Knowledge Check:
You should be familiar with different types of sequences and nth terms from GCSE.

n^{th} term

Before we get going with this section, there's some **notation** to learn:

a_n just means the nth **term** of the sequence — e.g. a_4 is the 4th term, and a_{n+1} is the term after a_n.

The idea behind the nth term is that you can use a formula to generate any term in a sequence from its **position**, n, in the sequence.

Example 1

A sequence has n^{th} term $a_n = 4n + 1$.
a) **Find the value of a_{10}.**

Just substitute 10 for n in the nth term expression:

$$a_{10} = 4(10) + 1 = \boxed{41}$$

b) **A term in the sequence is 33. Find the position of this term.**

Substitute 33 for a_n in the nth term and rearrange to find the value of n.

$33 = 4n + 1$
So $n = (33 - 1) \div 4 = 8$.
This means $\boxed{a_8 = 33}$

Example 2

A sequence has the nth term $an^2 + b$, where a and b are constants.
a) **If the 3rd term is 7 and the 5th term is 23, find the nth term formula.**

1. Form equations using the information given in the question.

For the 3rd term $n = 3$: $a(3^2) + b = \boxed{9a + b = 7}$

For the 5th term $n = 5$: $a(5^2) + b = \boxed{25a + b = 23}$

2. Solve the equations simultaneously to find the values of a and b.

$$\begin{array}{rl} 25a + b &= 23 \\ -(9a + b &= 7) \\ \hline 16a &= 16 \quad \Rightarrow a = 1 \end{array}$$

Use $a = 1$ to find b using one of the equations.

$9(1) + b = 7 \Rightarrow b = -2$. So the nth term is $\boxed{n^2 - 2}$.

b) **Is 35 a term in the sequence?**

Form and solve an equation in n and see if you get a positive whole number.

$n^2 - 2 = 35 \Rightarrow n^2 = 37 \Rightarrow n = \sqrt{37}$

$\sqrt{37}$ is not an integer, so $\boxed{35 \text{ is } \textbf{not} \text{ in the sequence.}}$

Increasing and decreasing sequences

There are a few types of sequences that you need to know:

- In an **increasing sequence**, each term is larger than the previous term, so $a_{k+1} > a_k$ for all terms — e.g. the square numbers 1, 4, 9, 16, 25, ...

- In a **decreasing sequence**, each term is smaller than the previous term, so $a_{k+1} < a_k$ for all terms — e.g. the sequence 16, 13, 10, 7, 4, ...

Example 3

a) Show that the sequence with n^{th} term $7n - 16$ is increasing.

1. Use the nth term formula to find a_k and a_{k+1}: $a_k = 7k - 16$ and $a_{k+1} = 7(k + 1) - 16 = 7k - 9$

2. Show that $a_{k+1} > a_k$ for all terms: $7k - 9 > 7k - 16 \Rightarrow -9 > -16$
   This is true so it is an increasing sequence.

b) Show that the sequence with n^{th} term $\dfrac{1}{2n-1}$ is decreasing.

1. Find a_k and a_{k+1}: $a_k = \dfrac{1}{2k-1}$ and $a_{k+1} = \dfrac{1}{2(k+1)-1} = \dfrac{1}{2k+1}$

2. Show that $a_{k+1} < a_k$ for all terms: $\dfrac{1}{2k+1} < \dfrac{1}{2k-1} \Rightarrow -1 < 1$
   (k has to be a positive integer, so it's okay to multiply both sides of the inequality by the denominators as $(2k + 1)$ and $(2k - 1)$ aren't 0 or negative.)   This is true so it is a decreasing sequence.

You may also see **periodic sequences**, where the terms **repeat** in a cycle. The number of repeated terms is known as the **order**. For example, the sequence 1, 0, 1, 0, 1, 0... is periodic with order 2.

Some sequences aren't increasing, decreasing or periodic. If you can show $a_{k+1} > a_k$ for some values of k and $a_{k+1} < a_k$ for some other values of k, then the sequence is **neither increasing nor decreasing**.

Exercise 5.1.1

Q1 A sequence has n^{th} term $a_n = 3n - 5$. Find the value of a_{20}.

Q2 Find the 4th term of the sequence with n^{th} term $n(n + 2)$.

Q3 Find the first 5 terms of the sequence with n^{th} term $(n - 1)(n + 1)$.

Q4 The kth term of a sequence is 29. The nth term of this sequence is $4n - 3$. Find the value of k.

Q5 A sequence has the nth term $13 - 6n$. Show that the sequence is decreasing.

Q6 Is the sequence with n^{th} term 3^{-n} increasing or decreasing?

Q7 A sequence has n^{th} term $= an^2 + b$, where a and b are constants.
If the 2nd term is 15, and the 5th term is 99, find a and b.

Q8 A sequence starts 9, 20, 37, ... Its nth term $= en^2 + fn + g$, where e, f and g are constants.
Find the values of e, f and g.

Q9 The nth term of the sequence is given by $(n - 1)^2$. A term in the sequence is 49. Find its position.

Q10 How many terms of the sequence with n^{th} term $15 - 2n$ are positive?

Recurrence relations

A **recurrence relation** is another way to describe a sequence.

> **Recurrence relations tell you how to work out a term in a sequence from the previous term.**

Tip: The notation using subscripts (see p.108) is used in recurrence relations, so you need to get used to it. Any letter can be used, e.g. $x_n = (n-1)(n+1)$. It just avoids having to repeat "with n^{th} term...".

So, using the new notation, what this is saying is that a recurrence relation describes how to work out a_{k+1} from a_k.

E.g. if each term in the sequence is **2 more** than the previous term:

$$a_{k+1} = a_k + 2$$

So, if $k = 5$, this says that $a_6 = a_5 + 2$, that is, the 6th term is equal to the 5th term + 2.

This recurrence relation will be true for loads of sequences, e.g. 1, 3, 5, 7..., and 4, 6, 8, 10...
So to describe a **particular sequence** you also have to give one term.
E.g. the sequence 1, 3, 5, 7... is described by:

$$a_{k+1} = a_k + 2, \ a_1 = 1$$

a_1 stands for the 1st term.

Tip: You might see f(x) notation used — e.g. $f(x+1) = f(x) + 2$, $f(1) = 1$ would also describe the sequence on the right.

Most of the sequences you'll see are **infinite** — they go on forever.
But you can have **finite** sequences which stop after a certain number of terms.

Example 1

Find the recurrence relation of the sequence 5, 8, 11, 14, 17, ...

1. Each term in this sequence equals the one before it, plus 3.
   The recurrence relation is written like this:

   $$a_{k+1} = a_k + 3$$

2. BUT, as you saw above $a_{k+1} = a_k + 3$ on its own isn't enough to describe 5, 8, 11, 14, 17, ... For example, the sequence 87, 90, 93, 96, ... also has each term being 3 more than the one before.

3. The description needs to be more specific, so you've got to give **one term** in the sequence, as well as the recurrence relation. Putting all of this together gives 5, 8, 11, 14, 17, ... as:

   $$a_{k+1} = a_k + 3, \ a_1 = 5$$

   Tip: You usually give the first value, a_1 — but using $a_2 = 8$ would also describe the sequence.

Example 2

A sequence is given by the recurrence relation $a_{k+1} = a_k - 4$, $a_1 = 20$. Find the first five terms of this sequence.

1. You're given the first term (a_1) — it's 20.
   Now you need to find the second term (a_2).
   If $a_1 = a_k$, then $a_2 = a_{k+1}$.

   $a_{k+1} = a_k - 4 \Rightarrow a_2 = a_1 - 4 = 20 - 4 = 16$

   This is 4 less than the first term.

2. Repeat this to find the third, fourth and fifth terms.

$a_3 = a_2 - 4 = 16 - 4 = \boxed{12}$

$a_4 = a_3 - 4 = 12 - 4 = \boxed{8}$

$a_5 = a_4 - 4 = 8 - 4 = \boxed{4}$

So the first five terms of the sequence are $\boxed{20, 16, 12, 8, 4.}$

Example 3

A sequence is generated by the recurrence relation: $u_{n+1} = 3u_n + k$, $u_1 = 2$.

a) Find u_3 in terms of k.

1. You're given the first term, u_1, so use this to generate the second term, u_2, in terms of k...

$u_{n+1} = 3u_n + k$

$\Rightarrow u_2 = 3u_1 + k = 3(2) + k = u_2 = 6 + k$

Substitute in the expression for u_2.

2. ...then use the second term to generate the third term, u_3.

$\Rightarrow u_3 = 3u_2 + k = 3(6 + k) + k = \boxed{18 + 4k}$

b) Given that $u_4 = 28$, find k.

1. Form an expression for u_4 using the recurrence relation:

$u_4 = 3u_3 + k = 3(18 + 4k) + k = 54 + 13k$

Substitute in the expression for u_3 from part a).

2. The question tells you that $u_4 = 28$, so form an equation and solve to find k.

$28 = 54 + 13k \Rightarrow 13k = -26 \Rightarrow \boxed{k = -2}$

The next example's a bit harder, as there's an n^2 in there. But the method works in exactly the same way — you just end up with a slightly more complicated formula for the recurrence relation.

Example 4

A sequence has the general term $x_n = n^2$.
Write down a recurrence relation which generates the sequence.

1. Start by finding the first few terms of the sequence (i.e. $n = 1, 2, 3, 4...$)

$x_1 = 1^2 = 1 \quad x_2 = 2^2 = 4 \quad x_3 = 3^2 = 9 \quad x_4 = 4^2 = 16$

So the first four terms are: 1, 4, 9, 16

2. You're now at the same point as you were at the start of Example 1. You use the same method to form the recurrence relation, but it's a little trickier as n in the general term is squared.

Look at the difference between each term:

$k =$	1	2	3	4
$x_k =$	1	4	9	16

+3   +5   +7
$(2\times1) + 1$ $(2\times2) + 1$ $(2\times3) + 1$

3. To get from term x_k to the next term, x_{k+1}, you take the value of term x_k and add $2k + 1$ to it.
E.g. 3rd term = 2nd term + 2(2) + 1.

So the recurrence relation is:
$$x_{k+1} = x_k + 2k + 1$$

4. To generate the sequence you need to give **one term** in the sequence, and there's no reason not to stick to convention and use the first term: (Try substituting in different k values to check your recurrence relation does generate the sequence.)

$$x_{k+1} = x_k + 2k + 1, x_1 = 1$$

5. It's sometimes helpful to draw some little diagrams where n^2 is involved. These diagrams let you see that it's $2k + 1$ added each time.

1st ●   2nd ● ●
                    ● ●

3rd ● ● ●   4th ● ● ● ●
      ● ● ●   ● ● ● ●
      ● ● ●   ● ● ● ●
                     ● ● ● ●

Exercise 5.1.2

Q1 A sequence is defined for $n \geq 1$ by $u_{n+1} = 3u_n$ and $u_1 = 10$.
Find the first 5 terms of the sequence.

Q2 Find the first 4 terms of the sequence in which $u_1 = 2$ and $u_{n+1} = u_n^2$ for $n \geq 1$.

Q3 Find the first 4 terms of the sequence in which $u_1 = 4$ and $u_{n+1} = \dfrac{-1}{u_n}$, and describe the type of sequence that this forms.

Q4 Write down a recurrence relation which produces the sequence 3, 6, 12, 24, 48, ...

Q5 a) Write down a recurrence relation which produces the sequence 12, 16, 20, 24, 28, ...

b) The sequence is finite and ends at 100. Find the number of terms.

Q6 Find a recurrence relation which generates the sequence 7, 4, 7, 4, 7, ...

> **Q6 Hint:** You need to find an operation that goes back and forth between 4 and 7. There's more than one possible answer — think about one of these number facts: 7 + 4 = 11 or 7 × 4 = 28.

Q7 In a sequence $u_1 = 4$ and $u_{n+1} = 3u_n - 1$ for $n \geq 1$.
Find the value of k if $u_k = 95$.

Q8 In a sequence $x_1 = 9$ and $x_{n+1} = (x_n + 1) \div 2$ for $n \geq 1$.
Find the value of r if $x_r = \dfrac{5}{4}$.

Q9 Find the first 5 terms of the sequence in which $u_1 = 7$ and $u_{n+1} = u_n + n$ for $n \geq 1$.

Q10 In a sequence $u_1 = 6$, $u_2 = 7$ and $u_3 = 8.5$. If the recurrence relation is of the form $u_{n+1} = au_n + b$, find the values of the constants a and b.

> **Q10 Hint:** Form all the equations you can from the information, and then solve them.

Q11 A sequence is generated by $u_1 = 8$ and $u_{n+1} = \dfrac{1}{2}u_n$ for $n \geq 1$.
Find the first 5 terms and a formula for u_n in terms of n.

5.2 Arithmetic Sequences

Now it's time to look at a particular kind of sequence in greater detail. When the terms of a sequence progress by adding a fixed amount each time, this is called an arithmetic sequence.

Learning Objective (Spec Ref 4.4):

- Find and use the formula for the nth term of an arithmetic sequence.

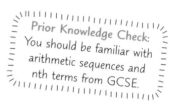

Prior Knowledge Check:
You should be familiar with arithmetic sequences and nth terms from GCSE.

Finding the nth term

Here are some examples of **arithmetic sequences**:

5, 7, 9, 11... (add 2 each time);
20, 17, 14, 11... (add –3 each time).

Arithmetic sequences are often referred to as **arithmetic progressions** — it's exactly the same thing.

The formula for the nth term of an arithmetic sequence is:

$$u_n = a + (n - 1)d$$

where:

a is the **first term** of the sequence.
d is the amount you add each time — the **common difference**.
n is the **position** of any term in the sequence.

This box shows you how the formula is derived:

Term	n	
1st	1	$u_1 = a$
2nd	2	$u_2 = u_1 + d = a + d$
3rd	3	$u_3 = u_2 + d = (a + d) + d = a + 2d$
4th	4	$u_4 = u_3 + d = (a + 2d) + d = a + 3d$
.	.	.
.	.	.
.	.	.
n^{th}	n	$u_n = a + (n - 1)d$

Tip: Each term is made up of the previous one, plus d. It's a recurrence relation.

This is the formula to find the nth term.

Example 1

For the arithmetic sequence 2, 5, 8, 11, ... find u_{20} and the formula for u_n.

1. Find a and d and plug them into the nth term formula with $n = 20$.

   $u_n = a + (n - 1)d$
   For this sequence, $a = 2$ and $d = 3$.
   $u_{20} = 2 + (20 - 1) \times 3 = 2 + 19 \times 3 = 59$
   So $u_{20} = 59$.

2. u_n is the general term, i.e. $a + (n - 1)d$. Just substitute in the a and d values and simplify:

   $u_n = 2 + (n - 1)3 \Rightarrow u_n = 3n - 1$

3. Finally, check the formula works with a couple of values of n.

   $n = 1$ gives $3(1) - 1 = 2$ ✓
   $n = 2$ gives $3(2) - 1 = 5$ ✓

You only actually need to know **two terms** of an arithmetic sequence (and their positions) — then you can work out any other term.

Example 2

The 2nd term of an arithmetic sequence is 21, and the 9th term is –7.
Find the 23rd term of this sequence.

1. Set up an equation for each of the known terms:

    2nd term = 21, so $a + (2 – 1)d = 21$
    $$a + d = 21$$

    9th term = –7, so $a + (9 – 1)d = –7$
    $$a + 8d = –7$$

2. You've now got two **simultaneous equations** — so solve them to find a and d:

    $a + d = 21$ —①

    $a + 8d = –7$ —②

    ①–②: $–7d = 28 \Rightarrow d = –4$

    ①: $a + d = 21 \Rightarrow a – 4 = 21 \Rightarrow a = 25$

3. Write the nth term formula...

    n^{th} term $= a + (n – 1)d$
    $$= 25 + (n – 1) \times –4$$
    $$= 29 – 4n$$

    Tip: The common difference and the first term have also been found along the way here (questions sometimes ask you to find these).

4. ... and use it to find the 23rd term ($n = 23$):

    23rd term $= 29 – 4 \times 23 = –63$

Exercise 5.2.1

Q1 An arithmetic progression has first term 7 and common difference 5. Find its 10th term.

Q2 Find the nth term for each of the following sequences:

    a) 6, 9, 12, 15, ...   b) 4, 9, 14, 19, ...   c) 12, 8, 4, 0, ...

    d) 1.5, 3.5, 5.5, 7.5 ...   e) 77, 69, 61, 53, ...   f) –2, –2.5, –3, –3.5, ...

Q3 In an arithmetic sequence, the fourth term is 19 and the tenth term is 43. Find the first term and common difference.

Q4 In an arithmetic progression, $u_1 = –5$ and $u_5 = 19$. Find u_{10}.

Q5 In an arithmetic progression, $u_7 = 8$ and $u_{11} = 10$. Find u_3.

Q6 In an arithmetic sequence, $u_3 = 15$ and $u_7 = 27$. Find the value of k if $u_k = 66$.

Q7 In an arithmetic sequence the first three terms are $\ln(x)$, $\ln(x + 8)$, $\ln(x + 48)$. Find the value of x and the next term in the sequence.

Q8 An arithmetic progression has exactly 20 terms greater than 0 and smaller than 100. All the terms are integers. Find two possible values for a if $u_{11} = 47$.

5.3 Arithmetic Series

You've seen that a sequence is a just list of terms that follow a pattern.
You'll often want to add these terms together — when you do this, it becomes a series.

Learning Objectives (Spec Ref 4.3-4.4):
- Use the nth term formula to solve arithmetic series problems.
- Find the sum of the first n terms of an arithmetic series.
- Use sigma notation (Σ) to refer to the sum of a series.
- Find the sum of the first n natural numbers.

Sequences and series

Here is an arithmetic sequence:
It's an infinite sequence — it goes on forever.

$$5, 8, 11, 14, 17, 20, ...$$

Now suppose you wanted to find the sum of the first 5 terms of this sequence.
You'd write this by replacing the commas with '+' signs like this:

$$5 + 8 + 11 + 14 + 17$$

This is now an **arithmetic series**. It's a finite series with 5 terms. And if you actually added up the numbers you'd find that the **sum** for this series is 55. So sequences become series when you add up their terms to find sums.

Sum of the first n terms

It would very quickly stop being fun if you had to find the sum of a 100-term series manually. Instead, you can use one of these **two formulas**. S_n represents the **sum of the first n terms**.

$$S_n = \frac{n}{2}[2a + (n-1)d]$$

For this formula, you just need to plug in the usual values of a, d and n

and $\quad S_n = \frac{1}{2}n(a + l)$

Here, l represents the **last term**. This formula is a bit easier to use if you know the value of the last term.

Tip: You can work out a, d and the nth term for a series, just as you would for a sequence. So in the 5-term series above, $a = 5$, $d = 3$ and n^{th} term = $3n + 2$ (for $1 \le n \le 5$). Also, because the series is finite, you can state its last term, which is 17.

It's given in the formula booklet like this, but can also be stated as $S_n = n \times \frac{(a + l)}{2}$.

There's a nice little proof for these formulas which you need to know:

- For any series, you can express S_n as:
  $S_n = a + (a + d) + (a + 2d) + ... + (a + (n - 3)d) + (a + (n - 2)d) + (a + (n - 1)d)$

- Now, if you reverse the order of the terms you can write it as:
  $S_n = (a + (n - 1)d) + (a + (n - 2)d) + (a + (n - 3)d) + ... + (a + 2d) + (a + d) + a$

- Adding the two expressions for S_n gives:
  $2S_n = (2a + (n - 1)d) + (2a + (n - 1)d) + (2a + (n - 1)d) + ... + (2a + (n - 1)d)$

- So we've now got the term "$(2a + (n - 1)d)$" repeated n times, which is:
  $2S_n = n \times (2a + (n - 1)d) \implies S_n = \frac{n}{2}[2a + (n-1)d]$

- So we've derived the first formula. Now to get the second, just replace "$a + (n - 1)d$" with l:
  $S_n = \frac{n}{2}[a + a + (n - 1)d]$, so $S_n = \frac{1}{2}n[a + l]$

Now it's time to try out the sum formulas in some worked examples.

Example 1

Find the sum of the series with first term 3, last term 87 and common difference 4.

1. You're told the last term,
   so use the S_n formula with l in:
   You know a (3) and l (87), but you don't know n yet.

   $$S_n = \frac{1}{2}n(a+l)$$

2. Find n by putting what you do
   know into the 'n^{th} term' formula:

   $$a + (n-1)d = 87$$
   $$3 + (n-1)4 = 87$$
   $$4n - 1 = 87$$
   $$n = 22$$

3. You're now all set to plug the values
   for a, l and n into the S_n formula:

   $$S_n = \frac{1}{2}n(a+l)$$

   $n = 22$ means that there are 22 terms in the series. $\longrightarrow$ $S_{22} = \frac{1}{2} \times 22 \times (3 + 87) = 11 \times 90$

   $$= 990$$

   The sum of the series is **990**.

Example 2

This question is about the sequence –5, –2, 1, 4, 7...

a) Is 67 a term in the sequence? If it is, give its position.

1. First, find the formula for the
   n^{th} term of the sequence:
   $a = -5$ and $d = 3$

   $$n^{\text{th}} \text{ term} = a + (n-1)d$$
   $$= -5 + (n-1)3$$
   $$= 3n - 8$$

2. Put 67 into the formula and see if
   this gives a whole number for n:

   $$67 = 3n - 8$$
   $$3n = 75 \implies n = 25$$

   67 **is** a term in the sequence. It's the **25th** term.

   Tip: This question could just have easily been "about the series $-5 + -2 + 1 + 4 + 7 + ...$" — the working would have been exactly the same.

b) Find the sum of the first 20 terms.

We know $a = -5$, $d = 3$ and $n = 20$,
so plug these values into the formula
$S_n = \frac{n}{2}[2a + (n-1)d]$:

$$S_{20} = \frac{20}{2}[2(-5) + (20-1)3]$$

$$S_{20} = 10[-10 + 19 \times 3]$$

$$S_{20} = 470$$

The sum of the first 20 terms is **470**.

Example 3

**Find the possible numbers of terms in the arithmetic series starting
21 + 18 + 15... if the sum of the series is 75.**

1. To work out n, the number of terms in the series,
    you need values for a, S_n and d:

    $a = 21$, $S_n = 75$, $d = -3$

2. You can then use the S_n formula:

    $S_n = \frac{n}{2}[2a + (n-1)d]$

    $S_n = \frac{n}{2}[2(21) + (n-1) \times -3]$

    $75 = \frac{n}{2}[42 - 3n + 3]$

    $75 = \frac{45n}{2} - \frac{3n^2}{2}$

    Divide through by –3 to simplify the quadratic. ⟶ $-3n^2 + 45n - 150 = 0$

    Solve this quadratic equation. ⟶ $n^2 - 15n + 50 = 0$

    $(n-5)(n-10) = 0$

    $n = 5$ or $n = 10$

    Tip: There are two answers because the series goes into
    negative numbers, so the sum of 75 is reached twice.
    Look at the first 10 terms of the series to see how:
    21 + 18 + 15 + 12 + 9 + 6 + 3 + 0 + (–3) + (–6).

    There are **5 or 10 terms**
    in the series.

Sigma notation

So far, the letter S has been used for the sum. The Greeks did a lot of work on this — their capital
letter for S is Σ or **sigma**. This is used today, together with the general term, to mean the sum of the
series. For example, the following means the sum of the series with n^{th} term $2n + 3$.

Starting with $n = 1$...

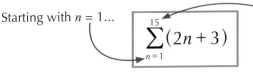

$$\sum_{n=1}^{15}(2n+3)$$

Tip: For all values of n, $\sum_1^n 1 = n$.

...and ending with $n = 15$

Example 4

Find $\sum_{n=1}^{15}(2n+3)$.

1. Put some values for n into
    $2n + 3$ to work out a, d and l
    for the sequence.

    First term ($n = 1$) is: $2(1) + 3 = 5$
    Second term ($n = 2$) is: $2(2) + 3 = 7$
    Last term ($n = 15$) is: $2(15) + 3 = 33$

    So $a = 5$, $d = 7 - 5 = 2$ and $l = 33$

2. You know all of a, d and l so
    you can use either formula
    to work out the sum of the
    first 15 terms (i.e. $n = 15$):

    $S_n = \frac{1}{2}n(a+l)$

    $S_n = \frac{n}{2}[2a + (n-1)d]$

    $S_{15} = \frac{1}{2} \times 15(5 + 33) = 285$

    $S_{15} = \frac{15}{2}[2 \times 5 + 14 \times 2] = 285$

    You get the same answer whichever formula you use.

Q1 An arithmetic series has first term 8 and common difference 3.
Find the 10th term and the sum of the first 10 terms.

Q2 In an arithmetic series $u_2 = 16$ and $u_5 = 10$. Find a, d and S_8.

Q3 In an arithmetic series $a = 12$ and $d = 6$. Find u_{100} and S_{100}.

Q4 An arithmetic progression has n^{th} term $8n - 6$. Find the sum of the first 20 terms.

Q5 An arithmetic series has first term -6 and the sum of the first 10 terms is 345.
Find the common difference.

Q6 Find the sum of the arithmetic series with first term 7, last term 79 and common difference 6.

Q7 Find: a) $\displaystyle\sum_{n=1}^{12}(5n-2)$, b) $\displaystyle\sum_{n=1}^{9}(20-2n)$.

Q8 In an arithmetic series $a = 3$ and $d = 2$. Find n if $S_n = 960$.

Q9 Given that $\displaystyle\sum_{n=1}^{k}(5n+2) = 553$, show that the value of k is 14.

Q10 An arithmetic sequence begins $x + 11$, $4x + 4$, $9x + 5$, ...
Find the sum of the first 11 terms.

Q11 An arithmetic progression begins 36, 32, 28, 24, ...
Find the possible values of n if $S_n = 176$.

Sum of the first n natural numbers

The **natural numbers** are the positive whole numbers, i.e. 1, 2, 3, 4...
They form a simple arithmetic progression with $a = 1$ and $d = 1$.

The sum of the first n natural numbers is: $\boxed{S_n = \frac{1}{2}n(n+1)}$

This formula can be derived from the previous sum formulas by plugging in values:

> The sum of the first n natural numbers is: $S_n = 1 + 2 + 3 + ... + (n-2) + (n-1) + n$
>
> So $a = 1$, $l = n$ and also $n = n$. $S_n = \frac{1}{2}n(a+l) \longrightarrow S_n = \frac{1}{2}n(n+1)$

You can also derive the formula from first principles —
the proof is almost identical to the one for a general arithmetic series on page 115:

> - $S_n = 1 + 2 + 3 + ... + (n-2) + (n-1) + n$ ①
> - Rewrite ① with the terms reversed:
> $S_n = n + (n-1) + (n-2) + ... + 3 + 2 + 1$ ②
> - ① + ② gives:
> $2S_n = (n+1) + (n+1) + (n+1) + ... + (n+1) + (n+1) + (n+1)$
> $\Rightarrow 2S_n = n(n+1) \Rightarrow S_n = \frac{1}{2}n(n+1)$

Tip: You could be asked to prove any of these sum formulas, so make sure you know these steps.

Example 1

Find the sum of the first 100 natural numbers.

Using $S_n = \frac{1}{2}n(n+1)$: $\qquad\qquad\qquad S_{100} = \frac{1}{2} \times 100 \times 101 = \boxed{5050}$

Sum of the first 100 natural numbers = $\boxed{5050}$

Example 2

The sum of the first k natural numbers is 861. Find the value of k.

1. Form an equation in k: $\qquad\qquad\qquad\qquad \frac{1}{2}k(k+1) = 861$

2. Expand the brackets and rearrange: $\qquad k^2 + k = 1722$
$\qquad\qquad\qquad\qquad\qquad\qquad\qquad\qquad k^2 + k - 1722 = 0$

3. So we have a quadratic in k to solve.
   We're looking for a whole number for k, $\qquad k^2 + k - 1722 = 0$
   so it should factorise. $\qquad\qquad\qquad\qquad (k \quad)(k \quad) = 0$

4. It looks tricky to factorise, but notice that
   '$b = 1$', so we're looking for two numbers $\qquad (k + 42)(k - 41) = 0$
   that are 1 apart and multiply to 1722. $\qquad\quad k = -42 \ $ or $\ k = 41$

   Tip: In this question we have k
   numbers added together, so an answer $\qquad$ We can ignore the negative solution here,
   of $k = -42$ wouldn't make any sense. $\qquad$ so the answer is $\boxed{k = 41}$.

Exercise 5.3.2

Q1 Find the sum of the first:

a) 10 natural numbers, $\qquad\qquad\qquad\qquad$ b) 2000 natural numbers.

Q2 Find $\displaystyle\sum_{n=1}^{32} n$.

Q3 Find $\displaystyle\sum_{n=1}^{10} n$ and $\displaystyle\sum_{n=1}^{20} n$. Hence find $\displaystyle\sum_{n=11}^{20} n$.

> **Q3 Hint:** This question uses a handy little trick for finding series sums that don't start from $n = 1$.

Q4 The sum of the first n natural numbers is 66. Find n.

Q5 Find k if $\displaystyle\sum_{n=1}^{k} n = 120$.

Q6 Find the sum of the series $16 + 17 + 18 + ... + 35$.

Q7 What is the first natural number k for which $\displaystyle\sum_{n=1}^{k} n$ is greater than 1 000 000?

5.4 Geometric Sequences and Series

On pages 113-119 you saw how to find the general term and how to find the sum of a number of terms for an arithmetic sequence. Now you'll do the same thing for geometric sequences and series.

Learning Objectives (Spec Ref 4.5):
- Recognise geometric sequences and series.
- Know and use the formula for the general term of a geometric sequence or series.
- Know and use the formula for the sum of the first *n* terms of a geometric sequence or series.
- Recognise convergent geometric series and find their sum to infinity.

Geometric sequences

Remember, with **arithmetic** sequences you get from one term to the next by **adding** a fixed amount each time. They have a **first term** (*a*), and the amount you add to get from one term to the next is called the **common difference** (*d*).

With **geometric sequences**, rather than adding, you get from one term to the next by **multiplying** by a **constant** called the **common ratio** (*r*).

Tip: Geometric sequences are also called geometric progressions.

- This is a **geometric sequence** where you find each term by **multiplying** the previous term by 2:

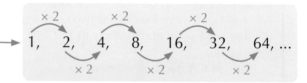

$$1, \quad 2, \quad 4, \quad 8, \quad 16, \quad 32, \quad 64, ...$$

- If the common ratio is **negative**, the signs of the sequence will **alternate**. For this geometric sequence the common ratio is –3.

$$2, -6, 18, -54, 162, -486, ...$$

- The common ratio might **not** be a **whole number**. Here, it's $\frac{3}{4}$.

$$16, 12, 9, \frac{27}{4}, \frac{81}{16}, \frac{243}{64}, ...$$

You get each term by multiplying the first term by the common ratio some number of times. In other words, each term is the **first term** multiplied by **some power** of the **common ratio**.

This is how you describe geometric sequences using **algebra**:

The **first term** (u_1) is called '*a*'.

The **common ratio** (the number you multiply by) is called '*r*'.

$$u_1 = a \qquad\qquad = a$$
$$u_2 = u_1 \times r = a \times r \qquad = ar$$
$$u_3 = u_2 \times r = ar \times r \qquad = ar^2$$
$$u_4 = u_3 \times r = ar^2 \times r \qquad = ar^3$$

Tip: In the first sequence above (1, 2, 4, 8, ...), $a = 1$ and $r = 2$.

So the **formula** that describes **any term** in a geometric sequence is: $\boxed{u_n = ar^{n-1}}$

The term u_n is called the 'n^{th} term', or 'general term' of the sequence. You need to learn this formula.

If you know the values of a and r, you can substitute them into the **general formula** to find an expression that describes the whole sequence:

Example 1

A chessboard has a 1p piece on the first square, 2p on the second square, 4p on the third, 8p on the fourth and so on until the board is full.
Find a formula for the amount of money on each square.

1. The trick with questions like this is to recognise that you're being asked about a **geometric sequence** (see p.129 for more on modelling).

   Geometric sequence:
   $u_1 = 1$, $u_2 = 2$, $u_3 = 4$, $u_4 = 8$, ...

2. Work out the values of a and r.

   $a = 1$ (you start with 1p on the first square)
   $r = 2$ (you get each term by multiplying the previous one by 2)

3. Plug these into the geometric sequence formula:

   $u_n = ar^{n-1} = 1 \times (2^{n-1}) = \boxed{2^{n-1}}$

You can also use the formula to find the **first term** a, the **common ratio** r or a **particular term** in the sequence, given other information about the sequence:

Example 2

a) **Find the 5th term in the geometric sequence 1, 3, 9, ...**

1. First find the common ratio r. Each term is the previous term multiplied by r, so you find the common ratio by dividing consecutive terms.

   second term = first term $\times r$
   $\Rightarrow r = \dfrac{\text{second term}}{\text{first term}} = \dfrac{3}{1} = 3$

2. Then find the 5th term.

   The 3rd term is 9, so:
   4th term = 3rd term $\times r = 9 \times 3 = 27$
   5th term = 4th term $\times r = 27 \times 3 = \boxed{81}$

b) **A geometric sequence has first term 2 and common ratio 1.2.
Find the 15th term in the sequence to 3 significant figures.**

1. When you're asked for a higher term, the best method is to find the nth term.

   $a = 2$ and $r = 1.2$, so $u_n = ar^{n-1} = 2 \times (1.2)^{n-1}$

2. Then find the 15th term ($n = 15$).

   $u_{15} = 2 \times (1.2)^{14} = 2 \times 12.839... = \boxed{25.7}$ to 3 s.f.

c) **A geometric sequence has first term 25 and 10th term 80.
Calculate the common ratio. Give your answer to 3 significant figures.**

1. Find the nth term in terms of r:

   $a = 25$, so $u_n = ar^{n-1} = 25r^{n-1}$.

2. Form and solve an equation using u_{10}.

   $u_{10} = 80 = 25r^9$
   $\Rightarrow r^9 = \dfrac{80}{25} \Rightarrow r = \sqrt[9]{\dfrac{80}{25}} = 1.137... = \boxed{1.14}$ to 3 s.f.

d) **The 8th term of a geometric sequence is 4374 and the common ratio is 3. What is the first term?**

1. Find the nth term in terms of a:

   $r = 3$, so $u_n = ar^{n-1} = a(3)^{n-1}$

2. Form and solve an equation using u_8.

   $u_8 = 4374 = a(3)^7 = 2187a \Rightarrow a = \dfrac{4374}{2187} = \boxed{2}$

Q1   Find the common ratio of the geometric progression 3125, 1875, 1125, 675, 405, ...

Q2   Find the seventh term in the geometric progression 2, 3, 4.5, 6.75 ...

Q3   The sixth and seventh terms of a geometric sequence are 2187 and 6561 respectively. What is the first term?

Q4   A geometric sequence is 24, 12, 6, ... What is the 9th term?

Q5   The 14th term of a geometric progression is 9216. The first term is 1.125. Calculate the common ratio.

Q6   The first and second terms of a geometric progression are 1 and 1.1 respectively. How many terms in this sequence are less than 4?

> **Q6 Hint:** Write yourself an equation or inequality and then solve it using logs. Look back at your Year 1 notes if you need a reminder of how to use logs.

Q7   A geometric progression has a common ratio of 0.6. If the first term is 5, what is the difference between the 10th term and the 15th term? Give your answer to 5 d.p.

Q8   A geometric sequence has a first term of 25 000 and a common ratio of 0.8. Which term is the first to be below 1000?

Q9   A geometric sequence is 5, –5, 5, –5, 5, ... Give the common ratio.

Q10 The first three terms of a geometric progression are $\frac{1}{4}$, $\frac{3}{16}$ and $\frac{9}{64}$.

     a) Calculate the common ratio.

     b) Find the 8th term. Give your answer as a fraction.

Q11 The 7th term of a geometric sequence is 196.608 and the common ratio is 0.8. What is the first term?

Q12 A geometric progression begins 2, 6, ... Which term of the geometric progression equals 1458?

Q13 3, –2.4, 1.92,... is a geometric progression.

     a) What is the common ratio?

     b) How many terms are there in the sequence before you reach a term with modulus less than 1?

Geometric series

A **sequence** becomes a **series** when you **add** the terms to find the **sum**. Geometric series work just like geometric sequences (they have a **first term** and a **common ratio**), but they're written as a **sum of terms** rather than a list:

geometric sequence:	geometric series:
3, 6, 12, 24, 48, ...	3 + 6 + 12 + 24 + 48 + ...

Sometimes you'll need to find the **sum** of the **first few terms** of a geometric series:

- The sum of the **first n terms** is called S_n.

- S_n can be written in terms of the first term a and the common ratio r:
$$S_n = u_1 + u_2 + u_3 + u_4 + ... \, u_n = a + ar + ar^2 + ar^3 + ... + ar^{n-1}$$

- There's a nice **formula** for finding S_n that doesn't involve loads of adding. You need to know the **proof** of the formula — luckily it's fairly straightforward:

Tip: Geometric series can be infinite sums (i.e. they can go on forever). We're just adding up bits of them for now, but summing a whole series is covered on page 127.

For any geometric sequence:
$$S_n = a + ar + ar^2 + ar^3 + ... \, ar^{n-2} + ar^{n-1} \quad \text{①}$$

Multiplying this by r gives:
$$rS_n = ar + ar^2 + ar^3 + ... \, ar^{n-2} + ar^{n-1} + ar^n \quad \text{②}$$

Subtract equation ② from equation ① : $\quad S_n - rS_n = a - ar^n$

Factorise both sides: $\quad (1 - r)S_n = a(1 - r^n)$

Then divide through by $(1 - r)$: $\quad S_n = \dfrac{a(1 - r^n)}{1 - r}$

Tip: You could also subtract equation ① from equation ② to get:
$$S_n = \frac{a(r^n - 1)}{r - 1}$$
Both versions are correct.

So the sum of the first n terms of a geometric series is: $\longrightarrow$ $\quad \boxed{S_n = \dfrac{a(1 - r^n)}{1 - r}}$

This formula is given in the formula book (but the proof isn't).

Example 1

a) **A geometric series has first term 3.5 and common ratio 5.**
   Find the sum of the first 6 terms.

   You're told that $a = 3.5$ and $r = 5$, and you're looking for the sum of the first 6 terms, so just stick these values into the formula for S_6:
   $$S_6 = \frac{a(1 - r^6)}{1 - r} = \frac{3.5(1 - 5^6)}{1 - 5} = \boxed{13\,671}$$

b) **The first two terms in a geometric series are 20, 22.**
   To 2 decimal places, the sum of the first k terms of the series is 271.59. Find k.

   1. $a = 20$, so find r and put a and r into the sum formula.

   $$r = \frac{\text{second term}}{\text{first term}} = \frac{22}{20} = 1.1$$

   $$S_k = \frac{a(1 - r^k)}{1 - r} = \frac{20(1 - (1.1)^k)}{1 - 1.1}$$
   $$= -200(1 - (1.1)^k)$$

2. Form and solve an equation using S_k.

$$271.59 = -200(1 - (1.1)^k)$$

$$\Rightarrow -\frac{271.59}{200} - 1 = -(1.1)^k$$

$$\Rightarrow -2.35795 = -(1.1)^k$$

$$\Rightarrow 2.35795 = 1.1^k$$

$$\Rightarrow \log(2.35795) = k\log(1.1)$$

$$\Rightarrow k = \frac{\log(2.35795)}{\log(1.1)} = \boxed{9}$$

Tip: You're looking for a number of terms so the answer must be a positive integer.

Sigma notation

You saw on page 117 that the **sum** of the first n **terms** of a series (S_n) can also be written using **sigma (Σ) notation**. For geometric series, sigma notation looks like this:

$$S_n = u_1 + u_2 + u_3 + \dots + u_n = a + ar + ar^2 + \dots + ar^{n-1} = \sum_{k=0}^{n-1} ar^k$$

Tip: Remember, Σ means sum (it's the Greek letter for S). Here, it's the sum of ar^k from $k = 0$ to $k = n - 1$. Be careful with the limits — it's $n - 1$ on top of the Σ, but the sum is S_n.

So, using the formula from the previous page, the sum of the first n terms can be written:

$$\sum_{k=0}^{n-1} ar^k = \frac{a(1 - r^n)}{1 - r}$$

Example 2

$a + ar + ar^2 + \dots$ is a geometric series, and $\sum_{k=0}^{4} ar^k = 85.2672$.

Given that $r = -1.8$, find the first term a.

1. Write the sum formula for the first 5 terms:

$$85.2672 = \sum_{k=0}^{4} ar^k = S_5 = \frac{a(1 - r^5)}{1 - r}$$

2. Plug in the value of r and solve for a:

$$85.2672 = \frac{a(1 - r^5)}{1 - r} = \frac{a(1 - (-1.8)^5)}{1 - (-1.8)} = a\frac{19.89568}{2.8}$$

$$85.2672 = 7.1056a$$

$$\Rightarrow a = \frac{85.2672}{7.1056} = \boxed{12}$$

Exercise 5.4.2

Q1 The first term of a geometric sequence is 8 and the common ratio is 1.2. Find the sum of the first 15 terms.

Q2 A geometric series has first term $a = 25$ and common ratio $r = 0.7$. Find $\sum_{k=0}^{9} 25(0.7)^k$.

Q3 The sum of the first n terms of a geometric series is 196 605. The common ratio of the series is 2 and the first term is 3. Find n.

Q4 A geometric progression starts with 4, 5, 6.25.
The first x terms add up to 103.2 to 4 significant figures. Find x.

Q5 The 3rd term of a geometric series is 6 and the 8th term is 192. Find:

a) the common ratio   b) the first term   c) the sum of the first 15 terms

Q6 $m + 10$, m, $2m - 21$, ... is a geometric progression, m is a positive constant.

a) Show that $m^2 - m - 210 = 0$.

b) Hence show that $m = 15$.

c) Find the common ratio of this series.

d) Find the sum of the first 10 terms.

> **Q6a) Hint:** The ratio of the first term to the second is the same as the ratio of the second term to the third.

Q7 The first three terms of a geometric series are 1, x, x^2.
The sum of these terms is 3 and each term has a different value.

a) Find x.   b) Calculate the sum of the first 7 terms.

Q8 a, ar, ar^2, ar^3, ... is a geometric progression. Given that $a = 7.2$ and $r = 0.38$, find $\sum_{k=0}^{9} ar^k$.

Q9 The sum of the first eight terms of a geometric series is 1.2.
Find the first term of the series, given that the common ratio is $-\frac{1}{3}$.

Q10 a, $-2a$, $4a$, $-8a$, ... is a geometric sequence. Given that $\sum_{k=0}^{12} a(-2)^k = -5735.1$, find a.

Convergent geometric series

Convergent sequences

Some geometric sequences **tend towards zero** — in other words, they get closer and closer to zero (but they never actually reach it). For example:

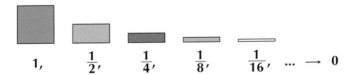

$$1, \quad \frac{1}{2}, \quad \frac{1}{4}, \quad \frac{1}{8}, \quad \frac{1}{16}, \quad \ldots \rightarrow 0$$

> **Tip:** The arrow here means 'tends to'.

Sequences like this are called **convergent** — the terms **converge** (get closer and closer) to a **limit** (the number they get close to). Geometric sequences either **converge to zero** or **don't converge** at all.

A sequence that doesn't converge is called **divergent**.

A geometric sequence a, ar, ar^2, ar^3, ... will converge to **zero** if each term is **closer** to zero than the one before. This happens when **$-1 < r < 1$**. You can write this as **$|r| < 1$**, where $|r|$ is the modulus of r (see p.28), so:

$$a, \, ar, \, ar^2, \, ar^3, \, \ldots \rightarrow 0 \text{ when } |r| < 1$$

You ignore the sign of r because you can still have a convergent sequence when r is negative. In that case the terms will alternate between > 0 and < 0, but they'll still be getting closer and closer to zero.

Convergent series

When you **sum** a geometric sequence that tends to zero you get a **convergent series**.

Because each term is getting closer and closer to zero, you're **adding smaller and smaller** amounts each time. The sum gets **closer and closer** to a certain number, but never reaches it — this is the **limit** of the series.

For example, the **sum** of the **convergent sequence** $1, \frac{1}{2}, \frac{1}{4}, \frac{1}{8}, \frac{1}{16}, \ldots$ gets closer and closer to 2:

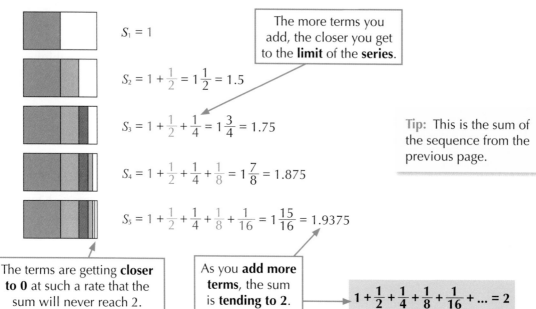

$S_1 = 1$

The more terms you add, the closer you get to the **limit** of the **series**.

$S_2 = 1 + \frac{1}{2} = 1\frac{1}{2} = 1.5$

$S_3 = 1 + \frac{1}{2} + \frac{1}{4} = 1\frac{3}{4} = 1.75$

Tip: This is the sum of the sequence from the previous page.

$S_4 = 1 + \frac{1}{2} + \frac{1}{4} + \frac{1}{8} = 1\frac{7}{8} = 1.875$

$S_5 = 1 + \frac{1}{2} + \frac{1}{4} + \frac{1}{8} + \frac{1}{16} = 1\frac{15}{16} = 1.9375$

The terms are getting **closer to 0** at such a rate that the sum will never reach 2.

As you **add more terms**, the sum is **tending to 2**.

$$1 + \frac{1}{2} + \frac{1}{4} + \frac{1}{8} + \frac{1}{16} + \ldots = 2$$

So when the **sequence** $a, ar, ar^2, ar^3, \ldots$ **converges** to zero, the **series** $a + ar + ar^2 + ar^3 + \ldots$ **converges** to a **limit**.

Like sequences, series converge when $|r| < 1$.

Geometric series $a + ar + ar^2 + ar^3 + \ldots$ with $|r| < 1$ are **convergent**	Geometric series $a + ar + ar^2 + ar^3 + \ldots$ with $|r| \geq 1$ are **divergent**

Tip: Not all sequences that tend to zero produce a convergent series — this rule is only true for geometric progressions. For example, the series $1 + \frac{1}{2} + \frac{1}{3} + \frac{1}{4} + \frac{1}{5} + \ldots$ diverges.

Example 1

Determine whether or not the following sequences are convergent.

a) **1, 2, 4, 8, 16, ...**

$r = \frac{2^{nd} \text{ term}}{1^{st} \text{ term}} = \frac{2}{1} = 2$, $|r| = |2| = 2 > 1$, so the series is not convergent

b) **81, –27, 9, –3, 1, ...**

$r = \frac{2^{nd} \text{ term}}{1^{st} \text{ term}} = \frac{-27}{81} = -\frac{1}{3}$, $|r| = \left|-\frac{1}{3}\right| = \frac{1}{3} < 1$, the series is convergent

Tip: You can usually spot straight away if a geometric series is convergent — the terms will be getting closer and closer to zero. But you still need to check $|r| < 1$ to prove it.

Summing to infinity

When a series is **convergent** you can find its **sum to infinity**. The sum to infinity is called S_∞ — it's the **limit** of S_n as $n \to \infty$. This just means that the sum of the first n terms of the series (S_n) gets closer and closer to S_∞ the more terms you add (the bigger n gets). In other words, it's the **number** that the **series converges to**.

Example 2

If $a = 2$ and $r = \frac{1}{2}$, find the sum to infinity of the geometric series.

1. Work out the sum to n terms after each term:

    The terms are getting **smaller** each time.

$u_1 = 2$ $\longrightarrow$ $S_1 = 2$

$u_2 = 2 \times \frac{1}{2} = 1$ $\longrightarrow$ $S_2 = 2 + 1 = 3$

$u_3 = 1 \times \frac{1}{2} = \frac{1}{2}$ $\longrightarrow$ $S_3 = 2 + 1 + \frac{1}{2} = 3\frac{1}{2}$

$u_4 = \frac{1}{2} \times \frac{1}{2} = \frac{1}{4}$ $\longrightarrow$ $S_4 = 2 + 1 + \frac{1}{2} + \frac{1}{4} = 3\frac{3}{4}$

$u_5 = \frac{1}{4} \times \frac{1}{2} = \frac{1}{8}$ $\longrightarrow$ $S_5 = 2 + 1 + \frac{1}{2} + \frac{1}{4} + \frac{1}{8} = 3\frac{7}{8}$

The sums are getting closer (**converging**) to 4. So the sum to infinity is $\boxed{4}$.

2. You can show this **graphically**. The line on the graph is getting **closer and closer** to 4, but it'll never actually get there.

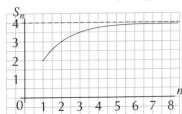

Luckily you don't have to find a list of sums like this to get the sum to infinity — there's a **formula** you use to work out the **sum to infinity** of a geometric series.

- The sum of the **first n terms** of a geometric series is $S_n = \dfrac{a(1 - r^n)}{1 - r}$

- If $|r| < 1$ and n is very, very big, then r^n will be very, very **small**, i.e. $r^n \to 0$ as $n \to \infty$.

- This means $(1 - r^n)$ will get really **close to 1**, so $(1 - r^n) \to 1$ as $n \to \infty$.

- Putting this back into the sum formula gives $S_n \to \dfrac{a \times 1}{1 - r} = \dfrac{a}{1 - r}$ as $n \to \infty$.

- So: $\boxed{S_\infty = \dfrac{a}{1 - r}}$

    Tip: The sum of the first n terms formula is on p.123. Both of these formulas are given on the formula sheet.

Example 3

a) If $a = 2$ and $r = \frac{1}{2}$, find the sum to infinity of the geometric series. $\longleftarrow$ This is the same as Example 2.

$|r| = \left|\frac{1}{2}\right| = \frac{1}{2} < 1$, so the series converges and you can find its sum to infinity using the formula for S_∞:

$S_\infty = \dfrac{a}{1 - r} = \dfrac{2}{1 - \frac{1}{2}} = \dfrac{2}{\frac{1}{2}} = \boxed{4}$

b) Find the sum to infinity of the geometric series 8 + 2 + 0.5 + 0.125 + ...

1. First find a and r as before:

$$a = 8, \ r = \frac{2^{\text{nd}} \text{ term}}{1^{\text{st}} \text{ term}} = \frac{2}{8} = 0.25$$

2. Again, $|r| < 1$, so the series converges and so you can find the sum to infinity:

$$S_\infty = \frac{a}{1-r} = \frac{8}{1-0.25} = \frac{32}{3} = 10\frac{2}{3}$$

Divergent series **don't** have a **sum to infinity**.

Because the terms aren't tending to zero, the size of the sum will just keep increasing as you add more terms, so there is **no limit** to the sum.

Exercise 5.4.3

Q1 State which of these sequences will converge and which will not.

a) 1, 1.1, 1.21, 1.331, ...

b) $0.8, \ 0.8^2, \ 0.8^3, \ ...$

c) $1, \ \dfrac{1}{4}, \ \dfrac{1}{16}, \ \dfrac{1}{64}, \ ...$

d) $3, \ \dfrac{9}{2}, \ \dfrac{27}{4}, \ ...$

e) $1, \ -\dfrac{1}{2}, \ \dfrac{1}{4}, \ -\dfrac{1}{8}, \ \dfrac{1}{16}, \ ...$

f) 5, 5, 5, 5, 5, ...

> **Q1 Hint:** If $r = 1$, the sequence is just the same term repeated, so it diverges. If $r = -1$, the sequence alternates between two terms forever.

Q2 A geometric series is 9 + 8.1 + 7.29 +...
Calculate the sum to infinity.

Q3 A geometric series has first term $a = 33$, common ratio $r = 0.25$. Find $\displaystyle\sum_{k=0}^{\infty} ar^k$ for this series.

Q4 $a, \ ar, \ ar^2, \ ...$ is a geometric sequence. Given that $S_\infty = 2a$, find r.

Q5 The sum to infinity of a geometric progression is 13.5 and the first 3 terms add up to 13.

a) Find the common ratio r

b) Find the first term a.

Q6 $a + ar + ar^2 + ...$ is a geometric series. $ra = 3$ and $S_\infty = 12$. Find r and a.

Q7 The sum to infinity of a geometric series is 10 and the first term is 6.

a) Find the common ratio.

b) What is the 5th term?

Q8 The 2nd term of a geometric progression is −48 and the 5th term is 0.75. Find:

a) the common ratio

b) the first term

c) the sum to infinity

Q9 The sum of the terms after the 10th term of a convergent geometric series is less than 1% of the sum to infinity. The first term is positive. Show that the common ratio $|r| < 0.631$.

Q10 In a convergent geometric series $S_\infty = \dfrac{9}{8} \times S_4$. Find the value of r, given that r is positive and real.

5.5 Modelling Problems

Sometimes a sequence or series is disguised by a 'real life' situation. You'll have to spot whether the sequence or series is arithmetic or geometric and turn the wordy question into the right maths.

Learning Objective (Spec Ref 4.6):

- Solve modelling problems involving arithmetic and geometric sequences and series.

Real life problems

Modelling problems might not say the words sequence, series, arithmetic or geometric in the question — you have to decide what you're dealing with. Look for questions that have a time period (e.g. each year) and describe how values increase or decrease over that time period.

Example 1

Mo is training for a 10 km running race. On the first day he runs 2 km. He schedules his training to increase by 0.5 km each day, so that he runs 2.5 km on the second day and 3 km on the third day and so on. This continues until he reaches the maximum distance of 10 km on the seventeenth day. The distance he runs each day then remains at 10 km until the race. There are 20 days before the race. What is the total distance Mo will run in training?

1. The question describes the sequence 2, 2.5, 3, ... , 10 which is arithmetic because each term increases by 0.5.

   Tip: You also know $l = 10$ for the series so you could use the formula $S_n = \frac{1}{2}n(a + l)$.

2. You are asked for the total distance, so use the series formula.

   $$S_n = \frac{n}{2}(2a + (n - 1)d)$$

3. The series contains 17 terms and you know that $a = 2$ and $d = 0.5$.

   $$S_{17} = \frac{17}{2}(2 \times 2 + (17 - 1) \times 0.5)$$
   $$= \frac{17}{2}(4 + 8) = 102 \text{ km}$$

4. There are also 3 extra days where he will run 10 km:

   $$3 \times 10 = 30 \text{ km}$$

5. So the total distance Mo will run is:

   $$102 + 30 = \boxed{132 \text{ km}}$$

Example 2

When a baby is born, £3000 is invested in an account with a fixed interest rate of 4% per year.

a) What will the account be worth at the start of the seventh year?

1. Start by working out the first few terms to see what the sequence is:

   $u_1 = a = 3000$

   $u_2 = 3000 + (4\% \text{ of } 3000)$ ← This is the interest.
   $= 3000 + (0.04 \times 3000)$
   $= 3000(1 + 0.04)$
   $= 3000 \times 1.04$

   $u_3 = u_2 \times 1.04 = (3000 \times 1.04) \times 1.04$
   $= 3000 \times (1.04)^2$

   Tip: You might recognise that the sequence is geometric with $r = 1.04$ straight away, if you know that a 4% interest rate means you multiply by 1.04.

   This is a geometric sequence with $r = 1.04$

2. Write down the nth term of the sequence: $u_n = ar^{n-1} = 3000 \times (1.04)^{n-1}$

3. The value of the account at the start of the first year is the 1st term, so the value of the account at the start of the seventh year is the 7th term. $u_7 = ar^6 = 3000 \times (1.04)^6 = 3795.957...$
So it's £3795.96 (to the nearest penny)

b) After how many full years will the account have doubled in value?

1. You need to know when $u_n > 3000 \times 2 = 6000$
From part **a)** you know $u_n = 3000 \times (1.04)^{n-1}$: $3000 \times (1.04)^{n-1} > 6000 \Rightarrow (1.04)^{n-1} > 2$

2. Solve the inequality using logs:

   Tip: It's OK to take logs of both sides of an inequality because logs are increasing functions, so if $x > y$, $\log x > \log y$.
   It's also fine to divide both sides by $\log 1.04$ because $1.04 > 1$ and the log of a number greater than 1 is positive.

   $\Rightarrow \qquad \log(1.04)^{n-1} > \log 2$

   $\Rightarrow \quad (n-1)\log(1.04) > \log 2$

   $\Rightarrow \qquad\qquad n - 1 > \dfrac{\log 2}{\log 1.04}$

   $\Rightarrow \qquad\qquad n - 1 > 17.67$

   $\Rightarrow \qquad\qquad\quad n > 18.67 \quad \text{(to 2 d.p.)}$

3. So u_n is more than 6000 when n is more than 18.67. Then u_{19} (the amount at the start of the 19th year) will be more than double the original amount.

After 18 years, the account will have doubled in value.

If you have to give an answer in years, make sure you think through which term belongs to which year carefully — it's easy to give the wrong answer even if you've done all the maths right.

Exercise 5.5.1

(MODELLING)

Q1 Morag starts a new job. In the first week she is paid £60, but this rises by £3 per week, so she earns £63 in the second week and £66 in the third week.
How much does she earn in her 12th week?

Q2 A collector has 8 china dolls that fit inside each other.
The smallest doll is 3 cm high and each doll is 25% taller than the previous one.
If he lines them up in height order (shortest to tallest), how tall is the 8th doll?

Q3 Mario opens a sandwich shop. On the first day he sells 40 sandwiches.
As people hear about the shop, sales increase and on the second day he sells 45 sandwiches.
Daily sales rise in an arithmetic sequence. On which day will he sell 80 sandwiches?

Q4 A retro cassette player is launched into the market.
In the first month after launch, the product takes £300 000 of revenue.
It takes £270 000 in the second month and £240 000 in the third.
If this pattern continues, when would you expect monthly sales to fall below £50 000?

Q5 A car depreciates by 15% each year. The value of the car after each year forms a geometric sequence. After 10 years from new the car is valued at £2362. How much was the car when new?

Q5 Hint: 'Depreciates' means 'decreases in value'.

Q6 A fishing licence cost £120 in 2011. The cost rose 3% each year for the next 5 years.

a) How much was a fishing licence in 2012?

b) Nigel bought a fishing licence every year between 2011 and 2016 (including 2011 and 2016). How much in total did he spend?

Q7 "Cornflake Collector" magazine sells 6000 copies in its first month of publication, 8000 in its second month and 10 000 in its third month.
If this pattern continues, how many copies will it sell in the first year of publication?

Q8 Ron is growing his prize leeks for the Village Show. The bag of compost he's using on his leeks says it will increase their height by 15% every 2 days. After 4 weeks the leeks' height has increased from 5 cm to 25 cm. Has the compost done what it claimed?

Q9 It's predicted that garden gnome value will go up by 2% each year, forming a geometric progression. Jean-Claude has a garden gnome currently valued at £80 000.
If the predicted rate of inflation is correct:

a) What will Jean-Claude's gnome be worth after 1 year?

b) What is the common ratio of the geometric progression?

c) What will Jean-Claude's gnome be worth after 10 years?

d) It will take k years for the value of Jean-Claude's gnome to exceed £120 000. Find k.

Q10 Frazer draws one dot in the first square of his calendar for July, two dots in the second square, and so on up to 31 dots in the last day of the month. How many dots does he draw in total?

Q11 The thickness of a piece of paper is 0.01 cm.
The Moon is 384 000 km from the Earth.
The piece of paper is on the Earth.
Assuming you can fold the piece of paper as many times as you like, how many times would you have to fold it for it to reach the Moon?

Q11 Hint: Have a go — it really works!*
*Disclaimer: it gets a bit tricky after 7 folds...

Q12 An athlete is preparing for an important event and sets herself a target of running 3% more each day. On day 1 she runs 12 miles.

a) How far does she run on day 10?

b) Her training schedule lasts for 20 days. To the nearest mile, how far does she run altogether?

Q13 Laura puts 1p in her jar on the first day, 2p in on the second day, 3p in on the third day, etc. How many days will it take her to collect over £10?

Q14 Chardonnay wants to invest her savings for the next 10 years. She wants her investment to double during this time. If interest is added annually, what interest rate does she need?

Q14 Hint: Call the initial value of her savings a.

Review Exercise

Q1 Find the 8th term of the sequence $x_n = n^2 - 3$. Is this sequence increasing or decreasing?

Q2 In the sequence $u_n = n^2 + 3n + 4$, $u_k = 44$. Find the value of k.

Q3 A sequence has the form $u_n = an^2 + bn$, where a and b are constants.
If the 3rd term is 18, and the 7th term is 70, find the values of a and b.

Q4 Find the first 5 terms of the sequence in which:
a) $x_1 = 7$ and $x_{n+1} = x_n + 3$ for $n \geq 1$.
b) $u_1 = 2$ and $u_{n+1} = 6 \div u_n$ for $n \geq 1$.

Q5 Find a recurrence relation which generates the sequence:
a) 65 536, 256, 16, 4, 2, ...
b) 40, 38, 34, 28, 20, ...
c) 1, 1, 2, 3, 5, 8, ...

Q6 A sequence is generated by a recurrence relation of the form $u_{n+1} = ku_n + 3$,
where k is a constant. If $u_1 = 4$ and $u_2 = 11$, find the values of k, u_3 and u_4.

Q7 A sequence is generated by $u_1 = 8$ and $u_{n+1} = 18 - u_n$ for $n \geq 1$. Find the first 5 terms and a
formula for u_n in terms of n. State whether the sequence is increasing, decreasing or periodic.

Q8 Find the common difference in a sequence that starts with –2, ends with 19 and has 29 terms.

Q9 In an arithmetic series, $u_7 = 8$ and $u_{11} = 10$. Find u_3.

Q10 An arithmetic series has seventh term 36 and tenth term 30. Find the nth term and S_5.

Q11 Find $\displaystyle\sum_{n=1}^{20}(3n-1)$.

Q12 Find: a) the sum of the first 24 natural numbers, b) $\displaystyle\sum_{n=13}^{24}n$, c) the value of k if $\displaystyle\sum_{n=1}^{k}n = 630$.

Q13 Write an expression for the nth term of the geometric sequence 3, –9, 27, –81, 243, ...

Q14 For the geometric progression 2, –6, 18, ..., find:
a) the 10th term,
b) the sum of the first 10 terms.

Q15 A geometric series has first term $a = 7$ and common ratio $r = 0.6$. Find $\displaystyle\sum_{k=0}^{5}7(0.6)^k$ to 2 d.p.

Q16 Show that the sum of the first n terms of a geometric sequence with
first term a and common ratio r is: $S_n = \dfrac{a(1-r^n)}{1-r}$.

Q17 For the geometric progression 24, 12, 6, ..., find:
a) the common ratio,
b) the seventh term,
c) the sum of the first 10 terms,
d) the sum to infinity.

Q18 A new shop takes £300 on its first day of business, £315 on its second day and £330 on
its third day. If this pattern continues, on which day will the shop first take over £500?

Q19 Hussain puts one stone on the wall on his way to school on the first day of term,
two stones on the wall on the second day of term and three on the third day of term.
The term has 13 weeks of 5 days each. If he continues like this, how many stones
will he have put on the wall in total by the holiday?

Exam-Style Questions

Q1   A series has recurrence relation:

$$u_{n+2} = \frac{u_{n+1} + 1}{u_n}, \text{ with } u_1 = 3 \text{ and } u_2 = 5.$$

a) Find u_6 and u_7.

[2 marks]

b) Find the sum of the first 25 terms.

[3 marks]

Q2   The 6th term of an arithmetic series is p and the 12th term is $4p$.

a) Write an expression for the common difference, d, in terms of p.

[3 marks]

b) The sum of the first 6 terms is 72 and the sum of the first 12 terms is 288. Find the first 3 terms of the series.

[4 marks]

Q3   Samira is training for a triathlon. She plans her training regime as follows:

- Run: Start with 30 minute run and increase by 5 minutes per day.
- Cycle: Start with 15 minute cycle then increase by 12% per day.
- Swim: Swim for 1 hour each day.

a) How long does Samira exercise for in total on day 3, to the nearest minute?

[3 marks]

b) On which day does the duration of the cycle and run both individually exceed the duration of the swim for the first time?

[4 marks]

c) For how long in total does Samira cycle in her second week of training? Give your answer in hours and minutes to the nearest minute.

[3 marks]

d) Explain one restriction of the models you have used in parts a)-c).

[1 mark]

Q4   A geometric series has common ratio r, 2nd term 6 and $S_\infty = 8k$.

a) Show that $4kr^2 - 4kr + 3 = 0$.

[3 marks]

b) Given that there is only one real value of r and $k \neq 0$, find the value of k and the first three terms in the series.

[5 marks]

6.1 The Binomial Expansion

You'll recognise binomial expansions from Year 1. This chapter should refresh your memory on the formula and take it further — including how to raise an expression to a fractional or negative power.

Learning Objectives (Spec Ref 4.1):

- Expand $(p + qx)^n$ for any rational n using the general formula for binomial expansions.
- State the validity of the expansion — i.e. the values of x for which the expansion is valid.

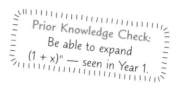

Prior Knowledge Check:
Be able to expand
$(1 + x)^n$ — seen in Year 1.

Expansions where n is a positive integer

The **binomial expansion** is a way to raise a given expression to any power. For simpler cases it's basically a fancy way of multiplying out brackets. You can also use it to approximate more complicated expressions. In Year 1, you met the formula for the binomial expansion of $(1 + x)^n$:

$$(1+x)^n = 1 + nx + \frac{n(n-1)}{1 \times 2}x^2 + \dots + \frac{n(n-1)\dots(n-r+1)}{1 \times 2 \times \dots \times r}x^r + \dots$$

From the formula, it looks like the expansion always goes on forever. But if **n is a positive integer**, the binomial expansion is **finite**.

Example 1

Give the binomial expansion of $(1 + x)^5$.

Use the formula and plug in **$n = 5$**:

$n = 5 \qquad n(n-1)$

$$(1+x)^5 = 1 + 5x + \frac{5(5-1)}{1 \times 2}x^2 + \frac{5(5-1)(5-2)}{1 \times 2 \times 3}x^3$$
$$+ \frac{5(5-1)(5-2)(5-3)}{1 \times 2 \times 3 \times 4}x^4 + \frac{5(5-1)(5-2)(5-3)(5-4)}{1 \times 2 \times 3 \times 4 \times 5}x^5$$
$$+ \frac{5(5-1)(5-2)(5-3)(5-4)(5-5)}{1 \times 2 \times 3 \times 4 \times 5 \times 6}x^6 + \dots$$

Tip: The expansion is finite because at some point you introduce an $(n - n)$ (i.e. zero) term in the numerator which then appears in every coefficient from that point on, making them all zero.

$$= 1 + 5x + \frac{5 \times 4}{1 \times 2}x^2 + \frac{5 \times 4 \times 3}{1 \times 2 \times 3}x^3 + \frac{5 \times 4 \times 3 \times 2}{1 \times 2 \times 3 \times 4}x^4$$
$$+ \frac{5 \times 4 \times 3 \times 2 \times 1}{1 \times 2 \times 3 \times 4 \times 5}x^5 + \frac{5 \times 4 \times 3 \times 2 \times 1 \times 0}{1 \times 2 \times 3 \times 4 \times 5 \times 6}x^6 + \dots$$

You can stop here — all the terms after this one are zero.

$$= 1 + 5x + \frac{20}{2}x^2 + \frac{60}{6}x^3 + \frac{120}{24}x^4 + \frac{120}{120}x^5 + \frac{0}{720}x^6 + \dots$$

$$= 1 + 5x + 10x^2 + 10x^3 + 5x^4 + x^5$$

The formula still works if the coefficient of x **isn't 1**, i.e. $(1 + ax)^n$ — just **replace** each 'x' in the formula with **(ax)**. The 'a' should be raised to the **same power** as the 'x' in each term, and included in the coefficient when you simplify at the end. This next example shows you how it's done.

Example 2

Give the binomial expansion of $(1 - 3x)^4$.

Use the **formula** with $n = 4$, but replace every x with $-3x$:

Think of this as $(1 + (-3x))^4$ — put the **minus** into the formula as well as the $3x$.

> **Tip:** Make life easier for yourself by cancelling down the fractions before you multiply.

$n = 4 \quad n(n-1)$

$(1 - 3x)^4 = 1 + 4(-3x) + \dfrac{4 \times 3}{1 \times 2}(-3x)^2 + \dfrac{4 \times \cancel{3} \times \cancel{2}}{1 \times \cancel{2} \times \cancel{3}}(-3x)^3$

$+ \dfrac{\cancel{4} \times \cancel{3} \times \cancel{2} \times \cancel{1}}{\cancel{1} \times \cancel{2} \times \cancel{3} \times \cancel{4}}(-3x)^4 + \dfrac{\cancel{4} \times \cancel{3} \times \cancel{2} \times \cancel{1} \times 0}{\cancel{1} \times \cancel{2} \times \cancel{3} \times \cancel{4} \times 5}(-3x)^5 + \ldots$

Don't forget to square the -3 as well.　　　Stop here.

$= 1 + 4(-3x) + \dfrac{12}{2}(9x^2) + \dfrac{4}{1}(-27x^3) + (81x^4) + \dfrac{0}{5}(-243x^5) + \ldots$

$= \boxed{1 - 12x + 54x^2 - 108x^3 + 81x^4}$

Validity

Some binomial expansions are **only valid for certain values of x**. When you find a binomial expansion, you usually have to state which values of x the expansion is valid for.

> If n is a **positive integer**, the binomial expansion of $(p + qx)^n$ is valid for **all values of x**.

So far you've only dealt with expansions of $(p + qx)^n$ where p is 1, but there are more complicated examples to come on page 140. There's more on the validity of other expansions on page 137.

Exercise 6.1.1

Use the formula to expand each of the following functions in ascending powers of x.

Q1　Expand fully: $(1 + x)^3$

Q2　Expand $(1 + x)^7$ up to and including the term in x^3.

Q3　Expand fully: $(1 - x)^4$

Q4　Give the first 3 terms of $(1 + 3x)^6$.

Q5　Give the first 4 terms of $(1 + 2x)^8$.

Q6　Expand $(1 - 5x)^5$ up to and including the term in x^2.

Q7　Expand fully: $(1 - 4x)^3$

Q8　Expand $(1 + 6x)^6$ up to and including the term in x^3.

> **Q3 Hint:** Watch out for that minus sign — replace 'x' in the formula with $(-x)$.

Expansions where _n_ is negative or a fraction

_n_ is negative

If _n_ is **negative**, the expansion gets more complicated. You can still use the **formula** in the same way, but it will produce an **infinite** number of terms (see the example below). You can just write down the **first few terms** in the series, but this will only be an **approximation** to the whole expansion. The question will usually tell you how many terms to give.

This type of expansion can be 'hidden' as a fraction — remember: $\dfrac{1}{(1+x)^n} = (1+x)^{-n}$

Example 1

Find the binomial expansion of $\dfrac{1}{(1+x)^2}$ up to and including the term in x^3.

1. First, **rewrite** the expression: $\dfrac{1}{(1+x)^2} = (1+x)^{-2}$

2. Now you can use the formula for $(1+x)^n$. This time $n = -2$:

$$(1+x)^{-2} = 1 + (-2)x + \frac{(-2)\times(-2-1)}{1\times 2}x^2$$
$$+ \frac{(-2)\times(-2-1)\times(-2-2)}{1\times 2\times 3}x^3 + \dots$$

where $n = -2$ and $n(n-1)$.

Tip: Again, you can cancel down before you multiply — but be careful with those minus signs.

$$= 1 + (-2)x + \frac{(-2)\times(-3)}{1\times 2}x^2 + \frac{(-2)\times(-3)\times(-4)}{1\times 2\times 3}x^3 + \dots$$

$$= 1 + (-2)x + \frac{3}{1}x^2 + \frac{(-4)}{1}x^3 + \dots$$

$$= \boxed{1 - 2x + 3x^2 - 4x^3 + \dots}$$

> With a negative _n_, you'll never get zero as a coefficient. If the question hadn't told you to stop, the expansion could go on forever.

3. We've left out all the terms after $-4x^3$, so the cubic expression you've ended up with is an **approximation** to the original expression.

4. You could also write the answer like this:

$$\frac{1}{(1+x)^2} \approx 1 - 2x + 3x^2 - 4x^3$$

_n_ is a fraction

The binomial expansion formula doesn't just work for integer values of _n_. If _n_ is a **fraction**, you'll have to take care multiplying out the fractions in the coefficients, but otherwise the formula is **exactly the same**.

Remember that **roots** are fractional powers: $\sqrt[n]{1+x} = (1+x)^{\frac{1}{n}}$

Example 2

Find the binomial expansion of $\sqrt[3]{1+2x}$, up to and including the term in x^3.

1. First rewrite the expression as a fractional power: $\sqrt[3]{1+2x} = (1+2x)^{\frac{1}{3}}$

2. This time $n = \frac{1}{3}$, and you also need to replace x with $2x$:

$$n = \frac{1}{3} \quad n(n-1)$$

$$(1 + 2x)^{\frac{1}{3}} = 1 + \frac{1}{3}(2x) + \frac{\frac{1}{3} \times \left(\frac{1}{3} - 1\right)}{1 \times 2}(2x)^2$$

$$+ \frac{\frac{1}{3} \times \left(\frac{1}{3} - 1\right) \times \left(\frac{1}{3} - 2\right)}{1 \times 2 \times 3}(2x)^3 + \ldots$$

Tip: Cancelling down is much trickier with this type of expansion — it's often safer to multiply everything out fully.

$$= 1 + \frac{2}{3}x + \frac{\frac{1}{3} \times \left(-\frac{2}{3}\right)}{1 \times 2}(4x^2) + \frac{\frac{1}{3} \times \left(-\frac{2}{3}\right) \times \left(-\frac{5}{3}\right)}{1 \times 2 \times 3}(8x^3) + \ldots$$

$$= 1 + \frac{2}{3}x + \frac{\left(-\frac{2}{9}\right)}{2}(4x^2) + \frac{\left(\frac{10}{27}\right)}{6}(8x^3) + \ldots$$

Tip: Exam questions often ask for the coefficients as simplified fractions.

$$= 1 + \frac{2}{3}x + \left(-\frac{1}{9}\right)(4x^2) + \left(\frac{5}{81}\right)(8x^3) + \ldots$$

$$= 1 + \frac{2}{3}x - \frac{4}{9}x^2 + \frac{40}{81}x^3 - \ldots$$

Validity when n is negative or a fraction

Binomial expansions where n is negative or a fraction are **not valid** for **all** values of x. The **rule** to work out the validity of an expansion is as follows:

> If n is a negative integer or a fraction, the binomial expansion of $(p + qx)^n$ is **valid** when $\left|\frac{qx}{p}\right| < 1$, i.e. when $|x| < \left|\frac{p}{q}\right|$.

This just means that the **absolute value** (or **modulus**) of x (i.e. ignoring any negative signs) must be **smaller** than the absolute value of $\frac{p}{q}$ for the expansion to be valid.

You might already know the rules $|ab| = |a||b|$ and $\left|\frac{a}{b}\right| = \frac{|a|}{|b|}$.

If you don't, then get to know them — they're handy for rearranging these limits.

Example 3

State the validity of the expansions given in the previous two examples.

a) Write down p and q for the expansion $(1 + x)^{-2} = 1 - 2x + 3x^2 - 4x^3 + \ldots$

$p = 1$ and $q = 1$.

...then put p and q in the inequality. So the expansion is valid if:

$\left|\frac{1x}{1}\right| < 1$, i.e. if $|x| < 1$

b) For $(1 + 2x)^{\frac{1}{3}} = 1 + \frac{2}{3}x - \frac{4}{9}x^2 + \frac{40}{81}x^3 - \ldots$

$p = 1$ and $q = 2$.

So the expansion is valid if:

$|2x| < 1 \Rightarrow 2|x| < 1 \Rightarrow |x| < \frac{1}{2}$

Combinations of expansions

- You can use the binomial expansion formula for more complicated combinations of expansions — e.g. where different brackets raised to different powers are **multiplied together**. Start by dealing with the different expansions **separately**, then **multiply** the expressions together at the end.

- For situations where one bracket is being **divided** by another, change the **sign** of the **power** and **multiply** instead — e.g. $\dfrac{(1+x)}{(1+2x)^3} = (1+x)(1+2x)^{-3}$.

- You'll usually be asked to give the expansion to a specified number of terms, so the multiplication shouldn't get too complicated as you can ignore terms in higher powers of x.

- For the **combined** expansion to be **valid**, x must be in the valid range for **both** expansions, i.e. where they overlap. In practice this just means sticking to the **narrowest** of the valid ranges for each separate expansion.

Example 4

Write down the first three terms in the expansion of $\dfrac{(1+2x)^3}{(1-x)^2}$.

State the range of x for which the expansion is valid.

1. Re-write as a product of two expansions:

$$\frac{(1+2x)^3}{(1-x)^2} = (1+2x)^3 (1-x)^{-2}$$

2. Expand each of these separately using the formula. (You only need to go up to the term in x^2, but it's better to have too many terms than too few at this stage.)

$$(1+2x)^3 = 1 + 3(2x) + \frac{3\times2}{1\times2}(2x)^2 + \frac{3\times2\times1}{1\times2\times3}(2x)^3$$

$$= 1 + 6x + 3(4x^2) + 8x^3 = 1 + 6x + 12x^2 + 8x^3$$

$$(1-x)^{-2} = 1 + (-2)(-x) + \frac{(-2)\times(-3)}{1\times2}(-x)^2 + \frac{(-2)\times(-3)\times(-4)}{1\times2\times3}(-x)^3 + \ldots$$

$$= 1 + 2x + 3x^2 + 4x^3 + \ldots$$

3. **Multiply** the two expansions together. Since you're only asked for the **first three terms**, ignore any terms with **higher powers** of x than x^2.

$$(1+2x)^3(1-x)^{-2} = (1 + 6x + 12x^2 + 8x^3)(1 + 2x + 3x^2 + 4x^3 + \ldots)$$

$$= 1(1 + 2x + 3x^2) + 6x(1 + 2x) + 12x^2(1) + \ldots$$

$$= 1 + 2x + 3x^2 + 6x + 12x^2 + 12x^2 + \ldots$$

$$= \boxed{1 + 8x + 27x^2 + \ldots}$$

4. Now find the **validity** of each expansion:

$(1+2x)^3$ is valid for all values of x, since n is a positive integer.

$(1-x)^{-2}$ is valid if $|-x| < 1 \Rightarrow |x| < 1$.

So the combined expression $\dfrac{(1+2x)^3}{(1-x)^2}$ is only valid if $\boxed{|x| < 1,}$ since this is the narrower range of the two separate expansions.

Exercise 6.1.2

Q1 Use the binomial formula to find the first four terms in the expansion of $(1 + x)^{-4}$.

Q2 a) Find the binomial expansion of $(1 - 6x)^{-3}$, up to and including the term in x^3.

b) For what values of x is this expansion valid?

Q3 Use the binomial formula to find the first three terms in the expansion of:

a) $(1 + 4x)^{\frac{1}{3}}$

b) $(1 + 4x)^{-\frac{1}{2}}$

c) For each of the expansions above, state the range of x for which the expansion is valid.

Q4 Find the binomial expansion of the following functions, up to and including the term in x^3.

a) $\dfrac{1}{(1 - 4x)^2}$ for $|x| < \dfrac{1}{4}$

b) $\sqrt{1 + 6x}$ for $|x| < \dfrac{1}{6}$

c) $\dfrac{1}{\sqrt{1 - 3x}}$ for $|x| < \dfrac{1}{3}$

d) $\sqrt[3]{1 + \dfrac{x}{2}}$ for $|x| < 2$

Q5 a) Find the coefficient of the x^3 term in the expansion of $\dfrac{1}{(1 + 7x)^4}$.

b) For what range of x is this expansion valid?

Q6 a) What is the coefficient of x^5 in the expansion of $\sqrt[4]{1 - 4x}$?

b) For what values of x is the binomial expansion of $\sqrt[4]{1 - 4x}$ valid?

> **Q5-6 Hint:** You don't need to bother doing the full expansion — just work out the coefficient of the term you need.

Q7 a) Find the first three terms of the expansion of $(1 - 5x)^{\frac{1}{6}}$.

b) Hence find the binomial expansion of $(1 + 4x)^4 (1 - 5x)^{\frac{1}{6}}$, up to and including the term in x^2.

c) State the validity of the expansion in b).

Q8 Expand, up to and including the term in x^2, giving the range for which the expansion is valid:

a) $(1 + x)^2(1 - 2x)^{-2}$

b) $(1 + 2x)^2(1 + 3x)^{-3}$

c) $(1 - 7x)(1 + 2x)^{\frac{1}{7}}$

d) $(1 - x)^2(1 + 4x)^{-\frac{1}{3}}$

Q9 a) Find the first three terms of the binomial expansion of $\dfrac{(1 + 3x)^4}{(1 + x)^3}$.

b) State the range of x for which the expansion is valid.

Q10 a) Write out the expansion of:

(i) $(1 + ax)^4$ (all terms)

(ii) $(1 - bx)^{-3}$, up to the term in x^2

b) Hence expand $\dfrac{(1 + ax)^4}{(1 - bx)^3}$, up to and including the term in x^2.

c) Find the two possible pairs of values of a and b if the first three terms of the expansion of $\dfrac{(1 + ax)^4}{(1 - bx)^3}$ are $1 + x + 24x^2$.

Expanding $(p + qx)^n$

You've seen over the last few pages that the binomial expansion of $(1 + x)^n$ works for **any** n, and that you can replace the x with other x-terms.

However, the 1 at the start **has to be a 1** before you can expand. If it's **not** a 1, you'll need to **factorise first** before you can use the formula.

This means you have to rewrite the expression as follows: $\quad (p + qx)^n = p^n\left(1 + \dfrac{qx}{p}\right)^n$

This rearrangement uses the power law $(ab)^k = a^k b^k$
— note that the p outside the brackets is still raised to the power n.

Example 1

Give the binomial expansion of $(3 - x)^4$ and state its validity.

> **Tip:** Don't forget to raise the 3 to the power 4.

1. To use the $(1 + x)^n$ formula, you need the constant term in the brackets to be 1 — you want an expression in the form $c(1 + dx)^n$, where c and d are constants, so factorise the 3 outside the brackets.

$$3 - x = 3\left(1 - \frac{1}{3}x\right)$$

$$\Rightarrow (3 - x)^4 = \left[3\left(1 - \frac{1}{3}x\right)\right]^4 = 3^4\left(1 - \frac{1}{3}x\right)^4$$

$$= 81\left(1 - \frac{1}{3}x\right)^4$$

2. Now use the $(1 + x)^n$ formula, with $n = 4$, and $-\frac{1}{3}x$ instead of x:

$$\left(1 - \frac{1}{3}x\right)^4 = 1 + 4\left(-\frac{1}{3}x\right) + \frac{4 \times 3}{1 \times 2}\left(-\frac{1}{3}x\right)^2$$

$$+ \frac{4 \times 3 \times 2}{1 \times 2 \times 3}\left(-\frac{1}{3}x\right)^3$$

$$+ \frac{4 \times 3 \times 2 \times 1}{1 \times 2 \times 3 \times 4}\left(-\frac{1}{3}x\right)^4$$

$$= 1 - \frac{4}{3}x + 6\left(\frac{1}{9}x^2\right) + 4\left(-\frac{1}{27}x^3\right) + \frac{1}{81}x^4$$

$$= 1 - \frac{4x}{3} + \frac{2x^2}{3} - \frac{4x^3}{27} + \frac{x^4}{81}$$

3. Finally, put this back into the original expression:

$$(3 - x)^4 = 81\left(1 - \frac{1}{3}x\right)^4$$

$$= 81\left(1 - \frac{4x}{3} + \frac{2x^2}{3} - \frac{4x^3}{27} + \frac{x^4}{81}\right)$$

$$= \boxed{81 - 108x + 54x^2 - 12x^3 + x^4}$$

4. The expansion is valid for all values of x.

   This is because n is a positive integer — so the expansion is finite.

For the example above, you could just pop $a = 3$ and $b = -x$ into the formula for $(a + b)^n$, which will be given to you in the exam.

This formula only works when n is a **natural number** (written $n \in \mathbb{N}$ — these are just positive integers), so you'll need to use the method shown here if the power is negative or a fraction.

Example 2

Give the first 3 terms in the binomial expansion of $(3x + 4)^{\frac{3}{2}}$.

1. Again, you need to **factorise** before using the formula, taking care to choose the **right factor**...

    $$3x + 4 = 4 + 3x = 4\left(1 + \frac{3}{4}x\right)$$

    $$\Rightarrow (3x + 4)^{\frac{3}{2}} = \left[4\left(1 + \frac{3}{4}x\right)\right]^{\frac{3}{2}}$$

    $$= 4^{\frac{3}{2}}\left(1 + \frac{3}{4}x\right)^{\frac{3}{2}}$$

    $$= 8\left(1 + \frac{3}{4}x\right)^{\frac{3}{2}}$$

    Tip: It's tempting to take the 3 outside the brackets because of the order the numbers are written in, but don't be fooled.

2. Use the $(1 + x)^n$ formula with $n = \frac{3}{2}$, and $\frac{3}{4}x$ instead of x:

    $$\left(1 + \frac{3}{4}x\right)^{\frac{3}{2}} = 1 + \frac{3}{2}\left(\frac{3}{4}x\right) + \frac{\frac{3}{2} \times \left(\frac{3}{2} - 1\right)}{1 \times 2}\left(\frac{3}{4}x\right)^2 + \ldots$$

    $$= 1 + \frac{9}{8}x + \frac{\frac{3}{2} \times \frac{1}{2}}{2}\left(\frac{9}{16}x^2\right) + \ldots$$

    $$= 1 + \frac{9x}{8} + \frac{27x^2}{128} + \ldots$$

3. Put this back into the **original expression**:

    $$(3x + 4)^{\frac{3}{2}} = 8\left(1 + \frac{3}{4}x\right)^{\frac{3}{2}} = 8\left(1 + \frac{9x}{8} + \frac{27x^2}{128} + \ldots\right)$$

    $$= 8 + 9x + \frac{27x^2}{16} + \ldots$$

    Tip: This expansion is only valid for $\left|\frac{qx}{p}\right| < 1$, i.e. $\left|\frac{3x}{4}\right| < 1 \Rightarrow |x| < \frac{4}{3}$.

Example 3

Expand $\dfrac{1 + 2x}{(2 - x)^2}$ up to the term in x^3. State the range of x for which the expansion is valid.

1. First **rearrange** and **separate** the different expansions:

    $$\frac{1 + 2x}{(2 - x)^2} = (1 + 2x)(2 - x)^{-2}$$

    $$p = 2 \qquad q = -1$$

    Tip: Take your time and set everything out in steps, then combine the expansions at the end.

2. The first bracket doesn't need expanding, so deal with the second bracket as usual, **factorising** first...

    $$2 - x = 2\left(1 - \frac{1}{2}x\right)$$

    $$\Rightarrow (2 - x)^{-2} = 2^{-2}\left(1 - \frac{1}{2}x\right)^{-2} = \frac{1}{4}\left(1 - \frac{1}{2}x\right)^{-2}$$

3. ... then using the **formula** with $n = -2$, and $-\frac{1}{2}x$ instead of x:

    $$\left(1 - \frac{1}{2}x\right)^{-2} = 1 + (-2)\left(-\frac{1}{2}x\right) + \frac{-2 \times -3}{1 \times 2}\left(-\frac{1}{2}x\right)^2$$

    $$+ \frac{-2 \times -3 \times -4}{1 \times 2 \times 3}\left(-\frac{1}{2}x\right)^3 + \ldots$$

    $$= 1 + x + \frac{3x^2}{4} + \frac{x^3}{2} + \ldots$$

4. So this means that:

$$(2-x)^{-2} = \frac{1}{4}\left(1 - \frac{1}{2}x\right)^{-2} = \frac{1}{4}\left(1 + x + \frac{3x^2}{4} + \frac{x^3}{2} + \ldots\right)$$

$$= \frac{1}{4} + \frac{x}{4} + \frac{3x^2}{16} + \frac{x^3}{8} + \ldots$$

5. Putting all this into the **original expression** gives:

$$\frac{1+2x}{(2-x)^2} = (1+2x)(2-x)^{-2} = (1+2x)\left(\frac{1}{4} + \frac{x}{4} + \frac{3x^2}{16} + \frac{x^3}{8} + \ldots\right)$$

$$= \frac{1}{4} + \frac{x}{4} + \frac{3x^2}{16} + \frac{x^3}{8} + 2x\left(\frac{1}{4} + \frac{x}{4} + \frac{3x^2}{16}\right) + \ldots$$

$$= \frac{1}{4} + \frac{x}{4} + \frac{3x^2}{16} + \frac{x^3}{8} + \frac{x}{2} + \frac{x^2}{2} + \frac{3x^2}{8} + \ldots$$

$$= \frac{1}{4} + \frac{3x}{4} + \frac{11x^2}{16} + \frac{x^3}{2} + \ldots$$

6. The **validity** of the whole expansion will depend on the validity of the expansion of $(2-x)^{-2}$. This is valid only if

$$\left|\frac{-x}{2}\right| < 1 \Rightarrow |x| < 2$$

Tip: Remember — if both expansions have a limited validity, choose the one with the narrower valid range of x for the combined expansion.

Exercise 6.1.3

Q1 Find the binomial expansion of the following functions, up to and including the term in x^3:

a) $(2 + 4x)^3$ b) $(3 + 4x)^5$ c) $(4 + x)^{\frac{1}{2}}$ d) $(8 + 2x)^{-\frac{1}{3}}$

Q2 If the x^2 coefficient of the binomial expansion of $(a + 5x)^5$ is 2000, what is the value of a?

Q3 a) Find the binomial expansion of $(2 - 5x)^7$ up to and including the term in x^2.

     b) Hence, or otherwise, find the binomial expansion of $(1 + 6x)^3(2 - 5x)^7$, up to and including the term in x^2.

Q4 a) Find the binomial expansion of $\left(1 + \frac{6}{5}x\right)^{-\frac{1}{2}}$, up to and including the term in x^3, stating the range of x for which it is valid.

     b) Hence, or otherwise, express $\sqrt{\dfrac{20}{5 + 6x}}$ in the form $a + bx + cx^2 + dx^3 + \ldots$

Q5 $f(x) = \dfrac{1}{\sqrt{5 - 2x}}$

     a) Find the binomial expansion of $f(x)$ in ascending powers of x, up to and including the x^2 term.

     b) Hence show that $\dfrac{3+x}{\sqrt{5-2x}} \approx \dfrac{3}{\sqrt{5}} + \dfrac{8x}{5\sqrt{5}} + \dfrac{19x^2}{50\sqrt{5}}$.

Q6 a) Find the binomial expansion of $(9 + 4x)^{-\frac{1}{2}}$, up to and including the term in x^2.

     b) Hence, or otherwise, find the binomial expansion of $\dfrac{(1 + 6x)^4}{\sqrt{9 + 4x}}$, up to and including the term in x^2.

6.2 Using the Binomial Expansion as an Approximation

One of the reasons that binomial expansions are so useful is that they can be used to estimate nasty-looking roots, powers and fractions. All you need to work out is the right value of x to use.

Learning Objective (Spec Ref 4.1):
- Substitute values into a binomial expansion in order to find approximations.

Approximating with binomial expansions

- When you've done an expansion, you can use it to work out the **value** of the original expression for **given values of** x, by **substituting** those values into the **expansion**.

- For most expansions this will only be an **approximate** answer, because you'll have had to limit the expansion to the first few terms.

- Often you'll have to do some **rearranging** of the expression so that you know what value of x to substitute. For example, $\sqrt[3]{1.3}$ can be written $(1 + 0.3)^{\frac{1}{3}}$, which can be approximated by expanding $(1 + x)^{\frac{1}{3}}$ and substituting $x = 0.3$ into the expansion.

- You also need to check the **validity** of the expansion — the approximation will only work for values of x in the valid range.

Example 1

The binomial expansion of $(1 + 3x)^{-1}$ up to the term in x^3 is: $(1 + 3x)^{-1} \approx 1 - 3x + 9x^2 - 27x^3$.

The expansion is valid for $|x| < \frac{1}{3}$.

Use this expansion to approximate $\frac{100}{103}$. Give your answer to 4 d.p.

1. For this type of question, you need to find the **right value of** x to make the expression you're expanding equal to the thing you're looking for.

2. This means a bit of clever **rearranging**: $\quad \frac{100}{103} = \frac{1}{1.03} = \frac{1}{1 + 0.03} = (1 + 0.03)^{-1}$

3. This is the same as an expansion of $(1 + 3x)^{-1}$ with $3x = 0.03$.
   $3x = 0.03 \implies x = 0.01$

4. Check this value is in the **valid range**: $\quad 0.01 < \frac{1}{3}$, so the expansion is valid for this value of x.

5. **Substituting** this value for x into the given expansion gives:

   $(1 + 3(0.01))^{-1} \approx 1 - 3(0.01) + 9(0.01^2) - 27(0.01^3)$

   Tip: You need to use a "$\approx$" when you give the answer — it's an approximation because you're only using the first few terms of the expansion.

   $= 1 - 0.03 + 0.0009 - 0.000027$

   $= 1.0009 - 0.030027$

   $= 0.970873$

   $(1 + 3(0.01))^{-1} \approx \boxed{0.9709 \text{ to 4 d.p.}}$

   $(\frac{100}{103} = 0.97087...$ so this is a pretty good approximation.$)$

In some cases you might have to **rearrange the expansion** first to get it into a form that fits with the given expression.

Example 2

The binomial expansion of $(1-5x)^{\frac{1}{2}}$ up to the term in x^2 is $(1-5x)^{\frac{1}{2}} \approx 1 - \dfrac{5x}{2} - \dfrac{25x^2}{8}$.

The expansion is valid for $|x| < \dfrac{1}{5}$.

a) Use $x = \dfrac{1}{50}$ in this expansion to show that $\sqrt{10} \approx \dfrac{800}{253}$.

1. First, substitute $x = \dfrac{1}{50}$ into **both sides** of the given expansion:

$$\sqrt{\left(1 - 5\left(\frac{1}{50}\right)\right)} \approx 1 - \frac{5}{2}\left(\frac{1}{50}\right) - \frac{25}{8}\left(\frac{1}{50}\right)^2$$

Tip: If you're not sure how to get the approximation you need from the expansion, try putting the numbers in and see what comes out. It should become clear where the $\sqrt{10}$ is coming from, even if it's not obvious at the start.

$$\sqrt{\left(1 - \frac{1}{10}\right)} \approx 1 - \frac{1}{20} - \frac{1}{800}$$

$$\sqrt{\frac{9}{10}} \approx \frac{759}{800}$$

2. Now **simplify the square root**...

$$\sqrt{\frac{9}{10}} = \frac{\sqrt{9}}{\sqrt{10}} = \frac{3}{\sqrt{10}} \approx \frac{759}{800}$$

3. ...and **rearrange** to find an estimate for $\sqrt{10}$:

$$\frac{3}{\sqrt{10}} \approx \frac{759}{800}$$

$$3 \times 800 \approx 759\sqrt{10}$$

$$\sqrt{10} \approx \frac{3 \times 800}{759}$$

$$\sqrt{10} \approx \frac{800}{253} \quad \text{as required.}$$

b) **Find the percentage error in your approximation, to 2 s.f.**

Work out the percentage error by finding the difference between your estimate and a calculated 'real' value, and give this as a percentage of the real value.

$$\left| \frac{\text{real value} - \text{estimate}}{\text{real value}} \right| \times 100$$

Tip: The modulus sign means you always get a positive answer, whether the estimate is bigger or smaller than the real value. You're only interested in the difference between them.

$$= \left| \frac{\sqrt{10} - \frac{800}{253}}{\sqrt{10}} \right| \times 100$$

$$= 0.0070\% \text{ (2 s.f.)}$$

(The % error is really small, so the approximation is very close to the real answer.)

Q1 a) Find the binomial expansion of $(1 + 6x)^{-1}$, up to and including the term in x^2.

b) What is the validity of the expansion in part a)?

c) Use an appropriate substitution to find an approximation for $\frac{100}{106}$.

d) What is the percentage error of this approximation? Give your answer correct to 1 significant figure.

> **Q1c) Hint:** Always check that the value you've decided to use for x is within the valid range for the expansion.

Q2 a) Use the binomial theorem to expand $(1 + 3x)^{\frac{1}{4}}$ in ascending powers of x, up to and including the term in x^3.

b) For what values of x is this expansion valid?

c) Use this expansion to find an approximate value of $\sqrt[4]{1.9}$ correct to 4 decimal places.

d) Find the percentage error of this approximation, correct to 3 significant figures.

Q3 a) Find the first four terms in the binomial expansion of $(1 - 2x)^{-\frac{1}{2}}$.

b) For what range of x is this expansion valid?

c) Use $x = \frac{1}{10}$ in this expansion to find an approximate value of $\sqrt{5}$.

d) Find the percentage error of this approximation, correct to 2 significant figures.

> **Q3c) Hint:** Put the value for x into both sides of the expansion, and rearrange the left-hand side until you get $\sqrt{5}$.

Q4 a) Expand $(2 - 5x)^6$ up to and including the x^2 term.

b) By substituting an appropriate value of x into the expansion in a), find an approximate value for 1.95^6.

c) What is the percentage error of this approximation? Give your answer to 2 significant figures.

Q5 a) Find the first three terms in the binomial expansion of $\sqrt{3 - 4x}$.

b) For what values of x is this expansion valid?

c) Use $x = \frac{3}{40}$ in this expansion to estimate the value of $\frac{3}{\sqrt{10}}$. Leave your answer as a fraction.

d) Find the percentage error of this approximation, correct to 1 significant figure.

Q6 a) Expand $\dfrac{(1 - 5x)}{(1 + 3x)^{\frac{1}{3}}}$ up to and including the term in x^2.

b) Give the range for which the expansion is valid.

c) Use $x = 0.1$ in this expansion to estimate the value of $\dfrac{1}{2\sqrt[3]{1.3}}$.

d) Find the percentage error of this approximation, correct to 2 significant figures.

6.3 Binomial Expansion and Partial Fractions

You'll need to deal with some tricky expressions — but you can use partial fractions to make things simpler. You met these back in Chapter 2.

Learning Objective (Spec Ref 4.1):
- Split rational functions into partial fractions, then find the binomial expansion of the function.

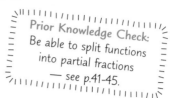

Prior Knowledge Check:
Be able to split functions into partial fractions
— see p.41-45.

Finding binomial expansions using partial fractions

You can find the binomial expansion of more complicated functions by:

- splitting them into **partial fractions** first,
- expanding **each fraction** using the formula (usually with $n = -1$),
- then **adding** the expansions together.

Example

$f(x) = \dfrac{x-1}{(3+x)(1-5x)}$ can be expressed as partial fractions in the form: $\dfrac{A}{(3+x)} + \dfrac{B}{(1-5x)}$.

a) Find the values of A and B, and hence express $f(x)$ as partial fractions.

1. Start by writing out the problem as an **identity**:

$$\frac{x-1}{(3+x)(1-5x)} \equiv \frac{A}{(3+x)} + \frac{B}{(1-5x)}$$

$$\Rightarrow \frac{x-1}{(3+x)(1-5x)} \equiv \frac{A(1-5x) + B(3+x)}{(3+x)(1-5x)}$$

$$\Rightarrow x - 1 \equiv A(1 - 5x) + B(3 + x)$$

2. You can then work out the values of A and B by putting in values of x that make each bracket in turn equal to zero.

   (This is known as the **'substitution'** method.)

Let $x = -3$, then: $-3 - 1 = A(1 - (-15))$

$$\Rightarrow -4 = 16A$$

$$\Rightarrow A = -\frac{1}{4}$$

Let $x = \frac{1}{5}$, then: $\frac{1}{5} - 1 = B\left(3 + \frac{1}{5}\right)$

$$\Rightarrow -\frac{4}{5} = \frac{16}{5}B$$

$$\Rightarrow B = -\frac{1}{4}$$

Tip: You could also **equate the coefficients** of x and the constant terms to find A and B.

Tip: Remember to put A and B back into the expression to give $f(x)$ as partial fractions.

So $f(x)$ can also be written as: $-\dfrac{1}{4(3+x)} - \dfrac{1}{4(1-5x)}$

b) Use your answer to part a) to find the binomial expansion of f(x), up to and including the term in x^2.

1. Start by **rewriting** the partial fractions from a) in $(p + qx)^n$ form:

$$f(x) = -\frac{1}{4}(3 + x)^{-1} - \frac{1}{4}(1 - 5x)^{-1}$$

2. Now do the two binomial expansions **separately**:

$$(3 + x)^{-1} = \left(3\left(1 + \frac{1}{3}x\right)\right)^{-1}$$
$$= \frac{1}{3}\left(1 + \frac{1}{3}x\right)^{-1}$$
$$= \frac{1}{3}\left(1 + (-1)\left(\frac{1}{3}x\right) + \frac{(-1)(-2)}{2}\left(\frac{1}{3}x\right)^2 + \ldots\right)$$
$$= \frac{1}{3}\left(1 - \frac{1}{3}x + \frac{1}{9}x^2 - \ldots\right)$$
$$= \frac{1}{3} - \frac{1}{9}x + \frac{1}{27}x^2 - \ldots$$

> **Tip:** Questions like these have lots of stages, which means lots of places that you could make a mistake — especially with all the negatives and fractions. Set your working out clearly and don't skip any stages.

$$(1 - 5x)^{-1} = 1 + (-1)(-5x) + \frac{(-1)(-2)}{2}(-5x)^2 + \ldots$$
$$= 1 + 5x + 25x^2 + \ldots$$

3. Finally, put everything together by adding the expansions in the rearranged form of f(x):

$$f(x) = -\frac{1}{4}(3 + x)^{-1} - \frac{1}{4}(1 - 5x)^{-1}$$
$$\approx -\frac{1}{4}\left(\frac{1}{3} - \frac{1}{9}x + \frac{1}{27}x^2\right) - \frac{1}{4}(1 + 5x + 25x^2)$$
$$= -\frac{1}{12} + \frac{x}{36} - \frac{x^2}{108} - \frac{1}{4} - \frac{5x}{4} - \frac{25x^2}{4}$$
$$= \boxed{-\frac{1}{3} - \frac{11x}{9} - \frac{169x^2}{27}}$$

c) Find the range of values of x for which your answer to part b) is valid.

1. The two expansions from b) are valid for **different values of x.**

> **Tip:** Remember, the expansion of $(p + qx)^n$ is valid when $\left|\frac{qx}{p}\right| < 1$.

2. The **combined** expansion of f(x) is valid where these **two ranges overlap**, i.e. over the **narrower** of the two ranges.

   (This is the same as when you combine expansions by multiplying them together, as shown on page 138.)

   The expansion of $(3 + x)^{-1}$ is valid when $\left|\frac{x}{3}\right| < 1 \Rightarrow |x| < 3$.

   The expansion of $(1 - 5x)^{-1}$ is valid when $|-5x| < 1 \Rightarrow |x| < \frac{1}{5}$.

3. The expansion of f(x) is valid for values of x in both ranges.

   So the expansion of f(x) is valid for $\boxed{|x| < \frac{1}{5}}$

Q1 a) $\dfrac{5-12x}{(1+6x)(4+3x)} \equiv \dfrac{A}{(1+6x)} + \dfrac{B}{(4+3x)}$. Find A and B.

b) (i) Find the binomial expansion of $(1+6x)^{-1}$, up to and including the term in x^2.

(ii) Find the binomial expansion of $(4+3x)^{-1}$, up to and including the term in x^2.

c) Hence find the binomial expansion of $\dfrac{5-12x}{(1+6x)(4+3x)}$, up to and including the term in x^2.

d) For what values of x is this expansion valid?

Q2 $f(x) = \dfrac{6}{(1-x)(1+x)(1+2x)}$

a) Show that $f(x)$ can be expressed as: $\dfrac{1}{(1-x)} - \dfrac{3}{(1+x)} + \dfrac{8}{(1+2x)}$

b) Give the binomial expansion of $f(x)$ in ascending powers of x, up to and including the term in x^2.

c) Find the percentage error when you use this expansion to estimate $f(0.01)$, giving your answer to 2 significant figures.

Q3 a) Factorise fully $2x^3 + 5x^2 - 3x$.

b) Hence express $\dfrac{5x-6}{2x^3 + 5x^2 - 3x}$ as partial fractions.

c) Find the binomial expansion of $\dfrac{5x-6}{2x^3 + 5x^2 - 3x}$, up to and including the term in x^2.

d) For what values of x is this expansion valid?

> **Q3c) Hint:** You'll end up with a term in x^{-1}, which you wouldn't usually get with a binomial expansion — this comes from the partial fractions and you can just leave it as it is.

Q4 $f(x) = \dfrac{55x+7}{(2x-5)(3x+1)^2}$

a) Express $f(x)$ in the form $\dfrac{A}{(2x-5)} + \dfrac{B}{(3x+1)} + \dfrac{C}{(3x+1)^2}$, where A, B and C are integers to be found.

b) Hence, or otherwise, use the binomial formula to expand $f(x)$ in ascending powers of x, up to and including the term in x^2.

Q5 a) Given that $f(0.5) = 0$, write $f(x) = 12x^3 - 8x^2 - x + 1$ in the form $(ax+b)(cx+d)^2$, where a, b, c and d are integers.

b) Use your answer to part a) to express $g(x) = \dfrac{8-x}{12x^3 - 8x^2 - x + 1}$ as partial fractions.

c) Find the first three terms in the binomial expansion of $\dfrac{8-x}{12x^3 - 8x^2 - x + 1}$.

d) For what values of x is the expansion in part c) valid?

e) Show that this expansion gives an estimate of $g(0.001)$ correct to 6 decimal places.

Review Exercise

Q1 Give the binomial expansion of:

a) $(1 + 2x)^3$ 　　b) $(1 - x)^5$ 　　c) $(1 - 4x)^4$ 　　d) $\left(1 - \frac{2}{3}x\right)^4$

Q2 For what values of n does the binomial expansion of $(1 + x)^n$ result in a finite expression?

Q3 a) If the x^2 coefficient of the binomial expansion of $(1 + ax)^{-2}$ is 48 and a is a positive integer, what is the value of a?

b) If the x^4 coefficient of the binomial expansion of $(1 - ax)^{\frac{1}{3}}$ is $-\frac{10}{3}$, and a is positive, what is the value of a?

Q4 If the full binomial expansion of $(c + dx)^n$ is an infinite series, what values of x is the expansion valid for?

Q5 Find the binomial expansion of each of the following, up to and including the term in x^3, stating the range of x for which the expansions are valid.

a) $\dfrac{1}{(1 + x)^5}$ 　　b) $\dfrac{1}{(1 - 3x)^3}$ 　　c) $\sqrt{1 - 5x}$ 　　d) $\dfrac{1}{\sqrt[3]{1 + 2x}}$

Q6 a) Give the binomial expansions of the following, up to and including the term in x^2. State the range of x for which each expansion is valid.

　　(i) $\dfrac{1}{(3 + 2x)^2}$ 　　　　(ii) $\sqrt[3]{8 - x}$

b) Use your answers to a) to give the binomial expansion of $\dfrac{\sqrt[3]{8 - x}}{(3 + 2x)^2}$, up to and including the term in x^2. State the range of x for which this expansion is valid.

c) (i) Use the expansion in a)(ii) to find an approximate value of $\sqrt[3]{7}$, leaving your answer as a fraction.

　　(ii) Find the percentage error of this approximation, correct to 2 significant figures.

Q7 a) Show that $\dfrac{5 - 10x}{(1 + 2x)(2 - x)}$ can be expressed as: $\dfrac{4}{(1 + 2x)} - \dfrac{3}{(2 - x)}$.

b) Give the binomial expansion of the expression in a), up to and including the term in x^2.

c) Find the percentage error when you use $x = 0.1$ in this expansion to estimate $\dfrac{4}{1.2 \times 1.9}$, giving your answer to 2 significant figures.

Q8 $f(x) = \dfrac{1}{(a - 2x)^2}$

a) Find the binomial expansion of $f(x)$, up to and including the term in x^2, in terms of a.

b) Give the range for which this expansion is valid in terms of a.

$g(x) = \dfrac{1}{\sqrt{4 - ax}}$

c) Find the binomial expansion of $g(x)$, up to and including the term in x^2, in terms of a.

d) Give the range for which this expansion is valid in terms of a.

e) Hence find the binomial expansion of $f(x) \times g(x)$, up to and including the term in x.

f) Write down the coefficient of x in the combined expansion of $f(x) \times g(x)$, given that $a = 2$.

Exam-Style Questions

Q1 Expand $\sqrt[3]{(1+2x)^2}$ up to and including x^2.

[2 marks]

Q2 The cubic term in the expansion $(1+ax)^{-4}$ is $-160x^3$. Find the value of a.

[3 marks]

Q3 a) Find the first three terms of the $\sqrt{1-3x}$ in ascending powers of x. State the range of values for which this expansion is valid.

[3 marks]

  b) Hence approximate $\sqrt{0.97}$.

[2 marks]

Q4 $\dfrac{3x^2 + x + 2}{(x+1)(x-1)(2x+1)} \equiv \dfrac{A}{(x+1)} + \dfrac{B}{(x-1)} + \dfrac{C}{(2x+1)}$

  a) Find the values of A, B and C.

[5 marks]

  b) Hence obtain the series expansion for $\dfrac{3x^2 + x + 2}{(x+1)(x-1)(2x+1)}$ giving all the terms up to and including the term in x^2.

[6 marks]

  c) State the values of x for which the expansion is valid.

[1 mark]

Q5 When $(1+ax)^n$ is expanded in ascending powers of x, the first three terms of the expansion are: $1 - 6x + \dfrac{45}{2}x^2$. Find the values of a and n when $n \neq 0$.

[6 marks]

Q6 a) Expand $\sqrt{\dfrac{1+x}{1-x}}$ up to and including the term x^3. State the value of x for which the expansion is valid.

[8 marks]

  b) Hence, by using an appropriate value of x, find an approximate fractional value for $\sqrt{3}$.

[2 marks]

7.1 Points of Inflection

You've already seen differentiation in Year 1, and used it to identify the maximum and minimum points of graphs. This section shows you how to use the second derivative to identify other parts of a curve.

Learning Objectives (Spec Ref 7.1 & 7.3):

- Understand the terms convex and concave in relation to curves.
- Use the second derivative of a function to work out when the graph of that function is concave or convex, and to identify points of inflection.
- Determine the nature of stationary points of a curve where the second derivative is zero.

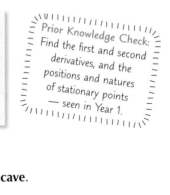

Prior Knowledge Check:
Find the first and second derivatives, and the positions and natures of stationary points — seen in Year 1.

Convex and concave curves

Continuous curves of the form $y = f(x)$ can be described as **convex** or **concave**.

- **Convex curves** are ones that curve **downwards**. A straight line joining any two points on a convex curve lies **above** the curve between those points.

- **Concave curves** are ones that curve **upwards**. A straight line joining any two points on a concave curve lies **below** the curve between those points.

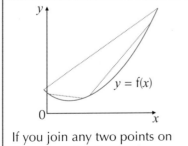

If you join any two points on this curve, the line is above the curve, so $y = f(x)$ is **convex**.

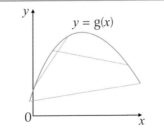

If you join any two points on this curve, the line is below the curve, so $y = g(x)$ is **concave**.

Tip: To help you remember: concave is the one that looks like the entrance to a cave.

In Year 1, you learnt how to find **first** and **second derivatives** of a function, and how they relate to the **graph** of that function.

$\dfrac{dy}{dx}$ or $f'(x)$ is the **gradient of the graph** $y = f(x)$ — the rate of change of x.

$\dfrac{d^2y}{dx^2}$ or $f''(x)$ is the **rate of change of the gradient** of $y = f(x)$.

Tip: Remember, $f'(x)$ is the first derivative and $f''(x)$ is the second derivative of a function $f(x)$ with respect to x.

Convex curves have an **increasing gradient** and **concave curves** have a **decreasing gradient**. This means you can use the **second derivative** to work out if a curve is convex or concave:

A curve $y = f(x)$ is **convex** if $f''(x) > 0$ for all values of x.

A curve $y = f(x)$ is **concave** if $f''(x) < 0$ for all values of x.

Most curves aren't **entirely** convex or concave — but the definitions of convex and concave can be applied to **parts** of these curves, so you can divide a curve into concave and convex **sections**.

Example 1

The graph of $y = x^3 + x^2 - x$ has concave and convex sections.
Find the range of values of x where the graph of $y = x^3 + x^2 - x$ is convex.

1. Find the second derivative.
$$\frac{dy}{dx} = 3x^2 + 2x - 1 \implies \frac{d^2y}{dx^2} = 6x + 2$$

2. The graph is convex when the second derivative is positive.
$$\frac{d^2y}{dx^2} > 0 \implies 6x + 2 > 0 \implies 6x > -2 \implies \boxed{x > -\frac{1}{3}}$$

Points of inflection

A point where the curve **changes** between concave and convex (i.e. where $f''(x)$ changes between positive and negative) is called a **point of inflection**.

At a point of inflection, $f''(x) = 0$, but not all points where $f''(x) = 0$ are points of inflection. You need to look what's happening on **either side** of the point to see if the sign of $f''(x)$ is changing. For example:

- The graph of $f(x) = x^3 - 6x^2 + 9x + 1$ has second derivative $f''(x) = 0$ when $x = 2$.

- When $x < 2$, $f''(x) < 0$ so the curve is **concave**, and when $x > 2$, $f''(x) > 0$ so the curve is **convex**.

- So $x = 2$ is a **point of inflection** of the curve.

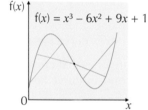

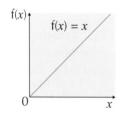

- On the graph of $f(x) = x$, $f''(x) = 0$ for **all** values of x.

- So at any particular value of x, $f''(x) = 0$, but it's **not** a point of inflection because $f''(x)$ **isn't changing** from positive to negative — it's just constant.

- On the graph of $f(x) = x^4$, $f''(x) = 12x^2$.

- At the point $(0, 0)$, $f''(x) = 0$, but it's **not** a point of inflection.

- $12x^2$ is positive for **all** non-zero values of x. The whole curve is convex, so it doesn't have any points of inflection.

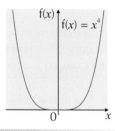

Example 2

Show that the graph of $y = x^3 - 3x^2 + 3$ has a point of inflection at $x = 1$.

1. Start by finding $f''(x)$.
$$f(x) = x^3 - 3x^2 + 3 \implies f'(x) = 3x^2 - 6x$$
$$\implies f''(x) = 6x - 6$$

2. Show that $f''(1) = 0$.
At $x = 1$, $f''(x) = 6(1) - 6 = 0$

3. Look at what happens either side of $x = 1$.
When $x < 1$, $6x < 6 \implies 6x - 6 < 0 \implies f''(x) < 0$
When $x > 1$, $6x > 6 \implies 6x - 6 > 0 \implies f''(x) > 0$

4. So at $x = 1$, $f''(x) = 0$ and $f''(x)$ changes sign from negative to positive.
So the graph of $y = x^3 - 3x^2 + 3$ has a point of inflection at $x = 1$.

Example 3

Find the coordinates of the points of inflection of the graph of $y = 2x^4 + 4x^3 - 72x^2$.

1. Find the second derivative of $y = 2x^4 + 4x^3 - 72x^2$.

    $$y = 2x^4 + 4x^3 - 72x^2 \Rightarrow \frac{dy}{dx} = 8x^3 + 12x^2 - 144x$$

    $$\Rightarrow \frac{d^2y}{dx^2} = 24x^2 + 24x - 144$$

2. Now find the points where $\frac{d^2y}{dx^2} = 0$. These could be points of inflection.

    $$\frac{d^2y}{dx^2} = 0 \Rightarrow 24x^2 + 24x - 144 = 0$$
    $$\Rightarrow x^2 + x - 6 = 0$$
    $$\Rightarrow (x + 3)(x - 2) = 0$$
    $$\Rightarrow x = -3 \text{ and } x = 2$$

3. So there could be points of inflection at $x = -3$ and $x = 2$. Think about what happens to $\frac{d^2y}{dx^2}$ either side of these points. The second derivative is a quadratic, so you can do this easily with a sketch.

    $\frac{d^2y}{dx^2} > 0$ for $x < -3$,

    $\frac{d^2y}{dx^2} < 0$ for $-3 < x < 2$,

    and $\frac{d^2y}{dx^2} > 0$ for $x > 2$.

    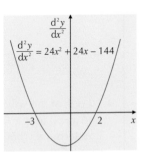

    Tip: If it's not easy to sketch, just work out whether $\frac{d^2y}{dx^2}$ is positive or negative either side of each point.

    $\frac{d^2y}{dx^2}$ changes sign at $x = -3$ and $x = 2$, so both are points of inflection.

4. The question asks for the coordinates of the points of inflection, so find the y-values.

    At $x = -3$, $y = 2(-3)^4 + 4(-3)^3 - 72(-3)^2 = -594$
    At $x = 2$, $y = 2(2)^4 + 4(2)^3 - 72(2)^2 = -224$

    So the points of inflection are at $(-3, -594)$ and $(2, -224)$.

Stationary points of inflection

In Year 1, you used the first and second derivatives of a function to find **maximum** and **minimum points** of its graph.

Stationary points are points where $f'(x) = 0$. A stationary point can be a **maximum** point, a **minimum** point or a **stationary point of inflection**. The value of $f''(x)$ can help you work out which type of stationary point it is:

- If $f'(x) = 0$ and $f''(x) > 0$, it's a **minimum**.
- If $f'(x) = 0$ and $f''(x) < 0$, it's a **maximum**.
- If $f'(x) = 0$ and $f''(x) = 0$, it could be **any one** of the three types — so you have to look at $f''(x)$ on either side of the stationary point.

If $f''(x) > 0$ on either side of a stationary point, the curve is **convex** near the point, so it's a **minimum**.
If $f''(x) < 0$ on either side of a stationary point, the curve is **concave** near the point, so it's a **maximum**.
And if $f''(x)$ **changes** sign either side of stationary point, it's a stationary **point of inflection**.

Example 4

For $f(x) = x^5 - 60x^3$, find the value of x at each stationary point of the graph of $y = f(x)$, and determine the nature of each one.

1. Find the first derivative to locate the stationary points (i.e. where $f'(x) = 0$).

   $f(x) = x^5 - 60x^3 \Rightarrow f'(x) = 5x^4 - 180x^2 = 5x^2(x^2 - 36)$
   $ = 5x^2(x + 6)(x - 6)$

   So $f'(x) = 0$ when $x = 0$, $x = -6$ and $x = 6$.

2. Now find the second derivative.

   $f'(x) = 5x^4 - 180x^2 \Rightarrow f''(x) = 20x^3 - 360x$

3. Use it to work out the nature of the three stationary points.

   $f''(-6) = 20(-6)^3 - 360(-6) = -2160$
   $f''(-6) < 0$, so the point at $x = -6$ is a maximum.

   $f''(6) = 20(6)^3 - 360(6) = 2160$
   $f''(6) > 0$, so the point at $x = 6$ is a minimum.

   $f''(0) = 20(0)^3 - 360(0) = 0$,
   so the type of point at $x = 0$ is unknown.

4. Look at the values of $f''(x)$ close to $x = 0$ (e.g. $x = -1$ and $x = 1$) to determine whether the stationary point at $x = 0$ could be a maximum, a minimum or a point of inflection.

   $f''(x) = 20x^3 - 360x$
   $f''(-1) = 20(-1)^3 - 360(-1) = -20 + 360 > 0$
   $f''(1) = 20(1)^3 - 360(1) = 20 - 360 < 0$
   The sign of $f''(x)$ changes at $x = 0$,
   so $x = 0$ is a point of inflection .

Exercise 7.1.1

Q1 Find the values of x for which the following graphs are concave:

a) $y = \frac{1}{6}x^3 - \frac{5}{2}x^2 + \frac{1}{4}x + \frac{1}{9}$

b) $y = 4x^2 - x^4$

Q2 The graph of $y = \frac{3}{2}x^4 - x^2 - 3x$ has two points of inflection. Find the x-coordinates of these two points.

> **Q2 Hint:** There are only two points where the second derivative is zero here, and the question tells you there are two points of inflection. So you don't actually need to prove they're points of inflection in this case, you just need to find them.

Q3 If $f(x) = \frac{1}{16}x^4 + \frac{3}{4}x^3 - \frac{21}{8}x^2 - 6x + 20$, identify the ranges of values of x for which the graph of $y = f(x)$ is concave and convex.

Q4 Show that the graph of $y = x^2 - \frac{1}{x}$ has a point of inflection at (1, 0).

Q5 For $f(x) = x^3 + 2x^2 + 3x + 3$, show that:

a) the graph of $y = f(x)$ has one point of inflection,

b) the point of inflection is not a stationary point.

Q6 Find the coordinates of the stationary points of the graph of $y = \frac{1}{10}x^5 - \frac{1}{3}x^3 + \frac{1}{2}x + 4$ and determine their nature.

7.2 Chain Rule

To differentiate complicated functions, you'll need some new rules not covered in Year 1. The first of these is the chain rule, which you use for differentiating functions of functions, like sin x².

Learning Objectives (Spec Ref 7.4):
- Identify which part of a function to use as *u* in the chain rule.
- Use the chain rule to differentiate functions of functions.
- Use the chain rule to convert $\frac{dx}{dy}$ into $\frac{dy}{dx}$.

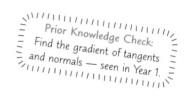

Prior Knowledge Check: Find the gradient of tangents and normals — seen in Year 1.

The chain rule

The **chain rule** helps you **differentiate** complicated functions by **splitting them up** into functions that are easier to differentiate. The trick is spotting **how** to split them up, and choosing the right bit to **substitute**.

Once you've worked out how to split up the function, you can differentiate it using this **formula**:

$$\text{If } y = f(u) \text{ and } u = g(x) \text{ then: } \frac{dy}{dx} = \frac{dy}{du} \times \frac{du}{dx}$$

To differentiate a function using the chain rule, just follow these steps:

- Pick a suitable function of *x* for '*u*' and rewrite *y* in terms of *u*.

- Differentiate *u* (with respect to *x*) to get $\frac{du}{dx}$...

- ...and differentiate *y* (with respect to *u*) to get $\frac{dy}{du}$.

- Stick it all in the formula and write everything in terms of *x*.

Tip: It may help you to think of the derivatives as fractions (they're not, but it's a good way to think of it). Then the d*u*'s cancel:
$$\frac{dy}{du} \times \frac{du}{dx} = \frac{dy}{dx}$$
If you remember this you'll never get the order wrong.

The important part is **choosing** which bit to make into *u*. The aim is to split it into **two separate functions** that you can **easily differentiate**.

- If you have a function inside **brackets**, then the part **inside** the brackets is normally *u*:

  $y = (x + 1)^2$ can be written as $y = u^2$ where $u = x + 1$.

  Now both u^2 and $x + 1$ are **easy to differentiate**, and the chain rule formula does the hard work for you.

- If there's a **trig function** or **log** involved, it's usually the part **inside** the trig function or log:

  Tip: Don't worry if you don't know how to differentiate trig functions yet — it's covered later in this chapter.

  $y = \sin x^2$ can be written as $y = \sin u$ where $u = x^2$

  Again, you end up with 2 functions that are **easy to differentiate**, so you just differentiate each one **separately** then put it all in the **formula**.

Example 1

Find $\frac{dy}{dx}$ if $y = (6x - 3)^5$.

1. Replace part of the function with u. The bit inside the brackets is easy to differentiate, so make that u.

   $y = (6x - 3)^5$,
   so let $y = u^5$ where $u = 6x - 3$

2. Next, differentiate the two parts separately.

   $\frac{dy}{du} = 5u^4$ and $\frac{du}{dx} = 6$

3. Finally, put everything back into the chain rule formula.

   $\frac{dy}{dx} = \frac{dy}{du} \times \frac{du}{dx} = 5u^4 \times 6$
   $= 30u^4 = \boxed{30(6x - 3)^4}$

Now that you can differentiate **functions of functions** using the chain rule, you can find the equation of a **tangent** or **normal** to a curve that has an equation given by a function of a function.

Example 2

Find the equation of the tangent to the curve $y = \dfrac{1}{\sqrt{x^2 + 3x}}$ at $(1, \frac{1}{2})$.

1. This function's a little more complicated than the previous one, so it will help to first rewrite it in terms of powers.

   $y = \dfrac{1}{\sqrt{x^2 + 3x}} = (x^2 + 3x)^{-\frac{1}{2}}$

2. Then identify which part to turn into u.

   $y = (x^2 + 3x)^{-\frac{1}{2}}$,
   so let $y = u^{-\frac{1}{2}}$ where $u = (x^2 + 3x)$

3. You now have two functions you can differentiate.

   $y = u^{-\frac{1}{2}} \Rightarrow \frac{dy}{du} = \left(-\frac{1}{2}\right)u^{-\frac{3}{2}} = -\dfrac{1}{2(\sqrt{x^2 + 3x})^3}$

   $u = x^2 + 3x \Rightarrow \frac{du}{dx} = 2x + 3$

4. Now put it all back into the chain rule formula.

   $\frac{dy}{dx} = \frac{dy}{du} \times \frac{du}{dx} = \left(-\dfrac{1}{2(\sqrt{x^2 + 3x})^3}\right) \times (2x + 3)$

   $= -\dfrac{2x + 3}{2(\sqrt{x^2 + 3x})^3}$

5. To find the equation of the tangent, you first need to know the gradient at the point $(1, \frac{1}{2})$, so put the x-value into your equation for $\frac{dy}{dx}$.

   $\frac{dy}{dx} = -\dfrac{(2 \times 1) + 3}{2(\sqrt{1^2 + (3 \times 1)})^3} = -\dfrac{5}{16}$

6. Then use your gradient and the values you're given to find c.

   $y = mx + c \Rightarrow \frac{1}{2} = (-\frac{5}{16} \times 1) + c$
   $\Rightarrow c = \frac{13}{16}$

7. Now you can write the equation of the tangent at $(1, \frac{1}{2})$.

   $\boxed{y = -\dfrac{5}{16}x + \dfrac{13}{16}}$

Q1 Differentiate with respect to x:

a) $y = (x + 7)^2$

b) $y = (2x - 1)^5$

c) $y = 3(4 - x)^8$

d) $y = (3 - 2x)^7$

e) $y = (x^2 + 3)^5$

f) $y = (5x^2 + 3)^2$

Q2 Find $f'(x)$ for the following:

a) $f(x) = (4x^3 - 9)^8$

b) $f(x) = (6 - 7x^2)^4$

c) $f(x) = (x^2 + 5x + 7)^6$

d) $f(x) = (x + 4)^{-3}$

e) $f(x) = (5 - 3x)^{-2}$

f) $f(x) = \dfrac{1}{(5 - 3x)^4}$

g) $f(x) = (3x^2 + 4)^{\frac{3}{2}}$

h) $f(x) = \dfrac{1}{\sqrt{5 - 3x}}$

i) $f(x) = \dfrac{1}{\sqrt{x^3 + 2x^2}}$

Q3 Find the exact value of $\dfrac{dy}{dx}$ when $x = 1$ for:

a) $y = \dfrac{1}{\sqrt{5x - 3x^2}}$

b) $y = \dfrac{12}{\sqrt[3]{x + 6}}$

Q4 Differentiate $\left(\sqrt{x} + \dfrac{1}{\sqrt{x}}\right)^2$ with respect to x by:

a) Multiplying the brackets out and differentiating term by term.

b) Using the chain rule.

Q5 Find the equation of the tangent to the curve $y = (x - 3)^5$ at $(1, -32)$.

Q6 Find the equation of the normal to the curve $y = \dfrac{1}{4}(x - 7)^4$ when $x = 6$.

> **Q6 Hint:**
> The gradient of the normal to a curve is just $-1 \div$ gradient of the tangent (this was covered in Year 1 if you need a refresher).

Q7 Find the value of $\dfrac{dy}{dx}$ when $x = 1$ for $y = (7x^2 - 3)^{-4}$.

Q8 Find $f'(x)$ if $f(x) = \dfrac{7}{\sqrt[3]{3 - 2x}}$.

Q9 Find the equation of the tangent to the curve $y = \sqrt{5x - 1}$ when $x = 2$, in the form $ax + by + c = 0$, $a, b, c \in \mathbb{Z}$.

> **Q9 Hint:** $a, b, c \in \mathbb{Z}$ just means that a, b and c are integers.

Q10 Find the equation of the normal to the curve $y = \sqrt[3]{3x - 7}$ when $x = 5$.

Q11 Find the equation of the tangent to the curve $y = (x^4 + x^3 + x^2)^2$ when $x = -1$.

Q12 Show that the curve $y = (2x - 3)^7$ has one point of inflection, and find the coordinates of that point.

> **Q12-13 Hint:**
> You'll need to use the chain rule twice for these questions.

Q13 Find the ranges of values of x for which the curve $y = \left(\dfrac{x}{4} - 2\right)^3$ is convex and concave.

Finding $\dfrac{dy}{dx}$ when $x = f(y)$

The principle of the chain rule can also be used where x **is given in terms of y** (i.e. $x = f(y)$). This comes from a little mathematical rearranging, and you'll find it's often quite useful:

$$\frac{dy}{dx} \times \frac{dx}{dy} = \frac{dy}{dy} = 1, \text{ so rearranging gives } \frac{dy}{dx} = \frac{1}{\left(\dfrac{dx}{dy}\right)}.$$

So to differentiate $x = f(y)$, use: $\quad \dfrac{dy}{dx} = \dfrac{1}{\left(\dfrac{dx}{dy}\right)}$

> **Tip:** As with the chain rule, treat the derivatives as fractions to make this result easier to follow (they're not actually fractions though).

Example

A curve has the equation $x = y^3 + 2y - 7$. Find $\dfrac{dy}{dx}$ at the point $(-4, 1)$.

1. Forget that the x's and y's are in the 'wrong' place and differentiate as usual.

    $x = y^3 + 2y - 7 \Rightarrow \dfrac{dx}{dy} = 3y^2 + 2$

2. Use $\dfrac{dy}{dx} = \dfrac{1}{\left(\dfrac{dx}{dy}\right)}$ to find $\dfrac{dy}{dx}$.

    $\dfrac{dy}{dx} = \dfrac{1}{3y^2 + 2}$

3. $y = 1$ at the point $(-4, 1)$, so put this in the equation:

    $\dfrac{dy}{dx} = \dfrac{1}{3(1)^2 + 2} = \dfrac{1}{5} = 0.2,$

    so $\dfrac{dy}{dx} = \boxed{0.2}$ at the point $(-4, 1)$.

Exercise 7.2.2

Q1 Find $\dfrac{dy}{dx}$ for each of the following functions at the given point. In each case, express $\dfrac{dy}{dx}$ in terms of y.

a) $x = 3y^2 + 5y + 7$ at $(5, -1)$

b) $x = y^3 - 2y$ at $(-4, -2)$

c) $x = (2y + 1)(y - 2)$ at $(3, -1)$

d) $x = \dfrac{4 + y^2}{y}$ at $(5, 4)$

Q2 Find $\dfrac{dy}{dx}$ in terms of y if $x = (2y^3 - 5)^3$.

Q3 Given that $x = \sqrt{4 + y}$, find $\dfrac{dy}{dx}$ in terms of x by:

a) finding $\dfrac{dx}{dy}$ first,

b) rearranging into the form $y = f(x)$.

Q4 Given that $x = \dfrac{1}{\sqrt{2y - 3}}$, find $\dfrac{dy}{dx}$ in terms of x by finding $\dfrac{dx}{dy}$ first.

7.3 Differentiation of e^x, ln x and a^x

Differentiating exponentials and logs is easier than you might think, as long as you know the rules.

Learning Objectives (Spec Ref 7.2 & 7.4):
- Differentiate e^x and ln x.
- Use the rules of differentiation for e^x and ln x to differentiate more complex functions using the chain rule.
- Use these methods to answer questions on tangents, normals, stationary points, convex and concave curves and points of inflection.
- Differentiate functions of the form $y = a^x$ and $y = a^{f(x)}$.

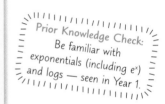

Differentiating e^x

Remember from Year 1 that 'e' is just a number for which the **gradient of e^x is e^x**, which makes it pretty simple to **differentiate:**

$$y = e^x \implies \frac{dy}{dx} = e^x$$

You can use the chain rule to show another useful relation involving exponentials.
If you replace x with $f(x)$, you have a **function of a function:**

$y = e^{f(x)}$, so let $y = e^u$ where $u = f(x)$. So $\dfrac{dy}{du} = e^u = e^{f(x)}$ and $\dfrac{du}{dx} = f'(x)$

Putting it into the chain rule formula you get: $\dfrac{dy}{dx} = \dfrac{dy}{du} \times \dfrac{du}{dx} = e^{f(x)} \times f'(x) = f'(x)e^{f(x)}$

This works because $e^{f(x)}$ is a special case — the 'e' part stays the same when you differentiate, so you only have to worry about the $f(x)$ part. You can just learn the formula:

$$y = e^{f(x)} \implies \frac{dy}{dx} = f'(x)e^{f(x)}$$

Use this formula to differentiate exponential functions.

Example 1

Find $\dfrac{dy}{dx}$ if $y = e^{(3x-2)}$

1. Use the formula and write down $f(x)$. $y = e^{f(x)}$, where $f(x) = 3x - 2$

2. Differentiate $f(x)$. $f'(x) = 3$

3. Now put the right parts back into the formula for $\dfrac{dy}{dx}$. $y = e^{(3x-2)} \implies \dfrac{dy}{dx} = f'(x)e^{f(x)} = \boxed{3e^{(3x-2)}}$

Example 2

If $f(x) = e^{x^2} + 2e^x$, find $f'(x)$ when $x = 0$.

1. The function is in 2 parts, so differentiate them separately. The second bit's easy so start with that. $g(x) = 2e^x \implies g'(x) = 2e^x$

2. For the first bit, you could use the formula used on the previous example, but let's use the chain rule here just to show how it works. $v = e^{x^2}$,
so let $v = e^u$ where $u = x^2$

---

3. Both u and v are now easy to differentiate.

$$\frac{dv}{du} = e^u \text{ and } \frac{du}{dx} = 2x$$

$$\frac{dv}{dx} = \frac{dv}{du} \times \frac{du}{dx} = e^u \times 2x = 2xe^{x^2}$$

4. Now put the bits back together.

$$f'(x) = 2xe^{x^2} + 2e^x$$

5. And finally, work out the value of $f'(x)$ at $x = 0$

$$f'(0) = (2 \times 0 \times e^{0^2}) + 2e^0$$
$$f'(0) = 0 + 2 = \boxed{2}$$

Example 3

The graph of $y = e^{2x} - 6x^2$ has one point of inflection. Find the exact coordinates of this point.

1. Start by finding $\frac{dy}{dx}$. The function is in two parts so differentiate them separately. The second bit's easy so start with that.

$$y = -6x^2 \implies \frac{dy}{dx} = -12x$$

2. For the first bit, use the formula given on the previous page.

$$y = e^{2x} = e^{f(x)}$$
$$f(x) = 2x \text{ so } f'(x) = 2 \implies \frac{dy}{dx} = f'(x)e^{f(x)} = 2e^{2x}$$

3. Now just put the two parts back together.

$$\frac{dy}{dx} = 2e^{2x} - 12x$$

4. Differentiate again to find $\frac{d^2y}{dx^2}$.

$$\frac{dy}{dx} = 2e^{2x} - 12x = 2e^{f(x)} - 12x$$
$$\frac{d^2y}{dx^2} = 2f'(x)e^{f(x)} - 12$$
$$= 2(2 \times e^{2x}) - 12 = 4e^{2x} - 12$$

> Take logs of both sides to solve for x:
> $\ln(e^x) = x$

5. To find the point of inflection, set $\frac{d^2y}{dx^2} = 0$.

$$4e^{2x} - 12 = 0 \implies e^{2x} = 3 \implies 2x = \ln 3$$
$$\implies x = \frac{1}{2}\ln 3 = \ln 3^{\frac{1}{2}} = \ln \sqrt{3}$$

> $k \log x = \log x^k$

Tip: The question says there's one point of inflection, so this is the point you're looking for — there's no need to prove it's a point of inflection.

> $2 \ln \sqrt{3} = \ln \sqrt{3}^2 = \ln 3$

6. Substitute $x = \ln \sqrt{3}$ into $y = e^{2x} - 6x^2$ to find the y-coordinate.

$$y = e^{2\ln\sqrt{3}} - 6(\ln\sqrt{3})^2 \implies y = e^{\ln 3} - 6(\ln\sqrt{3})^2$$
$$\implies y = 3 - 6(\ln\sqrt{3})^2$$

> $e^{\ln x} = x$

7. Write the coordinates for the point of inflection.

$$(\ln\sqrt{3}, \ 3 - 6(\ln\sqrt{3})^2)$$

Exercise 7.3.1

Q1 Differentiate with respect to x:

a) $y = e^{3x}$

b) $y = e^{2x-5}$

c) $y = e^{x+7}$

d) $y = e^{3x+9}$

e) $y = e^{7-2x}$

f) $y = e^{x^3}$

Q2 Find f′(x) if:

a) $f(x) = e^{x^3 + 3x}$

b) $f(x) = e^{x^3 - 3x - 5}$

c) $f(x) = e^{x(2x + 1)}$

Q3 Find f′(x) if:

a) $f(x) = \frac{1}{2}(e^x - e^{-x})$

b) $f(x) = e^{(x + 3)(x + 4)}$

c) $f(x) = e^{x^4 + 3x^2} + 2e^{2x}$

Q4 Find the equation of the tangent to the curve $y = e^{2x}$ at the point (0, 1).

Q5 Find the exact value of the x-coordinate of the point of the inflection on the curve $y = \frac{1}{2}x^2 - e^{2x - 6}$.

Q5-7 Hint: Where the questions ask for exact answers, that means they're likely to include e^a or ln a (where a is a number) rather than working out the actual numbers.

Q6 Find the equation of the tangent to the curve $y = e^{2x^2}$ when $x = 1$. Leave the numbers in your answer in exact form.

Q7 If $f(x) = \sqrt{(e^x + e^{2x})}$, find the exact value of f′(x) when $x = 0$.

Q8 Show that the curve $y = e^{2x - 4} - x$ is convex for all values of x.

Q9 Find the equation of the normal to the curve $y = e^{3x} + 3$ where it cuts the y-axis.

Q10 Find the exact coordinates of any points of inflection on the curve $y = 2e^{2x} - \frac{1}{2}e^{3 - 4x}$.

Q11 Show that the curve $y = e^{x^3 - 3x - 5}$ has stationary points at $x = \pm 1$.

Q12 Find the x-coordinate of the stationary point for the curve $y = e^{3x} - 6x$ and determine the nature of this point. Leave the numbers in your answer in exact form.

Q12 Hint: To determine the nature of the stationary point you need to look at the sign of $\frac{d^2y}{dx^2}$ at the point.

Differentiating ln x

The natural logarithm of a function is the logarithm with base e, written as ln x. Differentiating natural logarithms also uses the chain rule:

- If $y = \ln x$, then $x = e^y$.

- Differentiating gives $\frac{dx}{dy} = e^y$, and $\frac{dy}{dx} = \frac{1}{\left(\frac{dx}{dy}\right)} = \frac{1}{e^y} = \frac{1}{x}$ (since $x = e^y$).

Tip: Look back at p.158 for more on $\frac{dx}{dy}$.

- This gives the result: $y = \ln x \implies \frac{dy}{dx} = \frac{1}{x}$

Example 1

a) **Find $\dfrac{dy}{dx}$ if $y = \ln(2x + 3)$.**

1. It's a function of a function, so use the chain rule.

$y = \ln(2x + 3)$, so let $y = \ln u$ where $u = 2x + 3$

$\Rightarrow \dfrac{dy}{du} = \dfrac{1}{u} = \dfrac{1}{2x + 3}$ and $\dfrac{du}{dx} = 2$

2. Now put all the parts into the chain rule formula.

$\dfrac{dy}{dx} = \dfrac{dy}{du} \times \dfrac{du}{dx} = \dfrac{1}{2x + 3} \times 2 = \boxed{\dfrac{2}{2x + 3}}$

b) **Find $\dfrac{dy}{dx}$ if $y = \ln(x^2 + 3)$.**

1. Use the chain rule again for this one.

$y = \ln u$ and $u = x^2 + 3$, $\dfrac{dy}{du} = \dfrac{1}{u} = \dfrac{1}{x^2 + 3}$ and $\dfrac{du}{dx} = 2x$.

2. Put all the parts into the chain rule formula.

$\Rightarrow \dfrac{dy}{dx} = \dfrac{dy}{du} \times \dfrac{du}{dx} = \dfrac{1}{x^2 + 3} \times 2x = \boxed{\dfrac{2x}{x^2 + 3}}$

Look at the final answer from those examples. It comes out to $\dfrac{f'(x)}{f(x)}$.

This isn't a coincidence — it will always be the case for $y = \ln(f(x))$, so you can just learn the result:

$$y = \ln(f(x)) \implies \dfrac{dy}{dx} = \dfrac{f'(x)}{f(x)}$$

Example 2

Find $f'(x)$ if $f(x) = \ln(x^3 - 4x)$.

1. $f(x)$ is in the form $\ln(g(x))$, so use the formula above.

$f'(x) = \dfrac{g'(x)}{g(x)}$, $g(x) = x^3 - 4x \implies g'(x) = 3x^2 - 4$

2. Put this into the formula.

$f(x) = \ln(x^3 - 4x) \implies f'(x) = \dfrac{g'(x)}{g(x)} = \boxed{\dfrac{3x^2 - 4}{x^3 - 4x}}$

Exercise 7.3.2

Q1 Differentiate with respect to x:

a) $y = \ln(3x)$

b) $y = \ln(1 + x)$

c) $\ln(3 + 2x)$

d) $y = \ln(1 + 5x)$

e) $y = 4\ln(4x - 2)$

f) $9\ln(3x - 3)$

Q2 Differentiate with respect to x:

a) $y = \ln(1 + x^2)$

b) $y = \ln(2 + x)^2$

c) $\ln(2x - 8)^3$

d) $y = 3\ln x^3$

e) $y = \ln(x^3 + x^2)$

f) $\ln\sqrt{2x^2 - 4}$

Q3 Find f'(x) if:

a) $f(x) = \ln \dfrac{1}{x}$

b) $f(x) = \ln \sqrt{x}$

Q4 Find f'(x) if $f(x) = \ln ((2x + 1)^2 \sqrt{x - 4})$.
Give your answer as a single fraction.

Q4-6 Hint: You'll need to rewrite some of these questions as the sum or difference of two logarithms before differentiating them.

Q5 Find f'(x) if $f(x) = \ln (x - \sqrt{x - 4})$.

Q6 Find f'(x) if $f(x) = \ln \left(\dfrac{(3x + 1)^2}{\sqrt{2x + 1}} \right)$.

Q7 Find the equation of the tangent to the curve $y = \ln (3x)^2$:

a) when $x = -2$

b) when $x = 2$

Q7-8 Hint: Rewrite $\ln (f(x))^k$ as $k \ln (f(x))$ to make differentiation simpler.

Q8 Find the equation of the normal to the curve $y = \ln (x + 6)^2$:

a) when $x = -3$

b) when $x = 0$

Q9 Find any stationary points for the curve $y = \ln (x^3 - 3x^2 + 3x)$.

Differentiating a^x

For any constant a: $\quad \dfrac{\mathbf{d}}{\mathbf{dx}} (a^x) = a^x \ln a$

Tip: The proof for this rule uses implicit differentiation — you can see it on p.191.

Example 1

Differentiate the following:

a) $y = 2^x$ $\dfrac{dy}{dx} = 2^x \ln 2$

b) $y = \left(\dfrac{1}{2} \right)^x$ Use the log laws to tidy this up... $\dfrac{dy}{dx} = \left(\dfrac{1}{2} \right)^x \ln \left(\dfrac{1}{2} \right) = 2^{-x} \times (-\ln 2) = -2^{-x} \ln 2$

Differentiating $a^{f(x)}$

Use the **chain rule** (see p.155) to differentiate functions of the form $a^{f(x)}$, by differentiating $y = a^u$ and $u = f(x)$ separately, then using the **chain rule formula**: $\dfrac{dy}{dx} = \dfrac{dy}{du} \times \dfrac{du}{dx}$

Example 2

Find the equation of the tangent to the curve $y = 3^{-2x}$ at the point $\left(\dfrac{1}{2}, \dfrac{1}{3} \right)$.

1. Pick a function of x for 'u' and rewrite y in terms of u.   Let $u = -2x$ and $y = 3^u$

2. Differentiating separately gives. $\dfrac{du}{dx} = -2$ and $\dfrac{dy}{du} = 3^u \ln 3$

3. Put all the parts into the chain rule formula. $\dfrac{dy}{dx} = \dfrac{dy}{du} \times \dfrac{du}{dx} = 3^u \ln 3 \times -2 = -2(3^{-2x} \ln 3)$

---

4. Now we can find the **gradient** of the tangent.

At $\left(\frac{1}{2}, \frac{1}{3}\right)$, $\frac{dy}{dx} = -2(3^{-1} \ln 3) = -\frac{2}{3} \ln 3$

5. The tangent has an equation in the form $y = mx + c$ and meets the curve at $\left(\frac{1}{2}, \frac{1}{3}\right)$, so you can find c.

$\frac{1}{3} = (-\frac{2}{3} \ln 3)\frac{1}{2} + c \implies c = \frac{1}{3} + \frac{1}{3} \ln 3$

6. Now you can write out the equation of the tangent.

$y = -\frac{2x}{3} \ln 3 + \frac{1}{3} + \frac{1}{3} \ln 3$

or $3y = (1 - 2x)\ln 3 + 1$

Exercise 7.3.3

Q1 Differentiate the following:

a) $y = 5^x$

b) $y = 3^{2x}$

c) $y = 10^{-x}$

d) $y = p^{qx}$

Q2 A curve has the equation $y = 2^{4x}$.

a) Show that the gradient of the curve is $\frac{dy}{dx} = 4(2^{4x} \ln 2)$.

b) Find the equation of the tangent to the curve when $x = 2$.

Q2b) Hint: You can leave your answer in terms of ln if you're not asked for a specific degree of accuracy. That way you're giving the exact answer.

Q3 A curve $y = 2^{px}$ passes through the point (1, 32).

a) Find p.

b) Hence find the gradient of the curve at this point.

Q4 A curve has the equation $y = p^{x^3}$.

a) Show that the gradient of the curve is $\frac{dy}{dx} = 3x^2(p^{x^3} \ln p)$.

b) If the curve passes through the point (2, 6561), find p.

c) Hence find the equation of the tangent to the curve when $x = 1$.

Q4 Hint: Leave the ln's in your working and final answer.

Q5 The curve $y = 4^{\sqrt{x}}$ passes through the point (25, a).
Show that the equation of the tangent to the curve at (25, a) is $y = 142x - 2520$ (to 3 s.f.).

Q6 A curve C has the equation $y = 2^{-3x}$. It passes through the point (2, b).

a) Find the gradient $\frac{dy}{dx}$ of the curve.

b) Find b and the gradient of the curve at (2, b).

c) Hence show that the equation of the tangent to the curve at (2, b) is $64y = 1 + 6 \ln 2 - (3 \ln 2)x$.

Q7 A curve C has the equation $y = 3^{x^2}$. It passes through the point (2, p).

a) Find the gradient $\frac{dy}{dx}$ of the curve.

b) Find p and the gradient of the curve at (2, p).

c) Hence show that the equation of the normal to the curve at (2, p) is $y = 81 + \frac{2-x}{324 \ln 3}$.

7.4 Differentiating Trig Functions

Trig functions are pretty easy to differentiate once you learn the rules for sin, cos and tan. In this section you'll see how to differentiate trig functions and use the chain rule to differentiate the more tricky ones.

Learning Objectives (Spec Ref 7.1, 7.2 & 7.4):
- Differentiate sin, cos and tan.
- Differentiate sin and cos from first principles.
- Use the rules for differentiating trig functions in more complicated functions that require the chain rule.

Differentiating sin, cos and tan

For **trigonometric functions** where the angle is measured in **radians** the following rules apply:

$y = \sin x$	$y = \cos x$	$y = \tan x$
$\dfrac{dy}{dx} = \cos x$	$\dfrac{dy}{dx} = -\sin x$	$\dfrac{dy}{dx} = \sec^2 x$

You can prove the rules for sin x and cos x using **differentiation from first principles**. Recall the diagram from Year 1:

As h gets smaller, the gradient of the line passing through $(x, f(x))$ and $(x + h, f(x + h))$ gets closer to $f'(x)$.

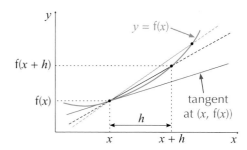

Example 1

Show using differentiation from first principles that if $y = \sin x$, $\dfrac{dy}{dx} = \cos x$.

1. Write down the formula for differentiating from first principles. $\longrightarrow$
$$\frac{dy}{dx} = \lim_{h \to 0}\left[\frac{f(x + h) - f(x)}{(x + h) - x}\right]$$

2. Use the fact that $y = f(x)$ to replace $f(x)$ with sin x. $\longrightarrow$
$$= \lim_{h \to 0}\left[\frac{\sin(x + h) - \sin x}{(x + h) - x}\right]$$

3. You can use the sin addition formula (see p.74) to expand sin $(x + h)$ on top of the fraction. $\longrightarrow$
$$= \lim_{h \to 0}\left[\frac{\sin x \cos h + \cos x \sin h - \sin x}{(x + h) - x}\right]$$

4. It's helpful to separate the sin x and cos x terms into two fractions at this point. $\longrightarrow$
$$= \lim_{h \to 0}\left[\frac{\sin x(\cos h - 1) + \cos x \sin h}{h}\right]$$
$$= \lim_{h \to 0}\left[\frac{\sin x(\cos h - 1)}{h} + \frac{\cos x \sin h}{h}\right]$$

5. Now, because you're interested in when h gets really small, you can use the small angle approximations sin $\theta \approx \theta$ and cos $\theta \approx 1 - \frac{1}{2}\theta^2$ (see p.55). $\longrightarrow$
$$= \lim_{h \to 0}\left[\frac{\sin x \times \left(-\frac{1}{2}h^2\right)}{h} + \frac{\cos x \times h}{h}\right]$$

6. As $h \to 0$, the first term $\to 0$, so it disappears. $\longrightarrow$
$$= \lim_{h \to 0}\left[-\frac{h \sin x}{2} + \cos x\right] = \boxed{\cos x}$$

The equations for differentiating trig functions can be combined
with the **chain rule** to differentiate **more complicated** functions.

Example 2

Differentiate the following with respect to x:

a) $y = \cos (2x)$

    1.   Rewrite the function in 'chain rule notation'. $y = \cos (2x)$, so let $y = \cos u$ where $u = 2x$

    2.   Differentiate the parts separately. $\dfrac{dy}{du} = -\sin u = -\sin (2x)$ and $\dfrac{du}{dx} = 2$

    3.   Put the parts back together
        using the chain rule formula. $\dfrac{dy}{dx} = \dfrac{dy}{du} \times \dfrac{du}{dx} = \boxed{-2 \sin (2x)}$

b) $y = 4 \sin (x^2 + 1)$

    1.   As before, work out which part
        needs to be u for the chain rule. $y = 4 \sin (x^2 + 1)$, so let $y = 4 \sin u$
                                         where $u = x^2 + 1$

    2.   Differentiate the parts separately. $\dfrac{dy}{du} = 4 \cos u = 4 \cos (x^2 + 1)$ and $\dfrac{du}{dx} = 2x$

    3.   Put the parts back together
        using the chain rule formula. $\dfrac{dy}{dx} = \dfrac{dy}{du} \times \dfrac{du}{dx} = 4 \cos (x^2 + 1) \times 2x$
                                                 $= \boxed{8x \cos (x^2 + 1)}$

c) **Find** $\dfrac{dy}{dx}$ **when** $x = \tan (3y)$.

    1.   Work out the part that needs to be u
        — this will be in terms of y in this case. $x = \tan u, u = 3y$

    2.   Differentiate the parts separately. $\dfrac{dx}{du} = \sec^2 u = \sec^2 (3y)$ and $\dfrac{du}{dy} = 3$

    3.   Find $\dfrac{dx}{dy}$ with the chain rule. $\dfrac{dx}{dy} = \dfrac{dx}{du} \times \dfrac{du}{dy} = 3 \sec^2 (3y)$

    4.   Then use $\dfrac{dy}{dx} = \dfrac{1}{\left(\dfrac{dx}{dy}\right)}$ to get the final answer. $\dfrac{dy}{dx} = \dfrac{1}{3 \sec^2 (3y)} = \boxed{\dfrac{1}{3} \cos^2 (3y)}$

Once you get the hang of it, you don't need to use the chain rule every time.
If it's a **simple function** inside, e.g. $\sin (kx)$, it just differentiates to $k \cos (kx)$.
If it's more **complicated** though, like $\sin (x^3)$, it's worth using the **chain rule**.

When differentiating trig functions it's important to know **which part of
the function** to turn into u. It's **not** always the part **inside the brackets**.

When you have a trig function multiplied by itself, like $\cos^2 x$, it's often easiest to turn the **trig function itself** into u.

Tip: Remember $\cos^2 x$ is another way of writing $(\cos x)^2$.

Example 3

Find $\dfrac{dy}{dx}$ if $y = \sin^3 x$.

1. Start off by rearranging the function so the chain rule can be used.

$$y = \sin^3 x = (\sin x)^3$$

Tip: Don't get $(\sin x)^3$ confused with $\sin x^3$ — for this, you'd take $u = x^3$, so end up with $3x^2 \cos x^3$ when you differentiate.

2. Now you have a function of a function and can rewrite y in 'chain rule' notation.

$y = (\sin x)^3$,
so let $y = u^3$ where $u = \sin x$

3. Differentiate y and u.

$$y = u^3 \Rightarrow \frac{dy}{du} = 3u^2 = 3 \sin^2 x \text{ and } \frac{du}{dx} = \cos x$$

4. Then put it all into the chain rule formula.

$$\frac{dy}{dx} = \frac{dy}{du} \times \frac{du}{dx} = \boxed{3 \sin^2 x \cos x}$$

When you're differentiating trig functions, you'll sometimes be asked to **rearrange** your answer to show it's equal to a **different** trig function. It's worth making sure you're familiar with **trig identities** (see Chapter 3) so you can spot which ones to use and when to use them.

Example 4

For $y = 2 \cos^2 x + \sin (2x)$, show that $\dfrac{dy}{dx} = 2(\cos (2x) - \sin (2x))$.

1. First rewrite the equation to make the chain rule easier to use.

$y = 2 \cos^2 x + \sin (2x)$
$\Rightarrow y = 2(\cos x)^2 + \sin (2x)$

2. Then differentiate the parts separately.

$y = 2u^2$ where $u = \cos x$
$\Rightarrow \dfrac{dy}{du} = 4u = 4 \cos x, \dfrac{du}{dx} = -\sin x$

$y = \sin u$ where $u = 2x$
$\Rightarrow \dfrac{dy}{du} = \cos u = \cos 2x, \dfrac{du}{dx} = 2$

3. Put it all back into the chain rule formula.

$\dfrac{dy}{dx} = [(4 \cos x) \times (-\sin x)] + [(\cos (2x)) \times 2]$
$= 2 \cos (2x) - 4 \sin x \cos x$

4. From the target answer in the question it looks like you need a $\sin (2x)$ from somewhere, so use the double angle formula for $\sin$ (page 81).

$\sin (2x) \equiv 2 \sin x \cos x \Rightarrow 4 \sin x \cos x \equiv 2 \sin (2x)$
$\Rightarrow \dfrac{dy}{dx} = 2 \cos (2x) - 2 \sin (2x)$
$= \boxed{2(\cos (2x) - \sin (2x))}$ as required.

Q1 Differentiate with respect to x:

a) $y = \sin(3x)$

b) $y = \cos(-2x)$

c) $y = \cos \frac{x}{2}$

d) $y = \sin\left(x + \frac{\pi}{4}\right)$

e) $y = 6 \tan \frac{x}{2}$

f) $y = 3 \tan(5x)$

> **Q1d) Hint:** Don't worry, you don't need to use the sin addition formula — use the chain rule with $u = x + \frac{\pi}{4}$.

Q2 Find $f'(x)$ if $f(x) = 3 \tan(2x - 1)$.

Q3 Find $f'(x)$ if $f(x) = 3 \tan x + \tan(3x)$.

Q4 Find $f'(x)$ if $f(x) = \sin\left(x^2 + \frac{\pi}{3}\right)$.

Q5 Find $f'(x)$ if $f(x) = \sin^2 x$.

Q6 Find $f'(x)$ if $f(x) = 2 \sin^3 x$.

Q7 a) Find $f'(x)$ if $f(x) = 3 \sin x + 2 \cos x$.

b) Find the value of x for which $f'(x) = 0$ and $0 \leq x \leq \frac{\pi}{2}$.

Q8 Find $\frac{dy}{dx}$ if $y = \frac{1}{\cos x}$.

Q9 Use differentiation from first principles to show that $\frac{dy}{dx} = -\sin x$ when $y = \cos x$.

Q10 Differentiate $y = \cos^2 x$ by:

a) Using the chain rule directly.

b) Expressing y in terms of $\cos(2x)$ and differentiating the result.

> **Q10-11 Hint:** You'll need the double angle formulas here — see page 81.

Q11 For $y = 6 \cos^2 x - 2 \sin(2x)$ show that $\frac{dy}{dx} = -6 \sin(2x) - 4 \cos(2x)$.

Q12 Find the gradient of the curve $y = \sin x$ when $x = \frac{\pi}{4}$.

Q13 Find the equation of the normal to the curve $y = \cos(2x)$ when $x = \frac{\pi}{4}$.

Q14 For the curve $x = \sin(2y)$:

a) Find the equation of the tangent at the point $\left(\frac{\sqrt{3}}{2}, \frac{\pi}{6}\right)$.

b) Find the equation of the normal at the point $\left(\frac{\sqrt{3}}{2}, \frac{\pi}{6}\right)$.

Q15 a) If $y = 2 \sin(2x) \cos x$, express y as a difference of two expressions involving $\sin x$ and $\sin^3 x$.

b) Hence find $\frac{dy}{dx}$.

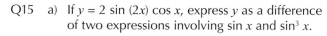

Differentiating by using the chain rule twice

Sometimes you'll have to use the chain rule **twice** when you have a function of a function of a function, like $\sin^3 (x^2)$.

Example

Find $\dfrac{dy}{dx}$ if $y = \sin^2 (2x + 1)$.

1. Start by setting up the first stage of differentiation with the **chain rule**, remembering to rewrite the $\sin^2$ part to make differentiating easier:

$y = \sin^2 (2x + 1) = [\sin (2x + 1)]^2$
$\Rightarrow\ y = u^2,\ u = \sin (2x + 1)$

2. Finding $\dfrac{dy}{du}$ is easy, so start with that.

$\dfrac{dy}{du} = 2u = 2 \sin (2x + 1)$

3. To find $\dfrac{du}{dx}$ you're going to need the **chain rule again**, so just set it up with u in terms of v instead of y in terms of u. Calling it v just means you don't end up with a load of u's floating around.

$u = \sin (2x + 1)$
so let $u = \sin v$ where $v = 2x + 1$

4. Then go through the usual stages.

$u = \sin v \Rightarrow \dfrac{du}{dv} = \cos v = \cos (2x + 1)$

$v = 2x + 1 \Rightarrow \dfrac{dv}{dx} = 2$

$\dfrac{du}{dx} = \dfrac{du}{dv} \times \dfrac{dv}{dx} = 2 \cos (2x + 1)$

5. Now you have the value of $\dfrac{du}{dx}$ needed to complete the question.

$\dfrac{dy}{dx} = \dfrac{dy}{du} \times \dfrac{du}{dx}$
$= [2 \sin (2x + 1)] \times [2 \cos (2x + 1)]$
$= \boxed{4 \sin (2x + 1) \cos (2x + 1)}$

Exercise 7.4.2

Q1 Find $\dfrac{dy}{dx}$ for the following functions:

a) $y = \sin^2 (x + 2)$

b) $y = \cos^2 (x^2)$

c) $y = \sqrt{\tan (4x)}$

Q2 Find $\dfrac{dy}{dx}$ if:

a) $y = \sin (\cos (2x))$

b) $y = 2 \ln (\cos (3x))$

c) $y = \ln (\tan^2 (x))$

d) $y = e^{\tan (2x)}$

> **Hint:** Differentiating e was covered on page 159 and differentiating ln was covered on page 161-162.

Q3 Differentiate the following functions with respect to x:

a) $y = \sin^4 (x^2)$

b) $y = e^{\sin^2 x}$

c) $y = \tan^2 (3x) + \sin x$

d) $y = e^{2 \cos (2x)} + \cos^2 (2x)$

7.5 Product Rule

The product rule is a way of differentiating two functions multiplied together.
It's fairly simple to use, but can get tricky when put together with other rules.

Learning Objectives (Spec Ref 7.4):
- Use the product rule for differentiation and recognise when it's needed.
- Use the product rule together with other rules for differentiation in order to differentiate more complicated functions.

Differentiating functions multiplied together

To differentiate two functions multiplied together, use the **product rule**:

$$\text{If } y = uv$$

$$\frac{dy}{dx} = u\frac{dv}{dx} + v\frac{du}{dx}$$

Where u and v are functions of x, i.e. $u(x)$ and $v(x)$.

Proving this rule is a lot trickier than anything covered in this section (and you won't need to know how to do it in the exam), but it goes like this:

You need the formula for differentiation from first principles:

$$f'(x) = \lim_{h \to 0} \frac{f(x+h) - f(x)}{h}$$

So when you have a product to differentiate, this can be written as:

$$(fg)'(x) = \lim_{h \to 0} \frac{fg(x+h) - fg(x)}{h} = \lim_{h \to 0} \frac{f(x+h)g(x+h) - f(x)g(x)}{h}$$

The numerator of this fraction can be seen as the area of a **rectangle f(x + h) by g(x + h)** minus the area of a **rectangle f(x) by g(x)**.

It can therefore be rewritten as a sum of the areas of the "extra bits" on the diagram:

$$f(x+h)g(x+h) - f(x)g(x) = \text{Area(A)} + \text{Area(B)}$$

$$\text{Area(A)} = g(x+h)[f(x+h) - f(x)] \qquad \text{Area(B)} = f(x)[g(x+h) - g(x)]$$

Tip: The length of the green arrow is $f(x + h) - f(x)$ and the length of the orange arrow is $g(x + h) - g(x)$.

$$(fg)'(x) = \lim_{h \to 0} \left(\frac{g(x+h)[f(x+h) - f(x)] + f(x)[g(x+h) - g(x)]}{h} \right)$$

$$= \lim_{h \to 0} \left(\frac{g(x+h)[f(x+h) - f(x)]}{h} \right) + \lim_{h \to 0} \left(\frac{f(x)[g(x+h) - g(x)]}{h} \right)$$

As $h \to 0$, $x + h \to x$ so this bit is just g(x).

This bit has no h's in it, so the limit as $h \to 0$ is just f(x).

$$= \lim_{h \to 0}(g(x + h)) \lim_{h \to 0}\left(\frac{f(x + h) - f(x)}{h}\right) + \lim_{h \to 0}(f(x)) \lim_{h \to 0}\left(\frac{g(x + h) - g(x)}{h}\right)$$

These are definitions of f′(x) and g′(x).

$$= g(x)f'(x) + f(x)g'(x)$$

Example 1

Differentiate $x^3 \tan x$ with respect to x.

1. The crucial thing is to write down everything in **steps**. Start by identifying 'u' and 'v'.

   $u = x^3$ and $v = \tan x$

   Tip: See p.165 for how to differentiate tan x.

2. Now differentiate these two **separately**, with respect to x.

   $\dfrac{du}{dx} = 3x^2$ and $\dfrac{dv}{dx} = \sec^2 x$

3. Very **carefully** put all the bits into the formula.

   $\dfrac{dy}{dx} = u\dfrac{dv}{dx} + v\dfrac{du}{dx} = (x^3 \times \sec^2 x) + (\tan x \times 3x^2)$

4. Finally, **rearrange** to make it look nicer.

   $\dfrac{dy}{dx} = x^3 \sec^2 x + 3x^2 \tan x$

You might have to differentiate functions using a mixture of the **product rule** and the **chain rule** (as well as the rules for e, ln and trig functions). In a question, you might be told which rules to use, but it's not guaranteed, so make sure you get used to spotting when the different rules are needed.

Example 2

Differentiate $e^{2x}\sqrt{2x - 3}$ with respect to x.

1. It's a **product** of two functions, so start by identifying 'u' and 'v'.

   $u = e^{2x}$ and $v = \sqrt{2x - 3}$

   Tip: The chain rule bit has been done all in one go here to save time, but if you need to, do it in steps just to make sure nothing goes wrong.

2. Each of these needs the **chain rule** to differentiate.

   $\dfrac{du}{dx} = 2e^{2x}$ and $\dfrac{dv}{dx} = \dfrac{1}{\sqrt{2x - 3}}$

3. Put it all into the **product rule formula**.

   $\dfrac{dy}{dx} = u\dfrac{dv}{dx} + v\dfrac{du}{dx}$

   $= \left(e^{2x} \times \dfrac{1}{\sqrt{2x - 3}}\right) + (\sqrt{2x - 3} \times 2e^{2x})$

4. As before, **rearrange** it and then **simplify**.

   $\dfrac{dy}{dx} = e^{2x}\left(\dfrac{1}{\sqrt{2x - 3}} + 2(\sqrt{2x - 3})\right)$

   $= e^{2x}\left(\dfrac{1 + 2(2x - 3)}{\sqrt{2x - 3}}\right) = \dfrac{e^{2x}(4x - 5)}{\sqrt{2x - 3}}$

You might also see questions that ask you to rearrange the final answer to 'show that' it's equal to something, or to find the stationary points of a graph.

Example 3

Show that the derivative of $x^2(2x-1)^3$ is $2x(2x-1)^2(5x-1)$.

1. As usual, **identify** u and v then differentiate them **separately**.

$u = x^2$ and $v = (2x-1)^3$

$\Rightarrow \dfrac{du}{dx} = 2x$ and $\dfrac{dv}{dx} = 2 \times 3(2x-1)^2$

(using the chain rule for $\dfrac{dv}{dx}$)

2. Then put it all into the **product rule formula**.

$\dfrac{dy}{dx} = u\dfrac{dv}{dx} + v\dfrac{du}{dx} = [x^2 \times 6(2x-1)^2] + [(2x-1)^3 \times 2x]$

$= 6x^2(2x-1)^2 + 2x(2x-1)^3$

3. This isn't exactly how the question wants the answer, so it needs a little more **rearranging**.

$6x^2(2x-1)^2 + 2x(2x-1)^3 = 2x(2x-1)^2(3x + (2x-1))$

$= 2x(2x-1)^2(5x-1)$

Example 4

The graph of $y = x^3 \ln x$ has two points of inflection.
Find the x-coordinates of these points, leaving your answers as exact values.

1. There'll be a point of inflection when $\dfrac{d^2y}{dx^2} = 0$. Start by finding $\dfrac{dy}{dx}$ — identify u and v and use the **product rule**.

$u = x^3$ and $v = \ln x$

$\Rightarrow \dfrac{du}{dx} = 3x^2$ and $\dfrac{dv}{dx} = \dfrac{1}{x}$

So $\dfrac{dy}{dx} = u\dfrac{dv}{dx} + v\dfrac{du}{dx} = \left(x^3 \times \dfrac{1}{x}\right) + (\ln x \times 3x^2)$

$= x^2 + 3x^2 \ln x$

2. Now differentiate again to find $\dfrac{d^2y}{dx^2}$, using the product rule again for the second part.

First part: $\dfrac{d}{dx}(x^2) = 2x$

Second part: $\dfrac{d}{dx}(3x^2 \ln x)$

$u = 3x^2$ and $v = \ln x$

$\Rightarrow \dfrac{du}{dx} = 6x$ and $\dfrac{dv}{dx} = \dfrac{1}{x}$

$v\dfrac{du}{dx} + u\dfrac{dv}{dx} = \left(3x^2 \times \dfrac{1}{x}\right) + (\ln x \times 6x)$

$= 3x + 6x \ln x$

3. Put these parts back together to get $\dfrac{d^2y}{dx^2}$ and work out when $\dfrac{d^2y}{dx^2} = 0$.

> **Tip:** You're told that there are two points of inflection, so these two x-coordinates must be the answers.

$\dfrac{d^2y}{dx^2} = 2x + 3x + 6x \ln x = x(5 + 6 \ln x)$

So $\dfrac{d^2y}{dx^2} = 0$ either when $x = 0$

or when $5 + 6 \ln x = 0 \Rightarrow 6 \ln x = -5$

$\Rightarrow \ln x = -\dfrac{5}{6}$

$\Rightarrow x = e^{-\frac{5}{6}}$

Q1 Differentiate $y = x(x + 2)$ with respect to x by:

a) Multiplying the brackets out and differentiating directly.

b) Using the product rule.

Q2 Differentiate with respect to x:

a) $y = x^2(x + 6)^3$

b) $y = x^3(5x + 2)^4$

c) $y = x^3e^x$

d) $y = xe^{4x}$

e) $y = xe^{x^2}$

f) $y = e^{2x}\sin x$

Q3 Find $f'(x)$ if:

a) $f(x) = x^3(x + 3)^{\frac{1}{2}}$

b) $f(x) = \dfrac{x^2}{\sqrt{x - 7}}$

c) $f(x) = x^4\ln x$

d) $f(x) = 4x \ln x^2$

e) $f(x) = 2x^3\cos x$

f) $f(x) = x^2\cos(2x)$

Q4 For parts a) and b), multiply out the brackets in your answer and simplify.

a) Differentiate $y = (x + 1)^2(x^2 - 1)$.

b) Differentiate $y = (x + 1)^3(x - 1)$.

c) Your answers to part a) and part b) should be the same.
Show by rearranging that the expressions for y in parts a) and b) are the same.

Q5 Find the range of values of x for which the curve $y = xe^x$ is concave.

> **Q5 Hint:** You'll have to differentiate twice here.

Q6 Find the equation of the tangent to the curve $y = (\sqrt{x + 2})(\sqrt{x + 7})$ at the point $(2, 6)$.
Write your answer in the form $ax + by + c = 0$, where a, b and c are integers.

Q7 For the curve $y = \dfrac{\sqrt{x - 1}}{\sqrt{x + 4}}$

a) Find the equation of the tangent to the curve when $x = 5$ in the form $ax + by + c = 0$ where a, b and c are integers.

b) Find the equation of the normal to the curve when $x = 5$ in the form $ax + by + c = 0$ where a, b and c are integers.

> **Q7 Hint:** To use the product rule here you'll need to rewrite the function at the bottom as a negative power.

Q8 Differentiate $y = e^{x^2\sqrt{x + 3}}$.

Q9 Find any stationary points for the curve $y = xe^{x - x^2}$.

Q10 a) Find any stationary points of the curve $y = (x - 2)^2(x + 4)^3$.

b) By writing the first derivative of $y = (x - 2)^2(x + 4)^3$ in the form $\dfrac{dy}{dx} = (Ax^2 + Bx + C)(x + D)^n$, find $\dfrac{d^2y}{dx^2}$ and hence identify the nature of the stationary points of the curve.

7.6 Quotient Rule

You've seen how to differentiate products with the product rule, and now you'll see how to differentiate quotients (divisions) with the quotient rule.

Learning Objectives (Spec Ref 7.4):
- Use the quotient rule for differentiation and understand when it's needed.
- Use the quotient rule alongside other methods for differentiating complex functions.

Differentiating a function divided by a function

In maths a **quotient** is one thing **divided** by another. As with the product rule, there's a rule that lets you differentiate quotients easily — the **quotient rule**:

$$\text{If } y = \frac{u}{v}$$

$$\frac{dy}{dx} = \frac{v\dfrac{du}{dx} - u\dfrac{dv}{dx}}{v^2}$$

Where u and v are functions of x, i.e. $u(x)$ and $v(x)$.

Tip: The quotient rule is basically just the product rule on $y = uv^{-1}$. It's usually quicker to use the quotient rule though.

There's also a proof for the quotient rule — again you won't need to know it for the exam, but you might find it helpful in understanding how it works.

- As before, start with the differentiation from first principles: $\dfrac{d}{dx}f(x) = \lim_{h \to 0} \dfrac{f(x+h) - f(x)}{h}$

- And so for the quotient $\dfrac{f(x)}{g(x)}$, this becomes: $\dfrac{d}{dx}\left(\dfrac{f(x)}{g(x)}\right) = \lim_{h \to 0} \dfrac{\dfrac{f(x+h)}{g(x+h)} - \dfrac{f(x)}{g(x)}}{h}$

- Put the top of the fraction over a common denominator $(g(x+h)g(x))$ and multiply this common denominator by the h.

$$\frac{d}{dx}\left(\frac{f(x)}{g(x)}\right) = \lim_{h \to 0} \frac{f(x+h)g(x) - f(x)g(x+h)}{g(x+h)g(x)h}$$

- The next stage is to add and subtract $f(x)g(x)$ and then factorise.

$$\frac{d}{dx}\left(\frac{f(x)}{g(x)}\right) = \lim_{h \to 0} \frac{f(x+h)g(x) - f(x)g(x) + f(x)g(x) - f(x)g(x+h)}{g(x+h)g(x)h}$$

$$\frac{d}{dx}\left(\frac{f(x)}{g(x)}\right) = \lim_{h \to 0} \frac{g(x)[f(x+h) - f(x)] - f(x)[g(x+h) - g(x)]}{g(x+h)g(x)h}$$

Tip: Adding and subtracting the same thing is a classic trick in algebra. It's like adding zero, and can get you from algebraic mess to perfectly formed equations.

- You might start to recognise the top row here. To make it a bit clearer, divide both the top and bottom by h, keeping f(x) and g(x) aside.

$$\frac{d}{dx}\left(\frac{f(x)}{g(x)}\right) = \lim_{h \to 0} \frac{g(x)\dfrac{f(x+h) - f(x)}{h} - f(x)\dfrac{g(x+h) - g(x)}{h}}{g(x+h)g(x)}$$

- The orange bits on top are the definition of $f'(x)$ and $g'(x)$. As h tends to zero, the blue bit at the bottom becomes $g(x)g(x)$, or $(g(x))^2$:

$$\frac{d}{dx}\left(\frac{f(x)}{g(x)}\right) = \frac{g(x)f'(x) - f(x)g'(x)}{(g(x))^2}$$

Tip: $\dfrac{f'(x)g(x) - f(x)g'(x)}{(g(x))^2}$ is just another way of writing the quotient rule. It's given like this on the formula sheet.

Example 1

Find $\dfrac{dy}{dx}$ if $y = \dfrac{\sin x}{2x + 1}$.

1. You can see that y is a **quotient** in the form of $\frac{u}{v}$. First identify u and v and differentiate them **separately**.

$u = \sin x \implies \dfrac{du}{dx} = \cos x$

and $v = 2x + 1 \implies \dfrac{dv}{dx} = 2$

2. Then just put the correct bits into the quotient rule. It's important that you get things in the right order, so concentrate on what's going where.

$$\frac{dy}{dx} = \frac{v\dfrac{du}{dx} - u\dfrac{dv}{dx}}{v^2} = \frac{(2x + 1)(\cos x) - (\sin x)(2)}{(2x + 1)^2}$$

3. Now just neaten it up.

$$\frac{dy}{dx} = \frac{(2x + 1)\cos x - 2\sin x}{(2x + 1)^2}$$

Example 2

Find the gradient of the tangent to the curve with equation $y = \dfrac{2x^2 - 1}{3x^2 + 1}$ at the point (1, 0.25).

1. 'Find the gradient of the tangent' means you have to **differentiate**. First identify u and v for the **quotient** rule, and differentiate **separately**.

$u = 2x^2 - 1 \implies \dfrac{du}{dx} = 4x$ and

$v = 3x^2 + 1 \implies \dfrac{dv}{dx} = 6x$

2. Then put everything into the quotient rule.

   Tip: Don't simplify straight away or you're more likely to get things mixed up.

$$\frac{dy}{dx} = \frac{v\dfrac{du}{dx} - u\dfrac{dv}{dx}}{v^2}$$

$$= \frac{(3x^2 + 1)(4x) - (2x^2 - 1)(6x)}{(3x^2 + 1)^2}$$

3. To make the expression **easier** to work with, **simplify** it where possible.

$$\frac{dy}{dx} = \frac{2x[2(3x^2 + 1) - 3(2x^2 - 1)]}{(3x^2 + 1)^2}$$

$$= \frac{2x[6x^2 + 2 - 6x^2 + 3]}{(3x^2 + 1)^2} = \frac{10x}{(3x^2 + 1)^2}$$

4. Finally, put in $x = 1$ to find the gradient at (1, 0.25).

$$\frac{dy}{dx} = \frac{10}{(3 + 1)^2} = 0.625$$

Example 3

Determine the nature of the stationary point of the curve $y = \dfrac{\ln x}{x^2}$ $(x > 0)$.

1. First use the quotient rule to find $\dfrac{dy}{dx}$.

   $u = \ln x \Rightarrow \dfrac{du}{dx} = \dfrac{1}{x}$ and $v = x^2 \Rightarrow \dfrac{dv}{dx} = 2x$

   $\dfrac{dy}{dx} = \dfrac{(x^2)\left(\dfrac{1}{x}\right) - (\ln x)(2x)}{x^4} = \dfrac{x - 2x\ln x}{x^4} = \dfrac{1 - 2\ln x}{x^3}$

2. The stationary point occurs where $\dfrac{dy}{dx} = 0$ (i.e. zero gradient).

   $\dfrac{1 - 2\ln x}{x^3} = 0 \Rightarrow \ln x = \dfrac{1}{2} \Rightarrow x = e^{\frac{1}{2}}$

3. To find out whether it's a maximum or minimum, differentiate $\dfrac{1 - 2\ln x}{x^3}$ using the quotient rule to get $\dfrac{d^2y}{dx^2}$.

   $u = 1 - 2\ln x \Rightarrow \dfrac{du}{dx} = -\dfrac{2}{x}$ and
   $v = x^3 \Rightarrow \dfrac{dv}{dx} = 3x^2$

   So $\dfrac{d^2y}{dx^2} = \dfrac{(x^3)\left(-\dfrac{2}{x}\right) - (1 - 2\ln x)(3x^2)}{x^6}$

   $= \dfrac{6x^2\ln x - 5x^2}{x^6} = \dfrac{6\ln x - 5}{x^4}$

4. Now put in the x-value of your stationary point and determine its nature.

   $\dfrac{d^2y}{dx^2} = \dfrac{6\ln e^{\frac{1}{2}} - 5}{(e^{\frac{1}{2}})^4} = \dfrac{3 - 5}{e^2} = -0.27\ldots$

   $\dfrac{d^2y}{dx^2} < 0$, so it's a $\boxed{\text{maximum}}$ stationary point.

As you saw on page 165, the derivative of $\tan x$ is $\sec^2 x$.

Because $\tan x = \dfrac{\sin x}{\cos x}$, you can prove this using the quotient rule.

Example 4

Prove that the derivative of $\tan x$ with respect to x is $\sec^2 x$.

1. First write $\tan x$ out as a quotient and set up u and v for the quotient rule.

   $\tan x = \dfrac{\sin x}{\cos x} = \dfrac{u}{v}$, so $u = \sin x$,
   $\dfrac{du}{dx} = \cos x$ and $v = \cos x$, $\dfrac{dv}{dx} = -\sin x$

2. Then just put all the right bits into the quotient rule.

   $\dfrac{d}{dx}(\tan x) = \dfrac{v\dfrac{du}{dx} - u\dfrac{dv}{dx}}{v^2}$

   $= \dfrac{\cos x \cos x - \sin x(-\sin x)}{\cos^2 x}$

   $= \dfrac{\cos^2 x + \sin^2 x}{\cos^2 x}$

   $= \dfrac{1}{\cos^2 x} = \boxed{\sec^2 x}$ as required

   Tip: The identity $\cos^2 x + \sin^2 x \equiv 1$ was used here to simplify.

Q1 Differentiate with respect to x:

a) $y = \dfrac{x+5}{x-3}$

b) $y = \dfrac{(x-7)^4}{(5-x)^3}$

c) $y = \dfrac{e^x}{x^2}$

d) $y = \dfrac{3x}{(x-1)^2}$

e) $y = \dfrac{\ln x^2}{5x}$

f) $y = \dfrac{4x^3}{e^x}$

Q2 Find $f'(x)$ for each of the following functions:

a) $f(x) = \dfrac{x^3}{(x+3)^3}$

b) $f(x) = \dfrac{x^2}{\sqrt{x-7}}$

c) $f(x) = \dfrac{e^{2x}}{e^{2x} + e^{-2x}}$

d) $f(x) = \dfrac{x}{\sin x}$

e) $f(x) = \dfrac{\sin x}{x}$

f) $f(x) = \dfrac{\cos x}{3x}$

Q3 Find $f'(x)$ if $f(x) = \dfrac{x^2}{\tan x}$, giving your answer in terms of $\cot x$ and $\operatorname{cosec} x$.

Q4 The graph of $y = \dfrac{5x-4}{2x^2}$ has one stationary point.
Find the coordinates of this point, and show that it is a maximum.

Q5 Use the quotient rule to find the coordinates of any points of inflection of the graph $y = \dfrac{x}{e^x}$.

> **Q5 Hint:** Remember from page 152 that if (a, b) is a point of inflection:
> $\dfrac{d^2y}{dx^2} = 0$ when $x = a$,
> and $\dfrac{d^2y}{dx^2}$ changes sign either side of $x = a$.

Q6 a) Differentiate $y = \dfrac{x}{\cos(2x)}$ with respect to x.

b) Show that $\dfrac{dy}{dx} = 0$ when $x = -\dfrac{1}{2}\cot(2x)$
(you do not need to solve this equation).

Q7 For the curve $y = \dfrac{1}{1+4\cos x}$:

a) Find the equation of the tangent to the curve when $x = \dfrac{\pi}{2}$.

b) Find the equation of the normal to the curve when $x = \dfrac{\pi}{2}$.

Q8 For the curve $y = \dfrac{2x}{\cos x}$, find the exact value of $\dfrac{dy}{dx}$ when $x = \dfrac{\pi}{3}$.

Q9 Show that if $y = \dfrac{x - \sin x}{1 + \cos x}$ then $\dfrac{dy}{dx} = \dfrac{x \sin x}{(1 + \cos x)^2}$.

Q10 Find any turning points on the curve $y = \dfrac{\cos x}{4 - 3\cos x}$ in the range $0 \le x \le 2\pi$.

Q11 Differentiate $y = e^{\frac{1+x}{1-x}}$ with respect to x.

Q12 Find the exact set of values of x for which $\dfrac{2 + 3x^2}{3x - 1}$ is increasing.

> **Q12 Hint:** You've seen increasing functions in Year 1 — a function $f(x)$ is increasing when its gradient $f'(x) > 0$.

7.7 More Differentiation

In this section you'll see how to differentiate reciprocals of trig functions —
sec x, cosec x and cot x. All of these can be derived from the quotient rule.

Learning Objectives (Spec Ref 7.4):
- Differentiate cosec, sec and cot.
- Use these results to differentiate more complicated functions.

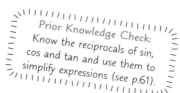

Prior Knowledge Check:
Know the reciprocals of sin,
cos and tan and use them to
simplify expressions (see p.61).

Differentiating cosec, sec and cot

Remember from page 61 the definitions of these trig functions:

$$\operatorname{cosec} x \equiv \frac{1}{\sin x} \qquad \sec x \equiv \frac{1}{\cos x} \qquad \cot x \equiv \frac{1}{\tan x} \equiv \frac{\cos x}{\sin x}$$

Since **cosec**, **sec** and **cot** are just **reciprocals** of **sin**, **cos** and **tan**,
the quotient rule can be used to differentiate them.

The following results are in the **formula booklet**, but it
will help a lot if you understand where they come from.

$y = \operatorname{cosec} x$	$y = \sec x$	$y = \cot x$
$\dfrac{dy}{dx} = -\operatorname{cosec} x \cot x$	$\dfrac{dy}{dx} = \sec x \tan x$	$\dfrac{dy}{dx} = -\operatorname{cosec}^2 x$

Tip: The trig functions
beginning with c give
negative results when
you differentiate them —
i.e. cos, cosec and cot.

The formula booklet actually gives these results in the form cosec *kx* etc
— but you can easily get these results by setting *k* = 1.

Example 1

a) Use the quotient rule to differentiate $y = \dfrac{\cos x}{\sin x}$,
and hence show that for $y = \cot x$, $\dfrac{dy}{dx} = -\operatorname{cosec}^2 x$.

PROBLEM SOLVING

1. Start off by identifying *u* and *v*.

$u = \cos x$ and $v = \sin x$

2. Differentiate them separately,
   and use the quotient rule (p.174).

$\dfrac{du}{dx} = -\sin x$ and $\dfrac{dv}{dx} = \cos x$ (see page 165)

$$\frac{dy}{dx} = \frac{v\dfrac{du}{dx} - u\dfrac{dv}{dx}}{v^2} = \frac{(\sin x \times -\sin x) - (\cos x \times \cos x)}{(\sin x)^2}$$

$$= \frac{-\sin^2 x - \cos^2 x}{\sin^2 x}$$

3. Simplify using a trig identity
   — sin² x + cos² x ≡ 1 seems fitting.

$$\frac{dy}{dx} = \frac{-(\sin^2 x + \cos^2 x)}{\sin^2 x} = -\frac{1}{\sin^2 x}$$

4. Link this back to the question.

$\tan x \equiv \dfrac{\sin x}{\cos x}$ and $\cot x \equiv \dfrac{1}{\tan x}$, so $y = \dfrac{\cos x}{\sin x} = \cot x$

5. You know $\operatorname{cosec} x \equiv \dfrac{1}{\sin x}$, so...

$$\frac{dy}{dx} = \frac{-1}{\sin^2 x} = \boxed{-\operatorname{cosec}^2 x}$$

b) Show that $\frac{d}{dx}$ cosec $x = -$cosec x cot x.

1. cosec $x \equiv \frac{1}{\sin x}$, so use the quotient rule.

   > **Tip:** You could also use the chain rule on $\frac{1}{\sin x} = (\sin x)^{-1}$.

   $u = 1 \Rightarrow \frac{du}{dx} = 0$ and $v = \sin x \Rightarrow \frac{dv}{dx} = \cos x$

   $\frac{dy}{dx} = \frac{v\frac{du}{dx} - u\frac{dv}{dx}}{v^2}$

   $= \frac{(\sin x \times 0) - (1 \times \cos x)}{\sin^2 x} = -\frac{\cos x}{\sin^2 x}$

2. Simplify using cot $x \equiv \frac{\cos x}{\sin x}$, and cosec $x \equiv \frac{1}{\sin x}$.

   $\frac{dy}{dx} = \frac{1}{\sin x} \times \left(-\frac{\cos x}{\sin x}\right) = \boxed{-\text{cosec } x \text{ cot } x}$

c) Show that $\frac{d}{dx}$ sec $x =$ sec x tan x.

1. sec $x \equiv \frac{1}{\cos x}$, so use the quotient rule.

   > **Tip:** You could also use the chain rule on $\frac{1}{\cos x} = (\cos x)^{-1}$.

   $u = 1 \Rightarrow \frac{du}{dx} = 0$ and $v = \cos x \Rightarrow \frac{dv}{dx} = -\sin x$

   $\frac{dy}{dx} = \frac{v\frac{du}{dx} - u\frac{dv}{dx}}{v^2}$

   $= \frac{(\cos x \times 0) - (1 \times -\sin x)}{\cos^2 x} = \frac{\sin x}{\cos^2 x}$

2. Simplify using tan $x \equiv \frac{\sin x}{\cos x}$, and sec $x \equiv \frac{1}{\cos x}$.

   $\frac{dy}{dx} = \frac{1}{\cos x} \times \frac{\sin x}{\cos x} = \boxed{\text{sec } x \text{ tan } x}$

As with other rules covered in this chapter, the rules for sec x, cosec x and cot x can be used with the **chain**, **product** and **quotient rules** and in combination with all the other functions you've seen so far.

Example 2

a) Find $\frac{dy}{dx}$ if $y =$ cot $\frac{x}{2}$.

This is a function (cot) of a function ($\frac{x}{2}$), so you need the **chain rule**.

> **Tip:** Although cot $x \equiv \frac{\cos x}{\sin x}$, you don't need the quotient rule as you know that cot x differentiates to give $-$cosec^2 x.

$y = \cot u$ where $u = \frac{x}{2}$

$\Rightarrow \frac{dy}{du} = -\text{cosec}^2 u = -\text{cosec}^2 \frac{x}{2}$ and $\frac{du}{dx} = \frac{1}{2}$

So $\frac{dy}{dx} = \frac{dy}{du} \times \frac{du}{dx} = \boxed{-\frac{1}{2} \text{cosec}^2 \frac{x}{2}}$

b) Find $\frac{dy}{dx}$ if $y =$ sec $(2x^2)$.

This is another function of a function, so use the chain rule again.

> **Tip:** Look back at p.155 for a reminder of the chain rule.

$y = \sec u$ where $u = 2x^2$

$\Rightarrow \frac{dy}{du} = \sec u \tan u = \sec (2x^2) \tan (2x^2)$ and $\frac{du}{dx} = 4x$

So $\frac{dy}{dx} = \frac{dy}{du} \times \frac{du}{dx} = \boxed{4x \sec (2x^2) \tan (2x^2)}$

c) Find $\dfrac{dy}{dx}$ if $y = e^x \cot x$.

This is a product of two functions, so think 'product rule' (p.170):

$u = e^x$ and $v = \cot x$

$\Rightarrow \dfrac{du}{dx} = e^x$ and $\dfrac{dv}{dx} = -\text{cosec}^2 x$

Tip: If the function inside 'cot' was more difficult, you'd do this in the same way but use the chain rule to work out $\dfrac{dv}{dx}$.

So $\dfrac{dy}{dx} = u\dfrac{dv}{dx} + v\dfrac{du}{dx} = (e^x \times -\text{cosec}^2 x) + (\cot x \times e^x)$

$= e^x(\cot x - \text{cosec}^2 x)$

Exercise 7.7.1

Q1 Differentiate with respect to x:

a) $y = \text{cosec}\,(2x)$

b) $y = \text{cosec}^2 x$

c) $y = \cot\,(7x)$

d) $y = \cot^7 x$

e) $y = x^4 \cot x$

f) $y = (x + \sec x)^2$

g) $y = \text{cosec}\,(x^2 + 5)$

h) $y = e^{3x} \sec x$

i) $y = (2x + \cot x)^3$

Q2 Find $f'(x)$ if:

a) $f(x) = \dfrac{\sec x}{x + 3}$

b) $f(x) = \sec \dfrac{1}{x}$

c) $f(x) = \sec \sqrt{x}$

Q3 Find $f'(x)$ if $f(x) = (\sec x + \text{cosec}\,x)^2$.

Q4 Find $f'(x)$ if $f(x) = \dfrac{1}{x \cot x}$.

Q5 Find $f'(x)$ if $f(x) = e^x \text{cosec}\,x$.

Q6 Find $f'(x)$ if $f(x) = e^{3x} \cot\,(4x)$.

Q7 Find $f'(x)$ if $f(x) = e^{-2x} \text{cosec}\,(4x)$.

Q8 Find $f'(x)$ if $f(x) = \ln\,(x)\,\text{cosec}\,x$.

Q9 Find $f'(x)$ if $f(x) = \sqrt{\sec x}$.

Q10 Find $f'(x)$ if $f(x) = e^{\sec x}$.

Q11 a) Find $f'(x)$ if $f(x) = \ln\,(\text{cosec}\,x)$.

b) Show that the function in part a) can be written as $-\ln\,(\sin x)$ and differentiate it — you should get the same answer as in part a).

Q11 Hint:
Remember the log laws from Year 1.

Q12 Find $f'(x)$ if $f(x) = \ln\,(x + \sec x)$.

Q13 Differentiate $y = \sec\,(\sqrt{x^2 + 5}\,)$.

7.8 Connected Rates of Change

A derivative is a 'rate of change' — e.g. the rate of change in y with respect to x. You can apply different rates of change to a given situation, and if they have variables in common they're 'connected'.

Learning Objective (Spec Ref 7.4 & 7.6):

- Form differential equations from situations involving connected rates of change.

Prior Knowledge Check:
Know formulas for surface areas and volumes of 3D solids — seen at GCSE.

Connected rates of change

Some situations have a number of **linked variables**, like length, surface area and volume or distance, speed and acceleration.

If you know the **rate of change** of one of these linked variables, and the equations that connect the variables, you can use the **chain rule** to help you find the rate of change of the other variables.

An equation connecting variables with their rates of change (i.e. with a derivative term) is called a **differential equation**.

When something changes over **time**, the derivative is $\frac{d}{dt}$ of that variable.

Tip: There's more on solving differential equations in Chapter 8 (see pages 241-248).

Example 1

a) If $y = 3e^{5x}$ and $\frac{dx}{dt} = 2$, work out $\frac{dy}{dt}$ when $x = -1$.

1. Start off by differentiating the expression for y, with respect to x.

$$y = 3e^{5x} \Rightarrow \frac{dy}{dx} = 15e^{5x}$$

2. Write out the chain rule for $\frac{dy}{dt}$, using the information available.

$$\frac{dy}{dt} = \frac{dy}{dx} \times \frac{dx}{dt}$$

3. Put in all the things you know to work out $\frac{dy}{dt}$.

$$\frac{dy}{dt} = 15e^{5x} \times 2 = 30e^{5x}$$

4. Now find the value of $\frac{dy}{dt}$ at $x = -1$.

$$\frac{dy}{dt} = \boxed{30e^{-5}}$$

b) y is the surface area of a sphere, and x is its radius.
The rate of change of the radius, $\frac{dx}{dt} = -2$. Find $\frac{dy}{dt}$ when $x = 2.5$.

1. This is trickier because you're not given the expression for y. But you should know (or be able to look up) the surface area of a sphere.

$$y = 4\pi x^2$$

Tip: This formula is in the formula booklet — given as $4\pi r^2$.

2. Now differentiate as before.

$$\frac{dy}{dx} = 8\pi x$$

3. Write out the chain rule for $\frac{dy}{dt}$.

$$\frac{dy}{dt} = \frac{dy}{dx} \times \frac{dx}{dt} = 8\pi x \times -2 = -16\pi x$$

4. Now find $\frac{dy}{dt}$ when $x = 2.5$.

$$\frac{dy}{dt} = -16\pi \times 2.5 = \boxed{-40\pi}$$

Often you'll see much wordier questions involving related rates of change, like the one in the example below, where you have to do a bit more work to figure out where to start.

Example 2

A scientist is testing how a new material expands when it is gradually heated. The diagram below shows the sample being tested, which is modelled as a triangular prism.

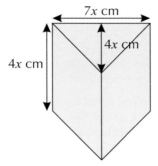

7x cm

4x cm

4x cm

After t minutes, the triangle that forms the base of the prism has base length $7x$ cm and height $4x$ cm, and the length of the prism is also $4x$ cm.

If the sample expands at a constant rate, given by $\frac{dx}{dt} = 0.05$ cm min⁻¹, find an expression in terms of x for $\frac{dV}{dt}$, where V is the volume of the prism.

Tip: If you've forgotten the formulas for areas and volumes of 3D solids, you should brush up on them now. They crop up quite a bit in these questions.

1. The best way to start this kind of question is to write down what you know. There's enough information to write an expression for the volume of the prism.

   Area of cross-section   Length of prism

   $V = \left(\frac{1}{2} \times 7x \times 4x \right) \times 4x$

   $\Rightarrow V = 56x^3$ cm³ .

2. Differentiate this expression for the volume with respect to x:

   $\frac{dV}{dx} = 168x^2$

3. You know that $\frac{dx}{dt} = 0.05$ cm min⁻¹. So you can use the chain rule to find $\frac{dV}{dt}$.

   $\frac{dV}{dt} = \frac{dV}{dx} \times \frac{dx}{dt}$

   $\Rightarrow \frac{dV}{dt} = 168x^2 \times 0.05 = 8.4x^2$ cm³ min⁻¹

There are a couple of tricks in this type of question that could catch you out if you're not prepared for them. In the example coming up on the next page, you have to spot that there's a hidden derivative described in words.

You also need to remember the rule $\frac{dy}{dx} = \frac{1}{\left(\frac{dx}{dy} \right)}$ (see p.158).

Example 3

A giant metal cube from space is cooling after entering the Earth's atmosphere. As it cools, the surface area of the cube is modelled as decreasing at a constant rate of 0.027 m² s⁻¹.

If the side length of the cube after t seconds is x m, find $\dfrac{dx}{dt}$ at the point when $x = 15$ m.

1. Start with what you know:

> The cube has side length x m.
>
> So the surface area of the cube is: $A = 6x^2 \implies \dfrac{dA}{dx} = 12x$
>
> A **decreases** at a constant rate of 0.027 m² s⁻¹.
>
> We can write this as $\dfrac{dA}{dt} = -0.027$. ← This value is negative because A is decreasing.
>
> Use $\dfrac{d}{dt}$ because it's a rate of time.

2. Now use the **chain rule** to find $\dfrac{dx}{dt}$.

$$\frac{dx}{dt} = \frac{dx}{dA} \times \frac{dA}{dt} = \frac{1}{\left(\dfrac{dA}{dx}\right)} \times \frac{dA}{dt} = \frac{1}{12x} \times -0.027 = -\frac{0.00225}{x}$$

3. Substitute in $x = 15$.

$$\frac{dx}{dt} = -\frac{0.00225}{x} = -\frac{0.00225}{15} = -0.00015 \text{ m s}^{-1}$$

Exercise 7.8.1

Q1 A cube with sides x cm is cooling and the sides are shrinking by 0.1 cm min⁻¹. Find an expression for $\dfrac{dV}{dt}$, the rate of change of volume with respect to time.

Q2 A cuboid block of sides $2x$ cm by $3x$ cm by $5x$ cm expands when heated such that x increases at a rate of 0.15 cm °C⁻¹. If the volume of the cuboid at temperature θ °C is V cm³, find $\dfrac{dV}{d\theta}$ when $x = 3$.

Q3 A snowball of radius r cm is melting. Its radius decreases by 1.6 cm h⁻¹. If the surface area of the snowball at time t hours is A cm², find $\dfrac{dA}{dt}$ when $r = 5.5$ cm. Give your answer to 2 d.p.

> **Q3 Hint:** Model the snowball as a sphere ($A = 4\pi r^2$).

Q4 A spherical satellite, radius r m, expands as it enters the atmosphere. It grows by 2×10^{-2} mm for every 1 °C rise in temperature. Find an expression $\dfrac{dV}{d\theta}$ for the rate of change of volume with respect to temperature.

Q5 Heat, H, is lost from a closed cylindrical tank of radius r cm and height $3r$ cm at a rate of 2 J cm⁻² of surface area, A. Find $\dfrac{dH}{dr}$ when $r = 12.3$. Give your answer to 2 d.p.

Q6 A cylindrical polishing block of radius r cm and length H cm is worn down at one circular end at a rate of 0.5 mm h^{-1}. Find an expression for the rate of change of the volume of the block with respect to time.

Q6 Hint: Treat r as a constant as the radius will not change.

Q7 A crystal of a salt is shaped like a prism. Its cross section is an equilateral triangle with sides x mm and the height of the crystal is 20 mm. New material is deposited only on the rectangular faces of the prism (i.e. the height does not change), so that x increases at a rate of 0.6 mm per day.

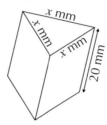

a) Find an expression for the area of the end of the prism in terms of x.

b) Find an expression for the rate of change of the volume of the crystal with respect to time.

c) Find the rate of change of the volume of the crystal with respect to time when $x = 0.5$.

Q8 The growth of a population of bacteria in a sample dish is modelled by the equation $D = 1 + 2^{\lambda t}$, where D is the diameter of the colony in mm, t is time in days, and λ is a constant. The number of bacteria in the colony, n, is directly proportional to the diameter. A biologist counts the bacteria in the colony when its diameter is 2 mm and estimates that there are approximately 208 bacteria.

a) Find an expression for the rate of change of n with respect to time.

b) Find the rate of increase in number of bacteria after 1 day if $\lambda = 5$.

Q9 Water is dripping from a hole in the base of a cylinder of radius r cm, where the water height is h cm, at a rate of 0.3 cm^3 s^{-1}.

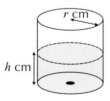

Q9 Hint: The amount of the water remaining is decreasing at a rate of 0.3 cm^3 s^{-1} — so this value should be negative.

a) Find an expression for $\frac{dh}{dt}$, the rate at which the water level falls in the cylinder.

b) Hence find the rate of change in the water level, per minute, in a cylinder of radius 6 cm when the height of water is 4 cm.

Q10 The volume, V, of a hemisphere of radius r cm, varies with its temperature, θ, at a rate of k cm^3 °C^{-1}, where k is a constant that depends on the material that the hemisphere is made of.

a) Find an expression for the rate of change of radius with respect to temperature.

b) Hence find $\frac{dr}{d\theta}$ for a material with $k = 1.5$, when $V = 4$ cm^3.

7.9 Differentiation with Parametric Equations

Differentiating parametric equations (like those you met in Chapter 4) is simpler than you might expect — but you'll have to combine this with all the other differentiation you've done in this chapter so far.

Learning Objectives (Spec Ref 7.5):
- Differentiate functions that are defined parametrically.
- Find the equations of tangents and normals to curves given parametrically.

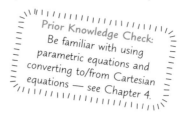

Prior Knowledge Check:
Be familiar with using parametric equations and converting to/from Cartesian equations — see Chapter 4.

Differentiating parametric equations

A curve can be defined by **two parametric equations**, often with the parameter t:

$$y = f(t) \text{ and } x = g(t)$$

To find the gradient, $\dfrac{dy}{dx}$, you could convert the equations into **Cartesian**

form (see pages 103-104), but this isn't always possible or convenient.

The **chain rule** you met on p.155 can be used to differentiate parametric equations without needing to convert to Cartesian form. It looks like this:

$$\frac{dy}{dx} = \frac{dy}{dt} \div \frac{dx}{dt}$$

So to find $\dfrac{dy}{dx}$ from parametric equations, **differentiate** each

equation with respect to the parameter t, then put them into the formula.

> **Tip:** On page 155, you saw this given in the form '$\times \dfrac{dt}{dx}$' rather than '$\div \dfrac{dx}{dt}$', but it means the same thing.

Example

The curve C is defined by the parametric equations
$x = t^2 - 1$ and $y = t^3 - 3t + 4$.

a) Find $\dfrac{dy}{dx}$ in terms of t.

1. Start by differentiating the two parametric equations with respect to t.

$$x = t^2 - 1 \ \Rightarrow \ \frac{dx}{dt} = 2t$$
$$y = t^3 - 3t + 4 \ \Rightarrow \ \frac{dy}{dt} = 3t^2 - 3 = 3(t^2 - 1)$$

2. Now use the chain rule to combine them.

$$\frac{dy}{dx} = \frac{dy}{dt} \div \frac{dx}{dt} = \frac{3(t^2 - 1)}{2t}$$

b) Find the gradient of C when $t = -2$.

Use the answer to a) to find the gradient for a specific value of t.
So, when $t = -2$:

$$\frac{dy}{dx} = \frac{3((-2)^2 - 1)}{2(-2)} = \frac{3(3)}{-4} = -\frac{9}{4}$$

c) Find the coordinates of the turning points.

1. The turning points occur when $\frac{dy}{dx} = 0$, so solve to find the values of t at the turning points:

$\frac{dy}{dx} = \frac{3(t^2 - 1)}{2t} = 0$

$\Rightarrow 3(t^2 - 1) = 0 \Rightarrow t^2 = 1 \Rightarrow t = \pm 1$

2. Now put these values for t into the original parametric equations to find the Cartesian coordinates of the turning points.

When $t = 1$, $x = (1)^2 - 1 = 0$,
$y = (1)^3 - 3(1) + 4 = 2$
So there's a turning point at $(0, 2)$.

When $t = -1$, $x = (-1)^2 - 1 = 0$,
$y = (-1)^3 - 3(-1) + 4 = 6$
So there's another turning point at $(0, 6)$.

> **Tip:** Remember — Cartesian coordinates are just the (x, y) coordinates.

Exercise 7.9.1

Q1 For each curve C, defined by the parametric equations given below, find $\frac{dy}{dx}$ in terms of t.

a) $x = t^2$, $y = t^3 - t$

b) $x = t^3 + t$, $y = 2t^2 + 1$

c) $x = t^4$, $y = t^3 - t^2$

d) $x = \cos t$, $y = 4t - t^2$

Q2 The curve C is defined by the parametric equations $x = t^2$, $y = e^{2t}$.

a) Find $\frac{dy}{dx}$ in terms of t.

b) Find the gradient of C when $t = 1$.

Q3 The curve C is defined by the parametric equations $x = e^{3t}$, $y = 4t^3 - 2t^2$.

a) Find $\frac{dy}{dx}$ in terms of t.

b) Find the gradient of C when $t = 0$.

Q4 The curve C is defined by the parametric equations $x = t^3$, $y = t^2 \cos t$.

a) Find $\frac{dy}{dx}$ in terms of t.

b) Find the gradient of C when $t = \pi$.

Q5 The curve C is defined by the parametric equations $x = t^2 \sin t$, $y = t^3 \sin t + \cos t$.

a) Find $\frac{dy}{dx}$ in terms of t.

b) Find the gradient of C when $t = \pi$.

Q6 The curve C is defined by the parametric equations $x = \ln t$, $y = 3t^2 - t^3$.

a) Find $\frac{dy}{dx}$ in terms of t.

b) Evaluate $\frac{dy}{dx}$ when $t = -1$.

c) Find the exact coordinates of the turning point of the curve C.

Q7 A curve is defined by the parametric equations $x = t^2$, $y = 3t^3 - 4t$.

a) Find $\frac{dy}{dx}$ for this curve.

b) Find the coordinates of the stationary points of the curve.

Finding tangents and normals

Once you've found the gradient of a parametric curve at a particular point, you can use this to find the **equation** of the **tangent** or **normal** to the curve at that point. You'll have seen this before, but here's a recap of the method:

- The gradient of the **tangent** is the **same** as the gradient of the curve at that point.

- The gradient of the **normal** at that point is $\dfrac{-1}{\text{gradient of tangent}}$.

- Put the values for the gradient, m, and the (x, y) coordinates of the point into $y = mx + c$ to find the equation of the line.

Tip: You could also use $y - y_1 = m(x - x_1)$ to get the equation.

Example

The curve C is defined by the following parametric equations: $x = \sin t$, $y = 2t \cos t$.

a) **Find the gradient of the curve, and the (x, y) coordinates, when $t = \pi$.**

1. Find $\dfrac{dx}{dt}$ and $\dfrac{dy}{dt}$.

   $\dfrac{dx}{dt} = \cos t$, $\dfrac{dy}{dt} = 2\cos t - 2t \sin t$

2. Use them to find $\dfrac{dy}{dx}$.

   $\dfrac{dy}{dx} = \dfrac{2\cos t - 2t \sin t}{\cos t} = 2 - 2t \tan t$

3. Substitute π into $\dfrac{dy}{dx}$ to get the gradient.

   When $t = \pi$, $\dfrac{dy}{dx} = 2 - 2\pi(0) = \boxed{2}$

4. Substitute π into the equations for x and y.

   When $t = \pi$, $x = 0$, and $y = -2\pi$, so the coordinates are $\boxed{(0, -2\pi)}$.

b) **Hence find the equation of the tangent to C when $t = \pi$.**

1. The equation of the tangent has an equation in the form $y = mx + c$, so substitute in m = 2, $x = 0$ and $y = -2\pi$ and find c.

   $y = mx + c$
   $-2\pi = 2(0) + c \implies c = -2\pi$

2. Putting c back into the equation gives:

   $\boxed{y = 2x - 2\pi}$ or $\boxed{y = 2(x - \pi)}$

c) **Find the equation of the normal to C when $t = \pi$.**

1. Find the gradient of the normal.

   gradient of normal
   $= -1 \div \text{gradient of tangent} = -\dfrac{1}{2}$

2. Substitute m $= -\dfrac{1}{2}$, $x = 0$ and $y = -2\pi$ into $y = mx + c$, to find c.

   $y = mx + c$
   $-2\pi = -\dfrac{1}{2}(0) + c \implies c = -2\pi$

3. Putting c back into the equation gives:

   $\boxed{y = -\dfrac{1}{2}x - 2\pi}$ or $\boxed{x + 2y + 4\pi = 0}$

Q1 A curve is defined by the parametric equations $x = t^2$, $y = t^3 - 6t$. Find the equation of the tangent to the curve at $t = 3$, giving your answer in the form $ax + by + c = 0$.

Q2 A curve C is defined parametrically by $x = t^3 - 2t^2$, $y = t^3 - t^2 + 5t$. Find the equation of the tangent at the point $t = -1$.

Q3 A curve C is defined by the parametric equations $x = \sin 2t$, $y = t \cos t + 2 \sin t$. Find the equation of the normal to the curve at $t = \pi$.

> **Q3 Hint:**
> You'll need
> to use the
> product rule.

Q4 The parametric representation of a curve is given by $x = t \ln t$, $y = t^3 - t^2 + 3$. Find the equation of the tangent to the curve at $t = 1$.

Q5 The path of a particle is given parametrically by $x = \theta \sin 2\theta$, $y = \theta^2 + \theta \cos \theta$. Find the equation of the normal to the particle's path at $\theta = \frac{\pi}{2}$.

Q6 The motion of a particle is modelled by the parametric equations $x = t^2 - t$, $y = 3t - t^3$.

    a) Find the equation of the tangent to the path of the particle when $t = 2$, giving your answer in a suitable form.

    b) Find the Cartesian coordinates of the point at which the normal to the path at $t = 2$ cuts the x-axis.

Q7 A particle moves along a path modelled by the parametric equations $x = \sin 2\theta + 2 \cos \theta$, $y = \theta \sin \theta$.

    a) Find the gradient $\dfrac{dy}{dx}$ of the particle's path in terms of θ.

    b) Evaluate $\dfrac{dy}{dx}$ at $\theta = \dfrac{\pi}{2}$ and hence obtain equations of the tangent and normal to the path at this point.

Q8 A particle moves along a path given parametrically by $x = s^3 \ln s$, $y = s^3 - s^2 \ln s$.

    a) Give the value(s) of s at which the path cuts the y-axis.

    b) Hence show that the equation of a tangent to the curve when $x = 0$ is $y = 2x + 1$.

Q9 A curve is given parametrically by $x = \theta^2 \sin \theta$, $y = \dfrac{\cos \theta}{\theta^3}$.

    a) Show that the gradient of the curve when $\theta = \pi$ is $-\dfrac{3}{\pi^6}$.

    b) Hence find the equation of the normal to the curve at this point.

Q10 Curve C is given by $x = \dfrac{\sin \theta}{\theta^2}$, $y = \theta \cos 2\theta$.

    a) Find the gradient of C when $\theta = \dfrac{\pi}{2}$.

    b) Hence find the equation of the tangent to the curve at this point.

    c) Find the values of θ where the curve cuts the x-axis ($\theta > 0$), and hence find the coordinates of the point with $0 < \theta \leq \dfrac{\pi}{2}$ where the curve cuts the x-axis.

7.10 Implicit Differentiation

For equations that you can't write in the form y = f(x), you need to use implicit differentiation. It works for equations that contain a mixture of x and y terms, such as xy².

> **Learning Objectives (Spec Ref 7.5):**
> - Differentiate functions defined implicitly.
> - Find the equations of tangents and normals to curves given implicitly.

Implicit differentiation

An **'implicit relation'** is the mathematical name for any equation in *x* and *y* that's written in the form **f(x, y) = g(x, y)** instead of *y* = f(x). For example, $y^2 = xy + x + 2$ is implicit.

Some implicit relations are either awkward or impossible to rewrite in the form *y* = f(x). This can happen, for example, if the equation contains a number of different powers of *y*, or terms where *x* is multiplied by *y*.

> **Tip:** f(x, y) and g(x, y) don't actually both have to include *x* and *y* — one of them could even be a constant.

This can make implicit relations tricky to differentiate — the solution is **implicit differentiation**:

To find $\dfrac{dy}{dx}$ **for an implicit relation between *x* and *y*:**

- **Step 1:** Differentiate terms in *x* **only** (and **constant** terms) with respect to *x*, as normal.

- **Step 2:** Use the **chain rule** to differentiate terms in *y* **only**:

$$\frac{d}{dx}f(y) = \frac{d}{dy}f(y)\frac{dy}{dx}$$

> In practice, this means 'differentiate with respect to *y*, and stick a $\dfrac{dy}{dx}$ on the end'.

- **Step 3:** Use the **product rule** to differentiate terms in **both *x* and *y*:**

$$\frac{d}{dx}u(x)v(y) = u(x)\frac{d}{dx}v(y) + v(y)\frac{d}{dx}u(x)$$

- **Step 4:** **Rearrange** the resulting equation in *x*, *y* and $\dfrac{dy}{dx}$ to make $\dfrac{dy}{dx}$ the subject.

> **Tip:** $\dfrac{d}{dx}f(y)$ just means 'the derivative of f(y) with respect to *x*'.

Example 1

Use implicit differentiation to find $\dfrac{dy}{dx}$ for $y^3 + y^2 = e^x + x^3$.

You need to differentiate each term of the equation with respect to *x*.

1. Start by sticking '$\dfrac{d}{dx}$' in front of each term.

$$\frac{d}{dx}y^3 + \frac{d}{dx}y^2 = \frac{d}{dx}e^x + \frac{d}{dx}x^3$$

2. Differentiate the terms in *x* only.

$$\frac{d}{dx}y^3 + \frac{d}{dx}y^2 = e^x + 3x^2$$

3. Use the **chain rule** for the terms in y only.

$$3y^2\frac{dy}{dx} + 2y\frac{dy}{dx} = e^x + 3x^2$$

4. There are no terms in both x and y to deal with, so **rearrange** to make $\frac{dy}{dx}$ the subject.

$$(3y^2 + 2y)\frac{dy}{dx} = e^x + 3x^2 \implies \frac{dy}{dx} = \frac{e^x + 3x^2}{3y^2 + 2y}$$

Take your time using the product rule as it's easy to forget terms if you're not careful. Always start by identifying $u(x)$ and $v(y)$, and do it in steps if you need to. Once you're happy with this method you might not need to write all the steps out separately, but you can do if you find it easier.

Example 2

a) **Use implicit differentiation to find $\frac{dy}{dx}$ for $2x^2y + y^3 = 6x^2 - 15$.**

1. Again, start by sticking '$\frac{d}{dx}$' in front of each term.

$$\frac{d}{dx}2x^2y + \frac{d}{dx}y^3 = \frac{d}{dx}6x^2 - \frac{d}{dx}15$$

2. First, deal with the **terms in x** and **constant** terms — in this case that's the two terms on the right-hand side.

$$\frac{d}{dx}2x^2y + \frac{d}{dx}y^3 = 12x + 0$$

3. Now use the **chain rule** on the term in y.

$$\frac{d}{dx}2x^2y + 3y^2\frac{dy}{dx} = 12x + 0$$

4. Use the **product rule** on the term in x and y, where $u(x) = 2x^2$ and $v(y) = y$.

$$2x^2\frac{d}{dx}(y) + y\frac{d}{dx}(2x^2) + 3y^2\frac{dy}{dx} = 12x + 0$$

$$\implies 2x^2\frac{dy}{dx} + 4xy + 3y^2\frac{dy}{dx} = 12x + 0$$

This comes from the chain rule:
$$\frac{d}{dx}(y) = \frac{d}{dy}(y)\frac{dy}{dx} = 1\frac{dy}{dx} = \frac{dy}{dx}$$

5. Finally, **rearrange** to make $\frac{dy}{dx}$ the subject.

$$\frac{dy}{dx}(2x^2 + 3y^2) = 12x - 4xy$$

$$\implies \frac{dy}{dx} = \frac{12x - 4xy}{2x^2 + 3y^2}$$

b) **Find the gradient of the curve $2x^2y + y^3 = 6x^2 - 15$ at the point (2, 1).**

Just put the values for x and y into $\frac{dy}{dx}$.

$$\frac{dy}{dx} = \frac{12(2) - 4(2)(1)}{2(2)^2 + 3(1)^2} = \frac{16}{11}$$

Exercise 7.10.1

Q1 Use implicit differentiation to find $\frac{dy}{dx}$ for each of these curves:

a) $y + y^3 = x^2 + 4$

b) $x^2 + y^2 = 2x + 2y$

c) $3x^3 - 4y = y^2 + x$

d) $5x - y^2 = x^5 - 6y$

e) $\cos x + \sin y = x^2 + y^3$

f) $x^3y^2 + \cos x = 4xy$

g) $e^x + e^y = x^3 - y$

h) $3xy^2 + 2x^2y = x^3 + 4x$

i) $4x^3y^2 + 3x^2y = 2\sin x - x^4$

Q2   Find the gradient, $\frac{dy}{dx}$, for each of these curves given below:

a) $x^3 + 2xy = y^4$

b) $x^2y + y^2 = x^3$

c) $y^3x + y = \sin x$

d) $y \cos x + x \sin y = xy$

e) $e^x + e^y = xy$

f) $\ln x + x^2 = y^3 + y$

g) $e^{2x} + e^{3y} = 3x^2y^2$

h) $x \ln x + y \ln x = x^5 + y^3$

> **Q3a) Hint:** Evaluate the left-hand and right-hand sides of the equation separately to show they're the same.

Q3   a) Show that the curve C, defined implicitly by $e^x + 2 \ln y = y^3$, passes through $(0, 1)$.

b) Find the gradient of the curve at this point.

Q4   A curve is defined implicitly by $x^3 + y^2 - 2xy = 0$.

a) Find $\frac{dy}{dx}$ for this curve.

b) Show that $y = -2 \pm 2\sqrt{3}$ when $x = -2$.

c) Evaluate the gradient at $(-2, -2 + 2\sqrt{3})$, leaving your answer in surd form.

Q5   The curve $x^3 - xy = 2y^2$ passes through the points $(1, -1)$ and $(1, a)$.

a) Find the value of a.

b) Evaluate the gradient of the curve at each of these points.

Q6   A curve is defined implicitly by $x^2y + y^2x = xy + 4$.

a) At which two values of y does the line $x = 1$ cut the curve?

b) By finding $\frac{dy}{dx}$, evaluate the gradient at each of these points.

Applications of implicit differentiation

Sometimes you can use implicit differentiation when you might not expect it.
For some equations of the form **y = f(x)**, the easiest way to differentiate them
is to **rearrange** them and use implicit differentiation.

For example, the proof of the rule for **differentiating a^x** from page 163 uses implicit differentiation:

- Take **ln** of both sides of the equation: $y = a^x \Rightarrow \ln y = \ln a^x$

- Use the **log laws** to rearrange the right-hand side: $\ln y = x \ln a$

- Now use **implicit differentiation**: $\frac{d}{dx}(\ln y) = \frac{d}{dx}(x \ln a)$

  Use the **chain rule** to deal with $\frac{d}{dx}(\ln y)$ $\frac{1}{y}\frac{dy}{dx} = \ln a$ Since **a** is a constant, **ln a** is also a constant.

  $\frac{dy}{dx} = y \ln a$

- Use the original equation to get rid of y: $\frac{dy}{dx} = a^x \ln a$

This method of rearranging and using implicit differentiation is also used to differentiate the **inverse trig functions**.

Example 1

Find $\dfrac{dy}{dx}$ if $y = \arcsin x$ for $-1 \leq x \leq 1$.

1. Rearrange the equation to get rid of the arcsin by taking sin of both sides.

$$\sin y = \sin(\arcsin x)$$
$$\Rightarrow \sin y = x$$

> **Tip:** Arcsin is the inverse of sin, so they cancel out.

2. Now use implicit differentiation:

$$\frac{d}{dx}(\sin y) = \frac{d}{dx}(x)$$

- Differentiate the x-term.

$$\frac{d}{dx}(\sin y) = 1$$

- Use the chain rule on the y-term.

$$\cos y \, \frac{dy}{dx} = 1$$

- Rearrange to give an equation for $\dfrac{dy}{dx}$.

$$\frac{dy}{dx} = \frac{1}{\cos y}$$

3. To get $\dfrac{1}{\cos y}$ in terms of x, first use the identity $\cos^2 x + \sin^2 x \equiv 1$ to write $\cos y$ in terms of $\sin y$.

$$\frac{dy}{dx} = \frac{1}{\sqrt{\cos^2 y}} = \frac{1}{\sqrt{1 - \sin^2 y}}$$

4. Now, use the equation $\sin y = x$ to get $\dfrac{dy}{dx}$ in terms of x.

$$\frac{dy}{dx} = \boxed{\frac{1}{\sqrt{1 - x^2}}}$$

You can use a similar method to differentiate the other inverse trig functions as well — the derivatives are given below:

$y = \arcsin x$	$y = \arccos x$	$y = \arctan x$
$\dfrac{dy}{dx} = \dfrac{1}{\sqrt{1 - x^2}}$	$\dfrac{dy}{dx} = -\dfrac{1}{\sqrt{1 - x^2}}$	$\dfrac{dy}{dx} = \dfrac{1}{1 + x^2}$

> **Tip:** You can have a go at finding the derivatives of arccos x and arctan x for yourself in Exercise 7.10.2 on p.195.

Most implicit differentiation questions aren't that different from any other differentiation questions. Once you've got an expression for the gradient, you'll have to use it to do the sort of things you'd normally expect, like finding **stationary points** of curves and equations of **tangents** and **normals**.

Example 2

Curve A has the equation $x^2 + 2xy - y^2 = 10x + 4y - 21$.

a) Show that when $\dfrac{dy}{dx} = 0$, $y = 5 - x$.

1. You need to find $\dfrac{dy}{dx}$ by implicit differentiation so stick $\dfrac{d}{dx}$ in front of each term.

$$\frac{d}{dx}x^2 + \frac{d}{dx}2xy - \frac{d}{dx}y^2 = \frac{d}{dx}10x + \frac{d}{dx}4y - \frac{d}{dx}21$$

2. Differentiate x^2, $10x$ and 21 with respect to x. $\Rightarrow 2x + \dfrac{d}{dx}2xy - \dfrac{d}{dx}y^2 = 10 + \dfrac{d}{dx}4y - 0$

3. Use the chain rule to differentiate y^2 and $4y$. $\Rightarrow 2x + \dfrac{d}{dx}2xy - 2y\dfrac{dy}{dx} = 10 + 4\dfrac{dy}{dx}$

4. Use the product rule to differentiate $2xy$. $\Rightarrow 2x + 2x\dfrac{dy}{dx} + y\dfrac{d}{dx}2x - 2y\dfrac{dy}{dx} = 10 + 4\dfrac{dy}{dx}$

$\Rightarrow 2x + 2x\dfrac{dy}{dx} + 2y - 2y\dfrac{dy}{dx} = 10 + 4\dfrac{dy}{dx}$

5. Rearrange to get $\dfrac{dy}{dx}$. $\Rightarrow 2x\dfrac{dy}{dx} - 2y\dfrac{dy}{dx} - 4\dfrac{dy}{dx} = 10 - 2x - 2y$

$\Rightarrow (2x - 2y - 4)\dfrac{dy}{dx} = 10 - 2x - 2y$

$\Rightarrow \dfrac{dy}{dx} = \dfrac{10 - 2x - 2y}{2x - 2y - 4} = \dfrac{5 - x - y}{x - y - 2}$

6. Find y in terms of x when $\dfrac{dy}{dx} = 0$. $\dfrac{5 - x - y}{x - y - 2} = 0 \Rightarrow 5 - x - y = 0 \Rightarrow \boxed{y = 5 - x}$

b) Find the coordinates of the stationary points of A.

1. Use the answer to part a) to find the points where $\dfrac{dy}{dx} = 0$ — i.e. substitute $y = 5 - x$ into the equation for the curve.

$x^2 + 2xy - y^2 = 10x + 4y - 21$
$\Rightarrow x^2 + 2x(5 - x) - (5 - x)^2 = 10x + 4(5 - x) - 21$

2. Expand and simplify the quadratic.

$\Rightarrow x^2 + 10x - 2x^2 - 25 + 10x - x^2$
$= 10x + 20 - 4x - 21$
$\Rightarrow -2x^2 + 14x - 24 = 0$
$\Rightarrow x^2 - 7x + 12 = 0$

3. Solve the quadratic to get the x-coordinates.

$\Rightarrow (x - 3)(x - 4) = 0 \Rightarrow x = 3 \text{ or } x = 4$

4. Find the y-coordinate for each stationary point using $y = 5 - x$.

$x = 3 \Rightarrow y = 5 - 3 = 2$
$x = 4 \Rightarrow y = 5 - 4 = 1$
So the stationary points of A are $\boxed{(3, 2)}$ and $\boxed{(4, 1)}$.

Example 3

A curve defined implicitly by $\sin x - y \cos x = y^2$ passes through two points (π, a) and (π, b), where $a < b$.

a) Find the values of a and b.

1. Put $x = \pi$ into the equation and solve for y.

$\sin \pi - y \cos \pi = y^2 \Rightarrow 0 + y = y^2$
$\Rightarrow y^2 - y = 0 \Rightarrow y(y - 1) = 0$
$\Rightarrow y = 0 \text{ and } y = 1$

2. You're looking for the y-coordinate of each point.

So $\boxed{a = 0}$ and $\boxed{b = 1}$.

b) Find the equations of the tangents to the curve at each of these points.

1. First find $\dfrac{dy}{dx}$ using implicit differentiation as usual.

$\cos x + y \sin x - \cos x \dfrac{dy}{dx} = 2y \dfrac{dy}{dx}$

$\Rightarrow \dfrac{dy}{dx} = \dfrac{\cos x + y \sin x}{2y + \cos x}$

2. Now put in $x = \pi$ and $y = 0$ to find the gradient at $(\pi, 0)$.

$\dfrac{dy}{dx} = \dfrac{\cos \pi + 0 \sin \pi}{2(0) + \cos \pi} = 1$

3. So the gradient of the tangent at $(\pi, 0)$ is 1. Put these values into $y = mx + c$ to find c.

$0 = \pi + c \Rightarrow c = -\pi$
So the equation of the tangent at $(\pi, 0)$ is $\boxed{y = x - \pi}$.

4. Do the same to find the equation of the tangent at $(\pi, 1)$.

$\dfrac{dy}{dx} = \dfrac{\cos \pi + \sin \pi}{2(1) + \cos \pi} = -1$
$1 = -\pi + c \Rightarrow c = 1 + \pi$
So the equation of the tangent at $(\pi, 1)$ is $\boxed{y = 1 + \pi - x}$.

c) Show that the tangents intersect at the point $\left(\dfrac{1 + 2\pi}{2}, \dfrac{1}{2}\right)$.

1. Set the equations of the tangents equal to one another to find where they intersect.

$x - \pi = 1 + \pi - x$
$\Rightarrow 2x = 1 + 2\pi$
$\Rightarrow x = \dfrac{1 + 2\pi}{2}$

2. Put this value of x into one of the equations.

$y = \left(\dfrac{1 + 2\pi}{2}\right) - \pi = \dfrac{1}{2} + \pi - \pi = \dfrac{1}{2}$

So they intersect at $\boxed{\left(\dfrac{1 + 2\pi}{2}, \dfrac{1}{2}\right)}$.

Exercise 7.10.2

Q1 A curve is defined implicitly by $x^2 + 2x + 3y - y^2 = 0$.

    a) Find the coordinates of the stationary points (to 2 decimal places).

    b) Show that the curve intersects the y-axis when $y = 0$ and $y = 3$.
       Hence find the equation of the tangent at each of these points.

Q2 A curve is defined implicitly by $x^3 + x^2 + y = y^2$.

    a) Find the coordinates of the stationary points (to 2 decimal places).

    b) Show that the curve intersects the line $x = 2$ when $y = 4$ and $y = -3$.
       Hence find the equation of the tangent at each of these points.

Q3 A curve is defined implicitly by $x^2y + y^3 = x + 7$.

    a) Calculate the x-coordinates of the points on the curve where $y = 1$
       and hence find the equations of the normals at these points.

    b) Find the coordinates of the point where the normals intersect.

Q4 $e^x + y^2 - xy = 5 - 3y$ is a curve passing through two points $(0, a)$ and $(0, b)$, where $a < b$.

   a) Find the values of a and b and show that one of these points is a stationary point of the curve.

   b) Find the equations of the tangent and normal to the curve at the other point.

Q5 Differentiate $\arccos x$ with respect to x.

Q6 If $y = \arctan x$, show that $\dfrac{dy}{dx} = \dfrac{1}{1 + x^2}$.

> **Q6 Hint:** You'll need to use the identity $\sec^2 \theta \equiv 1 + \tan^2 \theta$.

Q7 The curve C is defined by $\ln x + y^2 = x^2y + 6$.

   a) Show that C passes through $(1, 3)$ and $(1, -2)$.

   b) Find the equations of the normals to the curve at each of these points and explain why these normals cannot intersect.

Q8 A curve is defined implicitly by $e^y + x^2 = y^3 + 4x$.
Find the equations of the tangents that touch the curve at $(a, 0)$ and $(b, 0)$. Leave your answer in surd form.

Q9 Show that any point on the curve $y \ln x + x^2 = y^2 - y + 1$ which satisfies $y + 2x^2 = 0$ is a stationary point.

Q10 If $f(x) = \arccos(x^2)$ for $-1 \le x \le 1$, find the equation of the tangent to the graph of $y = f(x)$ when $x = \dfrac{1}{\sqrt{2}}$ and $0 \le y \le \pi$. Give your answer in the form $y = mx + c$, using exact values for m and c.

Q11 A curve is defined by $e^{2y} + e^x - e^4 = 2xy + 1$.

   a) Find the equation of the tangent to the curve when $y = 0$.

   b) Find the equation of the normal to the curve when $y = 0$.

   c) Show that these two lines intersect when $x = \dfrac{4e^8 + 144}{e^8 + 36}$.

> **Q11 Hint:** Remember, $\dfrac{1}{e^x}$ is the same as e^{-x}.

Q12 $y^2x + 2xy - 3x^3 = x^2 + 2$ passes through two points where $x = 2$. Find the equations of the tangents to the curve at these points, and hence show that they intersect at $\left(-\dfrac{14}{25}, -1\right)$.

Q13 The curve C is defined implicitly by $\cos y \cos x + \cos y \sin x = \dfrac{1}{2}$.

   a) Find y when $x = \dfrac{\pi}{2}$ and when $x = \pi$, $0 \le y \le \pi$.

   b) Find the equations of the tangents at these points.

> **Q13 Hint:** You won't need your calculator for the trig here but you will need to remember your common angles.

Q14 Find the coordinates of the stationary points of the graph $\dfrac{1}{3}y^2 = 6x^3 - 2xy$.

Review Exercise

Q1 A curve C has equation $y = 2x^3 - 12x^2 + 18x + 2$.

    a) Find the values of for which the curve is: (i) concave,   (ii) convex.

    b) (i) Find the coordinates of the point of inflection.

       (ii) Is this a stationary point of inflection? Explain your answer.

Q2 Differentiate with respect to x:

    a) $y = \sqrt{x^3 + 2x^2}$ b) $y = e^{5x^2}$ c) $y = \ln(6 - x^2)$

Q3 A curve C has the equation $y = (x^2 - 1)^3$.

    a) Differentiate y with respect to x.

    b) Hence find the equation of the normal to the curve C when $x = 2$ in the form $ax + by + c = 0$, where a, b and c are integers.

Q4 Differentiate the following with respect to x.

    a) $3e^{2x+1} - \ln(1 - x^2) + 2x^3$ b) $16x + e^{\sqrt{x}} + \ln(\cos x)$

Q5 a) Find $\dfrac{dy}{dx}$ as a function of x when: (i) $x = 2e^{2y}$ (ii) $x = \ln(2y + 3)$

    b) Find $\dfrac{dy}{dx}$ as a function of y when $x = \tan y$.

Q6 Find f$'(x)$ for the following functions:

    a) f$(x) = 2\cos(3x)$ b) f$(x) = \sqrt{\tan x}$ c) f$(x) = e^{\cos(3x)}$ d) f$(x) = \sin(4x)\tan(x^3)$

Q7 Find the value of the gradient for:

    a) $y = e^{2x}(x^2 - 3)$ when $x = 0$ b) $y = (\ln x)(\sin x)$ when $x = 1$

Q8 Find the exact value of $\dfrac{dy}{dx}$ when $x = 1$ if $y = e^{x^2}\sqrt{x + 1}$.

Q9 Find $\dfrac{dy}{dx}$ if $y = \dfrac{\sqrt{x^2 + 3}}{\cos(3x)}$.

Q10 Differentiate with respect to x:

    a) $y = \cos x \ln x^2$ b) $y = \dfrac{e^{x^2 - x}}{(x + 2)^4}$

Q11 Find the coordinates of the stationary point on the curve $y = \dfrac{e^x}{\sqrt{x}}$.

Q12 Find the equation of the tangent to the curve $y = \dfrac{6x^2 + 3}{4x^2 - 1}$ at the point $(1, 3)$.

Review Exercise

Q13 Find the equation of the normal to the curve for $y = 3\operatorname{cosec}\frac{x}{4}$ when $x = \pi$.

Q14 Find $\frac{dy}{dx}$ when $x = 0$ for $y = \sec(3x - 2)$.

Q15 Differentiate with respect to x:

     a) $y = \sqrt{\operatorname{cosec} x}$ b) $y = \dfrac{\sec x}{x^2}$ c) $y = \cot(x^2 + 5)$ d) $y = e^{2x}\operatorname{cosec}(5x)$

Q16 At the end of its life in the main sequence, a small star like our Sun first expands to a Red Giant and then shrinks to a White Dwarf.

     a) When the star becomes a Red Giant, it expands and cools. The rate of change of radius with respect to temperature is approximately -2500 km K^{-1}. Find an expression for the rate of change of volume (V) with temperature (θ). Model the star as a sphere.

     b) When the star collapses to a White Dwarf, density (ρ) and temperature both increase as the diameter (D) decreases. The rate of change of diameter with respect to temperature, $\frac{dD}{d\theta}$, is approximately -215 km K^{-1}.

       Using the expression $V = kD^3$ for the volume of the star, find an expression for the rate of change of density $\frac{d\rho}{d\theta}$, if the mass of the star is a constant, m kg ($m = \rho V$).

Q17 The path of a particle is described parametrically by $x = t^2 - 6t$, $y = 2t^3 - 6t^2 - 18t$.

     a) Find $\frac{dy}{dx}$ in terms of t.

     b) Hence find any stationary points on the path of the particle.

Q18 A curve is given parametrically by $x = 3se^s$, $y = e^{2s} + se^{2s}$

     a) Find the equations of the tangents to the curve at $s = 0$ and $s = 2$.

     b) Hence find the coordinates of the point of intersection of these tangents, leaving your answer in terms of e.

Q19 The curve $4y + x^2y^2 = 4x$ passes through the two points $(2, a)$ and $(2, b)$, where $a > b$.

     By finding a and b and the gradient $\frac{dy}{dx}$ of the curve, show that the tangents to the curve at $(2, a)$ and $(2, b)$ intersect at $(5, 1)$.

Q20 The curve $x\ln x + x^2y = y^2x - 6x$ passes through two points $(1, a)$ and $(1, b)$, where $a > b$.

     a) Find a and b.

     b) Use implicit differentiation to find the gradient of the curve at each of these points and hence the equations of the normals passing through the points.

     c) Find the coordinates of the point where the normals intersect.

Q1 a) Find $f'(x)$ given that $f(x) = (3x + 1)^5$.

[2 marks]

b) Show that $f(x)$ has one point of inflection and find the coordinates of that point.

[3 marks]

c) Give the range of values for which $f(x)$ is concave.

[1 mark]

Q2 A curve has the equation $y = \dfrac{\cos x^2}{\ln (2x)}$.

a) Find $\dfrac{dy}{dx}$.

[4 marks]

b) Hence calculate the gradient of the curve at $x = 2$.
    Give your answer to 3 significant figures.

[1 mark]

Q3 The curve C has the equation $4x^2 - 2y^2 = 7x^2y$.

a) Find an expression for the gradient of C using implicit differentiation.

[3 marks]

b) Hence find:

(i) the gradient of the tangent to C at $(1, -4)$.

[3 marks]

(ii) the equation of the normal to C at $(1, -4)$ in the form $ax + by + c = 0$.

[3 marks]

Q4 A curve is defined by the parametric equations $x = t \ln t$ and $y = 2t^3 - t^2$.

a) Find $\dfrac{dy}{dx}$ in terms of t.

[3 marks]

b) Hence find the equation of the tangent at $(0, 1)$.

[3 marks]

Q5 A cuboid has length x cm, width $2x$ cm and height $3x$ cm.
The temperature (θ) of the cuboid is increased, which causes it to expand.

a) Given that A is the surface area of the cuboid and V is its volume, find:

(i) $\dfrac{dA}{dx}$

(ii) $\dfrac{dV}{dx}$

[2 marks]

b) Use your answers from part a) to show that if $\dfrac{dV}{d\theta} = 3$ cm^3 K^{-1}, then $\dfrac{dA}{d\theta} = \dfrac{22}{3x}$ cm^2 K^{-1}.

[2 marks]

Q6 A curve C defined by $x = t^3 - t^2$, $y = t^3 + 3t^2 - 9t$ has two turning points.

a) Find the coordinates of the turning points.

[4 marks]

b) Find the values of t at the points where C cuts the x-axis and hence show that C passes through the origin. Leave your answers in surd form if necessary.

[2 marks]

c) Find the equation of the tangent to C when $t = 2$.

[2 marks]

Q7 The curve $x^2y + y^2 = x^2 + 1$ passes through the points $(1, -2)$ and $(1, a)$.

a) Find the gradient of the curve at $(1, -2)$.

[4 marks]

b) Find the value of a and show that $(1, a)$ is a turning point of the curve.

[2 marks]

Q8 A curve is defined by $x \cos x + y \sin x = y^3$.

a) Show that at the stationary points of the curve, $y = x \tan x - 1$.

[5 marks]

b) Show that there are three points on the curve which have the x-coordinate $\dfrac{\pi}{2}$.

[3 marks]

c) Find the gradients of the tangents at each of these points and hence show that two of these tangents will never intersect.

[2 marks]

8.1 Integration of $(ax + b)^n$

You've already seen how to integrate functions of the form x^n in Year 1. In this section you'll see how to integrate functions which are linear transformations of x^n — functions of the form $(ax + b)^n$.

Learning Objectives (Spec Ref 8.2):

- Integrate functions of the form $(ax + b)^n$, $n \neq -1$, where a, b and n are constants.
- Solve integration problems with functions of the form $(ax + b)^n$.

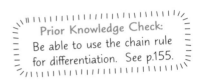

Prior Knowledge Check:
Be able to use the chain rule for differentiation. See p.155.

Integrating $(ax + b)^n$, $n \neq -1$

In Year 1, you learnt to think of **integration** as the **opposite of differentiation**. This means that if you differentiate a function, then **integrating** the result will get you back to the function you started with. Here's an example to show how you can use this technique to integrate functions of the form **$(ax + b)^n$**.

Example 1

a) **Differentiate $(3x + 4)^5$ with respect to x.**

Using the **chain rule**:

$$\frac{d}{dx}(3x + 4)^5 = 5(3x + 4)^4 \times 3$$
$$= 15(3x + 4)^4$$

Tip: See p.155 for a reminder on the chain rule.

b) **Use your answer to a) to find $\int (3x + 4)^4 \, dx$.**

1. From part a) you know that:

$$(3x + 4)^5 \xrightarrow{\text{Differentiation}} 15(3x + 4)^4$$

2. Integration is the opposite of differentiation so:

$$(3x + 4)^5 + C \xleftarrow{\text{Integration}} 15(3x + 4)^4$$

3. This means:

$$\int 15(3x + 4)^4 \, dx = (3x + 4)^5 + c$$
$$\Rightarrow 15\int (3x + 4)^4 \, dx = (3x + 4)^5 + c$$
$$\Rightarrow \int (3x + 4)^4 \, dx = \frac{1}{15}(3x + 4)^5 + \frac{c}{15}$$
$$= \frac{1}{15}(3x + 4)^5 + C$$

$\frac{c}{15}$ is just another constant term — you can call it C.

This method gives us a **general result** for integrating all functions of the form **$(ax + b)^n$**.

Differentiating **$(ax + b)^{n+1}$** using the chain rule gives **$a(n + 1)(ax + b)^n$**.

So $\int a(n + 1)(ax + b)^n \, dx = (ax + b)^{n+1} + c$

$a(n + 1)\int (ax + b)^n \, dx = (ax + b)^{n+1} + c$

Dividing by **$a(n + 1)$** gives the general expression:

$$\int (ax + b)^n \, dx = \frac{1}{a(n+1)}(ax + b)^{n+1} + C \quad \text{for } n \neq -1, a \neq 0$$

Tip: This doesn't work for $n = -1$ because you'd end up having to divide by $n + 1 = 0$. See page 204 for a method of integrating x^{-1} and $(ax + b)^{-1}$.

Example 2

Find $\int (3 - 4x)^2 \, dx$, using the general expression for $\int (ax + b)^n \, dx$.

Write down the values of
a, b and n and then substitute
them into the formula.

$a = -4$, $b = 3$ and $n = 2$

$$\int (3 - 4x)^2 \, dx = \frac{1}{-4 \times 3}(3 - 4x)^3 + C = \boxed{-\frac{1}{12}(3 - 4x)^3 + C}$$

$a = -4$ $\qquad$ $n + 1 = 3$

In Year 1, you learnt that definite integrals work out the **area** between a curve
and the x-axis. To find the area between a curve $y = f(x)$ and the x-axis over
an interval, just integrate f(x) with respect to x over that interval.

Example 3

Work out the area enclosed by the curve $y = (x - 2)^3$,
the x-axis and the lines $x = 2$ and $x = 3$.

You just need to integrate the curve $y = (x - 2)^3$
between $x = 2$ and $x = 3$, i.e. evaluate $\int_2^3 (x - 2)^3 \, dx$:

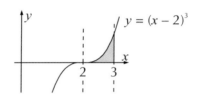
$y = (x - 2)^3$

1. Use the formula with $a = 1$, $b = -2$
    and $n = 3$ to work out the integral.

$$\int_2^3 (x - 2)^3 \, dx = \frac{1}{4}[(x - 2)^4]_2^3$$

$x = 3$ $\qquad$ $x = 2$

2. Substitute in the limits of
    integration to find the area.

$$\int_2^3 (x - 2)^3 \, dx = \frac{1}{4}[(3 - 2)^4] - \frac{1}{4}[(2 - 2)^4]$$

$$= \frac{1}{4}[1^4] - \frac{1}{4}[0^4]$$

$$= \frac{1}{4} - 0 = \boxed{\frac{1}{4}}$$

Exercise 8.1.1

Q1 Integrate with respect to x:

a) $(x + 10)^{10}$ $\qquad$ b) $(5x)^7$ $\qquad$ c) $(3 - 5x)^{-2}$ $\qquad$ d) $(3x - 4)^{-\frac{4}{3}}$

Q2 a) By using the general expression for $\int (ax + b)^n \, dx$,

show that the integral $A = \int 8(2x - 4)^4 \, dx = \frac{4(2x - 4)^5}{5} + C.$

b) Hence evaluate A between the values $x = \frac{3}{2}$ and $x = \frac{5}{2}$.

Q3 Evaluate $\int_0^1 (6x + 1)^{-3} \, dx$.

Q4 The curve $y = f(x)$ goes through the point $\left(1, \frac{3}{35}\right)$ and $f'(x) = (8 - 7x)^4$. Find f(x).

8.2 Integration of e^x and $\dfrac{1}{x}$

The functions e^x and $\dfrac{1}{x}$ are pretty easy to integrate — it's just the opposite of differentiating e^x and ln x.

Learning Objectives (Spec Ref 8.2):

- Integrate functions containing e^x and $\dfrac{1}{x}$ terms.
- Integrate linear transformations of e^x and $\dfrac{1}{x}$, i.e. functions of the form e^{ax+b} and $\dfrac{1}{ax+b}$.

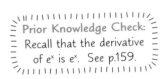
Prior Knowledge Check:
Recall that the derivative
of e^x is e^x. See p.159.

Integrating e^x and e^{ax+b}

e^x differentiates to give e^x, so it makes sense that e^x **integrates** to give **e^x + C**: $\boxed{\displaystyle\int e^x\,dx = e^x + C}$

Example 1

Integrate the function $6x^2 - 4x + 3e^x$ with respect to x.

1. Integrate each term separately:

$$\int 6x^2 - 4x + 3e^x\,dx = \int 6x^2\,dx - \int 4x\,dx + \int 3e^x\,dx$$

2. The first two terms are of the form x^n, but you need to use the rule above on the third term.

$$\int 6x^2\,dx = 2x^3 + c \qquad \int 4x\,dx = 2x^2 + c$$

$$\int 3e^x\,dx = 3\int e^x\,dx = 3e^x + c$$

3. Putting this all together gives:

$$\int 6x^2 - 4x + 3e^x\,dx = \boxed{2x^3 - 2x^2 + 3e^x + C}$$

On p.200 you saw how to integrate **linear transformations** of x^n by differentiating with the **chain rule** and working backwards. You can do the same with functions of the form e^{ax+b} where a and b are constants. Start by considering what you get when you **differentiate** functions of the form e^{ax+b} using the chain rule and work backwards.

This method of differentiating $f(ax + b)$ using the chain rule and working backwards to find an integral can be used with **any of the functions** that you know the derivative of.

Example 2

a) Differentiate the function e^{4x-1} with respect to x.

Use the chain rule:
$$\frac{d}{dx}(e^{4x-1}) = \boxed{4e^{4x-1}}$$

b) Using your answer to a), find the integral $\displaystyle\int e^{4x-1}\,dx$.

1. Reverse the process of differentiation to integrate.
$$\frac{d}{dx}(e^{4x-1}) = 4e^{4x-1} \Rightarrow \int 4e^{4x-1}\,dx = e^{4x-1} + c$$

2. Take out the factor of 4 and divide by it.
$$\Rightarrow 4\int e^{4x-1}\,dx = e^{4x-1} + c$$

$$\Rightarrow \int e^{4x-1}\,dx = \frac{1}{4}e^{4x-1} + C$$

This method gives you a **general rule** for integrating functions of the form e^{ax+b}:

$$\int e^{ax+b}\,dx = \frac{1}{a}e^{ax+b} + C \qquad \text{for } a \neq 0$$

This means you just need to **divide** by the **coefficient of** x
and add a constant of integration — the e^{ax+b} bit **doesn't change**.

Example 3

Integrate the following:

a) e^{7x}

If you differentiated e^{7x} you'd get $7e^{7x}$, so you need
to **divide by 7** (the coefficient of x) when integrating.

$$\int e^{7x}\,dx = \frac{1}{7}e^{7x} + C$$

b) $e^{\frac{x}{2}}$

If you differentiated this using the chain rule, you'd get $\frac{1}{2}e^{\frac{x}{2}}$,
so you need to **multiply by 2** (divide by $\frac{1}{2}$) to integrate.

$$\int e^{\frac{x}{2}}\,dx = \int e^{\frac{1}{2}x}\,dx = 2e^{\frac{x}{2}} + C$$

c) $2e^{4-3x}$

Multiplying by 2 doesn't change the integration —
the coefficient of x is -3, so **divide by -3** and you're done.

$$\int 2e^{4-3x}\,dx = -\frac{2}{3}e^{4-3x} + C$$

Exercise 8.2.1

Q1   Find the following indefinite integrals:

a) $\int 2e^x\,dx$

b) $\int 4x + 7e^x\,dx$

c) $\int e^{10x}\,dx$

d) $\int e^{-3x} + x\,dx$

e) $\int e^{\frac{7}{2}x}\,dx$

f) $\int e^{4x-2}\,dx$

g) $\int \frac{1}{2}e^{2-\frac{3}{2}x}\,dx$

h) $\int e^{4\left(\frac{x}{3}+1\right)}\,dx$

Q2   Find the equation of the curve that has the derivative $\frac{dy}{dx} = 10e^{-5x-1}$
and passes through the origin.

Q3   Integrate the function e^{8y+5} with respect to y.

Q4   Evaluate the following definite integrals, giving exact answers:

a) $\int_2^3 e^{2x}\,dx$

b) $\int_{-1}^0 12e^{12x+12}\,dx$

c) $\int_{-\frac{\pi}{2}}^{\frac{\pi}{2}} e^{\pi-2x}\,dx$

d) $\int_{-3}^6 \sqrt[6]{e^x} + \frac{1}{\sqrt[3]{e^x}}\,dx$

Q4 d) Hint:
Remember:
$$\sqrt[n]{e^x} = e^{\frac{x}{n}}$$
$$\frac{1}{\sqrt[n]{e^x}} = e^{-\frac{x}{n}}$$

Integrating $\frac{1}{x}$ and $\frac{1}{ax+b}$

The method for integrating x^n and $(ax + b)^n$ on p.200 doesn't work for $n = -1$. For these functions you need to consider the fact that $\frac{d}{dx}(\ln x) = \frac{1}{x}$, which you should remember from Chapter 7.

Prior Knowledge Check: Recall that the derivative of $\ln x$ is $\frac{1}{x}$. See p.161.

Example 1

Let $f(x) = \frac{1}{x}$, $x > 0$. Integrate $f(x)$ with respect to x, given that $\frac{d}{dx}(\ln x) = \frac{1}{x}$.

Given the derivative of $\ln x$, integration is the opposite of differentiation, so:

$$\ln x \xrightarrow{\text{Differentiation}} \frac{1}{x}$$

$$\ln x + C \xleftarrow{\text{Integration}} \frac{1}{x}$$

So $\int \frac{1}{x}\, dx = \boxed{\ln x + C}$

So now we have a general result for integrating $\frac{1}{x}$: $\boxed{\int \frac{1}{x}\, dx = \ln |x| + C}$

Notice that this result uses $|x|$ instead of just x. This is because the function $\ln x$ is not defined for negative values of x. Using the modulus means you'll never end up taking $\ln$ of a negative value.

You'll be working with logs all the time when integrating functions of the form $\frac{1}{x}$ — it'll help to remember the log laws:

$$\log(ab) = \log a + \log b$$
$$\log\left(\frac{a}{b}\right) = \log a - \log b$$
$$\log(a^b) = b \log a$$

Example 2

Find the following integrals:

a) $\int \frac{5}{x}\, dx$

5 is a constant coefficient — take it outside the integral so that you're just integrating $\frac{1}{x}$.

$$\int \frac{5}{x}\, dx = 5\int \frac{1}{x}\, dx = \boxed{5 \ln |x| + C}$$

b) $\int_3^9 \frac{1}{3x}\, dx$

1. Here $\frac{1}{3}$ is the coefficient, so it goes outside the integral:

$$\int_3^9 \frac{1}{3x}\, dx = \frac{1}{3}\int_3^9 \frac{1}{x}\, dx = \frac{1}{3}[\ln|x|]_3^9$$

2. Now put in the limits and use log laws to simplify:

$$= \frac{1}{3}(\ln|9| - \ln|3|) = \frac{1}{3}(\ln(\frac{9}{3})) = \boxed{\frac{1}{3}\ln 3}$$

$$\ln a - \ln b = \ln \frac{a}{b}$$

You can integrate **linear transformations** of $\frac{1}{x}$ (i.e. functions of the form $\frac{1}{ax+b}$) by considering the result of differentiating $\ln|ax+b|$.

Example 3

Given that $\frac{d}{dx}(\ln|4x+2|) = \frac{4}{4x+2}$, find $\int \frac{1}{4x+2}\,dx$.

Reverse the process of differentiation to integrate:

$$\frac{d}{dx}(\ln|4x+2|) = \frac{4}{4x+2} \implies \int \frac{4}{4x+2}\,dx = \ln|4x+2| + c$$

$$\implies 4\int \frac{1}{4x+2}\,dx = \ln|4x+2| + c$$

$$\implies \int \frac{1}{4x+2}\,dx = \frac{1}{4}\ln|4x+2| + C$$

This method gives a **general result** for integrating functions of the form $\frac{1}{ax+b}$:

$$\int \frac{1}{ax+b}\,dx = \frac{1}{a}\ln|ax+b| + C$$

Example 4

Find $\int \frac{1}{2x+5}\,dx$.

Using the general rule, $a = 2$ and $b = 5$:

$$\int \frac{1}{2x+5}\,dx = \frac{1}{2}\ln|2x+5| + C$$

Exercise 8.2.2

Q1 Find the following:

a) $\int \frac{19}{x}\,dx$ b) $\int \frac{1}{7x}\,dx$ c) $\int \frac{1}{7x+2}\,dx$ d) $\int \frac{4}{1-3x}\,dx$

Q2 Integrate $y = \frac{1}{8x} - \frac{20}{x}$ with respect to x.

Q3 a) Show that $\int \frac{6}{x} - \frac{3}{x}\,dx = \ln|x^3| + C$.

b) Evaluate $\int_4^5 \frac{6}{x} - \frac{3}{x}\,dx$, giving an exact answer.

> **Q3-4 Hint:** Use the log laws from Year 1 (given on p.204).

Q4 Show that $\int_b^a 15(5+3x)^{-1}\,dx = \ln\left|\frac{5+3a}{5+3b}\right|^5$.

Q5 The graph of the curve $y = f(x)$ passes through the point $(1, 2)$. The derivative of $f(x)$ is given by $f'(x) = \frac{4}{10-9x}$. Find $f(x)$.

Q6 a) Express the area bounded by the curve $y = \frac{-7}{16-2x}$, the x-axis, the y-axis, and the line $x = -3$ as an integral with respect to x.

b) Show that the area is equal to $\ln\left[\left(\frac{8}{11}\right)^{\frac{7}{2}}\right]$.

Q7 Given that $\int_1^A \frac{4}{6x-5}\,dx = 10$ and $A \geq 1$, find A in terms of e.

8.3 Integration of Trigonometric Functions

There are a few trig functions which are really easy to integrate — once you've learnt them, you'll be able to integrate loads of complicated-looking trig functions quickly.

Learning Objectives (Spec Ref 8.2):
- Integrate functions of sin x, cos x and sec^2 x.
- Integrate other trig functions by considering the derivatives of cosec x, sec x and cot x.

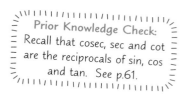
Prior Knowledge Check:
Recall that cosec, sec and cot are the reciprocals of sin, cos and tan. See p.61.

Integration of sin x and cos x

In Chapter 7 you learnt how to differentiate sin x and cos x. You should remember that sin x differentiates to cos x, and cos x differentiates to $-$sin x.

Working backwards from this, we get:

Tip: You won't be given the integrals for sin and cos in your formula booklet, so make sure you remember them.

$$\int \sin x \, dx = -\cos x + C \qquad \int \cos x \, dx = \sin x + C$$

Example 1

Find the following integrals:

a) $\int 4 \cos x \, dx$

$\int \cos x \, dx = \sin x + C$, so: $\qquad \int 4 \cos x \, dx = 4 \int \cos x \, dx = \boxed{4 \sin x + C}$

b) $\int_0^{\pi} \frac{\sin x}{2} + \frac{1}{\pi} \, dx$

1. Integrate each term separately. $\quad \int_0^{\pi} \frac{\sin x}{2} + \frac{1}{\pi} \, dx = \int_0^{\pi} \frac{1}{2} \sin x + \frac{1}{\pi} \, dx = \left[\frac{1}{2}(-\cos x) + \frac{1}{\pi}x \right]_0^{\pi}$

$$= \left[-\frac{1}{2} \cos x + \frac{1}{\pi}x \right]_0^{\pi}$$

2. Put in the limits.

$$\left[-\frac{1}{2}\cos x + \frac{1}{\pi}x \right]_0^{\pi} = \left[-\frac{1}{2} \cos \pi + \left(\frac{1}{\pi} \times \pi \right) \right] - \left[-\frac{1}{2}\cos 0 + \left(\frac{1}{\pi} \times 0 \right) \right]$$

$$= \left[-\frac{1}{2}(-1) + 1 \right] - \left[-\frac{1}{2}(1) + 0 \right]$$

$$= \left[\frac{1}{2} + 1 \right] - \left[-\frac{1}{2} + 0 \right] = \boxed{2}$$

c) $\int \frac{1}{2}(\cos x + 2 \sin x) \, dx$

Multiply out and integrate each term separately.

$$\int \frac{1}{2}(\cos x + 2 \sin x) \, dx = \int \frac{1}{2}\cos x + \sin x \, dx$$

$$= \frac{1}{2}\sin x + (-\cos x) + C$$

$$= \boxed{\frac{1}{2}\sin x - \cos x + C}$$

You can integrate **linear transformations** of sin x and cos x of the form sin($ax + b$) and cos($ax + b$).

- **Differentiating** sin($ax + b$) using the chain rule gives: $a\cos(ax + b)$

- So when **integrating** cos($ax + b$), you need to **divide** by a, giving: $\frac{1}{a}\sin(ax + b)$

The same can be done when integrating sin($ax + b$), so we get:

$$\int \sin(ax + b)\,dx = -\frac{1}{a}\cos(ax + b) + C$$
$$\int \cos(ax + b)\,dx = \frac{1}{a}\sin(ax + b) + C$$

Example 2

Find $\int \sin(1 - 6x)\,dx$.

Using the general formula with $a = -6$ and $b = 1$ gives: $\int \sin(1 - 6x)\,dx = \frac{1}{-6} \times -\cos(1 - 6x) + C$

$$= \frac{1}{6}\cos(1 - 6x) + C$$

Exercise 8.3.1

Q1 Integrate the following functions with respect to x.

a) $\frac{1}{7}\cos x$
b) $-3\sin x$
c) $-3\cos x - 3\sin x$

d) $\sin 5x$
e) $\cos\left(\frac{x}{7}\right)$
f) $2\sin(-3x)$

g) $5\cos\left(3x + \frac{\pi}{5}\right)$
h) $-4\sin\left(4x - \frac{\pi}{3}\right)$
i) $\cos(4x + 3) + \sin(3 - 4x)$

Q2 Integrate $\frac{1}{2}\cos 3\theta - \sin \theta$ with respect to θ.

Q3 Evaluate the following definite integrals:

a) $\int_0^{\frac{\pi}{2}} \sin x\,dx$
b) $\int_{\frac{\pi}{6}}^{\frac{\pi}{3}} \sin 3x\,dx$
c) $\int_{-1}^{2} 3\sin(\pi x + \pi)\,dx$

Q4 a) Integrate the function $y = 2\pi \cos\left(\frac{\pi x}{2}\right)$ with respect to x between the limits $x = 1$ and $x = 2$.

b) Given that the function doesn't cross the x-axis between these limits, state whether the area between the curve and the x-axis for $1 \leq x \leq 2$ lies above or below the x-axis, justifying your answer.

Q5 Show that $\int_{\frac{\pi}{3}}^{\frac{\pi}{2}} \sin(-x) + \cos(-x)\,dx = \frac{1 - \sqrt{3}}{2}$.

Q6 Evaluate the definite integral $\int_{-\frac{\pi}{3}}^{\frac{\pi}{3}} \sin(3x + 2) - \cos x\,dx$.

Q7 Show that the integral of the function $y = 5\cos\left(\frac{x}{6}\right)$ between $x = -2\pi$ and $x = \pi$ is $15(1 + \sqrt{3})$.

Integration of sec² x

Another trigonometric function which is easy to integrate is the derivative of tan x, **sec² x**. Since tan x differentiates to sec² x, you get:

$$\int \sec^2 x \, dx = \tan x + C$$

Tip: This integral is given in the formula book — it's given as $\int \sec^2 kx \, dx = \frac{1}{k} \tan kx + C$.

Example 1

Find $\int 2 \sec^2 x + 4x \, dx$.

Integrate each term separately: $\int 2 \sec^2 x + 4x \, dx = 2 \int \sec^2 x \, dx + \int 4x \, dx = \boxed{2 \tan x + 2x^2 + C}$

Unsurprisingly, you can use the chain rule in reverse to integrate functions of the form sec²(ax + b):

$$\int \sec^2 (ax + b) \, dx = \frac{1}{a} \tan(ax + b) + C$$

Example 2

Find $\int \cos 4x - 2 \sin 2x + \sec^2 \left(\frac{1}{2}x\right) dx$.

1. Integrate each term separately.

$$\int \cos 4x \, dx = \frac{1}{4} \sin 4x$$

$$\int -2 \sin 2x \, dx = -2 \left(-\frac{1}{2} \cos 2x\right) = \cos 2x$$

$$\int \sec^2 \left(\frac{1}{2}x\right) dx = \frac{1}{\left(\frac{1}{2}\right)} \tan \left(\frac{1}{2}x\right) = 2 \tan \left(\frac{1}{2}x\right)$$

2. Put them all together.

$$\int \cos 4x - 2 \sin 2x + \sec^2 \left(\frac{1}{2}x\right) dx$$

$$= \frac{1}{4} \sin 4x + \cos 2x + 2 \tan \left(\frac{1}{2}x\right) + C$$

Exercise 8.3.2

Q1 Find the following integrals:

a) $\int 2 \sec^2 x + 1 \, dx$

b) $\int \sec^2 9x \, dx$

c) $\int 20 \sec^2 3y \, dy$

d) $\int \sec^2 \frac{x}{7} \, dx$

e) $\int_0^{\frac{\pi}{3}} -\frac{1}{\cos^2 \theta} \, d\theta$

f) $\int_0^{\frac{\pi}{4}} 3 \sec^2 (-3x) \, dx$

Q2 Find the value of the integral of the function $y = \sec^2 x$ between the limits $x = \frac{2}{3}\pi$ and $x = \pi$.

Q3 Integrate sec²(x + α) + sec²(3x + β) with respect to x, where α and β are constants.

Q4 Let A be a constant. Integrate $5A \sec^2 \left(\frac{\pi}{3} - 2\theta\right)$ with respect to θ between the limits of $\theta = \frac{\pi}{12}$ and $\theta = \frac{\pi}{6}$.

Integration of other trigonometric functions

There are some other more complicated trig functions which are really easy to integrate.
They are the **derivatives** of the functions **cosec x, sec x** and **cot x**.

You may remember these derivatives from Chapter 7, but here's a recap:

$$\frac{d}{dx}(\cosec x) = -\cosec x \cot x \qquad \frac{d}{dx}(\sec x) = \sec x \tan x \qquad \frac{d}{dx}(\cot x) = -\cosec^2 x$$

Reversing the differentiation gives the following three integrals.
They'll be really useful when integrating complicated trig functions.

$$\int \cosec x \cot x \, dx = -\cosec x + C$$
$$\int \sec x \tan x \, dx = \sec x + C$$
$$\int \cosec^2 x \, dx = -\cot x + C$$

As always, you can integrate **linear transformations** of these functions (i.e. functions of the form
cosec($ax + b$)cot($ax + b$), sec($ax + b$)tan($ax + b$) and **cosec²($ax + b$)**) by **dividing** by the coefficient of x.

$$\int \cosec(ax + b)\cot(ax + b) \, dx = -\frac{1}{a}\cosec(ax + b) + C$$
$$\int \sec(ax + b)\tan(ax + b) \, dx = \frac{1}{a}\sec(ax + b) + C$$
$$\int \cosec^2(ax + b) \, dx = -\frac{1}{a}\cot(ax + b) + C$$

Tip: The $ax + b$ bit has to be the same in each trig function — you couldn't integrate sec x tan $3x$ using these formulas.

Example 1

Find the following:

a) $\int 2 \sec x \tan x \, dx$

Take the constant outside the integral, and integrate.

$$\int 2 \sec x \tan x \, dx = 2 \int \sec x \tan x \, dx = 2(\sec x + c)$$
$$= \boxed{2 \sec x + C}$$

b) $\int_0^\pi \cosec^2\left(\frac{x}{2} - \frac{\pi}{4}\right) dx$

This is a definite integral, so evaluate between the limits.

1. Integrate the function, dividing by the coefficient of x.

$$\int_0^\pi \cosec^2\left(\frac{x}{2} - \frac{\pi}{4}\right) dx = \left[-\frac{1}{\left(\frac{1}{2}\right)}\cot\left(\frac{x}{2} - \frac{\pi}{4}\right)\right]_0^\pi$$

$$= -2\left[\cot\left(\frac{x}{2} - \frac{\pi}{4}\right)\right]_0^\pi = -2\left[\frac{1}{\tan\left(\frac{x}{2} - \frac{\pi}{4}\right)}\right]_0^\pi$$

2. Put in the limits.

$$= -2\left(\frac{1}{\tan\left(\frac{\pi}{2} - \frac{\pi}{4}\right)} - \frac{1}{\tan\left(0 - \frac{\pi}{4}\right)}\right)$$

$$= -2\left(\frac{1}{\tan\left(\frac{\pi}{4}\right)} - \frac{1}{\tan\left(-\frac{\pi}{4}\right)}\right)$$

3. Evaluate the integral.

$$= -2\left(\frac{1}{1} - \frac{1}{(-1)}\right) = \boxed{-4}$$

c) $\int 8\,\mathrm{cosec}(2x+1)\cot(2x+1)\,dx$

1. Take the constant
   outside the integral. $\int 8\,\mathrm{cosec}(2x+1)\cot(2x+1)\,dx = 8\int \mathrm{cosec}(2x+1)\cot(2x+1)\,dx$

2. Integrate the function: $= 8\left(-\tfrac{1}{2}\,\mathrm{cosec}(2x+1)+c\right)$

   Don't forget to divide
   by the x coefficient. $= -4\,\mathrm{cosec}\,(2x+1)+C$

Example 2

Find $\int 10\sec 5x\tan 5x + \tfrac{1}{2}\,\mathrm{cosec}\,3x\cot 3x - \mathrm{cosec}^2(6x+1)\,dx.$

1. Integrate each bit in turn: $\int 10\sec 5x\tan 5x\,dx = 10\left(\tfrac{1}{5}\sec 5x\right) = 2\sec 5x$

$$\int \tfrac{1}{2}\,\mathrm{cosec}\,3x\cot 3x\,dx = \tfrac{1}{2}\left(-\tfrac{1}{3}\,\mathrm{cosec}\,3x\right)$$

$$= -\tfrac{1}{6}\,\mathrm{cosec}\,3x$$

Don't forget
the minus that
comes from
the integration.

$$\int -\mathrm{cosec}^2(6x+1)\,dx = -\left(-\tfrac{1}{6}\cot(6x+1)\right)$$

$$= \tfrac{1}{6}\cot(6x+1)$$

2. Putting the terms together and
   adding the constant gives: $\int 10\sec 5x\tan 5x + \tfrac{1}{2}\,\mathrm{cosec}\,3x\cot 3x - \mathrm{cosec}^2(6x+1)\,dx$

$$= 2\sec 5x - \tfrac{1}{6}\,\mathrm{cosec}\,3x + \tfrac{1}{6}\cot(6x+1)+C$$

Exercise 8.3.3

Q1 Find the following integrals:

a) $\int \mathrm{cosec}^2 11x\,dx$

b) $\int 5\sec 10\theta\tan 10\theta\,d\theta$

c) $\int -\mathrm{cosec}(x+17)\cot(x+17)\,dx$

d) $\int -3\,\mathrm{cosec}\,3x\cot 3x\,dx$

e) $\int 13\sec\left(\tfrac{\pi}{4}-x\right)\tan\left(\tfrac{\pi}{4}-x\right)dx$

f) $\int 4\,\mathrm{cosec}^2(5x+3)\,dx$

Q2 Find $\int 10\,\mathrm{cosec}^2\left(\alpha-\tfrac{x}{2}\right)-60\sec(\alpha-6x)\tan(\alpha-6x)\,dx$

Q3 Integrate the function $6\sec 2x\tan 2x + 6\,\mathrm{cosec}\,2x\cot x$ with respect to x
between the limits of $x = \tfrac{\pi}{12}$ and $x = \tfrac{\pi}{8}$.

Q4 Find the area of the region bounded by $y = \mathrm{cosec}^2(3x)$,
the x-axis and the lines $x = \tfrac{\pi}{12}$ and $x = \tfrac{\pi}{6}$.

8.4 Integration of $\dfrac{f'(x)}{f(x)}$

Fractions in which the numerator is the derivative of the denominator are pretty easy to integrate — there is a general formula which comes from the chain rule.

Learning Objectives (Spec Ref 8.5):
- Integrate functions of the form $\dfrac{f'(x)}{f(x)}$, including multiples of these functions.
- Integrate functions of tan, cosec, sec and cot.

Prior Knowledge Check:
Recall that the derivative of $\ln(f(x))$ is $\dfrac{f'(x)}{f(x)}$. See p.162.

Integrating $\dfrac{f'(x)}{f(x)}$

If you have a fraction that has a function of x as the numerator and a different function of x as the denominator, e.g. $\dfrac{x-2}{x^3+1}$, you'll probably struggle to integrate it.

However, if you have a fraction where the **numerator** is the **derivative** of the **denominator**, e.g. $\dfrac{3x^2}{x^3+1}$, it integrates to give ln of the denominator.

In general terms, this is written as:

$$\int \frac{f'(x)}{f(x)}\, dx = \ln|f(x)| + C$$

This rule won't surprise you if you remember differentiating ln $(f(x))$ using the chain rule (see p.162) — the derivative with respect to x of ln $(f(x))$ is $\dfrac{f'(x)}{f(x)}$.

You sometimes see this rule written without the modulus signs, but if it's possible for $f(x)$ to take a negative value, you need the modulus so you don't end up trying to take ln of a negative number.

The hardest bit about integrations like this is recognising that the denominator differentiates to give the numerator — once you've spotted that you can just use the formula.

Example 1

Integrate the following functions with respect to x.

a) $\dfrac{2x}{x^2+1}$

1. Differentiate the denominator to see what it gives:

   $\dfrac{d}{dx}(x^2 + 1) = 2x$ — this is the **numerator**.

2. The numerator is the derivative of the denominator, so use the formula:

   $\displaystyle\int \frac{2x}{x^2+1}\, dx = \boxed{\ln|x^2 + 1| + C}$

   You could leave out the modulus sign as $x^2 + 1 > 0$

---

b) $\dfrac{x(3x-4)}{x^3-2x^2-1}$

    1. Differentiate the denominator: $\dfrac{d}{dx}(x^3-2x^2-1)=3x^2-4x=x(3x-4)$

    2. $x(3x-4)$ is the numerator,
       so use the formula: $\displaystyle\int \dfrac{x(3x-4)}{x^3-2x^2-1}\,dx = \boxed{\ln|x^3-2x^2-1|+C}$

You might see questions where the numerator is a **multiple** of the derivative of the denominator just to confuse things. When this happens, just put the multiple **in front** of the ln.

Example 2

Find:

a) $\displaystyle\int \dfrac{8x^3-4}{x^4-2x}\,dx$

    1. Differentiate the denominator: $\dfrac{d}{dx}(x^4-2x)=4x^3-2$ and $8x^3-4=2(4x^3-2)$

                                      The numerator is $2 \times$ the derivative of the denominator.

    2. Take out the constant
       and use the formula: $\displaystyle\int \dfrac{8x^3-4}{x^4-2x}\,dx = 2\int \dfrac{4x^3-2}{x^4-2x}\,dx = \boxed{2\ln|x^4-2x|+C}$

b) $\displaystyle\int \dfrac{3\sin 3x}{\cos 3x + 2}\,dx$

    1. Differentiate the denominator: $\dfrac{d}{dx}(\cos 3x + 2)=-3\sin 3x$

                                        The numerator is $-1 \times$ the derivative of the denominator.

    2. Use the formula: $\displaystyle\int \dfrac{3\sin 3x}{\cos 3x + 2}\,dx = -\int \dfrac{-3\sin 3x}{\cos 3x + 2}\,dx = -\ln|\cos 3x + 2|+C$

    3. You can neaten your answer by
       combining it into one logarithm. $= -\ln|\cos 3x + 2| - \ln k = \boxed{-\ln|k(\cos 3x + 2)|}$

C is just a constant, so if we want we can express C as a logarithm — call it **ln k** or **−ln k**, where k is a constant. (Adding in a minus sign makes it easier to simplify in some cases, like in the example above.)

You can use this method to integrate **trig functions** by writing them as fractions:

> You can work out the integral of **tan x** using this method:
>
> $\tan x = \dfrac{\sin x}{\cos x}$, and $\dfrac{d}{dx}(\cos x)=-\sin x$
>
> The numerator is **−1** × the **derivative** of the **denominator**, so:
>
> $\displaystyle\int \tan x\,dx = \int \dfrac{\sin x}{\cos x}\,dx = -\ln|\cos x|+C$

This is a useful result — it's given in the formula booklet in the following form:

$$\boxed{\int \tan kx\,dx = \dfrac{1}{k}\ln|\sec kx|+C}$$

Tip: $-\ln|\cos x|$ is the same as $\ln|\sec x|$ by the laws of logs.

There are some other **trig functions** that you can integrate in the same way.

$$\int \operatorname{cosec} x \, dx = -\ln |\operatorname{cosec} x + \cot x| + C$$

$$\int \sec x \, dx = \ln |\sec x + \tan x| + C$$

$$\int \cot x \, dx = \ln |\sin x| + C$$

Tip: The formula booklet actually gives them in the form cosec kx etc — but you can easily get these results by setting $k = 1$.

As always, if you're integrating a linear transformation of any of these functions of the form f($ax + b$), then divide by a when you integrate.

You can check these results easily by using differentiation — differentiate the right-hand side of the results to get the left-hand sides. Remember that differentiating ln |f(x)| gives $\dfrac{f'(x)}{f(x)}$.

Example 3

Find the following integrals:

a) $\int 2 \sec x \, dx$

Take out the constant of 2 and use the result for sec x above:

$$\int 2 \sec x \, dx = \boxed{2 \ln|\sec x + \tan x| + C}$$

b) $\int \dfrac{\cot x}{5} \, dx$

Take out the constant of $\dfrac{1}{5}$ and use the result for cot x above.

$$\int \dfrac{\cot x}{5} \, dx = \boxed{\dfrac{1}{5} \ln|\sin x| + C}$$

c) $\int 2(\operatorname{cosec} x + \sec x) \, dx$

1. Expand the brackets and integrate each term separately:

$$\int 2(\operatorname{cosec} x + \sec x) \, dx = \int 2 \operatorname{cosec} x + 2 \sec x \, dx$$

$$= -2 \ln |\operatorname{cosec} x + \cot x| + 2 \ln |\sec x + \tan x| + C$$

2. Use log laws to simplify:

$$= \boxed{2 \ln \left| \dfrac{\sec x + \tan x}{\operatorname{cosec} x + \cot x} \right| + C}$$

d) $\int \dfrac{1}{2} \operatorname{cosec} 2x \, dx$

1. Work out what happens to the coefficient of x.

The coefficient of x is 2, so you need to divide by 2 when you integrate.

2. Use the result for cosec x:

$$\int \dfrac{1}{2} \operatorname{cosec} 2x \, dx = \boxed{-\dfrac{1}{4} \ln|\operatorname{cosec} 2x + \cot 2x| + C}$$

Divide $\dfrac{1}{2}$ by 2

Tip: Check this by differentiating (using the chain rule with $u = \operatorname{cosec} 2x + \cot 2x$).

Q1 Find the following integrals:

a) $\int \dfrac{4x^3}{x^4 - 1}\, dx$

b) $\int \dfrac{2x - 1}{x^2 - x}\, dx$

c) $\int \dfrac{x^4}{3x^5 + 6}\, dx$

d) $\int \dfrac{12x^3 + 18x^2 - 3}{x^4 + 2x^3 - x}\, dx$

e) $\int \dfrac{8x - 2}{(x - 2)(2x + 3)}\, dx$

f) $\int \dfrac{6 - 4x^2}{2x^3 - 9x + 7}\, dx$

Q2 Find the indefinite integrals below:

a) $\int \dfrac{e^x}{e^x + 6}\, dx$

b) $\int \dfrac{2(e^{2x} + 3e^x)}{e^{2x} + 6e^x}\, dx$

c) $\int \dfrac{e^x}{3(e^x + 3)}\, dx$

d) $\int \dfrac{10e^{4x} + 5}{5e^{4x} + 10x}\, dx$

Q3 Find the following integrals:

a) $\int \dfrac{2\cos 2x}{1 + \sin 2x}\, dx$

b) $\int \dfrac{\sin 3x}{\cos 3x - 1}\, dx$

c) $\int \dfrac{3\operatorname{cosec} x \cot x + 6x}{\operatorname{cosec} x - x^2 + 4}\, dx$

d) $\int \dfrac{\sec^2 x}{\tan x}\, dx$

e) $\int \dfrac{\sec x \tan x}{\sec x + 5}\, dx$

f) $\int \dfrac{\operatorname{cosec}^2 x}{2\cot x - 1}\, dx$

Q4 Show that $\int \dfrac{4\cos(2x + 7)}{\sin(2x + 7)}\, dx = 2\ln|k\,\sin(2x + 7)|$.

Q5 Prove that:

a) $\int \sec x\, dx = \ln|\sec x + \tan x| + C$

b) $\int \operatorname{cosec} x\, dx = -\ln|\operatorname{cosec} x + \cot x| + C$

Q5 Hint: Try multiplying the bit inside the integral by $\dfrac{\sec x + \tan x}{\sec x + \tan x}$ in part a) — there's a similar trick for part b) as well.

Q6 Find the following integrals:

a) $\int 2\tan x\, dx$

b) $\int \tan 2x\, dx$

c) $\int 4\operatorname{cosec} x\, dx$

d) $\int \cot 3x\, dx$

e) $\int \dfrac{1}{2}\sec 2x\, dx$

f) $\int 3\operatorname{cosec} 6x\, dx$

Q7 Find $\int \dfrac{4\sin(3 - 2x)}{3 + \cos(3 - 2x)} + \dfrac{x^2}{6x^3 - 5}\, dx$.

Q8 Find $\int \dfrac{\sec^2 x}{2\tan x} - 4\sec 2x \tan 2x + \dfrac{\operatorname{cosec} 2x \cot 2x - 1}{\operatorname{cosec} 2x + 2x}\, dx$.

8.5 Integrating $\dfrac{du}{dx}$ f'(u)

This section will show you how to integrate certain products of functions. You can use the chain rule in reverse to integrate special products of functions and their derivatives.

Learning Objectives (Spec Ref 8.5):

- Integrate products of the form $\dfrac{du}{dx}$ f'(u) using the chain rule in reverse.
- Know and use a result for integrating products of the form f'(x)[f(x)]ⁿ.

Integrating using the reverse of the chain rule

In Chapter 7, you saw the chain rule for differentiating a **function of a function**.

Here it is in the form it was given on page 155: If $y = f(u)$ and $u = g(x)$ then: $\dfrac{dy}{dx} = \dfrac{dy}{du} \times \dfrac{du}{dx}$

Since integration is the opposite of differentiation, you have:

$$y \xrightarrow{\quad\text{Differentiation}\quad} \dfrac{dy}{du} \times \dfrac{du}{dx} \qquad y + C \xleftarrow{\quad\text{Integration}\quad} \dfrac{dy}{du} \times \dfrac{du}{dx}$$

So $\displaystyle\int \dfrac{dy}{du} \times \dfrac{du}{dx}\, dx = y + C$. Then writing f(u) instead of y and f'(u) instead of $\dfrac{dy}{du}$ gives:

$$\int \dfrac{du}{dx} f'(u)\ dx = f(u) + C$$

Tip: To evaluate integrals like this, integrate with respect to u (because f'(u) is $\dfrac{dy}{du}$).

If you're integrating an expression which contains a **function of a function**, f(u), try differentiating the function u. If the **derivative** of u is also part of the expression, you might be able to use the formula above.

This result's quite difficult to grasp — but after a few examples it should make complete sense.

Example 1

a) Differentiate $y = e^{2x^2}$ using the chain rule.

Let $u = 2x^2$, then $y = e^u$.
Then by the chain rule:

$$\dfrac{dy}{dx} = \dfrac{dy}{du} \times \dfrac{du}{dx} = e^u \times 4x = e^{2x^2} \times 4x = \boxed{4xe^{2x^2}}$$

b) Find $\displaystyle\int 4xe^{2x^2}\, dx$ using your answer to part a).

Look for the bit that would have been u in the chain rule — here it's $2x^2$.

$$\int \underset{\text{f'}(u)}{4x} e^{2x^2}\ dx = \underset{\text{f}(u)}{e^{2x^2}} + C$$

$\dfrac{du}{dx}$

Example 2

Find the following integrals:

a) $\int 6x^5 e^{x^6} \, dx$

   1. Here, $u = x^6$ — it appears once differentiated ($6x^5$)
       and once within a function (e^{x^6}).

   2. Split the integral into $\dfrac{du}{dx}$ and $f'(u)$:

$$\int 6x^5 e^{x^6} \, dx$$
$$\underset{\frac{du}{dx}}{\nearrow} \qquad \underset{f'(u)}{\nwarrow}$$

   3. Use the formula $\int \dfrac{du}{dx} f'(u) \, dx = f(u) + C$
       to write down the result:

$$\int 6x^5 e^{x^6} \, dx = \boxed{e^{x^6} + C}$$
$$\underset{\frac{du}{dx}}{\nearrow} \qquad \underset{f'(u)}{\uparrow} \qquad \underset{f(u) = e^u}{\nwarrow}$$

b) $\int e^{\sin x} \cos x \, dx$

   1. Here, $u = \sin x$.

   2. Write $\dfrac{du}{dx}$ and $f'(u)$:
                                  $\dfrac{du}{dx} = \cos x$ and $f'(u) = e^{\sin x}$

   3. Use the formula to
       write down the result.

$$\int e^{\sin x} \cos x \, dx = \boxed{e^{\sin x} + C}$$
$$\underset{f'(u)}{\nearrow} \qquad \underset{\frac{du}{dx}}{\nwarrow} \qquad \underset{f(u) = e^u}{\nwarrow}$$

c) **(i)** **Find** $\int x^4 \sin(x^5) \, dx$

   1. Here, $u = x^5$.

   2. Take out a constant to get it
       in the form $\int \dfrac{du}{dx} f'(u) \, dx$. $\int x^4 \sin(x^5) \, dx = \dfrac{1}{5} \int 5x^4 \sin(x^5) \, dx$

   3. Now split up the integral: $\dfrac{du}{dx} = 5x^4$ and $f'(u) = \sin(x^5)$

                                                            $f(u) = -\cos u$

   4. Use the formula: $\dfrac{1}{5} \int 5x^4 \sin(x^5) \, dx = \dfrac{1}{5}(-\cos(x^5) + c)$
$$\underset{\frac{du}{dx}}{\qquad} \qquad \underset{f'(u)}{\qquad} \qquad\qquad = -\dfrac{1}{5}\cos(x^5) + C$$

(ii) **Hence find the exact value of** $\int_0^1 x^4 \sin(x^5) \, dx.$

    Put in the limits and simplify. $\int_0^1 x^4 \sin(x^5) \, dx = \left[-\dfrac{1}{5}\cos(x^5) \right]_0^1$

$$= \left[-\dfrac{1}{5}\cos(1^5) \right] - \left[-\dfrac{1}{5}\cos(0^5) \right]$$

$$= -\dfrac{1}{5}\cos 1 + \dfrac{1}{5} = \boxed{\dfrac{1}{5}(1 - \cos 1)}$$

Find the following integrals:

Q1 $\displaystyle\int 2xe^{x^2}\,dx$

Q2 $\displaystyle\int 6x^2e^{2x^3}\,dx$

Q3 $\displaystyle\int \frac{1}{2\sqrt{x}}e^{\sqrt{x}}\,dx$

Q4 $\displaystyle\int x^3e^{x^4}\,dx$

Q5 $\displaystyle\int (4x-1)e^{(x^2-\frac{1}{2}x)}\,dx$

Q6 $\displaystyle\int 2x\sin(x^2+1)\,dx$

Q7 $\displaystyle\int x^3\cos(x^4)\,dx$

Q8 $\displaystyle\int x\sec^2(x^2)\,dx$

Q9 $\displaystyle\int e^{\cos x}\sin x\,dx$

Q10 $\displaystyle\int \cos 2x\,e^{\sin 2x}\,dx$

Q11 $\displaystyle\int \sec^2x\,e^{\tan x}\,dx$

Q12 $\displaystyle\int \sec x\tan x\,e^{\sec x}\,dx$

Q13 $\displaystyle\int 2\operatorname{cosec}^2x\,e^{\cot x}\,dx$

Q14 $\displaystyle\int \operatorname{cosec}3x\cot 3x\,e^{\operatorname{cosec}3x}\,dx$

Q15 a) Find $\displaystyle\int 5\sin(2-5x)e^{\cos(2-5x)}\,dx$
    b) Hence evaluate $\displaystyle\int_0^1 5\sin(2-5x)e^{\cos(2-5x)}\,dx$.

Q16 a) Find $\displaystyle\int (8x-1)\cos(4x^2-x)\,e^{\sin(4x^2-x)}\,dx$
    b) Hence evaluate $\displaystyle\int_0^\pi (8x-1)\cos(4x^2-x)\,e^{\sin(4x^2-x)}\,dx$.

Integrating $f'(x) \times [f(x)]^n$

Some products are made up of a **function** and its **derivative**:

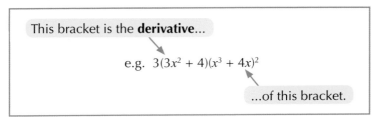

This bracket is the **derivative**...

e.g. $3(3x^2+4)(x^3+4x)^2$

...of this bracket.

If you spot that part of a product is the **derivative** of the other part of it (which is raised to a **power**), you can integrate it using this rule (which is just a special case of the 'reverse chain rule' on p.215):

This function is the **derivative**...

$$\int (n+1)f'(x)[f(x)]^n\,dx = [f(x)]^{n+1} + C$$

...of this function.

Remember that this result needs you to have a multiple of **n + 1** (not **n**) — you can check this by **differentiating** the right-hand side using the **chain rule**.

Watch out for any other multiples too — you might have to **multiply** or **divide** by a **constant**.

This will probably make more sense if you have a look at some examples:

Example 1

Evaluate $\int 12x^3(2x^4 - 5)^2 \, dx$.

1. Use the formula on
   p.217 to integrate:

   $f(x) = 2x^4 - 5$, so $f'(x) = 8x^3$. $n = 2$, so $n + 1 = 3$.

   So $\int (n + 1)f'(x)[f(x)]^n \, dx = [f(x)]^{n+1} + C$

   $\Rightarrow \int 3(8x^3)(2x^4 - 5)^2 = \int 24x^3(2x^4 - 5)^2 \, dx = (2x^4 - 5)^3 + C$

2. Divide everything by 2 to
   match the original integral:

   $\int 12x^3(2x^4 - 5)^2 \, dx = \boxed{\frac{1}{2}(2x^4 - 5)^3 + C}$

Example 2

Find $\int 8 \cosec^2 x \cot^3 x \, dx$.

1. Use the formula on
   p.217 to integrate:

   $f(x) = \cot x$, so $f'(x) = -\cosec^2 x$. $n = 3$, so $n + 1 = 4$.

   So $\int (n + 1)f'(x)[f(x)]^n \, dx = [f(x)]^{n+1} + C$

   $\Rightarrow \int -4 \cosec^2 x \cot^3 x \, dx = \cot^4 x + C$

2. Multiply everything by -2 to
   match the original integral:

   $\int 8 \cosec^2 x \cot^3 x \, dx = \boxed{-2 \cot^4 x + C}$

Example 3

a) Find $\int (x - 2)\sqrt{x^2 - 4x + 5} \, dx$.

1. You can write the square
   root as a fractional power:

   $\int (x - 2)\sqrt{x^2 - 4x + 5} \, dx = \int (x - 2)(x^2 - 4x + 5)^{\frac{1}{2}} \, dx$

2. Use the formula on
   p.217 to integrate:

   $f(x) = x^2 - 4x + 5$, so $f'(x) = 2x - 4$. $n = \frac{1}{2}$, so $n + 1 = \frac{3}{2}$.

   So $\int (n + 1)f'(x)[f(x)]^n \, dx = [f(x)]^{n+1} + C$

   $\Rightarrow \int \frac{3}{2}(2x - 4)(x^2 - 4x + 5)^{\frac{1}{2}} \, dx = (x^2 - 4x + 5)^{\frac{3}{2}} + C$

3. $\frac{3}{2}(2x - 4) = 3(x - 2)$, so you
   need to divide everything by 3
   to match the original integral:

   $\int (x - 2)\sqrt{x^2 - 4x + 5} \, dx = \boxed{\frac{1}{3}(x^2 - 4x + 5)^{\frac{3}{2}} + C}$

b) Hence solve $\int_2^6 (x - 2)\sqrt{x^2 - 4x + 5} \, dx$.

Put in the limits and simplify:

$\int_2^6 (x - 2)\sqrt{x^2 - 4x + 5} \, dx = \left[\frac{1}{3}(x^2 - 4x + 5)^{\frac{3}{2}} \right]_2^6$

$= \left[\frac{1}{3}(6^2 - 4(6) + 5)^{\frac{3}{2}} \right] - \left[\frac{1}{3}(2^2 - 4(2) + 5)^{\frac{3}{2}} \right]$

$= \frac{1}{3}\sqrt{17^3} - \frac{1}{3} = \boxed{\frac{1}{3}(17\sqrt{17} - 1)}$

Example 4

Evaluate $\int \dfrac{\cos x}{\sin^4 x}\,dx$.

1. Write $\dfrac{1}{\sin^4 x}$ as a negative power:

$$\int \frac{\cos x}{\sin^4 x}\,dx = \int \frac{\cos x}{(\sin x)^4}\,dx = \int \cos x (\sin x)^{-4}\,dx$$

2. Use the formula on p.217 to integrate:

$f(x) = \sin x$, so $f'(x) = \cos x$. $n = -4$, so $n + 1 = -3$.

So $\int (n + 1)f'(x)[f(x)]^n\,dx = [f(x)]^{n+1} + C$

$\Rightarrow \int -3\cos x(\sin x)^{-4}\,dx = (\sin x)^{-3} + C$

$\Rightarrow \int \dfrac{-3\cos x}{\sin^4 x}\,dx = \dfrac{1}{\sin^3 x} + C$

3. Divide everything by -3 to match the original integral:

$$\int \frac{\cos x}{\sin^4 x} = -\frac{1}{3\sin^3 x} + C$$

Exercise 8.5.2

Q1 Find the following indefinite integrals:

a) $\int 6x(x^2 + 5)^2\,dx$

b) $\int (2x + 7)(x^2 + 7x)^4\,dx$

c) $\int (x^3 + 2x)(x^4 + 4x^2)^3\,dx$

d) $\int \dfrac{2x}{(x^2 - 1)^3}\,dx$

e) $\int \dfrac{6e^{3x}}{(e^{3x} - 5)^2}\,dx$

f) $\int \sin x \cos^5 x\,dx$

g) $\int 2\sec^2 x \tan^3 x\,dx$

h) $\int 3e^x(e^x + 4)^2\,dx$

i) $\int 32\,(2e^{4x} - 3x)(e^{4x} - 3x^2)^7\,dx$

j) $\int \dfrac{\cos x}{(2 + \sin x)^4}\,dx$

k) $\int 5\,\text{cosec}\,x \cot x \,\text{cosec}^4 x\,dx$

l) $\int 2\,\text{cosec}^2 x \cot^3 x\,dx$

> **Q1-2 Hint:** You'll need the derivatives of cosec, sec and cot:
> $\dfrac{d}{dx}(\text{cosec}\,x) = -\text{cosec}\,x \cot x$
> $\dfrac{d}{dx}(\sec x) = \sec x \tan x$
> $\dfrac{d}{dx}(\cot x) = -\text{cosec}^2 x$

Q2 Find the following integrals:

a) $\int 6\tan x \sec^6 x\,dx$

b) $\int \cot x \,\text{cosec}^3 x\,dx$

Q3 Integrate the following functions with respect to x:

a) $4\cos x\, e^{\sin x}(e^{\sin x} - 5)^3$

b) $(\sin x\, e^{\cos x} - 4)(e^{\cos x} + 4x)^6$

Q4 Integrate:

a) $\int \dfrac{\sec^2 x}{\tan^4 x}\,dx$

b) $\int \cot x \,\text{cosec}\,x \sqrt{\text{cosec}\,x}\,dx$

Q5 a) Show that $\int e^{\cot 2x}\,\text{cosec}^2 2x\, e^{3\cot 2x}\,dx = -\dfrac{1}{8}\,e^{4\cot 2x} + C.$

b) Hence solve $\int_{\frac{1}{2}}^{1} e^{\cot 2x}\,\text{cosec}^2 2x\, e^{3\cot 2x}\,dx.$

8.6 Using Trigonometric Identities in Integration

You can sometimes use the trig identities that you learnt in Chapter 3 to manipulate nasty trig integrations to give functions you know how to integrate.

> **Learning Objective (Spec Ref 8.2):**
> - Use the double angle formulas for sin, cos and tan alongside the methods learnt throughout this chapter to simplify difficult trig integrals.

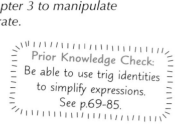

Prior Knowledge Check:
Be able to use trig identities to simplify expressions.
See p.69-85.

Integrating using trig identities

Integrating using the double angle formulas

If you're given a tricky **trig function** to integrate, you might be able to simplify it using one of the **double angle formulas**. They're especially useful for things like $\cos^2 x$, $\sin^2 x$ and $\sin x \cos x$.

Here are the double angle formulas again:

$$\sin 2x \equiv 2 \sin x \cos x \qquad \cos 2x \equiv \cos^2 x - \sin^2 x \qquad \tan 2x \equiv \frac{2 \tan x}{1 - \tan^2 x}$$

You came across two other ways of writing the double angle formula for cos, which come from using the identity $\cos^2 x + \sin^2 x \equiv 1$:

$$\cos 2x \equiv 2 \cos^2 x - 1 \qquad \cos 2x \equiv 1 - 2 \sin^2 x$$

Once you've rearranged the original function using one of the **double angle formulas**, the function you're left with should be easier to integrate using the rules you've seen in this chapter.

Example 1

Find the following:

a) $\int \sin^2 x \, dx$

> **Tip:** Use one of the cos double angle formulas when you've got a $\cos^2 x$ or a $\sin^2 x$ to integrate.

    1. Rearrange the cos double angle formula:

$$\cos 2x \equiv 1 - 2 \sin^2 x \implies \sin^2 x \equiv \tfrac{1}{2}(1 - \cos 2x)$$

    2. Rewrite the integration:

$$\int \sin^2 x \, dx = \int \tfrac{1}{2}(1 - \cos 2x) \, dx = \tfrac{1}{2} \int (1 - \cos 2x) \, dx$$

$$= \tfrac{1}{2}\left(x - \tfrac{1}{2} \sin 2x\right) + C = \tfrac{1}{2}x - \tfrac{1}{4} \sin 2x + C$$

b) $\int \cos^2 5x \, dx$

    1. Rearrange the cos double angle formula:

$$\cos 2x \equiv 2 \cos^2 x - 1 \implies \cos^2 x \equiv \tfrac{1}{2}(\cos 2x + 1)$$

    2. Rewrite the integration:

$$\int \cos^2 5x \, dx = \int \tfrac{1}{2}(\cos 10x + 1) \, dx = \tfrac{1}{2} \int (\cos 10x + 1) \, dx$$

$$= \tfrac{1}{2}\left(\tfrac{1}{10} \sin 10x + x\right) + C = \tfrac{1}{20} \sin 10x + \tfrac{1}{2}x + C$$

Example 2

Find the following integrals:

a) $\int \sin x \cos x \, dx$

1. Rearrange the **sin** double angle formula:

$$\sin 2x \equiv 2 \sin x \cos x \implies \sin x \cos x \equiv \frac{1}{2}\sin 2x$$

2. Rewrite the integration:

$$\int \sin x \cos x \, dx = \int \frac{1}{2}\sin 2x \, dx = \frac{1}{2}\left(-\frac{1}{2}\cos 2x\right) + C$$
$$= -\frac{1}{4}\cos 2x + C$$

b) $\int_0^{\frac{\pi}{4}} \sin 2x \cos 2x \, dx$

1. Rearrange the sin double angle formula with x replaced by $2x$:

$$\sin 4x \equiv 2 \sin 2x \cos 2x \implies \sin 2x \cos 2x \equiv \frac{1}{2}\sin 4x$$

2. Rewrite the integration:

$$\int_0^{\frac{\pi}{4}} \sin 2x \cos 2x \, dx = \int_0^{\frac{\pi}{4}} \frac{1}{2}\sin 4x \, dx = \left[\frac{1}{2}\left(-\frac{1}{4}\cos 4x\right)\right]_0^{\frac{\pi}{4}}$$
$$= -\frac{1}{8}[\cos 4x]_0^{\frac{\pi}{4}} = -\frac{1}{8}\left(\left[\cos \frac{4\pi}{4}\right] - [\cos 0]\right)$$
$$= \frac{1}{8}(\cos 0 - \cos \pi) = \frac{1}{8}(1 - (-1)) = \frac{1}{4}$$

c) $\int \dfrac{4 \tan \frac{x}{2}}{1 - \tan^2 \frac{x}{2}} \, dx$

1. Rearrange, then use the double angle formula for **tan**:

$$\frac{4 \tan \frac{x}{2}}{1 - \tan^2 \frac{x}{2}} = 2\left(\frac{2 \tan \frac{x}{2}}{1 - \tan^2 \frac{x}{2}}\right) = 2\left(\tan\left(2 \times \frac{x}{2}\right)\right) = 2 \tan x$$

2. Rewrite the integration:

$$\int \frac{4 \tan \frac{x}{2}}{1 - \tan^2 \frac{x}{2}} \, dx = \int 2 \tan x \, dx = -2 \ln|\cos x| + C$$

Integrating using other trigonometric identities

There are a couple of other **identities** you can use to simplify trig functions:

$$\boxed{\sec^2 x \equiv 1 + \tan^2 x} \qquad \boxed{\operatorname{cosec}^2 x \equiv 1 + \cot^2 x}$$

If you use one of these identities to get rid of a $\cot^2 x$ or a $\tan^2 x$, don't forget the stray 1's flying around — they'll just integrate to x. These identities are really useful if you have to integrate **tan²x** or **cot²x**, as you already know how to integrate sec²x and cosec²x (see pages 208-209).

$$\int \sec^2 x \, dx = \tan x + C \qquad \int \operatorname{cosec}^2 x \, dx = -\cot x + C$$

Example 3

a) Find $\int \tan^2 x - 1\ dx$

1. Rewrite the function in terms of $\sec^2 x$:

    $\tan^2 x - 1 = (\sec^2 x - 1) - 1$
    $ = \sec^2 x - 2$

2. Now integrate:

    $\int \tan^2 x - 1\ dx = \int \sec^2 x - 2\ dx = \boxed{\tan x - 2x + C}$

b) Find $\int \cot^2 3x\ dx$

1. Get the function in terms of $\operatorname{cosec}^2 x$:

    $\operatorname{cosec}^2 x \equiv 1 + \cot^2 x \implies \cot^2 3x = \operatorname{cosec}^2 3x - 1$

2. Integrate the function:

    $\int \cot^2 3x\ dx = \int \operatorname{cosec}^2 3x - 1\ dx = \boxed{-\dfrac{1}{3}\cot 3x - x + C}$

c) Find $\int \cos^3 x\ dx$

1. You don't know how to integrate $\cos^3 x$, but you can split it into $\cos^2 x$ and $\cos x$ and use identities.

    $\cos^3 x = \cos^2 x \cos x$
    $ = (1 - \sin^2 x)\cos x$
    $ = \cos x - \cos x \sin^2 x = \cos x - \cos x\,(\sin x)^2$

2. Now write out the integral:

    $\int \cos^3 x\ dx = \int \cos x\ dx - \int \cos x (\sin x)^2\ dx$

3. Using the method from p.217, if $f(x) = \sin x$, then $\cos x (\sin x)^2 = f'(x) \times [f(x)]^2$:

    So: $\int \cos x \sin^2 x\ dx = \dfrac{1}{3}\sin^3 x + c$

4. So the whole integral is:

    $\int \cos^3 x\ dx = \int \cos x\ dx - \int \cos x (\sin x)^2\ dx$
    $ = \boxed{\sin x - \dfrac{1}{3}\sin^3 x + C}$

d) Evaluate $\int_0^{\frac{\pi}{3}} 6 \sin 3x \cos 3x + \tan^2 \frac{1}{2}x + 1\ dx.$

1. Using the **sin** double angle formula:

    $6 \sin 3x \cos 3x \equiv 3 \sin 6x$

2. Using the identity for **$\tan^2 x$**:

    $\tan^2 \dfrac{1}{2}x + 1 \equiv \sec^2 \dfrac{1}{2}x$

3. Now integrate:

    $\displaystyle\int_0^{\frac{\pi}{3}} 6 \sin 3x \cos 3x + \tan^2 \dfrac{1}{2}x + 1\ dx$

    $= \displaystyle\int_0^{\frac{\pi}{3}} 3 \sin 6x + \sec^2 \dfrac{1}{2}x\ dx = \left[-\dfrac{3}{6}\cos 6x + 2\tan\dfrac{1}{2}x \right]_0^{\frac{\pi}{3}}$

    $= \left[-\dfrac{1}{2}\cos(2\pi) + 2\tan\left(\dfrac{\pi}{6}\right) \right] - \left[-\dfrac{1}{2}\cos(0) + 2\tan(0) \right]$

    $= \left[-\dfrac{1}{2}(1) + 2\left(\dfrac{1}{\sqrt{3}}\right) \right] - \left[-\dfrac{1}{2}(1) + 2(0) \right]$

    $= -\dfrac{1}{2} + \dfrac{2}{\sqrt{3}} + \dfrac{1}{2} = \dfrac{2}{\sqrt{3}} = \boxed{\dfrac{2\sqrt{3}}{3}}$

Q1   Find the following indefinite integrals:

a) $\int \cos^2 x \, dx$

b) $\int 6 \sin x \cos x \, dx$

c) $\int \sin^2 6x \, dx$

d) $\int \dfrac{2 \tan 2x}{1 - \tan^2 2x} \, dx$

e) $\int 2 \sin 4x \cos 4x \, dx$

f) $\int 2 \cos^2 4x \, dx$

g) $\int \cos x \sin x \, dx$

h) $\int \sin 3x \cos 3x \, dx$

i) $\int \dfrac{6 \tan 3x}{1 - \tan^2 3x} \, dx$

j) $\int 5 \sin 2x \cos 2x \, dx$

k) $\int (\sin x + \cos x)^2 \, dx$

l) $\int 4 \sin x \cos x \cos 2x \, dx$

> **Q1 l) Hint:**
> Use the sin double angle formula twice.

m) $\int (\cos x + \sin x)(\cos x - \sin x) \, dx$

n) $\int \sin^2 x \cot x \, dx$

Q2   Evaluate the following definite integrals, giving exact answers:

a) $\int_0^{\frac{\pi}{4}} \sin^2 x \, dx$

b) $\int_0^{\pi} \cos^2 2x \, dx$

c) $\int_0^{\pi} \sin \dfrac{x}{2} \cos \dfrac{x}{2} \, dx$

d) $\int_{\frac{\pi}{4}}^{\frac{\pi}{2}} \sin^2 2x \, dx$

e) $\int_0^{\frac{\pi}{4}} \cos 2x \sin 2x \, dx$

f) $\int_{\frac{\pi}{4}}^{\frac{\pi}{2}} \sin^2 x - \cos^2 x \, dx$

Q3   Find the exact value of $\int_0^{\frac{\pi}{6}} \dfrac{\tan 7x - \tan 5x}{1 + \tan 7x \tan 5x} \, dx$.

> **Q3 Hint:**
> Remember that $-\tan x = \tan(-x)$

Q4   Find the following integrals:

a) $\int \cot^2 x - 4 \, dx$

b) $\int \tan^2 x \, dx$

c) $\int 3 \cot^2 x \, dx$

d) $\int \tan^2 4x \, dx$

Q5   Find the exact value of $\int_0^{\frac{\pi}{4}} \tan^2 x + \cos^2 x - \sin^2 x \, dx$.

Find the integrals in Q6-9:

Q6 $\int (\sec x + \tan x)^2 \, dx$

Q7 $\int (\cot x + \cosec x)^2 \, dx$

Q8 $\int 4 + \cot^2 3x \, dx$

Q9 $\int \cos^2 4x + \cot^2 4x \, dx$

Q10   Integrate the following functions with respect to x:

a) $\tan^3 x + \tan^5 x$

b) $\cot^5 x + \cot^3 x$

c) $\sin^3 x$

Q11   Use the identity $\sin A + \sin B \equiv 2 \sin\left(\dfrac{A+B}{2}\right) \cos\left(\dfrac{A-B}{2}\right)$ to find $\int 2 \sin 4x \cos x \, dx$.

8.7 Finding Area using Integration

In Year 1 you saw how to find the area between a curve and the x-axis using integration.
But you can also use integration to find the area between a curve and a line, or even two curves.

Learning Objectives (Spec Ref 8.3):
- Use integration to find the area between two curves, or the area between a line and a curve.
- Use integration to find the area under a curve given its parametric equations.

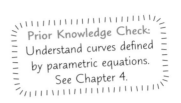
Prior Knowledge Check:
Understand curves defined
by parametric equations.
See Chapter 4.

Finding enclosed areas

To find the area between a curve, a line and the x-axis, you'll either have to **add** or **subtract** integrals to find the area you're after — it's always best to **draw a diagram** of the area.

Example 1

Find the area enclosed by the curve $y = x^2$, the line $y = 2 - x$ and the x-axis.

1. Draw a diagram of the curve and the line. You have to find **area A** — **split** it into two smaller bits.

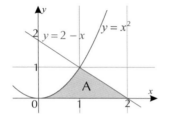

2. Find the limits by solving $x^2 = 2 - x$ to find where the line and curve intersect.

   $x^2 = 2 - x \Rightarrow x^2 + x - 2 = 0 \Rightarrow (x - 1)(x + 2) = 0$
   So they meet at $x = 1$ (and at $x = -2$, but this isn't relevant to A).

3. You also need to know the x-intercepts of the line and curve:

   $x^2 = 0 \Rightarrow x = 0$ and $2 - x = 0 \Rightarrow x = 2$

4. The area A is the area under the **red** curve between 0 and 1 added to the area under the **blue** line between 1 and 2.

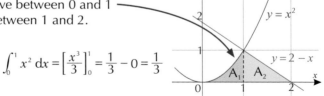

5. Integrate $y = x^2$ between 0 and 1 to find the area A_1:

   $$\int_0^1 x^2 \, dx = \left[\frac{x^3}{3}\right]_0^1 = \frac{1}{3} - 0 = \frac{1}{3}$$

6. Integrate $y = 2 - x$ between 1 and 2 to find the area A_2:

   $$\int_1^2 (2 - x) \, dx = \left[2x - \frac{x^2}{2}\right]_1^2$$

   $$= \left(2(2) - \frac{2^2}{2}\right) - \left(2(1) - \frac{1^2}{2}\right)$$

   $$= 2 - \frac{3}{2} = \frac{1}{2}$$

   Tip: A_2 is just a triangle with base 1 and height 1, so you could also calculate its area using the formula for the area of a triangle.

7. Add the areas together to find the area A:

   $$A = A_1 + A_2 = \frac{1}{3} + \frac{1}{2} = \frac{5}{6}$$

Sometimes you'll need to find the area **enclosed** by the graphs of two functions —
this usually means **subtracting** some area from another. Here is an example with two curves:

Example 2

The diagram on the right shows the curves
$y = \sin x + 1$ and $y = \cos x + 1$.

Find the area of the shaded grey region.

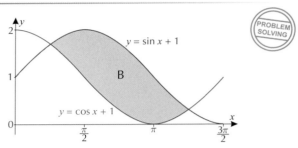

1. Find out where the graphs meet
   by solving $\sin x + 1 = \cos x + 1$:

$$\sin x + 1 = \cos x + 1 \Rightarrow \sin x = \cos x$$
$$\Rightarrow \frac{\sin x}{\cos x} = 1 \Rightarrow \tan x = 1$$
$$\Rightarrow x = \tan^{-1}(1) = \frac{\pi}{4}, \frac{5\pi}{4}$$

They meet at $x = \frac{\pi}{4}$ and $x = \frac{5\pi}{4}$.

2. The area of B is the area under the **red** curve
   between $\frac{\pi}{4}$ and $\frac{5\pi}{4}$ (B_1) minus the area
   under the **blue** curve between $\frac{\pi}{4}$ and $\frac{5\pi}{4}$ (B_2).

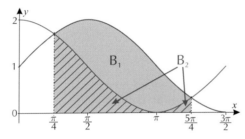

3. Integrate $\sin x + 1$ between
   $\frac{\pi}{4}$ and $\frac{5\pi}{4}$ to find B_1:

$$B_1 = \int_{\frac{\pi}{4}}^{\frac{5\pi}{4}} \sin x + 1 \, dx = [-\cos x + x]_{\frac{\pi}{4}}^{\frac{5\pi}{4}}$$
$$= \left(-\cos\left(\frac{5\pi}{4}\right) + \frac{5\pi}{4}\right) - \left(-\cos\left(\frac{\pi}{4}\right) + \frac{\pi}{4}\right)$$
$$= \left(-\left(-\frac{\sqrt{2}}{2}\right) + \frac{5\pi}{4}\right) - \left(-\frac{\sqrt{2}}{2} + \frac{\pi}{4}\right) = \sqrt{2} + \pi$$

4. Integrate $\cos x + 1$ between
   $\frac{\pi}{4}$ and $\frac{5\pi}{4}$ to find B_2:

$$B_2 = \int_{\frac{\pi}{4}}^{\frac{5\pi}{4}} \cos x + 1 \, dx = [\sin x + x]_{\frac{\pi}{4}}^{\frac{5\pi}{4}}$$
$$= \left(\sin\left(\frac{5\pi}{4}\right) + \frac{5\pi}{4}\right) - \left(\sin\left(\frac{\pi}{4}\right) + \frac{\pi}{4}\right)$$
$$= \left(-\frac{\sqrt{2}}{2} + \frac{5\pi}{4}\right) - \left(\frac{\sqrt{2}}{2} + \frac{\pi}{4}\right) = -\sqrt{2} + \pi$$

5. Subtract B_2 from B_1 to find the
   total area between the curves:

$$B = B_1 - B_2 = (\sqrt{2} + \pi) - (-\sqrt{2} + \pi) = \boxed{2\sqrt{2}}$$

Sometimes you might need to add **and** subtract integrals to find the right area.
You'll often need to do this when the curve goes **below** the x-axis.
The integrations you need to do should be obvious if you draw a **picture**.

Q1 Find the shaded area in the following diagrams:

a)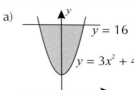

b)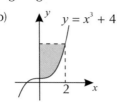

c)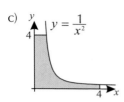

d)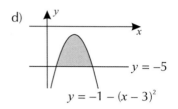

e)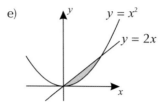

f)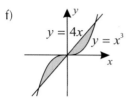

Q2 For each part, find the area enclosed by the curve and line:

a) $y = x^2 + 4$ and $y = x + 4$

b) $y = x^2 + 2x - 3$ and $y = 4x$

Q2b) Hint: Consider the bits above and below the x-axis separately.

Q3 Find the shaded area shown to the right:

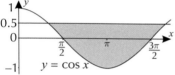

Q4 A company has designed a logo based on multiples of the sine curve, shown to the right. Calculate the total area of the grey sections of the logo.

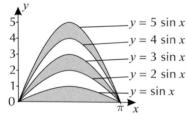

Parametric integration

Normally, to find the **area** under a graph, you can do a **simple integration**. But if you've got **parametric equations**, things are more difficult — you can't find $\int y \, dx$ if y isn't written in terms of x.

There's a sneaky way to get around this. Suppose your parameter is t. Then:

$$\int y \, dx = \int y \frac{dx}{dt} \, dt$$

This comes from the chain rule for differentiation (p.155) — if you think of dx as $\frac{dx}{1}$, then $\frac{dx}{1} = \frac{dx}{dt} \times \frac{dt}{1}$. Both y and $\frac{dx}{dt}$ are written **in terms of t**, so you can **multiply** them together to get an expression you can **integrate with respect to t**.

With a **definite integral**, you need to **alter the limits** as well. So if you have x-values as limits, work out the corresponding values of t before you integrate.

Example

The shaded region marked A on the sketch is bounded
by the x-axis, the line $x = 2$, and by the curve with
parametric equations $x = t^2 - 2$ and $y = t^2 - 9t + 20$,
$t \geq 0$, which crosses the x-axis at $x = 14$.

Find the area of A.

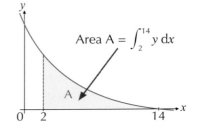

Area A $= \int_{2}^{14} y \, dx$

1. Find $\dfrac{dx}{dt}$:

$$\frac{dx}{dt} = \frac{d}{dt}(t^2 - 2) = 2t$$

2. Sort out the **limits** — 14 and 2
    are the limits for integrating **with
    respect to x**, so you need to find
    the **corresponding values of t.**

$$x = 2 \Rightarrow t^2 - 2 = 2$$
$$\Rightarrow t^2 = 4 \Rightarrow t = 2$$

$$x = 14 \Rightarrow t^2 - 2 = 14$$
$$\Rightarrow t^2 = 16 \Rightarrow t = 4$$

Tip: $t \geq 0$,
so ignore
the negative
square roots.

3. Now **integrate** to find the area of A:

$$A = \int_{2}^{14} y \, dx = \int_{2}^{4} y \frac{dx}{dt} \, dt = \int_{2}^{4} (t^2 - 9t + 20)(2t) \, dt$$

$$= \int_{2}^{4} 2t^3 - 18t^2 + 40t \, dt = \left[\frac{1}{2}t^4 - 6t^3 + 20t^2 \right]_{2}^{4}$$

$$= \left(\frac{1}{2}(4)^4 - 6(4)^3 + 20(4)^2 \right) - \left(\frac{1}{2}(2)^4 - 6(2)^3 + 20(2)^2 \right)$$

$$= 64 - 40 = \boxed{24}$$

Exercise 8.7.2

Q1 For each of the following curves, find an expression in parametric form
that is equivalent to the indefinite integral $\int y \, dx$.

a) $x = \dfrac{3}{t}, y = 4t^2$

b) $x = \tan 5\theta, y = \sec^2 5\theta$

Q2 For each of the following curves, find an expression equivalent to $\int y \, dx$ and integrate it.

a) $x = (4t - 5)^2, y = t^2 - 3t$

b) $x = t^2 + 3, y = 4t - 1$

Q3 A curve has parametric equations $x = 3t^2, y = \dfrac{5}{t}$, where $t > 0$.
Find an expression for $y \dfrac{dx}{dt}$, and hence evaluate $\int_{3}^{75} y \, dx$.

Q4 The curve shown here has parametric equations $x = 4t(t + 1), y = 3t^3$.

a) Find the values t_1 and t_2 that correspond to
$x = 8$ and $x = 120$, given that $t > 0$.

b) Hence find a parametric integral corresponding to $\int_{8}^{120} y \, dx$,
and evaluate this to find the area A.

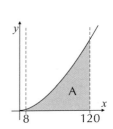

8.8 Integration by Substitution

Earlier, you saw how to use the chain rule in reverse to integrate a function of the form $\frac{du}{dx}f'(u)$. Integration by substitution is a more general version of this technique.

Learning Objectives (Spec Ref 8.5):

- Understand that integration by substitution is the reverse of differentiating using the chain rule.
- Use integration by substitution to integrate functions, including calculating definite integrals.
- Integrate using substitutions that require trig identities.

Integration by substitution

Integration by substitution is a way of integrating a **function of a function** by simplifying the integral. Like differentiating with the chain rule, to integrate by substitution you have to write part of the function in terms of u, where u is some **function** of x.

Here's the method:

- You'll be given an integral that's made up of **two functions of** x.
- **Substitute** u for one of the functions of x to give a function that's **easier to integrate**.
- Next, find $\frac{du}{dx}$, and **rewrite** it so that dx is on its own.
- **Rewrite** the original integral in terms of u and du.
- You should now be left with something that's **easier** to integrate — just **integrate** as normal, then at the last step **replace** u with the **original substitution**.

You won't always be told what substitution to use, so you might have to take an educated guess. Functions inside **brackets**, **denominators of fractions** and **square roots** are often good places to start. There might be **multiple different substitutions** that you could use to get the right answer.

Example 1

Use the substitution $u = x^2 - 2$ to find $\int 4x(x^2 - 2)^4\ dx$.

1. Differentiate u with respect to x:

$$u = x^2 - 2 \ \Rightarrow\ \frac{du}{dx} = 2x$$

2. Rearrange the equation for $\frac{du}{dx}$ to get dx on its own ($\frac{du}{dx}$ isn't really a fraction, but you can treat it like one for this bit):

$$\frac{du}{dx} = 2x \ \Rightarrow\ du = 2x\ dx \ \Rightarrow\ dx = \frac{1}{2x}du$$

3. Substitute what you've got so far back into the original expression and simplify:

$$\int 4x(x^2 - 2)^4\ dx = \int 4xu^4\frac{1}{2x}\ du = \int 2u^4\ du$$

4. Integrate this simpler expression with respect to u:

$$\int 2u^4\ du = \frac{2}{5}u^5 + C$$

5. Substitute $u = x^2 - 2$ back in:

$$= \frac{2}{5}(x^2 - 2)^5 + C$$

That first example worked out nicely, because the x's **cancelled out** when you substituted in the expressions for u and dx. It isn't always quite so straightforward — sometimes you need to get rid of some x's by **rearranging** the equation to get x in terms of u.

Example 2

Find $\int x(3x + 2)^3\, dx$, using the substitution $u = 3x + 2$.

> **Tip:** The expression in brackets is often the thing you substitute.

1. Start by finding $\dfrac{du}{dx}$ and then rearrange to get dx on its own:

$$u = 3x + 2 \implies \frac{du}{dx} = 3 \implies dx = \frac{1}{3}\, du$$

2. If you substitute for u and dx, you end up with an x still in the integral. To get rid of it, rearrange the equation for u:

$$\int x(3x + 2)^3\, dx = \int xu^3\, \frac{1}{3}\, du$$

$$u = 3x + 2 \implies x = \frac{u - 2}{3}$$

3. Integrate the function in terms of u:

$$\int x(3x + 2)^3\, dx = \int \left(\frac{u - 2}{3}\right)u^3\, \frac{1}{3}\, du$$

$$= \int \frac{u^4 - 2u^3}{9}\, du$$

$$= \frac{1}{9}\left(\frac{u^5}{5} - \frac{u^4}{2}\right) + C$$

$$= \frac{u^5}{45} - \frac{u^4}{18} + C$$

4. Substitute $u = 3x + 2$ back in at the end:

$$= \frac{(3x + 2)^5}{45} - \frac{(3x + 2)^4}{18} + C$$

Some integrations look really tricky, but with a clever substitution they can be made a lot simpler.

Example 3

Find $\int 3x\sqrt{2 - x^2}\, dx$, using a suitable substitution.

1. Choose u to make the integral simpler.

$\sqrt{2 - x^2}$ looks like the most awkward bit to integrate, so that might be a good choice for the substitution — let $u = \sqrt{2 - x^2}$.

2. Differentiate to find $\dfrac{du}{dx}$:

$$\frac{du}{dx} = -\frac{x}{\sqrt{2 - x^2}} = -\frac{x}{u} \implies u\, du = -x\, dx$$

$$\implies -\frac{u}{x}\, du = dx$$

3. Substitute what you've got into the original integral:

$$\int 3x\sqrt{2 - x^2}\, dx = \int 3x \times u \times -\frac{u}{x}\, du$$

$$= \int -3u^2\, du$$

$$= -u^3 + C$$

$$= -\left(\sqrt{2 - x^2}\right)^3 + C$$

Q1 Find the following integrals using the given substitutions:

a) $\int 12(x + 3)^5 \, dx, \quad u = x + 3$

b) $\int (11 - x)^4 \, dx, \quad u = 11 - x$

c) $\int 24x(x^2 + 4)^3 \, dx, \quad u = x^2 + 4$

d) $\int \sin^5 x \cos x \, dx, \quad u = \sin x$

e) $\int x(x - 1)^5 \, dx, \quad u = x - 1$

f) $\int 4x^3(x^2 - 3)^6 \, dx, \quad u = x^2 - 3$

Q2 Use an appropriate substitution to find:

a) $\int 21(x + 2)^6 \, dx$

b) $\int (5x + 4)^3 \, dx$

c) $\int x(2x + 3)^3 \, dx$

d) $\int 24x(x^2 - 5)^7 \, dx$

Q3 Use the given substitutions to find the following integrals:

a) $\int 6x\sqrt{x + 1} \, dx, \quad u = \sqrt{x + 1}$

b) $\int \frac{x}{\sqrt{4 - x}} \, dx, \quad u = \sqrt{4 - x}$

c) $\int \frac{15(\ln x)^4}{x} \, dx, \quad u = \ln x$

d) $\int \frac{3}{x(\ln(x^2))^3} \, dx, \quad u = \ln(x^2)$

Q4 Find the following integrals by substitution:

a) $\int \frac{4x}{\sqrt{(2x - 1)}} \, dx$

b) $\int \frac{1}{4 - \sqrt{x}} \, dx$

c) $\int \frac{e^{2x}}{1 + e^x} \, dx$

Q5 Use integration by substitution to prove that $\int (n + 1)f'(x)[f(x)]^n \, dx = [f(x)]^{n+1} + C.$

Q5 Hint: This is the formula from p.217.

Definite integrals

If you're given a **definite integral** to find using a substitution, it's important that you remember to **change the limits** to u. To do this, put the x-limits into the equation for u to find the corresponding values of u.

Doing it this way means you **don't** have to **put x back in** at the last step — just put the values of u into the integration for u.

Examples

a) **Use the substitution $u = \cos x$ to find $\int_{\frac{\pi}{2}}^{2\pi} -12 \sin x \cos^3 x \, dx.$**

Tip: You could also solve this using the method on p.217.

1. As with indefinite integrals, start by differentiating u, and rearranging to get dx on its own:

$u = \cos x \Rightarrow \dfrac{du}{dx} = -\sin x$

$\Rightarrow dx = -\dfrac{1}{\sin x} \, du$

2. Use the substitution to change the limits of the integral from x-values to u-values:

$x = \dfrac{\pi}{2} \Rightarrow u = \cos \dfrac{\pi}{2} = 0$

$x = 2\pi \Rightarrow u = \cos 2\pi = 1$

3. Substitute all that back into the original integral and solve:

$$\int_{\frac{\pi}{2}}^{2\pi} -12\sin x \cos^3 x \, dx = \int_0^1 -12\sin x \, u^3 \, \frac{-1}{\sin x} \, du$$

$$= \int_0^1 12u^3 \, du = [3u^4]_0^1$$

$$= [3(1)^4] - [3(0)^4] = 3 - 0 = \boxed{3}$$

b) Use a suitable substitution to find $\int_2^{\frac{7}{2}} x\sqrt{2x-3} \, dx$.

1. Choose u to make the integral simpler:

The square root looks like the most awkward part of the integral, so let $u = \sqrt{2x-3}$.

2. Differentiate the substitution, and rearrange to get dx on its own:

$$u = \sqrt{2x-3} \implies \frac{du}{dx} = \frac{1}{\sqrt{2x-3}} = \frac{1}{u}$$

$$\implies dx = u \, du$$

3. Rearrange the substitution to get an expression for x:

$$u = \sqrt{2x-3} \implies x = \frac{u^2+3}{2}$$

4. Convert the limits from x-values to u-values:

$$x = 2 \implies u = \sqrt{2(2)-3} = \sqrt{1} = 1$$

$$x = \frac{7}{2} \implies u = \sqrt{2\left(\frac{7}{2}\right)-3} = \sqrt{4} = 2$$

5. Substituting everything back into the original integral gives:

$$\int_2^{\frac{7}{2}} x\sqrt{2x-3} \, dx = \int_1^2 \frac{u^2+3}{2} \times u \times u \, du$$

$$= \frac{1}{2}\int_1^2 u^4 + 3u^2 \, du$$

$$= \frac{1}{2}\left[\frac{u^5}{5} + u^3\right]_1^2$$

$$= \left[\frac{2^5}{10} + \frac{2^3}{2}\right] - \left[\frac{1^5}{10} + \frac{1^3}{2}\right]$$

$$= \frac{36}{5} - \frac{3}{5} = \boxed{\frac{33}{5}}$$

Tip: Like Example 3 on p.229, there are other substitutions you could use. Try solving this on your own with the substitution $u = 2x - 3$.

Sometimes when you convert the limits of a definite integral, the **upper limit** converts to a **lower number** than the **lower limit** does.

You can either keep the converted limits in the **same places** as the corresponding original limits and carry on as normal or **swap them** so the higher value is the upper limit and stick a **minus sign** in front of the whole integral.

Swapping the limits and putting a minus in front of the integral might seem more complicated, but it often **cancels** with another minus, making the whole integration **easier**.

Q1 Find the exact values of the following using the given substitutions:

a) $\int_{\frac{2}{3}}^{1} (3x - 2)^4 \, dx, \quad u = 3x - 2$

b) $\int_{-2}^{1} 2x(x + 3)^4 \, dx, \quad u = x + 3$

c) $\int_{0}^{\frac{\pi}{6}} 8 \sin^3 x \cos x \, dx, \quad u = \sin x$

d) $\int_{0}^{3} x\sqrt{x + 1} \, dx, \quad u = \sqrt{x + 1}$

Q2 Use an appropriate substitution to find the exact value of each of the following:

a) $\int_{2}^{\sqrt{5}} x(x^2 - 3)^4 \, dx$

b) $\int_{1}^{2} x(3x - 4)^3 \, dx$

c) $\int_{2}^{10} \frac{x}{\sqrt{x - 1}} \, dx$

Q3 Integrate the function $y = \dfrac{1}{3 - \sqrt{x}}$ between $x = 1$ and $x = 4$, using a suitable substitution. Give your answer in the form $a + b \ln 2$, where a and b are integers.

Q4 Find $\int_{0}^{1} 2e^x(1 + e^x)^3 \, dx$, using the substitution $u = 1 + e^x$. Give your answer to 1 decimal place.

Q5 Use integration by substitution to find the integral of the function $y = \dfrac{x}{\sqrt{3x + 1}}$ between the limits $x = 1$ and $x = 5$.

Trig identities

As you know by now, there's a vast range of **trig identities** and **formulas** to deal with in A-level maths. This can make for some pretty tricky **integration questions** involving trig functions.

Here are a couple of examples:

> **Tip:** If you need a reminder of the trig identities, they're given in Chapter 3.

Examples

a) Use the substitution $u = \tan x$ to find $\int \dfrac{\sec^4 x}{\sqrt{\tan x}} \, dx$.

1. Work out what the substitutions will be — start by finding dx:

$$u = \tan x \implies \frac{du}{dx} = \sec^2 x \implies dx = \frac{1}{\sec^2 x} \, du$$

2. This substitution for dx leaves $\sec^2 x$ on the numerator — you need to find $\sec^2 x$ in terms of u:

From the trig identity, $\sec^2 x \equiv 1 + \tan^2 x$
$$u = \tan x \implies \sec^2 x \equiv 1 + u^2$$

3. Substitute all these bits into the integral:

$$\int \frac{\sec^4 x}{\sqrt{\tan x}} \, dx = \int \frac{(1 + u^2) \times \sec^2 x}{\sqrt{u}} \times \frac{1}{\sec^2 x} \, du$$

$$= \int \frac{1}{\sqrt{u}} + \frac{u^2}{\sqrt{u}} \, du = \int u^{-\frac{1}{2}} + u^{\frac{3}{2}} \, du$$

$$= 2u^{\frac{1}{2}} + \frac{2}{5} u^{\frac{5}{2}} + C = \boxed{2\sqrt{\tan x} + \frac{2}{5}\sqrt{\tan^5 x} + C}$$

b) Calculate $\int_{\frac{1}{2}}^{\frac{\sqrt{3}}{2}} \frac{4}{\sqrt{1-x^2}}\, dx$ using the substitution $x = \sin\theta$, where $-\frac{\pi}{2} \le \theta \le \frac{\pi}{2}$.

1. Differentiate x with respect to θ, and use the result to find dx:

$$x = \sin\theta \ \Rightarrow\ \frac{dx}{d\theta} = \cos\theta \ \Rightarrow\ dx = \cos\theta\, d\theta$$

2. Use the substitution to convert the limits from x to θ:

$$x = \sin\theta \ \Rightarrow\ \theta = \sin^{-1}x$$

$$\text{So } x = \frac{\sqrt{3}}{2} \ \Rightarrow\ \theta = \frac{\pi}{3}$$

$$\text{and } x = \frac{1}{2} \ \Rightarrow\ \theta = \frac{\pi}{6}$$

Tip: $\sin\theta$ has an inverse because θ is restricted to between $-\frac{\pi}{2}$ and $\frac{\pi}{2}$.

3. Now solve the integral:

$$\int_{\frac{1}{2}}^{\frac{\sqrt{3}}{2}} \frac{4}{\sqrt{1-x^2}}\, dx = \int_{\frac{\pi}{6}}^{\frac{\pi}{3}} \frac{4}{\sqrt{1-\sin^2\theta}} \cos\theta\, d\theta$$

$$= \int_{\frac{\pi}{6}}^{\frac{\pi}{3}} \frac{4\cos\theta}{\sqrt{\cos^2\theta}}\, d\theta$$

$$= \int_{\frac{\pi}{6}}^{\frac{\pi}{3}} 4\, d\theta = [4\theta]_{\frac{\pi}{6}}^{\frac{\pi}{3}} = \frac{4\pi}{3} - \frac{2\pi}{3} = \frac{2\pi}{3}$$

Exercise 8.8.3

Q1 Find the exact value of $\int_0^1 \frac{1}{1+x^2}\, dx$ using the substitution $x = \tan\theta$ where $-\frac{\pi}{2} < \theta < \frac{\pi}{2}$.

Q1-4 Hint: Remember, the phrase 'exact value' is usually a clue that the answer will include a surd or π.

Q2 Find the exact value of $\int_0^{\frac{\pi}{6}} 3\sin x \sin 2x\, dx$ using the substitution $u = \sin x$.

Q3 Use the substitution $x = 2\sin\theta$, where $-\frac{\pi}{2} \le \theta \le \frac{\pi}{2}$, to find the exact value of $\int_1^{\sqrt{3}} \frac{1}{(4-x^2)^{\frac{3}{2}}}\, dx$.

Q4 Find the exact value of $\int_{\frac{1}{2}}^1 \frac{1}{x^2\sqrt{1-x^2}}\, dx$. Use the substitution $x = \cos\theta$, where $0 \le \theta \le \pi$.

Q5 Find $\int 2\tan^3 x\, dx$ using the substitution $u = \sec^2 x$.

Q6 Find the exact value of the following integrals:

a) $\int_{-\pi}^{\frac{\pi}{2}} 3\sin\theta\cos^4\theta\, d\theta$, using $u = \cos\theta$

b) $\int_{\frac{\pi}{4}}^{\frac{\pi}{3}} \sec^4 x\tan x\, dx$, using $u = \sec x$

Q7 Find the exact value of $\int_{-1}^{\sqrt{3}} \frac{4x}{\sqrt{1+x^2}}\, dx$, using the substitution $x = \cot\theta$, where $-\frac{\pi}{2} \le \theta \le \frac{\pi}{2}$.

8.9 Integration by Parts

Sadly, not every integration problem can be solved with a nifty substitution. Integration by parts is another way to integrate a product of two functions — it involves both differentiation and integration.

Learning Objectives (Spec Ref 8.5):
- Understand that integration by parts comes from the product rule.
- Use integration by parts to integrate functions, including ln x.
- Integrate functions where integration by parts has to be applied more than once.

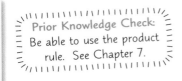
Prior Knowledge Check:
Be able to use the product rule. See Chapter 7.

Integration by parts

If you have a **product** to integrate but you can't use any of the methods you've learnt so far, you might be able to use **integration by parts**. The **formula** for integrating by parts is:

$$\int u \frac{dv}{dx} \, dx = uv - \int v \frac{du}{dx} \, dx$$

where u and v are both functions of x.

Here's the **proof** of this formula. You **don't need** to know it for the exam, but you might find it useful.

Start with the **product rule**:

- If u and v are both functions of x, then:

$$\frac{d}{dx} uv = u \frac{dv}{dx} + v \frac{du}{dx}$$

- Integrate both sides of the product rule with respect to x:

$$\int \frac{d}{dx} uv \, dx = \int u \frac{dv}{dx} \, dx + \int v \frac{du}{dx} \, dx$$

- On the left-hand side, uv is differentiated, then integrated — so you end up back at uv:

$$uv = \int u \frac{dv}{dx} \, dx + \int v \frac{du}{dx} \, dx$$

- Now just rearrange to get:

$$\int u \frac{dv}{dx} \, dx = uv - \int v \frac{du}{dx} \, dx$$

Tip: Take a look back at p.170 for more about the product rule.

Tip: The integration by parts formula is sometimes written $\int uv' \, dx = uv - \int vu' \, dx$ — you might find this version easier to use.

The hardest thing about integration by parts is **deciding** which bit of your product should be u and which bit should be $\frac{dv}{dx}$. There's no set rule for this — you just have to look at both parts, see which one **differentiates** to give something **nice**, then set that one as u.

For example, if you have a product that has a **single x** as one part of it, choose this to be u. It'll differentiate to **1**, which will make **integrating** $v \frac{du}{dx}$ very easy.

Example 1

Find $\int 2x\,e^x\,dx$.

1. Start by working out what should be u and what should be $\dfrac{dv}{dx}$
   — choose them so that $v\dfrac{du}{dx}$ is easier to integrate than $2x\,e^x$.

2. The two factors are $2x$ and e^x
   — try them both ways round:

   If $u = 2x$ and $\dfrac{dv}{dx} = e^x$, then $v\dfrac{du}{dx} = 2e^x$,

   or if $u = e^x$ and $\dfrac{dv}{dx} = 2x$, then $v\dfrac{du}{dx} = x^2 e^x$.

   $2e^x$ is easier to integrate than $x^2 e^x$,

   so let $u = 2x$ and $\dfrac{dv}{dx} = e^x$.

3. Put u, v, $\dfrac{du}{dx}$ and $\dfrac{dv}{dx}$ into the integration by parts formula:

   $u = 2x \;\Rightarrow\; \dfrac{du}{dx} = 2$ and $\dfrac{dv}{dx} = e^x \;\Rightarrow\; v = e^x$

   $\int 2x\,e^x\,dx = \int u\dfrac{dv}{dx}\,dx = uv - \int v\dfrac{du}{dx}\,dx$

   $\qquad = 2x\,e^x - \int 2e^x\,dx$

   $\qquad = 2x\,e^x - 2e^x + C$

   Don't forget the constant of integration.

You don't always need to work out both possible versions. In Example 1, e^x won't change whether you integrate it or differentiate it, so you just need to think about whether the integration would be made easier by differentiating $2x$ or by integrating it.

Example 2

Find $\int x^3 \ln x\,dx$.

1. Choose u and $\dfrac{dv}{dx}$:

   Let $u = \ln x$ and $\dfrac{dv}{dx} = x^3$

   $u = \ln x \;\Rightarrow\; \dfrac{du}{dx} = \dfrac{1}{x}$ and $\dfrac{dv}{dx} = x^3 \;\Rightarrow\; v = \dfrac{x^4}{4}$

2. Put u, v, $\dfrac{du}{dx}$ and $\dfrac{dv}{dx}$ into the integration by parts formula:

   $\int x^3 \ln x\,dx = \ln x \times \dfrac{x^4}{4} - \int \dfrac{x^4}{4} \times \dfrac{1}{x}\,dx$

   $\qquad = \dfrac{x^4 \ln x}{4} - \dfrac{1}{4}\int x^3\,dx$

   $\qquad = \dfrac{x^4 \ln x}{4} - \dfrac{x^4}{16} + C$

If you have a product that has $\ln x$ as one of its factors, let $u = \ln x$ —
it's easy to differentiate but quite tricky to integrate, as shown on the next page.

Until now, you haven't been able to integrate **ln x**, but **integration by parts** gives you a way to get around this. The trick is to write ln x as (1 × ln x).

You can write ln x as (ln x × 1). So let $u = \ln x$ and let $\frac{dv}{dx} = 1$.

$$u = \ln x \implies \frac{du}{dx} = \frac{1}{x} \qquad \frac{dv}{dx} = 1 \implies v = x$$

Putting these into the formula gives:

$$\int \ln x \, dx = \int (\ln x \times 1) \, dx = \ln x \times x - \int x \frac{1}{x} \, dx$$
$$= x \ln x - \int 1 \, dx = \mathbf{x \ln x - x + C}$$

You can use **integration by parts** on definite integrals too. The only change from the method for indefinite integrals is that you have to **apply the limits** of the integral to the *uv* bit.

The integration by parts formula for definite integrals can be written like this:

$$\int_a^b u \frac{dv}{dx} \, dx = [uv]_a^b - \int_a^b v \frac{du}{dx} \, dx$$

Example 3

Find the exact value of $\int_0^{\frac{\pi}{2}} 4x \sin\left(\frac{x}{2}\right) dx$.

1. Choose u and $\frac{dv}{dx}$.

$\sin\left(\frac{x}{2}\right)$ will give a cos function whether you integrate or differentiate it, so the only way to get a simpler $\int v \frac{du}{dx} \, dx$ is to make $u = 4x$.

So let $u = 4x$ and $\frac{dv}{dx} = \sin\left(\frac{x}{2}\right)$

$u = 4x \implies \frac{du}{dx} = 4$ and $\frac{dv}{dx} = \sin\left(\frac{x}{2}\right) \implies v = -2\cos\left(\frac{x}{2}\right)$

2. Substitute everything into the formula and complete the integration:

$$\int_0^{\frac{\pi}{2}} 4x \sin\left(\frac{x}{2}\right) dx = \left[-8x\cos\left(\frac{x}{2}\right)\right]_0^{\frac{\pi}{2}} - \int_0^{\frac{\pi}{2}} -8\cos\left(\frac{x}{2}\right) dx$$

> **Tip:** See p.206 for a reminder about integrating trig functions.

$$= -8\left[x\cos\left(\frac{x}{2}\right)\right]_0^{\frac{\pi}{2}} + 16\left[\sin\left(\frac{x}{2}\right)\right]_0^{\frac{\pi}{2}}$$

$$= -8\left[\frac{\pi}{2}\cos\left(\frac{\pi}{4}\right) - 0\cos(0)\right] + 16\left[\sin\left(\frac{\pi}{4}\right) - \sin(0)\right]$$

$$= -8\left[\frac{\pi}{2}\frac{1}{\sqrt{2}}\right] + 16\left[\frac{1}{\sqrt{2}}\right]$$

$$= -\frac{4\pi}{\sqrt{2}} + \frac{16}{\sqrt{2}}$$

$$= \boxed{8\sqrt{2} - 2\pi\sqrt{2}}$$

Q1 Use integration by parts to find:

a) $\int xe^x \, dx$

b) $\int xe^{-x} \, dx$

c) $\int xe^{-\frac{x}{3}} \, dx$

d) $\int x(e^x + 1) \, dx$

Q2 Use integration by parts to find:

a) $\int_0^\pi x \sin x \, dx$

b) $\int 2x \cos x \, dx$

c) $\int 3x \cos\left(\frac{1}{2}x\right) dx$

d) $\int_{\frac{\pi}{2}}^{\frac{\pi}{2}} 2x(1 - \sin x) \, dx$

Q3 Use integration by parts to find:

a) $\int 2 \ln x \, dx$

b) $\int x^4 \ln x \, dx$

c) $\int \ln 4x \, dx$

d) $\int \ln x^3 \, dx$

Q4 Use integration by parts to find:

a) $\int_{-1}^1 20x(x + 1)^3$

b) $\int_0^{1.5} 30x\sqrt{2x + 1} \, dx$

Q5 Use integration by parts to find the exact values of the following:

a) $\int_0^1 12x \, e^{2x} \, dx$

b) $\int_0^{\frac{\pi}{3}} 18x \sin 3x \, dx$

c) $\int_1^2 \frac{1}{x^2} \ln x \, dx$

Q6 Find:

a) $\int \frac{x}{e^{2x}} \, dx$

b) $\int (x + 1)\sqrt{x + 2} \, dx$

c) $\int \ln(x + 1) \, dx$

Repeated use of integration by parts

Sometimes **integration by parts** leaves you with a function for $v\frac{du}{dx}$ which is **simpler** than the function you started with, but still **tricky to integrate**.

You might have to carry out integration by parts **again** to find $\int v\frac{du}{dx} \, dx$.

Example 1

Find $\int x^2 \sin x \, dx$.

1. Choose u and $\frac{dv}{dx}$:

Let $u = x^2$ and let $\frac{dv}{dx} = \sin x$

Then $\frac{du}{dx} = 2x$ and $v = -\cos x$

2. Putting these into the formula gives:

$\int x^2 \sin x \, dx = -x^2\cos x - \int -2x \cos x \, dx$
$= -x^2\cos x + \int 2x \cos x \, dx$

3. $2x \cos x$ isn't very easy to integrate, but you can integrate by parts again:

Let $u_1 = 2x$ and let $\frac{dv_1}{dx} = \cos x$

Then $\frac{du_1}{dx} = 2$ and $v_1 = \sin x$

4. Putting these into the formula gives:

$\int 2x \cos x \, dx = 2x \sin x - \int 2 \sin x \, dx$
$= 2x \sin x + 2\cos x + C$

So $\int x^2 \sin x \, dx = -x^2\cos x + \int 2x \cos x \, dx$
$= -x^2\cos x + 2x \sin x + 2\cos x + C$

Example 2

Use integration by parts to find $\int_2^3 x^2(x-1)^{-4}\,dx$.

1. Choose u and $\dfrac{dv}{dx}$:

   Let $u = x^2$ and let $\dfrac{dv}{dx} = (x-1)^{-4}$.
   Then $\dfrac{du}{dx} = 2x$ and $v = -\dfrac{1}{3}(x-1)^{-3}$.

2. Putting these into the formula gives:

   $$\int_2^3 x^2(x-1)^{-4}\,dx = \left[-\frac{x^2}{3}(x-1)^{-3}\right]_2^3 - \int_2^3 -\frac{2x}{3}(x-1)^{-3}\,dx$$

   $$= \left[-\frac{x^2}{3}(x-1)^{-3}\right]_2^3 + \frac{2}{3}\int_2^3 x(x-1)^{-3}\,dx$$

3. This is still tricky to integrate, so use integration by parts again:

   Let $u_1 = x$ and let $\dfrac{dv_1}{dx} = (x-1)^{-3}$.
   Then $\dfrac{du_1}{dx} = 1$ and $v_1 = -\dfrac{1}{2}(x-1)^{-2}$.

4. Put these into the formula:

   $$\int_2^3 x(x-1)^{-3}\,dx = \left[-\frac{x}{2}(x-1)^{-2}\right]_2^3 - \int_2^3 -\frac{1}{2}(x-1)^{-2}\,dx$$

   $$= \left[-\frac{x}{2}(x-1)^{-2}\right]_2^3 - \frac{1}{2}\left[(x-1)^{-1}\right]_2^3$$

   $$= \left[-\frac{3}{2}(2)^{-2} + \frac{2}{2}(1)^{-2}\right] - \frac{1}{2}\left[2^{-1} - 1^{-1}\right]$$

   $$= \left[-\frac{3}{8} + 1\right] - \frac{1}{2}\left[\frac{1}{2} - 1\right]$$

   $$= \frac{5}{8} + \frac{1}{4} = \frac{7}{8}$$

   > **Tip:** The formula for integrating $(ax + b)^n$ is used a few times in this example — go back to p.200 if you've forgotten how it works.

5. Now you can evaluate the original integral:

   $$\int_2^3 x^2(x-1)^{-4}\,dx = \left[-\frac{x^2}{3}(x-1)^{-3}\right]_2^3 + \frac{2}{3}\int_2^3 x(x-1)^{-3}\,dx$$

   $$= \left[-\frac{x^2}{3}(x-1)^{-3}\right]_2^3 + \frac{2}{3}\left(\frac{7}{8}\right)$$

   $$= \left[\left(-\frac{9}{3}(2)^{-3}\right) - \left(-\frac{4}{3}(1)^{-3}\right)\right] + \frac{7}{12}$$

   $$= \left[-\frac{9}{24} + \frac{4}{3}\right] + \frac{7}{12}$$

   $$= \frac{23}{24} + \frac{7}{12} = \frac{37}{24}$$

Exercise 8.9.2

Q1 Use integration by parts twice to find:

   a) $\displaystyle\int x^2 e^x\,dx$ b) $\displaystyle\int x^2 \cos x\,dx$

   c) $\displaystyle\int 4x^2 \sin 2x\,dx$ d) $\displaystyle\int 40x^2(2x-1)^4\,dx$

Q2 Find $\displaystyle\int_{-1}^0 x^2(x+1)^4\,dx$ using integration by parts.

Q3 Use integration by parts to find the area enclosed by the curve $y = x^2 e^{-2x}$, the x-axis and the lines $x = 0$ and $x = 1$.

> **Q3 Hint:** Since $x^2 \geq 0$ and $e^{-2x} > 0$ for all x, the area will be entirely above the x-axis.

8.10 Integration Using Partial Fractions

By rewriting algebraic expressions as partial fractions, you can turn difficult-looking integrations into ones you're more familiar with.

Learning Objective (Spec Ref 8.6):

- Integrate rational expressions in which the denominator can be written as a product of linear factors, by splitting them into partial fractions.

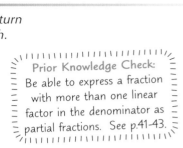

Prior Knowledge Check:
Be able to express a fraction with more than one linear factor in the denominator as partial fractions. See p.41-43.

Use of partial fractions

You can integrate algebraic fractions where the denominator can be written as a product of **linear factors** by splitting them up into **partial fractions**. Each fraction can then be **integrated separately** using the method on pages 204-205.

Example 1

Find $\int \dfrac{12x + 6}{4x^2 - 9}\,dx$ where $x > 2$.

1. The first step is to write the function as **partial fractions** as follows:

    - **Factorise** the denominator:

      $$\frac{12x + 6}{4x^2 - 9} \equiv \frac{12x + 6}{(2x + 3)(2x - 3)}$$

    - Write as an **identity** with partial fractions:

      $$\frac{12x + 6}{(2x + 3)(2x - 3)} \equiv \frac{A}{2x + 3} + \frac{B}{2x - 3}$$

    - **Add** the partial fractions and **cancel** the denominators:

      $$\frac{12x + 6}{(2x + 3)(2x - 3)} \equiv \frac{A(2x - 3) + B(2x + 3)}{(2x + 3)(2x - 3)}$$

      $$\Rightarrow 12x + 6 \equiv A(2x - 3) + B(2x + 3)$$

    - Use the **substitution method** to find A and B:

      Substituting $x = \dfrac{3}{2}$ into the identity gives:

      $$18 + 6 = 0A + 6B \Rightarrow 24 = 6B \Rightarrow B = 4$$

      > **Tip:** You could also use the 'equating coefficients' method to find A and B.

      Substituting $x = -\dfrac{3}{2}$ into the identity gives:

      $$-18 + 6 = -6A + 0B \Rightarrow -12 = -6A \Rightarrow A = 2$$

    - Replace A and B in the **original identity**:

      $$\frac{12x + 6}{4x^2 - 9} \equiv \frac{2}{2x + 3} + \frac{4}{2x - 3}$$

2. Integrate each term **separately**:

    $$\int \frac{12x + 6}{4x^2 - 9}\,dx = \int \frac{2}{2x + 3} + \frac{4}{2x - 3}\,dx$$

    $x > 2$ so $2x + 3 > 7$ and $2x - 3 > 1$ so remove the modulus signs.

    $$= 2 \times \frac{1}{2}\ln|2x + 3| + 4 \times \frac{1}{2}\ln|2x - 3| + C$$

    $$= \ln|2x + 3| + 2\ln|2x - 3| + C$$

    $$= \ln(2x + 3) + 2\ln(2x - 3) + C$$

    > **Tip:** It's a good idea to tidy up your answers using the log laws.

    $$= \ln(2x + 3)(2x - 3)^2 + C$$

Example 2

Find the exact value of $\int_3^4 \dfrac{2}{x(x-2)}\,dx$, **writing it as a single logarithm.**

1. Start by writing $\dfrac{2}{x(x-2)}$ as **partial fractions**.

    -   Write as an **identity** with partial fractions:

        $$\frac{2}{x(x-2)} \equiv \frac{A}{x} + \frac{B}{x-2} \equiv \frac{A(x-2)+Bx}{x(x-2)}$$
        $$\Rightarrow 2 \equiv A(x-2) + Bx$$

    -   Use the **equating coefficients method** to find A and B.

        Equating constant terms:
        $2 = -2A \Rightarrow A = -1$
        Equating x coefficients:
        $0 = A + B \Rightarrow 0 = -1 + B \Rightarrow \mathbf{B = 1}$

    -   Replace A and B in the **original identity**:

        $$\frac{2}{x(x-2)} \equiv \frac{-1}{x} + \frac{1}{x-2} \equiv \frac{1}{x-2} - \frac{1}{x}$$

2. Integrate each term separately:

    $$\int_3^4 \frac{2}{x(x-2)}\,dx = \int_3^4 \frac{1}{(x-2)} - \frac{1}{x}\,dx$$
    $$= \Big[\ln|x-2| - \ln|x|\Big]_3^4$$
    $$= \Big[\ln\Big|\frac{x-2}{x}\Big|\Big]_3^4$$
    $$= \ln\Big|\frac{4-2}{4}\Big| - \ln\Big|\frac{3-2}{3}\Big|$$

3. Fully simplify your answer by using the law $\log a - \log b = \log\left(\frac{a}{b}\right)$. $\longrightarrow$ $= \ln\left(\frac{1}{2}\right) - \ln\left(\frac{1}{3}\right) = \boxed{\ln\left(\frac{3}{2}\right)}$

Exercise 8.10.1

Q1 Integrate the following functions by writing them as partial fractions:

a) $\displaystyle\int \frac{24(x-1)}{9-4x^2}\,dx$

b) $\displaystyle\int \frac{21x-82}{(x-2)(x-3)(x-4)}\,dx$

Q2 Find $\displaystyle\int_0^1 \frac{x}{(x-2)(x-3)}\,dx$ by expressing as partial fractions.
Give your answer as a single logarithm.

Q3 a) Express $\dfrac{6}{2x^2-5x+2}$ in partial fractions.

b) Hence find $\displaystyle\int \frac{6}{2x^2-5x+2}\,dx$ where $x > 2$.

c) Evaluate $\displaystyle\int_3^5 \frac{6}{2x^2-5x+2}\,dx$, expressing your answer as a single logarithm.

Q4 Given that f$(x) = 3x + 5$ and g$(x) = x(x + 10)$, find $\displaystyle\int_1^2 \frac{f(x)}{g(x)}\,dx$ to 3 d.p.
by expressing $\dfrac{f(x)}{g(x)}$ as partial fractions.

Q5 Show that $\displaystyle\int_0^{\frac{2}{3}} \frac{-(t+3)}{(3t+2)(t+1)}\,dt = 2\ln\frac{5}{3} - \frac{7}{3}\ln 2$.

Q6 Use the substitution $u = \sqrt{x}$ to find the exact value of $\displaystyle\int_9^{16} \frac{4}{\sqrt{x}(9x-4)}\,dx$.

8.11 Differential Equations

Differential equations involve differentiation as well as integration. The differentiation comes in because they always include a derivative term, and integration is used to solve them.

Learning Objectives (Spec Ref 8.7 & 8.8):
- Formulate a differential equation for a given situation.
- Find general and particular solutions to differential equations.
- Formulate and solve differential equations that model real-life situations and interpret the results in context.
- Identify the limitations of a model and suggest refinements to address them.

Differential equations

A **differential equation** is an equation that includes a **derivative term** such as $\frac{dy}{dx}$ (or $\frac{dP}{dt}$, $\frac{ds}{dt}$, $\frac{dV}{dr}$ etc, depending on the variables), as well as **other variables** (like x and y).

Before you even think about **solving** them, you have to be able to **set up** ('**formulate**') differential equations. Differential equations tend to involve a **rate of change** (giving a derivative term) and a **proportion relation**, where the rate of change will be directly or inversely proportional to some function of the variables.

It'll help to think about what the derivative **actually means**. $\frac{dy}{dx}$ is defined as 'the **rate of change** of y with respect to x'. In other words, it tells you how y changes as x changes. One of the variables in a differential equation is often **time**, t, so the question will be about how something **changes over time**.

Example 1

The number of bacteria in a petri dish, b, is increasing over time, t, at a rate directly proportional to the number of bacteria. Formulate a differential equation that shows this information.

1. The question tells you that you need to write a differential equation, so you know there'll be a **derivative term** — work this out first.

   The number of bacteria (b) increases as time (t) increases — so that's the rate of change of b with respect to t, or $\frac{db}{dt}$.

2. The rate of change, $\frac{db}{dt}$, is proportional to b:

   $$\frac{db}{dt} \propto b$$

3. We're looking for an equation, not a proportion relation, so rewrite it:

   $$\frac{db}{dt} = kb \text{ for some constant } k, k > 0.$$

Example 2

The volume of interdimensional space jelly, V, in a container is decreasing over time, t, at a rate inversely proportional to the square of its volume. Show this as a differential equation.

1. Find the derivative term:

   V decreases as t increases, so the derivative term is the rate of change of V with respect to t, or $\frac{dV}{dt}$.

2. $\dfrac{dV}{dt}$ is inversely proportional V^2, so:

$$\dfrac{dV}{dt} \propto \dfrac{1}{V^2}$$

3. The equation needs a minus sign because V is decreasing as t increases.

$$\dfrac{dV}{dt} = -\dfrac{k}{V^2} \text{ for some constant } k,\, k > 0.$$

Example 3

The rate of cooling of a hot liquid is proportional to the difference between the temperature of the liquid and the temperature of the room. Formulate a differential equation to represent this situation.

1. Find the derivative term:

Let L = temperature of the liquid, R = room temperature and t = time.

Then the derivative term is the rate of change of L with respect to t, or $\dfrac{dL}{dt}$.

2. $\dfrac{dL}{dt}$ is proportional to the difference between L and R:

$$\dfrac{dL}{dt} \propto (L - R)$$

3. $(L - R)$ decreases as t increases, so you need a minus sign in the equation again.

$$\dfrac{dL}{dt} = -k(L - R) \text{ for some constant } k,\, k > 0$$

Exercise 8.11.1

Q1 The number of fleas (N) on a cat is increasing over time, t, at a rate directly proportional to the number of fleas. Show this as a differential equation.

Q2 The value, x, of a house is increasing over time, t, at a rate inversely proportional to the square of x. Formulate a differential equation to show this.

Q3 The rate of depreciation of the amount (£A) a car is worth is directly proportional to the square root of A. Show this as a differential equation.

Q4 The rate of decrease of a population, y, with respect to time is directly proportional to the difference between y and λ where λ is a constant. Show this as a differential equation.

Q5 The volume of water which is being poured into a container is directly proportional to the volume of water (V) in the container. The container has a hole in it from which water flows out at a rate of 20 cm³s⁻¹. Formulate a differential equation to show this.

Q5 Hint: The rate of change of V is the difference between the rate water flows in and the rate it flows out.

Solving differential equations

Solving a differential equation means using it to find an **equation** in terms of the two variables, **without** a derivative term. To do this, you need to use **integration**.

The only differential equations containing x and y terms that you'll have to solve in A-Level Maths are ones with **separable variables** — where x and y can be separated into functions **f**(x) and **g**(y). Note that other variables might be used instead — they won't always be x and y.

Solving differential equations

Step 1: Write the differential equation in the form $\frac{dy}{dx} = f(x)g(y)$.

Step 2: **Rearrange** the equation into the form: $\frac{1}{g(y)}dy = f(x)\ dx$.

To do this, get all the terms containing y on the **left-hand side**,

and all the terms containing x on the **right-hand side** and split up the $\frac{dy}{dx}$.

Step 3: Now **integrate both sides**: $\int \frac{1}{g(y)}\ dy = \int f(x)\ dx$.

Don't forget the **constant of integration** (you only need one — not one on each side). It might be useful to write the constant as **ln k** rather than **C** (see p.244).

Step 4: **Rearrange** your answer to get it in a **nice form** — you might be asked to find it in the form $y = h(x)$.

Step 5: If you're asked for a **general solution**, leave C (or k) in your answer. If they want a **particular solution**, they'll give you x and y values for a certain point. All you do is put these values into your equation and use them to **find C** (or k).

Example 1

Find the general solution of the differential equation $\frac{ds}{dt} = -6t^2$.

Step 1 is already done: $f(t) = -6t^2,\ g(s) = 1$

Step 2 — rearrange the equation: $ds = -6t^2\ dt$

Step 3 — integrate both sides: $\int 1\ ds = \int -6t^2\ dt\ \Rightarrow\ \boxed{s = -2t^3 + C}$

Steps 4 and 5 aren't needed here — the equation doesn't need rearranging, and you're only looking for the general solution, so you're done.

Example 2

Find the particular solution of $\frac{dy}{dx} = 2y(1 + x)^2$ when $x = -1$ and $y = 4$.

1. Identify $f(x)$ and $g(y)$: $f(x) = 2(1 + x)^2$ and $g(y) = y$

2. Separate the variables: $\frac{1}{y}\ dy = 2(1 + x)^2\ dx$

3. And integrate: $\int \frac{1}{y}\ dy = \int 2(1 + x)^2\ dx\ \Rightarrow\ \ln |y| = \frac{2}{3}(1 + x)^3 + C$

4. Work out the value of C for the given values of x and y: $\ln 4 = \frac{2}{3}(1 + (-1))^3 + C\ \Rightarrow\ \ln 4 = C$

     So $\boxed{\ln |y| = \frac{2}{3}(1 + x)^3 + \ln 4}$

Example 3

Find the general solution of $(x - 2)(2x + 3)\dfrac{dy}{dx} = xy + 5y$, where $x > 2$.

Give your answer in the form $y = f(x)$.

1. First, separate the variables:

$$\frac{dy}{dx} = \frac{x + 5}{(x - 2)(2x + 3)} \times y \implies \frac{1}{y}\,dy = \frac{x + 5}{(x - 2)(2x + 3)}\,dx$$

2. Write the right-hand side as partial fractions (see p.239):

$$\frac{x + 5}{(x - 2)(2x + 3)} \equiv \frac{A}{x - 2} + \frac{B}{2x + 3}$$

$$\implies x + 5 \equiv A(2x + 3) + B(x - 2)$$

Solving for A and B gives $A = 1$, $B = -1$, so:

$$\frac{1}{y}\,dy = \frac{1}{x - 2} - \frac{1}{2x + 3}\,dx$$

3. Now you can integrate:

$$\int \frac{1}{y}\,dy = \int \frac{1}{x - 2} - \frac{1}{2x + 3}\,dx$$

> **Tip:** Since all the other terms are ln(something), it makes sense to use ln k as the constant of integration, then use the log laws to simplify.

$$\implies \ln|y| = \ln|x - 2| - \frac{1}{2}\ln|2x + 3| + \ln k$$

$$\implies \ln|y| = \ln\left|\frac{k(x - 2)}{\sqrt{2x + 3}}\right|$$

$$\implies y = \frac{k(x - 2)}{\sqrt{2x + 3}}$$

You know $x > 2$, so $x - 2$ is positive and the modulus can be removed.

Example 4

Find the particular solution to the differential equation $\dfrac{db}{dt} = 4\sqrt{b}$,

given that when $t = 12$, $b = 900$. Give your answer in the form $b = f(t)$.

1. Separate the variables:

$$\frac{1}{\sqrt{b}}\,db = 4\,dt$$

2. Integrate both sides:

$$\int b^{-\frac{1}{2}}\,db = \int 4\,dt \implies 2b^{\frac{1}{2}} = 4t + C$$

3. In this case, it's easier to find C for the given values of b and t before you rearrange the equation — rearranging then finding C would give you a quadratic to solve.

$$2\sqrt{b} = 4t + C \implies 2\sqrt{900} = 4(12) + C$$
$$\implies 60 = 48 + C$$
$$\implies C = 12$$

4. Now rearrange to get the form $b = f(t)$:

$$2\sqrt{b} = 4t + 12 \implies \sqrt{b} = 2t + 6$$

$$\implies b = 4t^2 + 24t + 36$$

Q1 Find the general solutions of the following differential equations where $x \geq 0$.
Give your answers in the form $y = f(x)$.

a) $\dfrac{dy}{dx} = 8x^3$

b) $\dfrac{dy}{dx} = 5y$

c) $\dfrac{dy}{dx} = 6x^2y$

d) $\dfrac{dy}{dx} = \dfrac{y}{x}$

e) $\dfrac{dy}{dx} = (y + 1)\cos x$

f) $\dfrac{dy}{dx} = \dfrac{3xy - 6y}{(x - 4)(2x - 5)}$

> **Q1f) Hint:** You'll need to do some work before you can integrate with respect to x.

Q2 Find the particular solutions of the following differential equations at the given conditions:

a) $\dfrac{dy}{dx} = -\dfrac{x}{y}$ $x = 0, y = 2$

b) $\dfrac{dx}{dt} = \dfrac{2}{\sqrt{x}}$ $t = 5, x = 9$

c) $\dfrac{dV}{dt} = 3(V - 1)$ $t = 0, V = 5$

d) $\dfrac{dy}{dx} = \dfrac{\tan y}{x}$ $x = 2, y = \dfrac{\pi}{2}$

e) $\dfrac{dx}{dt} = 10x(x + 1)$ $t = 0, x = 1$

Q3 a) Find the general solution of the equation $\dfrac{dx}{d\theta} = \cos^2x \cot \theta$.

     b) Given that $x = \dfrac{\pi}{4}$ when $\theta = \dfrac{\pi}{2}$, find a particular solution.

     c) Hence find the value of x when $\theta = \dfrac{\pi}{6}$, for $0 < x < \dfrac{\pi}{2}$.

Q4 The rate of increase of the variable V at time t satisfies the differential equation $\dfrac{dV}{dt} = a - bV$, where a and b are positive constants.

     a) Show that $V = \dfrac{a}{b} - Ae^{-bt}$, where A is a positive constant.

     b) Given that $V = \dfrac{a}{4b}$ when $t = 0$, find A in terms of a and b.

     c) Find the value V approaches as t gets very large.

Applying differential equations to real-life problems

- Some questions involve taking **real-life problems** and using differential equations to **model** them.

- **Population** questions come up quite often — the population might be **increasing** or **decreasing**, and you have to find and solve differential equations to show it. In cases like this, one variable will usually be t, **time**.

- You might be given a **starting condition** — e.g. the **initial population**.
  The important thing to remember is that the starting condition occurs when $t = 0$

- Once you've solved the differential equation you can use it to **answer questions** about the model. For example, if the equation is for population you might be asked to find the **population** after a certain number of years, or the **number of years** it takes to reach a certain population. Don't forget to relate the answer back to the situation given in the question.

You may also have to identify **limitations** of the model, as well as suggest possible **changes** that would **improve** it. Common things that you should think about are:

- Is there any information **missing** from the model?

- What happens to the model when the variables get really **big/small**?

- Is the model appropriate? Is a **continuous** function used for a **discrete** variable? Does the function allow **negative** values that don't make sense?

- Are there **other factors** that have not been accounted for in the model? Some examples might be **natural immunity** to a disease, **immigration/emigration** of a population or **seasonal variation** in weather.

When suggesting some refinements to the model, you don't have to make up a whole new model — just identify what the changes would be and how you could make them.

Questions like the following examples can seem a bit **overwhelming** at first, but follow things through **step by step** and they shouldn't be too bad.

Example 1

The population of rabbits in a park is decreasing as winter approaches. The rate of decrease is directly proportional to the current number of rabbits (*P*).

a) **Explain why this situation can be modelled by the differential equation $\frac{dP}{dt} = -kP$, where *t* is the time in days and *k* is a positive constant.**

1. The model states that the rate of decrease in the rabbit population (i.e. $\frac{dP}{dt}$) is **proportional** to *P*.

   So $\frac{dP}{dt} \propto P$

2. By introducing a constant of proportionality, the model becomes:

   $\frac{dP}{dt} = -kP$ (where the minus sign shows that the population is decreasing.)

b) **If the initial population is P_0, solve your differential equation to find *P* in terms of P_0, *k* and *t*.**

1. Solve the differential equation to find the general solution:

   $\frac{dP}{dt} = -kP \Rightarrow \frac{1}{P}\,dP = -k\,dt$

   $\Rightarrow \int \frac{1}{P}\,dP = \int -k\,dt$

   $\Rightarrow \ln P = -kt + C$

2. At $t = 0$, $P = P_0$ — putting these values into the equation gives:

   $\ln P_0 = -k(0) + C \Rightarrow \ln P_0 = C$

3. So the equation becomes:

   $\ln P = -kt + \ln P_0 \Rightarrow P = e^{(-kt + \ln P_0)} = e^{-kt}e^{\ln P_0}$

   $\Rightarrow P = P_0 e^{-kt}$

   Tip: You don't need modulus signs when you integrate to get $\ln P$ here. $P \geq 0$ as you can't have a negative population.

c) **Given that $k = 0.1$, find the time at which the population of rabbits will have halved, to the nearest day.**

When the population of rabbits has halved, $P = \frac{1}{2}P_0$.

And you've also been told that $k = 0.1$, so substitute these values into the equation above and solve for t.

$$\frac{1}{2}P_0 = P_0 e^{-0.1t} \Rightarrow \frac{1}{2} = e^{-0.1t}$$
$$\Rightarrow \ln\frac{1}{2} = -0.1t$$
$$\Rightarrow -0.6931 = -0.1t$$
$$\Rightarrow t = 6.931$$

So to the nearest day, $t = 7$.

This means that it will take 7 days for the population to halve.

d) **Give a limitation of the model and suggest a possible improvement that could be made to address it.**

There are several ways to answer this:

- The value of P_0 is not given — the model could be improved by finding a suitable value of P_0.

- As t becomes very large, the population becomes increasingly small but never reaches 0 — it may be more realistic to choose a model where the population can reach 0.

- The population of rabbits is a discrete variable while the model is continuous — choosing a function that limits the possible values of P to integers would solve this problem.

- The situation being modelled is the approach of winter — the model could give a limit on t to show at which point the model stops being appropriate.

Example 2

Water is leaking from the bottom of a water tank shaped like a vertical cylinder, so that at time t seconds the depth, D, of water in the tank is decreasing at a rate proportional to $\frac{1}{D^2}$.

MODELLING

a) **Explain why the depth of water satisfies the differential equation $\dfrac{dD}{dt} = -\dfrac{k}{D^2}$ for some constant $k > 0$.**

The question tells you that the rate at which D decreases (i.e. $\frac{dD}{dt}$) is inversely proportional to D^2.

$$\frac{dD}{dt} \propto \frac{1}{D^2} \Rightarrow \frac{dD}{dt} = -\frac{k}{D^2} \text{ for some } k > 0,$$

where the minus sign indicates that the depth of the water is decreasing.

b) **Given that D is decreasing at a rate of 2 cm s^{-1} when $D = 40$ cm, find k.**

Use the differential equation for D:

$$\frac{dD}{dt} = -\frac{k}{D^2}$$

$$\frac{dD}{dt} = -2 \text{ when } D = 40$$

$$\Rightarrow -\frac{k}{40^2} = -2 \Rightarrow k = 2 \times 40^2 = 3200$$

c) **Given that $D = 60$ cm at $t = 0$ s, find a particular solution to the differential equation for D, and hence calculate how long it takes for the tank to empty.**

There are a few steps to part c) — first you have to find the general solution, then sub in the values given to find the particular solution, then use this solution to answer the question.

1. Solve the differential equation, using the value of k from part b), to find the general solution:

$$\frac{dD}{dt} = -\frac{3200}{D^2} \Rightarrow D^2\,dD = -3200\,dt$$
$$\Rightarrow \int D^2\,dD = \int -3200\,dt$$
$$\Rightarrow \tfrac{1}{3}D^3 = -3200t + C$$

2. When $t = 0$, $D = 60$ — putting these values into the equation gives:

$$\tfrac{1}{3}60^3 = -3200(0) + C \Rightarrow C = 72\,000$$
So $\tfrac{1}{3}D^3 = 72\,000 - 3200t$

3. The tank is empty when $D = 0$:

$$D = 0 \Rightarrow 72\,000 = 3200t \Rightarrow t = 22.5 \text{ s}$$

d) **Given that the radius of the cylinder is 20 cm, calculate the rate at which the volume of water in the tank is decreasing when $t = 10$ s.**

Tip: Part d) is a 'connected rates of change' question — see p.181 if you've forgotten how to tackle them.

1. Find an expression for the volume of water in the tank and differentiate:

$$V = \pi r^2 h = \pi(20)^2 D = 400\pi D \Rightarrow \frac{dV}{dD} = 400\pi$$

2. Use the chain rule:

$$\frac{dV}{dt} = \frac{dV}{dD} \times \frac{dD}{dt} = 400\pi \times -\frac{3200}{D^2} = -\frac{1280000\pi}{D^2}$$

3. Find D when $t = 10$:

$$\tfrac{1}{3}D^3 = 72000 - 3200(10) = 40000$$
$$\Rightarrow D = \sqrt[3]{3 \times 40000} = 49.324\dots \text{ cm}$$

4. Use this value of D to calculate $\frac{dV}{dt}$:

$$\frac{dV}{dt} = \frac{-1280000\pi}{49.324^2} = -1652.87\dots \text{ cm}^3\text{s}^{-1}$$

So the volume is decreasing at a rate of $1650 \text{ cm}^3\text{s}^{-1}$ (3 s.f.)

Exercise 8.11.3

MODELLING

Q1 A virus spreads so that t hours after infection, the rate of increase of the number of germs (N) in the body of an infected person is directly proportional to the number of germs in the body.

a) Given that this can be represented by the differential equation $\frac{dN}{dt} = kN$, show that the general solution of this equation is $N = Ae^{kt}$, where A and k are positive constants.

b) Given that a person catching the virus will initially be infected with 200 germs and that this will double to 400 germs in 8 hours, find the number of germs an infected person has after 24 hours.

c) Give one possible limitation of this model.

Q2 The rate of depreciation of the value (V) of a car at time t after it is first purchased is directly proportional to V.

a) If the initial value of the car is V_0, show that $V = V_0 e^{-kt}$, where k is a positive constant.

b) If the car drops to one half of its initial value in the first year after purchase, how long (to the nearest month) will it take to be worth 5% of its initial value?

Q3 The population of squirrels is increasing suspiciously quickly.
The rate of increase is directly proportional to the number of squirrels, S.

a) Formulate a differential equation to model the rate of increase in terms of S, t (time in weeks) and k, a positive constant.

b) The squirrels need a population of 150 to take over the forest. If, initially, $S = 30$ and $\frac{dS}{dt} = 6$, how long (to the nearest week) will it be before they take over?

Q4 It is thought that the rate of increase of the number of field mice (N) in a given area is directly proportional to N.

a) Formulate a differential equation for N.

b) Given that in 4 weeks the number of mice in a particular field has risen from 20 to 30, find the length of time, to the nearest week, before the field is over-run with 1000 mice.

A biologist believes that the rate of increase of the number field mice is actually directly proportional to the square root of N when natural factors such as predators and disease are taken into account.

c) Repeat parts a) and b) using this new model.

d) Suggest another refinement that could be made to improve this model.

Q5 A cube has side length x. At time t seconds, the side length is increasing at a rate of $\frac{1}{x^2(t+1)}$ cms^{-1}.

a) Show that the volume (V) is increasing at a rate which satisfies
the differential equation $\frac{dV}{dt} = \frac{3}{t+1}$.

b) Given that the volume of the cube is initially 15 cm^3, find the length of time, to 3 s.f., for it to reach a volume of 18 cm^3.

Q6 A local activist is trying to get lots of signatures on his petition, and has just launched a new online campaign. The rate of increase of the number of signatures (y) he's gathered can be represented by the differential equation $\frac{dy}{dt} = k(p - y)$, where p is the population of his town and t is the time in days since the new campaign was launched.

a) Find the general solution of this equation.

b) Given that the population of his town is 30 000, he initially has 10 000 signatures on his petition and it takes 5 days for him to reach 12 000 signatures, how long, to the nearest day, will it take for him to reach 25 000 signatures?

c) Draw a graph to show this particular solution.

d) The activist wants 28 000 signatures within 92 days of launching his new campaign. According to the model, will he achieve this?

e) What is a likely limitation of this model and how could it be addressed?

Review Exercise

Q1   a) Find $\int \dfrac{1}{\sqrt[3]{(2-11x)}} \, dx$

      b) Show that the area under the curve $y = \dfrac{1}{\sqrt[3]{(2-11x)}}$ from $x = -\dfrac{123}{11}$ to $x = -\dfrac{62}{11}$ is $\dfrac{27}{22}$.

Q2   Find the equation of the curve with derivative $\dfrac{dy}{dx} = (1-7x)^{\frac{1}{2}}$ that goes through the point (0, 1).

Q3   Find the following integrals, giving your answers in terms of e or ln.

      a) $\int 4e^{2x} \, dx$
      b) $\int e^{3x-5} \, dx$
      c) $\int \dfrac{2}{3x} \, dx$
      d) $\int \dfrac{2}{2x+1} \, dx$

Q4   If $\int \dfrac{8}{2-x} - \dfrac{8}{x} \, dx = \ln P + C$, where P is an expression in terms of x and C is a constant, find P.

Q5   Find the following integrals (A and B are constants):

      a) $\int \cos(x+A) \, dx$
                 b) $\int \operatorname{cosec}^2((A+B)t + A + B) \, dt$

Q6   Find the following integrals:

      a) $\int \cos 4x - \sec^2 7x \, dx$
            b) $\int 6\sec 3x \tan 3x - \operatorname{cosec}^2 \dfrac{x}{5} \, dx$

Q7   Find the following integrals:

      a) $\int \dfrac{\cos x}{\sin x} \, dx$
            b) $\int \dfrac{20x^4 + 12x^2 - 12}{x^5 + x^3 - 3x} \, dx$

Q8   Find the following integrals:

      a) $\int 3x^2 e^{x^3} \, dx$
      b) $\int 2x\cos(x^2)e^{\sin(x^2)} \, dx$
      c) $\int \sec 4x \tan 4x \, e^{\sec 4x} \, dx$

Q9   Use an appropriate trig identity to find $\int \dfrac{2\tan 3x}{1 - \tan^2 3x} \, dx$.

Q10   Find the following integrals:

      a) $\int 2\sin^2 x \, dx$
      b) $\int \sin 2x \cos 2x \, dx$
      c) $\int \tan^2 x + 1 \, dx$

Q11   Find the exact shaded area in each of these graphs:

      a)

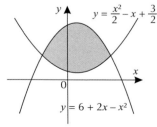

$y = \dfrac{x^2}{2} - x + \dfrac{3}{2}$

$y = 6 + 2x - x^2$

      b)

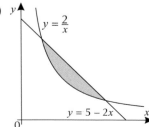

$y = \dfrac{2}{x}$

$y = 5 - 2x$

Review Exercise

Q12 Find the areas enclosed by the following:

a) The curve $y = \arctan x$, the y-axis and the lines $y = \frac{\pi}{6}$ and $y = \frac{\pi}{4}$.

b) The curve $y = \frac{1}{x^2}$, the y-axis and the lines $y = 4$ and $y = 16$.

Q13 The curve on the right has the parametric equations $x = t^2 + 3$, $y = 4t - 1$.

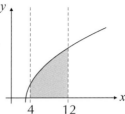

a) Given that $t > 0$, find the values of t when $x = 4$ and $x = 12$.

b) Hence find the shaded area.

Q14 Find the following integrals, using the given substitution in each case. Where appropriate, give your answers as exact values.

a) $\int 16x(5 - x^2)^5 \, dx$, using $u = 5 - x^2$

b) $\int e^x(e^x + 1)(e^x - 1)^2 \, dx$, using $u = e^x - 1$

c) $\int_2^4 x(x^2 - 4)^3 \, dx$, using $u = x^2 - 4$

d) $\int_3^{11} \frac{2x}{\sqrt{3x - 8}} \, dx$, using $u = \sqrt{3x - 8}$

Q15 Find $\int_0^{\frac{\pi}{2}} \frac{1}{4} \cos x \sin 2x \, dx$, using the substitution $u = \cos x$.

Q16 Use integration by parts to solve:

a) $\int 3x^2 \ln x \, dx$

b) $\int 4x \cos 4x \, dx$

c) $\int_0^4 e^{\frac{x}{2}} x^2 \, dx$

Q17 Use integration by parts twice to find $\int 10x^2 e^{5x} \, dx$.

Q18 Given that $\frac{3x + 10}{(2x + 3)(x - 4)} \equiv \frac{A}{2x + 3} + \frac{B}{x - 4}$, find $\int \frac{3x + 10}{(2x + 3)(x - 4)} \, dx$.

Q19 Given that $f(x) = \frac{13x - 18}{(x - 3)^2(2x + 1)} \equiv \frac{A}{(x - 3)^2} + \frac{B}{(x - 3)} + \frac{C}{(2x + 1)}$, find $\int_4^9 f(x) \, dx$.

Q20 Find the general solution to the differential equation $\frac{dy}{dx} = \frac{1}{y} \cos x$. Give your answer in the form $y^2 = f(x)$.

Q21 Given that $x = 0$ when $t = 1$ and $x = -3$ when $t = 0$, find the particular solution of the differential equation $\frac{dx}{dt} = kte^t$, where k is a constant.

Q22 The rate of decrease of temperature ($T \, ^\circ C$) of a cup of tea with time (t minutes) satisfies the differential equation $\frac{dT}{dt} = -k(T - 21)$, where k is a positive constant.

a) Given that the initial temperature of the tea is 90 $^\circ$C, and it cools to 80 $^\circ$C in 5 minutes, find a particular solution for T.

b) Use this solution to find: (i) the temperature of the tea after 15 minutes,
(ii) the time it takes to drop to 40 $^\circ$C.

c) Sketch the graph of T against t.

Q1 Find $\int_{\frac{\pi}{3}}^{\frac{\pi}{2}} \sin(3x - \pi)\, dx$.

[3 marks]

Q2 Find the exact value of $\int_2^7 \frac{8}{4x - 3}\, dx$.

[4 marks]

Q3 Given that $\int_0^A e^{5x}\, dx = \frac{31}{5}$, find the exact value of A.

[4 marks]

Q4 Find $\int 4x \operatorname{cosec}^2(x^2) e^{\cot(x^2)}\, dx$.

[4 marks]

Q5 Evaluate $\int_0^{\frac{\pi}{4}} 3 \sin 2x \cos 2x\, dx$.

[4 marks]

Q6 The graph below shows a shaded region R bounded by the line $y = \frac{3}{2}x - 1$, the curve $y = \frac{5x}{1 + x^2}$ and the y-axis.

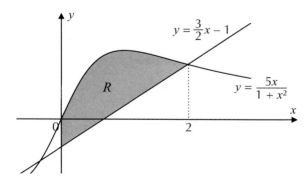

Calculate the exact area of the region R.

[7 marks]

Q7   The curve below has parametric equations $x = 2t^3$ and $y = \frac{2}{t}$, $t \neq 0$.

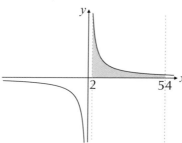

       Find the shaded area between the curve, the lines $x = 2$ and $x = 54$ and the x-axis.

[6 marks]

Q8   Use an appropriate substitution to find $\int x(x+1)^3 \, dx$.

[3 marks]

Q9   Use the substitution $x = 3 \tan u$ to find $\int \frac{1}{9+x^2} \, dx$.

[6 marks]

Q10   Evaluate $\int_0^1 2x^2 e^{3x} \, dx$, giving your answer as an exact value in terms of e.

[7 marks]

Q11   Find $\int \frac{5x+7}{x^2+2x-3} \, dx$.

[6 marks]

Q12   A population of birds is infected by a disease. The rate of change of the bird population as a result of the disease is thought to be proportional to the number of birds, P. Initially, there are 75 birds, and after three weeks, the population falls to 58 birds.

    a) Show that the number of birds after t weeks can be modelled by the equation $P = Ae^{-kt}$, where A and k are constants to be found.

[5 marks]

    b) Find the time it takes, to the nearest week, for the population to fall below 30 birds.

[3 marks]

9.1 Location of Roots

Sometimes finding the solutions of an equation algebraically can be tricky. In these situations, it's often helpful to find roughly where the roots are (the points where f(x) = 0) by looking at the graph of y = f(x).

Learning Objectives (Spec Ref 9.1):

- Locate the roots of f(x) = 0 by finding changes in the sign of f(x) between two values of *x*.
- Choose upper and lower bounds to show that a root is accurate to a certain number of decimal places.
- Sketch functions and use the sketches to find approximate locations of roots.

Prior Knowledge Check:
Be familiar with finding the roots of polynomial functions numerically and graphically — seen in Year 1.

Locating roots by changes of sign

'Solving' or 'finding the roots of' an equation (where f(x) = 0) is the same as finding the values of *x* where the graph crosses the *x*-axis.

- The graph of the function gives you a rough idea of **how many** roots there are and **where** they are. E.g. the function $f(x) = 3x^2 - x^3 - 2$ (below) has 3 roots, since it crosses the *x*-axis three times (i.e. there are 3 solutions to the equation $3x^2 - x^3 - 2 = 0$). From the graph you can see there's a root at $x = 1$ and two others near $x = -1$ and $x = 3$.

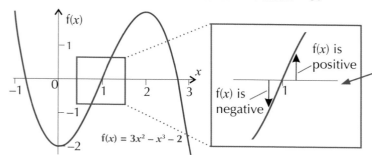

For each root in the graph, f(x) goes from positive to negative or vice versa —
f(x) changes sign as it passes through a root. So to find if there's a root between two values 'a' and 'b', work out f(a) and f(b). If the signs are different, there's a root somewhere between them.

- Be careful though — this only applies when the **range of x** you're interested in is **continuous** (no break or jump in the line of the graph). Some graphs, like tan *x*, have an **asymptote** where the line jumps from positive to negative without actually crossing the *x*-axis, so you might think there's a root when there isn't.

- This method might **fail** to find a particular root. If the function **touches** the *x*-axis but doesn't cross it, then there won't be a change of sign. An accurate sketch of the graph will help to avoid this.

- Often you'll be given an **approximation** to a root and be asked to show that it's correct to a certain accuracy. To do this, choose the right **upper and lower bounds** and work out if there's a sign change between them.

> The **lower bound** is the **lowest** value a number could have and still be **rounded up** to the correct answer. The **upper bound** is the **upper limit** of the values which will be **rounded down** to the correct answer.

Example

Show that one root of the equation $x^3 - x^2 - 9 = 0$ is $x = 2.472$, correct to 3 d.p.

1. If $x = 2.472$ is a root rounded to 3 decimal places, the exact root must lie between the **upper and lower bounds** of this value — **2.4715** and **2.4725**. Any value in this interval would be rounded to 2.472 to 3 d.p.

2. The function $f(x) = x^3 - x^2 - 9$ is **continuous**, so a root lies in the interval $2.4715 \leq x < 2.4725$ if $f(2.4715)$ and $f(2.4725)$ have **different signs**.

    > **Tip:** The function is continuous because it's just a cubic curve — it has no breaks or jumps.

    $f(2.4715) = 2.4715^3 - 2.4715^2 - 9$
    $\qquad\qquad = \boxed{-0.0116...}$

    $f(2.4725) = 2.4725^3 - 2.4725^2 - 9$
    $\qquad\qquad = \boxed{0.0017...}$

3. $f(2.4715)$ and $f(2.4725)$ have different signs, so a root must lie between them. Since any value between them would be rounded to 2.472 to 3 d.p. this answer must be correct.

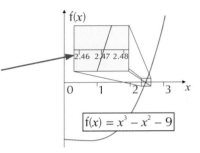

Exercise 9.1.1

Q1 $f(x) = x^3 - 5x + 1$. Show that there is a root of $f(x) = 0$ in the interval $2 < x < 3$.

Q2 $f(x) = \sin 2x - x$ (x is in radians). Show that there is a root of $f(x) = 0$ between $x = 0.9$ and $x = 1.0$.

Q3 $f(x) = x^3 + \ln x - 2$, $x > 0$. Show that there is a root of $f(x) = 0$ in the interval $[1.2, 1.3]$.

Q4 Explain why change of sign methods cannot be used to identify a solution of the equation $f(x) = 0$, where $f(x) = x^2 + 4x + 4$.

Q5 A bird is observed diving into the sea. Its height above the water after x seconds is modelled by the equation $f(x) = 2x^2 - 8x + 7$, where $f(x)$ is the height in metres. Show that the bird hits the water in the interval $1.2 < x < 1.3$ seconds.

Q6 Show that there are 2 solutions, α and β, to the equation $3x - x^4 + 3 = 0$, such that $1.6 < \alpha < 1.7$ and $-1 < \beta < 0$.

Q7 Show that there are 2 solutions, α and β, to the equation $e^{x-2} - \sqrt{x} = 0$, such that $0.01 < \alpha < 0.02$ and $2.4 < \beta < 2.5$.

Q8 Show that $x = 2.8$ is a solution to the equation $x^3 - 7x - 2 = 0$ to 1 d.p.

Q9 Show that $x = 0.7$ is a solution to the equation $2x - \dfrac{1}{x} = 0$ to 1 d.p.

Q10 $f(x) = e^x - x^3 - 5x$. Verify that a root of the equation $f(x) = 0$ is $x = 0.25$ correct to 2 d.p.

Q11 Show that a solution to the equation $4x - 2x^3 = 15$ lies between -2.3 and -2.2.

Q12 Show that a solution to the equation $\ln(x + 3) = 5x$ lies between 0.23 and 0.24.

Q13 Show that a solution to the equation $e^{3x}\sin x = 5$ lies between $x = 0$ and $x = 1$ (x is in radians).

Sketching graphs to find approximate roots

Sometimes it's easier to find the number of roots and roughly where they are with a **sketch**.

- In some questions you might be asked to **sketch** the graphs of **two equations** on the same set of axes. Sketching graphs was covered in Year 1 if you need a reminder.

- At the points where they **cross** each other, the two equations are equal. So for $y = x + 3$ and $y = x^2$, at the points of intersection you know that $x + 3 = x^2$, which you can rearrange to get $x^2 - x - 3 = 0$.

> The **number of roots** of this 'combined' equation is the same as the number of **points of intersection** of the original two graphs. The sketch you made will also show roughly **where** the roots are (it's the same x-value for both), so locating them is a bit easier.

> **Tip:** Setting the equations equal to each other and then rearranging them to get $f(x) = 0$ gets you to where you were in the previous section.

Example

a) On the same set of axes, sketch the graphs $y = \ln x$ and $y = (x - 3)^2$.

Just sketch the two graphs on a set of axes.
(Don't worry about trying to make your sketch perfect — the important things are that the graphs are the correct shape and that they cross the axes in the right places.)

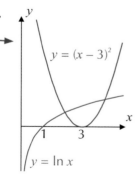

b) Hence work out the number of roots of the equation $\ln x - (x - 3)^2 = 0$.

This equation is a combination of the previous two.
The graphs cross twice, so the equation has   two roots.

c) Show that there is a solution between 2 and 3, and find this solution to 1 decimal place.

1. Put 2 and 3 into the equation and check for a sign change:

   $\ln 2 - (2 - 3)^2 = -0.306...$
   $\ln 3 - (3 - 3)^2 = 1.098...$

2. The sign has changed:

   There is a   root between 2 and 3.

3. On the sketch, it looks like the root is much closer
    to 2 than 3, so try again using $x = 2$ and $x = 2.2$
    (You might need to choose a wider interval
    depending on how accurate your sketch is.) $\qquad$ $\ln 2.2 - (2.2 - 3)^2 = 0.148...$

4. $f(2.2)$ is positive, so the root is between 2 and 2.2.
    Try again with $x = 2.1$, as it's halfway between $\qquad$ $\ln 2.1 - (2.1 - 3)^2 = -0.068...$
    the two and will tell you which it's closer to: $\qquad$ $\Rightarrow$ root is between 2.1 and 2.2.

5. Check if it rounds up to 2.2 or down to 2.1 — try 2.15 $\qquad$ $\ln 2.15 - (2.15 - 3)^2 = 0.0429...$
    as it's the upper bound for 2.1 and lower bound for 2.2. $\qquad$ $\Rightarrow$ root is between 2.1 and 2.15.

6. So the answer rounds down, and the value of the root to 1 d.p. is $\boxed{2.1}$.

Exercise 9.1.2

Sketch all graphs in this exercise for $-5 < x < 5$ unless otherwise stated.

Q1 a) On the same axes, sketch the graphs of $y = \dfrac{1}{x}$ and $y = x - 2$.

    b) Using your graph from part a) write down the number of solutions of the equation $\dfrac{1}{x} = x - 2$
    in this interval.

    c) Show that one solution of the equation $\dfrac{1}{x} = x - 2$ lies in the interval $2.4 < x < 2.5$.

Q2 a) On the same axes, sketch the graphs of $y = 2x^3 - 7x$ and $y = x^2$.

    b) Using your graph from part a) write down the number of solutions
    of the equation $2x^3 - x^2 - 7x = 0$ in this interval.

    c) Show that the equation $2x^3 - x^2 - 7x = 0$ has a root between $x = -2$ and $x = -1$.

Q3 a) Sketch the graphs of $y = 2^x - 3$ and $y = \ln x$ on the same axes.

    b) $f(x) = \ln x - 2^x + 3$. Using your graph write down the number of roots of the equation $f(x) = 0$.

    c) Show that the equation $f(x) = 0$ has a root between 1.8 and
    2.2 and find this root to 1 decimal place.

Q4 a) Sketch the graphs of $y = \sqrt{x + 1}$ and $y = 2x$ on the same axes.

    b) Write down the number of solutions of the equation $\sqrt{x + 1} = 2x$.

    c) Show that the equation $\sqrt{x + 1} = 2x$ has a solution in the interval $(0.6, 0.7)$.

    d) By rearranging the equation $\sqrt{x + 1} = 2x$, use the quadratic formula to find the solution of the
    equation from part c) to 3 s.f.

Q5 a) Sketch the graphs of $y = e^{2x}$ and $y = 3 - x^2$ on the same axes.

    b) Using your graph from part a), explain how you know that
    the equation $e^{2x} + x^2 = 3$ has two solutions.

    c) Show that the negative solution of the equation $e^{2x} + x^2 = 3$ lies
    between $x = -2$ and $x = -1$, and find this solution to 1 d.p.

9.2 Iterative Methods

Another way of finding roots of an equation is with iteration formulas.
They can seem fiddly to work with but are actually pretty simple to use.

Learning Objectives (Spec Ref 9.2):

- Use iteration formulas to find a solution of an equation to a given level of accuracy.
- Find and rearrange iteration formulas and understand that some don't converge to a solution of an equation.

Using iteration formulas

Some equations are too difficult to solve algebraically, so you need to find **approximations** to the roots to a certain level of accuracy. In exam questions you'll usually be told the value of x that a root is close to, and then **iteration** does the rest.

Iteration is a numerical method for **solving equations**, like **trial and improvement**:

- You put an approximate value of a root x into an iteration formula, and it gives you a **slightly more accurate** value.

- You then put the new value into the iteration formula, and keep going until your answers are the same when rounded to the level of accuracy needed.

Example 1

Use the iteration formula $x_{n+1} = \sqrt[3]{x_n + 4}$ to solve $x^3 - 4 - x = 0$, to 2 d.p. Start with $x_0 = 2$.

1. The notation x_n just means the approximation of x at the nth iteration. Putting x_0 in the formula for x_n gives you x_1 — the first iteration:

$$x_0 = 2, \text{ so } x_1 = \sqrt[3]{x_0 + 4}$$
$$= \sqrt[3]{2 + 4} = 1.8171...$$

2. This value now gets put back into the formula to find x_2:

$$x_2 = \sqrt[3]{x_1 + 4} = \sqrt[3]{1.8171... + 4} = 1.7984...$$

3. Carry on until you get answers that are the same when rounded to 2 d.p:

$$x_3 = \sqrt[3]{x_2 + 4} = \sqrt[3]{1.7984... + 4} = 1.7965...$$

4. x_2, x_3 and all further iterations are the same when rounded to 2 d.p., so:

The root is $x = 1.80$ to 2 d.p.

Sometimes an iteration formula will just **not find a root**. In these cases, no matter how close to the root you have x_0, the iteration sequence **diverges** — the numbers get further and further apart. The iteration might also **stop working**, like if you have to take the square root of a negative number.

However, you'll nearly always be given a formula that converges to a certain root, otherwise there's not much point in using it. If your formula diverges when it shouldn't, chances are you went wrong somewhere, so go back and double check every stage.

This doesn't mean you'll never see a diverging formula in an exam, but if you do it will usually be followed by a question like 'what do you notice about the iterations?'. If the iterations seem to bounce up and down, or do something else unexpected, then it probably diverges.

Example 2

The equation $x^3 - x^2 - 9 = 0$ has a root close to $x = 2.5$.
What is the result of using $x_{n+1} = \sqrt{x_n^3 - 9}$ with $x_0 = 2.5$ to find this root?

1. Start with x_1: $\qquad\qquad\qquad\qquad$ $x_1 = \sqrt{2.5^3 - 9} = 2.5739...$ (seems okay so far).

2. Subsequent iterations give: $\quad$ $x_2 = 2.8376...$, $x_3 = 3.7214...$, $x_4 = 6.5221...$

3. The results are getting further and further apart with each iteration. So $\boxed{\text{the sequence diverges.}}$

You can use the ANS button on your calculator to speed things up. Enter the starting value, then type the iteration formula replacing x_n with '**ANS**' — each time you press enter you'll get another iteration.

Exercise 9.2.1

Q1 a) Show that the equation $x^3 + 3x^2 - 7 = 0$ has a root in the interval $(1, 2)$.

b) Use the iterative formula $x_{n+1} = \sqrt{\dfrac{7 - x_n^3}{3}}$ with $x_0 = 1$ to find values for x_1, x_2, x_3 and x_4 to 3 d.p.

Q2 An intersection of the curves $y = \ln x$ and $y = x - 2$ is at the point $x = \alpha$, where α is 3.1 to 1 d.p.

a) Starting with $x_0 = 3.1$, use the iterative formula $x_{n+1} = 2 + \ln x_n$ to find the first 5 iterations, giving your answers to 4 decimal places.

b) Write down an estimate of the value of α to 3 decimal places.

Q3 a) Show that the equation $x^4 - 5x + 3 = 0$ has a root between $x = 1.4$ and $x = 1.5$.

b) Use the iterative formula $x_{n+1} = \sqrt[3]{5 - \dfrac{3}{x_n}}$ and $x_0 = 1.4$ to find iterations x_1 to x_6 to 3 d.p.

c) Hence write down an approximation of the root from part a), to 2 decimal places.

Q4 a) Show that the function $f(x) = x^2 - 5x - 2$ has a root that lies between $x = 5$ and $x = 6$.

b) The root in part a) can be estimated using the iterative formula $x_{n+1} = \dfrac{2}{x_n} + 5$. Using a starting value of $x_0 = 5$ find the values of x_1, x_2, x_3 and x_4, giving your answers to 4 significant figures.

Q5 Use the iterative formula $x_{n+1} = 2 - \ln x_n$ with $x_0 = 1.5$ to find the root of the equation $\ln x = 2 - x$ to 2 decimal places.

Q6 a) Show that the equation $e^x - 10x = 0$ has a root in the interval $(3, 4)$.

b) Using the iterative formula $x_{n+1} = \ln(10x_n)$ with an appropriate starting value, find values for x_1, x_2, x_3 and x_4 to 3 d.p.

c) Verify that the value of the root from part a) is $x = 3.577$ to 3 d.p.

d) Describe what happens when you use the alternative formula $x_{n+1} = \dfrac{e^{x_n}}{10}$ with $x_0 = 3$.

Q7 The iterative formula $x_{n+1} = \dfrac{x_n^2 - 3x_n}{2} - 5$ is used to try and find
approximations to a root of $f(x) = x^2 - 5x - 10$.

a) Find the values of x_1, x_2, x_3 and x_4, starting with $x_0 = -1$ and describe
what is happening to the sequence $x_1, x_2, x_3, x_4 \ldots$

b) Using the alternative iterative formula $x_{n+1} = \sqrt{5x_n + 10}$ with starting value $x_0 = 6$, find a root to the
equation $f(x) = 0$ to 3 significant figures. Verify your answer is correct to this level of accuracy.

Finding iteration formulas

The **iteration formula** is just a **rearrangement** of the equation, leaving a single 'x' on **one side**.

There are often lots of **different ways** to rearrange the equation, so in the exam you might be asked to
'**show that**' it can be rearranged in a **certain way**, rather than starting from scratch.

Sometimes a rearrangement of the equation leads to a **divergent** iteration when
you come to working out the steps. This is the reason you probably **won't** be asked
to **both** rearrange **and** use a formula to find a root without **prompting**.

Example

**a) Show that $x^3 - x^2 - 9 = 0$ can be rearranged into $x = \sqrt{\dfrac{9}{x-1}}$. Use this to make an
iteration formula and find the value of a root to 2 d.p. with starting value $x_0 = 2.5$.**

1. The '9' is on its own in the fraction so try: $\qquad\qquad x^3 - x^2 - 9 = 0 \implies x^3 - x^2 = 9$

2. The LHS can be factorised now: $\qquad\qquad\qquad\quad x^2(x - 1) = 9$

3. Get the x^2 on its own by dividing by $x - 1$: $\qquad\quad x^2 = \dfrac{9}{x-1}$

4. Finally take the square root of both sides: $\qquad\quad \boxed{x = \sqrt{\dfrac{9}{x-1}}}$ as required

5. You can now use the iteration formula
    $x_{n+1} = \sqrt{\dfrac{9}{x_n - 1}}$ to find approximations of the roots:

    $x_1 = \sqrt{\dfrac{9}{2.5 - 1}} = 2.449\ldots$

    $x_2 = \sqrt{\dfrac{9}{2.449 - 1}} = 2.491\ldots$

    ...etc., until after 16 iterations you get the
    value of the root, to 2 d.p.: $\boxed{x = 2.47}$

**b) Show that $x^3 - x^2 - 9 = 0$ can also be rearranged into $x = \sqrt{x^3 - 9}$
and use this to make an iteration formula.**

1. Start by isolating the x^2 term: $\qquad\qquad\qquad x^2 = x^3 - 9$

2. Now just take the square root of both sides: $\quad \boxed{x = \sqrt{x^3 - 9}}$ as required

3. This makes the iteration formula: $\qquad\qquad \boxed{x_{n+1} = \sqrt{x_n^3 - 9}}$

This is the iteration formula used in the example on page 259, so if you tried to use it to find a
root you'd end up with a diverging sequence and it wouldn't find a root. (This shows why you'll
never just be given an equation and told to find a root by first making an iteration formula.)

Q1 Show that $x^4 + 7x - 3 = 0$ can be written in the form:

a) $x = \sqrt[4]{3 - 7x}$

b) $x = \dfrac{3 - 5x - x^4}{2}$

c) $x = \dfrac{\sqrt{3 - 7x}}{x}$

> **Q1 Hint:** Think about which parts you need to get on their own before starting to rearrange the equation. In part b), for example, turn $7x$ into $5x + 2x$ to get where you want.

Q2 a) Show that the equation $x^3 - 2x^2 - 5 = 0$ can be rewritten as $x = 2 + \dfrac{5}{x^2}$.

b) Use the iterative formula $x_{n+1} = 2 + \dfrac{5}{x_n^2}$ with starting value $x_0 = 2$ to find x_5 to 1 decimal place.

c) Verify that the value found in part b) is a root of the equation $x^3 - 2x^2 - 5 = 0$ to 1 d.p.

Q3 a) Rearrange the equation $x^2 + 3x - 8 = 0$ into the form $x = \dfrac{a}{x} + b$ where a and b are values to be found.

b) Verify that a root of the equation $x^2 + 3x - 8 = 0$ lies in the interval $(-5, -4)$.

c) Use the iterative formula $x_{n+1} = \dfrac{a}{x_n} + b$ with $x_0 = -5$ to find the values for $x_1, x_2, ..., x_6$, giving your answers to 3 d.p. Hence find a value of the root of the equation $x^2 + 3x - 8 = 0$ to 2 d.p.

Q4 a) Show that the equation $2^{x-1} = 4\sqrt{x}$ can be written as $x = 2^{2x - 6}$.

b) Use the iterative formula $x_{n+1} = 2^{2x_n - 6}$ starting with $x_0 = 1$ to find the values of x_1, x_2, x_3 and x_4, giving your answers to 4 d.p.

c) Verify that the value for x_4 is a correct approximation to 4 d.p. for the root of the equation $2^{x-1} = 4\sqrt{x}$.

> **Q4 Hint:** Start by rewriting everything as powers of 2 or x if you're struggling. You're going to need the rules for multiplying powers for this question.

Q5 $f(x) = \ln 2x + x^3$

a) Show that $f(x) = 0$ has a solution in the interval $0.4 < x < 0.5$.

b) Show that $f(x) = 0$ can be rewritten in the form $x = \dfrac{e^{-x^3}}{2}$.

c) Using an iterative formula based on part b) and an appropriate value for x_0, find an approximation of the root of the equation $f(x) = 0$ to 3 decimal places.

Q6 $f(x) = x^2 - 9x - 20$

a) Find an iterative formula for $f(x) = 0$ in the form $x_{n+1} = \sqrt{px_n + q}$ where p and q are constants to be found.

b) By using the formula in part a) and a starting value of $x_0 = 10$, find an approximation to a root of the equation $f(x) = 0$. Give your answer to 3 significant figures.

c) Show that an alternative iterative formula is $x_{n+1} = \dfrac{x_n^2 - 4x_n}{5} - 4$.

d) By using the iterative formula in part c) with starting value $x_0 = 1$, find the value of $x_1, x_2, ..., x_8$.

e) Describe the behaviour of this sequence.

9.3 Sketching Iterations

*Once you've calculated a sequence of iterations, you can show
on a diagram whether your sequence converges or diverges.*

Learning Objectives (Spec Ref 9.2):
- Sketch cobweb and staircase diagrams.
- Identify diagrams of iterations that show convergence or divergence.

Cobweb and staircase diagrams

The instructions below show you how to sketch an iteration diagram.

- First, sketch the graphs of $y = x$ and $y = f(x)$ (where f(x) is the iterative formula).
  The point where the two graphs **meet** is the **root** you're aiming for.

- Draw a **vertical line** from the x-value of your starting point (x_0)
  until it meets the curve $y = f(x)$.

- Now draw a **horizontal line** from this point to the line $y = x$.
  At this point, the x-value is x_1, the value of your first iteration. This is one **step**.

- Draw another step — a **vertical line** from this point to the curve,
  and a **horizontal line** joining it to the line $y = x$. Repeat this for each of your iterations.

- If your steps are getting **closer and closer** to the root, the sequence of iterations is **converging**.

- If the steps are moving **further and further away** from the root, the sequence is **diverging**.

The method above produces two different types of diagrams — **cobweb** diagrams and **staircase** diagrams.

Cobweb diagrams

Cobweb diagrams look like they're **spiralling** in to the root (or away from it).
The example below shows a **convergent cobweb diagram**.

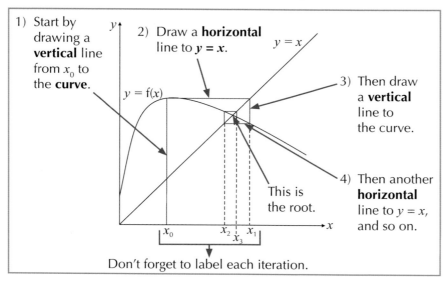

1) Start by drawing a **vertical** line from x_0 to the **curve**.

2) Draw a **horizontal** line to $y = x$.

3) Then draw a **vertical** line to the curve.

4) Then another **horizontal** line to $y = x$, and so on.

This is the root.

Don't forget to label each iteration.

Tip: A divergent cobweb diagram would have a similar shape, but each iteration would spiral away from the root rather than towards it.

Staircase diagrams

Staircase diagrams look like a set of **steps** leading to (or away from) the root.
The examples below show a **convergent** and a **divergent** staircase diagram.

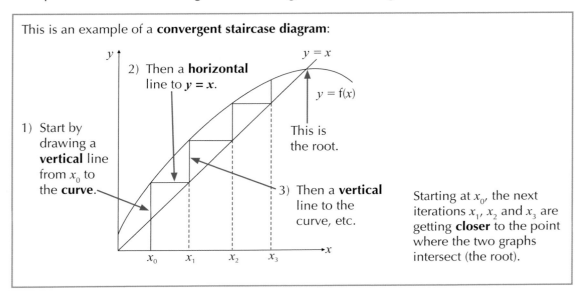

This is an example of a **convergent staircase diagram**:

2) Then a **horizontal** line to $y = x$.

1) Start by drawing a **vertical** line from x_0 to the **curve**.

This is the root.

3) Then a **vertical** line to the curve, etc.

$y = x$

$y = f(x)$

Starting at x_0, the next iterations x_1, x_2 and x_3 are getting **closer** to the point where the two graphs intersect (the root).

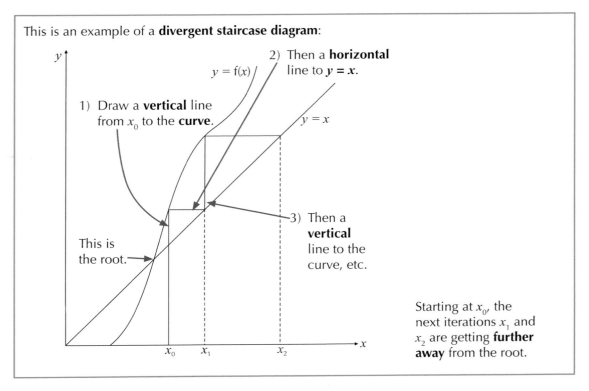

This is an example of a **divergent staircase diagram**:

2) Then a **horizontal** line to $y = x$.

$y = f(x)$

1) Draw a **vertical** line from x_0 to the **curve**.

$y = x$

This is the root.

3) Then a **vertical** line to the curve, etc.

Starting at x_0, the next iterations x_1 and x_2 are getting **further away** from the root.

In general, these diagrams will only converge if your starting value of x_0 is **close enough** to the root, and if the graph of f(x) **isn't too steep**. For a root, a, of a function f(x), the iterations **will converge** if the gradient of f(x) at a is **between –1 and 1** (i.e. $|f'(a)| < 1$) for a suitable choice of x_0.

Q1   Using the position of x_0 as given on the graph on the right, draw a staircase or cobweb diagram showing how the sequence converges. Label x_1 and x_2 on the diagram.

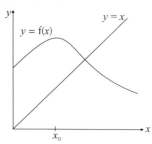

Q2   For each graph below, draw a diagram to show the convergence or divergence of the iterative sequence for the given value of x_0, and say whether it is a convergent or divergent staircase or cobweb diagram. Label x_0, x_1 and x_2 on each diagram where possible.

a) $x_0 = 3.5$

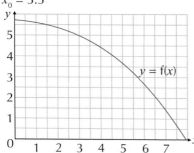

b) $x_0 = 3$

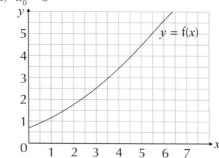

c) $x_0 = 1.75$

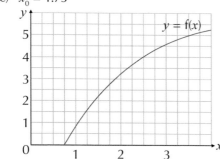

d) $x_0 = 2$

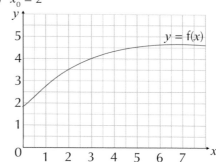

e) $x_0 = 4$

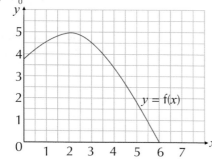

f) $x_0 = 2.5$

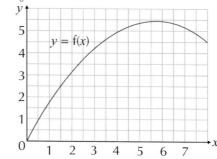

9.4 The Newton-Raphson Method

The next numerical method that you need to know for finding the root of an equation is the Newton-Raphson method, which uses differentiation.

Learning Objectives (Spec Ref 9.3):
- Use the Newton-Raphson method to find the root of an equation.
- Answer questions that combine multiple numerical methods.

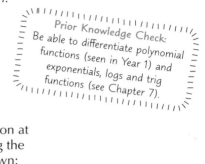
Prior Knowledge Check:
Be able to differentiate functions (seen in Year 1) and exponentials, logs and trig functions (see Chapter 7).

The Newton-Raphson method

The **Newton-Raphson method** works by finding the **tangent** to a function at a point x_0, and using its **x-intercept** for the next iteration, x_1. Repeating the process **iteratively** to find x_2, x_3, etc. gets you **closer** to the root, as shown:

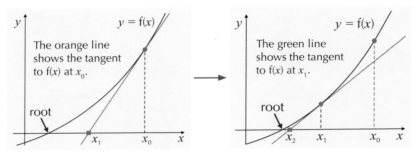

The iteration formula for this method can be derived as follows:

- The tangent to f(x) at the point x_n is a straight line that can be written in the form: $y - y_n = m(x - x_n)$ gradient at x_n

$$\Rightarrow y - f(x_n) = f'(x_n)(x - x_n)$$

- The next iteration, x_{n+1}, should be at the x-intercept of this tangent line, i.e. $x = x_{n+1}$ when $y = 0$. So substitute $(x_{n+1}, 0)$ into the equation:

$$0 - f(x_n) = f'(x_n)(x_{n+1} - x_n) \Rightarrow x_{n+1} - x_n = \frac{-f(x_n)}{f'(x_n)} \Rightarrow \boxed{x_{n+1} = x_n - \frac{f(x_n)}{f'(x_n)}}$$

Example

Use the Newton-Raphson method with a starting point of $x_0 = -2$ to find a root of $f(x) = x^3 - 3x + 5$ correct to 5 decimal places.

Tip: Make sure you use the ANS button on your calculator when you're doing these iterations, to avoid rounding errors.

1. First, differentiate: $f(x) = x^3 - 3x + 5 \Rightarrow f'(x) = 3x^2 - 3$.

2. $x_n = x_{n+1} - \dfrac{f(x_n)}{f'(x_n)}$: $x_{n+1} = x_n - \dfrac{x_n^3 - 3x_n + 5}{3x_n^2 - 3}$

3. $x_0 = -2$, so: $x_1 = -2 - \dfrac{(-2)^3 - 3(-2) + 5}{3(-2)^2 - 3} = -\dfrac{7}{3}$

     $x_2 = -2.280555...$, $x_3 = -2.279020...$, $x_4 = -2.279018...$, $x_5 = -2.279018...$

4. So the root is -2.27902 to 5 d.p.

There are times when the Newton-Raphson method can't be used to find a root.

- If the function $f(x)$ cannot be differentiated, then you won't be able to form an iteration formula to use.

- Like other iterative methods, if you choose a start point too far away from the root, the sequence might diverge.

- If the tangent to $f(x)$ is **horizontal** at the point x_n (i.e. if x_n is a **stationary point**) the method will fail. This is shown on the diagram below:

The tangent does not meet the x-axis, so there is no x_{n+1} value to continue the iterations with.

> **Tip:** You know from the definition of a stationary point that $f'(x) = 0$ at that point. So you'd have to divide by zero in the iteration formula, which will cause the method to fail.

- Similarly, if you try a point where $f(x)$ has a **shallow gradient**, the tangent meets the x-axis a really long way away from the root, which could cause the iterations to diverge:

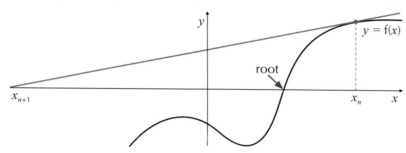

Exercise 9.4.1

Q1 Using the Newton-Raphson method, give an iteration formula for finding the roots of the following:

a) $f(x) = 5x^2 - 6$ b) $g(x) = e^{3x} - 4x^2 - 1$ c) $h(x) = \sin x + x^3 - 1$

Q2 Use the Newton-Raphson method to find a root of $x^4 - 2x^3 - 5 = 0$ to 5 s.f., starting with $x_0 = 2.5$.

Q3 Use the Newton-Raphson method to find the negative root of $f(x) = x^2 - 5x - 12$ to 5 s.f. Use $x_0 = -1$ as your start value.

Q4 Find the root to the equation $\sin x - x + 1$ to 5 s.f., using $x_0 = 1$.

Q5 Find a root to the equation $x^2 \ln x = 5$ to 5 s.f., using $x_0 = 2$.

Q6 Find a root to the equation $e^{-x} - 2 \cos \frac{1}{2}x$ to 5 s.f., using $x_0 = 1$.

Q7 Show that the Newton-Raphson method will fail to find a root of the equation $2x^3 - 15x^2 + 109 = 0$ if $x_0 = 1$ is used as the starting value.

Combining the methods

You might see a question that **combines** all (or at least most) of the methods covered so far in this chapter into one long question.

Here you can see an **exam-style question** worked from start to finish, just how they'd want you to do it in the real thing.

Example

The graph below shows both roots of the continuous function $f(x) = 6x - x^2 + 13$.

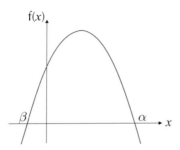

Tip: Remember to show all of your working. That way, even if you get your final answer wrong, you can still get some marks for showing that you understood what the question was asking.

a) **Show that the positive root, α, lies in the interval $7 < x < 8$.**

1. $f(x)$ is a **continuous function**, so if $f(7)$ and $f(8)$ have **different signs** then there is a root in the interval $7 < x < 8$:

$f(7) = (6 \times 7) - 7^2 + 13 = 6$
$f(8) = (6 \times 8) - 8^2 + 13 = -3$

2. There is a change of sign so $7 < \alpha < 8$.

b) **Show that $6x - x^2 + 13 = 0$ can be rearranged into the formula $x = \sqrt{6x + 13}$**

1. Get the x^2 on its own.

$6x + 13 = x^2$

2. Now take the (positive) square root.

$x = \sqrt{6x + 13}$

c) **Use the iteration formula $x_{n+1} = \sqrt{6x_n + 13}$ and $x_0 = 7$ to find α to 1 d.p.**

1. Using $x_{n+1} = \sqrt{6x_n + 13}$ with $x_0 = 7$, find x_1.

$x_1 = \sqrt{6 \times 7 + 13} = 7.4161...$

2. Continue the iterations.

$x_2 = \sqrt{6 \times 7.4161... + 13} = 7.5826...$

$x_3 = \sqrt{6 \times 7.5826... + 13} = 7.6482...$

$x_4 = \sqrt{6 \times 7.6482... + 13} = 7.6739...$

$x_5 = \sqrt{6 \times 7.6739... + 13} = 7.6839...$

3. Stop when you reach two successive iterations that round to the same number to 1 d.p.

$x_4 = 7.7$ to 1 d.p. and $x_5 = 7.7$ to 1 d.p., so $\alpha = 7.7$ (1 d.p.)

d) Sketch a diagram to show the convergence of the sequence for x_1, x_2 and x_3.

In an exam question, $y = \sqrt{6x + 13}$ and $y = x$ would usually be drawn on a graph for you, and the position of x_0 would be marked.

All you have to do is draw on the lines and label the values of x_1, x_2 and x_3.

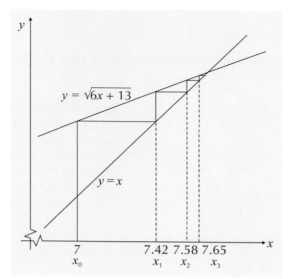

Tip: Here the values of x_1, x_2 and x_3 have been rounded to 2 d.p. to make it easier to label them on the graph.

e) Use the Newton-Raphson formula to find the negative root, β, to 5 s.f. Start with $x_0 = -1$.

1. Differentiate f(x).

    $f'(x) = 6 - 2x$.

2. Put this into the Newton-Raphson formula.

    $x_{n+1} = x_n - \dfrac{f(x_n)}{f'(x_n)} = x_n - \dfrac{6x_n - x_n^2 + 13}{6 - 2x_n}$

3. Starting with $x_0 = -1$, find x_1.

    $x_1 = -1 - \dfrac{6(-1) - (-1)^2 + 13}{6 - 2(-1)} = -1.75$

4. Continue the iterations until you reach two successive iterations that round to the same number to 5 s.f.

    $x_2 = -1.690789...$
    $x_3 = -1.690415...$
    $x_4 = -1.690415...$
    So, $\boxed{\beta = -1.6904}$ (5 s.f.)

Exercise 9.4.2

Q1   Let $f(x) = x^4 + 2x^3 - 4x^2 - 7x + 2$ and $g(x) = x^3 - 4x + 1$.

a) Show that $f(x) = (x + 2)g(x)$. Hence give an integer root of f(x).

b) Show that a root of g(x), α, lies between 1 and 2.

c) Show that g(x) = 0 can be rearranged into the formula $x = \sqrt[3]{4x - 1}$.

d) Use the iteration formula $x_{n+1} = \sqrt[3]{4x_n - 1}$ with $x_0 = 2$ to find α to 3 s.f.

e) Use the Newton-Raphson method with $x_0 = -2$ to find another root of g(x), β, to 4 s.f.

f) Explain why the Newton-Raphson method for g(x) fails when $x_n = \dfrac{2\sqrt{3}}{3}$.

9.5 The Trapezium Rule

It's not always possible to integrate a function using the methods you learn at A-level, and some functions can't be integrated at all. When this happens, you can approximate the integral using the trapezium rule.

Learning Objectives (Spec Ref 9.4):
- Use the trapezium rule to approximate the value of definite integrals.
- Calculate an upper and lower bound of the area beneath a curve.
- Explain and use the fact that integration is the limit of a sum of rectangles.

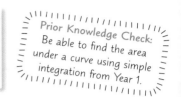

Prior Knowledge Check:
Be able to find the area under a curve using simple integration from Year 1.

The trapezium rule

When you find yourself with a function which is too difficult to integrate, you can **approximate** the area under the curve using lots of **trapeziums**, which gives an approximate value of the integral.

- The **area** under this curve between a and b can be approximated by the green **trapezium** shown.

- It has height $(b - a)$ and parallel sides of length $f(a)$ and $f(b)$.

- The area of the trapezium is an **approximation** of the integral $\int_a^b f(x)\,dx$.

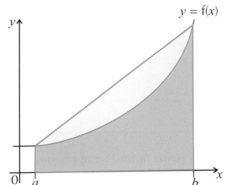

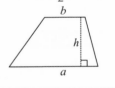

Tip: The area of a trapezium is given by the formula $\frac{h}{2}(a + b)$.

It's not a very good approximation, but if you split the area up into **more** trapeziums of equal width, the approximation will get more and more **accurate** because the **difference** between the trapeziums and the curve will get **smaller**.

The **trapezium rule** for approximating $\int_a^b f(x)\,dx$ works like this:

- n is the **number** of strips i.e. trapeziums.

- h is the **width** of each strip —it's equal to $\dfrac{(b-a)}{n}$.

- The x-values go up in steps of h, starting with $x_0 = a$.

- The y-values are found by putting the x-values into the equation of the curve — so $y_1 = f(x_1)$. They give the **heights** of the sides of the trapeziums.

- The **area** of each trapezium is $A = \dfrac{h}{2}(y_r + y_{r+1})$.

Then an **approximation** for $\int_a^b f(x)\,dx$ is found by **adding** the **areas** of all the trapeziums:

$$\int_a^b f(x)\,dx \approx \frac{h}{2}(y_0 + y_1) + \frac{h}{2}(y_1 + y_2) + \ldots + \frac{h}{2}(y_{n-1} + y_n)$$

$$= \frac{h}{2}[y_0 + 2(y_1 + y_2 + \ldots + y_{n-1}) + y_n]$$

So the **trapezium rule** says:

$$\int_a^b f(x)\,dx \approx \frac{h}{2}[y_0 + 2(y_1 + y_2 + \dots + y_{n-1}) + y_n]$$

Tip: The trapezium rule is given as $\int_a^b y\,dx$, but this is the same since $y = f(x)$.

This may seem like a lot of information, but it's simple if you follow this **step by step** method:

To approximate the integral $\int_a^b f(x)\,dx$:

- **Split** the interval up into a number of equal sized strips, n. You'll always be told what n is (it could be 4, 5 or even 6).

- Work out the **width** of each strip: $h = \dfrac{(b-a)}{n}$

- Make a **table** of x and y values:

x	$x_0 = a$	$x_1 = a + h$	$x_2 = a + 2h$	...	$x_n = b$
y	$y_0 = f(x_0)$	$y_1 = f(x_1)$	$y_2 = f(x_2)$	...	$y_n = f(x_n)$

- Put all the values into the **trapezium rule**:
$$\int_a^b f(x)\,dx \approx \frac{h}{2}[y_0 + 2(y_1 + y_2 + \dots + y_{n-1}) + y_n]$$

Example 1

Use the trapezium rule with 3 strips to find an approximate value for $\int_0^{1.5} \sqrt{x^2 + 2x}\,dx$.

1. Work out the width of each strip.

   $n = 3$, $a = 0$ and $b = 1.5$, so $h = \dfrac{1.5 - 0}{3} = 0.5$

2. Work out the x-values.

   $x_0 = 0$, $x_1 = 0.5$, $x_2 = 1$ and $x_3 = 1.5$

3. Calculate the value of y for each of x_0, x_1, x_2, x_3.

x	$y = \sqrt{x^2 + 2x}$
$x_0 = 0$	$y_0 = 0$
$x_1 = 0.5$	$y_1 = \sqrt{1.25} = 1.118\dots$
$x_2 = 1$	$y_2 = \sqrt{3} = 1.732\dots$
$x_3 = 1.5$	$y_3 = \sqrt{5.25} = 2.291\dots$

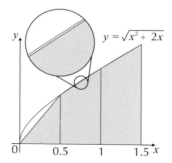

$y = \sqrt{x^2 + 2x}$

Tip: The graph shows that the estimate here is less than the actual value of the integral — there's a gap between the curve and the top of each strip. Even where it looks like the curve and the top of the trapezium are the same, if you zoom in far enough there will always be a gap.

4. Now use the formula to find the approximate value of the integral:

$$\int_0^{1.5} \sqrt{x^2 + 2x}\,dx \approx \frac{h}{2}[y_0 + 2(y_1 + y_2) + y_3]$$

$$= \frac{0.5}{2}\,[0 + 2(1.118\dots + 1.732\dots) + 2.291\dots]$$

$$= \frac{1}{4}\,[7.991\dots] = 2.00 \text{ (3 s.f.)}$$

The **approximation** that the trapezium rule gives will either be an **overestimate** (too big) or an **underestimate** (too small).

This will depend on the **shape** of the graph — a sketch can show whether the tops of the trapeziums lie **above** the curve or stay **below** it.

Tip: An exam question might ask you to draw the trapeziums on a given graph.

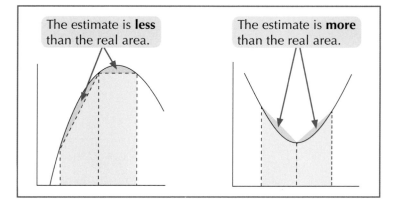

The estimate is **less** than the real area.

The estimate is **more** than the real area.

Tip: Another way to say this is that the trapezium rule gives an underestimate if the curve is concave and an overestimate if the curve is convex — see p.151 for more on convex and concave curves.

Using **more strips** (i.e. **increasing** n) gives you a **more accurate** approximation.

Example 2

Use the trapezium rule to approximate $\int_0^4 \dfrac{6x^2}{x^3 + 2}\, dx$ to 3 d.p. using:

a) $n = 2$

1. Work out the width for 2 strips.

$$h = \frac{4 - 0}{2} = 2$$

2. Work out the x-values.

$x_0 = 0$, $x_1 = 2$ and $x_2 = 4$.

3. Calculate the corresponding y-values:

> **Tip:** If you have to round the y-values, make sure you leave enough decimal places. For example, if your final answer has to be to 3 d.p., find the y-values to at least 4 d.p.

x	$y = \dfrac{6x^2}{x^3 + 2}$
$x_0 = 0$	$y_0 = 0$
$x_1 = 2$	$y_1 = 2.4$
$x_2 = 4$	$y_2 = 1.4545$ (4 d.p.)

4. Put these values into the formula.

$$\int_0^4 \frac{6x^2}{x^3 + 2}\, dx \approx \frac{h}{2}[y_0 + 2y_1 + y_2]$$
$$= \frac{2}{2}[0 + 2(2.4) + 1.4545]$$
$$= 6.255 \ (3 \text{ d.p.})$$

b) $n = 4$

1. Work out the width for 4 strips.

$$h = \frac{4 - 0}{4} = 1$$

2. Work out the x-values.

$x_0 = 0$, $x_1 = 1$, $x_2 = 2$, $x_3 = 3$ and $x_4 = 4$.

3. Calculate the corresponding y-values:

Tip: Increasing the number of strips increases the accuracy because the gaps between curve and line are smaller:

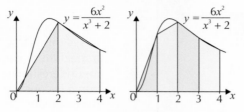

x	$y = \dfrac{6x^2}{x^3 + 2}$
$x_0 = 0$	$y_0 = 0$
$x_1 = 1$	$y_1 = 2$
$x_2 = 2$	$y_2 = 2.4$
$x_3 = 3$	$y_3 = 1.8621$ (4 d.p.)
$x_4 = 4$	$y_4 = 1.4545$ (4 d.p.)

4. Put these values into the formula.

$$\int_0^4 \frac{6x^2}{x^3 + 2}\, dx \approx \frac{h}{2}[y_0 + 2(y_1 + y_2 + y_3) + y_4]$$

$$= \frac{1}{2}[0 + 2(2 + 2.4 + 1.8621) + 1.4545]$$

$$= \frac{1}{2}[13.9787] = \boxed{6.989}\ (3\ \text{d.p.})$$

Upper and lower bounds

You can calculate an **upper** and **lower bound** for the area under a curve using a simplified version of the trapezium rule that uses rectangles:

$$\int_a^b f(x)\,dx \approx h[y_0 + y_1 + y_2 + \ldots + y_{n-1}]$$

This formula sums the areas of the rectangles which meet f(x) with their **left hand corner**.

In this example, the rectangles are **below** the curve, so they calculate a **lower bound**.

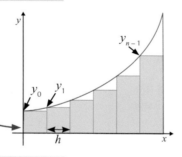

$$\int_a^b f(x)\,dx \approx h[y_1 + y_2 + \ldots + y_{n-1} + y_n]$$

This formula sums the areas of the rectangles which meet f(x) with their **right hand corner**.

In this example, the rectangles are **above** the curve, so they calculate an **upper bound**.

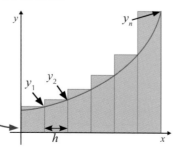

Tip: For an increasing function like the one shown here, calculating the bound using the 'left hand corner' will give the lower bound, and using the 'right hand corner' will give the upper bound. But for a decreasing function, it's the other way around. So to calculate a bound of a curve across a turning point, do a separate calculation either side of the turning point — one will use the right hand corner, and the other will use the left.

When you approximate the area under a curve using the **trapezium rule**, that value will lie **between** these two bounds.

Integration as the limit of a sum

When **differentiating** a function, you're finding the **gradient** of the curve. You saw in Year 1 that you do this by finding the gradient of a straight line over a smaller and smaller interval, until the interval is virtually nothing. So, for a function f(x):

Tip: On page 165, you saw this with h instead, but it's the same formula. δ is the Greek letter delta, and δx just means "change in x".

$$f'(x) = \lim_{\delta x \to 0} \left[\frac{f(x + \delta x) - f(x)}{(x + \delta x) - x} \right]$$

Similarly, you can define the **integral** of a curve f(x) between two points a and b using limits:

$$\int_a^b f(x)\, dx = \lim_{\delta x \to 0} \sum_{x=a}^{b} f(x) \times \delta x$$

You saw on the previous page that you can find upper and lower bounds for the area under a curve by adding up the area of rectangles. These are **approximations** of the actual area under the curve.

Tip: It doesn't matter if you use rectangles above or below the curve — the result will be the same.

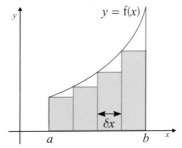

- The area of each rectangle is height × width.
  Its height is the y-value, f(x), and its width is just δx.

  So the area of each rectangle is $R = f(x) \times \delta x$.

Tip: You're summing the areas of the rectangles where the left hand corner meets the curve. So, to avoid adding on an extra rectangle beyond the point b, you need to sum only up to the point $b - \delta x$. If you use rectangles above the curve, then you would sum the 'right hand corner' rectangles from $a + \delta x$ to b.

- Then the **sum** of all the rectangles between a and $b - \delta x$ is:

$$\sum_{x=a}^{b-\delta x} R = \sum_{x=a}^{b-\delta x} f(x)\, \delta x$$

- As δx gets smaller and smaller, this sum of rectangles comes closer and closer to the actual area under the curve. This is how we **define** an integral — as the **limit of a sum** of areas.

- So as the width δx approaches 0, the sum of areas is indistinguishable from the actual area. And as $\delta x \to 0$, $b - \delta x \to b$, so the upper value of the sum can be replaced with b:

$$\lim_{\delta x \to 0} \sum_{x=a}^{b-\delta x} f(x)\, \delta x = \int_a^b f(x)\, dx$$

- This is really just a **change in notation**, so that you don't have to write out the whole limit of a sum each time you want to write an integral.

- When you're writing the **exact** integral, you use **d** instead of δ, and you replace $\sum$ with $\int$, which are both just ways of writing 'S' (for 'sum').

Q1 Use the trapezium rule to find approximations of each of the following integrals.
Use the given number of intervals in each case. Give your answers to 3 significant figures.

a) $\int_0^2 \sqrt{x+2}\ dx$, 2 intervals

b) $\int_1^3 2(\ln x)^2\ dx$, 4 intervals

c) $\int_0^{0.4} e^{x^2}\ dx$, 2 intervals

d) $\int_{-\frac{\pi}{4}}^{\frac{\pi}{4}} 4x\tan x\ dx$, 4 intervals

e) $\int_0^{0.3} \sqrt{e^x+1}\ dx$, 6 intervals

f) $\int_0^{\pi} \ln(2+\sin x)\ dx$, 6 intervals

Q2 For Q1a) and b) above, find an upper and lower bound for the area beneath the curve to 4 s.f.

Q3 Use the trapezium rule with 3 intervals to find an estimate to $\int_0^{\frac{\pi}{2}} \sin^3\theta\ d\theta$.
Give your answer to 3 d.p.

Q4 The shape of an aeroplane's wing is modelled by the curve $y = \sqrt{\ln x}$, where
x and y are measured in metres. Use the trapezium rule with 5 intervals to
estimate the area of a cross-section of the wing enclosed by the curve
$y = \sqrt{\ln x}$, the x-axis and the lines $x = 2$ and $x = 7$. Give your answer to 3 d.p.

Q5 a) Complete the following table of values to 3 d.p. for $y = e^{\sin x}$.

x	0	$\frac{\pi}{8}$	$\frac{\pi}{4}$	$\frac{3\pi}{8}$	$\frac{\pi}{2}$
y	1	1.466			2.718

b) (i) Using the trapezium rule with 2 intervals, estimate $\int_0^{\frac{\pi}{2}} e^{\sin x}\ dx$ to 2 d.p.

(ii) Repeat the calculation using 4 intervals.

c) Which is the better estimate? Explain your answer.

Q6 The diagram below shows part of the curve $y = \dfrac{3}{\ln x}$.

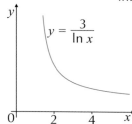

a) Using the trapezium rule with 4 intervals, find an estimate to 2 d.p. for $\int_2^4 \dfrac{3}{\ln x}\ dx$.

b) Without further calculation, state whether your answer to part a) is
an over-estimate or under-estimate of the true area. Explain your answer.

Q7 a) Using the trapezium rule with $h = \frac{\pi}{6}$, show that $\int_{-\frac{\pi}{2}}^{\frac{\pi}{2}} \cos x\ dx$ can be approximated as $\dfrac{\pi(2+\sqrt{3})}{6}$.

b) Without further calculation, state whether this approximation
is an under- or over-estimation. Explain your answer.

Review Exercise

Q1 Show that there is a root in the interval:

    a) $3 < x < 4$ for $\sin(2x) = 0$ (x in radians)
    b) $2.1 < x < 2.2$ for $\ln(x - 2) + 2 = 0$

    c) $4.3 < x < 4.5$ for $x^3 - 4x^2 = 7$
    d) $0 < x < 0.5$ for $e^{2x} + 2e^x = 4$

Q2 By selecting an appropriate interval, show that, to 1 d.p.,
$x = 1.2$ is a root of the equation $x^3 + x - 3 = 0$.

Q3
    a) On the same axes, sketch the graphs of $y = \ln x$ and $y = \dfrac{2}{x}$.

        Hence find the number of roots of the equation $\ln x - \dfrac{2}{x} = 0$.

    b) Show that there is a root of the equation $\ln x - \dfrac{2}{x} = 0$ between $x = 2$ and $x = 3$.

Q4
    a) Sketch the graphs of $y = \dfrac{1}{x + 1}$ and $y = x - 2$ on the same axes.

    b) $f(x) = \dfrac{1}{x + 1} - x + 2$. Show that a root of the equation $f(x) = 0$ lies between $x = -1.4$ and -1.3.

    c) Show that the equation $f(x) = 0$ can be written in the form $x^2 - x - 3 = 0$.

Q5 Use the formula $x_{n+1} = \sqrt{\ln x_n + 4}$, with $x_0 = 2$, to find a root of $x^2 - \ln x - 4 = 0$ to 3 d.p.

Q6
    a) Show that the equation $x^x = 3$ has a root between $x = 1.5$ and $x = 2$.

    b) Using the iterative formula $x_{n+1} = 3^{\frac{1}{x_n}}$, with an appropriate value for x_0,
        find an approximation for the root of the equation $x^x = 3$ to 1 decimal place.

Q7
    a) Show that a solution to the equation $2x - 5\cos x = 0$ (x in radians) lies in the interval $(1.1, 1.2)$.

    b) Show that the equation in part a) can be written as $x = p\cos x$, stating the value of p.

    c) Using an iterative formula based on part b) and a starting value of $x_0 = 1.1$, find the values
        up to and including x_8, giving your answers to 4 decimal places. Comment on your findings.

Q8 Use the Newton-Raphson method with $x_0 = 1$
to find a root, to 3 d.p., of the following functions:

    a) $f(x) = x^2 + 9x - 4$
    b) $f(x) = x^3 + 3x^2 + 5x + 7$

    c) $f(x) = e^x - x^4$
    d) $f(x) = \sin x \cos x$

Q9 Use the trapezium rule with n intervals to estimate the following to 3 s.f.:

    a) $\displaystyle\int_0^3 (9 - x^2)^{\frac{1}{2}}\, dx$, $n = 3$
    b) $\displaystyle\int_{0.2}^{1.2} x^{x^2}\, dx$, $n = 5$
    c) $\displaystyle\int_1^3 2^{x^2}\, dx$, $n = 5$

Q10 Use the trapezium rule to estimate the value of $\displaystyle\int_0^6 (6x - 12)(x^2 - 4x + 3)^2\, dx$, first using
4 strips and then again with 6 strips. Calculate the percentage error for each answer.

Exam-Style Questions

Q1   The function $f(x) = \cos x + 2x$ has a root where $f(x) = 0$.

a) Show that $f(x)$ can be written as $x = -\dfrac{1}{2} \cos x$.

[1 mark]

b) Hence, with $x_0 = -1$, find the root of $\cos x + 2x = 0$ to 2 d.p.

[2 marks]

c) Draw a sketch to show $f(x) = 0$ has only one root.

[2 marks]

Q2 $f(x) = 5 - 2x - x^2$ has a positive root α and a negative root β.

a) Show that α lies in the interval $1.4 < x < 1.5$.

[2 marks]

b) Use the iteration formula $x_{n+1} = \sqrt{5 - 2x_n}$
with an appropriate value for x_0 to find α to 3 s.f.

[2 marks]

c) Use the Newton-Raphson method with $x_0 = -4$ to find β to 3 s.f.

[3 marks]

Q3

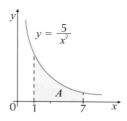

The diagram above shows part of the curve $y = \dfrac{5}{x^2}$.

a) Use the trapezium rule with $n = 4$ to find an estimate for the area A to 2 d.p.

[3 marks]

b) Without further calculation, explain whether or not your answer
to part a) is an overestimate or underestimate of the true area.

[1 mark]

c) Calculate the exact value of $\displaystyle\int_1^7 \dfrac{5}{x^2}\, dx$.

[3 marks]

d) Hence find the percentage error in your estimate.

[1 mark]

10.1 Vectors in Three Dimensions

In Year 1 you learnt how to represent, calculate with, and model situations using vectors in two dimensions. Now you're going to find out how to do all of that in three dimensions. You might want to look back at your notes on 2D vectors first, to refresh your memory.

Learning Objectives (Spec Ref 10.1 & 10.3):

- Understand how to represent vectors in three dimensions, using both unit vectors and column vectors.
- Add and subtract 3D vectors and multiply them by scalars.
- Show that two 3D vectors are parallel, and three points are collinear.

Prior Knowledge Check:
Be able to add and subtract 2D vectors, and to find if they're parallel or collinear — seen in Year 1.

Three-dimensional position vectors

- **Three-dimensional vectors** have components in the direction of the **x-**, **y-** and **z-axes**. Imagine that the x- and y-axes lie flat on the page. Then imagine a **third axis** sticking straight through the page at right angles to it — this is the **z-axis**.

- The points in three dimensions are given **(x, y, z) coordinates**.

- The **unit vector** in the direction of the z-axis is **k**, so three-dimensional vectors can be written like this: ⟶ $x\mathbf{i} + y\mathbf{j} + z\mathbf{k}$ or $\begin{pmatrix} x \\ y \\ z \end{pmatrix}$

- Three-dimensional vectors are used to describe things in **three-dimensional space**, e.g. an aeroplane moving through the sky.

- Calculating with 3D vectors is just the same as with 2D vectors, as the next example shows.

Example 1

The diagram on the right shows the position of the points P and Q.

a) Write the position vectors $\overrightarrow{OP}$ and $\overrightarrow{OQ}$ as column vectors.

$$\overrightarrow{OP} = 4\mathbf{i} + 3\mathbf{j} + 0\mathbf{k} = \begin{pmatrix} 4 \\ 3 \\ 0 \end{pmatrix} \qquad \overrightarrow{OQ} = 2\mathbf{i} + 5\mathbf{j} + 4\mathbf{k} = \begin{pmatrix} 2 \\ 5 \\ 4 \end{pmatrix}$$

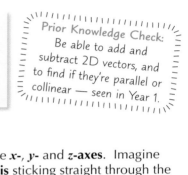

b) Hence find $\overrightarrow{PQ}$ as a column vector.

Add along each row of the column, just like with 2D column vectors — don't forget, you've multiplied $\overrightarrow{OP}$ by the scalar '−1' so all its entries will change signs.

$$\overrightarrow{PQ} = -\overrightarrow{OP} + \overrightarrow{OQ} = -\begin{pmatrix} 4 \\ 3 \\ 0 \end{pmatrix} + \begin{pmatrix} 2 \\ 5 \\ 4 \end{pmatrix} = \begin{pmatrix} 2-4 \\ 5-3 \\ 4-0 \end{pmatrix} = \begin{pmatrix} -2 \\ 2 \\ 4 \end{pmatrix}$$

The point R lies on the line PQ such that PR:RQ = 3:1.

c) Find the position vector of point R, in unit vector form.

1. The ratio tells you that point R is $\frac{3}{4}$ of the way along the line PQ from point P:

$$\overrightarrow{PR} = \frac{3}{4}\overrightarrow{PQ} = \frac{3}{4} \times \begin{pmatrix} -2 \\ 2 \\ 4 \end{pmatrix} = \begin{pmatrix} -1.5 \\ 1.5 \\ 3 \end{pmatrix}$$

2. Position vector $\overrightarrow{OR} = \overrightarrow{OP} + \overrightarrow{PR}$:
(You could draw a vector triangle if you need to.)

$$\overrightarrow{OR} = \begin{pmatrix} 4 \\ 3 \\ 0 \end{pmatrix} + \begin{pmatrix} -1.5 \\ 1.5 \\ 3 \end{pmatrix} = \begin{pmatrix} 4-1.5 \\ 3+1.5 \\ 0+3 \end{pmatrix} = \begin{pmatrix} 2.5 \\ 4.5 \\ 3 \end{pmatrix}$$

$$= 2.5\mathbf{i} + 4.5\mathbf{j} + 3\mathbf{k}$$

Don't get confused between a point and its position vector. Points are given by (x, y, z) coordinates and position vectors are the movement needed to get to the point from the origin, given in the form $x\mathbf{i} + y\mathbf{j} + z\mathbf{k}$. You'll need to be able to swap between the forms.

Parallel lines and collinear points

As with two-dimensional vectors, **parallel** vectors in three dimensions are **scalar multiples** of each other.

To determine whether two vectors are parallel, check whether one vector can be produced by multiplying the other by a scalar.

If two vectors are **parallel**, and also have a **point in common**, then they must lie on the same straight line — their points are **collinear**.

Example 2

Show that points A, B and C are collinear, if:
$$\overrightarrow{OA} = 2\mathbf{i} - \mathbf{j} + \mathbf{k}, \ \overrightarrow{OB} = \mathbf{i} + 2\mathbf{j} + 3\mathbf{k} \text{ and } \overrightarrow{OC} = -\mathbf{i} + 8\mathbf{j} + 7\mathbf{k}.$$

1. First, find vectors $\overrightarrow{AB}$ and $\overrightarrow{BC}$:

$$\overrightarrow{AB} = -\overrightarrow{OA} + \overrightarrow{OB}$$
$$= (-2 + 1)\mathbf{i} + (1 + 2)\mathbf{j} + (-1 + 3)\mathbf{k}$$
$$= -\mathbf{i} + 3\mathbf{j} + 2\mathbf{k}$$

$$\overrightarrow{BC} = -\overrightarrow{OB} + \overrightarrow{OC}$$
$$= (-1 - 1)\mathbf{i} + (-2 + 8)\mathbf{j} + (-3 + 7)\mathbf{k}$$
$$= -2\mathbf{i} + 6\mathbf{j} + 4\mathbf{k}$$

2. Show that $\overrightarrow{AB}$ and $\overrightarrow{BC}$ are parallel by finding a **scalar multiple**.

$$\overrightarrow{BC} = -2\mathbf{i} + 6\mathbf{j} + 4\mathbf{k}$$
$$= 2(-\mathbf{i} + 3\mathbf{j} + 2\mathbf{k})$$
$$= 2\,\overrightarrow{AB}$$

3. $\overrightarrow{BC}$ is a scalar multiple of $\overrightarrow{AB}$, so they are **parallel**, and also have a **point in common** (B).

So A, B and C must all lie on the same line — they are collinear.

Make sure you're comfortable working with vectors in all forms — as column vectors, using $\mathbf{i}$, $\mathbf{j}$, $\mathbf{k}$ notation, and as the movement between points given as Cartesian coordinates.

Q1 R is the point (4, –5, 1) and S is the point (–3, 0, –1).
Write down the position vectors of R and S, giving your answers:

a) as column vectors

b) in unit vector form.

Q2 Give $\overrightarrow{GH}$ and $\overrightarrow{HG}$ as column vectors, where $\overrightarrow{OG} = \begin{pmatrix} 2 \\ -3 \\ 4 \end{pmatrix}$ and $\overrightarrow{OH} = \begin{pmatrix} -1 \\ 4 \\ 9 \end{pmatrix}$.

Q3 A 3D printer is being used to make the plastic toy sketched below.

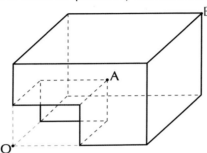

The toy can be modelled as a large cuboid with a smaller cuboid section missing. The large cuboid section is an enlargement of the smaller, 'missing' cuboid, by a scale factor of 2, centred at point O.

a) Prove that $\overrightarrow{AB} = \overrightarrow{OA}$.

b) Find the position vector of point B, if $\overrightarrow{OA} = 3\mathbf{i} + \mathbf{j} + 2\mathbf{k}$.

Q4 Hint: The question doesn't mention **i** and **j** components or column vectors so you can answer it using either.

Q4 Triangle JKL has vertices at the points J (4, 0, –3), K (–1, 3, 0) and L (2, 2, 7). Find the vectors $\overrightarrow{JK}$, $\overrightarrow{KL}$ and $\overrightarrow{LJ}$.

Q5 M is a point on the line CD, where C has coordinates (–1, 3, –5),

M has coordinates (1, 1, –2) and $\overrightarrow{CD} = \begin{pmatrix} 4 \\ -4 \\ 6 \end{pmatrix}$.

Show that M is the midpoint of CD.

Q6 Show that vectors $\mathbf{a} = \frac{3}{4}\mathbf{i} + \frac{1}{3}\mathbf{j} - 2\mathbf{k}$ and $\mathbf{b} = \frac{1}{4}\mathbf{i} + \mathbf{j} - \frac{2}{3}\mathbf{k}$ are <u>not</u> parallel.

Q7 In a 3D board game, players take turns to position counters at points inside a cuboid grid. Players score by forming a straight line with three of their counters, unblocked by their opponent.

Show that counters placed at coordinates (1, 0, 3), (3, 1, 2) and (7, 3, 0) lie on a straight line.

Q8 The points with position vectors $\overrightarrow{OP} = \begin{pmatrix} -2 \\ a \\ -8 \end{pmatrix}$, $\overrightarrow{OQ} = \begin{pmatrix} 1 \\ b \\ -4 \end{pmatrix}$ and $\overrightarrow{OR} = \begin{pmatrix} -5 \\ 6 \\ 3b \end{pmatrix}$ are collinear.

Find the values of a and b.

10.2 Calculating with Vectors

Calculating with 2D vectors should already be familiar to you, and 3D vector calculations are pretty similar. Magnitude is a scalar quantity that tells you a vector's length. You can use Pythagoras' theorem and trigonometry to find the magnitude of any vector.

Learning Objectives (Spec Ref 10.2 & 10.4):

- Find the magnitude of any vector in three dimensions.
- Find the unit vector in the direction of any vector in three dimensions.
- Find the distance between any two three-dimensional points using vectors.
- Calculate the angle between any two vectors in three dimensions using trigonometry.

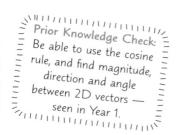

Prior Knowledge Check:
Be able to use the cosine rule, and find magnitude, direction and angle between 2D vectors — seen in Year 1.

Calculating with 3D vectors

Magnitude of a 3D vector

- The **magnitude** (sometimes called **modulus**) of a vector **v** is written as $|\mathbf{v}|$, and for a vector $\overrightarrow{AB}$ it is written $|\overrightarrow{AB}|$.

- Magnitude is always a **positive**, **scalar** quantity.

You will have used **Pythagoras' theorem** to find the length of a 2D vector, and it works in **three dimensions** too:

The **distance** of point (a, b, c) from the origin is: $\sqrt{a^2 + b^2 + c^2}$

You can **derive** this formula from the **two-dimensional** Pythagoras' theorem:

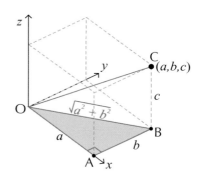

The **orange** line shows the distance of the point (a, b, c) from the origin.

First use Pythagoras on the **green triangle**.

OB is $\sqrt{a^2 + b^2}$.

Tip: Remember the position vector of the point (a, b, c) is $a\mathbf{i} + b\mathbf{j} + c\mathbf{k}$, or as a column vector: $\begin{pmatrix} a \\ b \\ c \end{pmatrix}$

Now use Pythagoras on the **blue triangle**.

OC is the distance from the origin to (a, b, c).

So the distance from the origin to (a, b, c) is:
$\sqrt{\left(\sqrt{a^2 + b^2}\right)^2 + c^2} = \sqrt{a^2 + b^2 + c^2}$

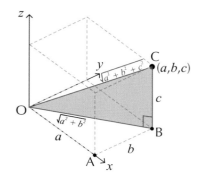

So the **magnitude** of any vector $\mathbf{v} = a\mathbf{i} + b\mathbf{j} + c\mathbf{k}$ is the same as the distance of point (a, b, c) from the origin:

$$|\mathbf{v}| = |a\mathbf{i} + b\mathbf{j} + c\mathbf{k}| = \sqrt{a^2 + b^2 + c^2}$$

The **unit vector** in the direction of $\mathbf{v}$ is $\dfrac{\mathbf{v}}{|\mathbf{v}|}$, as it is for 2D vectors.

> **Tip:** A unit vector has a magnitude of 1. Magnitude is always a positive scalar, so the unit vector is always parallel to the vector, and has the same direction.

Example 1

The diagram on the right shows the position of point Q.

a) Find $|\overrightarrow{OQ}|$, giving your answer in reduced surd form.

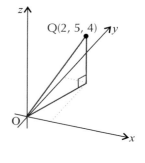

$\overrightarrow{OQ} = 2\mathbf{i} + 5\mathbf{j} + 4\mathbf{k}$

Plug the coordinates, which are the $\mathbf{i}$, $\mathbf{j}$ and $\mathbf{k}$ coefficients in $\overrightarrow{OQ}$, into the formula:

$$|\overrightarrow{OQ}| = \sqrt{x^2 + y^2 + z^2}$$
$$= \sqrt{2^2 + 5^2 + 4^2}$$
$$= \sqrt{45} = 3\sqrt{5}$$

b) Find the unit vector in the direction of $\overrightarrow{OQ}$.

To find a **unit vector**, divide the vector by its magnitude:

$$\frac{\overrightarrow{OQ}}{|\overrightarrow{OQ}|} = \frac{1}{3\sqrt{5}}(2\mathbf{i} + 5\mathbf{j} + 4\mathbf{k})$$
$$= \frac{2}{3\sqrt{5}}\mathbf{i} + \frac{5}{3\sqrt{5}}\mathbf{j} + \frac{4}{3\sqrt{5}}\mathbf{k}$$
$$= \frac{2\sqrt{5}}{15}\mathbf{i} + \frac{\sqrt{5}}{3}\mathbf{j} + \frac{4\sqrt{5}}{15}\mathbf{k}$$

Distance between two points in three dimensions

The **distance** between any two points $P(x_1, y_1, z_1)$ and $Q(x_2, y_2, z_2)$ is the **magnitude** of the vector $\overrightarrow{PQ}$:

$$\overrightarrow{PQ} = \overrightarrow{OQ} - \overrightarrow{OP} = (x_2\mathbf{i} + y_2\mathbf{j} + z_2\mathbf{k}) - (x_1\mathbf{i} + y_1\mathbf{j} + z_1\mathbf{k}) = (x_2 - x_1)\mathbf{i} + (y_2 - y_1)\mathbf{j} + (z_2 - z_1)\mathbf{k}$$

> So the magnitude of the vector $\overrightarrow{PQ} = (x_2 - x_1)\mathbf{i} + (y_2 - y_1)\mathbf{j} + (z_2 - z_1)\mathbf{k}$
> is $\sqrt{(x_2 - x_1)^2 + (y_2 - y_1)^2 + (z_2 - z_1)^2}$, by Pythagoras' theorem.

Example 2

The position vector of point A is $3\mathbf{i} + 2\mathbf{j} + 4\mathbf{k}$, and the position vector of point B is $2\mathbf{i} + 6\mathbf{j} - 5\mathbf{k}$. Find $|\overrightarrow{AB}|$ to 1 decimal place.

1. A has the coordinates $(3, 2, 4)$, B has the coordinates $(2, 6, -5)$. Use these to write $\overrightarrow{AB}$.

$$\overrightarrow{AB} = (x_2 - x_1)\mathbf{i} + (y_2 - y_1)\mathbf{j} + (z_2 - z_1)\mathbf{k}$$
$$= (2 - 3)\mathbf{i} + (6 - 2)\mathbf{j} + (-5 - 4)\mathbf{k}$$

2. Use the formula for magnitude.

$$|\overrightarrow{AB}| = \sqrt{(x_2 - x_1)^2 + (y_2 - y_1)^2 + (z_2 - z_1)^2}$$
$$= \sqrt{(2-3)^2 + (6-2)^2 + (-5-4)^2}$$
$$= \sqrt{1 + 16 + 81} = \sqrt{98} = 9.9 \text{ (1 d.p.)}$$

Example 3

A = (−3, −6, 4), B = (2t, 1, −t). $|\overrightarrow{AB}| = 3\sqrt{11}$. Find the possible values of t.

Put the coordinates in the formula and solve the resulting quadratic for t.

$$|\overrightarrow{AB}| = \sqrt{(2t+3)^2 + (1+6)^2 + (-t-4)^2}$$

$$\Rightarrow \sqrt{(2t+3)^2 + (1+6)^2 + (-t-4)^2} = 3\sqrt{11}$$

$$\Rightarrow 4t^2 + 12t + 9 + 49 + t^2 + 8t + 16 = 99$$

$$\Rightarrow 5t^2 + 20t + 74 = 99$$

$$\Rightarrow 5t^2 + 20t - 25 = 0$$

$$\Rightarrow t^2 + 4t - 5 = 0$$

$$\Rightarrow (t+5)(t-1) = 0$$

$$\Rightarrow \boxed{t = -5 \text{ or } t = 1}$$

The angle between two vectors

To find the angle between two vectors:

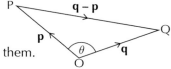

- Create a **triangle** with the vectors as two sides, and angle θ between them.
- Find the **magnitude** (i.e. the length) of each side of the triangle.
- Use the **cosine rule** to find the angle θ from these lengths: $\longrightarrow$ $\cos A = \dfrac{b^2 + c^2 - a^2}{2bc}$

Example 4

The flight path of two different aeroplanes taking off from a runway are modelled as position vectors a = 5i −2j + k, and b = −3i + 3j + k. Find the angle between the two flight paths, in degrees, to 1 d.p.

MODELLING

1. **a** and **b** form two sides of the triangle AOB: $\longrightarrow$

2. Find the lengths of **a** and **b**.

$$|a| = \sqrt{5^2 + (-2)^2 + 1^2} = \sqrt{30}$$
$$|b| = \sqrt{(-3)^2 + 3^2 + 1^2} = \sqrt{19}$$

3. Find the length of $\overrightarrow{AB}$ (= **b** − **a** = −8i + 5j + 0k).

$$|\overrightarrow{AB}| = \sqrt{(-8)^2 + 5^2 + 0^2} = \sqrt{89}$$

4. Use the cosine rule, $\cos A = \dfrac{b^2 + c^2 - a^2}{2bc}$.

$$\cos \theta = \frac{(\sqrt{30})^2 + (\sqrt{19})^2 - (\sqrt{89})^2}{2 \times \sqrt{30} \times \sqrt{19}} = \frac{-40}{2\sqrt{570}}$$

$$\Rightarrow \theta = \cos^{-1}\left(\frac{-40}{2\sqrt{570}}\right) = \boxed{146.9° \text{ (1 d.p.)}}$$

Exercise 10.2.1

Unless specified, give each answer in this exercise as an integer or as a simplified surd.

Q1 Find the magnitude of each of the following vectors:

a) **i + 4j + 8k**

b) $\begin{pmatrix} 4 \\ 2 \\ 4 \end{pmatrix}$

c) $\begin{pmatrix} -4 \\ -5 \\ 20 \end{pmatrix}$

d) **7i + j − 7k**

Q2 Find the magnitude of the resultant of each pair of vectors.

a) $\mathbf{i} + \mathbf{j} + 2\mathbf{k}$ and $\mathbf{i} + 2\mathbf{j} + 4\mathbf{k}$

b) $2\mathbf{i} + 11\mathbf{j} + 25\mathbf{k}$ and $3\mathbf{j} - 2\mathbf{k}$

c) $\begin{pmatrix} 4 \\ 2 \\ 8 \end{pmatrix}$ and $\begin{pmatrix} -2 \\ 4 \\ 1 \end{pmatrix}$

d) $\begin{pmatrix} 3 \\ 0 \\ 10 \end{pmatrix}$ and $\begin{pmatrix} -1 \\ 5 \\ 4 \end{pmatrix}$

Q3 Two vectors, $\mathbf{a}$ and $\mathbf{b}$, are given by the column vectors $\mathbf{a} = \begin{pmatrix} 8 \\ 4 \\ 10 \end{pmatrix}$ and $\mathbf{b} = \begin{pmatrix} 2 \\ -2 \\ 4 \end{pmatrix}$.
Find $|\mathbf{a} + \mathbf{b}|$.

Q4 Find the distances between each of the following pairs of points:

a) (3, 4, 5), (5, 6, 6)

b) (7, 2, 9), (–11, 1, 15)

c) (10, –2, –1), (6, 10, –4)

d) (0, –4, 10), (7, 0, 14)

e) (–4, 7, 10), (2, 4, –12)

f) (7, –1, 4), (30, 9, –6)

Q5 The flight path of a toy aeroplane is modelled by the vector $2\mathbf{m} - \mathbf{n}$,

where $\mathbf{m} = \begin{pmatrix} -5 \\ -2 \\ 6 \end{pmatrix}$ metres, and $\mathbf{n} = \begin{pmatrix} -4 \\ 1 \\ 2 \end{pmatrix}$ metres.

Find the distance of the plane's destination from its starting position.
Give your answer in metres to 1 decimal place.

Q6 $\overrightarrow{OA} = \mathbf{i} - 4\mathbf{j} + 3\mathbf{k}$ and $\overrightarrow{OB} = -\mathbf{i} - 3\mathbf{j} + 5\mathbf{k}$. Find $|\overrightarrow{AO}|$, $|\overrightarrow{BO}|$ and $|\overrightarrow{BA}|$.
Show that triangle AOB is right-angled.

Q7 Find the unit vector in the direction of the following vectors:

a) $\mathbf{t} = 4\mathbf{i} - 4\mathbf{j} - 7\mathbf{k}$

b) $\mathbf{u} = -\mathbf{i} + 2\mathbf{j} - 2\mathbf{k}$

c) $\mathbf{v} = 2\mathbf{i} + 3\mathbf{j} - \mathbf{k}$

Q8 P is the point (2, –1, 4) and Q is the point $(q - 2, 5, 2q + 1)$. Given that the length of the line PQ is 11, find the possible coordinates of the point Q.

Q9 Find the angle, in degrees to 1 d.p., that the vector $\begin{pmatrix} 1 \\ 3 \\ 2 \end{pmatrix}$ makes with:

a) vector $\begin{pmatrix} 3 \\ 2 \\ 1 \end{pmatrix}$

b) the unit vector $\mathbf{j}$

c) vector $\begin{pmatrix} -3 \\ 1 \\ -2 \end{pmatrix}$

d) vector $\begin{pmatrix} 2 \\ 2 \\ 2 \end{pmatrix}$

Q10 A toy rocket is launched at an angle of 60° to the unit vector in the $\mathbf{i}$ direction,
with a velocity $\mathbf{v} = (\mathbf{i} + a\mathbf{j} + \mathbf{k})$ ms^{-1}.
Find the possible values of a, in surd form, and hence the launch speed of the rocket.

Q11 The position of a bee during its flight can be modelled using the vector $\begin{pmatrix} 15t \cos 36° \\ 15t \sin 36° \\ 8t \end{pmatrix}$,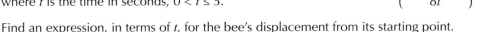
where t is the time in seconds, $0 < t \le 5$.

Find an expression, in terms of t, for the bee's displacement from its starting point.

Review Exercise

Q1   Give, in unit vector form, the position vector of point P, which has the coordinates (2, –4, 5).

Q2   X is the point (6, –1, 0) and Y is the point (4, –4, 7).
Write the vectors $\overrightarrow{XO}$ and $\overrightarrow{YO}$ in unit vector form and in column vector form.

Q3   Give two vectors that are parallel to each of the following:

a) 2**a**   b) 3**i** + 4**j** – 2**k**   c) $\begin{pmatrix} 1 \\ 2 \\ -1 \end{pmatrix}$

Q4   Given that **a** = 2**i** – 3**j** + **k**, **b** = –**i** + 4**j** –7**k** and **c** = –6**i** + 4**j** + 10**k**, show that 2**a** + **b** is parallel to **c**.

Q5   Show that points A, B and C are collinear, given that $\overrightarrow{OA} = \begin{pmatrix} 2 \\ 1 \\ 3 \end{pmatrix}$, $\overrightarrow{OB} = \begin{pmatrix} 1 \\ 5 \\ 7 \end{pmatrix}$ and $\overrightarrow{OC} = \begin{pmatrix} -2 \\ 17 \\ 19 \end{pmatrix}$.

Q6   Find the exact magnitudes of these vectors: a) 3**i** + 4**j** – 2**k**   b) $\begin{pmatrix} 1 \\ 2 \\ -1 \end{pmatrix}$

Q7   If A is (1, 2, 3) and B is (3, –1, –2), find: a) $|\overrightarrow{OA}|$ b) $|\overrightarrow{OB}|$ c) $|\overrightarrow{AB}|$

Q8   Find the unit vectors in the direction of each of these vectors:

a) **i** – 3**k**   b) –2**i** + 2**j** + 5**k**   c) $\begin{pmatrix} -1 \\ -3 \\ 3 \end{pmatrix}$ d) $\begin{pmatrix} 7 \\ -1 \\ 12 \end{pmatrix}$

Q9   Find the exact distance between points P and Q given by
position vectors $\overrightarrow{OP}$ = –**i** + 2**j** + 3**k** and $\overrightarrow{OQ}$ = 2**i** – 2**j** + 4**k**.

Q10   X is the point (–2, 1, 0).

The distance between X and Y is 6. The unit vector in the direction $\overrightarrow{XY}$ is $\begin{pmatrix} \frac{2}{3} \\ \frac{2}{3} \\ -\frac{1}{3} \end{pmatrix}$.

Find the coordinates of Y.

Q11   Given that $\overrightarrow{OA} = \begin{pmatrix} 4 \\ 3 \\ -3 \end{pmatrix}$, $\overrightarrow{OB} = \begin{pmatrix} -1 \\ 2 \\ -4 \end{pmatrix}$, find the angle between $\overrightarrow{AB}$ and $\overrightarrow{OB}$ to one decimal place.

Q12   A simple mathematical model of the motion of two asteroids following a collision
is given in terms of vectors. The velocity of asteroid R is given by **r** = 5**i** + 3**j** – **k** ms⁻¹.
The velocity of asteroid S is given by **s** = –2**i** – 2**j** + 7**k** ms⁻¹.

a) Calculate the exact speed of each asteroid.

b) After 5 seconds, how much further has S travelled than R?
Give your answer to the nearest metre.

c) Calculate the angle between the two asteroids' paths to the nearest degree.

d) Comment on the suitability of this model.

Exam-Style Questions

Q1 L, M and N are three collinear points.

The point L has position vector $L = 3\mathbf{i} + \mathbf{j} + 8\mathbf{k}$, and $\overrightarrow{LM} = 2\mathbf{i} - \mathbf{j} - 2\mathbf{k}$.

Given that M divides $\overrightarrow{LN}$ in the ratio $2:3$, find the position vector for N.

[3 marks]

Q2 The diagram below shows a sketch of the parallelogram $ABCD$.

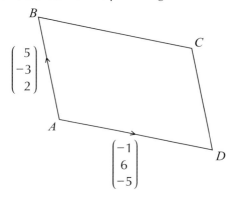

a) Write $\overrightarrow{AC}$ as a single column vector.

[2 marks]

b) Find the length of the vector $\overrightarrow{AC}$.

[2 marks]

Q3 The diagram on the right shows a sketch of the triangle XYZ.

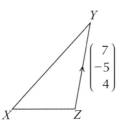

The unit vector in the direction $\overrightarrow{XZ}$ is $\begin{pmatrix} \frac{2}{3} \\ \frac{1}{2} \\ -\frac{\sqrt{11}}{6} \end{pmatrix}$ and $|\overrightarrow{XZ}| = \frac{\sqrt{10}}{5}|\overrightarrow{YZ}|$.

a) Show that $\overrightarrow{XZ} = \begin{pmatrix} 4 \\ 3 \\ -\sqrt{11} \end{pmatrix}$.

[4 marks]

b) Hence or otherwise find the angle XZY.

[5 marks]

Practice Paper

Q1 Prove that $\cot^2 \theta + \sin^2 \theta \equiv \csc^2 \theta - \cos^2 \theta$.

[2 marks]

Q2 π is an irrational number. Prove by contradiction that $\pi + 1$ is also irrational.

[3 marks]

Q3 A charity received £20 000 of public donations in its first year, Y_1.
The charity predicts that public donations will increase by 8% each year.

a) Write down an expression for the predicted donations in Y_n.

[1 mark]

b) Assuming the prediction is correct, calculate how much money
the charity will receive in total from Y_6 to Y_{10}, including Y_6 and Y_{10}.

[3 marks]

Q4 For the function, $f(x) = x^3 - 4x^2 - 5x + 6$:

a) Show $f(x) = 0$ has a root, α, in the interval $4.7 < x < 4.8$.

[2 marks]

b) Rearrange $f(x) = 0$ to give an equation for x in the form $x = \sqrt[3]{g(x)}$.

[1 mark]

c) Using your answer to part b) as an iterative formula and a starting value of 4.7,
find the root α to 3 s.f.

[2 marks]

d) Use the Newton-Raphson method and $x_0 = -1.5$
to find the negative root, β, of $f(x) = 0$ to 3 s.f.

[3 marks]

Q5 Find the inverse of function $g(x) = 5^x - 3$.

[3 marks]

Q6 The trajectory of a particle is given by the parametric equations $x = t^3 + t^2$, $y = \frac{1}{2}t^2 - 6t$.

a) Find the gradient $\frac{dy}{dx}$ of the trajectory in terms of t.

[2 marks]

b) Hence find the turning point of the trajectory.

[2 marks]

c) Find the equation of the tangent to the trajectory when $t = 12$.

[3 marks]

Q7 The diagram below shows the triangle ABC.

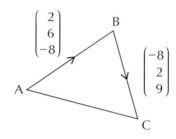

a) Find $\overrightarrow{AC}$.

[1 mark]

D is a point such that A, B and D are collinear and AB : AD = 2 : 5.

b) Find the angle ACD in degrees to 1 d.p.

[5 marks]

Q8 The curve C has the equation $x^4 - 3x^2y^2 = y^3$.
Find the equation of the tangent to C at $(4, 4)$.

[5 marks]

Q9 The arithmetic sequence begins with the terms -3, 1, 5, 9, ...
The nth term is given by the expression $kn + m$, where k and m are constants.

a) Find the values of k and m.

[2 marks]

b) Using your answer to part a), find the value of the 20th term.

[1 mark]

c) Hence find the sum of the first 20 terms of the sequence.

[2 marks]

Q10 $f(x) = \cos x$

    a) On the same set of axes, sketch the following in the interval $0 \le x \le 2\pi$, and give the range of each:

        (i) $|f(x)|$

        (ii) $f(2x) + 1$

[4 marks]

    b) Hence or otherwise, find all solutions to the equation $|f(x)| = f(2x) + 1$ in the interval $0 \le x \le 2\pi$.

[5 marks]

Q11 The curve C has parametric equations:

$$x = \frac{1 - \cos\theta}{3} \quad \text{and} \quad y = \frac{\cos\theta\sin 2\theta}{2\sin\theta}, \quad 0 < \theta < 2\pi$$

    a) Find the Cartesian equation of the curve in the form $y = f(x)$.

[3 marks]

    b) Hence determine whether the curve intersects the line $y + 3 = 2x$.

[2 marks]

Q12 a) Show that $\dfrac{\cos x}{(\cos x + 1)(\cos x - 1)} \equiv -\operatorname{cosec} x \cot x$.

[3 marks]

    b) Hence find $\displaystyle\int \frac{\cos x \cdot e^{\frac{1}{\sin x}}}{(\cos x + 1)(\cos x - 1)}\, dx$.

[4 marks]

Q13 The volume of a pond (V m³) is modelled by the equation $V = \sqrt{h^4 + 2}$, where h is the depth of the pond in metres.

    a) Find the value of $\dfrac{dV}{dh}$ to 3 s.f. when $h = 0.4$.

[3 marks]

    b) Given that the volume of the pond increases at a constant rate of 0.15 m³ per hour, find the rate at which the depth of the water is increasing with time when $h = 0.4$. Give your answer to 3 s.f.

[2 marks]

Practice Paper

Q14 The table shows values of $y = \dfrac{3x^2}{x^3 + 4}$ to 3 d.p. where appropriate.

x	1	1.1	1.2	1.3	1.4	1.5
y	0.6	0.681	0.754		0.872	

a) Find the missing values for $x = 1.3$ and $x = 1.5$.

[1 mark]

b) Use the trapezium rule and the values from the table
and part a) to estimate $\displaystyle\int_1^{1.5} \dfrac{3x^2}{x^3 + 4}\,\mathrm{d}x$ to 2 d.p.

[3 marks]

c) (i) Find the exact value of $\displaystyle\int_1^{1.5} \dfrac{3x^2}{x^3 + 4}\,\mathrm{d}x$ in the form $\ln k$, where k is a rational number.

[3 marks]

   (ii) Hence find the percentage error of your estimate from part b).

[1 mark]

Q15 $f(x) = x^3 + 5x^2 - 8x - 48$ and $g(x) = \dfrac{3x + 40}{x^3 + 5x^2 - 8x - 48}$

a) Given that $(x + 4)$ is a factor of f(x), fully factorise f(x).

[3 marks]

b) Express g(x) in partial fractions.

[4 marks]

c) Hence obtain the series expansion for g(x) giving all the terms
up to and including the term in x^2.

[6 marks]

Q16 The diagram below shows a sketch of the curve C,
which can be given by the differential equation $y = 2\dfrac{\mathrm{d}y}{\mathrm{d}x}$.

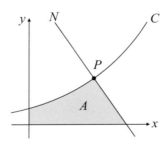

The point $P(1, e)$ lies on the curve, and the line N is normal to C at point P.
Find the area A, bounded by the curve C, the line N and both axes.

[10 marks]

Answers

Chapter 1: Proof

1.1 Proof by Contradiction

Exercise 1.1.1 — Proof by contradiction

Q1 Suppose that there is a number x that is the largest multiple of 3, so it can be written as $x = 3k$ for some integer k. Then $x + 3 = 3k + 3 = 3(k + 1)$ is also a multiple of 3 and is larger than x, which contradicts the initial assumption. So there cannot be a largest multiple of 3.

Q2 Suppose that there is some even number x for which x^2 is odd. Since x is even, it can be written as $x = 2n$ for some integer n. Then $x^2 = (2n)^2 = 4n^2 = 2(2n^2)$ which is even, which contradicts the assumption that x^2 is odd. So if x^2 is odd, then x must also be odd.

Q3 a) Suppose that there is a rational number $x \neq 0$ and an irrational number y such that xy is rational. This means that x can be written as $x = \frac{a}{b}$ and xy can be written as $xy = \frac{c}{d}$, where a, b, c and d are all non-zero integers.
So $xy = \frac{a}{b} y = \frac{c}{d} \Rightarrow y = \frac{bc}{ad}$
Since bc and ad are both integers, this means that y is a rational number, which contradicts the assumption that y is irrational. So the product of a non-zero rational number and an irrational number is always irrational.

b) To disprove the statement, find a counter-example.
$\sqrt{2}$ is an irrational number, but $\sqrt{2} \times \sqrt{2} = 2$ which is rational, so the statement is false.

Q4 Suppose that there is a smallest positive rational number, and call it x. Since x is rational, it can be written as $x = \frac{a}{b}$, and since it is positive, a and b are both positive integers (or both negative, in which case you can simplify the fraction by dividing top and bottom by -1 to get a and b positive). Then $\frac{a}{b+1}$ is also a positive rational number, and is smaller than x, which contradicts the assumption that x is the smallest positive rational number. So there cannot be a smallest positive rational number.

Q5 Assume that $1 + \sqrt{2}$ is rational, so it can be written as $\frac{a}{b}$ where a and b are non-zero integers.
So $1 + \sqrt{2} = \frac{a}{b} \Rightarrow \sqrt{2} = \frac{a}{b} - 1 \Rightarrow \sqrt{2} = \frac{a-b}{b}$
Since a and b are integers, $(a - b)$ is also an integer, which means that $\sqrt{2}$ is rational, which is not true. So $1 + \sqrt{2}$ must be irrational.

Exam-Style Questions — Chapter 1

Q1 Suppose there is some even number x for which x^3 is odd. Since x is even, it can be written as $x = 2n$ for some integer n. Then $x^3 = (2n)^3 = 8n^3 = 2(4n^3)$ which is even, which contradicts the assumption that x^3 is odd. So if x^3 is odd, then x must also be odd.

[2 marks available — 1 mark for an appropriate expression for the cube of an even number, 1 mark for correct interpretation]

Q2 Suppose that there is a number x that is the largest odd integer, so it can be written as $x = 2k + 1$ for some integer k. Then $x + 2 = 2k + 3 = 2(k + 1) + 1$ is also an odd integer and is larger than x, which contradicts the initial assumption. So there cannot be a largest odd integer.

[2 marks available — 1 mark for appropriate expressions for consecutive odd numbers, 1 mark for correct interpretation]

Q3 Suppose there is some odd number x for which $x^2 + 3$ is odd. Since x is odd, it can be written as $x = 2n + 1$ for some integer n.
Then $x^2 + 3 = (2n + 1)^2 + 3 = 4n^2 + 4n + 1 + 3$
$= 4n^2 + 4n + 4 = 2(2n^2 + 2n + 2)$ which is even,
which contradicts the assumption that $x^2 + 3$ is odd.
So if $x^2 + 3$ is odd, then x must be even.

[2 marks available — 1 mark for an appropriate expression for $x^2 + 3$ for an odd number, 1 mark for correct interpretation]

Q4 a) Suppose that the sum of a rational number x and an irrational number y is a rational number.
Then $x + y$ can be written as $\frac{a}{b} + y = \frac{c}{d}$ for some non-zero integers a and b that share no common factors and some non-zero integers c and d that share no common factors.
So $y = \frac{c}{d} - \frac{a}{b} = \frac{bc - ad}{bd}$. As a, b, c and d are all integers, $(bc - ad)$ and bd are also integers and so y is a rational number, which contradicts the initial assumption. So the sum of a rational number and an irrational number must be an irrational number.

[3 marks available — 1 mark for correctly expressing the sum using fractions, 1 mark for a correct expression for y, 1 mark for correct interpretation]

b) E.g. Suppose there is a number z that is the largest irrational number. Then as proven above, $z + 1$ is also irrational, since 1 is a rational number. $z + 1$ is larger than z, which contradicts the initial assumption. So there cannot be a largest irrational number.

[2 marks available — 1 mark for adding a positive rational number to z, 1 mark for correct interpretation]
You could have added any positive rational number here.

Q5 a) Suppose that there is an integer x such that x^2 is a multiple of 3 but x is not. If x is not a multiple of 3, then there are two cases to consider: $x = 3k + 1$ and $x = 3k + 2$ for some integer k.
If $x = 3k + 1$, then $x^2 = (3k + 1)^2 = 9k^2 + 6k + 1$
$= 3(3k^2 + 2k) + 1$
So x^2 is not a multiple of 3.
If $x = 3k + 2$, then $x^2 = (3k + 2)^2 = 9k^2 + 12k + 4$
$= 3(3k^2 + 4k + 1) + 1$
So x^2 is not a multiple of 3.
Therefore, by exhaustion, x^2 cannot be a multiple of 3, which contradicts the initial assumption. So if x^2 is a multiple of 3, then x must also be a multiple of 3.

[3 marks available — 1 mark for each correct expression for x^2, 1 mark for correct interpretation]

b) Suppose that $\sqrt{3}$ is rational, so $\sqrt{3} = \frac{a}{b}$ for some non-zero integers a and b that share no common factors.
So $b\sqrt{3} = a \Rightarrow 3b^2 = a^2 \Rightarrow a^2$ is a multiple of 3.
From part a), this means that a is also a multiple of 3, so write $a = 3k$ for some integer k.
$3b^2 = (3k)^2 \Rightarrow 3b^2 = 9k^2 \Rightarrow b^2 = 3k^2$
$\Rightarrow b^2$ is a multiple of 3.
Again, from part a), this means b is a multiple of 3. But it was assumed at the start that a and b had no common factors.
So $\sqrt{3}$ cannot be written as an integer fraction, so it is irrational.

[3 marks available — 1 mark for setting $\sqrt{3}$ equal to $\frac{a}{b}$, 1 mark for correct deduction that a and b must both be multiples of 3, 1 mark for correct interpretation]

Q6 a) Suppose that the difference between a rational number x and an irrational number y is a rational number.

$x - y$ can be written as $\frac{a}{b} - y = \frac{c}{d}$ for some non-zero integers a and b that share no common factors and some non-zero integers c and d that share no common factors.

So $y = \frac{a}{b} - \frac{c}{d} = \frac{ad - bc}{bd}$. As a, b, c and d are all integers, $(ad - bc)$ and bd are also integers and so y is a rational number, which contradicts the initial assumption.

So $y - x$ is irrational.

Since $x - y = -(y - x)$, and the negative of an irrational number will also be irrational, the difference $x - y$ is also irrational. So the difference between a rational number and an irrational number must be an irrational number.

[4 marks available — 1 mark for correctly expressing $x - y$ or $y - x$ using fractions, 1 mark for considering the other case, 1 mark for showing a contradiction, 1 mark for correct interpretation]

b) E.g. $1 - \sqrt{2}$ is irrational (from part a)). $\sqrt{2}$ is also irrational.

$(1 - \sqrt{2}) + \sqrt{2} = 1$, which is rational.

So the sum of an irrational number and an irrational number cannot always be irrational.

[2 marks available — 1 mark for choosing two appropriate irrational numbers, 1 mark for correct interpretation]

Q7 Suppose that $\sqrt[3]{5}$ is rational, so $\sqrt[3]{5} = \frac{a}{b}$

for some non-zero integers a and b that share no common factors.

So $b\sqrt[3]{5} = a \Rightarrow 5b^3 = a^3 \Rightarrow a^3$ is a multiple of 5.

Using the assumption given, this means that a is also a multiple of 5, so write $a = 5k$ for some integer k.

$5b^3 = (5k)^3 \Rightarrow 5b^3 = 125k^3 \Rightarrow b^3 = 25k^3 = 5(5k^3)$
$\Rightarrow b^3$ is a multiple of 5.

Again, from the given assumption, this means b is a multiple of 5. But it was assumed at the start that a and b had no common factors. So $\sqrt[3]{5}$ cannot be written as an integer fraction, so it is irrational.

[3 marks available — 1 mark for setting $\sqrt[3]{5}$ equal to $\frac{a}{b}$, 1 mark for correct deduction that a and b must both be multiples of 5, 1 mark for correct interpretation]

Chapter 2: Algebra and Functions

2.1 Simplifying Expressions

Exercise 2.1.1 — Simplifying algebraic fractions

Q1 $\frac{4}{2x + 10} = \frac{4}{2(x + 5)} = \frac{2}{x + 5}$

Q2 $\frac{5x}{x^2 + 2x} = \frac{5x}{x(x + 2)} = \frac{5}{x + 2}$

Q3 $\frac{6x^2 - 3x}{3x^2} = \frac{3x(2x - 1)}{3x^2} = \frac{2x - 1}{x}$

Q4 $\frac{4x^3}{x^3 + 3x^2} = \frac{4x^3}{x^2(x + 3)} = \frac{4x}{x + 3}$

Q5 $\frac{3x + 6}{x^2 + 3x + 2} = \frac{3(x + 2)}{(x + 1)(x + 2)} = \frac{3}{x + 1}$

Q6 $\frac{x^2 + 3x}{x^2 + x - 6} = \frac{x(x + 3)}{(x - 2)(x + 3)} = \frac{x}{x - 2}$

Q7 $\frac{2x - 6}{x^2 - 9} = \frac{2(x - 3)}{(x - 3)(x + 3)} = \frac{2}{x + 3}$

Q8 $\frac{5x^2 - 20x}{2x^2 - 5x - 12} = \frac{5x(x - 4)}{(2x + 3)(x - 4)} = \frac{5x}{2x + 3}$

Q9 $\frac{3x^2 - 7x - 6}{2x^2 - x - 15} = \frac{(3x + 2)(x - 3)}{(2x + 5)(x - 3)} = \frac{3x + 2}{2x + 5}$

Q10 $\frac{x^3 - 4x^2 - 19x - 14}{x^2 - 6x - 7} = \frac{(x + 1)(x + 2)(x - 7)}{(x + 1)(x - 7)} = x + 2$

To factorise the cubic, try a few different values for x — once you've spotted that $f(-1) = 0$ (and so $(x + 1)$ is a factor) you can take that out and see what's left to factorise.

Q11 $\frac{x^3 - 2x^2}{x^3 - 4x} = \frac{x^2(x - 2)}{x(x^2 - 4)} = \frac{x^2(x - 2)}{x(x - 2)(x + 2)} = \frac{x}{x + 2}$

Q12 $\frac{1 + \frac{1}{x}}{x + 1} = \frac{\left(1 + \frac{1}{x}\right)x}{(x + 1)x} = \frac{x + 1}{x(x + 1)} = \frac{1}{x}$

Q13 $\frac{3 + \frac{1}{x}}{2 + \frac{1}{x}} = \frac{\left(3 + \frac{1}{x}\right)x}{\left(2 + \frac{1}{x}\right)x} = \frac{3x + 1}{2x + 1}$

Q14 $\frac{1 + \frac{1}{2x}}{2 + \frac{1}{x}} = \frac{\left(1 + \frac{1}{2x}\right)2x}{\left(2 + \frac{1}{x}\right)2x} = \frac{2x + 1}{4x + 2} = \frac{2x + 1}{2(2x + 1)} = \frac{1}{2}$

Q15 $\frac{\frac{1}{3x} - 1}{3x^2 - x} = \frac{\left(\frac{1}{3x} - 1\right)3x}{(3x^2 - x)3x} = \frac{-(3x - 1)}{3x^2(3x - 1)} = -\frac{1}{3x^2}$

Q16 $\frac{2 + \frac{1}{x}}{6x^2 + 3x} = \frac{\left(2 + \frac{1}{x}\right)x}{(6x^2 + 3x)x} = \frac{2x + 1}{3x^2(2x + 1)} = \frac{1}{3x^2}$

Q17 $\frac{\frac{3x}{x + 2}}{\frac{x}{x + 2} + \frac{1}{x + 2}} = \frac{\left(\frac{3x}{x + 2}\right)(x + 2)}{\left(\frac{x}{x + 2} + \frac{1}{x + 2}\right)(x + 2)} = \frac{3x}{x + 1}$

Q18 $\frac{2 + \frac{1}{x + 1}}{3 + \frac{1}{x + 1}} = \frac{\left(2 + \frac{1}{x + 1}\right)(x + 1)}{\left(3 + \frac{1}{x + 1}\right)(x + 1)} = \frac{2(x + 1) + 1}{3(x + 1) + 1} = \frac{2x + 3}{3x + 4}$

Q19 $\frac{1 - \frac{2}{x + 3}}{x + 2} = \frac{\left(1 - \frac{2}{x + 3}\right)(x + 3)}{(x + 2)(x + 3)} = \frac{x + 3 - 2}{(x + 2)(x + 3)}$
$= \frac{x + 1}{(x + 2)(x + 3)}$

Q20 $\frac{4 - \frac{1}{x^2}}{2 - \frac{1}{x} - \frac{1}{x^2}} = \frac{\left(4 - \frac{1}{x^2}\right)x^2}{\left(2 - \frac{1}{x} - \frac{1}{x^2}\right)x^2} = \frac{4x^2 - 1}{2x^2 - x - 1}$
$= \frac{(2x + 1)(2x - 1)}{(x - 1)(2x + 1)} = \frac{2x - 1}{x - 1}$

Q21 $\frac{\frac{4}{x} + \frac{x}{4} + 2}{\frac{4}{x} + 1} \times \frac{4x}{4x} = \frac{\frac{16x}{x} + \frac{4x^2}{4} + 8x}{\frac{16x}{x} + 4x}$
$= \frac{16 + x^2 + 8x}{16 + 4x} = \frac{(4 + x)^2}{4(4 + x)} = \frac{4 + x}{4}$

Q22 Factorise the numerator $f(x) = x^3 + 6x^2 - x - 6$:
$f(1) = 1 + 6 - 1 - 6 = 0$, so $(x - 1)$ is a factor.
$f(-1) = -1 + 6 + 1 - 6 = 0$, so $(x + 1)$ is a factor.
By equating coefficients, you can see that:
$x^3 + 6x^2 - x - 6 = (x^2 - 1)(x + 6) = (x - 1)(x + 1)(x + 6)$
And for the denominator $g(x) = x^3 + 7x^2 + 4x - 12$:
$g(1) = 1 + 7 + 4 - 12 = 0$, so $(x - 1)$ is a factor.
Divide $g(x)$ by $(x - 1)$ to fully factorise:
$x^3 + 7x^2 + 4x - 12 = (x - 1)(Ax^2 + Bx + C)$
By equating coefficients, you can see that $A = 1$ and $C = 12$. Also, $B - A = 7 \Rightarrow B = 7 + A = 8$. So:
$x^3 + 7x^2 + 4x - 12 = (x - 1)(x^2 + 8x + 12) = (x - 1)(x + 2)(x + 6)$
So $\frac{x^3 + 6x^2 - x - 6}{x^3 + 7x^2 + 4x - 12} = \frac{f(x)}{g(x)}$
$= \frac{(x - 1)(x + 1)(x + 6)}{(x - 1)(x + 2)(x + 6)} = \frac{x + 1}{x + 2}$

Exercise 2.1.2 — Adding and subtracting algebraic fractions

Q1 $\frac{2x}{3} + \frac{x}{5} = \frac{10x}{15} + \frac{3x}{15} = \frac{13x}{15}$

Q2 $\frac{2}{3x} - \frac{1}{5x} = \frac{10}{15x} - \frac{3}{15x} = \frac{7}{15x}$

Q3 $\frac{3}{x^2} + \frac{2}{x} = \frac{3}{x^2} + \frac{2x}{x^2} = \frac{3 + 2x}{x^2}$

Q4
$$\frac{x+1}{3} + \frac{x+2}{4} = \frac{4(x+1)}{12} + \frac{3(x+2)}{12}$$
$$= \frac{4x+4+3x+6}{12} = \frac{7x+10}{12}$$

Q5
$$\frac{2x}{3} + \frac{x-1}{7x} = \frac{14x^2}{21x} + \frac{3(x-1)}{21x} = \frac{14x^2+3x-3}{21x}$$

Q6
$$\frac{3x}{4} - \frac{2x-1}{5x} = \frac{15x^2}{20x} - \frac{4(2x-1)}{20x} = \frac{15x^2-8x+4}{20x}$$

Q7
$$\frac{2}{x-1} + \frac{3}{x} = \frac{2x}{x(x-1)} + \frac{3(x-1)}{x(x-1)} = \frac{2x+3x-3}{x(x-1)} = \frac{5x-3}{x(x-1)}$$

Q8
$$\frac{3}{x+1} + \frac{2}{x+2} = \frac{3(x+2)}{(x+1)(x+2)} + \frac{2(x+1)}{(x+1)(x+2)}$$
$$= \frac{3x+6+2x+2}{(x+1)(x+2)} = \frac{5x+8}{(x+1)(x+2)}$$

Q9
$$\frac{4}{x-3} - \frac{1}{x+4} = \frac{4(x+4)}{(x-3)(x+4)} - \frac{x-3}{(x-3)(x+4)}$$
$$= \frac{4x+16-x+3}{(x-3)(x+4)} = \frac{3x+19}{(x-3)(x+4)}$$

Q10
$$\frac{6}{x+2} + \frac{6}{x-2} = \frac{6(x-2)}{(x+2)(x-2)} + \frac{6(x+2)}{(x+2)(x-2)}$$
$$= \frac{6x-12+6x+12}{(x+2)(x-2)} = \frac{12x}{(x+2)(x-2)}$$

Q11
$$\frac{3}{x-2} - \frac{5}{2x+3} = \frac{3(2x+3)}{(x-2)(2x+3)} - \frac{5(x-2)}{(x-2)(2x+3)}$$
$$= \frac{6x+9-5x+10}{(x-2)(2x+3)} = \frac{x+19}{(x-2)(2x+3)}$$

Q12
$$\frac{3}{x+2} + \frac{x}{x+1} = \frac{3(x+1)}{(x+2)(x+1)} + \frac{x(x+2)}{(x+2)(x+1)}$$
$$= \frac{3x+3+x^2+2x}{(x+2)(x+1)} = \frac{x^2+5x+3}{(x+2)(x+1)}$$

Q13
$$\frac{5x}{(x+1)^2} - \frac{3}{x+1} = \frac{5x}{(x+1)^2} - \frac{3(x+1)}{(x+1)^2}$$
$$= \frac{5x-3x-3}{(x+1)^2} = \frac{2x-3}{(x+1)^2}$$

Q14
$$\frac{5}{x(x+3)} + \frac{3}{x+2} = \frac{5(x+2)}{x(x+3)(x+2)} + \frac{3x(x+3)}{x(x+3)(x+2)}$$
$$= \frac{5x+10+3x^2+9x}{x(x+3)(x+2)} = \frac{3x^2+14x+10}{x(x+3)(x+2)}$$

Q15
$$\frac{x}{x^2-4} - \frac{1}{x+2} = \frac{x}{(x+2)(x-2)} - \frac{1}{x+2}$$
$$= \frac{x}{(x+2)(x-2)} - \frac{x-2}{(x+2)(x-2)} = \frac{x-x+2}{(x+2)(x-2)} = \frac{2}{(x+2)(x-2)}$$

Q16
$$\frac{3}{x+1} + \frac{6}{2x^2+x-1} = \frac{3}{x+1} + \frac{6}{(x+1)(2x-1)}$$
$$= \frac{3(2x-1)}{(x+1)(2x-1)} + \frac{6}{(x+1)(2x-1)} = \frac{6x-3+6}{(x+1)(2x-1)} = \frac{3(2x+1)}{(x+1)(2x-1)}$$

Q17
$$\frac{2}{x} + \frac{3}{x+1} + \frac{4}{x+2}$$
$$= \frac{2(x+1)(x+2)}{x(x+1)(x+2)} + \frac{3x(x+2)}{x(x+1)(x+2)} + \frac{4x(x+1)}{x(x+1)(x+2)}$$
$$= \frac{2x^2+6x+4+3x^2+6x+4x^2+4x}{x(x+1)(x+2)} = \frac{9x^2+16x+4}{x(x+1)(x+2)}$$

Q18
$$\frac{3}{x+4} - \frac{2}{x+1} + \frac{1}{x-2}$$
$$= \frac{3(x+1)(x-2)}{(x+4)(x+1)(x-2)} - \frac{2(x+4)(x-2)}{(x+4)(x+1)(x-2)} + \frac{(x+4)(x+1)}{(x+4)(x+1)(x-2)}$$
$$= \frac{3x^2-3x-6-2x^2-4x+16+x^2+5x+4}{(x+4)(x+1)(x-2)} = \frac{2(x^2-x+7)}{(x+4)(x+1)(x-2)}$$

Q19
$$2 - \frac{3}{x+1} + \frac{4}{(x+1)^2} = \frac{2(x+1)^2}{(x+1)^2} - \frac{3(x+1)}{(x+1)^2} + \frac{4}{(x+1)^2}$$
$$= \frac{2x^2+4x+2-3x-3+4}{(x+1)^2} = \frac{2x^2+x+3}{(x+1)^2}$$

Q20
$$\frac{2x^2-x-3}{x^2-1} + \frac{1}{x(x-1)} = \frac{(x+1)(2x-3)}{(x+1)(x-1)} + \frac{1}{x(x-1)}$$
$$= \frac{2x-3}{x-1} + \frac{1}{x(x-1)} = \frac{x(2x-3)}{x(x-1)} + \frac{1}{x(x-1)}$$
$$= \frac{2x^2-3x+1}{x(x-1)} = \frac{(x-1)(2x-1)}{x(x-1)} = \frac{2x-1}{x}$$

Exercise 2.1.3 — Multiplying and dividing algebraic fractions

Q1
a) $\frac{2x}{3} \times \frac{5x}{4} = \frac{x}{3} \times \frac{5x}{2} = \frac{x \times 5x}{3 \times 2} = \frac{5x^2}{6}$

b) $\frac{6x^3}{7} \times \frac{2}{x^2} = \frac{6x}{7} \times \frac{2}{1} = \frac{6x \times 2}{7 \times 1} = \frac{12x}{7}$

c) $\frac{8x^2}{3y^2} \times \frac{x^3}{4y} = \frac{2x^2}{3y^2} \times \frac{x^3}{y} = \frac{2x^2 \times x^3}{3y^2 \times y} = \frac{2x^5}{3y^3}$

d) $\frac{8x^4}{3y} \times \frac{6y^2}{5x} = \frac{8x^3}{1} \times \frac{2y}{5} = \frac{8x^3 \times 2y}{1 \times 5} = \frac{16x^3y}{5}$

Q2
a) $\frac{x}{3} \div \frac{3}{x} = \frac{x}{3} \times \frac{x}{3} = \frac{x \times x}{3 \times 3} = \frac{x^2}{9}$

b) $\frac{4x^3}{3} \div \frac{x}{2} = \frac{4x^3}{3} \times \frac{2}{x} = \frac{4x^2}{3} \times \frac{2}{1} = \frac{4x^2 \times 2}{3 \times 1} = \frac{8x^2}{3}$

c) $\frac{3}{2x} \div \frac{6}{x^3} = \frac{3}{2x} \times \frac{x^3}{6} = \frac{1}{2} \times \frac{x^2}{2} = \frac{1 \times x^2}{2 \times 2} = \frac{x^2}{4}$

d) $\frac{2x^3}{3y} \div \frac{4x}{y^2} = \frac{2x^3}{3y} \times \frac{y^2}{4x} = \frac{x^2}{3} \times \frac{y}{2} = \frac{x^2 \times y}{3 \times 2} = \frac{x^2y}{6}$

Q3 $\frac{x+2}{4} \times \frac{x}{3x+6} = \frac{x+2}{4} \times \frac{x}{3(x+2)} = \frac{x}{12}$

Q4 $\frac{4x}{5} \div \frac{4x^2+8x}{15} = \frac{4x}{5} \times \frac{15}{4x(x+2)} = \frac{3}{(x+2)}$

Q5 $\frac{2x^2-2}{x} \times \frac{5x}{3x-3} = \frac{2(x-1)(x+1)}{x} \times \frac{5x}{3(x-1)}$
$$= \frac{2(x+1)}{1} \times \frac{5}{3} = \frac{2(x+1) \times 5}{1 \times 3} = \frac{10(x+1)}{3}$$

Q6 $\frac{2x^2+8x}{x^2-2x} \times \frac{x-1}{x+4} = \frac{2x(x+4)}{x(x-2)} \times \frac{x-1}{x+4}$
$$= \frac{2}{x-2} \times \frac{x-1}{1} = \frac{2(x-1)}{x-2}$$

Q7 $\frac{x^2-4}{9} \div \frac{x-2}{3} = \frac{(x+2)(x-2)}{9} \times \frac{3}{x-2} = \frac{x+2}{3} \times \frac{1}{1} = \frac{x+2}{3}$

Q8 $\frac{2}{x^2+4x} \div \frac{1}{x+4} = \frac{2}{x(x+4)} \times \frac{x+4}{1} = \frac{2}{x} \times \frac{1}{1} = \frac{2}{x}$

Q9 $\frac{x^2-1}{3} \div \frac{x^2+x}{6} = \frac{(x+1)(x-1)}{3} \times \frac{6}{x(x+1)} = \frac{2(x-1)}{x}$

Q10 $\frac{2x^2-2x-24}{x^2+7x+12} \div \frac{2}{x+4} = \frac{2(x^2-x-12)}{x^2+7x+12} \times \frac{x+4}{2}$
$$= \frac{2(x-4)(x+3)}{(x+4)(x+3)} \times \frac{x+4}{2} = x-4$$

Q11 $\frac{x^2+4x+3}{x^2+5x+6} \times \frac{x^2+2x}{x+1} = \frac{(x+1)(x+3)}{(x+2)(x+3)} \times \frac{x(x+2)}{x+1} = \frac{1}{1} \times \frac{x}{1} = x$

Q12 $\frac{x^2+5x+6}{x^2-2x-3} \times \frac{3x+3}{x^2+2x} = \frac{(x+2)(x+3)}{(x-3)(x+1)} \times \frac{3(x+1)}{x(x+2)}$
$$= \frac{x+3}{x-3} \times \frac{3}{x} = \frac{3(x+3)}{x(x-3)}$$

Q13 $\frac{x^2-4}{6x-3} \times \frac{2x^2+5x-3}{x^2+2x} = \frac{(x+2)(x-2)}{3(2x-1)} \times \frac{(2x-1)(x+3)}{x(x+2)}$
$$= \frac{x-2}{3} \times \frac{x+3}{x} = \frac{(x-2)(x+3)}{3x}$$

Q14 $\frac{x^2+7x+6}{4x-4} \div \frac{x^2+8x+12}{x^2-x}$
$$= \frac{(x+1)(x+6)}{4(x-1)} \times \frac{x(x-1)}{(x+2)(x+6)} = \frac{x(x+1)}{4(x+2)}$$

Q15 $\frac{x^2+4x+4}{x^2-4x+3} \times \frac{x^2-2x-3}{2x^2-2x} \times \frac{4x-4}{x^2+2x}$
$$= \frac{(x+2)^2}{(x-3)(x-1)} \times \frac{(x-3)(x+1)}{2x(x-1)} \times \frac{4(x-1)}{x(x+2)}$$
$$= \frac{x+2}{x-1} \times \frac{x+1}{x} \times \frac{2}{x} = \frac{2(x+2)(x+1)}{x^2(x-1)}$$

Q16 $\frac{x}{6x+12} \div \frac{x^2-x}{x+2} \times \frac{3x-3}{x+1}$
$$= \frac{x}{6(x+2)} \times \frac{x+2}{x(x-1)} \times \frac{3(x-1)}{x+1} = \frac{1}{2(x+1)}$$

Q17 $\frac{x^2+5x}{2x^2+7x+3} \times \frac{2x+1}{x^3-x^2} \div \frac{x+5}{x^2+x-6}$
$$= \frac{x(x+5)}{(2x+1)(x+3)} \times \frac{2x+1}{x^2(x-1)} \times \frac{(x+3)(x-2)}{x+5}$$
$$= \frac{1}{1} \times \frac{1}{x(x-1)} \times \frac{x-2}{1} = \frac{x-2}{x(x-1)}$$

Q18 $\dfrac{3x}{x+2} \div \dfrac{x-2}{x-3} \div \dfrac{x^2-3x}{x^2-4} = \left(\dfrac{3x}{x+2} \times \dfrac{x-3}{x-2}\right) \div \dfrac{x^2-3x}{x^2-4}$

$= \dfrac{3x(x-3)}{(x+2)(x-2)} \times \dfrac{(x+2)(x-2)}{x(x-3)} = 3$

Exercise 2.1.4 — Algebraic division

Q1 **a)** $x^3 - 14x^2 + 6x + 11 \equiv (Ax^2 + Bx + C)(x+1) + D$
The degree of the quotient is the difference between the degrees of the polynomial and the divisor, in this case $3 - 1 = 2$. The degree of the remainder must be less than the degree of the divisor (1) so it must be 0.
Set $x = -1$: $-1 - 14 - 6 + 11 = D$, so $D = -10$.
Set $x = 0$: $11 = C + D$, so $C = 21$.
Equating the coefficients of x^3 gives $1 = A$.
Equating the coefficients of x^2 gives:
$-14 = A + B$, so $B = -15$.
So $x^3 - 14x^2 + 6x + 11 \equiv (x^2 - 15x + 21)(x + 1) - 10$.
Quotient: $x^2 - 15x + 21$
Remainder: -10

b) $2x^3 + 5x^2 - 8x - 17 \equiv (Ax^2 + Bx + C)(x - 2) + D$
Set $x = 2$: $16 + 20 - 16 - 17 = D$, so $D = 3$.
Set $x = 0$: $-17 = -2C + D$, so $C = 10$.
Equating the coefficients of x^3 gives $2 = A$.
Equating the coefficients of x^2 gives:
$5 = -2A + B$, so $B = 9$.
So $2x^3 + 5x^2 - 8x - 17 \equiv (2x^2 + 9x + 10)(x - 2) + 3$.
Quotient: $2x^2 + 9x + 10$
Remainder: 3

c) $6x^3 + x^2 - 11x - 5 \equiv (Ax^2 + Bx + C)(2x + 1) + D$
Set $x = -\dfrac{1}{2}$: $-\dfrac{6}{8} + \dfrac{1}{4} + \dfrac{11}{2} - 5 = D$, so $D = 0$.
Set $x = 0$: $-5 = C + D$, so $C = -5$.
Equating the coefficients of x^3 gives $6 = 2A$, so $A = 3$.
Equating the coefficients of x^2 gives:
$1 = A + 2B$, so $B = -1$.
So $6x^3 + x^2 - 11x - 5 \equiv (3x^2 - x - 5)(2x + 1)$.
Quotient: $3x^2 - x - 5$
Remainder: 0

Q2 $3x^4 - 8x^3 - 6x - 4 \equiv (Ax^3 + Bx^2 + Cx + D)(x - 3) + E$
Set $x = 3$: $243 - 216 - 18 - 4 = E$, so $E = 5$.
Set $x = 0$: $-4 = -3D + E$, so $D = 3$.
Equating the coefficients:
x^4 terms $\Rightarrow 3 = A$.
x^3 terms $\Rightarrow -8 = -3A + B$, so $B = 1$.
x terms $\Rightarrow -6 = -3C + D$, so $C = 3$.
So $3x^4 - 8x^3 - 6x - 4 \equiv (3x^3 + x^2 + 3x + 3)(x - 3) + 5$
or $(3x^4 - 8x^3 - 6x - 4) \div (x - 3) = 3x^3 + x^2 + 3x + 3$ remainder 5

Q3 **a)**
$$x + 1 \overline{)\, x^3 - 14x^2 + 6x + 11} \quad \text{r} -10$$
quotient line: $x^2 - 15x + 21$
$- (x^3 + x^2)$
$-15x^2 + 6x$
$- (-15x^2 - 15x)$
$21x + 11$
$- (21x + 21)$
-10
Quotient: $x^2 - 15x + 21$, remainder: -10

b)
$$x + 3 \overline{)\, x^3 + 10x^2 + 15x - 13} \quad \text{r } 5$$
quotient: $x^2 + 7x - 6$
$- (x^3 + 3x^2)$
$7x^2 + 15x$
$- (7x^2 + 21x)$
$-6x - 13$
$- (-6x - 18)$
5
Quotient: $x^2 + 7x - 6$, remainder: 5

c)
$$x - 2 \overline{)\, 2x^3 + 5x^2 - 8x - 17} \quad \text{r } 3$$
quotient: $2x^2 + 9x + 10$
$- (2x^3 - 4x^2)$
$9x^2 - 8x$
$- (9x^2 - 18x)$
$10x - 17$
$- (10x - 20)$
3
Quotient: $2x^2 + 9x + 10$, remainder: 3

d)
$$x + 5 \overline{)\, 3x^3 + 0x^2 - 78x + 9} \quad \text{r } 24$$
quotient: $3x^2 - 15x - 3$
$- (3x^3 + 15x^2)$
$-15x^2 - 78x$
$- (-15x^2 - 75x)$
$-3x + 9$
$- (-3x - 15)$
24
Quotient: $3x^2 - 15x - 3$, remainder: 24

e)
$$x - 1 \overline{)\, x^4 + 0x^3 + 0x^2 + 0x - 1}$$
quotient: $x^3 + x^2 + x + 1$
$- (x^4 - x^3)$
$x^3 + 0x^2$
$- (x^3 - x^2)$
$x^2 + 0x$
$- (x^2 - x)$
$x - 1$
$- (x - 1)$
0
Quotient: $x^3 + x^2 + x + 1$, remainder: 0

f)
$$2x - 3 \overline{)\, 8x^3 - 6x^2 + x - 10} \quad \text{r } 25$$
quotient: $4x^2 + 3x + 5$
$- (8x^3 - 12x^2)$
$6x^2 + x$
$- (6x^2 - 9x)$
$10x + 10$
$- (10x - 15)$
25
Quotient: $4x^2 + 3x + 5$, remainder: 25

For Questions 4-10, we've given the algebraic long division method, but you could also have used the formula method — you should get the same quotient and remainder.

Q4
$$2x + 1 \overline{)\, 10x^3 + 7x^2 - 5x + 21} \quad \text{r } 24$$
quotient: $5x^2 + x - 3$
$- (10x^3 + 5x^2)$
$2x^2 - 5x$
$- (2x^2 + x)$
$-6x + 21$
$- (-6x - 3)$
24
Quotient: $5x^2 + x - 3$, remainder: 24

Q5
$$x - 2 \overline{)\, 3x^3 - 8x^2 + 15x - 12} \quad \text{r } 10$$
quotient: $3x^2 - 2x + 11$
$- (3x^3 - 6x^2)$
$-2x^2 + 15x$
$- (-2x^2 + 4x)$
$11x - 12$
$- (11x - 22)$
10
Quotient: $3x^2 - 2x + 11$, remainder: 10

Q6

$$2x - 3 \overline{\smash{\big)}\ 16x^4 + 0x^3 + 0x^2 + 0x + 0}$$ with quotient $8x^3 + 12x^2 + 18x + 27$ r 81

$$
\begin{array}{r}
8x^3 + 12x^2 + 18x + 27 \ \text{r} \ 81 \\
2x-3{\overline{\smash{\big)}\,16x^4 + 0x^3 + 0x^2 + 0x + 0\,}} \\
-\ \underline{(16x^4 - 24x^3)} \\
24x^3 + 0x^2 \\
-\ \underline{(24x^3 - 36x^2)} \\
36x^2 + 0x \\
-\ \underline{(36x^2 - 54x)} \\
54x + 0 \\
-\ \underline{(54x - 81)} \\
81
\end{array}
$$

Quotient: $8x^3 + 12x^2 + 18x + 27$, remainder: 81

Q7

$$
\begin{array}{r}
x^2 - x - 12 \ \text{r} \ 0 \\
2x-3{\overline{\smash{\big)}\,2x^3 - 5x^2 - 21x + 36\,}} \\
-\ \underline{(2x^3 - 3x^2)} \\
-2x^2 - 21x \\
-\ \underline{(-2x^2 + 3x)} \\
-24x + 36 \\
-\ \underline{(-24x + 36)} \\
0
\end{array}
$$

$2x^3 - 5x^2 - 21x + 36 = (2x - 3)(x^2 - x - 12) = (2x - 3)(x - 4)(x + 3)$

So $2x^3 - 5x^2 - 21x + 36 = 0$ has solutions $x = \frac{3}{2}$, $x = 4$ and $x = -3$

Q8

$$
\begin{array}{r}
x^3 + 2x^2 - x + 1 \ \text{r} \ 0 \\
x+1{\overline{\smash{\big)}\,x^4 + 3x^3 + x^2 + 0x + 1\,}} \\
-\ \underline{(x^4 + x^3)} \\
2x^3 + x^2 \\
-\ \underline{(2x^3 + 2x^2)} \\
-x^2 + 0x \\
-\ \underline{(-x^2 - x)} \\
x + 1 \\
-\ \underline{(x + 1)} \\
0
\end{array}
$$

$(x + 1)$ is a factor of $x^4 + 3x^3 + x^2 + 1$.
$\Rightarrow x = -1$ is a solution to $x^4 + 3x^3 + x^2 + 1 = 0$

Q9

$$
\begin{array}{r}
x^3 + x^2 - x - 2 \ \text{r} \ 0 \\
3x-2{\overline{\smash{\big)}\,3x^4 + x^3 - 5x^2 - 4x + 4\,}} \\
-\ \underline{(3x^4 - 2x^3)} \\
3x^3 - 5x^2 \\
-\ \underline{(3x^3 - 2x^2)} \\
-3x^2 - 4x \\
-\ \underline{(-3x^2 + 2x)} \\
-6x + 4 \\
-\ \underline{(-6x + 4)} \\
0
\end{array}
$$

So $(3x^4 + x^3 - 5x^2 - 4x + 4) \div (3x - 2) = x^3 + x^2 - x - 2$

Q10

$$
\begin{array}{r}
3x^3 + 13x^2 + 4x \ \text{r} \ 0 \\
x-2{\overline{\smash{\big)}\,3x^4 + 7x^3 - 22x^2 - 8x\,}} \\
-\ \underline{(3x^4 - 6x^3)} \\
13x^3 - 22x^2 \\
-\ \underline{(13x^3 - 26x^2)} \\
4x^2 - 8x \\
-\ \underline{(4x^2 - 8x)} \\
0
\end{array}
$$

$3x^4 + 7x^3 - 22x^2 - 8x = (x - 2)(3x^3 + 13x^2 + 4x)$
$= x(x - 2)(3x^2 + 13x + 4) = x(x - 2)(3x + 1)(x + 4)$
So $3x^4 + 7x^3 - 22x^2 - 8x = 0$ has solutions
$x = 0$, $x = 2$, $x = -\frac{1}{3}$, $x = -4$

Q11 For $f(x) = 2x^4 - 5x^3 - 50x^2 - 85x - 42$, $f(-1) = 0$, so $(x + 1)$ is a factor. Use this as the divisor:

$$
\begin{array}{r}
2x^3 - 7x^2 - 43x - 42 \ \text{r} \ 0 \\
x+1{\overline{\smash{\big)}\,2x^4 - 5x^3 - 50x^2 - 85x - 42\,}} \\
-\ \underline{(2x^4 + 2x^3)} \\
-7x^3 - 50x^2 \\
-\ \underline{(-7x^3 - 7x^2)} \\
-43x^2 - 85x \\
-\ \underline{(-43x^2 - 43x)} \\
-42x - 42 \\
-\ \underline{(-42x - 42)} \\
0
\end{array}
$$

You need to use algebraic long division again.
For $g(x) = 2x^3 - 7x^2 - 43x - 42$, $g(-2) = 0$, so $(x + 2)$ is a factor.
Use this as the divisor for $g(x)$:

$$
\begin{array}{r}
2x^2 - 11x - 21 \ \text{r} \ 0 \\
x+2{\overline{\smash{\big)}\,2x^3 - 7x^2 - 43x - 42\,}} \\
-\ \underline{(2x^3 + 4x^2)} \\
-11x^2 - 43x \\
-\ \underline{(-11x^2 - 22x)} \\
-21x - 42 \\
-\ \underline{(-21x - 42)} \\
0
\end{array}
$$

You're left with a quadratic, which can be easily factorised:
$2x^2 - 11x - 21 = (2x + 3)(x - 7)$
$\Rightarrow 2x^4 - 5x^3 - 50x^2 - 85x - 42 = (x + 1)(x + 2)(2x + 3)(x - 7)$
$\Rightarrow 2x^4 - 5x^3 - 50x^2 - 85x - 42 = 0$ has solutions
$x = -1$, $x = -2$, $x = -\frac{3}{2}$, $x = 7$

2.2 Mappings and Functions

Exercise 2.2.1 — Mappings and functions

Q1

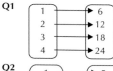

Q2

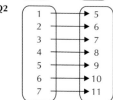

Q3 a) b)

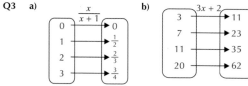

Q4 $g(0) = \dfrac{1}{2(0) + 1} = 1$, $g(2) = \dfrac{1}{2(2) + 1} = \dfrac{1}{5}$

Q5 $f(1) = \dfrac{1}{2 + \log_{10} 1} = \dfrac{1}{2 + 0} = \dfrac{1}{2}$

$f(100) = \dfrac{1}{2 + \log_{10} 100} = \dfrac{1}{2 + 2} = \dfrac{1}{4}$

Q6 a) The minimum value of $h(x)$ in the domain is $\sin 0° = 0$, and the maximum is $\sin 90° = 1$. So the range is $0 \le h(x) \le 1$

b) The minimum value of $j(x)$ in this domain is $\cos 180° = -1$, and the maximum is $\cos 0° = 1$. So the range is $-1 \le j(x) \le 1$

Q7 a) 3^x is defined for all $x \in \mathbb{R}$, so the domain of $f(x)$ is $\mathbb{R}$.
The value of 3^x gets closer to 0 as x becomes more negative, so its range is $3^x > 0$. So the range of f is $f(x) > -1$

b) ln x is not defined for $x \le 0$, so the largest possible domain of
$g(x)$ is $x > 0$. The range of ln x is $\mathbb{R}$, but squaring the result
means that $g(x)$ will always be positive.
So the range is $g(x) \ge 0$.

Q8 **a)** Yes, it is a function.

b) No, because the map is not defined for elements 4 and 5 of
the domain.

c) No, because a value in the domain can map to more than
one value in the range.

Exercise 2.2.2 — Graphs of functions

Q1 **a)** Yes, it is a function.

b) No, because a value of x can map to more than one value of
$f(x)$.

Q2 **a)** 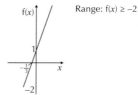 Range: $f(x) \ge -2$

b) 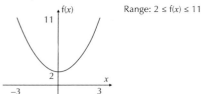 Range: $2 \le f(x) \le 11$

c) 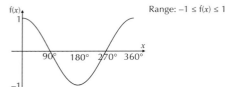 Range: $-1 \le f(x) \le 1$

d) 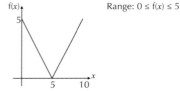 Range: $0 \le f(x) \le 5$

Q3 **a)** The range shown is $3 \le f(x) \le 11$, so the domain is:
$\frac{3-1}{2} \le x \le \frac{11-1}{2}$, which is $1 \le x \le 5$.
In set notation, this is $\{x : 1 \le x \le 5\}$.

b) The domain shown is $-1 \le x \le 4$. The range is between $f(2)$
and $f(-1)$: $((2)^2 - 4(2) + 5) \le f(x) \le ((-1)^2 - 4(-1) + 5)$,
which is $1 \le f(x) \le 10$, i.e. $\{f(x) : 1 \le f(x) \le 10\}$.

Q4 When $x = 0$, $f(x) = 2$. For large x, $x + 2 \approx x + 1$ so as $x \to \infty$,
$\frac{x+2}{x+1} \to 1$. So $f(x) = 1$ is an asymptote.
So the range is $1 < f(x) \le 2$.

Q5 The function $f(x) = \frac{1}{x-2}$ is undefined when $x = 2$, so $a = 2$.

Q6 The function $f(x) = +\sqrt{9 - x^2}$ is only defined when
$x^2 \le 9$, i.e. when $-3 \le x \le 3$. So $a = -3$ and $b = 3$

Q7 The graph of $h(x) = +\sqrt{x+1}$ is shown below.

$h(x)$ is undefined when x is less than -1.
Restricting the domain to $\{x : x \ge -1\}$
would make $h(x)$ a function.

Q8 The graph of k : $x \to \tan x$ is shown below.

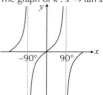

$\tan x$ is undefined at e.g. $-90°$ and $90°$
(it is also undefined periodically either side).
Restricting the domain to e.g. $-90° < x < 90°$ would make this a
function.

Q9 The function $m(x) = \frac{1}{x^2 - 4}$ is undefined when $x = 2$
and when $x = -2$.
So the largest continuous domain that makes it a function would
be either $x > 2$ or $x < -2$.

Q10 **a)** It is not a function because it is not defined for all values of
x in the domain (it's not defined at $x = 0$ or $x = 4$).

b) $x \in \mathbb{R}$, $x \ne 0$, $x \ne 4$

Exercise 2.2.3 — Types of function

It helps to sketch the graph of each function to identify its type.

Q1 **a)** One-to-one: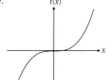

b) Many-to-one: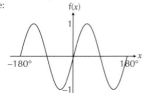

c) One-to-one: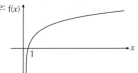

d) Many-to-one:

e) Many-to-one:

2.3 Composite Functions

Exercise 2.3.1 — Composite functions

Q1 **a)** Do $g(3) = 2(3) + 1 = 7$ then $f(7) = 7^2 = 49$, so $fg(3) = 49$.
b) $gf(3) = g(3^2) = g(9) = 2(9) + 1 = 19$
c) $f^2(5) = f(5^2) = f(25) = 25^2 = 625$
d) $g^2(2) = g(2(2) + 1) = g(5) = 2(5) + 1 = 11$

Q2 $fg(90°) = f(2(90°)) = f(180°) = \sin 180° = 0$
$gf(90°) = g(\sin 90°) = g(1) = 2(1) = 2$

Q3 **a)** $gf(1) = g\left(\frac{3}{1+2}\right) = g(1) = 2(1) = 2.$

$fg(1) = f(2(1)) = f(2) = \frac{3}{2+2} = \frac{3}{4}.$

$f^2(4) = f\left(\frac{3}{4+2}\right) = f\left(\frac{1}{2}\right) = \frac{3}{\frac{1}{2}+2} = \frac{3}{1+4} = \frac{6}{5}$

b) $g(-1) = -2$, and $f(-2)$ has a denominator of 0 (which is undefined).

Q4 **a)** $fg(x) = f(2x) = \cos 2x$
b) $gf(x) = g(\cos x) = 2 \cos x$

Q5 **a)** $fg(x) = f(2^x) = 2(2^x) - 1 \; (= 2^{x+1} - 1)$
b) $gf(x) = g(2x - 1) = 2^{(2x-1)}$
c) $f^2(x) = f(2x - 1) = 2(2x - 1) - 1 = 4x - 3$

Q6 $fg(x) = f(x + 4) = \frac{2}{x+4-1} = \frac{2}{x+3}$

$gf(x) = g\left(\frac{2}{x-1}\right) = \frac{2}{x-1} + 4$

$= \frac{2}{x-1} + \frac{4x-4}{x-1} = \frac{4x-2}{x-1} = \frac{2(2x-1)}{x-1}$

Q7 $f^2(x) = f\left(\frac{x}{1-x}\right) = \frac{\frac{x}{1-x}}{1 - \frac{x}{1-x}} = \frac{x}{(1-x) - x} = \frac{x}{1-2x}$

$gfg(x) = gf(x^2) = g\left(\frac{x^2}{1-x^2}\right) = \left(\frac{x^2}{1-x^2}\right)^2 = \frac{x^4}{(1-x^2)^2}$

Q8 **a)** $fg(x) = f(2x - 3) = (2x - 3)^2$, range: $fg(x) \geq 0$.
b) $gf(x) = g(x^2) = 2x^2 - 3$, range: $gf(x) \geq -3$.

Q9 **a)** $gf(x) = g\left(\frac{1}{x}\right) = \ln\left(\frac{1}{x} + 1\right)$
Domain: $\{x : x > 0\}$ (domain of g = range of f = $\{x : x > 0\}$)
Range: $\{gf(x) : gf(x) > 0\}$.
b) $fg(x) = f(\ln (x + 1)) = \frac{1}{\ln(x+1)}$
Domain: $\{x : x > 0\}$ (domain of f = range of g = $\{x : x > 0\}$)
Range: $\{fg(x) : fg(x) > 0\}$

Q10 $fgh(x) = fg(x^2 + 1) = f(5(x^2 + 1) - 1)$
$= f(5x^2 + 4) = 3(5x^2 + 4) + 2 = 15x^2 + 14$

Exercise 2.3.2 — Solving composite function equations

Q1 **a)** $fg(x) = f(3x - 4) = 2(3x - 4) + 1 = 6x - 7$
$6x - 7 = 23 \Rightarrow x = 5$
b) $gf(x) = g\left(\frac{1}{x}\right) = \frac{2}{x} + 5 \Rightarrow \frac{2}{x} + 5 = 6 \Rightarrow x = 2$
c) $gf(x) = g(x^2) = \frac{x^2}{x^2 - 3}$
$\frac{x^2}{x^2 - 3} = 4 \Rightarrow x^2 = 4x^2 - 12 \Rightarrow x^2 = 4 \Rightarrow x = 2 \text{ or } x = -2$
d) $fg(x) = f(3x - 2) = (3x - 2)^2 + 1$
$(3x - 2)^2 + 1 = 50 \Rightarrow x = \frac{\pm\sqrt{49} + 2}{3} \Rightarrow x = 3 \text{ or } x = -\frac{5}{3}$
e) $fg(x) = f(\sqrt{x}) = 2(\sqrt{x}) + 1$
$2(\sqrt{x}) + 1 = 17 \Rightarrow \sqrt{x} = 8 \Rightarrow x = 64$
f) $fg(x) = f(3 - x) = \log_{10} (3 - x)$
$\log_{10} (3 - x) = 0 \Rightarrow 3 - x = 1 \Rightarrow x = 2$

g) $fg(x) = f(x^2 + 2x) = 2^{(x^2 + 2x)} \Rightarrow 2^{(x^2 + 2x)} = 8 \Rightarrow x^2 + 2x = 3$
$\Rightarrow (x - 1)(x + 3) = 0 \Rightarrow x = 1 \text{ or } x = -3$

h) $fg(x) = f(2x - 1) = \frac{2x - 1}{2x - 1 + 1} = \frac{2x - 1}{2x} = 1 - \frac{1}{2x}$

$gf(x) = g\left(\frac{x}{x+1}\right) = 2\left(\frac{x}{x+1}\right) - 1 = \frac{x-1}{x+1}$

$1 - \frac{1}{2x} = \frac{x-1}{x+1} \Rightarrow 2x(x + 1) - (x + 1) = 2x(x - 1)$
$2x^2 + 2x - x - 1 - 2x^2 + 2x = 0 \Rightarrow 3x = 1 \Rightarrow x = \frac{1}{3}$

Q2 **a)** $fg(x) = f(b - 3x) = (b - 3x)^2 + b$
Range: $(b - 3x)^2 \geq 0$, so $fg(x) \geq b$

$gf(x) = g(x^2 + b) = b - 3(x^2 + b) = -3x^2 - 2b$
Range: $-3x^2 \leq 0$, so $gf(x) \leq -2b$

b) $gf(2) = -3(2)^2 - 2b = -8 \Rightarrow 12 + 2b = 8 \Rightarrow b = -2$
$fg(2) = (-2 - 3(2))^2 - 2 = (-8)^2 - 2 = 64 - 2 = 62$

2.4 Inverse Functions

Exercise 2.4.1 — Inverse functions and their graphs

Q1 **a)** Yes, as the graph shows a one-to-one function.
b) No, as it is a many-to-one map, and many-to-one functions do not have inverse functions.

Q2 **a)** No, as $\sin x$ is a many-to-one function over the domain $x \in \mathbb{R}$.
b) No, as it is a many-to-one function over the domain $x \in \mathbb{R}$.
c) Yes, as it is a one-to-one function over the domain $\{x : x \geq 4\}$.

Q3 **a)** $f(x) = 3x + 4$ with domain $x \in \mathbb{R}$ has a range $f(x) \in \mathbb{R}$.
Replace $f(x)$ with y: $y = 3x + 4$
Rearrange: $x = \frac{y - 4}{3}$
Replace with $f^{-1}(x)$ and x: $f^{-1}(x) = \frac{x - 4}{3}$.
The domain of $f^{-1}(x)$ is $x \in \mathbb{R}$ and the range is $f^{-1}(x) \in \mathbb{R}$.

b) $f(x) = 5(x - 2)$ with domain $x \in \mathbb{R}$ has a range $f(x) \in \mathbb{R}$.
Replace $f(x)$ with y: $y = 5(x - 2)$
Rearrange: $x = \frac{y}{5} + 2$
Replace with $f^{-1}(x)$ and x: $f^{-1}(x) = \frac{x}{5} + 2$.
The domain of $f^{-1}(x)$ is $x \in \mathbb{R}$ and the range is $f^{-1}(x) \in \mathbb{R}$.

c) $f(x) = \frac{1}{x+2}$ with domain $x > -2$ has a range $f(x) > 0$.
Replace $f(x)$ with y: $y = \frac{1}{x+2}$
Rearrange: $x = \frac{1}{y} - 2$
Replace with $f^{-1}(x)$ and x: $f^{-1}(x) = \frac{1}{x} - 2$.
The domain of $f^{-1}(x)$ is the range of $f(x)$: $x > 0$.
The range of $f^{-1}(x)$ is the domain of $f(x)$: $f^{-1}(x) > -2$.

d) $f(x) = x^2 + 3$ with domain $\{x : x > 0\}$ has a range $\{f(x) : f(x) > 3\}$.
Replace $f(x)$ with y: $y = x^2 + 3$
Rearrange: $x = \sqrt{y - 3}$
Replace with $f^{-1}(x)$ and x: $f^{-1}(x) = \sqrt{x - 3}$.
The domain of $f^{-1}(x)$ is the range of $f(x)$: $\{x : x > 3\}$.
The range of $f^{-1}(x)$ is the domain of $f(x)$: $\{f^{-1}(x) : f^{-1}(x) > 0\}$.

Q4 **a)** $f(x) = \frac{3x}{x+1}$ with domain $x > -1$ has a range
$f(x) < 3$ — you can work this out by sketching the graph. If you consider what happens as $x \to \infty$ you'll see that $f(x)$ approaches 3.

Replace $f(x)$ with y: $y = \frac{3x}{x+1}$
Rearrange: $y(x + 1) = 3x \Rightarrow yx + y = 3x$
$\Rightarrow (3 - y)x = y \Rightarrow x = \frac{y}{3 - y}$
Replace with $f^{-1}(x)$ and x: $f^{-1}(x) = \frac{x}{3 - x}$.
The domain of $f^{-1}(x)$ is the range of $f(x)$: $x < 3$.
The range of $f^{-1}(x)$ is the domain of $f(x)$: $f^{-1}(x) > -1$.

b) $f^{-1}(2) = \dfrac{2}{3-2} = 2$

c) $f^{-1}\left(\dfrac{1}{2}\right) = \dfrac{\frac{1}{2}}{3-\frac{1}{2}} = \dfrac{1}{6-1} = \dfrac{1}{5}$

Q5 a) $f(x) = \dfrac{x-4}{x+3}$ with domain $\{x : x > -3\}$ has a range $\{f(x) : f(x) < 1\}$ — again, sketching the graph will help. If you consider what happens as $x \to \infty$ you'll see that $f(x)$ approaches 1.

Replace $f(x)$ with y: $y = \dfrac{x-4}{x+3}$

Rearrange: $y(x+3) = x-4 \implies yx + 3y = x - 4$

$x(1-y) = 3y + 4 \implies x = \dfrac{3y+4}{1-y}$

Replace with $f^{-1}(x)$ and x: $f^{-1}(x) = \dfrac{3x+4}{1-x}$.

The domain of $f^{-1}(x)$ is the range of $f(x)$: $\{x : x < 1\}$.
The range of $f^{-1}(x)$ is the domain of $f(x)$: $\{f^{-1}(x) : f^{-1}(x) > -3\}$.

b) $f^{-1}(0) = \dfrac{3(0)+4}{1-0} = 4$

c) $f^{-1}\left(-\dfrac{2}{5}\right) = \dfrac{3\left(-\frac{2}{5}\right)+4}{1+\frac{2}{5}} = \dfrac{-6+20}{5+2} = \dfrac{14}{7} = 2$

Q6 a) $f(x)$ has domain $x > 3$, and range $f(x) \in \mathbb{R}$.
So $f^{-1}(x)$ has domain $x \in \mathbb{R}$ and range $f^{-1}(x) > 3$.

b) $f(x)$ has domain of $1 \le x \le 7$, which will give a range of $(4(1)-2) \le f(x) \le (4(7)-2)$, $2 \le f(x) \le 26$.
So $f^{-1}(x)$ has domain $2 \le x \le 26$ and range $1 \le f^{-1}(x) \le 7$.

c) $f(x)$ has domain $\{x : x < 2\}$ and range $\{f(x) : f(x) < 1\}$.
So $f^{-1}(x)$ has domain $\{x : x < 1\}$ and range $\{f^{-1}(x) : f^{-1}(x) < 2\}$.

d) $f(x)$ has domain $\{x : x \ge 2\}$ and range $\{f(x) : f(x) \ge 3\}$.
So $f^{-1}(x)$ has domain $\{x : x \ge 3\}$ and range $\{f^{-1}(x) : f^{-1}(x) \ge 2\}$.

e) $f(x)$ has domain $0° \le x < 90°$ and range $f(x) \ge 0$.
So $f^{-1}(x)$ has domain $x \ge 0$ and range $0° \le f^{-1}(x) < 90°$.

f) $f(x)$ has domain $\{x : 3 \le x \le 4\}$, which will give a range of $\{f(x) : \ln 9 \le f(x) \le \ln 16\}$.
So $f^{-1}(x)$ has domain $\{x : \ln 9 \le x \le \ln 16\}$ and range $\{f^{-1}(x) : 3 \le f^{-1}(x) \le 4\}$.

Q7 a) $y = e^{x+1} \implies \ln y = x + 1 \implies (\ln y) - 1 = x$
So $f^{-1}(x) = (\ln x) - 1$
$f(x)$ has domain $x \in \mathbb{R}$ and range $f(x) > 0$,
so $f^{-1}(x)$ has domain $x > 0$ and range $f^{-1}(x) \in \mathbb{R}$.

b) $y = x^3 \implies \sqrt[3]{y} = x$
So $f^{-1}(x) = \sqrt[3]{x}$
$f(x)$ has both domain $x < 0$ and range $f(x) < 0$,
so $f^{-1}(x)$ also has domain $x < 0$ and range $f^{-1}(x) < 0$.

c) $y = 2 - \log_2(x) \implies \log_2(x) = 2 - y \implies x = 2^{2-y}$
So $f^{-1}(x) = 2^{2-x}$
$f(x)$ has domain $x \ge 1$, which means that $\log_2(x) \ge 0$.
So the range of f is $f(x) \le 2$.
So $f^{-1}(x)$ has domain $x \le 2$ and range $f^{-1}(x) \ge 1$.

d) $y = \dfrac{1}{x-2} \implies \dfrac{1}{y} = x - 2 \implies \dfrac{1}{y} + 2 = x$
So $f^{-1}(x) = \dfrac{1}{x} + 2$
$f(x)$ has domain $\{x : x \ne 2\}$ and range $\{f(x) : f(x) \ne 0\}$,
so $f^{-1}(x)$ has domain $\{x : x \ne 0\}$ and range $\{f^{-1}(x) : f^{-1}(x) \ne 2\}$.
You can see the range of f(x) more easily from the graph of y = f(x) — there is a horizontal asymptote at y = 0.

e) $y = \dfrac{1}{e^x} = e^{-x} \implies \ln y = -x \implies x = -\ln y$
So $f^{-1}(x) = -\ln x$
$f(x)$ has domain $x \in \mathbb{R}$ and range $f(x) > 0$.
So $f^{-1}(x)$ has domain $x > 0$ and range $f^{-1}(x) \in \mathbb{R}$.

f) $y = \log_{10}e^x \implies 10^y = e^x \implies \ln 10^y = x$
So $f^{-1}(x) = \ln 10^x = x\ln 10$
$f(x)$ has domain $x \in \mathbb{R}$ and range $f(x) \in \mathbb{R}$
So $f^{-1}(x)$ has domain $x \in \mathbb{R}$ and range $f^{-1}(x) \in \mathbb{R}$.
Even though the functions f(x) and f⁻¹(x) look complicated, they're both just straight lines through the origin.

Q8

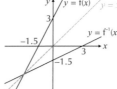

Q9 a)

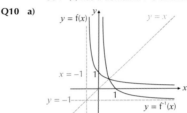

b) $f(x)$ has a domain of $x > 0$, giving a range of $f(x) > 3$.
So $f^{-1}(x)$ has a domain $x > 3$ and range $f^{-1}(x) > 0$.

Q10 a)

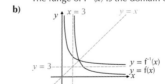

b) There is one point where the graphs intersect.

Q11 a) $f(x) = \dfrac{1}{x-3}$ with domain $x > 3$ has a range $f(x) > 0$.
Replace $f(x)$ with y: $y = \dfrac{1}{x-3}$
Rearrange: $x = \dfrac{1}{y} + 3$
Replace with $f^{-1}(x)$ and x: $f^{-1}(x) = \dfrac{1}{x} + 3$.
The domain of $f^{-1}(x)$ is the range of $f(x)$: $x > 0$.
The range of $f^{-1}(x)$ is the domain of $f(x)$: $f^{-1}(x) > 3$.

b)

c) There is one solution as the graphs intersect once.

d) $\dfrac{1}{x-3} = \dfrac{1}{x} + 3 \implies x = (x-3) + 3x(x-3)$
$\implies x^2 - 3x - 1 = 0$
So using the quadratic formula gives $x = \dfrac{3 + \sqrt{13}}{2}$
You can ignore the negative solution to the quadratic equation because you're only considering the domain x > 3.

Q12 a) $y = \dfrac{3x+6}{x^2 - 2x - 8} = \dfrac{3(x+2)}{(x-4)(x+2)} = \dfrac{3}{x-4}$
$\implies x - 4 = \dfrac{3}{y} \implies x = \dfrac{3}{y} + 4$. So $f^{-1}(x) = \dfrac{3}{x} + 4$
$f(x)$ has domain $x < 4$ and range $f(x) < 0$
So $f^{-1}(x)$ has domain $x < 0$ and range $f^{-1}(x) < 4$.

b) $f^2(x) = f(f(x)) = f\left(\dfrac{3}{x-4}\right) = \dfrac{3}{\dfrac{3}{x-4} - 4}$

$= \dfrac{3}{\dfrac{3}{x-4} - \dfrac{4(x-4)}{x-4}} = \dfrac{3}{\dfrac{3-4(x-4)}{x-4}} = \dfrac{3(x-4)}{19-4x}$

$f^2(x) = f^{-1}(x) \implies \dfrac{3(x-4)}{19-4x} = \dfrac{3}{x} + 4$

$\implies 3x(x-4) = 3(19-4x) + 4x(19-4x)$

$\implies 3x^2 - 12x = 57 - 12x + 76x - 16x^2$

$\implies 19x^2 - 76x - 57 = 0 \implies x^2 - 4x - 3 = 0$

$\implies x = \dfrac{4 \pm \sqrt{(-4)^2 - 4 \times 1 \times -3}}{2} = 2 \pm \sqrt{7}$

But $f^{-1}(x)$ has domain $x < 0$, so only
$x = 2 - \sqrt{7}$ is a valid solution.

2.5 Modulus

Exercise 2.5.1 — The modulus function

Q1 **a)** 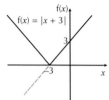 Range: $f(x) \geq 0$

$f(x) = |x + 3|$

b) 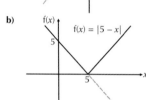 Range: $f(x) \geq 0$

$f(x) = |5 - x|$

c) 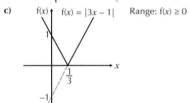 $f(x) = |3x - 1|$ Range: $f(x) \geq 0$

d) 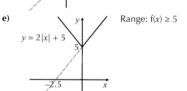 $y = |x| - 9$ Range: $f(x) \geq -9$

e) 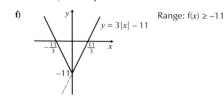 Range: $f(x) \geq 5$

$y = 2|x| + 5$

f) Range: $f(x) \geq -11$

$y = 3|x| - 11$

Q2 **a)** 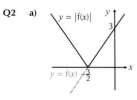 $y = |f(x)|$

b) 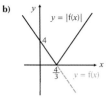 $y = |f(x)|$

c) 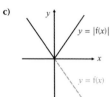 $y = |f(x)|$

d) $y = |f(x)|$

e) 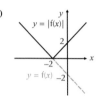 $y = |f(x)|$

f) $y = |f(x)|$

Q3 **a)** 2 **b)** 1 **c)** 4 **d)** 3

Q4 **a)** **(i)** 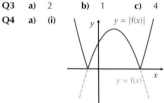 $y = |f(x)|$ $y = f(|x|)$

(ii) 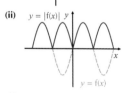 $y = |f(x)|$ 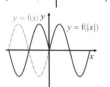 $y = f(|x|)$

(iii) 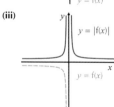 $y = |f(x)|$

b) 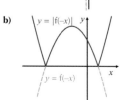 $y = |f(-x)|$

Q5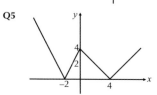

298   Answers

Q6 a)

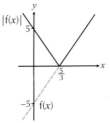

b)

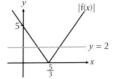

The line $y = 2$ intersects with the line $y = |3x - 5|$ in two places so there are 2 solutions to $|3x - 5| = 2$.

Q7 a)

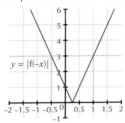

b) There are two solutions to $|-4x + 1| = 3$.
Reading off the graph, these are: $x = -0.5$ and $x = 1$.

Q8 a)

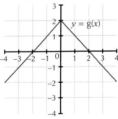

b)

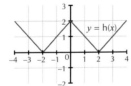

Exercise 2.5.2 — Solving modulus equations and inequalities

Q1 a)

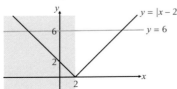

The graph shows that there are two solutions to
$|x - 2| = 6$. $x - 2 \geq 0$ for $x \geq 2$
                   $x - 2 < 0$ for $x < 2$ (shaded)
So there are two equations to solve:
① $x - 2 = 6 \Rightarrow x = 8$ (this is valid as it's in the range $x \geq 2$)
② (shaded) $-(x - 2) = 6 \Rightarrow x = -4$
     (this is also valid as it's in the range $x < 2$)
So the two solutions are $x = 8$ and $x = -4$.

b)

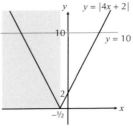

The graph shows that there are two solutions to
$|4x + 2| = 10$. $4x + 2 \geq 0$ for $x \geq -\frac{1}{2}$

$\qquad\qquad\qquad 4x + 2 < 0$ for $x < -\frac{1}{2}$ (shaded)
So there are two equations to solve:
① $4x + 2 = 10 \Rightarrow x = 2$
(this is valid as it's in the range $x \geq -\frac{1}{2}$)
② (shaded) $-(4x + 2) = 10 \Rightarrow x = -3$
(this is also valid as it's in the range $x < -\frac{1}{2}$)
So the two solutions are $x = 2$ and $x = -3$.

c) Rearranging the equation gives $|3x - 4| = 1$.

The graph shows that there are two solutions to $|3x - 4| = 1$.
$3x - 4 \geq 0$ for $x \geq \frac{4}{3}$

$3x - 4 < 0$ for $x < \frac{4}{3}$ (shaded)
So there are two equations to solve:
① $3x - 4 = 1 \Rightarrow x = \frac{5}{3}$
(this is valid as it's in the range $x \geq \frac{4}{3}$)
② (shaded) $-(3x - 4) = 1 \Rightarrow x = 1$
(this is also valid as it's in the range $x < \frac{4}{3}$)
So the two solutions are $x = \frac{5}{3}$ and $x = 1$.

d) Rearranging the equation gives $|x + 3| = 9$.

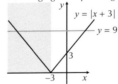

The graph shows that there are two solutions to $|x + 3| = 9$.
$x + 3 \geq 0$ for $x \geq -3$
$x + 3 < 0$ for $x < -3$ (shaded)

So there are two equations to solve:
① $x + 3 = 9 \Rightarrow x = 6$
(this is valid as it's in the range $x \geq -3$)
② (shaded) $-(x + 3) = 9 \Rightarrow x = -12$
(this is also valid as it's in the range $x < -3$)
So the two solutions are $x = 6$ and $x = -12$.

e)

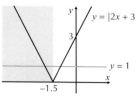

The graph shows that there are two solutions to $|2x + 3| = 1$.
$2x + 3 \geq 0$ for $x \geq -1.5$
$2x + 3 < 0$ for $x < -1.5$ (shaded)

So there are two equations to solve:
① $2x + 3 = 1 \Rightarrow x = -1$
(this is valid as it's in the range $x \geq -1.5$)

② (shaded) $-(2x + 3) = 1 \Rightarrow x = -2$
(this is also valid as it's in the range $x < -1.5$)
So the two solutions are $x = -1$ and $x = -2$.

f)

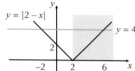

The graph shows that there are two solutions to $|2 - x| = 4$.
$2 - x \geq 0$ for $x < 2$
$2 - x < 0$ for $x \geq 2$ (shaded)

So there are two equations to solve:
① $2 - x = 4 \Rightarrow x = -2$
(this is valid as it's in the range $x < 2$)

② (shaded) $-(2 - x) = 4 \Rightarrow x = 6$
(this is also valid as it's in the range $x \geq 2$)
So the two solutions are $x = -2$ and $x = 6$.

Q2 $|x| = 5 \Rightarrow x = 5$ or $x = -5$
If $x = 5$, $|3x + 2| = |15 + 2| = 17$
If $x = -5$, $|3x + 2| = |-15 + 2| = |-13| = 13$

Q3 $|x| - 2 = -1 \Rightarrow |x| = 1 \Rightarrow x = 1$ or $x = -1$
If $x = 1$, $|7x - 1| = |6| = 6$
If $x = -1$, $|7x - 1| = |-8| = 8$

Q4 $|x| = 3 \Rightarrow x = 3$ or $x = -3$
If $x = 3$, $|-2x + 1| = |-6 + 1| = |-5| = 5$
If $x = -3$, $|-2x + 1| = |6 + 1| = |7| = 7$

Q5 **a)**

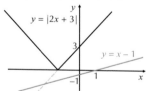

b) You can see from the graph that the lines do not intersect, so there are no solutions to $|f(x)| = g(x)$.

Q6 **a)**

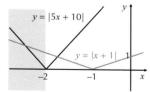

b) There are two solutions to $|f(x)| = |g(x)|$, one where $-2 < x < -1$ and one where $x < -2$ (shaded).
So there are two equations to solve:
① $5x + 10 = -(x + 1) \Rightarrow 6x = -11 \Rightarrow x = -\frac{11}{6}$
(this is valid as it's in the range $-2 < x < -1$)

② (shaded) $-(5x + 10) = -(x + 1) \Rightarrow -4x = 9 \Rightarrow x = -\frac{9}{4}$
(this is also valid as it's in the range $x < -2$)
So the two solutions to $|f(x)| = |g(x)|$ are
$x = -\frac{11}{6}$ and $x = -\frac{9}{4}$.

Q7 **a)**

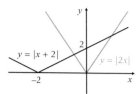

The graph shows that there are two solutions, one where both $x + 2$ and $2x$ are positive, and one where $x + 2$ is positive but $2x$ is negative.
So there are two equations to solve:
① $x + 2 = 2x \Rightarrow x = 2$
② $x + 2 = -2x \Rightarrow x = -\frac{2}{3}$
So the two solutions are $x = 2$ and $x = -\frac{2}{3}$.

Or using the algebraic method, solve:
$(x + 2)^2 = (2x)^2 \Rightarrow x^2 + 4x + 4 = 4x^2$
$\Rightarrow 3x^2 - 4x - 4 = 0 \Rightarrow (3x + 2)(x - 2) = 0$
So $x = 2$ and $x = -\frac{2}{3}$

b)

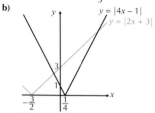

The graph shows that there are two solutions, one where both $2x + 3$ and $4x - 1$ are positive, and one where $2x + 3$ is positive but $4x - 1$ is negative.
So there are two equations to solve:
① $4x - 1 = 2x + 3 \Rightarrow x = 2$
② $-(4x - 1) = 2x + 3 \Rightarrow x = -\frac{1}{3}$
So the two solutions are $x = 2$ and $x = -\frac{1}{3}$.

Or using the algebraic method, solve:
$(2x + 3)^2 = (4x - 1)^2 \Rightarrow 4x^2 + 12x + 9 = 16x^2 - 8x + 1$
$\Rightarrow 12x^2 - 20x - 8 = 0 \Rightarrow 3x^2 - 5x - 2 = 0$
$\Rightarrow (3x + 1)(x - 2) = 0$
So $x = 2$ and $x = -\frac{1}{3}$.

c) Solving algebraically:
$|3x - 6| = |10 - 5x| \Rightarrow (3x - 6)^2 = (10 - 5x)^2$
$9x^2 - 36x + 36 = 100 - 100x + 25x^2$
$16x^2 - 64x + 64 = 0 \Rightarrow x^2 - 4x + 4 = 0 \Rightarrow (x - 2)^2 = 0$
So there is only one solution at $x = 2$.
If you wanted to solve this graphically, you would see that the graphs look like this:

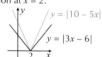

Q8 $|4x + 1| = 3 \quad \Rightarrow 4x + 1 = 3$ or $-(4x + 1) = 3$
$\Rightarrow x = \frac{1}{2}$ or $x = -1$

If $x = \frac{1}{2}$, $2|x - 1| + 3 = 2\left|-\frac{1}{2}\right| + 3 = 1 + 3 = 4$

If $x = -1$, $2|x - 1| + 3 = 2|-2| + 3 = 4 + 3 = 7$

Q9 **a)** $|x| < 8 \Rightarrow -8 < x < 8$
b) $|x| \geq 5 \Rightarrow x \leq -5$ and $x \geq 5$
c) $|2x| > 12 \Rightarrow 2x < -12$ and $2x > 12 \Rightarrow x < -6$ and $x > 6$
d) $|4x + 2| \leq 6 \Rightarrow -6 \leq 4x + 2 \leq 6 \Rightarrow -8 \leq 4x \leq 4 \Rightarrow -2 \leq x \leq 1$
e) $3 \geq |3x - 3| \Rightarrow -3 \leq 3x - 3 \leq 3 \Rightarrow 0 \leq 3x \leq 6 \Rightarrow 0 \leq x \leq 2$
f) $6 - 2|x + 4| < 0 \Rightarrow 6 < 2|x + 4| \Rightarrow 3 < |x + 4|$
$x + 4 < -3$ and $x + 4 > 3 \Rightarrow x < -7$ and $x > -1$

g)

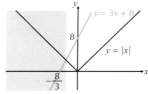

The shaded region shows the values of x that satisfy the inequality. The graph shows that there is one solution to $3x + 8 = |x|$, where $x < 0$.
So the equation to solve is:
$3x + 8 = -x \Rightarrow 4x = -8 \Rightarrow x = -2$ (valid since $-2 < 0$)
So the region that satisfies the inequality is $x < -2$.

h)

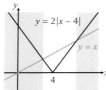

The shaded regions shows the values of x that satisfy the inequality. The graph shows that there are two solutions to $2|x - 4| = x$, one where $x > 4$ and one where $x < 4$.
So there are two equations to solve:
① $2(x - 4) = x \Rightarrow x = 8$ (valid since $8 > 4$)
② $-2(x - 4) = x \Rightarrow x = \frac{8}{3}$ (valid since $\frac{8}{3} < 4$)
So the regions that satisfy the inequality are $x \le \frac{8}{3}$ and $x \ge 8$.

i)

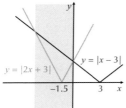

The shaded region shows the values of x that satisfy the inequality. The graph shows that there are two solutions to $|x - 3| = |2x + 3|$, one where both $(x - 3)$ and $(2x + 3)$ are negative (i.e. $x < -1.5$) and one where $(x - 3)$ is negative and $(2x + 3)$ is positive (i.e. $-1.5 < x < 3$).
So there are two equations to solve:
① $-(x - 3) = -(2x + 3) \Rightarrow -x + 3 = -2x - 3$
$\Rightarrow x = -6$ (valid since $-6 < -1.5$)
② $-(x - 3) = 2x + 3 \Rightarrow -x + 3 = 2x + 3$
$\Rightarrow x = 0$ (valid since $-1.5 < 0 < 3$)
So the region that satisfies the inequality is $-6 \le x \le 0$.

Q10

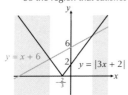

The shaded regions shows the values of x that satisfy the inequality. The graph shows that there are two solutions to $x + 6 = |3x + 2|$, one where $(3x + 2) > 0 \left(x > -\frac{2}{3} \right)$
and one where $(3x + 2) < 0 \left(x < -\frac{2}{3} \right)$.
So there are two equations to solve:
① $x + 6 = 3x + 2 \Rightarrow 4 = 2x \Rightarrow x = 2$ (valid since $2 > -\frac{2}{3}$)
② $x + 6 = -3x - 2 \Rightarrow 4x = -8 \Rightarrow x = -2$ (valid since $-2 < -\frac{2}{3}$)
So the regions that satisfy the inequality are $x \ge 2$ and $x \le -2$.
In set notation, this is $\{x : x \ge 2\} \cup \{x : x \le -2\}$

Q11 $|1 + 2x| \le 3 \Rightarrow -3 \le 1 + 2x \le 3 \Rightarrow -4 \le 2x \le 2 \Rightarrow -2 \le x \le 1$
Draw the graph of $y = |5x + 4|$ for these values:

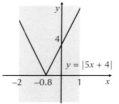

You can see from the graph that the minimum possible value of $|5x + 4|$ is 0, and the maximum is when $x = 1$,
i.e. $|5x + 4| = |5 + 4| = |9| = 9$.
So the possible values are $0 \le |5x + 4| \le 9$

2.6 Transformations of Graphs

Exercise 2.6.1 — Transformations of graphs

Q1

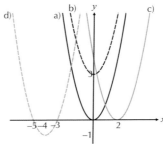

a) Turning point at $(0, 0)$

b) Turning point at $(0, 3)$, translation vector $\begin{pmatrix} 0 \\ 3 \end{pmatrix}$

c) Turning point at $(2, 0)$, translation vector $\begin{pmatrix} 2 \\ 0 \end{pmatrix}$

d) Turning point at $(-4, -1)$, translation vector $\begin{pmatrix} -4 \\ -1 \end{pmatrix}$

Q2 a)

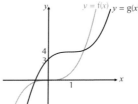

b) $\begin{pmatrix} 1 \\ 4 \end{pmatrix}$ **c)** $y = (x - 1)^3 + 4 \ (= x^3 - 3x^2 + 3x + 3)$

Q3

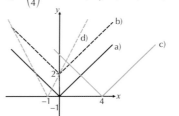

The transformations can be described as follows:

b) A translation of 2 up / by the column vector $\begin{pmatrix} 0 \\ 2 \end{pmatrix}$.

c) A translation of 4 right / by the column vector $\begin{pmatrix} 4 \\ 0 \end{pmatrix}$.

d) A translation of 1 left / by the column vector $\begin{pmatrix} -1 \\ 0 \end{pmatrix}$

and a stretch vertically by a scale factor of 2.

Q4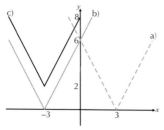

Q5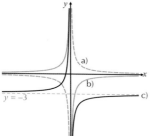

Q6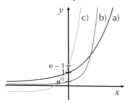

Q7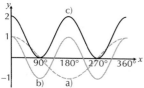

d) The minimum points on c) are (90°, 0) and (270°, 0).

Q8 The maximum value of sin x is 1, and the minimum is –1:

Transformed Function	New equation	Max value	Min value
$f(x) + 2$	$\sin x + 2$	3	1
$f(x - 90°)$	$\sin(x - 90°)$	1	–1
$f(3x)$	$\sin 3x$	1	–1
$4f(x)$	$4 \sin x$	4	–4

Q9 The point of inflection of x^3 is at (0, 0), so:

Transformed Function	New equation	Coordinates of point of inflection
$f(x) + 1$	$x^3 + 1$	(0, 1)
$f(x - 2)$	$(x - 2)^3$	(2, 0)
$-f(x) - 3$	$-x^3 - 3$	(0, –3)
$f(-x) + 4$	$-x^3 + 4$	(0, 4)

Q10 a)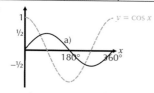

b) $y = \frac{1}{2} \cos(x - 90°)$ $\left(= \frac{1}{2} \sin x\right)$

Q11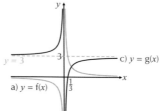

b) Reflect in the y-axis (or x-axis) and translate by $\begin{pmatrix} 0 \\ 3 \end{pmatrix}$ (3 upwards).

Q12

Original graph	New graph	Sequence of transformations
$y = x^3$	$y = (x - 4)^3 + 5$	Translate by $\begin{pmatrix} 4 \\ 5 \end{pmatrix}$ i.e. 4 right and 5 up.
$y = 4^x$	$y = 4^{3x} - 1$	Stretch horizontally by a factor of $\frac{1}{3}$ and translate by $\begin{pmatrix} 0 \\ -1 \end{pmatrix}$ i.e. 1 down.
$y = \|x + 1\|$	$y = 1 - \|2x + 1\|$	Stretch horizontally by a factor of $\frac{1}{2}$, reflect in the x-axis and translate by $\begin{pmatrix} 0 \\ 1 \end{pmatrix}$ i.e. 1 up.
$y = \sin x$	$y = -3 \sin 2x + 1$	Stretch horizontally by a factor of $\frac{1}{2}$, stretch vertically by a factor of 3, reflect in the x-axis and translate by $\begin{pmatrix} 0 \\ 1 \end{pmatrix}$ i.e. 1 up.

Q13 a) $y = 2x^2 - 4x + 6 = 2[x^2 - 2x + 3] = 2[(x - 1)^2 + 2]$

b) Translate by $\begin{pmatrix} 1 \\ 2 \end{pmatrix}$ i.e. 1 right, then 2 up, then stretch vertically by a factor of 2.

c)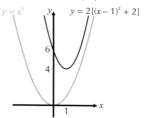

d) The minimum point is at (1, 4).
You can work this out by doing the transformations on the minimum point of the graph $y = x^2$ (which is (O, O)).

Q14 a) Stretch horizontally, scale factor $\frac{1}{3}$, then stretch vertically, scale factor 4.

b) Stretch horizontally, scale factor $\frac{1}{2}$, then reflect in the x-axis, then translate by $\begin{pmatrix} 0 \\ 4 \end{pmatrix}$ i.e. 4 up.

c) Translate by $\begin{pmatrix} 60° \\ 0 \end{pmatrix}$ i.e. 60° right, then stretch vertically, scale factor 2.

Q15 a)

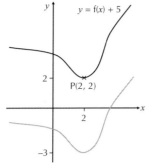

b)

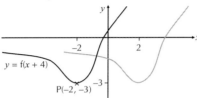

c)

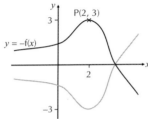

Q16 a)

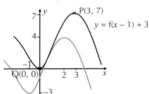

b)

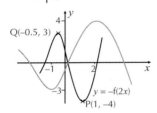

c)

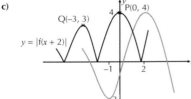

Q17 $f^{-1}(x + 1) = \ln x$. f^{-1} can be treated just as any other function, so using rules of transformation, you know that $f^{-1}(x) = \ln (x - 1)$.
Find the inverse: let $y = \ln (x - 1) \Rightarrow e^y = x - 1 \Rightarrow x = e^y - 1$
So $f(x) = e^x - 1$.
The transformation can be described as follows: starting with the graph of $y = f(x)$, shift the curve up by 1, and then reflect the curve in the line $y = x$.

2.7 Partial Fractions

Exercise 2.7.1 —
Expressing in partial fractions

Q1
$$\frac{3x + 3}{(x - 1)(x - 4)} \equiv \frac{A}{(x - 1)} + \frac{B}{(x - 4)}$$
$$\Rightarrow \frac{3x + 3}{(x - 1)(x - 4)} \equiv \frac{A(x - 4) + B(x - 1)}{(x - 1)(x - 4)}$$
$$\Rightarrow 3x + 3 \equiv A(x - 4) + B(x - 1)$$
Substitution: $x = 4 \Rightarrow 15 = 3B \Rightarrow B = 5$
$\qquad\qquad\quad x = 1 \Rightarrow 6 = -3A \Rightarrow A = -2$
This gives: $\dfrac{3x + 3}{(x - 1)(x - 4)} \equiv -\dfrac{2}{(x - 1)} + \dfrac{5}{(x - 4)}$

Q2 $\dfrac{5x - 1}{x(2x + 1)} \equiv \dfrac{A}{x} + \dfrac{B}{(2x + 1)} \Rightarrow 5x - 1 \equiv A(2x + 1) + Bx$
Equating coefficients: x terms: $5 = 2A + B$
$\qquad\qquad\qquad\qquad$ constants: $-1 = A$
$A = -1$, putting this into the first equation gives:
$5 = -2 + B \Rightarrow B = 7$
This gives: $\dfrac{5x - 1}{x(2x + 1)} \equiv -\dfrac{1}{x} + \dfrac{7}{(2x + 1)}$

Q3
$$\frac{3x - 2}{x^2 + x - 12} \equiv \frac{3x - 2}{(x + 4)(x - 3)} \equiv \frac{A}{(x + 4)} + \frac{B}{(x - 3)}$$
$$\Rightarrow \frac{3x - 2}{(x + 4)(x - 3)} \equiv \frac{A(x - 3) + B(x + 4)}{(x + 4)(x - 3)}$$
$$\Rightarrow 3x - 2 \equiv A(x - 3) + B(x + 4)$$
Equating coefficients: x terms: $3 = A + B$
$\qquad\qquad\qquad\qquad$ constants: $-2 = -3A + 4B$
Solving simultaneously gives: $A = 2$, $B = 1$
This gives: $\dfrac{3x - 2}{x^2 + x - 12} \equiv \dfrac{2}{(x + 4)} + \dfrac{1}{(x - 3)}$

Q4
$$\frac{2}{x^2 - 16} \equiv \frac{2}{(x + 4)(x - 4)} \equiv \frac{A}{(x + 4)} + \frac{B}{(x - 4)}$$
$$\Rightarrow 2 \equiv A(x - 4) + B(x + 4)$$
Substitution: $x = 4 \Rightarrow 2 = 8B \Rightarrow B = \dfrac{1}{4}$
$\qquad\qquad\quad x = -4 \Rightarrow 2 = -8A \Rightarrow A = -\dfrac{1}{4}$
This gives: $\dfrac{2}{x^2 - 16} \equiv -\dfrac{1}{4(x + 4)} + \dfrac{1}{4(x - 4)}$
Don't worry if you get fractions for your coefficients — just put the numerator on the top of your partial fraction and the denominator on the bottom.

Q5 $x^2 - x - 6 = (x - 3)(x + 2)$
$$\frac{5}{(x - 3)(x + 2)} \equiv \frac{A}{(x - 3)} + \frac{B}{(x + 2)} \Rightarrow 5 \equiv A(x + 2) + B(x - 3)$$
Equating coefficients: x terms: $0 = A + B$
$\qquad\qquad\qquad\qquad$ constants: $5 = 2A - 3B$
Solving simultaneously gives: $A = 1$, $B = -1$
This gives: $\dfrac{5}{x^2 - x - 6} \equiv \dfrac{1}{(x - 3)} - \dfrac{1}{(x + 2)}$

Q6 $\dfrac{11x}{2x^2 + 5x - 12} \equiv \dfrac{11x}{(2x - 3)(x + 4)} \equiv \dfrac{A}{(2x - 3)} + \dfrac{B}{(x + 4)}$
$\Rightarrow 11x \equiv A(x + 4) + B(2x - 3)$
Equating coefficients: x terms: $11 = A + 2B$
$\qquad\qquad\qquad\qquad$ constants: $0 = 4A - 3B$
Solving simultaneously gives: $A = 3$, $B = 4$
This gives: $\dfrac{11x}{2x^2 + 5x - 12} \equiv \dfrac{3}{(2x - 3)} + \dfrac{4}{(x + 4)}$

Q7 a) $x^3 - 9x = x(x^2 - 9) = x(x + 3)(x - 3)$
b) $\dfrac{12x + 18}{x(x + 3)(x - 3)} \equiv \dfrac{A}{x} + \dfrac{B}{(x + 3)} + \dfrac{C}{(x - 3)}$
$\Rightarrow 12x + 18 \equiv A(x + 3)(x - 3) + Bx(x - 3) + Cx(x + 3)$
Substitution: $x = 0 \Rightarrow 18 = -9A \Rightarrow A = -2$
$\qquad\qquad\quad x = -3 \Rightarrow -18 = 18B \Rightarrow B = -1$
$\qquad\qquad\quad x = 3 \Rightarrow 54 = 18C \Rightarrow C = 3$
This gives: $\dfrac{12x + 18}{x^3 - 9x} \equiv -\dfrac{2}{x} - \dfrac{1}{(x + 3)} + \dfrac{3}{(x - 3)}$

Q8 $\dfrac{3x+9}{x^3-36x} \equiv \dfrac{3x+9}{x(x^2-36)} \equiv \dfrac{3x+9}{x(x+6)(x-6)}$

$\dfrac{3x+9}{x(x+6)(x-6)} \equiv \dfrac{A}{x} + \dfrac{B}{(x+6)} + \dfrac{C}{(x-6)}$

$\Rightarrow 3x+9 \equiv A(x+6)(x-6) + Bx(x-6) + Cx(x+6)$

Substitution:

$x = 0 \Rightarrow 9 = -36A \Rightarrow A = -\dfrac{9}{36} = -\dfrac{1}{4}$

$x = -6 \Rightarrow -9 = 72B \Rightarrow B = -\dfrac{9}{72} = -\dfrac{1}{8}$

$x = 6 \Rightarrow 27 = 72C \Rightarrow C = \dfrac{27}{72} = \dfrac{3}{8}$

This gives: $\dfrac{3x+9}{x^3-36x} \equiv -\dfrac{1}{4x} - \dfrac{1}{8(x+6)} + \dfrac{3}{8(x-6)}$

Q9 **a)** $f(x) = x^3 - 7x - 6$

$f(-1) = -1 + 7 - 6 = 0 \Rightarrow (x+1)$ is a factor

Once you've found one factor using the Factor Theorem you can use e.g. algebraic long division to get:
$x^3 - 7x - 6 = (x+1)(x^2 - x - 6)$
Then you can factorise the quadratic:
$x^3 - 7x - 6 = (x+1)(x-3)(x+2)$

b) $\dfrac{6x+2}{x^3-7x-6} \equiv \dfrac{6x+2}{(x+1)(x-3)(x+2)}$

$\dfrac{6x+2}{(x+1)(x-3)(x+2)} \equiv \dfrac{A}{(x+1)} + \dfrac{B}{(x-3)} + \dfrac{C}{(x+2)}$

$\Rightarrow 6x+2 \equiv A(x-3)(x+2) + B(x+1)(x+2) + C(x+1)(x-3)$
Substitution: $x = -1 \Rightarrow -4 = -4A \Rightarrow A = 1$
$x = 3 \Rightarrow 20 = 20B \Rightarrow B = 1$
$x = -2 \Rightarrow -10 = 5C \Rightarrow C = -2$

This gives: $\dfrac{6x+2}{x^3-7x-6} \equiv \dfrac{1}{(x+1)} + \dfrac{1}{(x-3)} - \dfrac{2}{(x+2)}$

Q10 **a)** $\dfrac{6x+4}{(x+4)(x-1)(x+1)} \equiv \dfrac{A}{(x+4)} + \dfrac{B}{(x-1)} + \dfrac{C}{(x+1)}$

$\Rightarrow 6x+4 \equiv A(x-1)(x+1) + B(x+4)(x+1) + C(x+4)(x-1)$

Substitution: $x = -4 \Rightarrow -20 = 15A \Rightarrow A = -\dfrac{4}{3}$
$x = 1 \Rightarrow 10 = 10B \Rightarrow B = 1$
$x = -1 \Rightarrow -2 = -6C \Rightarrow C = \dfrac{1}{3}$

This gives:
$\dfrac{6x+4}{(x+4)(x-1)(x+1)} \equiv -\dfrac{4}{3(x+4)} + \dfrac{1}{(x-1)} + \dfrac{1}{3(x+1)}$

b) $\dfrac{15x-27}{x^3-6x^2+3x+10} \equiv \dfrac{15x-27}{(x+1)(x-2)(x-5)}$

You get this by using the factor theorem, as in Q9.

$\dfrac{15x-27}{(x+1)(x-2)(x-5)} \equiv \dfrac{A}{(x+1)} + \dfrac{B}{(x-2)} + \dfrac{C}{(x-5)}$

$\Rightarrow 15x-27 \equiv A(x-2)(x-5) + B(x+1)(x-5) + C(x+1)(x-2)$

Substitution: $x = -1 \Rightarrow -42 = 18A \Rightarrow A = -\dfrac{7}{3}$
$x = 2 \Rightarrow 3 = -9B \Rightarrow B = -\dfrac{1}{3}$
$x = 5 \Rightarrow 48 = 18C \Rightarrow C = \dfrac{8}{3}$

This gives:
$\dfrac{15x-27}{x^3-6x^2+3x+10} \equiv -\dfrac{7}{3(x+1)} - \dfrac{1}{3(x-2)} + \dfrac{8}{3(x-5)}$

c) $\dfrac{2x+7}{x^3-2x^2-5x+6} \equiv \dfrac{2x+7}{(x-1)(x+2)(x-3)}$

$\equiv \dfrac{A}{x-1} + \dfrac{B}{x+2} + \dfrac{C}{x-3}$

$2x+7 \equiv A(x+2)(x-3) + B(x-1)(x-3) + C(x-1)(x+2)$

Substitution: $x = 1$: $9 = -6A \Rightarrow A = -\dfrac{3}{2}$

$x = -2$: $3 = 15B \Rightarrow B = \dfrac{1}{5}$

$x = 3$: $13 = 10C \Rightarrow C = \dfrac{13}{10}$

$\dfrac{2x+7}{x^3-2x^2-5x+6} \equiv \dfrac{1}{5(x+2)} + \dfrac{13}{10(x-3)} - \dfrac{3}{2(x-1)}$

d) $\dfrac{162}{x^3-81x} \equiv \dfrac{162}{x(x+9)(x-9)} \equiv \dfrac{A}{x} + \dfrac{B}{x+9} + \dfrac{C}{x-9}$

$162 \equiv A(x+9)(x-9) + Bx(x-9) + Cx(x+9)$
Substitution: $x = 0$: $162 = -81A \Rightarrow A = -2$
$x = -9$: $162 = 162B \Rightarrow B = 1$
$x = 9$: $162 = 162C \Rightarrow C = 1$
$\dfrac{162}{x^3-9x} \equiv \dfrac{1}{x-9} + \dfrac{1}{x+9} - \dfrac{2}{x}$

e) The coefficients of the cubic in the denominator add to 0, so $(x-1)$ is a factor. Then using e.g. algebraic long division you can fully factorise the denominator:

$\dfrac{6-x}{2x^3-7x^2+7x-2} \equiv \dfrac{6-x}{(2x-1)(x-2)(x-1)}$

$\equiv \dfrac{A}{2x-1} + \dfrac{B}{x-2} + \dfrac{C}{x-1}$

$6-x \equiv A(x-2)(x-1) + B(2x-1)(x-1) + C(2x-1)(x-2)$

Substitution: $x = 2$: $4 = 3B \Rightarrow B = \dfrac{4}{3}$

$x = 1$: $5 = -C \Rightarrow C = -5$

$x = \dfrac{1}{2}$: $\dfrac{11}{2} = \dfrac{3}{4}A \Rightarrow A = \dfrac{22}{3}$

$\dfrac{6-x}{2x^3-7x^2+7x-2} \equiv \dfrac{22}{3(2x-1)} + \dfrac{4}{3(x-2)} - \dfrac{5}{x-1}$

f) $\dfrac{x+4}{15x^3-x^2-2x} \equiv \dfrac{x+4}{x(3x+1)(5x-2)}$

$\equiv \dfrac{A}{x} + \dfrac{B}{3x+1} + \dfrac{C}{5x-2}$

$x+4 \equiv A(3x+1)(5x-2) + Bx(5x-2) + Cx(3x+1)$
Substitution: $x = 0$: $4 = -2A \Rightarrow A = -2$

$x = -\dfrac{1}{3}$: $\dfrac{11}{3} = \dfrac{11}{9}B \Rightarrow B = 3$

$x = \dfrac{2}{5}$: $\dfrac{22}{5} = \dfrac{22}{25}C \Rightarrow C = 5$

$\dfrac{x+4}{15x^3-x^2-2x} \equiv \dfrac{3}{3x+1} + \dfrac{5}{5x-2} - \dfrac{2}{x}$

Exercise 2.7.2 — Repeated factors

Q1 $\dfrac{3x}{(x+5)^2} \equiv \dfrac{A}{(x+5)} + \dfrac{B}{(x+5)^2} \Rightarrow 3x \equiv A(x+5) + B$

Equating coefficients: x terms: $3 = A$
constants: $0 = 5A + B \Rightarrow B = -15$
This gives: $\dfrac{3x}{(x+5)^2} \equiv \dfrac{3}{(x+5)} - \dfrac{15}{(x+5)^2}$

Q2 $\dfrac{5x+2}{x^2(x+1)} \equiv \dfrac{A}{x} + \dfrac{B}{x^2} + \dfrac{C}{(x+1)}$

$\Rightarrow 5x+2 \equiv Ax(x+1) + B(x+1) + Cx^2$
Equating coefficients:
constants: $2 = B$
x terms: $5 = A + B \Rightarrow A = 3$
x^2 terms: $0 = A + C \Rightarrow C = -3$
This gives: $\dfrac{5x+2}{x^2(x+1)} \equiv \dfrac{3}{x} + \dfrac{2}{x^2} - \dfrac{3}{(x+1)}$

Q3 **a)** $\dfrac{2x-7}{(x-3)^2} \equiv \dfrac{A}{(x-3)} + \dfrac{B}{(x-3)^2} \Rightarrow 2x-7 \equiv A(x-3) + B$

Substitution: $x = 3 \Rightarrow -1 = B$
Equating coefficients of the x terms: $2 = A$
This gives: $\dfrac{2x-7}{(x-3)^2} \equiv \dfrac{2}{(x-3)} - \dfrac{1}{(x-3)^2}$

b) $\dfrac{6x+7}{(2x+3)^2} \equiv \dfrac{A}{(2x+3)} + \dfrac{B}{(2x+3)^2} \Rightarrow 6x+7 \equiv A(2x+3) + B$

Substitution: $x = -\dfrac{3}{2} \Rightarrow -2 = B$
Equating coefficients of x: $A = 3$
This gives: $\dfrac{3x+7}{(2x+3)^2} \equiv \dfrac{3}{(2x+3)} - \dfrac{2}{(2x+3)^2}$

c) $\dfrac{7x}{(x+4)^2(x-3)} \equiv \dfrac{A}{(x+4)} + \dfrac{B}{(x+4)^2} + \dfrac{C}{(x-3)}$

$\Rightarrow 7x \equiv A(x+4)(x-3) + B(x-3) + C(x+4)^2$
Substitution: $x = -4 \Rightarrow -28 = -7B \Rightarrow B = 4$
$x = 3 \Rightarrow 21 = 49C \Rightarrow C = \dfrac{3}{7}$
Equating coefficients of the x^2 terms:
$0 = A + C \Rightarrow A = -\dfrac{3}{7}$

This gives: $\dfrac{7x}{(x+4)^2(x-3)} \equiv -\dfrac{3}{7(x+4)} + \dfrac{4}{(x+4)^2} + \dfrac{3}{7(x-3)}$

d) $\dfrac{11x - 10}{x(x - 5)^2} \equiv \dfrac{A}{x} + \dfrac{B}{(x - 5)} + \dfrac{C}{(x - 5)^2}$

$\Rightarrow 11x - 10 \equiv A(x - 5)^2 + Bx(x - 5) + Cx$

Substitution: $x = 5 \Rightarrow 45 = 5C \Rightarrow C = 9$

$x = 0 \Rightarrow -10 = 25A \Rightarrow A = -\dfrac{2}{5}$

Equating the coefficients of x^2:

$0 = A + B \Rightarrow B = \dfrac{2}{5}$

This gives: $\dfrac{11x - 10}{x(x - 5)^2} \equiv -\dfrac{2}{5x} + \dfrac{2}{5(x - 5)} + \dfrac{9}{(x - 5)^2}$

Q4 $x^3 - 10x^2 + 25x = x(x^2 - 10x + 25) = x(x - 5)(x - 5)$

So $\dfrac{5x + 10}{x^3 - 10x^2 + 25x} \equiv \dfrac{5x + 10}{x(x - 5)^2} \equiv \dfrac{A}{x} + \dfrac{B}{(x - 5)} + \dfrac{C}{(x - 5)^2}$

$\Rightarrow 5x + 10 \equiv A(x - 5)^2 + Bx(x - 5) + Cx$

Substitution: $x = 0 \Rightarrow 10 = 25A \Rightarrow A = \dfrac{2}{5}$

$x = 5 \Rightarrow 35 = 5C \Rightarrow C = 7$

Equating coefficients of x^2 terms:

$0 = A + B \Rightarrow B = -\dfrac{2}{5}$

This gives: $\dfrac{5x + 10}{x^3 - 10x^2 + 25x} \equiv \dfrac{2}{5x} - \dfrac{2}{5(x - 5)} + \dfrac{7}{(x - 5)^2}$

Q5 $(x - 2)(x^2 - 4) = (x - 2)(x + 2)(x - 2) = (x + 2)(x - 2)^2$

$\dfrac{3x + 2}{(x - 2)(x^2 - 4)} \equiv \dfrac{3x + 2}{(x + 2)(x - 2)^2} \equiv \dfrac{A}{(x + 2)} + \dfrac{B}{(x - 2)} + \dfrac{C}{(x - 2)^2}$

$\Rightarrow 3x + 2 \equiv A(x - 2)^2 + B(x + 2)(x - 2) + C(x + 2)$

Substitution: $x = 2 \Rightarrow 8 = 4C \Rightarrow C = 2$

$x = -2 \Rightarrow -4 = 16A \Rightarrow A = -\dfrac{1}{4}$

Equating coefficients of x^2 terms:

$0 = A + B \Rightarrow B = \dfrac{1}{4}$

This gives: $\dfrac{3x + 2}{(x - 2)(x^2 - 4)} \equiv -\dfrac{1}{4(x + 2)} + \dfrac{1}{4(x - 2)} + \dfrac{2}{(x - 2)^2}$

Q6 $\dfrac{7x + 3}{x^2(3 - 2x)} \equiv \dfrac{A}{x} + \dfrac{B}{x^2} + \dfrac{C}{3 - 2x}$

$\Rightarrow 7x + 3 \equiv Ax(3 - 2x) + B(3 - 2x) + Cx^2$

Substitution: $x = 0 \Rightarrow 3 = 3B \Rightarrow B = 1$

$x = \dfrac{3}{2} \Rightarrow \dfrac{27}{2} = \dfrac{9}{4}C \Rightarrow C = 6$

Equating coefficients of x^2 terms:

$0 = -2A + C \Rightarrow A = 3$

This gives: $\dfrac{7x + 3}{x^2(3 - 2x)} \equiv \dfrac{3}{x} + \dfrac{1}{x^2} + \dfrac{6}{3 - 2x}$

Q7 $\dfrac{x + 17}{(x + 1)(x + c)^2} \equiv \dfrac{1}{(x + 1)} - \dfrac{1}{(x + c)} + \dfrac{5}{(x + c)^2}$

$\Rightarrow x + 17 \equiv (x + c)^2 - (x + c)(x + 1) + 5(x + 1)$

$x + 17 \equiv x^2 + 2cx + c^2 - x^2 - cx - x - c + 5x + 5$

$x + 17 \equiv (2c - c - 1 + 5)x + (c^2 - c + 5)$

$x + 17 \equiv (c + 4)x + (c^2 - c + 5)$

Equating coefficients of x:

$1 = c + 4 \Rightarrow c = -3$

You can check this by equating constant terms:

$(-3)^2 - (-3) + 5 = 9 + 3 + 5 = 17$

Q8 **a)** You know that $(x + 2)$ is a factor, so e.g. using algebraic long division, you can factorise the expression as:

$2x^3 + 7x^2 + 4x - 4 = (x + 2)(x + 2)(2x - 1)$

b) $\dfrac{x - 13}{(x + 2)^2(2x - 1)} \equiv \dfrac{A}{x + 2} + \dfrac{B}{(x + 2)^2} + \dfrac{C}{2x - 1}$

$\Rightarrow x - 13 \equiv A(x + 2)(2x - 1) + B(2x - 1) + C(x + 2)^2$

Substitution: $x = -2 \Rightarrow -15 = -5B \Rightarrow B = 3$

$x = \dfrac{1}{2} \Rightarrow -\dfrac{25}{2} = \dfrac{25}{4}C \Rightarrow C = -2$

Equating coefficients of x^2 terms:

$0 = 2A + C \Rightarrow A = 1$

This gives: $\dfrac{x - 13}{(x + 2)^2(2x - 1)} \equiv \dfrac{1}{x + 2} + \dfrac{3}{(x + 2)^2} - \dfrac{2}{2x - 1}$

Review Exercise — Chapter 2

Q1 **a)** $\dfrac{4x^2 - 25}{6x - 15} = \dfrac{(2x + 5)(2x - 5)}{3(2x - 5)} = \dfrac{(2x + 5)}{3}$

b) $\dfrac{2x + 3}{x - 2} \times \dfrac{4x - 8}{2x^2 - 3x - 9} = \dfrac{(2x + 3) \times 4(x - 2)}{(x - 2)(2x + 3)(x - 3)} = \dfrac{4}{(x - 3)}$

c) $\dfrac{x^2 - 3x}{x + 1} \div \dfrac{x}{2} = \dfrac{x(x - 3)}{x + 1} \times \dfrac{2}{x} = \dfrac{2(x - 3)}{x + 1}$

Q2 **a)** $\dfrac{x}{2x + 1} + \dfrac{3}{x^2} + \dfrac{1}{x} = \dfrac{x^3}{x^2(2x + 1)} + \dfrac{3(2x + 1)}{x^2(2x + 1)} + \dfrac{(2x + 1)x}{x^2(2x + 1)}$

$= \dfrac{x^3 + 2x^2 + 7x + 3}{x^2(2x + 1)}$

b) $\dfrac{2}{x^2 - 1} - \dfrac{3x}{x - 1} + \dfrac{x}{x + 1} = \dfrac{2}{x^2 - 1} - \dfrac{3x(x + 1)}{(x - 1)(x + 1)} + \dfrac{x(x - 1)}{(x - 1)(x + 1)}$

$= \dfrac{2(1 - 2x - x^2)}{(x - 1)(x + 1)}$

c) $\dfrac{2}{(x + 1)^2} - \dfrac{x}{x + 1} + \dfrac{1}{3x} = \dfrac{6x}{3x(x + 1)^2} - \dfrac{3x^2(x + 1)}{3x(x + 1)^2} + \dfrac{(x + 1)^2}{3x(x + 1)^2}$

$= -\dfrac{3x^3 + 2x^2 - 8x - 1}{3x(x + 1)^2}$

Q3 $2x^3 + 8x^2 + 7x + 8 \equiv (Ax^2 + Bx + C)(x + 3) + D$

Set $x = -3$: $-54 + 72 - 21 + 8 = D$, so $D = 5$.

Set $x = 0$: $8 = 3C + D$, so $3C = 3 \Rightarrow C = 1$.

Equating the coefficients of x^3 gives $2 = A$.

Equating the coefficients of x^2 gives

$8 = 3A + B$, so $B = 2$.

So $2x^3 + 8x^2 + 7x + 8 \equiv (2x^2 + 2x + 1)(x + 3) + 5$

The result when $2x^3 + 8x^2 + 7x + 8$ is divided by $(x + 3)$ is $(2x^2 + 2x + 1)$ remainder 5.

Q4 $x^4 + x^3 - 5x^2 - 7x - 2 \equiv (Ax^3 + Bx^2 + Cx + D)(x + 1) + E$

Set $x = -1$: $1 - 1 - 5 + 7 - 2 = E$, so $E = 0$

Set $x = 0$: $-2 = D + E$, so $D = -2$

Equating the coefficients of x^4 gives $1 = A$.

Equating the coefficients of x^3 gives $1 = A + B$, so $B = 0$

Equating the coefficients of x^2 gives

$-5 = B + C$, so $C = -5$

So $x^4 + x^3 - 5x^2 - 7x - 2 \equiv (x^3 - 5x - 2)(x + 1)$

$x^4 + x^3 - 5x^2 - 7x = 2 \Rightarrow x^4 + x^3 - 5x^2 - 7x - 2 = 0$

$\Rightarrow (x^3 - 5x - 2)(x + 1) = 0$, so one solution of

$x^4 + x^3 - 5x^2 - 7x = 2$ is $x = -1$

Q5 **a)** Range $f(x) \geq -16$. This is a function, and it's one-to-one (the domain is restricted so every x-value is mapped to only one value of $f(x)$).

b) Complete the square: $x^2 - 7x + 10 = (x - \dfrac{7}{2})^2 - \dfrac{9}{4}$

Sketching this gives:

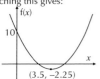

So range $f(x) \geq -2.25$. This is a function, and it's many-to-one.

c) Range $f(x) \geq 0$. This is not a function as $f(x)$ doesn't exist for $x < 0$.

$\sqrt{x}$ *means the positive root of x.*

Q6 **a)** $f(0) = 5$, $f\left(\dfrac{1}{2}\right) = 2\left(\dfrac{1}{2}\right)$

b)

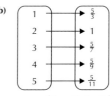

Range $\left\{\dfrac{5}{3}, 1, \dfrac{5}{7}, \dfrac{5}{9}, \dfrac{5}{11}\right\}$

c) $f(x)$ is not defined when $2x + 1 = 0 \Rightarrow x = -\frac{1}{2}$,
but is defined for all other values of x.
$-\frac{1}{2} \notin \mathbb{Z}$, so the mapping is a function for $x \in \mathbb{Z}$

d) No — the mapping is not defined for $x = -\frac{1}{2}$.

Q7 a)

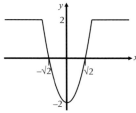

b) $-2 \le f(x) \le 2$

Q8 a) $fg(x) = f(2x + 3) = \frac{3}{2x + 3}$

$fg(2) = \frac{3}{7}$

$gf(x) = g\left(\frac{3}{x}\right) = \frac{6}{x} + 3$, so $gf(1) = 9$

b) $fg(x) = f(x + 4) = 3(x + 4)^2$
$fg(2) = 3 \times 6^2 = 108$
$gf(x) = g(3x^2) = 3x^2 + 4$, so $gf(1) = 7$

Q9 a) $fg(1) = f(g(1)) = f(100) = 2$
$gf(1) = g(f(1)) = g(0) = 10$
$f^2(10) = f(f(10)) = f(1) = 0$
$g^2(-1) = g(g(-1)) = g(1) = 100$

b) Because $f(1) = \log_{10} 1 = 0$, and $f(0) = \log_{10} 0$,
which is undefined.

Q10 $fg(x) = f(g(x)) = f(x + 7) = 3(x + 7) = 3x + 21$
$gf(x) = g(f(x)) = g(3x) = 3x + 7$
$g^2(x) = g(g(x)) = g(x + 7) = x + 7 + 7 = x + 14$

Q11 f is a one-to-one function so it has an inverse.
Domain: $x \ge 3$, range: $f^{-1}(x) \in \mathbb{R}$.

Q12 Replace $f(x)$ with y: $y = \sqrt{2x - 4} \Rightarrow y^2 = 2x - 4$
$\Rightarrow 2x = y^2 + 4 \Rightarrow x = \frac{y^2}{2} + 2$

Replace with $f^{-1}(x)$ and x: $f^{-1}(x) = \frac{x^2}{2} + 2$

The domain is $x \ge 0$ and the range is $f^{-1}(x) \ge 2$.

Q13 In the domain $0 \le x \le \frac{\pi}{2}$, $\cos x$ is a one-to-one function:

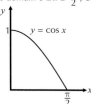

so $f^{-1}(x)$ does exist.

Q14 $y = \frac{x}{x - 1} \Rightarrow y(x - 1) = x \Rightarrow yx - y = x$

$\Rightarrow yx - x = y \Rightarrow x(y - 1) = y \Rightarrow x = \frac{y}{y - 1}$

Replace with $f^{-1}(x)$ and x: $f^{-1}(x) = \frac{x}{x - 1}$
This shows that $f(x) = f^{-1}(x) \Rightarrow f(f(x)) = f(f^{-1}(x)) \Rightarrow f^2(x) = x$

Q15 Replace $f(x)$ with y:
$y = \log_{10}(x + 4) \Rightarrow 10^y = x + 4 \Rightarrow x = 10^y - 4$.
Replace with $f^{-1}(x)$ and x: $f^{-1}(x) = 10^x - 4$

Q16 a)

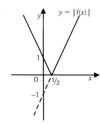

b)

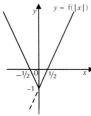

Q17 Solving algebraically:
$|3x - 1| = |4 - x| \Rightarrow (3x - 1)^2 = (4 - x)^2$
$\Rightarrow 9x^2 - 6x + 1 = 16 - 8x + x^2$
$\Rightarrow 8x^2 + 2x - 15 = 0 \Rightarrow (4x - 5)(2x + 3) = 0$
So $x = \frac{5}{4}$ and $x = -\frac{3}{2}$

Q18 a)

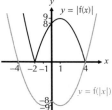

b) There are two solutions to $f(|x|) = -5$ — they correspond to
the positive solution to $f(x) = -5$, and the negative solution to
$-f(x) = -5$. These are symmetrical about the y-axis.
$f(x) = -5$: $x^2 - 2x - 8 = -5$
$\Rightarrow x^2 - 2x - 3 = 0 \Rightarrow (x - 3)(x + 1) = 0$.
So the positive solution is $x = 3$.
By symmetry, the other solution is $x = -3$.

Q19 Do the transformation in stages:

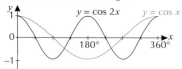

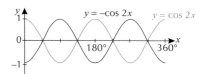

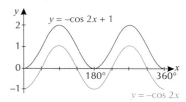

Q20 a)

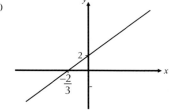

b)

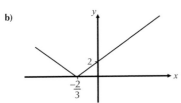

c)

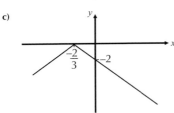

Q21 $\dfrac{2x}{(x-5)(x+5)} \equiv \dfrac{A}{(x-5)} + \dfrac{B}{(x+5)} \;\Rightarrow\; 2x \equiv A(x+5) + B(x-5)$

$x = 5:\; 10 = 10A \;\Rightarrow\; A = 1$
$x = -5:\; -10 = -10B \;\Rightarrow\; B = 1$
$\Rightarrow\; \dfrac{2x}{(x-5)(x+5)} \equiv \dfrac{1}{(x-5)} + \dfrac{1}{(x+5)}$

Q22 $\dfrac{2-x}{(3x+2)(x+1)} \equiv \dfrac{A}{(3x+2)} + \dfrac{B}{(x+1)}$

$\Rightarrow\; 2 - x \equiv A(x+1) + B(3x+2)$
$x = -1:\; 3 = B(-1) \;\Rightarrow\; B = -3$
$x = 0:\; 2 = A + 2B = A - 6 \;\Rightarrow\; A = 8$

Q23 $\dfrac{x-3}{x^2+3x+2} \equiv \dfrac{A}{(x+1)} + \dfrac{B}{(x+2)}$

$\Rightarrow\; x - 3 \equiv A(x+2) + B(x+1)$
$x = -1:\; -4 = A(1) \;\Rightarrow\; A = -4$
$x = -2:\; -5 = B(-1) \;\Rightarrow\; B = 5$

Q24 a) $\dfrac{4}{x^2+x} \equiv \dfrac{4}{x(x+1)} \equiv \dfrac{A}{x} + \dfrac{B}{x+1}$

$\Rightarrow\; 4 = A(x+1) + Bx$
$x = 0:\; 4 = A$
$x = -1:\; 4 = -B \;\Rightarrow\; B = -4$
$\Rightarrow\; \dfrac{4}{x^2+x} \equiv \dfrac{4}{x} - \dfrac{4}{(x+1)}$

b) $\dfrac{4x+5}{(x+4)(2x-3)} \equiv \dfrac{A}{x+4} + \dfrac{B}{2x-3}$

$\Rightarrow\; 4x + 5 \equiv A(2x-3) + B(x+4)$
$x = -4:\; -11 = -11A \;\Rightarrow\; A = 1$
$x = 0:\; 5 = -3A + 4B = -3 + 4B \;\Rightarrow\; B = 2$
$\Rightarrow\; \dfrac{4x+5}{(x+4)(2x-3)} \equiv \dfrac{1}{x+4} + \dfrac{2}{2x-3}$

c) $\dfrac{5x}{x^2+x-6} \equiv \dfrac{5x}{(x+3)(x-2)} \equiv \dfrac{A}{x+3} + \dfrac{B}{x-2}$

$\Rightarrow\; 5x \equiv A(x-2) + B(x+3)$
$x = 2:\; 10 = 5B \;\Rightarrow\; B = 2$
$x = -3:\; -15 = -5A \;\Rightarrow\; A = 3$
$\Rightarrow\; \dfrac{5x}{x^2+x-6} \equiv \dfrac{3}{x+3} + \dfrac{2}{x-2}$

d) $\dfrac{10x}{(x+3)(2x+4)} \equiv \dfrac{5x}{(x+3)(x+2)} \equiv \dfrac{A}{x+3} + \dfrac{B}{x+2}$

$\Rightarrow\; 5x \equiv A(x+2) + B(x+3)$
$x = -3:\; -15 = A(-1) \;\Rightarrow\; A = 15$
$x = -2:\; -10 = B$
$\Rightarrow\; \dfrac{10x}{(x+3)(2x+4)} \equiv \dfrac{15}{x+3} - \dfrac{10}{x+2}$

e) $\dfrac{6x+10}{(2x+1)(2-3x)} \equiv \dfrac{A}{2x+1} + \dfrac{B}{2-3x}$

$\Rightarrow\; 6x + 10 \equiv A(2-3x) + B(2x+1)$
$x = \tfrac{2}{3}:\; 14 = \tfrac{7}{3}B \;\Rightarrow\; B = 6$

$x = -\tfrac{1}{2}:\; 7 = \tfrac{7}{2}A \;\Rightarrow\; A = 2$

$\Rightarrow\; \dfrac{6x+10}{(2x+1)(2-3x)} \equiv \dfrac{2}{2x+1} + \dfrac{6}{2-3x}$

f) $\dfrac{2x+1}{x^2+3x} \equiv \dfrac{2x+1}{(x+3)x} \equiv \dfrac{A}{x+3} + \dfrac{B}{x}$

$\Rightarrow\; 2x + 1 \equiv Ax + B(x+3)$
$x = 0:\; 1 = 3B \;\Rightarrow\; B = \dfrac{1}{3}$
$x = -3:\; -5 = -3A \;\Rightarrow\; A = \dfrac{5}{3}$

$\Rightarrow\; \dfrac{2x+1}{x^2+3x} \equiv \dfrac{5}{3(x+3)} + \dfrac{1}{3x}$

Q25 $\dfrac{2x-5}{(x-5)^2} = \dfrac{A}{(x-5)} + \dfrac{B}{(x-5)^2}$,

so $2x - 5 = A(x-5) + B \;\Rightarrow\; 2x - 5 = Ax - 5A + B$
Equating x coefficients gives: $A = 2$
Equating constants gives:
$-5 = -5A + B \;\Rightarrow\; -5 = -10 + B \;\Rightarrow\; B = 5$.
This gives $\dfrac{2}{(x-5)} + \dfrac{5}{(x-5)^2}$, as required.

Q26 a) $\dfrac{2x+2}{(x+3)^2} \equiv \dfrac{A}{x+3} + \dfrac{B}{(x+3)^2}$

$\Rightarrow\; 2x + 2 \equiv A(x+3) + B$
$x = -3:\; -4 = B$
$x = 0:\; 2 = 3A + B = 3A - 4 \;\Rightarrow\; A = 2$
$\Rightarrow\; \dfrac{2x+2}{(x+3)^2} \equiv \dfrac{2}{x+3} - \dfrac{4}{(x+3)^2}$

b) $\dfrac{-18x+14}{(2x-1)^2(x+2)} \equiv \dfrac{A}{(2x-1)} + \dfrac{B}{(2x-1)^2} + \dfrac{C}{(x+2)}$

$\Rightarrow\; -18x + 14 \equiv A(2x-1)(x+2) + B(x+2) + C(2x-1)^2$
$x = -2:\; 50 = 25C \;\Rightarrow\; C = 2$
$x = \tfrac{1}{2}:\; 5 = 2\tfrac{1}{2}B \;\Rightarrow\; B = 2$
$x = 0:\; 14 = -2A + 2B + C \;\Rightarrow\; 8 = -2A \;\Rightarrow\; A = -4$
$\Rightarrow\; \dfrac{-18x+14}{(2x-1)^2(x+2)} \equiv \dfrac{-4}{(2x-1)} + \dfrac{2}{(2x-1)^2} + \dfrac{2}{(x+2)}$

c) $\dfrac{x-5}{x^3-x^2} \equiv \dfrac{x-5}{x^2(x-1)} \equiv \dfrac{A}{x^2} + \dfrac{B}{x} + \dfrac{C}{(x-1)}$

$\Rightarrow\; x - 5 \equiv A(x-1) + Bx(x-1) + Cx^2$
$x = 1:\; -4 = C$
$x = 0:\; -5 = -A \;\Rightarrow\; A = 5$
$x = -1:\; -6 = -2A + 2B + C \;\Rightarrow\; 8 = 2B \;\Rightarrow\; B = 4$
$\Rightarrow\; \dfrac{x-5}{x^3-x^2} \equiv \dfrac{5}{x^2} + \dfrac{4}{x} - \dfrac{4}{(x-1)}$

Q27 $\dfrac{bx+7}{(x+1)^2(x+2)} = \dfrac{3}{x+1} + \dfrac{2}{(x+1)^2} - \dfrac{3}{x+2}$

$\Rightarrow\; bx + 7 = 3(x+1)(x+2) + 2(x+2) - 3(x+1)^2$
$\qquad = 3(x^2+3x+2) + 2(x+2) - 3(x^2+2x+1)$
$\qquad = 3x^2 + 9x + 6 + 2x + 4 - 3x^2 - 6x - 3$
$\qquad = 5x + 7 \;\Rightarrow\; b = 5$

Exam-Style Questions — Chapter 2

Q1 a) $\dfrac{1}{x} - \dfrac{2x}{x+1} = \dfrac{x+1}{x(x+1)} - \dfrac{2x^2}{x(x+1)}$

$= \dfrac{x+1-2x^2}{x(x+1)} = \dfrac{(2x+1)(1-x)}{x(x+1)}$

[3 marks available — 1 mark for attempting to subtract the algebraic fractions, 1 mark for correct factorised denominator, 1 mark for correct factorised numerator]

b) The vertical asymptotes occur where the denominator h(x) = 0.
$h(x) = x(x+1) = 0 \;\Rightarrow\; x = 0,\; x = -1$.
[2 marks available — 1 mark for each correct asymptote]

Q2 a) Solutions are where the graphs intersect, so sketch the two curves and find where they meet.

    (i) Sketching $y = -f(x)$: $y = f(x)$

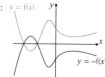

So there are two solutions — at $x = -9$ and $x = -5$. There are no unknown solutions.
[2 marks available — 1 mark for both solutions, 1 mark for stating that there are no unknown solutions]

    (ii) Sketching $y = f(|x|)$ on the interval $-12 \le x \le 0$:

So there is one known solution at $x = 0$. There are two more unknown solutions.
[2 marks available — 1 mark for correct solution, 1 mark for stating that there are two unknown solutions]

    (iii) Sketching $y = f^{-1}(x)$:

So there is one solution, and it is unknown.
[2 marks available — 1 mark for identifying that there is one solution, 1 mark for stating that it is unknown]

b)

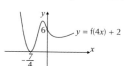

The curve has undergone a horizontal stretch by a factor of $\frac{1}{4}$, which means that all x-coordinates (including the limits of the domain) are divided by 4. The curve is then shifted vertically by +2, which means the y-coordinates increase by 2. So the curve is valid over the interval $-3 \le x \le 3$
[4 marks available — 1 mark for correct curve that touches the x-axis, 1 mark for each correct axis-intercept, 1 mark for correct interval]

Q3 a) E.g. by using algebraic long division:

$$\require{enclose}
\begin{array}{r}
x^2 + 2x + 1 \ \text{r} \ 0 \\
x - 1 \enclose{longdiv}{x^3 + x^2 \ -x - 1} \\
\end{array}$$

$-\ (x^3 - x^2)$
    $2x^2 - x$
$-\ (2x^2 - 2x)$
    $x - 1$
$-\ (x - 1)$
    0

So $g(x) = (x - 1)(x^2 + 2x + 1) = (x - 1)(x + 1)^2$
[3 marks available — 1 mark for a suitable method to find the quadratic factor, 1 mark for the correct quadratic, 1 mark for the correct final answer fully factorised]

b) $\dfrac{x - 5}{x^3 + x^2 - x - 1} \equiv \dfrac{x - 5}{(x - 1)(x + 1)^2}$

$\equiv \dfrac{A}{x - 1} + \dfrac{B}{x + 1} + \dfrac{C}{(x + 1)^2}$

$\Rightarrow x - 5 \equiv A(x + 1)^2 + B(x - 1)(x + 1) + C(x - 1)$
Substitution: $x = 1$: $-4 = 4A \Rightarrow A = -1$
$x = -1$: $-6 = -2C \Rightarrow C = 3$
$x = 0$: $-5 = A - B - C = -1 - B - 3 \Rightarrow B = 1$
So $\dfrac{x - 5}{x^3 + x^2 - x - 1} \equiv \dfrac{3}{(x + 1)^2} + \dfrac{1}{x + 1} - \dfrac{1}{x - 1}$

[4 marks available — 1 mark for writing the expression as the sum of three fractions, 1 mark for finding one unknown, 1 mark for finding the other two unknowns, 1 mark for the correct answer]

Q4 $2x^3 + 9x^2 - 5x - 39 = x + 1 \Rightarrow 2x^3 + 9x^2 - 6x - 40 = 0$
So call this new function $s(x) = 2x^3 + 9x^2 - 6x - 40$, and solve $s(x) = 0$.
$s(2) = 2(2)^3 + 9(2)^2 - 6(2) - 40 = 16 + 36 - 12 - 40 = 0$
So by the Factor Theorem $(x - 2)$ is a factor of $s(x)$.
Dividing $s(x)$ by $(x - 2)$:

$$\begin{array}{r}
2x^2 + 13x + 20 \ \text{r} \ 0 \\
x - 2 \enclose{longdiv}{2x^3 + 9x^2 - 6x - 40} \\
\end{array}$$

$-\ (2x^3 - 4x^2)$
    $13x^2 - 6x$
$-\ (13x^2 - 26x)$
    $20x - 40$
$-\ (20x - 40)$
    0

$s(x) = (x - 2)(2x^2 + 13x + 20) = (x - 2)(2x + 5)(x + 4)$
So the solutions to $r(x) = x + 1$ are $x = 2$, $x = -\frac{5}{2}$, $x = -4$
[6 marks available — 1 mark for rewriting as one single function, 1 mark for finding one factor of this new function, 1 mark for a suitable method to find a quadratic factor, 1 mark for correct quadratic factor, 1 mark for correctly factorising the quadratic, 1 mark for correct solutions]

Q5 a) **(i)** $fg(x) = f\left(\dfrac{1}{x}\right) = 2\left(\dfrac{1}{x}\right) - 3 = \dfrac{2}{x} - 3$
Domain: $x > 0$, Range: $fg(x) > -3$
[2 marks available — 1 mark for correct (or equivalent) expression for fg(x), 1 mark for both domain and range correct]

    (ii) $gf(x) = g(2x - 3) = \dfrac{1}{2x - 3}$
Domain: $x > \dfrac{3}{2}$, Range: $gf(x) > 0$
[2 marks available — 1 mark for correct (or equivalent) expression for fg(x), 1 mark for both domain and range correct]

b) $hf(x)$ is linear, so can be written as $y = mx + c$, where m and c are constants to be found.
$hf(x)$ intercepts the y-axis at -10, so $c = -10$
$\Rightarrow y = mx - 10$.
$hf(x)$ also passes through the point $(0.8, 0)$:
$0 = m(0.8) - 10 \Rightarrow 10 = 0.8m \Rightarrow m = 12.5$
$\Rightarrow hf(x) = 12.5x - 10$
$h(x)$ is also linear, so can be written as $h(x) = ax + b$, where a and b are constants to be found. And you know that $f(x) = 2x - 3$, so $hf(x) = h(2x - 3) = a(2x - 3) + b = 12.5x - 10$
$\Rightarrow 2ax - 3a + b = 12.5x - 10$
Equating coefficients: $2a = 12.5 \Rightarrow a = 6.25$
$-3a + b = -10 \Rightarrow b - 18.75 = -10 \Rightarrow b = 8.75$
So $h(x) = 6.25x + 8.75$
[4 marks available — 1 mark for finding the expression for hf(x), 1 mark for writing h(x) in terms of unknowns, 1 mark for equating coefficients, 1 mark for correct expression for h(x)]

Q6 **a)** **(i)** and **(ii)**

[4 marks available — 1 mark for correct shape and position for y = f(x), 1 mark for correct axis-intercepts labelled for y = f(x), 1 mark for correct shape and position for y = g(x), 1 mark for correct axis-intercept labelled for y = g(x)]

b) Looking at the sketch, f(x) and g(x) intersect twice.
To the left of the y-axis:
$-(2x - 5) = 3(-x) + 4 \Rightarrow x = -1$
To the right of the y-axis:
$-(2x - 5) = 3x + 4 \Rightarrow x = \frac{1}{5}$
f(x) > g(x) between these two values, i.e. when $-1 < x < \frac{1}{5}$
[3 marks available — 1 mark for each correct point of intersection, 1 mark for correct answer]

c) By looking at the sketch, you can see that if you shift g(x) up by 1, then f(x) will never be above g(x) + k, and so there will be no real solutions to the new inequality.
So the smallest value of k is 1 *[1 mark]*

Chapter 3: Trigonometry

3.1 Arcs and Sectors

Exercise 3.1.1 — Radians

Q1 **a)** π **b)** $\frac{3\pi}{4}$ **c)** $\frac{3\pi}{2}$

    d) $\frac{7\pi}{18}$ **e)** $\frac{5\pi}{6}$ **f)** $\frac{5\pi}{12}$

Q2 **a)** 45°   **b)** 90°   **c)** 60°

    d) 450°   **e)** 135°   **f)** 420°

Exercise 3.1.2 — Arc length and sector area

Q1 $s = r\theta = 6 \times 2 = 12$ cm
$A = \frac{1}{2}r^2\theta = \frac{1}{2} \times 6^2 \times 2 = 36$ cm²

Q2 Get the angle in radians:
$46° = \frac{46 \times \pi}{180} = 0.802...$ radians
$s = r\theta = 8 \times 0.802... = 6.4$ cm (1 d.p.)
$A = \frac{1}{2}r^2\theta = \frac{1}{2} \times 8^2 \times 0.802... = 25.7$ cm² (1 d.p.)

Q3 $A = \frac{1}{2}r^2\theta \Rightarrow 6\pi = \frac{1}{2} \times 4^2 \times \theta \Rightarrow 6\pi = 8\theta \Rightarrow \theta = \frac{6\pi}{8} = \frac{3\pi}{4}$

Q4 **a)** $s = r\theta = 5 \times 1.2 = 6$ cm
$A = \frac{1}{2}r^2\theta = \frac{1}{2} \times 5^2 \times 1.2 = 15$ cm²

    b) $s = r\theta = 4 \times 0.6 = 2.4$ cm
$A = \frac{1}{2}r^2\theta = \frac{1}{2} \times 4^2 \times 0.6 = 4.8$ cm²

    c) Get the angle in radians:
$80° = \frac{80 \times \pi}{180} = \frac{4\pi}{9}$ radians
$s = r\theta = 9 \times \frac{4\pi}{9} = 4\pi$ cm = 12.6 cm (3 s.f.)
$A = \frac{1}{2}r^2\theta = \frac{1}{2} \times 9^2 \times \frac{4\pi}{9} = 18\pi$ cm² = 56.5 cm² (3 s.f.)

    d) $s = r\theta = 4 \times \frac{5\pi}{12} = \frac{5\pi}{3}$ cm = 5.24 cm (3 s.f.)
$A = \frac{1}{2}r^2\theta = \frac{1}{2} \times 4^2 \times \frac{5\pi}{12} = \frac{10\pi}{3}$ cm² = 10.5 cm² (3 s.f.)

Q5 Find the radius, r:
$A = \frac{1}{2}r^2\theta \Rightarrow 16.2 = \frac{1}{2} \times r^2 \times 0.9$
$16.2 = 0.45r^2 \Rightarrow 36 = r^2 \Rightarrow r = 6$ cm
$s = r\theta = 6 \times 0.9 = 5.4$ cm

Q6 Get the angle in radians: $20° = \frac{20 \times \pi}{180} = \frac{\pi}{9}$ radians
$s = r\theta = 3 \times \frac{\pi}{9} = \frac{\pi}{3}$ cm
$A = \frac{1}{2}r^2\theta = \frac{1}{2} \times 3^2 \times \frac{\pi}{9} = \frac{\pi}{2}$ cm²

Q7 Find the radius, r: $s = r\theta \Rightarrow r = \frac{s}{\theta} = \frac{7}{1.4} = 5$ cm
$A = \frac{1}{2}r^2\theta = \frac{1}{2} \times 5^2 \times 1.4 = 17.5$ cm²

Q8 Get the angle in radians: $50° = \frac{50 \times \pi}{180} = \frac{5}{18}\pi$ radians
Find the radius, r:
$A = \frac{1}{2}r^2\theta \Rightarrow 20\pi = \frac{1}{2} \times r^2 \times \frac{5}{18}\pi$
$\Rightarrow r^2 = 144 \Rightarrow r = 12$ cm
Then $s = r\theta = 12 \times \frac{5}{18}\pi = \frac{10\pi}{3}$ cm

Q9 $s = r\theta \Rightarrow r\theta = 16\pi$ ①
$A = \frac{1}{2}r^2\theta \Rightarrow \frac{1}{2}r^2\theta = 80\pi \Rightarrow r^2\theta = 160\pi$ ②
② ÷ ①: $\frac{r^2\theta}{r\theta} = \frac{160\pi}{16\pi} \Rightarrow r = 10$ cm
①: $10\theta = 16\pi \Rightarrow \theta = \frac{8\pi}{5} = 5.03$ radians (3 s.f.)

Q10 Area A = $\frac{1}{2}r^2\theta = \frac{1}{2}(2)^2\theta = 2\theta$
Area B = $\frac{1}{2}(2)^2(\pi - \theta) - \frac{1}{2}(1)^2(\pi - \theta)$
$= 2(\pi - \theta) - \frac{1}{2}(\pi - \theta) = \frac{3}{2}(\pi - \theta)$
A = B, so $2\theta = \frac{3}{2}(\pi - \theta) \Rightarrow 4\theta = 3\pi - 3\theta$
$\Rightarrow 7\theta = 3\pi \Rightarrow \theta = \frac{3\pi}{7}$
The angle of the missing sector would be $\pi - \theta$, since they lie on a straight line.

3.2 Small Angle Approximations

Exercise 3.2.1 — The small angle approximations

Q1 **a)** $\sin 0.23 \approx 0.23$
From a calculator, sin 0.23 = 0.228 (3 d.p.)

    b) $\cos 0.01 \approx 1 - \frac{1}{2}(0.01)^2 = 1 - 0.00005 = 0.99995$
From a calculator, cos 0.01 = 0.999950 (6 d.p.)

    c) $\tan 0.18 \approx 0.18$
From a calculator, tan 0.18 = 0.182 (3 d.p.)

Q2 $f(\theta) = \sin \theta + \cos \theta \approx \theta + 1 - \frac{1}{2}\theta^2$

    a) $f(0.3) \approx 0.3 + 1 - \frac{1}{2}(0.3)^2 = 1.255$
f(0.3) = 1.2509 (4 d.p.)

    b) $f(0.5) \approx 0.5 + 1 - \frac{1}{2}(0.5)^2 = 1.375$
f(0.5) = 1.3570 (4 d.p.)

    c) $f(0.25) \approx 0.25 + 1 - \frac{1}{2}(0.25)^2 = 1.21875$
f(0.25) = 1.216316 (6 d.p.)

    d) $f(0.01) \approx 0.01 + 1 - \frac{1}{2}(0.01)^2 = 1.00995$
f(0.01) = 1.009950 (6 d.p.)

Q3 **a)** $\sin \theta \cos \theta \approx \theta\left(1 - \frac{1}{2}\theta^2\right) = \theta - \frac{1}{2}\theta^3$

    b) $\theta \tan 5\theta \sin \theta \approx \theta(5\theta)(\theta) = 5\theta^3$

    c) $\frac{\sin 4\theta \cos 3\theta}{2\theta} \approx \frac{4\theta\left(1 - \frac{1}{2}(3\theta)^2\right)}{2\theta} = 2\left(1 - \frac{9}{2}\theta^2\right) = 2 - 9\theta^2$

    d) $3 \tan \theta + \cos 2\theta \approx 3\theta + 1 - \frac{1}{2}(2\theta)^2 = 1 + 3\theta - 2\theta^2$

    e) $\sin \frac{1}{2}\theta - \cos \theta \approx \frac{1}{2}\theta - 1 + \frac{1}{2}\theta^2 = \frac{1}{2}(\theta^2 + \theta - 2)$

    f) $\frac{\cos \theta - \cos 2\theta}{1 - (\cos 3\theta + 3 \sin \theta \tan \theta)} \approx \frac{\left(1 - \frac{1}{2}\theta^2\right) - \left(1 - \frac{1}{2}(2\theta)^2\right)}{1 - \left(1 - \frac{1}{2}(3\theta)^2\right) - 3(\theta)(\theta)}$

$= \frac{-\frac{1}{2}\theta^2 + 2\theta^2}{\frac{9}{2}\theta^2 - 3\theta^2} = \frac{\frac{3}{2}\theta^2}{\frac{3}{2}\theta^2} = 1$

Q4 **a)** $\mathbf{d} = 6\sin\theta\,\mathbf{i} + 6(1 - \cos\theta)\mathbf{j}$

$|\mathbf{d}| = \sqrt{(6\sin\theta)^2 + (6 - 6\cos\theta)^2}$

$= \sqrt{36\sin^2\theta + 36 - 72\cos\theta + 36\cos^2\theta}$

$= \sqrt{36(\sin^2\theta + \cos^2\theta) + 36 - 72\cos\theta}$

$= \sqrt{36 + 36 - 72\cos\theta}$

$= \sqrt{72(1 - \cos\theta)} = 6\sqrt{2(1 - \cos\theta)}$ as required

b) Arc length $s = 6\theta$

$|\mathbf{d}| = 6\sqrt{2(1 - \cos\theta)} \approx 6\sqrt{2\left(1 - \left(1 - \tfrac{1}{2}\theta^2\right)\right)}$

$= 6\sqrt{2\left(\tfrac{1}{2}\theta^2\right)} = 6\sqrt{\theta^2} = 6\theta = s$ as required

3.3 Inverse Trig Functions
Exercise 3.3.1 — Arcsin, arccos and arctan

Q1 **a)** If $x = \arccos 1$ then $1 = \cos x$ so $x = 0$.

b) If $x = \arcsin\dfrac{\sqrt{3}}{2}$ then $\dfrac{\sqrt{3}}{2} = \sin x$ so $x = \dfrac{\pi}{3}$.

c) If $x = \arctan\sqrt{3}$ then $\sqrt{3} = \tan x$ so $x = \dfrac{\pi}{3}$.

d) If $x = \arccos\dfrac{1}{\sqrt{2}}$ then $\dfrac{1}{\sqrt{2}} = \cos x$ so $x = \dfrac{\pi}{4}$.

Q2 **a)** $y = 2\arccos x$

The graph is the same as $y = \arccos x$ but stretched vertically by a factor of 2, so the y-coordinates of the endpoints and y-intercept are doubled.

b)

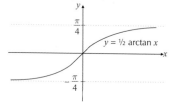

$y = \tfrac{1}{2}\arctan x$

The range is $-\dfrac{\pi}{4} < \dfrac{1}{2}\arctan x < \dfrac{\pi}{4}$.

The graph is the same as $y = \arctan x$ but stretched vertically by a factor of $\dfrac{1}{2}$, so the y-coordinates of the asymptotes are halved.

Q3 $y = \cos^{-1} x$

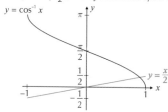

$y = \dfrac{x}{2}$

The graphs intersect once, so there is one real root of the equation $\cos^{-1} x = \dfrac{x}{2}$.

Q4 **a)** $\sin^{-1}(-1) = -\dfrac{\pi}{2}$.

This is one of the endpoints of the arcsin x graph.

b) To find $\cos^{-1}\left(-\dfrac{\sqrt{3}}{2}\right)$, first find the angle a

for which $\cos a = \dfrac{\sqrt{3}}{2}$:

So $\cos\dfrac{\pi}{6} = \dfrac{\sqrt{3}}{2}$.

Now use the CAST diagram to find the negative solutions that lie in the domain $0 \le x \le \pi$:

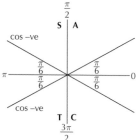

The only negative solution in that domain is $\pi - \dfrac{\pi}{6} = \dfrac{5\pi}{6}$. So $\cos^{-1}\left(-\dfrac{\sqrt{3}}{2}\right) = \dfrac{5\pi}{6}$.

c) To find $\tan^{-1}\left(-\dfrac{1}{\sqrt{3}}\right)$, first find the angle a

for which $\tan a = \dfrac{1}{\sqrt{3}}$:

So $\tan\dfrac{\pi}{6} = \dfrac{1}{\sqrt{3}}$.

Now use the CAST diagram to find the negative solutions that lie in the domain $-\dfrac{\pi}{2} < x < \dfrac{\pi}{2}$:

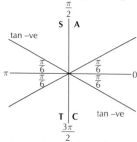

The only negative solution in that domain is $0 - \dfrac{\pi}{6} = -\dfrac{\pi}{6}$. So $\tan^{-1}\left(-\dfrac{1}{\sqrt{3}}\right) = -\dfrac{\pi}{6}$.

d) To find $\sin^{-1}\left(-\dfrac{1}{2}\right)$, first find the angle a

for which $\sin a = \dfrac{1}{2}$:

So $\sin\dfrac{\pi}{6} = \dfrac{1}{2}$.

Now use the CAST diagram to find the negative solutions that lie in the domain $-\dfrac{\pi}{2} \le x \le \dfrac{\pi}{2}$:

The only negative solution in that domain
is $0 - \frac{\pi}{6} = -\frac{\pi}{6}$. So $\sin^{-1}\left(-\frac{1}{2}\right) = -\frac{\pi}{6}$.

Q5 **a)** $\arcsin \frac{1}{2} = \frac{\pi}{6}$, so $\tan\left(\arcsin \frac{1}{2}\right) = \tan \frac{\pi}{6} = \frac{1}{\sqrt{3}}$.

b) This is just the cos function followed by its inverse function so the answer is $\frac{2\pi}{3}$.

c) $\arcsin \frac{1}{2} = \frac{\pi}{6}$, so $\cos\left(\arcsin \frac{1}{2}\right) = \cos \frac{\pi}{6} = \frac{\sqrt{3}}{2}$.

Q6 To find the inverse of the function, first write as
$y = 1 + \sin 2x$, then rearrange to make x the subject:

$\sin 2x = y - 1 \Rightarrow 2x = \sin^{-1}(y - 1) \Rightarrow x = \frac{1}{2}\sin^{-1}(y - 1)$
Now replace x with $f^{-1}(x)$ and y with x:

$f^{-1}(x) = \frac{1}{2}\sin^{-1}(x - 1) = \frac{1}{2}\arcsin(x - 1)$

3.4 Cosec, Sec and Cot
Exercise 3.4.1 — Graphs of cosec, sec and cot

Q1 **a)**
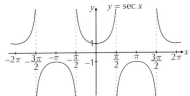

b) The minimum points are at $(-2\pi, 1)$, $(0, 1)$ and $(2\pi, 1)$.
c) The maximum points are at $(-\pi, -1)$ and $(\pi, -1)$.
d) The range is $y \geq 1$ or $y \leq -1$.
You could also say that y is undefined for $-1 < y < 1$.

Q2 **a)**
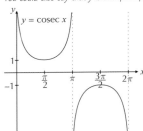

b) There is a maximum at $\left(\frac{3\pi}{2}, -1\right)$ and a minimum at $\left(\frac{\pi}{2}, 1\right)$.
c) The domain is $x \in \mathbb{R}$, $x \neq n\pi$ (where n is an integer).
The range is $y \geq 1$ or $y \leq -1$.
The domain is all real numbers except those for which cosec x is undefined (i.e. at the asymptotes).

Q3 A horizontal translation right by $\frac{\pi}{2}$ (or 90°) or
a horizontal translation left by $\frac{3\pi}{2}$ (or 270°).

Q4 **a)** If $f(x) = \cot x$, then $y = \cot \frac{x}{4} = f\left(\frac{x}{4}\right)$.
This is a horizontal stretch scale factor 4.

b) The period of $y = \cot x$ is 180°, so the period of
$y = \cot \frac{x}{4}$ is 180° × 4 = 720°.

c)
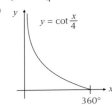

Q5 **a)** $y = 2 + \sec x$ is the graph of $y = \sec x$ translated
vertically up by 2:
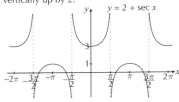

b) The minimum points are at $(-2\pi, 3)$, $(0, 3)$ and $(2\pi, 3)$.
The maximum points are at $(-\pi, 1)$ and $(\pi, 1)$.
The maximum and minimum points have the same x-coordinates as on the graph of y = sec x, but the y-coordinates have all been increased by 2.

c) The domain is $x \in \mathbb{R}$, $x \neq \left(n\pi + \frac{\pi}{2}\right)$ (where n is an integer).
The range is $y \geq 3$ or $y \leq 1$.

Q6 **a)** $y = 2 \operatorname{cosec} 2x$ is the graph of $y = \operatorname{cosec} x$ stretched
horizontally by a factor of $\frac{1}{2}$ and stretched vertically
by a factor of 2.
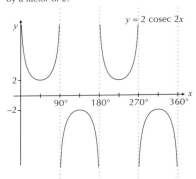

b) The minimum points are at (45°, 2) and (225°, 2).
c) The maximum points are at (135°, −2) and (315°, −2).
d) $y = 2 \operatorname{cosec} 2x$ is undefined when $x = 0°$, 90°, 180°, 270°
and 360°.

Q7 **a)** If $f(x) = \operatorname{cosec} x$, then $y = 2 + 3\operatorname{cosec} x = 3f(x) + 2$,
which is a vertical stretch scale factor 3,
followed by a vertical translation of 2 up.
Vertical transformations do not affect the position of the
asymptotes, so they are in the same position as for the graph
of $y = \operatorname{cosec} x$, i.e. at $n\pi$ or 180n°, where n is an integer.

b) The period of the graph will be the same as
for the graph of $y = \operatorname{cosec} x$, i.e. 360°.
Vertical transformations will not affect how often the graph repeats itself.

c)
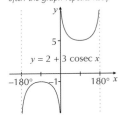

d) The range is $y \geq 5$ or $y \leq -1$.

Exercise 3.4.2 — Evaluating cosec, sec and cot

Q1 **a)** $\operatorname{cosec} 80° = \frac{1}{\sin 80°} = 1.02$

b) $\sec 75° = \frac{1}{\cos 75°} = 3.86$

c) $\cot 30° = \dfrac{1}{\tan 30°} = 1.73$

d) $\sec(-70)° = \dfrac{1}{\cos(-70°)} = 2.92$

e) $3 - \cot 250° = 3 - \dfrac{1}{\tan 250°} = 2.64$

f) $2 \operatorname{cosec} 25° = \dfrac{2}{\sin 25°} = 4.73$

Q2 a) $\sec 3 = \dfrac{1}{\cos 3} = -1.01$

b) $\cot 0.6 = \dfrac{1}{\tan 0.6} = 1.46$

c) $\operatorname{cosec} 1.8 = \dfrac{1}{\sin 1.8} = 1.03$

d) $\sec(-1) = \dfrac{1}{\cos(-1)} = 1.85$

e) $\operatorname{cosec} \dfrac{\pi}{8} = \dfrac{1}{\sin \frac{\pi}{8}} = 2.61$

f) $8 + \cot \dfrac{\pi}{8} = 8 + \dfrac{1}{\tan \frac{\pi}{8}} = 10.4$

g) $\dfrac{1}{1 + \sec \frac{\pi}{10}} = \dfrac{1}{1 + \frac{1}{\cos \frac{\pi}{10}}} = 0.487$

h) $\dfrac{1}{6 + \cot \frac{\pi}{5}} = \dfrac{1}{6 + \frac{1}{\tan \frac{\pi}{5}}} = 0.136$

Q3 a) $\sec 60° = \dfrac{1}{\cos 60°} = \dfrac{1}{\left(\frac{1}{2}\right)} = 2$

b) $\operatorname{cosec} 30° = \dfrac{1}{\sin 30°} = \dfrac{1}{\left(\frac{1}{2}\right)} = 2$

c) $\cot 45° = \dfrac{1}{\tan 45°} = \dfrac{1}{1} = 1$

d) $\operatorname{cosec} \dfrac{\pi}{3} = \dfrac{1}{\sin \frac{\pi}{3}} = \dfrac{1}{\left(\frac{\sqrt{3}}{2}\right)} = \dfrac{2}{\sqrt{3}} = \dfrac{2\sqrt{3}}{3}$

e) $\sec(-180°) = \dfrac{1}{\cos(-180°)} = \dfrac{1}{\cos 180°} = -1$

The graph of y = cos x is symmetrical about the y-axis, so cos (−x) = cos x.

f) $\operatorname{cosec} 135° = \operatorname{cosec} (180° - 45°) = \dfrac{1}{\sin(180° - 45°)}$

The CAST diagram below shows that sin 135° is the same size as sin 45°, and also lies in a positive quadrant for sin:

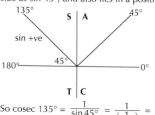

So $\operatorname{cosec} 135° = \dfrac{1}{\sin 45°} = \dfrac{1}{\left(\frac{1}{\sqrt{2}}\right)} = \sqrt{2}$

g) $\cot 330° = \cot (360° - 30°) = \dfrac{1}{\tan(360° - 30°)}$

The CAST diagram below shows that tan 330° is the same size as tan 30°, but lies in a negative quadrant for tan:

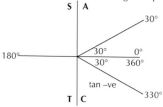

So $\cot 330° = \dfrac{1}{-\tan 30°} = \dfrac{1}{\left(-\frac{1}{\sqrt{3}}\right)} = -\sqrt{3}$

h) $\sec \dfrac{5\pi}{4} = \sec \left(\pi + \dfrac{\pi}{4}\right) = \dfrac{1}{\cos\left(\pi + \frac{\pi}{4}\right)}$

The CAST diagram below shows that $\cos\left(\pi + \dfrac{\pi}{4}\right)$ is the same size as $\cos \dfrac{\pi}{4}$, but lies in a negative quadrant for cos:

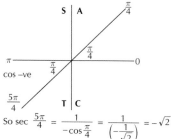

So $\sec \dfrac{5\pi}{4} = \dfrac{1}{-\cos \frac{\pi}{4}} = \dfrac{1}{\left(-\frac{1}{\sqrt{2}}\right)} = -\sqrt{2}$

i) $\operatorname{cosec} \dfrac{5\pi}{3} = \operatorname{cosec} \left(2\pi - \dfrac{\pi}{3}\right) = \dfrac{1}{\sin\left(2\pi - \frac{\pi}{3}\right)}$

The CAST diagram shows that $\sin\left(2\pi - \dfrac{\pi}{3}\right) = -\sin \dfrac{\pi}{3}$, so:

$\dfrac{1}{\sin\left(2\pi - \frac{\pi}{3}\right)} = \dfrac{1}{-\sin \frac{\pi}{3}} = \dfrac{1}{-\left(\frac{\sqrt{3}}{2}\right)} = -\dfrac{2}{\sqrt{3}} = -\dfrac{2\sqrt{3}}{3}$

j) $\operatorname{cosec} \dfrac{2\pi}{3} = \operatorname{cosec} \left(\pi - \dfrac{\pi}{3}\right) = \dfrac{1}{\sin\left(\pi - \frac{\pi}{3}\right)}$

The CAST diagram shows that $\sin\left(\pi - \dfrac{\pi}{3}\right) = \sin \dfrac{\pi}{3}$, so:

$\dfrac{1}{\sin\left(\pi - \frac{\pi}{3}\right)} = \dfrac{1}{\sin \frac{\pi}{3}} = \dfrac{1}{\left(\frac{\sqrt{3}}{2}\right)} = \dfrac{2}{\sqrt{3}} = \dfrac{2\sqrt{3}}{3}$

k) $3 - \cot \dfrac{3\pi}{4} = 3 - \cot \left(\pi - \dfrac{\pi}{4}\right) = 3 - \dfrac{1}{\tan\left(\pi - \frac{\pi}{4}\right)}$

$= 3 - \dfrac{1}{-\tan \frac{\pi}{4}} = 3 - \left(\dfrac{1}{-1}\right) = 4$

l) $\dfrac{\sqrt{3}}{\cot \frac{\pi}{6}} = \dfrac{\sqrt{3}}{\left(\frac{1}{\tan \frac{\pi}{6}}\right)} = \sqrt{3}\left(\tan \dfrac{\pi}{6}\right) = \sqrt{3} \times \dfrac{1}{\sqrt{3}} = 1$

Q4 a) $\dfrac{1}{1 + \sec 60°} = \dfrac{1}{1 + \left(\frac{1}{\cos 60°}\right)} = \dfrac{1}{1 + \frac{1}{\left(\frac{1}{2}\right)}} = \dfrac{1}{3}$

b) $\cot 315° = \cot (360° - 45°) = \dfrac{1}{\tan(360° - 45°)}$

$= \dfrac{1}{-\tan 45°} = -1$, so:

$\dfrac{2}{6 + \cot 315°} = \dfrac{2}{6 + (-1)} = \dfrac{2}{5}$

c) $\dfrac{1}{\sqrt{3} - \sec 30°} = \dfrac{1}{\sqrt{3} - \left(\frac{1}{\cos 30°}\right)}$

$= \dfrac{\cos 30°}{\sqrt{3}(\cos 30°) - 1} = \dfrac{\left(\frac{\sqrt{3}}{2}\right)}{\sqrt{3}\left(\frac{\sqrt{3}}{2}\right) - 1} = \dfrac{\sqrt{3}}{3 - 2} = \sqrt{3}$

d) $1 + \cot 420° = 1 + \cot (360° + 60°) = 1 + \cot 60°$

$= 1 + \dfrac{1}{\tan 60°} = 1 + \dfrac{1}{\sqrt{3}} = \dfrac{3 + \sqrt{3}}{3}$

e) $\cot 150° = \cot(180° - 30°) = \dfrac{1}{\tan(180° - 30°)}$

$= \dfrac{1}{-\tan 30°} = \dfrac{1}{-\left(\frac{1}{\sqrt{3}}\right)} = -\sqrt{3}$, so:

$\dfrac{2}{7 + \sqrt{3}\cot 150°} = \dfrac{2}{7 + \sqrt{3}(-\sqrt{3})} = \dfrac{2}{7 - 3} = \dfrac{1}{2}$

f) $1 - \operatorname{cosec} 330° = 1 - \operatorname{cosec}(360° - 30°)$

$= 1 - \dfrac{1}{\sin(360° - 30°)} = 1 - \dfrac{1}{-\sin 30°} = 1 - \dfrac{1}{-0.5} = 3$, so:

$\dfrac{2}{1 - \operatorname{cosec} 330°} = \dfrac{2}{3}$

Exercise 3.4.3 — Simplifying expressions and solving equations

Q1 a) $\dfrac{1}{\cos x} = \sec x$, so $\sec x + \sec x = 2\sec x$

b) $(\operatorname{cosec}^2 x)(\sin^2 x) = \dfrac{1}{\sin^2 x}(\sin^2 x) = 1$

c) $\dfrac{1}{\tan x} = \cot x$, so $2\cot x + \cot x = 3\cot x$

d) $\dfrac{\sec x}{\operatorname{cosec} x} = \dfrac{\left(\frac{1}{\cos x}\right)}{\left(\frac{1}{\sin x}\right)} = \dfrac{\sin x}{\cos x} = \tan x$

e) $(\cos x)(\operatorname{cosec} x) = \dfrac{\cos x}{\sin x} = \dfrac{1}{\left(\frac{\sin x}{\cos x}\right)} = \dfrac{1}{\tan x} = \cot x$

f) $\dfrac{\operatorname{cosec}^2 x}{\cot x} = \dfrac{\left(\frac{1}{\sin^2 x}\right)}{\left(\frac{1}{\tan x}\right)} = \dfrac{\tan x}{\sin^2 x} = \dfrac{\left(\frac{\sin x}{\cos x}\right)}{\sin^2 x}$

$= \dfrac{\sin x}{\cos x \sin^2 x} = \dfrac{1}{\cos x \sin x} = \sec x \operatorname{cosec} x$

g) $5\cot x - \dfrac{\operatorname{cosec} x}{\sec x} = 5\cot x - \dfrac{\left(\frac{1}{\sin x}\right)}{\left(\frac{1}{\cos x}\right)}$

$= 5\cot x - \cot x = 4\cot x$

h) $\dfrac{1}{\sec^2 x} + \dfrac{1}{\operatorname{cosec}^2 x} = \dfrac{1}{\left(\frac{1}{\cos^2 x}\right)} + \dfrac{1}{\left(\frac{1}{\sin^2 x}\right)} = \cos^2 x + \sin^2 x = 1$

Q2 a) $\sin x \cot x = \sin x \left(\dfrac{1}{\tan x}\right) = \sin x \left(\dfrac{\cos x}{\sin x}\right) = \cos x$

b) $\sec x - \cos x = \dfrac{1}{\cos x} - \cos x = \dfrac{1 - \cos^2 x}{\cos x}$

Use the identity $\sin^2 x + \cos^2 x \equiv 1$:

$= \dfrac{\sin^2 x}{\cos x} = \left(\dfrac{\sin x}{\cos x}\right)\sin x = \tan x \sin x$

c) $\dfrac{\sec x}{\cot x} = \dfrac{\frac{1}{\cos x}}{\frac{1}{\tan x}} = \dfrac{\tan x}{\cos x} = \dfrac{\frac{\sin x}{\cos x}}{\cos x} = \dfrac{\sin x}{\cos^2 x} = \sin x \sec^2 x$

d) $\tan x \operatorname{cosec} x = \left(\dfrac{\sin x}{\cos x}\right)\left(\dfrac{1}{\sin x}\right) = \dfrac{1}{\cos x} = \sec x$

e) $\dfrac{(\tan^2 x)(\operatorname{cosec} x)}{\sin x} = \dfrac{\left(\frac{\sin^2 x}{\cos^2 x}\right)\left(\frac{1}{\sin x}\right)}{\sin x}$

$= \dfrac{\left(\frac{\sin x}{\cos^2 x}\right)}{\sin x} = \dfrac{1}{\cos^2 x} = \sec^2 x$

f) $\operatorname{cosec} x (\sin x + \cos x) = \dfrac{1}{\sin x}(\sin x + \cos x)$

$= \dfrac{\sin x}{\sin x} + \dfrac{\cos x}{\sin x} = 1 + \cot x$

Q3 a) $\sec x = 1.9 \Rightarrow \cos x = \dfrac{1}{1.9} = 0.52631...$

$x = \cos^{-1}(0.52631...) = 58.2°$ (1 d.p.)

There is another positive solution in the interval $0 \le x \le 360°$ at $(360° - 58.2°)$ so $x = 301.8°$ (1 d.p.)

Remember, you can use the graphs or the CAST diagram to find other solutions in the interval.

b) $\cot x = 2.4 \Rightarrow \tan x = 0.41666...$

$\tan^{-1}(0.41666...) = 22.6°$ (1 d.p.)

There is another positive solution in the interval $0 \le x \le 360°$ at $(180° + 22.6°)$, so $x = 202.6°$ (1 d.p.)

c) $\operatorname{cosec} x = -2 \Rightarrow \sin x = -0.5$

$\sin^{-1}(-0.5) = -30°$ which is not in the interval $0° \le x \le 360°$.

There are two negative solutions in the interval $0 \le x \le 360°$ at $(180° + 30°)$ and $(360° - 30°)$, so $x = 210°$ and $330°$.

d) $\sec x = -1.3 \Rightarrow \cos x = -0.76923...$

$\cos^{-1}(-0.76923...) = 140.3°$ (1 d.p.)

There are two negative solutions in the interval $0 \le x \le 360°$ at $140.3°$ and $(360° - 140.3°)$, so $x = 140.3°$ and $219.7°$ (1 d.p.)

e) $\cot x = -2.4 \Rightarrow \tan x = -0.41666...$

$\tan^{-1}(-0.41666...) = -22.6°$ (1 d.p.)

There are two negative solutions in the interval $0 \le x \le 360°$ at $(-22.6° + 180°)$ and $(-22.6° + 360°)$, so $x = 157.4°$ and $337.4°$ (1 d.p.)

f) $\dfrac{1}{2}\operatorname{cosec} x = 0.7 \Rightarrow \operatorname{cosec} x = 1.4 \Rightarrow \sin x = 0.71428...$

$\sin^{-1}(0.71428...) = 45.6°$ (1 d.p.)

There are two positive solutions in the interval $0 \le x \le 360°$ at $45.6°$ and $(180° - 45.6°)$, so $x = 45.6°$ and $134.4°$ (1 d.p.)

g) $4\sec 2x = -7 \Rightarrow \sec 2x = -1.75 \Rightarrow \cos 2x = -0.57142...$

$\cos^{-1}(-0.57142...) = 124.84990...$

You need to find all solutions for x in the interval $0 \le x \le 360°$ so $0 \le 2x \le (2 \times 360°)$ so you'll need to look for solutions for 2x in the interval $0 \le 2x \le 720°$.

There are four negative solutions for $2x$ in the interval $0 \le x \le 720°$ at $124.849...$, $(360° - 124.849...°)$, $(360° + 124.849...°)$ and $(720° - 124.849...°)$ and each of these needs to be divided by 2 to give x. So $x = 62.4°$, $117.6°$, $242.4°$ and $297.6°$ (1 d.p.)

h) $5\cot 3x = 4 \Rightarrow \cot 3x = 0.8 \Rightarrow \tan 3x = 1.25$

$\tan^{-1}(1.25) = 51.3°$ (1 d.p.)

You need to find all solutions for x in the interval $0 \le x \le 360°$ so $0 \le 3x \le (3 \times 360°)$ so you'll need to look for solutions for 3x in the interval $0 \le 3x \le 1080°$.

There are six positive solutions for $3x$ in the interval $0 \le x \le 1080°$ at $51.34...°$, $(180° + 51.34...°)$, $(360° + 51.34...°)$, $(540° + 51.34...°)$, $(720° + 51.34...°)$ and $(900° + 51.34...°)$ and each of these needs to be divided by 3 to give x. So $x = 17.1°$, $77.1°$, $137.1°$, $197.1°$, $257.1°$ and $317.1°$ (1 d.p.)

Q4 a) $\sec x = 2 \Rightarrow \cos x = 0.5 \Rightarrow x = \cos^{-1}(0.5) = \dfrac{\pi}{3}$

There is another positive solution in the interval $0 \le x \le 2\pi$ at $\left(2\pi - \dfrac{\pi}{3}\right)$, so $x = \dfrac{5\pi}{3}$.

b) $\operatorname{cosec} x = -2 \Rightarrow \sin x = -0.5 \Rightarrow x = \sin^{-1}(-0.5) = -\dfrac{\pi}{6}$

There are two negative solutions in the interval $0 \le x \le 2\pi$ at $\left(\pi + \dfrac{\pi}{6}\right)$ and $\left(2\pi - \dfrac{\pi}{6}\right)$, so $x = \dfrac{7\pi}{6}$ and $\dfrac{11\pi}{6}$.

c) $\cot 2x = 1 \Rightarrow \tan 2x = 1 \Rightarrow 2x = \tan^{-1}(1) = \dfrac{\pi}{4}$

Don't forget to double the interval for the next bit — you're looking for solutions for 2x instead of x.

There are 3 other positive solutions for $2x$ in the interval $0 \le 2x \le 4\pi$, at $\left(\pi + \dfrac{\pi}{4}\right)$, $\left(2\pi + \dfrac{\pi}{4}\right)$ and $\left(3\pi + \dfrac{\pi}{4}\right)$, so $x = \dfrac{\pi}{8}$, $\dfrac{5\pi}{8}$, $\dfrac{9\pi}{8}$ and $\dfrac{13\pi}{8}$.

d) $\sec 5x = -1 \Rightarrow \cos 5x = -1 \Rightarrow 5x = \cos^{-1}(-1) = \pi$

In this case you're looking for solutions for 5x — the interval you'll need to look in is $0 \le 5x \le 10\pi$ since $0 \le x \le 2\pi$. Use the fact that the cos graph repeats itself every 2π. $(\pi, -1)$ is a minimum point on the graph, so this will be repeated every 2π.

There are 4 other solutions for $5x$ in the interval $0 \le 5x \le 10\pi$, at 3π, 5π, 7π, and 9π, so $x = \dfrac{\pi}{5}$, $\dfrac{3\pi}{5}$, π, $\dfrac{7\pi}{5}$ and $\dfrac{9\pi}{5}$.

e) $\csc 3x = -\sqrt{2} \implies \sin 3x = -\frac{1}{\sqrt{2}}$

$\implies 3x = \sin^{-1}\left(-\frac{1}{\sqrt{2}}\right) = -\frac{\pi}{4}$, which isn't in the interval.

Remember to multiply the interval by 3 for the next bit — you're looking for solutions for 3x instead of x.

There are six negative solutions in the interval $0 \le 3x \le 6\pi$ at $\left(\pi + \frac{\pi}{4}\right)$, $\left(2\pi - \frac{\pi}{4}\right)$, $\left(3\pi + \frac{\pi}{4}\right)$, $\left(4\pi - \frac{\pi}{4}\right)$, $\left(5\pi + \frac{\pi}{4}\right)$ and

$\left(6\pi - \frac{\pi}{4}\right)$, so $x = \frac{5\pi}{12}, \frac{7\pi}{12}, \frac{13\pi}{12}, \frac{5\pi}{4}, \frac{7\pi}{4}, \frac{23\pi}{12}$.

f) $\cot 4x = \frac{1}{\sqrt{3}} \implies \tan 4x = \sqrt{3} \implies 4x = \tan^{-1}(\sqrt{3}) = \frac{\pi}{3}$

Remember to multiply the interval by 4 to find the solutions for 4x instead of x.

There are eight positive solutions in the interval $0 \le 4x \le 8\pi$ at $\frac{\pi}{3}$, $\left(\pi + \frac{\pi}{3}\right)$, $\left(2\pi + \frac{\pi}{3}\right)$, $\left(3\pi + \frac{\pi}{3}\right)$, $\left(4\pi + \frac{\pi}{3}\right)$, $\left(5\pi + \frac{\pi}{3}\right)$,

$\left(6\pi + \frac{\pi}{3}\right)$, $\left(7\pi + \frac{\pi}{3}\right)$

so $x = \frac{\pi}{12}, \frac{\pi}{3}, \frac{7\pi}{12}, \frac{5\pi}{6}, \frac{13\pi}{12}, \frac{4\pi}{3}, \frac{19\pi}{12}, \frac{11\pi}{6}$.

Q5 $\cot 2x - 4 = -5 \implies \tan 2x = -1 \implies 2x = \tan^{-1}(-1) = -\frac{\pi}{4}$

There are 4 negative solutions for $2x$ in the interval $0 \le 2x \le 4\pi$, at $\left(\pi - \frac{\pi}{4}\right)$, $\left(2\pi - \frac{\pi}{4}\right)$, $\left(3\pi - \frac{\pi}{4}\right)$

and $\left(4\pi - \frac{\pi}{4}\right)$, so $x = \frac{3\pi}{8}, \frac{7\pi}{8}, \frac{11\pi}{8}$ and $\frac{15\pi}{8}$.

Q6 $2 \csc 2x = 3 \implies \sin 2x = \frac{2}{3}$

$2x = \sin^{-1}\left(\frac{2}{3}\right) = 41.81031...°$

There are three other positive solutions for $2x$ in the interval $0 \le 2x \le 720°$ at $(180° - 41.81...°)$, $(360° + 41.81...°)$ and $(540° - 41.81...°)$, so $x = 20.9°, 69.1°, 200.9°$ and $249.1°$ (1 d.p.)

Q7 $-2 \sec x = 4 \implies \cos x = -0.5 \implies x = \cos^{-1}(-0.5) = \frac{2\pi}{3}$

There are 2 negative solutions in the interval $0 \le x \le 2\pi$ at $\frac{2\pi}{3}$ and $\left(2\pi - \frac{2\pi}{3}\right)$, so $x = \frac{2\pi}{3}$ and $\frac{4\pi}{3}$.

Q8 $\sqrt{3} \csc 3x = 2 \implies \sin 3x = \frac{\sqrt{3}}{2} \implies 3x = \sin^{-1}\left(\frac{\sqrt{3}}{2}\right) = \frac{\pi}{3}$

There are 5 other positive solutions in the interval $0 \le 3x \le 6\pi$, at $\left(\pi - \frac{\pi}{3}\right)$, $\left(2\pi + \frac{\pi}{3}\right)$, $\left(3\pi - \frac{\pi}{3}\right)$, $\left(4\pi + \frac{\pi}{3}\right)$

and $\left(5\pi - \frac{\pi}{3}\right)$, so $x = \frac{\pi}{9}, \frac{2\pi}{9}, \frac{7\pi}{9}, \frac{8\pi}{9}, \frac{13\pi}{9}$ and $\frac{14\pi}{9}$.

Q9 a) $\sec^2 x - 2\sqrt{2} \sec x + 2$ factorises to $(\sec x - \sqrt{2})^2$.

$(\sec x - \sqrt{2})^2 = 0 \implies \sec x = \sqrt{2} \implies \cos x = \frac{1}{\sqrt{2}} \implies x = 45°$

b) $2 \cot^2 x + 3 \cot x - 2$ factorises to give $(2 \cot x - 1)(\cot x + 2)$

So $(2 \cot x - 1)(\cot x + 2) = 0$

$\implies \cot x = \frac{1}{2}$ or $\cot x = -2 \implies \tan x = 2$ or $\tan x = -\frac{1}{2}$

The solution for $\tan x = 2$ is $x = 63.4°$.

$\tan^{-1} -\frac{1}{2} = -26.6°$, so the other solution is

$x = -26.6° + 180° = 153.4°$. So $x = 63.4°$ and $153.4°$ (1 d.p.)

Q10 $(\csc x - 3)(2 \tan x + 1) = 0$ means that either $\csc x = 3$ (and so $\sin x = \frac{1}{3}$) or $\tan x = -\frac{1}{2}$.

The solutions for $\sin x = \frac{1}{3}$ are $x = 19.5°$

or $x = 180° - 19.5° = 160.5°$.

The solutions for $\tan x = -\frac{1}{2}$ are

$x = -26.6° + 180° = 153.4°$ or $x = -26.6° + 360° = 333.4°$.

So $x = 19.5°, 160.5°, 153.4°, 333.4°$ (1 d.p.) are all solutions.

3.5 Identities Involving Cosec, Sec and Cot

Exercise 3.5.1 — Using the identities

Q1 $\csc^2 x + 2 \cot^2 x = \csc^2 x + 2(\csc^2 x - 1) = 3 \csc^2 x - 2$

Q2 $\tan^2 x - \frac{1}{\cos^2 x} = \tan^2 x - \sec^2 x = \tan^2 x - (1 + \tan^2 x) = -1$

Q3 $x + \frac{1}{x} = \sec\theta + \tan\theta + \frac{1}{\sec\theta + \tan\theta} = \frac{(\sec\theta + \tan\theta)^2 + 1}{\sec\theta + \tan\theta}$

$= \frac{\sec^2\theta + 2\sec\theta\tan\theta + \tan^2\theta + 1}{\sec\theta + \tan\theta}$

But since $\sec^2\theta = \tan^2\theta + 1$:

$x + \frac{1}{x} = \frac{\sec^2\theta + 2\sec\theta\tan\theta + \sec^2\theta}{\sec\theta + \tan\theta}$

$= \frac{2\sec\theta(\sec\theta + \tan\theta)}{\sec\theta + \tan\theta} = 2\sec\theta$ as required.

Q4 a) $\tan^2 x = 2\sec x + 2 \implies \sec^2 x - 1 = 2\sec x + 2$
$\implies \sec^2 x - 2\sec x - 3 = 0$

b) Solve $\sec^2 x - 2\sec x - 3 = 0$

This factorises to give: $(\sec x - 3)(\sec x + 1) = 0$

So $\sec x = 3 \implies \cos x = \frac{1}{3}$ and $\sec x = -1 \implies \cos x = -1$

Solving these over the interval $0° \le x \le 360°$ gives:

$x = 70.5°, 180°$ and $289.5°$ (1 d.p.)

Just use the graph of cos x or the CAST diagram as usual to find all the solutions in the interval.

Q5 a) $2 \csc^2 x = 5 - 5 \cot x \implies 2(1 + \cot^2 x) = 5 - 5 \cot x$
$\implies 2 \cot^2 x + 5 \cot x - 3 = 0$

b) Solve $2 \cot^2 x + 5 \cot x - 3 = 0$

This factorises to give: $(2 \cot x - 1)(\cot x + 3) = 0$

So $\cot x = \frac{1}{2} \implies \tan x = 2$ and $\cot x = -3 \implies \tan x = -\frac{1}{3}$

Solving these over the interval $-\pi \le x \le \pi$ gives:

$x = -2.03, -0.32, 1.11, 2.82$ (2 d.p.)

Q6 a) $2 \cot^2 A + 5 \csc A = 10$
$\implies 2(\csc^2 A - 1) + 5 \csc A = 10$
$\implies 2 \csc^2 A - 2 + 5 \csc A = 10$
$\implies 2 \csc^2 A + 5 \csc A - 12 = 0$

b) Solve $2 \csc^2 A + 5 \csc A - 12 = 0$

This factorises to give:

$(\csc A + 4)(2 \csc A - 3) = 0$

So $\csc A = -4 \implies \sin A = -\frac{1}{4}$

Or $\csc x = \frac{3}{2} \implies \sin A = \frac{2}{3}$

The solutions (to 1 d.p.) are

$A = 194.5°, 345.5°, 41.8°, 138.2°$.

Q7 $\sec^2 x + \tan x = 1 \implies 1 + \tan^2 x + \tan x = 1$
$\implies \tan^2 x + \tan x = 0 \implies \tan x(\tan x + 1) = 0$

So $\tan x = 0 \implies x = 0, \pi, 2\pi$.

And $\tan x = -1 \implies x = \frac{3\pi}{4}, \frac{7\pi}{4}$.

Q8 a) $\csc^2\theta + 2 \cot^2\theta = 2 \implies \csc^2\theta + 2(\csc^2\theta - 1) = 2$
$\implies 3 \csc^2\theta - 2 = 2 \implies 3 \csc^2\theta = 4$

$\implies \csc^2\theta = \frac{4}{3} \implies \csc\theta = \pm\frac{2}{\sqrt{3}} \implies \sin\theta = \pm\frac{\sqrt{3}}{2}$

b) Solving $\sin\theta = \pm\frac{\sqrt{3}}{2}$ over the interval $0° \le x \le 180°$ gives: $\theta = 60°, 120°$.

Q9 $\sec^2 x = 3 + \tan x \implies (1 + \tan^2 x) = 3 + \tan x$
$\implies \tan^2 x - \tan x - 2 = 0 \implies (\tan x - 2)(\tan x + 1) = 0$

So $\tan x = 2$ or $\tan x = -1$.

Solving over the interval $0° \le x \le 360°$ gives:

$x = 63.4°, 135°, 243.4°$ and $315°$ (1 d.p.)

Q10 $\cot^2 x + \csc^2 x = 7 \implies \cot^2 x + (1 + \cot^2 x) = 7$
$\implies 2 \cot^2 x + 1 = 7 \implies \cot^2 x = 3 \implies \cot x = \pm\sqrt{3} \implies \tan x = \pm\frac{1}{\sqrt{3}}$

Solving over the interval $0 \le x \le 2\pi$ gives:

$x = \frac{\pi}{6}$ and $\frac{7\pi}{6}$ when $\tan x = +\frac{1}{\sqrt{3}}$

and $x = \frac{5\pi}{6}$ and $\frac{11\pi}{6}$ when $\tan x = -\frac{1}{\sqrt{3}}$.

Q11 $\tan^2 x + 5 \sec x + 7 = 0 \implies (\sec^2 x - 1) + 5 \sec x + 7 = 0$
$\implies \sec^2 x + 5 \sec x + 6 = 0 \implies (\sec x + 2)(\sec x + 3) = 0$
So $\sec x = -2 \implies \cos x = -\frac{1}{2}$ and $\sec x = -3 \implies \cos x = -\frac{1}{3}$
Solving over the interval $0 \le x \le 2\pi$ gives:
$x = 1.91, 2.09, 4.19$ and 4.37 (2 d.p.)

Q12 Drawing a right-angled triangle will help to solve this question:

$\tan \theta = \frac{60}{11}$

Notice that $180° \le \theta \le 270°$ — this puts us in the 3rd quadrant of the CAST diagram so sin will be –ve, cos will be –ve and tan will be +ve.

a) From the triangle, $\sin \theta = -\frac{\text{opp}}{\text{hyp}} = -\frac{60}{61}$.

b) $\cos \theta = -\frac{\text{adj}}{\text{hyp}} = -\frac{11}{61} \implies \sec \theta = \frac{1}{\left(-\frac{11}{61}\right)} = -\frac{61}{11}$.

c) $\csc \theta = \frac{1}{\sin \theta} = \frac{1}{\left(-\frac{60}{61}\right)} = -\frac{61}{60}$.

Q13 Drawing a right-angled triangle will help to solve this question:

$\csc \theta = -\frac{17}{15}$

$\sin \theta = -\frac{15}{17}$

Notice that $180° \le \theta \le 270°$ — this puts us in the 3rd quadrant of the CAST diagram so sin will be –ve, cos will be –ve and tan will be +ve.

a) $\cos \theta = -\frac{\text{adj}}{\text{hyp}} = -\frac{8}{17}$.

b) $\sec \theta = \frac{1}{\cos \theta} = -\frac{17}{8}$.

c) $\tan \theta = \frac{\text{opp}}{\text{adj}} = \frac{15}{8}$ so $\cot \theta = \frac{1}{\tan \theta} = \frac{8}{15}$.

Q14 $\cos x = \frac{1}{6} \implies \sec x = 6 \implies \sec^2 x = 36$
So $1 + \tan^2 x = 36 \implies \tan^2 x = 35 \implies \tan x = \pm\sqrt{35}$

Exercise 3.5.2 — Proving other identities

Q1 a) $\sec^2 \theta - \csc^2 \theta \equiv (1 + \tan^2 \theta) - (1 + \cot^2 \theta) \equiv \tan^2 \theta - \cot^2 \theta$

b) $\tan^2 \theta - \cot^2 \theta$ is the difference of two squares, and so can be written as $(\tan \theta + \cot \theta)(\tan \theta - \cot \theta)$.
So is $\sec^2 \theta - \csc^2 \theta$, so it can be written $(\sec \theta + \csc \theta)(\sec \theta - \csc \theta)$.
So using the result from part a),
$(\sec \theta + \csc \theta)(\sec \theta - \csc \theta) \equiv (\tan \theta + \cot \theta)(\tan \theta - \cot \theta)$.

Q2 $\csc x - \sin x \equiv \frac{1}{\sin x} - \sin x \equiv \frac{1}{\sin x} - \frac{\sin^2 x}{\sin x}$
$\equiv \frac{1 - \sin^2 x}{\sin x} \equiv \frac{\cos^2 x}{\sin x} \equiv \cos x \frac{\cos x}{\sin x} \equiv \cos x \cot x$

Q3 First expand the bracket:
$(\tan x + \cot x)^2 \equiv \tan^2 x + \cot^2 x + 2 \tan x \cot x$
$\equiv \tan^2 x + \cot^2 x + \frac{2 \tan x}{\tan x}$
$\equiv \tan^2 x + \cot^2 x + 2$
Split up that '+2' into two lots of '+1' so it starts to resemble the identities...
$\equiv (1 + \tan^2 x) + (1 + \cot^2 x)$
$\equiv \sec^2 x + \csc^2 x$

Q4 $\frac{1 - \sec x}{\tan x} \equiv \frac{1 - \frac{1}{\cos x}}{\frac{\sin x}{\cos x}} \equiv \frac{\cos x - 1}{\sin x} \equiv \frac{\cos x}{\sin x} - \frac{1}{\sin x}$
$\equiv \cot x - \csc x$

Q5 $\tan^2 x + \cos^2 x \equiv (\sec^2 x - 1) + (1 - \sin^2 x) \equiv \sec^2 x - \sin^2 x$
This is the difference of two squares...
$\equiv (\sec x + \sin x)(\sec x - \sin x)$

Q6 $(\sec x + \cot x)(\sec x - \cot x) \equiv \sec^2 x - \cot^2 x$
$\equiv (1 + \tan^2 x) - (\csc^2 x - 1) \equiv \tan^2 x - \csc^2 x + 2$

Q7 $\sec^2 \theta \csc^2 \theta \equiv (1 + \tan^2 \theta)(1 + \cot^2 \theta)$
$\equiv 1 + \cot^2 \theta + \tan^2 \theta + \tan^2 \theta \cot^2 \theta$
$\equiv 1 + \cot^2 \theta + \tan^2 \theta + (\tan^2 \theta)\left(\frac{1}{\tan^2 \theta}\right)$
$\equiv 1 + \cot^2 \theta + \tan^2 \theta + 1 \equiv 2 + \cot^2 \theta + \tan^2 \theta$

Q8 $\frac{\sec^2 x + 1}{\tan^2 x} \equiv \frac{(\sec^2 x + 1)(\sec^2 x - 1)}{\tan^2 x(\sec^2 x - 1)}$
The numerator on the right-hand side of the identity is the difference of two squares, so you multiply the top and bottom of the fraction on the left by $(\sec^2 x - 1)$.
$\equiv \frac{\sec^4 x - 1}{\tan^2 x(\sec^2 x - 1)} \equiv \frac{\sec^4 x - 1}{\tan^2 x(\tan^2 x)} \equiv \frac{\sec^4 x - 1}{\tan^4 x}$
You could also start by multiplying top and bottom by $\tan^2 x$.

Q9 $\frac{\cos \theta}{\sin \theta} + \frac{\sin \theta}{\cos \theta} \equiv \frac{\cos \theta \cos \theta}{\sin \theta \cos \theta} + \frac{\sin \theta \sin \theta}{\sin \theta \cos \theta} \equiv \frac{\cos^2 \theta + \sin^2 \theta}{\sin \theta \cos \theta}$
$\equiv \frac{1}{\sin \theta \cos \theta} \equiv \frac{1}{\sin \theta} \times \frac{1}{\cos \theta} \equiv \csc \theta \sec \theta$

Q10 $\frac{(\sec x - \tan x)(\tan x + \sec x)}{\csc x - \cot x} \equiv \frac{\sec^2 x - \tan^2 x}{\csc x - \cot x}$
$\equiv \frac{(1 + \tan^2 x) - \tan^2 x}{\csc x - \cot x} \equiv \frac{1}{\csc x - \cot x}$
Multiply top and bottom by $(\csc x + \cot x)$...
$\frac{1}{\csc x - \cot x} \equiv \frac{\csc x + \cot x}{(\csc x - \cot x)(\csc x + \cot x)}$
$\equiv \frac{\csc x + \cot x}{\csc^2 x - \cot^2 x} \equiv \frac{\csc x + \cot x}{(1 + \cot^2 x) - \cot^2 x} \equiv \cot x + \csc x$

Q11 $\frac{\cot x}{1 + \csc x} + \frac{1 + \csc x}{\cot x} \equiv \frac{\cot^2 x + (1 + \csc x)^2}{\cot x(1 + \csc x)}$
$\equiv \frac{(\csc^2 x - 1) + (1 + 2\csc x + \csc^2 x)}{\cot x(1 + \csc x)}$
$\equiv \frac{2\csc x(1 + \csc x)}{\cot x(1 + \csc x)} \equiv \frac{2\csc x}{\cot x} \equiv \frac{2\tan x}{\sin x}$
$\equiv \frac{2\sin x}{\sin x \cos x} \equiv \frac{2}{\cos x} \equiv 2 \sec x$

Q12 $\frac{\csc x + 1}{\csc x - 1} \equiv \frac{(\csc x + 1)(\csc x + 1)}{(\csc x - 1)(\csc x + 1)}$
$\equiv \frac{\csc^2 x + 2\csc x + 1}{\csc^2 x - 1} \equiv \frac{\csc^2 x + 2\csc x + 1}{(1 + \cot^2 x) - 1}$
$\equiv \frac{\csc^2 x + 2\csc x + 1}{\cot^2 x} \equiv \frac{\csc^2 x}{\cot^2 x} + \frac{2\csc x}{\cot^2 x} + \frac{1}{\cot^2 x}$
$\equiv \frac{\tan^2 x}{\sin^2 x} + \frac{2\tan^2 x}{\sin x} + \tan^2 x \equiv \frac{\sin^2 x}{\cos^2 x \sin^2 x} + \frac{2\sin^2 x}{\cos^2 x \sin x} + \tan^2 x$
$\equiv \frac{1}{\cos^2 x} + \frac{2\sin x}{\cos x \cos x} + \tan^2 x \equiv \frac{1}{\cos^2 x} + \frac{2\tan x}{\cos x} + \tan^2 x$
$\equiv \sec^2 x + 2\tan x \sec x + (\sec^2 x - 1) \equiv 2\sec^2 x + 2\tan x \sec x - 1$

3.6 The Addition Formulas

Exercise 3.6.1 — Finding exact values

Q1 a) $\cos 72° \cos 12° + \sin 72° \sin 12°$
$= \cos(72° - 12°) = \cos 60° = \frac{1}{2}$

b) $\cos 13° \cos 17° - \sin 13° \sin 17°$
$= \cos(13° + 17°) = \cos 30° = \frac{\sqrt{3}}{2}$

c) $\frac{\tan 12° + \tan 18°}{1 - \tan 12° \tan 18°} = \tan(12° + 18°) = \tan 30° = \frac{1}{\sqrt{3}}$

d) $\frac{\tan 500° - \tan 140°}{1 + \tan 500° \tan 140°} = \tan(500° - 140°) = \tan 360° = 0$

e) $\sin 35° \cos 10° + \cos 35° \sin 10° = \sin(35° + 10°)$
$= \sin 45° = \frac{1}{\sqrt{2}}$

f) $\sin 69° \cos 9° - \cos 69° \sin 9° = \sin(69° - 9°) = \sin 60° = \frac{\sqrt{3}}{2}$

Q2 **a)** $\sin \frac{2\pi}{3} \cos \frac{\pi}{2} - \cos \frac{2\pi}{3} \sin \frac{\pi}{2} = \sin \left(\frac{2\pi}{3} - \frac{\pi}{2}\right)$

$\qquad\qquad = \sin \frac{\pi}{6} = \frac{1}{2}$

b) $\cos 4\pi \cos 3\pi + \sin 4\pi \sin 3\pi = \cos (4\pi - 3\pi) = \cos \pi = -1$

c) $\dfrac{\tan \frac{5\pi}{12} + \tan \frac{5\pi}{4}}{1 - \tan \frac{5\pi}{12} \tan \frac{5\pi}{4}} = \tan \left(\frac{5\pi}{12} + \frac{5\pi}{4}\right)$

$\qquad = \tan \frac{5\pi}{3} = \tan \left(2\pi - \frac{\pi}{3}\right) = -\tan \frac{\pi}{3} = -\sqrt{3}$

d) $\cos \frac{\pi}{9} \cos \frac{5\pi}{9} - \sin \frac{\pi}{9} \sin \frac{5\pi}{9} = \cos \left(\frac{\pi}{9} + \frac{5\pi}{9}\right)$

$\qquad = \cos \left(\frac{2\pi}{3}\right) = -0.5$

Q3 **a)** $\sin (5x - 2x) = \sin 3x$

b) $\cos (4x + 6x) = \cos 10x$

c) $\tan (7x + 3x) = \tan 10x$

d) $5 \sin (2x + 3x) = 5 \sin 5x$

e) $8 \cos (7x - 5x) = 8 \cos 2x$

f) $\tan (8x - 5x) = \tan 3x$

Q4 Before answering a)-d), calculate cos x and sin y:

$\sin x = \frac{5}{13} \implies \sin^2 x = \frac{25}{169}$

$\implies \cos^2 x = 1 - \frac{25}{169} = \frac{144}{169} \implies \cos x = \frac{12}{13}$

x is acute, meaning cos x must be positive, so take the positive square root.

$\cos y = \frac{24}{25} \implies \cos^2 y = \frac{576}{625}$

$\qquad \implies \sin^2 y = 1 - \frac{576}{625} = \frac{49}{625} \implies \sin y = \frac{7}{25}$

Again, y is acute, so sin y must be positive, so you can take the positive square root. You could have used the triangle method to work out sin y and cos x instead.

a) $\sin (x - y) = \sin x \cos y - \cos x \sin y$

$= \left(\frac{5}{13} \times \frac{24}{25}\right) - \left(\frac{12}{13} \times \frac{7}{25}\right) = \left(\frac{120}{325}\right) - \left(\frac{84}{325}\right) = \frac{36}{325}$

b) $\cos (x + y) = \cos x \cos y - \sin x \sin y$

$= \left(\frac{12}{13} \times \frac{24}{25}\right) - \left(\frac{5}{13} \times \frac{7}{25}\right) = \left(\frac{288}{325}\right) - \left(\frac{35}{325}\right) = \frac{253}{325}$

c) $\cos (x - y) = \cos x \cos y + \sin x \sin y$

$= \left(\frac{12}{13} \times \frac{24}{25}\right) + \left(\frac{5}{13} \times \frac{7}{25}\right) = \left(\frac{288}{325}\right) + \left(\frac{35}{325}\right) = \frac{323}{325}$

d) $\tan (x + y) = \dfrac{\sin (x + y)}{\cos (x + y)}$

$\sin (x + y) = \sin x \cos y + \cos x \sin y$

$\qquad = \left(\frac{120}{325}\right) + \left(\frac{84}{325}\right) = \frac{204}{325}$, so:

$\tan (x + y) = \dfrac{\left(\frac{204}{325}\right)}{\left(\frac{253}{325}\right)} = \frac{204}{253}$

Q5 Before answering a)-d), calculate cos x and sin y:

$\sin x = \frac{3}{4} \implies \sin^2 x = \frac{9}{16}$

$\implies \cos^2 x = 1 - \frac{9}{16} = \frac{7}{16} \implies \cos x = \frac{\sqrt{7}}{4}$

x is acute, meaning cos x must be positive, so take the positive square root.

$\cos y = \frac{3}{\sqrt{10}} \implies \cos^2 y = \frac{9}{10}$

$\qquad \implies \sin^2 y = 1 - \frac{9}{10} = \frac{1}{10} \implies \sin y = \frac{1}{\sqrt{10}}$

Again, y is acute, so sin y must be positive, so you can take the positive square root. If you don't like using this method, you can use the triangle method to work out sin y and cos x.

a) $\sin (x + y) = \sin x \cos y + \cos x \sin y$

$= \left(\frac{3}{4} \times \frac{3}{\sqrt{10}}\right) + \left(\frac{\sqrt{7}}{4} \times \frac{1}{\sqrt{10}}\right) = \frac{9 + \sqrt{7}}{4\sqrt{10}} = \frac{9\sqrt{10} + \sqrt{70}}{40}$

b) $\cos (x - y) = \cos x \cos y + \sin x \sin y$

$= \left(\frac{\sqrt{7}}{4} \times \frac{3}{\sqrt{10}}\right) + \left(\frac{3}{4} \times \frac{1}{\sqrt{10}}\right) = \frac{3\sqrt{7} + 3}{4\sqrt{10}} = \frac{3\sqrt{70} + 3\sqrt{10}}{40}$

c) $\operatorname{cosec} (x + y) = \dfrac{1}{\sin (x + y)} = \dfrac{40}{9\sqrt{10} + \sqrt{70}} = \frac{18\sqrt{10} - 2\sqrt{70}}{37}$

d) $\sec (x - y) = \dfrac{1}{\cos (x - y)} = \dfrac{40}{3\sqrt{70} + 3\sqrt{10}} = \frac{2\sqrt{70} - 2\sqrt{10}}{9}$

Q6 $\cos \frac{\pi}{12} = \cos \left(\frac{\pi}{4} - \frac{\pi}{6}\right) = \cos \frac{\pi}{4} \cos \frac{\pi}{6} + \sin \frac{\pi}{4} \sin \frac{\pi}{6}$

$\qquad = \left(\frac{1}{\sqrt{2}} \times \frac{\sqrt{3}}{2}\right) + \left(\frac{1}{\sqrt{2}} \times \frac{1}{2}\right) = \frac{\sqrt{3} + 1}{2\sqrt{2}}$

Now rationalise the denominator...

$\qquad = \dfrac{(\sqrt{3} + 1) \times \sqrt{2}}{(2\sqrt{2}) \times \sqrt{2}} = \frac{\sqrt{6} + \sqrt{2}}{4}$

Q7 $\sin 75° = \sin (30° + 45°) = \sin 30° \cos 45° + \cos 30° \sin 45°$

$= \left(\frac{1}{2} \times \frac{1}{\sqrt{2}}\right) + \left(\frac{\sqrt{3}}{2} \times \frac{1}{\sqrt{2}}\right) = \frac{1 + \sqrt{3}}{2\sqrt{2}} = \frac{(1 + \sqrt{3}) \times \sqrt{2}}{(2\sqrt{2}) \times \sqrt{2}} = \frac{\sqrt{6} + \sqrt{2}}{4}$

Q8 $\tan 75° = \tan (45° + 30°) = \dfrac{\tan 45° + \tan 30°}{1 - \tan 45° \tan 30°}$

$= \dfrac{1 + \frac{1}{\sqrt{3}}}{1 - 1 \times \frac{1}{\sqrt{3}}} = \dfrac{\left(\frac{\sqrt{3} + 1}{\sqrt{3}}\right)}{\left(\frac{\sqrt{3} - 1}{\sqrt{3}}\right)} = \frac{\sqrt{3} + 1}{\sqrt{3} - 1}.$

Exercise 3.6.2 — Simplifying, solving equations and proving identities

Q1 $\tan (A - B) \equiv \dfrac{\sin (A - B)}{\cos (A - B)} \equiv \dfrac{\sin A \cos B - \cos A \sin B}{\cos A \cos B + \sin A \sin B}$

Divide through by cos A cos B...

$\equiv \dfrac{\left(\frac{\sin A \cos B}{\cos A \cos B}\right) - \left(\frac{\cos A \sin B}{\cos A \cos B}\right)}{\left(\frac{\cos A \cos B}{\cos A \cos B}\right) + \left(\frac{\sin A \sin B}{\cos A \cos B}\right)} \equiv \dfrac{\left(\frac{\sin A}{\cos A}\right) - \left(\frac{\sin B}{\cos B}\right)}{1 + \left(\frac{\sin A}{\cos A}\right)\left(\frac{\sin B}{\cos B}\right)}$

Now use tan = sin / cos...

$\equiv \dfrac{\tan A - \tan B}{1 + \tan A \tan B}$

Q2 **a)** $\dfrac{\cos (A - B) - \cos (A + B)}{\cos A \sin B}$

$\equiv \dfrac{(\cos A \cos B + \sin A \sin B) - (\cos A \cos B - \sin A \sin B)}{\cos A \sin B}$

$\equiv \dfrac{2 \sin A \sin B}{\cos A \sin B} \equiv \dfrac{2 \sin A}{\cos A} \equiv 2 \tan A$

b) $\frac{1}{2} [\cos (A - B) - \cos (A + B)]$

$\equiv \frac{1}{2} [(\cos A \cos B + \sin A \sin B) - (\cos A \cos B - \sin A \sin B)]$

$\equiv \frac{1}{2} (2 \sin A \sin B) \equiv \sin A \sin B$

c) $\sin (x + 90°) \equiv \sin x \cos 90° + \cos x \sin 90°$

$\qquad\qquad \equiv \sin x (0) + \cos x (1) \equiv \cos x$

d) $\cos (x + 180°) \equiv \cos x \cos 180° - \sin x \sin 180°$

$\qquad\qquad \equiv \cos x (-1) - \sin x (0) \equiv -\cos x$

Q3 $4 \sin x \cos \frac{\pi}{3} - 4 \cos x \sin \frac{\pi}{3} = \cos x$

$\implies 2 \sin x - 2\sqrt{3} \cos x = \cos x \implies 2 \sin x = (1 + 2\sqrt{3}) \cos x$

$\implies \dfrac{\sin x}{\cos x} = \dfrac{1 + 2\sqrt{3}}{2} = \tan x \implies x = -1.99$ and 1.15 (2 d.p.)

Q4 **a)** $\tan \left(-\frac{\pi}{12}\right) = \tan \left(\frac{\pi}{6} - \frac{\pi}{4}\right) \equiv \dfrac{\tan \frac{\pi}{6} - \tan \frac{\pi}{4}}{1 + \tan \frac{\pi}{6} \tan \frac{\pi}{4}}$

$\equiv \dfrac{\frac{1}{\sqrt{3}} - 1}{1 + \frac{1}{\sqrt{3}}} \equiv \dfrac{1 - \sqrt{3}}{\sqrt{3} + 1}$

Now rationalise the denominator...

$\equiv \dfrac{1 - \sqrt{3}}{\sqrt{3} + 1} \times \dfrac{\sqrt{3} - 1}{\sqrt{3} - 1} \equiv \dfrac{2\sqrt{3} - 4}{2} \equiv \sqrt{3} - 2$

b) $\cos x = \cos x \cos \frac{\pi}{6} - \sin x \sin \frac{\pi}{6}$

$\Rightarrow \cos x = \frac{\sqrt{3}}{2} \cos x - \frac{1}{2} \sin x \Rightarrow (2 - \sqrt{3}) \cos x = -\sin x$

$\Rightarrow \frac{\sin x}{\cos x} = \tan x = \sqrt{3} - 2$

From a), $\tan\left(-\frac{\pi}{12}\right) = \sqrt{3} - 2$, so one solution for x is $-\frac{\pi}{12}$.

To get an answer in the correct interval, add π, since $\tan x$ repeats itself every π radians.

So $x = \frac{11\pi}{12}$.

Q5 $2 \sin(x + 30°) \equiv 2 \sin x \cos 30° + 2 \cos x \sin 30°$

$\equiv 2 \sin x \left(\frac{\sqrt{3}}{2}\right) + 2 \cos x \left(\frac{1}{2}\right) \equiv \sqrt{3} \sin x + \cos x$

Q6 **a)** $\sin(\theta - 45°) \equiv \sin \theta \cos 45° - \cos \theta \sin 45°$

$\equiv \frac{1}{\sqrt{2}} \sin \theta - \frac{1}{\sqrt{2}} \cos \theta \equiv \frac{1}{\sqrt{2}} (\sin \theta - \cos \theta)$

b) $4 \sin(\theta - 45°) = \sqrt{2} \cos \theta \Rightarrow \frac{4}{\sqrt{2}} (\sin \theta - \cos \theta) = \sqrt{2} \cos \theta$

$\Rightarrow \sin \theta - \cos \theta = \frac{1}{2} \cos \theta \Rightarrow \sin \theta = \frac{3}{2} \cos \theta$

$\Rightarrow \tan \theta = \frac{3}{2} \Rightarrow \theta = \tan^{-1}\left(\frac{3}{2}\right) \Rightarrow \theta = 56.30...°$

There is another positive solution at $180° + 56.30...°$ so $\theta = 56.3°$ and $236°$ (3 s.f.)

Q7 $\tan\left(\frac{\pi}{3} - x\right) \equiv \frac{\tan \frac{\pi}{3} - \tan x}{1 + \tan \frac{\pi}{3} \tan x} \equiv \frac{\sqrt{3} - \tan x}{1 + \sqrt{3} \tan x}$

Q8 $\tan(A + B) = \frac{\tan A + \tan B}{1 - \tan A \tan B} = \frac{1}{4}$

$\Rightarrow \frac{\frac{3}{8} + \tan B}{1 - \frac{3}{8} \tan B} = \frac{1}{4} \Rightarrow \frac{3}{8} + \tan B = \frac{1}{4}\left(1 - \frac{3}{8} \tan B\right)$

$\Rightarrow \frac{3}{8} + \tan B = \frac{1}{4} - \frac{3}{32} \tan B$

$\Rightarrow \tan B + \frac{3}{32} \tan B = \frac{1}{4} - \frac{3}{8} = -\frac{1}{8}$

$\Rightarrow \frac{35}{32} \tan B = -\frac{1}{8} \Rightarrow \tan B = -\frac{1}{8} \times \frac{32}{35} = -\frac{4}{35}$

Q9 Starting with the addition formulas for sin:
$\sin(x + y) \equiv \sin x \cos y + \cos x \sin y$
$\sin(x - y) \equiv \sin x \cos y - \cos x \sin y$

So $\sin(x + y) + \sin(x - y)$
$\equiv \sin x \cos y + \cos x \sin y + \sin x \cos y - \cos x \sin y \equiv 2 \sin x \cos y$

Substitute $A = x + y$ and $B = x - y$.

Then $A + B = 2x$ and $A - B = 2y$, so $x = \left(\frac{A+B}{2}\right)$ and $y = \left(\frac{A-B}{2}\right)$.

Putting this back into the identity gives:
$\sin A + \sin B \equiv 2 \sin\left(\frac{A+B}{2}\right) \cos\left(\frac{A-B}{2}\right)$

Q10 **a)** $\sin x \cos y + \cos x \sin y = 4 \cos x \cos y + 4 \sin x \sin y$

Dividing through by $\cos x \cos y$ gives:

$\frac{\sin x}{\cos x} + \frac{\sin y}{\cos y} = 4 + \frac{4 \sin x \sin y}{\cos x \cos y}$

$\Rightarrow \tan x + \tan y = 4 + 4 \tan x \tan y$

$\Rightarrow \tan x - 4 \tan x \tan y = 4 - \tan y$

$\Rightarrow \tan x (1 - 4 \tan y) = 4 - \tan y \Rightarrow \tan x = \frac{4 - \tan y}{1 - 4 \tan y}$

b) $\tan x = \frac{4 - \tan \frac{\pi}{4}}{1 - 4 \tan \frac{\pi}{4}}$

Comparing the equation you have to solve to the one in part a) you can see that $y = \frac{\pi}{4}$.

$\Rightarrow \tan x = \frac{4 - 1}{1 - 4} = -1 \Rightarrow x = \frac{3\pi}{4}$ and $\frac{7\pi}{4}$

Q11 **a)** Use the sin addition formula on $\sin(\theta + 45°)$:
$\sqrt{2} (\sin \theta \cos 45° + \cos \theta \sin 45°) = 3 \cos \theta$
$\sqrt{2}\left(\frac{1}{\sqrt{2}} \sin \theta + \frac{1}{\sqrt{2}} \cos \theta\right) = 3 \cos \theta$

$\sin \theta + \cos \theta = 3 \cos \theta \Rightarrow \sin \theta = 2 \cos \theta$
$\frac{\sin \theta}{\cos \theta} = 2 \Rightarrow \tan \theta = 2$
So $\theta = 63.43°$ (2 d.p.) and $63.43° + 180° = 243.43°$ (2 d.p.).

b) Use the cos addition formula:
$2 \cos\left(\theta - \frac{2\pi}{3}\right) - 5 \sin \theta = 0$
$2\left(\cos \theta \cos \frac{2\pi}{3} + \sin \theta \sin \frac{2\pi}{3}\right) - 5 \sin \theta = 0$
$2\left(-\frac{1}{2} \cos \theta + \frac{\sqrt{3}}{2} \sin \theta\right) - 5 \sin \theta = 0$
$-\cos \theta + \sqrt{3} \sin \theta - 5 \sin \theta = 0$
$-\cos \theta + (\sqrt{3} - 5) \sin \theta = 0$
$\cos \theta = (\sqrt{3} - 5) \sin \theta$
$\frac{1}{(\sqrt{3} - 5)} = \frac{\sin \theta}{\cos \theta} = \tan \theta$

So $\theta = -0.296... + \pi = 2.84$ (2 d.p.)
and $-0.296... + 2\pi = 5.99$ (2 d.p.).

c) Use the addition formulas:
$\sin(\theta - 30°) - \cos(\theta + 60°) = 0$
$(\sin \theta \cos 30° - \cos \theta \sin 30°)$
$\quad - (\cos \theta \cos 60° - \sin \theta \sin 60°) = 0$
$\left(\frac{\sqrt{3}}{2} \sin \theta - \frac{1}{2} \cos \theta\right) - \left(\frac{1}{2} \cos \theta - \frac{\sqrt{3}}{2} \sin \theta\right) = 0$
$\frac{\sqrt{3}}{2} \sin \theta - \frac{1}{2} \cos \theta - \frac{1}{2} \cos \theta + \frac{\sqrt{3}}{2} \sin \theta = 0$
$\sqrt{3} \sin \theta - \cos \theta = 0$
$\sqrt{3} \sin \theta = \cos \theta$
$\frac{\sin \theta}{\cos \theta} = \frac{1}{\sqrt{3}} \Rightarrow \tan \theta = \frac{1}{\sqrt{3}}$
$\theta = 30°$ and $30° + 180° = 210°$

Q12 Use the sin addition formula for $\sin\left(x + \frac{\pi}{6}\right)$:
$\sin\left(x + \frac{\pi}{6}\right) = \sin x \cos \frac{\pi}{6} + \cos x \sin \frac{\pi}{6} = \frac{\sqrt{3}}{2} \sin x + \frac{1}{2} \cos x$
Use the small angle approximations for sin and cos:
$\approx \frac{\sqrt{3}}{2} x + \frac{1}{2}\left(1 - \frac{1}{2}x^2\right) = \frac{\sqrt{3}}{2} x + \frac{1}{2} - \frac{1}{4}x^2 = \frac{1}{2} + \frac{\sqrt{3}}{2} x - \frac{1}{4}x^2$

3.7 The Double Angle Formulas
Exercise 3.7.1 — Using the double angle formulas

Q1 **a)** $\sin 2A \equiv 2 \sin A \cos A \Rightarrow 4 \sin A \cos A \equiv 2 \sin 2A$
$\Rightarrow 4 \sin \frac{\pi}{12} \cos \frac{\pi}{12} = 2 \sin \frac{\pi}{6} = 2 \times \frac{1}{2} = 1$

b) $\cos 2A \equiv 2 \cos^2 A - 1$
$\Rightarrow \cos \frac{2\pi}{3} = 2 \cos^2 \frac{\pi}{3} - 1 = 2\left(\frac{1}{2}\right)^2 - 1 = -\frac{1}{2}$

c) $\sin 2A \equiv 2 \sin A \cos A \Rightarrow \frac{\sin 2A}{2} \equiv \sin A \cos A$
$\Rightarrow \frac{\sin 120°}{2} = \sin 60° \cos 60° = \frac{\sqrt{3}}{2} \times \frac{1}{2} = \frac{\sqrt{3}}{4}$

d) $\tan 2A \equiv \frac{2 \tan A}{1 - \tan^2 A} \Rightarrow \frac{\tan A}{2 - 2 \tan^2 A} \equiv \frac{\tan 2A}{4}$
$\Rightarrow \frac{\tan 15°}{2 - 2 \tan^2 15°} = \frac{\tan 30°}{4} = \frac{1}{4\sqrt{3}} = \frac{\sqrt{3}}{12}$

e) $\cos 2A \equiv 1 - 2 \sin^2 A \Rightarrow 2 \sin^2 A - 1 \equiv -\cos 2A$
$\Rightarrow 2 \sin^2 15° - 1 = -\cos 30° = -\frac{\sqrt{3}}{2}$

f) $\tan 2A \equiv \frac{2 \tan A}{1 - \tan^2 A} \Rightarrow \tan^2 A = 1 - \frac{2 \tan A}{\tan 2A}$
$\Rightarrow \tan^2 \frac{\pi}{3} = 1 - \frac{2 \tan \frac{\pi}{3}}{\tan \frac{2\pi}{3}} = 1 - \frac{2\sqrt{3}}{-\sqrt{3}} = 1 - (-2) = 3$

Q2 **a)** $\cos 2A \equiv 1 - 2 \sin^2 A$
$\Rightarrow \cos 2x = 1 - 2 \sin^2 x = 1 - 2\left(\frac{1}{6}\right)^2 = \frac{17}{18}$

b) First find cos x:

$$\cos^2 x = 1 - \sin^2 x = 1 - \left(\frac{1}{6}\right)^2 = \frac{35}{36} \implies \cos x = \frac{\sqrt{35}}{6}$$

x is acute so take the positive root for cos x. Again, if you find it easier you can use the triangle method here.

$$\sin 2A \equiv 2 \sin A \cos A \implies \sin 2x = 2\left(\frac{1}{6} \times \frac{\sqrt{35}}{6}\right) = \frac{\sqrt{35}}{18}$$

c) $\tan 2x = \frac{\sin 2x}{\cos 2x} = \frac{\sqrt{35}}{17}$

d) $\sec 2x = \frac{1}{\cos 2x} = \frac{18}{17}$

e) $\operatorname{cosec} 2x = \frac{1}{\sin 2x} = \frac{18}{\sqrt{35}} \left(= \frac{18\sqrt{35}}{35}\right)$

f) $\cot 2x = \frac{1}{\tan 2x} = \frac{17}{\sqrt{35}} \left(= \frac{17\sqrt{35}}{35}\right)$

Q3 a) $\cos 2x = 1 - 2\sin^2 x = 1 - 2\left(-\frac{1}{4}\right)^2 = \frac{7}{8}$

b) First find cos x:

$$\cos^2 x = 1 - \sin^2 x = 1 - \left(-\frac{1}{4}\right)^2 = \frac{15}{16} \implies \cos x = -\frac{\sqrt{15}}{4}$$

x is in the 3rd quadrant of the CAST diagram where cos x is negative, so take the negative root for cos x.

$$\sin 2A \equiv 2 \sin A \cos A \implies \sin 2x = 2\left(-\frac{1}{4} \times -\frac{\sqrt{15}}{4}\right) = \frac{\sqrt{15}}{8}$$

c) $\tan 2x = \frac{\sin 2x}{\cos 2x} = \frac{\sqrt{15}}{7}$

d) $\sec 2x = \frac{1}{\cos 2x} = \frac{8}{7}$

e) $\operatorname{cosec} 2x = \frac{1}{\sin 2x} = \frac{8}{\sqrt{15}} \left(= \frac{8\sqrt{15}}{15}\right)$

f) $\cot 2x = \frac{1}{\tan 2x} = \frac{7}{\sqrt{15}} \left(= \frac{7\sqrt{15}}{15}\right)$

Q4 a) Using the sin double angle formula: $\frac{\sin 3\theta \cos 3\theta}{3} \equiv \frac{\sin 6\theta}{6}$

b) Using the cos double angle formula:

$$\sin^2\left(\frac{2y}{3}\right) - \cos^2\left(\frac{2y}{3}\right) \equiv -\cos\left(\frac{4y}{3}\right)$$

c) Using the tan double angle formula:

$$\frac{1 - \tan^2\left(\frac{x}{2}\right)}{2\tan\left(\frac{x}{2}\right)} \equiv \frac{1}{\tan x} \equiv \cot x$$

Exercise 3.7.2 — Solving equations and proving identities

Q1 a) Using the cos double angle formula involving sin:
$4(1 - 2\sin^2 x) - 14 \sin x = 0 \implies 4 - 8\sin^2 x - 14\sin x = 0$
$\implies 8\sin^2 x + 14\sin x - 4 = 0 \implies 4\sin^2 x + 7\sin x - 2 = 0$
$\implies (4\sin x - 1)(\sin x + 2) = 0$

So $\sin x = \frac{1}{4}$ or $\sin x = -2$ (not valid)

Solving $\sin x = \frac{1}{4}$ in the interval $0 \le x \le 360°$:
$x = 14.5°$ (1 d.p.) and $(180° - 14.5°) = 165.5°$ (1 d.p.)

b) Using the cos double angle formula involving cos:
$5(2\cos^2 x - 1) + 9\cos x + 7 = 0$
$\implies 10\cos^2 x + 9\cos x + 2 = 0$
$\implies (2\cos x + 1)(5\cos x + 2) = 0$

So $\cos x = -\frac{1}{2}$ or $\cos x = -\frac{2}{5}$
$\implies x = 113.6°, 120°, 240°, 246.4°$ (1 d.p.)

c) Using the tan double angle formula:

$\frac{4(1 - \tan^2 x)}{2\tan x} + \frac{1}{\tan x} = 5 \implies 2(1 - \tan^2 x) + 1 = 5\tan x$

$\implies 3 - 2\tan^2 x = 5\tan x \implies 0 = 2\tan^2 x + 5\tan x - 3$
$\implies 0 = (2\tan x - 1)(\tan x + 3)$

So $\tan x = \frac{1}{2}$ or $\tan x = -3$
$\implies x = 26.6°, 108.4°, 206.6°, 288.4°$ (1 d.p.)

d) $\tan x - 5(2\sin x \cos x) = 0 \implies \frac{\sin x}{\cos x} = 10\sin x \cos x$
$\implies \sin x = 10\sin x \cos^2 x \implies \sin x - 10\sin x \cos^2 x = 0$
$\implies \sin x(1 - 10\cos^2 x) = 0$

So $\sin x = 0$ or $\cos x = \pm\frac{1}{\sqrt{10}}$

Don't forget to find $\cos^{-1}$ of both the positive and negative root...
$x = 0°, 71.6°, 108.4°, 180°, 251.6°, 288.4°, 360°$.

Q2 a) $4(2\cos^2 x - 1) - 10\cos x + 1 = 0$
$\implies 8\cos^2 x - 10\cos x - 3 = 0$
$\implies (4\cos x + 1)(2\cos x - 3) = 0$

So $\cos x = -\frac{1}{4}$ or $\cos x = \frac{3}{2}$ (not valid)
$\implies x = 1.82$ and 4.46 (3 s.f.)

b) $\cos 2x - 3 = 6\sin^2 x - 3$
$\implies (1 - 2\sin^2 x) - 3 - 6\sin^2 x + 3 = 0 \implies 1 - 8\sin^2 x = 0$
So $\sin x = \pm\frac{1}{2\sqrt{2}} \implies x = 0.361, 2.78, 3.50, 5.92$ (3 s.f.)

c) $2\sin x \cos x = 4\cos^2 x - 4\sin^2 x$
$\implies \sin 2x = 4\cos 2x \implies \tan 2x = 4$
$\implies 2x = 1.325..., 4.467..., 7.609..., 10.75...$
$\implies x = 0.662, 2.23, 3.80, 5.38$ (3 s.f.)

d) $2\cos 4x + \sin 2x = -1 \implies 2(1 - 2\sin^2 2x) + \sin 2x + 1 = 0$
$\implies 2 - 4\sin^2 2x + \sin 2x + 1 = 0 \implies 4\sin^2 2x - \sin 2x - 3 = 0$
$\implies (\sin 2x - 1)(4\sin 2x + 3) = 0$

So $\sin 2x = 1$ or $\sin 2x = -\frac{3}{4}$.

$\sin 2x = 1 \implies 2x = \frac{\pi}{2}, \frac{5\pi}{2} \implies x = \frac{\pi}{4}, \frac{5\pi}{4}$
$\implies x = 0.785, 3.93$ (3 s.f.)

$\sin 2x = -\frac{3}{4} \implies 2x = -0.848...$ which is outside the interval.
$2x = 3.989..., 5.435..., 10.272..., 11.718...$
There are six negative solutions in total in the interval
$0 \le 2x \le 4\pi$: $x = 0.785, 1.99, 2.72, 3.93, 5.14, 5.86$ (3 s.f)

Q3 a) $2\cos^2 x - 1 + 7\cos x = -4 \implies 2\cos^2 x + 7\cos x + 3 = 0$
$\implies (2\cos x + 1)(\cos x + 3) = 0$
So $\cos x = -\frac{1}{2}$ or $\cos x = -3$ (not valid)
$\implies x = \frac{2\pi}{3}$ and $\frac{4\pi}{3}$

b) $2\sin\frac{x}{2}\cos\frac{x}{2} + \cos\frac{x}{2} = 0 \implies \cos\frac{x}{2}\left(2\sin\frac{x}{2} + 1\right) = 0$
So $\cos\frac{x}{2} = 0$ or $\sin\frac{x}{2} = -\frac{1}{2}$

*There are no solutions for $\sin\frac{x}{2} = -\frac{1}{2}$ in the interval $0 \le x \le \pi$
(they both lie in the 3rd and 4th quadrants of the CAST diagram,
$\pi \le x \le 2\pi$) so...*

$\implies \frac{x}{2} = \frac{\pi}{2} \implies x = \pi$

c) $\sin x - \cos 2x = 0 \implies \sin x - (1 - 2\sin^2 x) = 0$
$\implies 2\sin^2 x + \sin x - 1 = 0 \implies (\sin x + 1)(2\sin x - 1) = 0$
So $\sin x = -1$ or $\sin x = \frac{1}{2}$.

$x = \sin^{-1}(-1) = \frac{3\pi}{2}$ and $x = \sin^{-1}\left(\frac{1}{2}\right) = \frac{\pi}{6}, \frac{5\pi}{6}$

So $x = \frac{\pi}{6}, \frac{5\pi}{6}, \frac{3\pi}{2}$

d) $\cos x = 7\cos\frac{x}{2} + 3 \implies 2\cos^2\frac{x}{2} - 1 = 7\cos\frac{x}{2} + 3$
$\implies 2\cos^2\frac{x}{2} - 7\cos\frac{x}{2} - 4 = 0$
$\implies \left(\cos\frac{x}{2} - 4\right)\left(2\cos\frac{x}{2} + 1\right) = 0$
$\implies \cos\frac{x}{2} = 4$ (not valid) or $\cos\frac{x}{2} = -\frac{1}{2}$
$\cos\frac{x}{2} = -\frac{1}{2} \implies \frac{x}{2} = \frac{2\pi}{3} \implies x = \frac{4\pi}{3}$

Q4 a) $\sin 2x \sec^2 x \equiv (2\sin x \cos x)\left(\frac{1}{\cos^2 x}\right) \equiv \frac{2\sin x}{\cos x} \equiv 2\tan x$

b) $\frac{2}{1 + \cos 2x} \equiv \frac{2}{1 + 2\cos^2 x - 1} \equiv \frac{2}{2\cos^2 x} \equiv \frac{1}{\cos^2 x} \equiv \sec^2 x$

c) $\cot x - 2 \cot 2x \equiv \dfrac{1}{\tan x} - \dfrac{2}{\tan 2x}$

$\equiv \dfrac{1}{\tan x} - \dfrac{2(1-\tan^2 x)}{2\tan x} \equiv \dfrac{1-(1-\tan^2 x)}{\tan x} \equiv \dfrac{\tan^2 x}{\tan x} \equiv \tan x$

d) $\tan 2x + \cot 2x \equiv \dfrac{\sin 2x}{\cos 2x} + \dfrac{\cos 2x}{\sin 2x} \equiv \dfrac{\sin^2 2x + \cos^2 2x}{\sin 2x \cos 2x}$

Use $\sin^2 x + \cos^2 x \equiv 1$, and $\sin 4x \equiv 2 \sin 2x \cos 2x$...

$\equiv \dfrac{1}{\frac{1}{2}\sin 4x} \equiv \dfrac{2}{\sin 4x} \equiv 2 \, \text{cosec} \, 4x$

Q5 a) $\dfrac{1+\cos 2x}{\sin 2x} \equiv \dfrac{1+(2\cos^2 x - 1)}{2\sin x \cos x}$

$\equiv \dfrac{2\cos^2 x}{2 \sin x \cos x} \equiv \dfrac{\cos x}{\sin x} \equiv \cot x$

b) Use $4\theta = 2x$, so $x = 2\theta$ and so $\dfrac{1+\cos 4\theta}{\sin 4\theta} \equiv \cot 2\theta$

Solve $\cot 2\theta = 7 \Rightarrow \tan 2\theta = \dfrac{1}{7}$

$\Rightarrow 2\theta = 8.130°, 188.130°, 368.130°, 548.130°$
$\Rightarrow \theta = 4.1°, 94.1°, 184.1°, 274.1°$ (1 d.p.)

Q6 a) $\dfrac{\cot^2 x + 1}{\cot^2 x - 1} \equiv \dfrac{\text{cosec}^2 x}{\frac{\cos^2 x}{\sin^2 x} - 1} \equiv \dfrac{\frac{1}{\sin^2 x}}{\frac{\cos^2 x}{\sin^2 x} - 1}$

$\equiv \dfrac{1}{\cos^2 x - \sin^2 x} \equiv \dfrac{1}{\cos 2x} \equiv \sec 2x$

b) $\dfrac{\cot^2 2\alpha + 1}{\cot^2 2\alpha - 1} = \sec 4\alpha$, so solve for $-4\pi \leq 4\alpha \leq 4\pi$:

$\sec 4\alpha = -3 \Rightarrow \cos 4\alpha = -\dfrac{1}{3} \Rightarrow 4\alpha = 1.910...$

There are 7 other negative solutions at
$(0 - 1.910...), (2\pi - 1.910...), (2\pi + 1.910...), (-2\pi - 1.910...),$
$(-2\pi + 1.910...), (4\pi - 1.910...), (-4\pi + 1.910...)$
so $4\alpha = -10.656..., -8.193..., -4.373..., -1.910...,$
$\quad\quad 1.910..., 4.373..., 8.193..., 10.656...$
$\alpha = -2.66, -2.05, -1.09, -0.478, 0.478, 1.09, 2.05, 2.66$ (3 s.f.)

Q7 $\cot x = \tan \dfrac{x}{2} \Rightarrow \dfrac{1}{\tan x} = \tan \dfrac{x}{2} \Rightarrow \dfrac{1-\tan^2 \frac{x}{2}}{2\tan \frac{x}{2}} = \tan \dfrac{x}{2}$

$\Rightarrow 1 - \tan^2 \dfrac{x}{2} = 2\tan^2 \dfrac{x}{2} \Rightarrow \tan^2 \dfrac{x}{2} = \dfrac{1}{3}$

So $\tan \dfrac{x}{2} = \pm\dfrac{1}{\sqrt{3}} \Rightarrow \dfrac{x}{2} = \dfrac{\pi}{6}, \dfrac{5\pi}{6} \Rightarrow x = \dfrac{\pi}{3}, \dfrac{5\pi}{3}$

Q8 a) $\text{cosec} \, x - \cot \dfrac{x}{2} \equiv \dfrac{1}{\sin x} - \dfrac{\cos \frac{x}{2}}{\sin \frac{x}{2}}$

$\equiv \dfrac{1}{2\sin \frac{x}{2}\cos \frac{x}{2}} - \dfrac{\cos \frac{x}{2}}{\sin \frac{x}{2}} \equiv \dfrac{1-2\cos^2 \frac{x}{2}}{2\sin \frac{x}{2}\cos \frac{x}{2}}$

Here we've let $2A = x$ so $x = \dfrac{A}{2}$.

$\equiv \dfrac{-\left(2\cos^2 \frac{x}{2} - 1\right)}{2\sin \frac{x}{2}\cos \frac{x}{2}} \equiv \dfrac{-\cos x}{\sin x}$

$\equiv -\dfrac{1}{\left(\frac{\sin x}{\cos x}\right)} \equiv -\dfrac{1}{\tan x} \equiv -\cot x.$

b) Rearranging, $\text{cosec} \, y - \cot \dfrac{y}{2} = -2 = -\cot y$

$\Rightarrow \cot y = 2 \Rightarrow \tan y = \dfrac{1}{2}.$
There are 2 solutions in the interval $-\pi \leq y \leq \pi$, at $y = 0.464$
(3 s.f.) and $y = 0.464 - \pi = -2.68$ (3 s.f.)

Q9 First find $\cos \theta$. You know $\sin \theta = \dfrac{5}{13}$,
so using the triangle method, $\cos \theta = \dfrac{12}{13}$.

a) (i) $\cos^2 \left(\dfrac{\theta}{2}\right) = \dfrac{1}{2}(1 + \cos \theta) = \dfrac{1}{2}\left(1 + \dfrac{12}{13}\right) = \dfrac{25}{26}$

So $\cos \left(\dfrac{\theta}{2}\right) = \sqrt{\dfrac{25}{26}} = \dfrac{5}{\sqrt{26}}$.

θ is acute, so $\dfrac{\theta}{2}$ is also acute, and $\cos \left(\dfrac{\theta}{2}\right)$ is +ve so we can ignore the negative root.

(ii) $\sin^2 \left(\dfrac{\theta}{2}\right) = \dfrac{1}{2}(1 - \cos \theta) = \dfrac{1}{2}\left(1 - \dfrac{12}{13}\right) = \dfrac{1}{26}$

So $\sin \left(\dfrac{\theta}{2}\right) = \sqrt{\dfrac{1}{26}} = \dfrac{1}{\sqrt{26}}$.

Again, θ is acute so $\sin \left(\dfrac{\theta}{2}\right)$ must be positive.

b) $\tan \left(\dfrac{\theta}{2}\right) = \dfrac{\sin\left(\frac{\theta}{2}\right)}{\cos\left(\frac{\theta}{2}\right)} = \dfrac{\left(\frac{1}{\sqrt{26}}\right)}{\left(\frac{5}{\sqrt{26}}\right)} = \dfrac{1}{5}$

3.8 The R Addition Formulas
Exercise 3.8.1 — Expressions of the form a cos θ + b sin θ

Q1 $3 \sin x - 2 \cos x \equiv R \sin (x - \alpha)$
$\Rightarrow 3 \sin x - 2 \cos x \equiv R \sin x \cos \alpha - R \cos x \sin \alpha$
$\Rightarrow \text{①} \, R \cos \alpha = 3$ and $\text{②} \, R \sin \alpha = 2$
$\text{②} \div \text{①}$ gives $\tan \alpha = \dfrac{2}{3} \Rightarrow \alpha = 33.7°$ (1 d.p.)
$\text{①}^2 + \text{②}^2$ gives: $R^2 \cos^2 \alpha + R^2 \sin^2 \alpha = 3^2 + 2^2 = 13$
$\Rightarrow R^2 (\cos^2 \alpha + \sin^2 \alpha) = 13$
$\Rightarrow R^2 = 13 \Rightarrow R = \sqrt{13}$
So $3 \sin x - 2 \cos x \equiv \sqrt{13} \, \sin (x - 33.7°)$.

Q2 $6 \cos x - 5 \sin x \equiv R \cos (x + \alpha)$
$\Rightarrow 6 \cos x - 5 \sin x \equiv R \cos x \cos \alpha - R \sin x \sin \alpha$
$\Rightarrow \text{①} \, R \cos \alpha = 6$ and $\text{②} \, R \sin \alpha = 5$
$\text{②} \div \text{①}$ gives $\tan \alpha = \dfrac{5}{6} \Rightarrow \alpha = 39.8°$ (1 d.p.)
$\text{①}^2 + \text{②}^2$ gives: $R^2 \cos^2 \alpha + R^2 \sin^2 \alpha = 6^2 + 5^2 = 61$
$\Rightarrow R = \sqrt{61}$
So $6 \cos x - 5 \sin x \equiv \sqrt{61} \, \cos (x + 39.8°)$.

Q3 $\sin x + \sqrt{7} \, \cos x \equiv R \sin (x + \alpha)$
$\Rightarrow \sin x + \sqrt{7} \, \cos x \equiv R \sin x \cos \alpha + R \cos x \sin \alpha$
$\Rightarrow \text{①} \, R \cos \alpha = 1$ and $\text{②} \, R \sin \alpha = \sqrt{7}$
$\text{②} \div \text{①}$ gives $\tan \alpha = \sqrt{7} \Rightarrow \alpha = 1.21$ (3 s.f.)
$\text{①}^2 + \text{②}^2$ gives: $R^2 \cos^2 \alpha + R^2 \sin^2 \alpha = 1^2 + (\sqrt{7})^2 = 8$
$\Rightarrow R = \sqrt{8} = \sqrt{4 \times 2} = \sqrt{4} \times \sqrt{2} = 2\sqrt{2}$
So $\sin x + \sqrt{7} \, \cos x \equiv 2\sqrt{2} \, \sin (x + 1.21)$.

Q4 $5 \sin \theta - 6 \cos \theta \equiv R \sin (\theta - \alpha)$
$5 \sin \theta - 6 \cos \theta \equiv R \sin \theta \cos \alpha - R \cos \theta \sin \alpha$
$\Rightarrow \text{①} \, R \cos \alpha = 5$ and $\text{②} \, R \sin \alpha = 6$
$\text{②} \div \text{①}$ gives $\tan \alpha = \dfrac{6}{5} \Rightarrow \alpha = 50.19°$ (2 d.p.)
$\text{①}^2 + \text{②}^2$ gives:
$R^2 \cos^2 \alpha + R^2 \sin^2 \alpha = 5^2 + 6^2 = 61 \Rightarrow R = \sqrt{61}$
So $5 \sin \theta - 6 \cos \theta \equiv \sqrt{61} \, \cos (\theta - 50.19°)$

Q5 $\sqrt{2} \, \sin x - \cos x \equiv R \sin (x - \alpha)$
$\Rightarrow \sqrt{2} \, \sin x - \cos x \equiv R \sin x \cos \alpha - R \cos x \sin \alpha$
$\Rightarrow \text{①} \, R \cos \alpha = \sqrt{2}$ and $\text{②} \, R \sin \alpha = 1$
$\text{②} \div \text{①}$ gives $\tan \alpha = \dfrac{1}{\sqrt{2}}$
$\text{①}^2 + \text{②}^2$ gives: $R^2 \cos^2 \alpha + R^2 \sin^2 \alpha = (\sqrt{2})^2 + 1^2 = 3$
$\Rightarrow R^2 (\cos^2 \alpha + \sin^2 \alpha) = 3 \Rightarrow R^2 = 3 \Rightarrow R = \sqrt{3}$
So $\sqrt{2} \, \sin x - \cos x \equiv \sqrt{3} \, \sin (x - \alpha)$, where $\tan \alpha = \dfrac{1}{\sqrt{2}}$.

Q6 $3 \cos 2x + 5 \sin 2x \equiv R \cos (2x - \alpha)$
$3 \cos 2x + 5 \sin 2x \equiv R \cos 2x \cos \alpha + R \sin 2x \sin \alpha$
$\Rightarrow \text{①} \, R \cos \alpha = 3$ and $\text{②} \, R \sin \alpha = 5$
$\text{②} \div \text{①}$ gives $\tan \alpha = \dfrac{5}{3}$
$\text{①}^2 + \text{②}^2$ gives: $R^2 \cos^2 \alpha + R^2 \sin^2 \alpha = 3^2 + 5^2 = 34 \Rightarrow R = \sqrt{34}$
So $3 \cos 2x + 5 \sin 2x \equiv \sqrt{34} \, \cos (2x - \alpha)$, where $\tan \alpha = \dfrac{5}{3}$.

Q7 a) $\sqrt{3}\ \sin x + \cos x \equiv R \sin (x + \alpha)$

$\Rightarrow \sqrt{3}\ \sin x + \cos x \equiv R \sin x \cos \alpha + R \cos x \sin \alpha$

$\Rightarrow$ ① $R \cos \alpha = \sqrt{3}$ and ② $R \sin \alpha = 1$

② $\div$ ① gives $\tan \alpha = \dfrac{1}{\sqrt{3}}$ $\Rightarrow \alpha = \dfrac{\pi}{6}$

①² $+$ ②² gives: $R^2 \cos^2 \alpha + R^2 \sin^2 \alpha = (\sqrt{3})^2 + 1^2 = 4$

$\Rightarrow R = \sqrt{4} = 2$

So $\sqrt{3}\ \sin x + \cos x \equiv 2 \sin \left(x + \dfrac{\pi}{6}\right)$.

b) The graph of $y = 2 \sin \left(x + \dfrac{\pi}{6}\right)$ is the graph

of $y = \sin x$ transformed in the following way:
a horizontal translation left by $\dfrac{\pi}{6}$, then a vertical stretch by
a factor of 2.

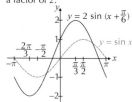

c) The graph of $y = \sin x$ has a minimum at $\left(-\dfrac{\pi}{2}, -1\right)$,

a maximum at $\left(\dfrac{\pi}{2}, 1\right)$, and cuts the x-axis

at $(-\pi, 0)$, $(0, 0)$ and $(\pi, 0)$. To describe the graph of

$y = 2 \sin \left(x + \dfrac{\pi}{6}\right)$, each of these points needs to have $\dfrac{\pi}{6}$

subtracted from the x-coordinates, and the y-coordinates

multiplied by 2. So the graph of $y = 2 \sin \left(x + \dfrac{\pi}{6}\right)$ has a

minimum at $\left(-\dfrac{2\pi}{3}, -2\right)$, a maximum at $\left(\dfrac{\pi}{3}, 2\right)$, and cuts

the x-axis at $\left(-\dfrac{\pi}{6}, 0\right)$ and $\left(\dfrac{5\pi}{6}, 0\right)$.

To find the y-intercept, put $x = 0$ into the equation:
$y = 2 \sin \left(0 + \dfrac{\pi}{6}\right) = 2 \times \dfrac{1}{2} = 1$

So the y-intercept is at $(0, 1)$.

Exercise 3.8.2 — Applying the R addition formulas

Q1 a) $5 \cos \theta - 12 \sin \theta \equiv R \cos (\theta + \alpha)$

$\equiv R \cos \theta \cos \alpha - R \sin \theta \sin \alpha$

$\Rightarrow R \cos \alpha = 5$, $R \sin \alpha = 12$

$\tan \alpha = \dfrac{12}{5}$ $\Rightarrow \alpha = 67.4°$ (1 d.p.)

$R = \sqrt{5^2 + 12^2} = \sqrt{169} = 13$

$\Rightarrow 5 \cos \theta - 12 \sin \theta \equiv 13 \cos (\theta + 67.4°)$

b) $13 \cos (\theta + 67.4°) = 4$, in the interval
$67.4° \leq (\theta + 67.4°) \leq 427.4°$

$\cos (\theta + 67.4°) = \dfrac{4}{13}$

$\Rightarrow \theta + 67.4° = \cos^{-1} \dfrac{4}{13}$

$= 72.1°$ and $(360° - 72.1°) = 287.9°$

$\Rightarrow \theta = (72.1° - 67.4°)$ and $(287.9° - 67.4°)$
$= 4.7°$ and $220.5°$ (1 d.p.)

c) The maximum and minimum values of $\cos \theta$
are at ± 1. So the maximum and minimum
values of $13 \cos (\theta + 67.4°)$ are at ± 13.

Q2 a) $2 \sin 2\theta + 3 \cos 2\theta \equiv R \sin (2\theta + \alpha)$

$\equiv R \sin 2\theta \cos \alpha + R \cos 2\theta \sin \alpha$

$\Rightarrow R \cos \alpha = 2$, $R \sin \alpha = 3$

$\tan \alpha = \dfrac{3}{2}$ $\Rightarrow \alpha = 0.983$ (3 s.f.)

$R = \sqrt{2^2 + 3^2} = \sqrt{13}$

$\Rightarrow 2 \sin 2\theta + 3 \cos 2\theta \equiv \sqrt{13}\ \sin (2\theta + 0.983)$

b) $\sqrt{13}\ \sin (2\theta + 0.983) = 1$ in the interval
$0.983 \leq (2\theta + 0.983) \leq 13.549$.

$\sin (2\theta + 0.983) = \dfrac{1}{\sqrt{13}}$

$\Rightarrow 2\theta + 0.983 = 0.281$ (not in correct interval),
$(\pi - 0.281)$, $(2\pi + 0.281)$, $(3\pi - 0.281)$, $(4\pi + 0.281)$.
*There will be 4 solutions for θ between 0 and 2π
because you're dealing with sin 2θ.*

$\Rightarrow 2\theta + 0.983 = 2.861$, 6.564, 9.144, 12.847

$\Rightarrow \theta = 0.939$, 2.79, 4.08, 5.93 (3 s.f.)

Q3 a) $3 \sin \theta - 2\sqrt{5}\ \cos \theta \equiv R \sin (\theta - \alpha)$

$\equiv R \sin \theta \cos \alpha - R \cos \theta \sin \alpha$

$\Rightarrow R \cos \alpha = 3$, $R \sin \alpha = 2\sqrt{5}$

$\tan \alpha = \dfrac{2\sqrt{5}}{3}$ $\Rightarrow \alpha = 56.1°$ (1 d.p.)

$R = \sqrt{3^2 + (2\sqrt{5})^2} = \sqrt{29}$

$\Rightarrow 3 \sin \theta - 2\sqrt{5}\ \cos \theta \equiv \sqrt{29}\ \sin (\theta - 56.1°)$

b) $\sqrt{29}\ \sin (\theta - 56.1°) = 5$ in the interval
$-56.1° \leq (\theta - 56.1°) \leq 303.9°$.

$\sin (\theta - 56.1°) = \dfrac{5}{\sqrt{29}}$

$\Rightarrow \theta - 56.1° = 68.2°$ and $(180° - 68.2°) = 111.8°$

$\Rightarrow \theta = 124.3°$ and $167.9°$ (1 d.p.)

c) $f(x) = \sqrt{29}\ \sin (x - 56.1°)$. The maximum of $\sin x$ is 1, so the
maximum value of $f(x)$ is $f(x) = \sqrt{29}$.

When $f(x) = \sqrt{29}$, $\sin (x - 56.1°) = 1$

$\Rightarrow x - 56.1° = 90°$ $\Rightarrow x = 146.1°$ (1 d.p.)

Q4 a) $3 \sin x + \cos x \equiv R \sin (x + \alpha) \equiv R \sin x \cos \alpha + R \cos x \sin \alpha$

$\Rightarrow R \cos \alpha = 3$, $R \sin \alpha = 1$

$\tan \alpha = \dfrac{1}{3}$ $\Rightarrow \alpha = 18.4°$ (1 d.p.)

$R = \sqrt{3^2 + 1^2} = \sqrt{10}$

$\Rightarrow 3 \sin x + \cos x \equiv \sqrt{10}\ \sin (x + 18.4°)$

b) $\sqrt{10}\ \sin (x + 18.4°) = 2$ in the interval
$18.4° \leq (x + 18.4°) \leq 378.4°$

$\sin (x + 18.4°) = \dfrac{2}{\sqrt{10}}$

$\Rightarrow x + 18.4° = 39.2°$ and $(180° - 39.2°) = 140.8°$

$\Rightarrow x = 20.8°$ and $122.4°$ (1 d.p.)

c) The maximum and minimum values of $f(x)$ are $\pm\sqrt{10}$.

Q5 a) $4 \sin x + \cos x \equiv R \sin (x + \alpha)$

$\equiv R \sin x \cos \alpha + R \cos x \sin \alpha$

$\Rightarrow R \cos \alpha = 4$, $R \sin \alpha = 1$

$\tan \alpha = \dfrac{1}{4}$ $\Rightarrow \alpha = 0.245$ (3 s.f.)

$R = \sqrt{4^2 + 1^2} = \sqrt{17}$

$\Rightarrow 4 \sin x + \cos x \equiv \sqrt{17}\ \sin (x + 0.245)$

b) Maximum value of $4 \sin x + \cos x = \sqrt{17}$, so the greatest
value of $(4 \sin x + \cos x)^4 = (\sqrt{17})^4 = 289$.

c) $\sqrt{17}\ \sin (x + 0.245) = 1$ in the interval
$0.245 \leq (x + 0.245) \leq 3.387$.

$\sin (x + 0.245) = \dfrac{1}{\sqrt{17}}$

$\Rightarrow x + 0.245 = 0.245$ and $(\pi - 0.245) = 2.897$

$\Rightarrow x = 0$ and 2.65 (3 s.f.)

Q6 a) $8 \cos x + 15 \sin x \equiv R \cos (x - \alpha)$

$\equiv R \cos x \cos \alpha + R \sin x \sin \alpha$

$\Rightarrow R \cos \alpha = 8$, $R \sin \alpha = 15$

$\tan \alpha = \dfrac{15}{8}$ $\Rightarrow \alpha = 1.08$ (3 s.f.)

$R = \sqrt{8^2 + 15^2} = \sqrt{289} = 17$

$\Rightarrow 8 \cos x + 15 \sin x \equiv 17 \cos (x - 1.08)$.

b) So solve for $17 \cos (x - 1.08) = 5$ in the interval $-1.08 \le (x - 1.08) \le 5.20$.

$\cos (x - 1.08) = \frac{5}{17}$

$\Rightarrow x - 1.08 = 1.27$ and $(2\pi - 1.27) = 5.01$

$\Rightarrow x = 2.35$ and 6.09 (3 s.f.)

c) $g(x) = (8 \cos x + 15 \sin x)^2 = 17^2 \cos^2 (x - 1.08)$

$= 289 \cos^2 (x - 1.08)$

The function $\cos^2 x$ has a minimum value of 0 (since all negative values of $\cos x$ become positive when you square it) so the minimum of $g(x)$ is 0.

This minimum occurs when $\cos^2(x - 1.08) = 0$

so $\cos(x - 1.08) = 0 \Rightarrow x - 1.08 = \frac{\pi}{2} \Rightarrow x = 2.65$ (3 s.f.).

Q7 a) $2 \cos x + \sin x \equiv R \cos (x - \alpha) \equiv R \cos x \cos \alpha + R \sin x \sin \alpha$

$\Rightarrow R \cos \alpha = 2, \ R \sin \alpha = 1$

$\tan \alpha = \frac{1}{2} \Rightarrow \alpha = 26.6°$ (3 s.f.)

$R = \sqrt{2^2 + 1^2} = \sqrt{5}$

$\Rightarrow 2 \cos x + \sin x \equiv \sqrt{5} \cos (x - 26.6°).$

b) The range of $g(x)$ is between the maximum and minimum values, which are at $\pm \sqrt{5}$.

So $-\sqrt{5} \le g(x) \le \sqrt{5}$.

Q8 $3 \sin \theta - \frac{3}{2} \cos \theta \equiv R \sin (\theta - \alpha) \equiv R \sin \theta \cos \alpha - R \cos \theta \sin \alpha$

$\Rightarrow R \cos \alpha = 3, \ R \sin \alpha = \frac{3}{2}$

$\tan \alpha = \frac{1}{2} \Rightarrow \alpha = 0.464$ (3 s.f.)

$R = \sqrt{3^2 + \left(\frac{3}{2}\right)^2} = \sqrt{\frac{45}{4}} = \frac{3\sqrt{5}}{2}$

$\Rightarrow 3 \sin \theta - \frac{3}{2} \cos \theta \equiv \frac{3\sqrt{5}}{2} \sin (\theta - 0.464)$

So solve $\frac{3\sqrt{5}}{2} \sin (\theta - 0.464) = 3$ in the interval $-0.464 \le (\theta - 0.464) \le 5.819$.

$\sin (\theta - 0.464) = \frac{2}{\sqrt{5}}$

$\Rightarrow \theta - 0.464 = 1.107$ and $(\pi - 1.107) = 2.034$

$\Rightarrow \theta = 1.57$ and 2.50 (3 s.f.)

Q9 $4 \sin 2\theta + 3 \cos 2\theta \equiv R \sin (2\theta + \alpha)$

$\equiv R \sin 2\theta \cos \alpha + R \cos 2\theta \sin \alpha$

$\Rightarrow R \cos \alpha = 4, \ R \sin \alpha = 3$

$\tan \alpha = \frac{3}{4} \Rightarrow \alpha = 0.644$ (3 s.f.)

$R = \sqrt{3^2 + 4^2} = 5$

$\Rightarrow 4 \sin 2\theta + 3 \cos 2\theta \equiv 5 \sin (2\theta + 0.644)$

So solve $5 \sin (2\theta + 0.644) = 2$ in the interval $0.644 \le (2\theta + 0.644) \le 6.927$.

$\sin (2\theta + 0.644) = \frac{2}{5}$

$\Rightarrow 2\theta + 0.644 = 0.412$ (not in the interval),

$(\pi - 0.412) = 2.730$, and $(2\pi + 0.412) = 6.695$

$\Rightarrow \theta = 1.04$ and 3.03 (3 s.f.)

You could also solve this by writing the function in the form $R \cos (2\theta - \alpha)$ $(R = 5, \alpha = 0.927)$ — you should get the same solutions for θ either way.

3.9 Modelling with Trig Functions

Exercise 3.9.1 — Trigonometry in modelling

Q1 For each sector of the circle, $r = 20$ so

Area $= \frac{1}{2} r^2 \theta = (200\theta)$ m², and

Perimeter $= 2r + r\theta = (40 + 200\theta)$ m

Convert each angle to radians then find the area and perimeter:

$120° = \frac{120 \times \pi}{180} = \frac{2\pi}{3}$

Area $= 200 \times \frac{2\pi}{3} = 419$ m² (3 s.f.)

Perimeter $= 40 + 20 \times \frac{2\pi}{3} = 81.9$ m (3 s.f.)

$144° = \frac{144 \times \pi}{180} = \frac{4\pi}{5}$

Area $= 200 \times \frac{4\pi}{5} = 503$ m² (3 s.f.)

Perimeter $= 40 + 20 \times \frac{4\pi}{5} = 90.3$ m (3 s.f.)

$96° = \frac{96 \times \pi}{180} = \frac{8\pi}{15}$

Area $= 200 \times \frac{8\pi}{15} = 335$ m² (3 s.f.)

Perimeter $= 40 + 20 \times \frac{8\pi}{15} = 73.5$ m (3 s.f.)

Q2 a) $\cos \theta$ has a maximum of 1 and a minimum of -1.

You want $A + B \cos \theta$ to have a maximum of 17 and a minimum of 7. So form two equations:

① $A + B(1) = 17$ (at maximum)

② $A + B(-1) = 7$ (at minimum)

① + ②: $2A = 24 \Rightarrow A = 12$

Sub back into ①: $12 + B = 17 \Rightarrow B = 5$

So $f(\theta) = 12 + 5 \cos \theta$

You could also think of this as a transformation of the graph of $\cos \theta$ — a vertical stretch with scale factor 5 followed by a translation up by 12.

b) The longest day ($t = 0$) will have 17 hours of daylight, which is the maximum of the function. This will occur when $\cos (Ct + D) = 1$, i.e. when $Ct + D = 0$.

Similarly, the shortest day ($t = 6$) will occur when $\cos (Ct + D) = -1$ i.e. when $Ct + D = \pi$.

So $C(0) + D = 0$ (longest day) $\Rightarrow D = 0$

$C(6) + D = \pi$ (shortest day) $\Rightarrow 6C + 0 = \pi \Rightarrow C = \frac{\pi}{6}$

So $g(t) = 12 + 5 \cos \left(\frac{\pi}{6} t\right)$

Because cos is periodic, you might have found $D = 2\pi$.

Also, because cos is symmetrical, $C = -\frac{\pi}{6}$ will give you the same answer — either one is fine.

Q3 $h(t) = 14 + 5 \sin t + 5 \cos t \equiv 14 + R \cos (t - \alpha)$

$\equiv 14 + R \cos t \cos \alpha + R \sin t \sin \alpha$

$\Rightarrow R \cos \alpha = 5, \ R \sin \alpha = 5$

$\tan \alpha = 1 \Rightarrow \alpha = \frac{\pi}{4}$

$R = \sqrt{5^2 + 5^2} = \sqrt{50} = 5\sqrt{2}$

$\Rightarrow h(t) \equiv 14 + 5\sqrt{2} \cos \left(t - \frac{\pi}{4}\right)$

The maximum and minimum of cos are 1 and -1, so the maximum of $h(t) = 14 + 5\sqrt{2} = 21.1$ m (1 d.p.) and the minimum of $h(t) = 14 - 5\sqrt{2} = 6.9$ m (1 d.p.)

Q4 a) $H = 10 + \frac{7}{2} \sin t - \frac{7\sqrt{3}}{2} \cos t \equiv 10 + R \sin (t - \alpha)$

$\equiv 10 + R \sin t \cos \alpha - R \cos t \sin \alpha$

$\Rightarrow R \cos \alpha = \frac{7}{2}, \ R \sin \alpha = \frac{7\sqrt{3}}{2}$

$\tan \alpha = \sqrt{3} \Rightarrow \alpha = \frac{\pi}{3}$

$R = \sqrt{\left(\frac{7}{2}\right)^2 + \left(\frac{7\sqrt{3}}{2}\right)^2} = \sqrt{\frac{49}{4} + \frac{147}{4}}$

$= \sqrt{\frac{196}{4}} = \sqrt{49} = 7$

$\Rightarrow H \equiv 10 + 7 \sin \left(t - \frac{\pi}{3}\right)$

b) Replace $\left(t - \frac{\pi}{3}\right)$ with x to make the working clearer:

$h = 10 + 7 \sin x - \cos 2x$

Write $\cos 2x$ in terms of $\sin x$, i.e. $1 - 2 \sin^2 x$

$h = 10 + 7 \sin x - (1 - 2 \sin^2 x)$

$= 10 + 7 \sin x - 1 + 2 \sin^2 x = 9 + 7 \sin x + 2 \sin^2 x$

i.e. $A = 9$ and $B = 2$.

c) You need to find $h = 13$, i.e.
$9 + 7 \sin x + 2 \sin^2 x = 13$
$2 \sin^2 x + 7 \sin x - 4 = 0$
This is a quadratic in $\sin x$, so factorise:
$(2 \sin x - 1)(\sin x + 4) = 0$
$\Rightarrow \sin x = \frac{1}{2}$ or $\sin x = -4$ (not valid since $-1 < \sin x < 1$)

So $\sin x = \frac{1}{2}$ i.e. $\sin \left(t - \frac{\pi}{3} \right) = \frac{1}{2}$
You need to find the smallest t that satisfies this equation.
$\sin \left(t - \frac{\pi}{3} \right) = \frac{1}{2} \Rightarrow t - \frac{\pi}{3} = -\frac{7\pi}{6}, \frac{\pi}{6}, \frac{5\pi}{6}$, etc.

$\Rightarrow t = -\frac{5\pi}{6}, \frac{\pi}{2}, \frac{7\pi}{6}$, etc.
Time cannot be negative, so the smallest solution is $t = \frac{\pi}{2}$
i.e. $t = 1.57$ s (3 s.f.)

Review Exercise — Chapter 3

Q1 **a)** **(i)** $\frac{\pi}{12}$ **(ii)** $\frac{5\pi}{18}$ **(iii)** $\frac{11\pi}{6}$ **(iv)** $\frac{5\pi}{4}$

b) **(i)** $105°$ **(ii)** $210°$ **(iii)** $300°$ **(iv)** $195°$

Q2 Arc length $BC = r\theta = 10 \times 0.7 = 7$ cm
Area $= A = \frac{1}{2} r^2 \theta = \frac{1}{2} \times 10^2 \times 0.7 = 35$ cm^2

Q3 $\tan \theta \approx \theta$, $\cos \theta \approx 1 - \frac{1}{2} \theta^2$
so $\tan \theta - \cos \theta \approx \theta - (1 - \frac{1}{2} \theta^2) = \theta - 1 + \frac{1}{2} \theta^2$.

a) $0.13 - 1 + \frac{1}{2} (0.13)^2 = -0.86155$

b) $0.07 - 1 + \frac{1}{2} (0.07)^2 = -0.92755$

c) $0.26 - 1 + \frac{1}{2} (0.26)^2 = -0.7062$

Q4 **a)** $\sin 3\theta \tan 4\theta \approx 3\theta \times 4\theta = 12\theta^2$

b) $\cos 4\theta + \cos 8\theta \approx (1 - \frac{1}{2} (4\theta)^2) + (1 - \frac{1}{2} (8\theta)^2)$

$= 1 - 8\theta^2 + 1 - 32\theta^2 = 2 - 40\theta^2$

c) $\frac{2\theta^3}{\sin 2\theta \cos \theta} \approx \frac{2\theta^3}{2\theta \times (1 - \frac{1}{2}\theta^2)} = \frac{2\theta^3}{2\theta - \theta^3} = \frac{2\theta^2}{2 - \theta^2}$

Q5 Using common trig angles:

a) If $x = \sin^{-1} \frac{1}{\sqrt{2}}$, then $\frac{1}{\sqrt{2}} = \sin x$ so $x = \frac{\pi}{4}$.

b) If $x = \cos^{-1} \frac{1}{2}$, then $\frac{1}{2} = \cos x$ so $x = \frac{\pi}{3}$.

c) If $x = \tan^{-1} \frac{1}{\sqrt{3}}$, then $\frac{1}{\sqrt{3}} = \tan x$ so $x = \frac{\pi}{6}$.

Q6

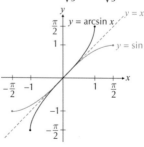

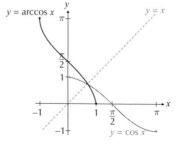

Q7 **a)** Rearrange to make x the subject:
$1 + \cos x = \frac{1}{y} \Rightarrow \cos x = \frac{1}{y} - 1 \Rightarrow x = \cos^{-1}(\frac{1}{y} - 1)$
Replace x with $f^{-1}(x)$ and y with x:
$f^{-1}(x) = \cos^{-1}(\frac{1}{x} - 1) = \arccos(\frac{1}{x} - 1)$

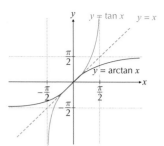

b) The range for $f(x)$ is $\frac{1}{2} \le f(x) \le 1$,
so the domain for $f^{-1}(x)$ is $\frac{1}{2} \le x \le 1$
The domain for $f(x)$ is $0 \le x \le \frac{\pi}{2}$,
so the range for $f^{-1}(x)$ is $0 \le f^{-1}(x) \le \frac{\pi}{2}$.

c)

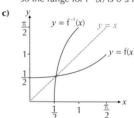

$y = f(x)$ has been reflected in $y = x$.

Q8 **a)** $f(1) = \sin^{-1}(1) + \cos^{-1}(1) + \tan^{-1}(1) = \frac{\pi}{2} + 0 + \frac{\pi}{4} = \frac{3\pi}{4}$

b) $f(-1) = \sin^{-1}(-1) + \cos^{-1}(-1) + \tan^{-1}(-1) = -\frac{\pi}{2} + \pi + -\frac{\pi}{4} = \frac{\pi}{4}$

Q9 **a)** $\operatorname{cosec} 30° = \frac{1}{\sin 30°} = 1 \div \frac{1}{2} = 2$

b) $\sec 30° = \frac{1}{\cos 30°} = 1 \div \frac{\sqrt{3}}{2} = \frac{2}{\sqrt{3}}$

c) $\cot 30° = \frac{1}{\tan 30°} = 1 \div \frac{1}{\sqrt{3}} = \sqrt{3}$

Q10

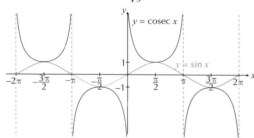

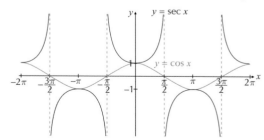

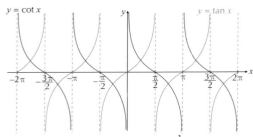

Q11 a) A horizontal stretch with scale factor $\frac{1}{4}$.

b) The period of $y = \sec x$ is 2π, so the period of $y = \sec 4x = 2\pi \div 4 = \frac{\pi}{2}$.

c)

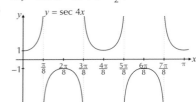

d) $y = \sec 4x$ is undefined when $x = \frac{\pi}{8}, \frac{3\pi}{8}, \frac{5\pi}{8}$ and $\frac{7\pi}{8}$.

Q12 $y = \cot^2 \theta$
By rearranging the identity $\text{cosec}^2\, \theta = 1 + \cot^2 \theta$, you get $\cot^2 \theta = \text{cosec}^2\, \theta - 1$:
Since $x = \text{cosec}\, \theta$, $y = x^2 - 1$ as required.

Q13 Square $y = 2 \tan \theta$ to get $y^2 = 4 \tan^2 \theta$.
By rearranging the identity $\sec^2 \theta = 1 + \tan^2 \theta$, you get $\tan^2 \theta = \sec^2 \theta - 1$:
So $y^2 = 4(\sec^2 \theta - 1) = 4(x^2 - 1) \Rightarrow y = \pm 2\sqrt{x^2 - 1}$

Q14 a) $\text{cosec}^2\, x = \frac{3 \cot x + 4}{2} \Rightarrow 2\,\text{cosec}^2\, x = 3 \cot x + 4$
$\Rightarrow 2(1 + \cot^2 x) = 3 \cot x + 4$
$\Rightarrow 2 \cot^2 x - 3 \cot x + 2 - 4 = 0$
$\Rightarrow 2 \cot^2 x - 3 \cot x - 2 = 0$

b) Factorise the quadratic in $\cot x$:
$(\cot x - 2)(2 \cot x + 1) = 0$
So $\cot x = 2$ or $\cot x = -\frac{1}{2}$.
$\Rightarrow \tan x = \frac{1}{2}$ or $\tan x = -2$
For $\tan x = \frac{1}{2}$, the first solution is $x = 0.463...$
There is another solution at $0.463... + \pi = 3.605...$
You can find other solutions by sketching a graph or using a CAST diagram.
For $\tan x = -2$, $x = -1.107...$ — this is outside the interval, so add π: $-1.107... + \pi = 2.034...$
There is another solution at $2.034... + \pi = 5.176...$
So $x = 0.46, 3.61, 2.03$ and 5.18 (all to 2 d.p.)

Q15 a) $\sec \theta = \frac{1}{\cos \theta} = 1 \div \frac{1}{2} = 2$

b) Draw a right angled triangle to find the third side: $\sqrt{2^2 - 1^2} = \sqrt{3}$.
So $\tan \theta = \frac{\sqrt{3}}{1} = \sqrt{3}$.

c) From a), $\sec \theta = 2$, so $\sec^2 \theta = 4$
$\Rightarrow 1 + \tan^2 \theta = 4 \Rightarrow \tan^2 \theta = 3 \Rightarrow \tan \theta = \sqrt{3}$

d) $\cot \theta = \frac{1}{\tan \theta} = \frac{1}{\sqrt{3}}$

e) From d), $\cot^2 \theta = \frac{1}{3}$, so $\text{cosec}^2\, \theta = 1 + \frac{1}{3} = \frac{4}{3}$
$\Rightarrow \text{cosec}\, \theta = \frac{2}{\sqrt{3}} \Rightarrow \sin \theta = \frac{1}{\text{cosec}\, \theta} = \frac{\sqrt{3}}{2}$

You're told θ is acute, so you know all the trig ratios will be positive.

Q16 a) Using the sin addition formula:
$\sin 2x \cos 9x + \cos 2x \sin 9x = \sin (2x + 9x) = \sin 11x$

b) Using the cos addition formula:
$3 \cos 5x \cos 7x - 3 \sin 5x \sin 7x = 3 \cos (5x + 7x)$
$= 3 \cos 12x$

c) Using the tan addition formula:
$\frac{\tan 12x - \tan 8x}{1 + \tan 12x \tan 8x} = \tan (12x - 8x) = \tan 4x$

d) Using the sin addition formula:
$12 \sin \frac{7x}{2} \cos \frac{3x}{2} - 12 \cos \frac{7x}{2} \sin \frac{3x}{2}$
$= 12 \sin (\frac{7x}{2} - \frac{3x}{2}) = 12 \sin 2x$

Q17 $\cos \frac{7\pi}{12} = \cos \left(\frac{\pi}{3} + \frac{\pi}{4}\right) = \cos \frac{\pi}{3} \cos \frac{\pi}{4} - \sin \frac{\pi}{3} \sin \frac{\pi}{4}$
$= \frac{1}{2} \times \frac{1}{\sqrt{2}} - \frac{\sqrt{3}}{2} \times \frac{1}{\sqrt{2}} = \frac{1}{2\sqrt{2}} - \frac{\sqrt{3}}{2\sqrt{2}} = \frac{1 - \sqrt{3}}{2\sqrt{2}}$
$= \frac{1 - \sqrt{3}}{2\sqrt{2}} \times \frac{\sqrt{2}}{\sqrt{2}} = \frac{\sqrt{2} - \sqrt{2}\sqrt{3}}{4} = \frac{\sqrt{2} - \sqrt{6}}{4}$

Q18 $\sin A = \frac{4}{5}$, so using the triangle on the right, $\cos A = \frac{3}{5}$.

$\sin B = \frac{7}{25}$, so from the triangle, $\cos B = \frac{24}{25}$.

$\sin (A + B) = \sin A \cos B + \cos A \sin B$
$= \frac{4}{5} \times \frac{24}{25} + \frac{3}{5} \times \frac{7}{25} = \frac{96}{125} + \frac{21}{125} = \frac{117}{125} = 0.936$

Q19 $\sin 2\theta = 2 \sin \theta \cos \theta$, so rewrite the equation as:
$2 \sin \theta \cos \theta = -\sqrt{3} \sin \theta \Rightarrow \sin \theta (2 \cos \theta + \sqrt{3}) = 0$
$\Rightarrow \sin \theta = 0$ or $\cos \theta = -\frac{\sqrt{3}}{2}$
$\sin \theta = 0 \Rightarrow \theta = 0°, 180°, 360°$
From the common angles,
$\cos \theta = \frac{\sqrt{3}}{2} \Rightarrow \theta = 30°$
So, using the CAST diagram to find negative values for cos:
$\cos \theta = -\frac{\sqrt{3}}{2} \Rightarrow \theta = 150°, 210°$
So $\theta = 0°, 150°, 180°, 210°, 360°$.

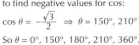

Q20 a) Using the double angle formula with $A = \frac{x}{2}$:
$4 \sin x = \sin \frac{x}{2} \Rightarrow 4 (2 \sin \frac{x}{2} \cos \frac{x}{2}) = \sin \frac{x}{2}$
$\Rightarrow \sin \frac{x}{2} (8 \cos \frac{x}{2} - 1) = 0$
$\Rightarrow \sin \frac{x}{2} = 0$ or $\cos \frac{x}{2} = \frac{1}{8}$
$\sin \frac{x}{2} = 0 \Rightarrow \frac{x}{2} = 0, \pi \Rightarrow x = 0, 2\pi$
$\cos \frac{x}{2} = \frac{1}{8} \Rightarrow \frac{x}{2} = 1.445... \Rightarrow x = 2.89$ (3 s.f.)
So $x = 0, 2.89$ (3 s.f.), 6.28 (3 s.f.).

b) Using the double angle formula with $A = \frac{x}{2}$:
$\tan \frac{x}{2} \tan x = 2 \Rightarrow \tan \frac{x}{2} \frac{2 \tan \frac{x}{2}}{1 - \tan^2 \frac{x}{2}} = 2$
$\Rightarrow 2 \tan^2 \frac{x}{2} = 2(1 - \tan^2 \frac{x}{2})$
$\Rightarrow 2 \tan^2 \frac{x}{2} = 1 \Rightarrow \tan \frac{x}{2} = \pm \frac{1}{\sqrt{2}}$
$\tan \frac{x}{2} = \frac{1}{\sqrt{2}} \Rightarrow \frac{x}{2} = 0.6154... \Rightarrow x = 1.23$ (3 s.f.)
$\tan \frac{x}{2} = -\frac{1}{\sqrt{2}} \Rightarrow \frac{x}{2} = -0.6154...$
This is outside the interval so add π:
$\frac{x}{2} = -0.6154... + \pi = 2.526... \Rightarrow x = 5.05$ (3 s.f.)
So $x = 1.23, 5.05$ (to 3 s.f.)

Q21 a) $2 \tan 2x = \tan x \implies \dfrac{4\tan x}{1 - \tan^2 x} = \tan x$

$\implies 4 \tan x = \tan x (1 - \tan^2 x)$

$\implies 4 \tan x = \tan x - \tan^3 x$

$\implies \tan x (3 + \tan^2 x) = 0$

$\implies \tan x = 0 \ \text{or} \ \tan^2 x = -3 \ \text{(not valid)}$

$\tan x = 0 \implies x = 0, \pi, 2\pi$

b) $\sin 6x - \cos 3x = 0$

$\implies 2 \sin 3x \cos 3x - \cos 3x = 0$

$\implies \cos 3x (2 \sin 3x - 1) = 0$

$\implies \cos 3x = 0 \ \text{or} \ \sin 3x = \dfrac{1}{2}$

$\cos 3x = 0 \implies 3x = \dfrac{\pi}{2}, \dfrac{3\pi}{2}, \dfrac{5\pi}{2}, \dfrac{7\pi}{2}, \dfrac{9\pi}{2}, \dfrac{11\pi}{2}$

$\implies x = \dfrac{\pi}{6}, \dfrac{\pi}{2}, \dfrac{5\pi}{6}, \dfrac{7\pi}{6}, \dfrac{3\pi}{2}, \dfrac{11\pi}{6}$

$\sin 3x = \dfrac{1}{2} \implies 3x = \dfrac{\pi}{6}, \dfrac{5\pi}{6}, \dfrac{13\pi}{6}, \dfrac{17\pi}{6}, \dfrac{25\pi}{6}, \dfrac{29\pi}{6}$

$\implies x = \dfrac{\pi}{18}, \dfrac{5\pi}{18}, \dfrac{13\pi}{18}, \dfrac{17\pi}{18}, \dfrac{25\pi}{18}, \dfrac{29\pi}{18}$

Q22 a) $3 \cos \theta - 8 \sin \theta \equiv R \cos (\theta + \alpha)$
$\equiv R \cos \theta \cos \alpha - R \sin \theta \sin \alpha$

$\implies R \cos \alpha = 3, \ R \sin \alpha = 8$

$\tan \alpha = \dfrac{8}{3} \implies \alpha = 69.44...° = 69.4° \ \text{(1 d.p.)}$

$R = \sqrt{3^2 + 8^2} = \sqrt{73}$

$\implies 3 \cos \theta - 8 \sin \theta \equiv \sqrt{73} \ \cos (\theta + 69.4°)$

b) $\sqrt{73} \ \cos (\theta + 69.4°) = 1.2$, in the interval
$69.4° \le (\theta + 69.4°) \le 429.4°$

$\cos (\theta + 69.4°) = \dfrac{1.2}{\sqrt{73}}$

$\implies \theta + 69.4° = \cos^{-1} \left(\dfrac{1.2}{\sqrt{73}} \right) = 81.9...°$

Using the symmetry of the graph
of cos, there is another solution at
$\theta + 69.4° = (360° - 81.9...°) = 278.0...°$

$\implies \theta = (81.9...° - 69.4°) \ \text{and} \ (278.0...° - 69.4°)$
$= 12.5° \ \text{and} \ 208.6° \ \text{(1 d.p.)}$

Q23 $5 \sin t + 3 \cos t \equiv R \sin (t + \alpha) \equiv R \sin t \cos \alpha + R \cos t \sin \alpha$

$\implies R \cos \alpha = 5 \ \text{and} \ R \sin \alpha = 3$

$\tan \alpha = \dfrac{3}{5} \implies \alpha = 30.9637...° = 30.964° \ \text{(3 d.p.)}$

$R = \sqrt{5^2 + 3^2} = \sqrt{34}$

So $h = \sqrt{34} \ \sin (t + 30.964°) + 2$

The maximum height occurs when $\sin (t + 30.964°) = 1$,

so $h_{max} = \sqrt{34} \times 1 + 2 = 5.83... + 2 = 7.83 \ \text{m} \ \text{(2 d.p.)}$

Exam-Style Questions — Chapter 3

Q1 The domain of $\cos x$ is limited to $0 \le x \le \pi$ in defining $\cos^{-1} x$,
so $y = \cos^{-1} x$ is defined on the domain $-1 \le x \le 1$.
A and C are endpoints, so the x-coordinate of A is -1 and the
x-coordinate of C is 1. $\cos x = 1$ when $x = 0$, so $\cos^{-1} 1 = 0$.
Similarly, $\cos x = -1$ when $x = \pi$, so $\cos^{-1} -1 = \pi$.
B is the y-intercept so its x-coordinate is 0.
$\cos x = 0$ when $x = \dfrac{\pi}{2}$, so $\cos^{-1} 0 = \dfrac{\pi}{2}$.

So A $(-1, \pi)$, B $(0, \dfrac{\pi}{2})$ and C $(1, 0)$.

[3 marks available — 1 mark for each correct pair of coordinates]

Q2 a) $\tan \dfrac{5\pi}{12} = \tan \left(\dfrac{\pi}{6} + \dfrac{\pi}{4} \right) = \dfrac{\tan \frac{\pi}{6} + \tan \frac{\pi}{4}}{1 - \tan \frac{\pi}{6} \tan \frac{\pi}{4}}$

$= \dfrac{\frac{1}{\sqrt{3}} + 1}{1 - \frac{1}{\sqrt{3}} \times 1} = \dfrac{\frac{1 + \sqrt{3}}{\sqrt{3}}}{\frac{\sqrt{3} - 1}{\sqrt{3}}} = \dfrac{1 + \sqrt{3}}{\sqrt{3} - 1}$

$= \dfrac{1 + \sqrt{3}}{\sqrt{3} - 1} \times \dfrac{\sqrt{3} + 1}{\sqrt{3} + 1} = \dfrac{4 + 2\sqrt{3}}{2} = 2 + \sqrt{3}$

[3 marks available — 1 mark for splitting $\frac{5\pi}{12}$ into a suitable sum, 1 mark for using the tan addition formula correctly, 1 mark for simplifying to get the correct answer]

b) $\cot \dfrac{5\pi}{12} = \dfrac{1}{\tan \frac{5\pi}{12}} = \dfrac{1}{2 + \sqrt{3}} = \dfrac{1}{2 + \sqrt{3}} \times \dfrac{2 - \sqrt{3}}{2 - \sqrt{3}}$

$= \dfrac{2 - \sqrt{3}}{1} = 2 - \sqrt{3}$

[1 mark for correct answer]

Q3 $2 \sin 2\theta - \cos \theta = 0 \implies 4 \sin \theta \cos \theta - \cos \theta = 0$

$\implies \cos \theta (4 \sin \theta - 1) = 0 \implies \cos \theta = 0 \ \text{or} \ \sin \theta = \dfrac{1}{4}$

$\cos \theta = 0 \implies \theta = \dfrac{\pi}{2}, \dfrac{3\pi}{2}$

$\sin \theta = \dfrac{1}{4} \implies \theta = 0.252..., \pi - 0.252...$

So $\theta = 0.253, 1.57, 2.89$ and 4.71 (3 s.f.)

[5 marks available — 1 mark for using the identity $\sin 2\theta = 2 \sin \theta \cos \theta$, 1 mark for factorising the equation, 1 mark for finding one correct solution of $\cos \theta = 0$, 1 mark for finding one correct solution of $\sin \theta = \dfrac{1}{4}$, 1 mark for all four solutions correctly given to 3 s.f.]

Q4 a) Find the angle in radians: $40° = \dfrac{40\pi}{180} = \dfrac{2\pi}{9}$

Area $= \dfrac{1}{2} r^2 \theta = \dfrac{1}{2} \times 100^2 \times \dfrac{2\pi}{9} = 3490 \ \text{m}^2 \ \text{(3 s.f.)}$

[3 marks available — 1 mark for converting the angle into radians, 1 mark for using the formula for the area of a sector, 1 mark for the correct answer]

b) Length of arc $= s = r\theta = 100 \times \dfrac{2\pi}{9} = 69.81... \ \text{m}$

Boundary length $= 100 + 100 + s = 270 \ \text{m} \ \text{(3 s.f.)}$

[2 marks available — 1 mark for finding the arc length, 1 mark for the correct answer]

Q5 a) Find the angle in radians: $5° = \dfrac{5\pi}{180} = \dfrac{\pi}{36}$

$\tan x \approx x$, so $\tan \dfrac{\pi}{36} \approx \dfrac{\pi}{36} = 0.0873 \ \text{(3 s.f.)}$

[2 marks available — 1 mark for correct conversion, 1 mark for the correct answer]

b) $\tan 5° = 0.0874...$ so the percentage error
is $\dfrac{0.0874... - 0.0872...}{0.0874...} \times 100 = 2.54\% \ \text{(3 s.f.)}$

[2 marks available — 1 mark for correct method to find percentage error, 1 mark for correct answer]

Q6 a) $7 \cos x - 11 \sin x \equiv R \cos (x + \alpha)$
$\equiv R \cos x \cos \alpha - R \sin x \sin \alpha$

$\implies R \cos \alpha = 7, \ R \sin \alpha = 11$

$\tan \alpha = \dfrac{11}{7} \implies \alpha = 57.5° \ \text{(3 s.f.)}$

$R = \sqrt{7^2 + 11^2} = \sqrt{170}$

$\implies 7 \cos x - 11 \sin x \equiv \sqrt{170} \cos (x + 57.5°)$.

[3 marks available — 1 mark for finding $\tan \alpha$, 1 mark for finding α, 1 mark for finding R]

b) $y = \cos x$ has been translated $57.5°$ to the left and
vertically stretched by a scale factor of $\sqrt{170}$.

[2 marks available — 1 mark for correct translation, 1 mark for correct vertical stretch]

c) The maximum value is $\sqrt{170}$.

$y = 7 \cos x - 11 \sin x$ takes a maximum value when
$\cos(x + 57.5°) = 1$, i.e. when $x + 57.5° = 0 \Rightarrow x = -57.5°$ (3 s.f.)
You could have given x as −57.5° ± 360°, ±720°, etc.
[2 marks available — 1 mark for correct
maximum value, 1 mark for correct x value]

d) $\sqrt{170} \cos(x + 57.5°) = 3$

$\Rightarrow (x + 57.5°) = \cos^{-1}\left(\dfrac{3}{\sqrt{170}}\right) = 76.69...°$

Look for solutions in the interval $57.5° \le x + 57.5° \le 417.5°$
There is another solution at $360° - 76.69...°$,
so $x + 57.5° = 76.69...°$, $283.30...°$.
$\Rightarrow x = 19.2°$ and $225.8°$ (1 d.p.)
[4 marks available — 1 mark for using the form
R cos (x + α), 1 mark for using the inverse
cos function, 1 mark for a method seen to convert the
solutions of (x + 57.5°) to the solutions of x, 1 mark
for both correct values of x rounded to 1 d.p.]

Q7 $\operatorname{cosec}^2 x = 4 + 2 \cot x \Rightarrow 1 + \cot^2 x = 4 + 2 \cot x$
$\Rightarrow \cot^2 x - 2 \cot x - 3 = 0 \Rightarrow (\cot x + 1)(\cot x - 3) = 0$
$\Rightarrow \cot x = -1$ or $\cot x = 3$

$\cot x = -1 \Rightarrow \tan x = -1 \Rightarrow x = \tan^{-1}(-1) = -\dfrac{\pi}{4}$

This is outside the interval — there are two solutions in the
interval at $\pi - \dfrac{\pi}{4}$ and $2\pi - \dfrac{\pi}{4}$ so $x = \dfrac{3\pi}{4}, \dfrac{7\pi}{4}$.

$\cot x = 3 \Rightarrow \tan x = \dfrac{1}{3} \Rightarrow x = \tan^{-1}\left(\dfrac{1}{3}\right) = 0.3217...$

There is another solution in the interval at
$\pi + 0.317...$, so $x = 0.322, 3.46$ (3 s.f.)

So $x = 0.322, 2.36, 3.46, 5.50$ (3 s.f.)

[7 marks available — 1 mark for using the identity
cosec² x ≡ 1 + cot² x, 1 mark for rearranging to form a quadratic
in cot x, 1 mark for factorising the quadratic, 1 mark for finding
the two correct values of cot x, 1 mark for using cot x = 1/tan x,
1 mark for using tan⁻¹ and the periodicity of tan to get two
correct values of x, 1 mark for all four values of x correct]

Q8 a) $\cot \theta + \tan \theta \equiv \dfrac{\cos \theta}{\sin \theta} + \dfrac{\sin \theta}{\cos \theta} \equiv \dfrac{\cos \theta \cos \theta}{\sin \theta \cos \theta} + \dfrac{\sin \theta \sin \theta}{\sin \theta \cos \theta}$

$\equiv \dfrac{\cos^2 \theta + \sin^2 \theta}{\sin \theta \cos \theta} \equiv \dfrac{1}{\sin \theta \cos \theta} \equiv \dfrac{1}{\frac{1}{2}\sin 2\theta} \equiv 2 \operatorname{cosec} 2\theta$

[3 marks available — 1 mark for expressing cot and tan
in terms of sin and cos, 1 mark for combining into a single
fraction, 1 mark for using the sine double angle formula
to show the required result]

b) By replacing θ with 2θ in the result from a):
$\cot 2\theta + \tan 2\theta \equiv 2 \operatorname{cosec} 4\theta$.

So $2 \operatorname{cosec} 4\theta = \dfrac{7}{2} \Rightarrow \operatorname{cosec} 4\theta = \dfrac{7}{4} \Rightarrow \sin 4\theta = \dfrac{4}{7}$

$\Rightarrow 4\theta = \sin^{-1}\left(\dfrac{4}{7}\right) = 0.6082...$

Look for solutions in the interval $0 \le 4\theta \le 4\pi$.
There are three more solutions in this interval at
$\pi - 0.6082...$, $2\pi + 0.6082...$ and $3\pi - 0.6082...$,
so $4\theta = 0.6082..., 2.533..., 6.891... 8.816...$
$\Rightarrow \theta = 0.152, 0.633, 1.72$ and 2.20 (all to 3 s.f.)

[5 marks available — 1 mark for adjusting the identity from
part a), 1 mark for an equation in terms of sin, 1 mark for
finding the first solution for 4θ, 1 mark for a method to
convert the solutions for 4θ into solutions for θ, 1 mark
for all four correct solutions]

Q9 a) The minimum value of h(t) occurs when
$\sin\left(\frac{1}{2}(t - \pi)\right) = -1$, so $9 = a + b(-1) = a - b$.
The maximum value occurs when
$\sin\left(\frac{1}{2}(t - \pi)\right) = 1$, so $17 = a + b$.
Solving simultaneously by adding the equations together:
$17 + 9 = 2a \Rightarrow 26 = 2a \Rightarrow a = 13$.
Then $9 = 13 - b \Rightarrow b = 4$.

[3 marks available — 1 mark for using the maximum
and minimum properties of sin to generate two equations,
1 mark for solving simultaneously, 1 mark for the correct
values of both a and b]

b) Low tide occurs when $\sin\left(\frac{1}{2}(t - \pi)\right) = -1$
$\Rightarrow \left(\frac{1}{2}(t - \pi)\right) = -\dfrac{\pi}{2} \Rightarrow t = 0$ *[1 mark]*
And when h(t) = 11:

$13 + 4 \sin\left(\frac{1}{2}(t - \pi)\right) = 11 \Rightarrow \sin\left(\frac{1}{2}(t - \pi)\right) = -\dfrac{1}{2}$ *[1 mark]*

$\Rightarrow \frac{1}{2}(t - \pi) = \sin^{-1}\left(\dfrac{1}{2}\right) = -\dfrac{\pi}{6} \Rightarrow t - \pi = -\dfrac{\pi}{3}$ *[1 mark]*

$\Rightarrow t = \dfrac{2\pi}{3} = 2.09$ (3 s.f.)

The tide reaches 11 feet at
$2.09 - 0 = 2.09$ hours after low tide. *[1 mark]*
[4 marks available — as above]

Q10 $\tan x (\operatorname{cosec} 2x + \cot 2x) \equiv \tan x \left(\dfrac{1}{\sin 2x} + \dfrac{1}{\tan 2x}\right)$

$\equiv \tan x \left(\dfrac{1}{\sin 2x} + \dfrac{\cos 2x}{\sin 2x}\right) \equiv \tan x \left(\dfrac{1 + \cos 2x}{\sin 2x}\right)$

$\equiv \tan x \left(\dfrac{1 + (2\cos^2 x - 1)}{2 \sin x \cos x}\right) \equiv \tan x \left(\dfrac{2\cos^2 x}{2 \sin x \cos x}\right)$

$\equiv \tan x \left(\dfrac{\cos x}{\sin x}\right) \equiv \tan x \left(\dfrac{1}{\tan x}\right) \equiv 1$

[5 marks available — 1 mark for using the identity
cosec 2x = $\frac{1}{\sin 2x}$, 1 mark for using cot 2x = $\frac{\cos 2x}{\sin 2x}$,
1 mark for using cos 2x = 2 cos² x − 1, 1 mark for
sin 2x = 2 sin x cos x, 1 mark for cancelling to get
tan x × $\frac{1}{\tan x}$ or tan x × cot x]
There are often many ways to prove an identity —
you'll get the marks for it as long as each step makes sense.

Chapter 4: Coordinate Geometry in the (x, y) Plane

4.1 Parametric Equations of Curves

Exercise 4.1.1 — Finding coordinates from parametric equations

Q1 a) $x = 3t = 3 \times 5 = 15$
$y = t^2 = 5^2 = 25$
So coordinates are (15, 25).

b) $18 = 3t \Rightarrow t = 6$

c) $36 = t^2 \Rightarrow t = \pm 6 \Rightarrow x = \pm 18$

Q2 a) $x = 2t - 1 = (2 \times 7) - 1 = 13$
$y = 4 - t^2 = 4 - 7^2 = -45$
So coordinates are (13, −45).

b) $2t - 1 = 15 \Rightarrow t = 8$

c) $4 - t^2 = -5 \Rightarrow t = \pm 3 \Rightarrow x = -7$ or 5

Q3 a) $x = 2 + \sin \theta = 2 + \sin \dfrac{\pi}{4} = \dfrac{4 + \sqrt{2}}{2}$

$y = -3 + \cos \theta = -3 + \cos \dfrac{\pi}{4} = \dfrac{\sqrt{2} - 6}{2}$

So coordinates are $\left(\dfrac{4 + \sqrt{2}}{2}, \dfrac{\sqrt{2} - 6}{2}\right)$.

b) $2 + \sin \theta = \frac{4 + \sqrt{3}}{2} = 2 + \frac{\sqrt{3}}{2}$

$\Rightarrow \sin \theta = \frac{\sqrt{3}}{2} \Rightarrow \theta = \frac{\pi}{3}$

c) $-3 + \cos \theta = -\frac{7}{2} \Rightarrow \cos \theta = -\frac{1}{2} \Rightarrow \theta = \frac{2\pi}{3}$

The angle in a) was given in radians so make sure you use radians for b) and c). They're both cos values you should know an angle for off by heart. The cos value in part c) is negative so you can use the CAST diagram (have a look at your Year 1 notes) to figure out which angle you need (cos is negative in the 2nd and 3rd quadrants).

Q4 a) $33 = 6 + 3t^2 \Rightarrow t^2 = 9 \Rightarrow t = \pm3$

b) $6 = t^2 + 5t \Rightarrow t^2 + 5t - 6 = 0 \Rightarrow (t + 6)(t - 1) = 0$
$\Rightarrow t = -6 \text{ or } t = 1$
$\Rightarrow y = 6 + 3(-6)^2 = 114 \text{ or } y = 6 + 3(1)^2 = 9$
So $y = 9$ or 114

Q5

t	−5	−4	−3	−2	−1	1	2	3	4	5
x	−25	−20	−15	−10	−5	5	10	15	20	25
y	$-\frac{2}{5}$	$-\frac{1}{2}$	$-\frac{2}{3}$	−1	−2	2	1	$\frac{2}{3}$	$\frac{1}{2}$	$\frac{2}{5}$

When $t = 0$, y is undefined, so there must be an asymptote.

Q6

θ	0	$\frac{\pi}{4}$	$\frac{\pi}{3}$	$\frac{\pi}{2}$	$\frac{2\pi}{3}$	$\frac{3\pi}{4}$	π	$\frac{4\pi}{3}$	$\frac{3\pi}{2}$	$\frac{5\pi}{3}$	2π
x	1	1.71	1.87	2	1.87	1.71	1	0.13	0	0.13	1
y	3	2.71	2.5	2	1.5	1.29	1	1.5	2	2.5	3

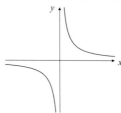

Q7 a) When $y = 1$, $x = a$, so:
$1 = 10 - t^2 \Rightarrow t^2 = 9 \Rightarrow t = \pm3$
When $t = 3$, $x = 2(3)^2 - 7(3) = -3$.
When $t = -3$, $x = 2(-3)^2 - 7(-3) = 39$.
$a > 1$, so $a = 39$.

b) At $(-6, 4)$, $x = -6 \Rightarrow -6 = 2t^2 - 7t$
$\Rightarrow 2t^2 - 7t + 6 = 0 \Rightarrow (2t - 3)(t - 2) = 0$
$\Rightarrow t = \frac{3}{2}, t = 2$
$t = \frac{3}{2} \Rightarrow y = 10 - \left(\frac{3}{2}\right)^2 = \frac{31}{4} \neq 4$
$t = 2 \Rightarrow y = 10 - 2^2 = 6 \neq 4$
So neither of the t-values when $x = -6$ corresponds to $y = 4$, so $(-6, 4)$ is not on the curve.
You could have started with $y = 4$ and used a similar method to show that $x \neq -6$ at this point.

Q8 a) When $\theta = 0$: $x = 3 \sin 0 = 3(0) = 0$
$y = 7 + 9 \cos 0 = 7 + 9(1) = 16$
The comet is at $(0, 16)$, so the distance to the Sun at $(0, 0)$ is 16 AU.

b) When $\theta = \frac{\pi}{2}$: $x = 3 \sin \frac{\pi}{2} = 3(1) = 3$
$y = 7 + 9 \cos \frac{\pi}{2} = 7 + 9(0) = 7$
The comet is at $(3, 7)$, so the distance to the Sun at $(0, 0)$ is $\sqrt{3^2 + 7^2} = \sqrt{58} = 7.62$ AU (to 3 s.f.).

Q9 a) When $t = 2$, $x = 2^2 + 4(2) = 4 + 8 = 12$
The plane travels 12 m horizontally in the first 2 s.

b) Sonia is standing at the point $x = 21$.
$x = 21 \Rightarrow t^2 + 4t = 21 \Rightarrow t^2 + 4t - 21 = 0$
$\Rightarrow (t + 7)(t - 3) = 0 \Rightarrow t = -7 \text{ or } t = 3$
The parametric equations are only valid for $0 \leq t \leq 5$, so the plane is at $x = 21$ when $t = 3$.
When $t = 3$, $y = 25 - 3^2 = 25 - 9 = 16$
The plane passes over Sonia's head at a height of 16 m.

Exercise 4.1.2 — Finding intersections

Q1 At A: $y = 0 \Rightarrow -2 + t = 0 \Rightarrow t = 2$
$x = 3 + t = 3 + 2 = 5$
At B: $x = 0 \Rightarrow 3 + t = 0 \Rightarrow t = -3$
$y = -2 + (-3) = -5$
So the coordinates are A(5, 0) and B(0, −5).

Q2 a) The curve meets the x-axis when $y = 0$, so:
$3t^3 - 24 = 0 \Rightarrow 3(t^3 - 8) = 0 \Rightarrow t^3 = 8 \Rightarrow t = 2$

b) The curve meets the y-axis when $x = 0$, so:
$2t^2 - 50 = 0 \Rightarrow 2(t^2 - 25) = 0 \Rightarrow t^2 = 25 \Rightarrow t = \pm5$
If you'd have been asked to give the coordinates you would then just put the t values into the parametric equations.

Q3 The curve meets the y-axis when $x = 0$, so:
$64 - t^3 = 0 \Rightarrow t^3 = 64 \Rightarrow t = 4$
$y = \frac{1}{t} = \frac{1}{4}$, so P is $\left(0, \frac{1}{4}\right)$.

Q4 $y = x - 3 \Rightarrow 4t = (2t + 1) - 3 \Rightarrow 2t = -2 \Rightarrow t = -1$
To find the coordinates when $t = -1$, just put this value back into the parametric equations...
$x = (2 \times -1) + 1 = -1$, $y = 4 \times -1 = -4$
So P is $(-1, -4)$.

Q5 $y = x^2 + 32 \Rightarrow 6t^2 = (2t)^2 + 32 \Rightarrow 6t^2 = 4t^2 + 32$
$\Rightarrow 2t^2 = 32 \Rightarrow t^2 = 16 \Rightarrow t = \pm4$
When $t = 4$: $x = 2 \times 4 = 8$, $y = 6 \times 4^2 = 96$
So one point of intersection is (8, 96).
When $t = -4$: $x = 2 \times -4 = -8$, $y = 6 \times (-4)^2 = 96$
So the other point of intersection is (−8, 96).

Q6 $x^2 + y^2 = 32 \Rightarrow (t^2)^2 + (2t)^2 = 32 \Rightarrow t^4 + 4t^2 - 32 = 0$
$\Rightarrow (t^2 - 4)(t^2 + 8) = 0 \Rightarrow t^2 = 4 \Rightarrow t = \pm2$
(there are no real solutions to $t^2 = -8$).
When $t = 2$: $x = 2^2 = 4$, $y = 2 \times 2 = 4$
So one point of intersection is (4, 4).
When $t = -2$: $x = (-2)^2 = 4$, $y = 2 \times -2 = -4$
So the other point of intersection is (4, −4).

Q7 a) At the point (0, 4):
$x = 0 \Rightarrow a(t - 2) = 0 \Rightarrow t = 2$ (as $a \neq 0$)
$y = 4 \Rightarrow 2at^2 + 3 = 4 \Rightarrow 2a(2^2) + 3 = 4$
$\Rightarrow 8a + 3 = 4 \Rightarrow a = \frac{1}{8}$.

b) The curve would meet the x-axis when $y = 0$.
$y = 2at^2 + 3 = \frac{2t^2}{8} + 3 = \frac{t^2}{4} + 3$
So at the x-axis, $\frac{t^2}{4} + 3 = 0 \Rightarrow t^2 = -12$.
This has no real solutions, so the curve does not meet the x-axis.

Q8 a) The curve crosses the x-axis when $y = 0$.
$t^2 - 9 = 0 \Rightarrow t = \pm3$
When $t = 3$, $x = \frac{2}{3}$, so one point is $\left(\frac{2}{3}, 0\right)$.
When $t = -3$, $x = -\frac{2}{3}$, so the other point is $\left(-\frac{2}{3}, 0\right)$.

b) The curve would meet the y-axis when $x = 0$, i.e. when $\frac{2}{t} = 0$. This has no solutions, so the curve does not meet the y-axis.

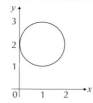

c) $y = \dfrac{10}{x} - 3 \Rightarrow t^2 - 9 = \dfrac{10t}{2} - 3 \Rightarrow t^2 - 5t - 6 = 0$

$\Rightarrow (t+1)(t-6) = 0 \Rightarrow t = -1$ and $t = 6$

When $t = -1$: $x = -2$, $y = (-1)^2 - 9 = -8$

So one point of intersection is $(-2, -8)$.

When $t = 6$: $x = \dfrac{2}{6} = \dfrac{1}{3}$, $y = 6^2 - 9 = 27$

So the other point of intersection is $\left(\dfrac{1}{3}, 27\right)$.

Q9 a) The curve meets the x-axis when $y = 0$.

$5 \cos t = 0 \Rightarrow \cos t = 0 \Rightarrow t = \dfrac{\pi}{2}$ and $\dfrac{3\pi}{2}$.

When $t = \dfrac{\pi}{2}$, $x = 3 \sin\left(\dfrac{\pi}{2}\right) = 3$, so $(3, 0)$.

When $t = \dfrac{3\pi}{2}$, $x = 3 \sin\left(\dfrac{3\pi}{2}\right) = -3$, so $(-3, 0)$.

So the curve crosses the x-axis twice in the domain $0 \le t \le 2\pi$, at $(-3, 0)$ and $(3, 0)$.

The curve meets the y-axis when $x = 0$.

$3 \sin t = 0 \Rightarrow \sin t = 0 \Rightarrow t = 0$, π and 2π.

When $t = 0$, $y = 5 \cos 0 = 5$, so $(0, 5)$.

When $t = \pi$, $y = 5 \cos \pi = -5$, so $(0, -5)$.

When $t = 2\pi$, $y = 5 \cos 2\pi = 5$, so $(0, 5)$.

So the curve crosses the y-axis twice in the domain $0 \le t \le 2\pi$, at $(0, -5)$ and $(0, 5)$.

b) $y = \left(\dfrac{5\sqrt{3}}{9}\right)x \Rightarrow 5 \cos t = \left(\dfrac{5\sqrt{3}}{3}\right)\sin t$

$\Rightarrow \dfrac{15}{5\sqrt{3}} = \dfrac{\sin t}{\cos t} = \tan t \Rightarrow \tan t = \dfrac{3}{\sqrt{3}} = \sqrt{3}$

$\Rightarrow t = \dfrac{\pi}{3}$ and $\left(\pi + \dfrac{\pi}{3}\right) \Rightarrow t = \dfrac{\pi}{3}$ and $\dfrac{4\pi}{3}$

When $t = \dfrac{\pi}{3}$: $x = 3 \sin \dfrac{\pi}{3} = \dfrac{3\sqrt{3}}{2}$

$y = 5 \cos \dfrac{\pi}{3} = \dfrac{5}{2}$

So one point of intersection is $\left(\dfrac{3\sqrt{3}}{2}, \dfrac{5}{2}\right)$

When $t = \dfrac{4\pi}{3}$: $x = 3 \sin \dfrac{4\pi}{3} = -\dfrac{3\sqrt{3}}{2}$

$y = 5 \cos \dfrac{4\pi}{3} = -\dfrac{5}{2}$

So the other point of intersection is $\left(-\dfrac{3\sqrt{3}}{2}, -\dfrac{5}{2}\right)$

Q10 The ships will collide if they have the same x- and y-coordinates at the same time. To find the value of t when they both have the same x-coordinate, set the two equations for x equal to each other:

$x_1 = x_2 \Rightarrow 24 - t = t + 10 \Rightarrow 14 = 2t \Rightarrow t = 7$

Now see if the y-coordinates are the same when $t = 7$:

$t = 7 \Rightarrow y_1 = 10 + 3(7) = 31$,

$\qquad y_2 = 12 + 2(7) - 0.1(7)^2 = 21.1$

$t = 7$ minutes is the only time when $x_1 = x_2$, but $y_1 \neq y_2$ at this time, so they will not collide.

You could have done this the other way around, by setting $y_1 = y_2$ to find the values of t when the y-coordinates are equal. In this case, that's a much more difficult way to solve the question — it gives you a fairly awkward quadratic to solve, and you end up with two values of t to test instead of one.

This question shows how parametric equations can be useful in modelling — if you drew the two Cartesian graphs, you'd find they cross in two places, so you might think the ships would collide. It's only when you think about how the ships' positions depend on time that you can work out what actually happens.

4.2 Parametric and Cartesian Equations

Exercise 4.2.1 — Converting parametric equations to Cartesian equations

Q1 a) $x = t + 3 \Rightarrow t = x - 3$,

so $y = t^2 = (x - 3)^2 = x^2 - 6x + 9$

b) $x = 3t \Rightarrow t = \dfrac{x}{3}$ so $y = \dfrac{6}{t} = \dfrac{18}{x}$

c) $x = 2t^3 \Rightarrow t = \left(\dfrac{x}{2}\right)^{\frac{1}{3}}$, so $y = t^2 = \left(\dfrac{x}{2}\right)^{\frac{2}{3}}$

d) $x = t + 7 \Rightarrow t = x - 7$,

so $y = 12 - 2t = 12 - 2(x - 7) = 26 - 2x$

e) $x = t + 4 \Rightarrow t = x - 4$,

so $y = t^2 - 9 = (x - 4)^2 - 9 = x^2 - 8x + 7$

f) $x = \dfrac{t + 2}{3} \Rightarrow t = 3x - 2$,

so $y = t^2 - t = (3x - 2)^2 - (3x - 2)$

$= 9x^2 - 12x + 4 - 3x + 2 = 9x^2 - 15x + 6$

g) $y = 5 - 8t \Rightarrow t = \dfrac{5 - y}{8}$,

so $x = t^2 - \dfrac{t}{2} = \left(\dfrac{5-y}{8}\right)^2 - \dfrac{5-y}{16} = \dfrac{y^2 - 6y + 5}{64}$

Here you have to find t in terms of y first and substitute into the equation for x.

h) $x = \sin\theta$, $y = \cos\theta$

Use trig identities here rather than rearranging...

$\sin^2\theta + \cos^2\theta \equiv 1 \Rightarrow x^2 + y^2 = 1$

i) $x = \sin\theta$, $y = \cos 2\theta$

The 2θ should make you think of the double angle formulae...

$\cos 2\theta \equiv 1 - 2\sin^2\theta \Rightarrow y = 1 - 2x^2$

j) $x = 1 + \sin\theta \Rightarrow \sin\theta = x - 1$

$y = 2 + \cos\theta \Rightarrow \cos\theta = y - 2$

$\sin^2\theta + \cos^2\theta \equiv 1 \Rightarrow (x - 1)^2 + (y - 2)^2 = 1$

You can leave this equation in the form it's in — it's the equation of a circle radius 1, centre (1, 2).

k) $x = \cos\theta$, $y = \cos 2\theta$

$\cos 2\theta \equiv 2\cos^2\theta - 1 \Rightarrow y = 2x^2 - 1$

l) $x = \cos\theta - 5 \Rightarrow \cos\theta = x + 5$

$y = \cos 2\theta \equiv 2\cos^2\theta - 1 \Rightarrow y = 2(x + 5)^2 - 1$

$= 2x^2 + 20x + 49$

Q2 $x = \tan\theta$, $y = \sec\theta$

Using the identity $\sec^2\theta \equiv 1 + \tan^2\theta$ gives: $y^2 = 1 + x^2$

Q3 $x = 2 \cot\theta \Rightarrow \cot\theta = \dfrac{x}{2}$

$y = 3 \operatorname{cosec}\theta \Rightarrow \operatorname{cosec}\theta = \dfrac{y}{3}$

Using the identity $\operatorname{cosec}^2\theta \equiv 1 + \cot^2\theta$ gives:

$\dfrac{y^2}{9} = 1 + \dfrac{x^2}{4} \Rightarrow y^2 = 9 + \dfrac{9x^2}{4}$

Q4 a) From the parametric equations the centre of the circle is $(5, -3)$, and the radius is 1.

b) $x = 5 + \sin\theta \Rightarrow \sin\theta = x - 5$

$y = -3 + \cos\theta \Rightarrow \cos\theta = y + 3$

Using the identity $\sin^2\theta + \cos^2\theta \equiv 1$ gives:

$(x - 5)^2 + (y + 3)^2 = 1$

Q5 a) $x = \dfrac{1 + 2t}{t} \Rightarrow xt = 1 + 2t \Rightarrow xt - 2t = 1$

$\Rightarrow t(x - 2) = 1 \Rightarrow t = \dfrac{1}{(x - 2)}$

b) $y = \dfrac{3 + t}{t^2} = \dfrac{3 + \dfrac{1}{(x-2)}}{\dfrac{1}{(x-2)^2}} = 3(x - 2)^2 + (x - 2)$

$= 3(x^2 - 4x + 4) + x - 2$

$= 3x^2 - 11x + 10$

$= (3x - 5)(x - 2)$

c)

Q6 $x = \dfrac{2 - 3t}{1 + t} \Rightarrow x(1 + t) = 2 - 3t \Rightarrow x + xt = 2 - 3t$

$\Rightarrow xt + 3t = 2 - x \Rightarrow t(x + 3) = 2 - x \Rightarrow t = \dfrac{2 - x}{x + 3}$

$y = \dfrac{5 - t}{4t + 1} = \dfrac{5 - \left(\dfrac{2-x}{x+3}\right)}{4\left(\dfrac{2-x}{x+3}\right) + 1} = \dfrac{5(x+3) - (2-x)}{4(2-x) + (x+3)}$

$\Rightarrow y = \dfrac{6x + 13}{11 - 3x}$

You could also write this as $6x - 11y + 3xy + 13 = 0$

Q7 $x = 5 \sin^2\theta \Rightarrow \sin^2\theta = \dfrac{x}{5}$, $y = \cos\theta$

Using the identity $\sin^2\theta + \cos^2\theta \equiv 1$ gives:

$\dfrac{x}{5} + y^2 = 1 \Rightarrow y^2 = 1 - \dfrac{x}{5}$

Q8 **a)** $x = a \sin \theta \Rightarrow \sin \theta = \frac{x}{a}$

$y = b \cos \theta \Rightarrow \cos \theta = \frac{y}{b}$

Using the identity $\sin^2 \theta + \cos^2 \theta \equiv 1$ gives: $\left(\frac{x}{a}\right)^2 + \left(\frac{y}{b}\right)^2 = 1$

b) To sketch the graph, find the x- and y-intercepts.

When $x = 0$, $\left(\frac{y}{b}\right)^2 = 1 \Rightarrow y = \pm b$.

When $y = 0$, $\left(\frac{x}{a}\right)^2 = 1 \Rightarrow x = \pm a$.

So the curve looks like this:

c) An ellipse.
If a and b were equal it would be a circle.

Q9 **a)** $y = 2t - 1 \Rightarrow t = \frac{y+1}{2}$

$x = 3t^2 = 3\left(\frac{y+1}{2}\right)^2 = \frac{3}{4}(y+1)^2$

b) Substitute $y = 4x - 3$ into the equation:

$x = \frac{3}{4}(4x - 3 + 1)^2 \Rightarrow 4x = 3(4x - 2)^2$

$4x = 3(16x^2 - 16x + 4) \Rightarrow 4x = 48x^2 - 48x + 12$

$12x^2 - 13x + 3 = 0 \Rightarrow (3x - 1)(4x - 3) = 0$

$x = \frac{1}{3}$ and $x = \frac{3}{4}$

$y = 4\left(\frac{1}{3}\right) - 3 = -\frac{5}{3}$ and $y = 4\left(\frac{3}{4}\right) - 3 = 0$

So the curve and the line intersect at $\left(\frac{1}{3}, -\frac{5}{3}\right)$ and $\left(\frac{3}{4}, 0\right)$.

Q10 $x = 7t + 2 \Rightarrow t = \frac{x-2}{7}$

$y = \frac{5}{t} = \frac{5}{\left(\frac{x-2}{7}\right)} = \frac{35}{x-2}$

This is the graph of $y = \frac{1}{x}$ stretched vertically by a factor of 35 and translated right by 2.

The y-intercept is at $x = 0$, so $y = \frac{35}{-2} = -17.5$.

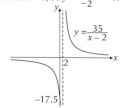

Review Exercise — Chapter 4

Q1 **a)** $x = \frac{1}{t} \Rightarrow t = \frac{1}{x}$. So when $x = \frac{1}{4}$, $t = 4$, and

$y = \frac{2}{t^2} = \frac{2}{4^2} = \frac{1}{8}$.

b) $\frac{2}{t^2} = \frac{1}{50} \Rightarrow t^2 = 100 \Rightarrow t = \pm 10$

Q2 The curve crosses the y-axis at $x = 0$, so:

$0 = t^3 + t^2 - 6t \Rightarrow t(t^2 + t - 6) = 0 \Rightarrow t(t + 3)(t - 2) = 0$

So $t = 0$, -3 or 2.

When $t = 0$, $y = 4(0) - 5 = -5$.

When $t = -3$, $y = 4(-3) - 5 = -17$.

When $t = 2$, $y = 4(2) - 5 = 3$.

So the coordinates are $(0, -5)$, $(0, -17)$ and $(0, 3)$.

Q3 **a)** When $t = 0$, $x = \frac{6-0}{2} = 3$, $y = 2(0)^2 + 0 + 4 = 4$,

When $t = 1$, $x = \frac{6-1}{2} = 2.5$, $y = 2(1)^2 + 1 + 4 = 7$

When $t = 2$, $x = \frac{6-2}{2} = 2$, $y = 2(2)^2 + 2 + 4 = 14$,

When $t = 3$, $x = \frac{6-3}{2} = 1.5$, $y = 2(3)^2 + 3 + 4 = 25$

b) **(i)** $-7 = \frac{6-t}{2} \Rightarrow -14 = 6 - t \Rightarrow t = 20$

(ii) $19 = 2t^2 + t + 4 \Rightarrow 2t^2 + t - 15 = 0$

$\Rightarrow (2t - 5)(t + 3) = 0 \Rightarrow t = 2.5, t = -3$

c) $x = \frac{6-t}{2} \Rightarrow t = 6 - 2x$

$y = 2(6 - 2x)^2 + (6 - 2x) + 4$

$y = 2(36 - 24x + 4x^2) + 6 - 2x + 4$

$y = 8x^2 - 50x + 82$

Q4 Substitute the parametric equations for x and y in $y = 10x - 8$:

$t^2 - t = 10\left(\frac{t+3}{5}\right) - 8 \Rightarrow t^2 - t = 2t + 6 - 8$

$\Rightarrow t^2 - 3t + 2 = 0 \Rightarrow (t - 2)(t - 1) = 0$

So they cross when $t = 1$ and $t = 2$.

When $t = 1$, $x = \frac{1+3}{5} = \frac{4}{5}$, $y = 1^2 - 1 = 0$.

When $t = 2$, $x = \frac{2+3}{5} = 1$, $y = 2^2 - 2 = 2$.

So the coordinates are $\left(\frac{4}{5}, 0\right)$ and $(1, 2)$.

Q5 **a)** **(i)** $x = 2 \sin \frac{\pi}{4} = \sqrt{2}$

$y = \cos^2 \frac{\pi}{4} + 4 = \frac{9}{2}$

So the coordinates are $\left(\sqrt{2}, \frac{9}{2}\right)$.

(ii) $x = 2 \sin \frac{\pi}{6} = 1$

$y = \cos^2 \frac{\pi}{6} + 4 = \frac{19}{4}$

So the coordinates are $\left(1, \frac{19}{4}\right)$.

b) $x = 2 \sin \theta \Rightarrow \sin \theta = \frac{x}{2}$

$y = \cos^2 \theta + 4$

$\cos^2 \theta \equiv 1 - \sin^2 \theta \Rightarrow y = 1 - \left(\frac{x}{2}\right)^2 + 4$

$\Rightarrow y = 5 - \frac{x^2}{4}$

c) $-1 \leq \sin \theta \leq 1 \Rightarrow -2 \leq 2 \sin \theta \leq 2 \Rightarrow -2 \leq x \leq 2$

Q6 $x = \frac{\sin \theta}{3} \Rightarrow \sin \theta = 3x$, $y = 3 + 2 \cos 2\theta$

Use one of the double angle formulae here:

$\cos 2\theta \equiv 1 - 2 \sin^2 \theta \Rightarrow y = 3 + 2(1 - 2 \sin^2 \theta)$

$\Rightarrow y = 3 + 2(1 - 2(3x)^2) \Rightarrow y = 3 + 2 - 4(9x^2) \Rightarrow y = 5 - 36x^2$

Q7 **a)** The curve crosses the y-axis at $x = 0$, so:

$t^2 - 1 = 0 \Rightarrow t = \pm 1$

When $t = -1$, $y = 4 - 3 = 1$.

When $t = 1$, $y = 4 + 3 = 7$.

So the coordinates are $(0, 1)$ and $(0, 7)$.

b) Substitute the parametric equations for x and y in $x + 2y = 14$:

$t^2 - 1 + 2(4 + \frac{3}{t}) = 14$

$\Rightarrow t^2 - 1 + 8 + \frac{6}{t} - 14 = 0$

$\Rightarrow t^3 - 7t + 6 = 0$

The coefficients add up to 0, so $(t - 1)$ is a factor.
Using e.g. algebraic division:

$(t - 1)(t^2 + t - 6) = 0 \Rightarrow (t - 1)(t - 2)(t + 3) = 0$

So $t = 1$, 2 or -3.

When $t = 1$, $x = 1^2 - 1 = 0$, $y = 4 + \frac{3}{1} = 7$.

When $t = 2$, $x = 2^2 - 1 = 3$, $y = 4 + \frac{3}{2} = 5.5$.

When $t = -3$, $x = (-3)^2 - 1 = 8$, $y = 4 + \frac{3}{-3} = 3$.

So the coordinates are $(0, 7)$, $(3, 5.5)$ and $(8, 3)$.

Q8 **a)** $x = 4 - \cos \frac{2\pi}{3} = \frac{9}{2}$

$y = \sin^4 \frac{\pi}{3} - \frac{1}{2} = \frac{1}{16}$

So the coordinates are $\left(\frac{9}{2}, \frac{1}{16}\right)$

b) $x = 0$ on the y-axis, but $x = 4 - \cos 2\theta$ can never be zero, as $-1 \leq \cos 2\theta \leq 1$, so $3 \leq x \leq 5$.

c) $x = 4 - \cos 2\theta$

Using $\cos 2\theta \equiv 1 - 2\sin^2\theta$:

$x = 4 - (1 - 2\sin^2\theta) \Rightarrow x - 3 = 2\sin^2\theta$

$\Rightarrow \sin^2\theta = \frac{x-3}{2}$

$y = \sin^4\theta - \frac{1}{2} = \left(\frac{x-3}{2}\right)^2 - \frac{1}{2}$

$\Rightarrow y = \frac{x^2 - 6x + 9}{4} - \frac{1}{2} \Rightarrow y = \frac{x^2 - 6x + 7}{4}$

Q9 a) $e^t \cos 2t = 0$

Since $e^t \neq 0$, $\cos 2t = 0$

$\Rightarrow 2t = \frac{\pi}{2}, \frac{3\pi}{2}, \frac{5\pi}{2}, \frac{7\pi}{2} \ldots$

$\Rightarrow t = \frac{\pi}{4}, \frac{3\pi}{4}, \frac{5\pi}{4}, \frac{7\pi}{4}$

When $t = \frac{\pi}{4}$, $x = -e^{\frac{\pi}{4}} \sin\frac{\pi}{2} = -e^{\frac{\pi}{4}}$

When $t = \frac{3\pi}{4}$, $x = -e^{\frac{3\pi}{4}} \sin\frac{3\pi}{2} = e^{\frac{3\pi}{4}}$

When $t = \frac{5\pi}{4}$, $x = -e^{\frac{5\pi}{4}} \sin\frac{5\pi}{2} = -e^{\frac{5\pi}{4}}$

When $t = \frac{7\pi}{4}$, $x = -e^{\frac{7\pi}{4}} \sin\frac{7\pi}{2} = e^{\frac{7\pi}{4}}$

So when $y = 0$, $x = -e^{\frac{\pi}{4}}, e^{\frac{3\pi}{4}}, -e^{\frac{5\pi}{4}}, e^{\frac{7\pi}{4}}$

b) (i) Use $d = \sqrt{x^2 + y^2}$ to find the distance of the particle from the origin. Substitute in the equations for x and y...

$d = \sqrt{(-e^t \sin 2t)^2 + (e^t \cos 2t)^2}$

$\Rightarrow d = \sqrt{e^{2t}\sin^2 2t + e^{2t}\cos^2 2t}$

$\Rightarrow d = \sqrt{e^{2t}(\sin^2 2t + \cos^2 2t)}$

...and use the identity $\sin^2\theta + \cos^2\theta \equiv 1$:

$\Rightarrow d = \sqrt{e^{2t}} \Rightarrow d = e^t$

(ii) From b)(i), $d = e^t$, so when $d = e^{\frac{\pi}{8}}$, $t = \frac{\pi}{8}$,

and so $x = -e^{\frac{\pi}{8}} \sin\frac{\pi}{4} = -\frac{\sqrt{2}}{2} e^{\frac{\pi}{8}}$, and

$y = e^{\frac{\pi}{8}} \cos\frac{\pi}{4} = \frac{\sqrt{2}}{2} e^{\frac{\pi}{8}}$.

So the coordinates are $\left(-\frac{\sqrt{2}}{2} e^{\frac{\pi}{8}}, \frac{\sqrt{2}}{2} e^{\frac{\pi}{8}}\right)$.

Exam-Style Questions — Chapter 4

Q1 a) At $x = 0$, $\frac{2t-3}{t} = 0 \Rightarrow t = \frac{3}{2}$

$\Rightarrow y = 2\left(\frac{3}{2}\right) + 6 = 9$

At $y = 0$, $2t + 6 = 0 \Rightarrow t = -3$

$\Rightarrow x = \frac{2(-3)-3}{-3} = 3$

So the curve crosses the coordinate axes at points $(0, 9)$ and $(3, 0)$.

[3 marks available — 1 mark for a correct method, 1 mark for each correct pair of coordinates]

b) Rearrange the equation for y:

$y = 2t + 6 \Rightarrow t = \frac{y-6}{2}$

Substitute into the equation for x:

$x = \frac{2\left(\frac{y-6}{2}\right)-3}{\left(\frac{y-6}{2}\right)} = \frac{2(y-6)-6}{y-6} = \frac{2y-18}{y-6}$

Rearrange to make y the subject:

$xy - 6x = 2y - 18 \Rightarrow xy - 2y = 6x - 18$

$\Rightarrow y(x - 2) = 6x - 18 \Rightarrow y = \frac{6(x-3)}{x-2}$

[3 marks available — 1 mark for equation for t in terms of x or y, 1 mark for substituting t into other equation, 1 mark for correct final answer given as $y = f(x)$]

c) $1 < t \leq 6$. When $t = 1$, $y = f(x) = 2(1) + 6 = 8$.

When $t = 6$, $y = f(x) = 2(6) + 6 = 18$.

So the range of $f(x)$ is $8 < f(x) \leq 18$.

[2 marks available — 1 mark for substituting the limits of t in an equation for y, 1 mark for correct final answer]

Q2 a) $x = 2t \Rightarrow t = \frac{x}{2}$

$\Rightarrow y = \frac{x}{2}\left(\frac{ax}{2} + 6\right) = \frac{a}{4}x^2 + 3x$

If $y = ax - 4$ is a tangent then it touches the curve once, at the point where $\frac{a}{4}x^2 + 3x = ax - 4$

$\Rightarrow ax^2 + 12x - 4ax + 16 = 0$

$\Rightarrow ax^2 + (12 - 4a)x + 16 = 0$

There should be one solution to this equation, so the discriminant should be zero:

$(12 - 4a)^2 - 4 \times a \times 16 = 0$

$\Rightarrow 144 - 96a + 16a^2 - 64a = 0$

$\Rightarrow a^2 - 10a + 9 = 0 \Rightarrow (a-1)(a-9) = 0$

So $a = 1$ or $a = 9$.

[4 marks available — 1 mark for Cartesian equation, 1 mark for equating the tangent and the curve to form a quadratic, 1 mark for using the discriminant = 0 (or otherwise using the fact that there is only one solution to this quadratic), 1 mark for both correct solutions for a]

b) From a), $a = 1$ or 9, so the Cartesian equation of the curve will be: $y = \frac{1}{4}x^2 + 3x = x\left(\frac{1}{4}x + 3\right)$

or $y = \frac{9}{4}x^2 + 3x = 3x\left(\frac{3}{4}x + 1\right)$.

$y = x\left(\frac{1}{4}x + 3\right)$ is a u-shaped quadratic (shown in black) through $(0, 0)$ and $(-12, 0)$, with a minimum point where $x = -6$ and $y = \frac{1}{4}(-6)^2 + 3(-6) = -9$.

$y = 3x\left(\frac{3}{4}x + 1\right)$ is a u-shaped quadratic (shown in grey) through $(0, 0)$ and $\left(-\frac{4}{3}, 0\right)$, with a minimum point where $x = -\frac{2}{3}$ and $y = \frac{9}{4}\left(-\frac{2}{3}\right)^2 + 3\left(-\frac{2}{3}\right) = -1$.

[4 marks available — 1 mark for two graphs with the correct shape, 1 mark for correct intersection at $(0, 0)$, 1 mark for correct axis-intercepts shown on one curve, 1 mark for correct axis-intercepts shown on the other curve]

Q3 a) Use an addition formula to write $y = 5\cos 3t$ in terms of $\cos 2t$, $\cos t$, $\sin 2t$ and $\sin t$:

$y = 5\cos(2t + t) = 5(\cos 2t \cos t - \sin 2t \sin t)$

Use double angle formulae to write everything in terms of $\cos t$ and $\sin t$:

$y = 5[(2\cos^2 t - 1)\cos t - (2\sin t \cos t)\sin t]$

$\quad = 5[2\cos^3 t - \cos t - 2\sin^2 t \cos t]$

Replace $\sin^2 t$ with $1 - \cos^2 t$:

$y = 5[2\cos^3 t - \cos t - 2(1 - \cos^2 t)\cos t]$

$\quad = 5[2\cos^3 t - \cos t - 2\cos t + 2\cos^3 t] = 5\cos t(4\cos^2 t - 3)$

Substitute $\cos t = \frac{x}{2}$:

$y = \frac{5x}{2}\left(\frac{4x^2}{4} - 3\right) = \frac{5}{2}x(x^2 - 3)$ as required,

i.e. $A = \frac{5}{2}$ and $B = 3$.

$-\pi < t < \pi \Rightarrow -1 < \cos t < 1 \Rightarrow -2 < 2\cos t < 2$, so the domain is $-2 < x < 2$.

[6 marks available — 1 mark for correct use of addition angle formula, 1 mark for correct use of double angle formula for $\cos 2t$, 1 mark for correct use of double angle formula for $\sin 2t$, 1 mark for writing y in terms of $\cos t$ only, 1 mark for correct Cartesian equation, 1 mark for correct domain]

b) The range of $y = 5\cos 3t$ is $-5 \leq y \leq 5$, so $y = 6$ cannot cross the curve *[1 mark]*.

c) A quick sketch will help. C is a positive cubic going through $(0, 0)$ and $(\pm\sqrt{3}, 0)$, with domain $-2 \le x \le 2$, and $y = kx$ is a straight line with a positive gradient through the origin:

From the graph, any line $y = kx$ whose gradient is greater than the line shown will not cross the curve 3 times. So the gradient of the line shown is the maximum value of k.

When $x = -2$, $y = \frac{5}{2}(-2)(4 - 3) = -5$

When $x = 2$, $y = \frac{5}{2}(2)(4 - 3) = 5$

So the straight line passes through $(-2, -5)$ and $(2, 5)$ when k is at its largest value.

So the gradient of the straight line, $k \le \frac{5 - (-5)}{2 - (-2)} \Rightarrow k \le 2.5$

You're told k is positive, so $0 < k \le 2.5$.

[4 marks available — 1 mark for identifying the limit of k relating to the domain of C, 1 mark for correct end points of the curve, 1 mark for using the end points to find the max gradient of the straight line, 1 mark for a correct range given for k]

Q4 a) When $x < 0$, $2t^2 + 3t < 0 \Rightarrow t(2t + 3) < 0 \Rightarrow -\frac{3}{2} < t < 0$

When $y < 0$, $2t^2 - 3t < 0 \Rightarrow t(2t - 3) < 0 \Rightarrow 0 < t < \frac{3}{2}$

These ranges do not overlap, so there are no values for t for which both x and y are negative.

[3 marks available — 1 mark for finding the values of t for a negative x, 1 mark for finding the values of t for a negative y, 1 mark for showing that they do not overlap]

b) t cannot easily be isolated in either equation. There is an xy term in the final answer, and multiplying the parametric equations together gives the difference of two squares:

$xy = (2t^2 + 3t)(2t^2 - 3t) = 4t^4 - 9t^2$

Adding the parametric equations gives:

$x + y = 2t^2 + 3t + 2t^2 - 3t = 4t^2 \Rightarrow t^2 = \frac{x + y}{4}$

Substitute $t^2 = \frac{x + y}{4}$ into xy and rearrange:

$xy = 4\left(\frac{x + y}{4}\right)^2 - 9\left(\frac{x + y}{4}\right)$

$\Rightarrow xy = \frac{1}{4}(x^2 + 2xy + y^2) - \frac{9}{4}(x + y)$

$\Rightarrow 4xy = x^2 + 2xy + y^2 - 9(x + y)$

$\Rightarrow 0 = x^2 + y^2 - 2xy - 9(x + y)$ — as required, where $A = -2$ and $B = -9$.

[5 marks available — 1 mark for finding xy, 1 mark for finding x + y, 1 mark for substituting for t², 1 mark for attempt to rearrange in the correct form, 1 mark for final answer with correct values of A and B]

Chapter 5: Sequences and Series

5.1 Sequences

Exercise 5.1.1 — n^{th} term

Q1 $a_{20} = 3(20) - 5 = 55$

Q2 4th term $= 4(4 + 2) = 24$

Q3 1st term $= (1 - 1)(1 + 1) = 0$
2nd term $= (2 - 1)(2 + 1) = 3$
Using the same method, 3rd, 4th and 5th terms $= 8, 15, 24$

Q4 $29 = 4k - 3 \Rightarrow k = 8$

Q5 $a_k = 13 - 6k$ and $a_{k+1} = 13 - 6(k + 1) = 7 - 6k$
The sequence is decreasing if $a_{k+1} < a_k$ for all values of k.
$7 - 6k < 13 - 6k \Rightarrow 7 < 13$, which is true so the sequence is decreasing.

Q6 $3^{-n} = \frac{1}{3^n}$, so $a_k = \frac{1}{3^k}$ and $a_{k+1} = \frac{1}{3^{k+1}}$
The sequence is decreasing if $a_{k+1} < a_k$ for all values of k.
Since k is a positive integer, so is 3^k, so you can multiply through by this without affecting the inequality:
$\frac{1}{3^{k+1}} < \frac{1}{3^k} \Rightarrow \frac{3^k}{3^{k+1}} < \frac{3^k}{3^k} \Rightarrow \frac{1}{3} < 1$
This is true, so the sequence is decreasing.

Q7 Form equations for the 2nd and 5th terms:
$15 = a(2^2) + b$, $99 = a(5^2) + b$
Solve the equations simultaneously to get $a = 4$, $b = -1$

Q8 Form equations for the first 3 terms:
$9 = (1^2)e + f + g$
$20 = (2^2)e + 2f + g$
$37 = (3^2)e + 3f + g$
Solve the equations simultaneously to get $e = 3$, $f = 2$, $g = 4$.
To solve simultaneous equations with 3 unknowns, you use a similar method to when there are 2 unknowns — it just takes a few more steps.

Q9 $49 = (n - 1)^2$, $n = 8$

Q10 This first 8 terms of the sequence are: 13, 11, 9, 7, 5, 3, 1, -1,... The sequence continues to decrease. So 7 terms are positive.
A different way to solve this one would be to use an inequality — set $15 - 2n > 0$ and solve for n (taking the integer value of n).

Exercise 5.1.2 — Recurrence relations

Q1 $u_1 = 10$
$u_2 = 3u_1 = 3(10) = 30$
$u_3 = 3u_2 = 3(30) = 90$
$u_4 = 3u_3 = 3(90) = 270$
$u_5 = 3u_4 = 3(270) = 810$

Q2 $u_1 = 2$
$u_2 = u_1^2 = 2^2 = 4$
$u_3 = u_2^2 = 4^2 = 16$
$u_4 = u_3^2 = 16^2 = 256$

Q3 $u_1 = 4$
$u_2 = \frac{-1}{u_1} = -\frac{1}{4}$
$u_3 = \frac{-1}{u_2} = \frac{-1}{\left(\frac{-1}{4}\right)} = 4$
$u_4 = \frac{-1}{u_3} = -\frac{1}{4}$
The sequence is periodic with order 2.

For Q4, 5, 6, you can use any letter in place of u.

Q4 Each term is the previous term doubled and the first term is 3.
$u_{n+1} = 2u_n$, $u_1 = 3$

Q5 a) Each term is 4 more than the previous term. The first term is 12.
$u_{n+1} = u_n + 4$, $u_1 = 12$

b) Work out the number of 'jumps' of 4 needed to get from 28 to 100:
$100 - 28 = 72$, $72 \div 4 = 18$
Add on the first 5 terms given in the question:
$18 + 5 = 23$ terms
You could have written an nth term expression and used it to find the position of 100 in the sequence (it's the last term). The nth term expression would be $4n + 8$.

Q6 $u_{n+1} = 11 - u_n$ or $u_{n+1} = 28 \div u_n$, with $u_1 = 7$.
This one is tricky. It's the sort you suddenly go "aah" with. There are other possible answers here, but these are the two simplest.

Q7 $u_1 = 4$, $u_2 = 3(4) - 1 = 11$, $u_3 = 3(11) - 1 = 32$
$u_4 = 3(32) - 1 = 95$, so $k = 4$

Q8 $x_1 = 9$, $x_2 = (9 + 1) \div 2 = 5$

Keep substituting the result into the formula until...

$x_6 = (\frac{3}{2} + 1) \div 2 = \frac{5}{4}$, so $r = 6$

Q9 $u_1 = 7$, $u_2 = 7 + 1 = 8$, $u_3 = 8 + 2 = 10$
$u_4 = 10 + 3 = 13$, $u_5 = 13 + 4 = 17$

Q10 Form an equation for getting u_2 from u_1, and an equation for getting u_3 from u_2:
$7 = 6a + b$
$8.5 = 7a + b$

Solve the equations simultaneously to get $a = 1.5$, $b = -2$

Q11 First 5 terms:
$u_1 = 8$, $u_2 = \frac{1}{2}(8) = 4$, $u_3 = \frac{1}{2}(4) = 2$
$u_4 = \frac{1}{2}(2) = 1$, $u_5 = \frac{1}{2}(1) = \frac{1}{2}$
The terms are all powers of 2:
$8 = 2^3$, $4 = 2^2$, $2 = 2^1$, $1 = 2^0$, $\frac{1}{2} = 2^{-1}$
so $u_n = 2^{(4-n)}$ or $u_n = 16 \div 2^n$

5.2 Arithmetic Sequences
Exercise 5.2.1 — Finding the nth term

Q1 $a = 7$, $d = 5$
n^{th} term $= a + (n-1)d = 7 + (n-1)5 = 5n + 2$
10th term $= 5(10) + 2 = 52$

Q2 **a)** $a = 6$, $d = 3$, so n^{th} term $= 6 + (n-1)3 = 3n + 3$

b) $a = 4$, $d = 5$, n^{th} term $= 5n - 1$

c) $a = 12$, $d = -4$, n^{th} term $= -4n + 16$

d) $a = 1.5$, $d = 2$, n^{th} term $= 2n - 0.5$

e) $a = 77$, $d = -8$, n^{th} term $= 85 - 8n$

f) $a = -2$, $d = -0.5$, n^{th} term $= -0.5n - 1.5$

Q3 Form equations for 4th and 10th terms:
n^{th} term $= a + (n-1)d$
$19 = a + (4-1)d \Rightarrow 19 = a + 3d$
$43 = a + (10-1)d \Rightarrow 43 = a + 9d$
Solving the simultaneous equations: $a = 7$, $d = 4$.

Q4 1st term $= u_1 = a = -5$
Form an equation for the 5th term:
n^{th} term $= a + (n-1)d$
$19 = a + (5-1)d \Rightarrow 19 = -5 + 4d \Rightarrow d = 6$
So $u_{10} = -5 + 9 \times 6 = 49$

Q5 Form equations for 7th and 11th terms:
n^{th} term $= a + (n-1)d$
$8 = a + (7-1)d \Rightarrow 8 = a + 6d$
$10 = a + (11-1)d \Rightarrow 10 = a + 10d$
Solving the simultaneous equations: $a = 5$, $d = 0.5$
So $u_3 = 5 + 2(0.5) = 6$

Q6 Form equations for 3rd and 7th terms:
n^{th} term $= a + (n-1)d$
$15 = a + (3-1)d \Rightarrow 15 = a + 2d$
$27 = a + (7-1)d \Rightarrow 27 = a + 6d$
Solving the simultaneous equations: $a = 9$, $d = 3$.
Now write an equation for the kth term: $66 = 9 + (k-1)3 = 6 + 3k$
And solve to find $k = 20$

Q7 The difference between all the terms is the same in an arithmetic sequence. Use this fact to set up an equation:
$\ln(x + 8) - \ln x = \ln(x + 48) - \ln(x + 8)$
$\Rightarrow \ln\left(\frac{x+8}{x}\right) = \ln\left(\frac{x+48}{x+8}\right) \Rightarrow \frac{x+8}{x} = \frac{x+48}{x+8}$
$\Rightarrow (x+8)^2 = (x+48)x \Rightarrow x^2 + 16x + 64 = x^2 + 48x$
$\Rightarrow 64 = 32x \Rightarrow x = 2$
So the common difference is $\ln(2 + 8) - \ln 2 = \ln 5$.
Add $\ln 5$ to the third term to get the next term:
$\ln(x + 48) + \ln 5 = \ln(2 + 48) + \ln 5 = \ln 250$.

Q8 For there to be 20 integer terms above 0 and below 100, there must be 19 'gaps' between the terms. The size of the gap is the common difference, d, where:
$1 + 19d < 100$ or $99 - 19d > 0$
$\Rightarrow d < 99 \div 19 = 5.2105...$ so the progression must have a common difference of $d = \pm 5$.
Using $d = 5$, $n = 11$ and $u_n = 47$:
$47 = a + 10 \times 5 \Rightarrow a = -3$
Using $d = -5$, $n = 11$ and $u_n = 47$:
$47 = a + 10 \times -5 \Rightarrow a = 97$

5.3 Arithmetic Series
Exercise 5.3.1 Sequences and Series

Q1 $a = 8$, $d = 3$
n^{th} term $= a + (n-1)d = 8 + (n-1)3 = 3n + 5$
10th term $= 3(10) + 5 = 35$
$S_n = \frac{n}{2}[2a + (n-1)d]$
$S_{10} = \frac{10}{2}[2(8) + 9(3)] = 215$
Alternatively, you could have used the $S_n = \frac{1}{2}n(a + l)$ formula here. You'd worked out the last term earlier in the question.

Q2 Form equations for 2nd and 5th terms:
n^{th} term $= a + (n-1)d$
$16 = a + d$
$10 = a + 4d$
Solving the simultaneous equations: $a = 18$, $d = -2$.
$S_n = \frac{n}{2}[2a + (n-1)d]$
$S_8 = \frac{8}{2}[2(18) + 7(-2)] = 88$

Q3 $a = 12$, $d = 6$
n^{th} term $= a + (n-1)d = 12 + (n-1)6 = 6n + 6$
$u_{100} = 6(100) + 6 = 606$
$S_n = \frac{1}{2}n(a + l)$
$S_{100} = \frac{1}{2} \times 100(12 + 606) = 30\,900$

Q4 1st term $a = 8(1) - 6 = 2$
20th term $l = 8(20) - 6 = 154$
$S_n = \frac{1}{2}n(a + l)$
$S_{20} = \frac{1}{2} \times 20(2 + 154) = 1560$
You could also read off $d = 8$ from the nth term and use the other formula.

Q5 $S_n = \frac{n}{2}[2a + (n-1)d]$
$S_{10} = \frac{10}{2}[2(-6) + 9d] = 345$
$-60 + 45d = 345$
So $d = 9$

Q6 $u_n = a + (n-1)d$
For the last term: $79 = 7 + 6(n-1) \Rightarrow n = 13$
$S_n = \frac{1}{2}n(a + l)$
$S_{13} = \frac{1}{2} \times 13(7 + 79) = 559$

Q7 **a)** $a = 5(1) - 2 = 3$
$l = 5(12) - 2 = 58$
$S_n = \frac{1}{2}n(a + l)$
$S_{12} = \frac{1}{2} \times 12(3 + 58) = 366$

b) $a = 20 - 2(1) = 18$, $l = 20 - 2(9) = 2$
$S_n = \frac{1}{2}n(a + l)$
$S_9 = \frac{1}{2} \times 9(18 + 2) = 90$

Q8 $a = 3, d = 2$

$$S_n = \frac{n}{2}[2a + (n-1)d]$$

$$960 = \frac{n}{2}[2(3) + 2(n-1)]$$

$$960 = n^2 + 2n$$

$$n^2 + 2n - 960 = 0$$

You're expecting a whole number for n, so you should be able to factorise the quadratic — you need two numbers that are 2 apart and multiply to give 960.

$$(n + 32)(n - 30) = 0$$

Ignore the negative solution since n needs to be positive, so $n = 30$.

Q9 $a = 5(1) + 2 = 7,\ l = 5k + 2$

$$S_n = \frac{1}{2}n(a + l)$$

$$553 = \frac{1}{2}k(7 + 5k + 2)$$

$$1106 = 5k^2 + 9k$$

$$5k^2 + 9k - 1106 = 0$$

Factorising gives: $(5k + 79)(k - 14) = 0$

Now we can ignore the negative solution, so $k = 14$.

This one looked very tricky to factorise, but you can cheat a little here — you know you're trying to get to k = 14, so one of the brackets is going to be (k − 14)...

Q10 The first thing to do is use the fact that it's an arithmetic progression to write down some equations — remember, there's a common difference, d, between each term.

$x + 11 + d = 4x + 4 \Rightarrow -3x + d = -7$

$x + 11 + 2d = 9x + 5 \Rightarrow -8x + 2d = -6$

You've now got a pair of simultaneous equations in d and x. Solving these gives $x = -4$, $d = -19$

So the first term is $a = -4 + 11 = 7$.

Now you can put $a = 7$, $d = -19$ and $n = 11$ into the formula for S_n:

$$S_n = \frac{n}{2}[2a + (n-1)d]$$

$$S_{11} = \frac{11}{2}[2(7) + 10(-19)]$$

$$S_{11} = \frac{11}{2} \times -176 = -968$$

Q11 $a = 36, d = -4$

$$S_n = \frac{n}{2}[2a + (n-1)d]$$

$$176 = \frac{n}{2}[2(36) - 4(n-1)]$$

$$88 = 19n - n^2$$

$$n^2 - 19n + 88 = 0$$

You know you should be able to factorise the quadratic as n is a whole number:

$$(n - 8)(n - 11) = 0$$

So $n = 8$ or 11.

Exercise 5.3.2 — Sum of the first n natural numbers

Q1 **a)** $S_n = \frac{1}{2}n(n + 1)$

$$S_{10} = \frac{1}{2} \times 10 \times 11 = 55$$

b) $S_{2000} = \frac{1}{2} \times 2000 \times 2001 = 2\,001\,000$

Q2 $S_{32} = \frac{1}{2} \times 32 \times 33 = 528$

Q3 $\sum\limits_{n=11}^{20} n = \sum\limits_{n=1}^{20} n - \sum\limits_{n=1}^{10} n = S_{20} - S_{10}$

$$S_{10} = \frac{1}{2} \times 10 \times 11 = 55$$

$$S_{20} = \frac{1}{2} \times 20 \times 21 = 210$$

$$\sum\limits_{n=11}^{20} n = 210 - 55 = 155$$

Q4 $66 = \frac{1}{2}n(n + 1)$

$$132 = n^2 + n$$

$$0 = n^2 + n - 132$$

$$(n + 12)(n - 11) = 0$$

$n = -12$ or 11 — so ignoring the negative answer, the sum of the first 11 terms is 66, so $n = 11$.

Q5 $S_n = \frac{1}{2}n(n + 1)$

$$120 = \frac{1}{2}k(k + 1)$$

$$240 = k^2 + k$$

$$0 = k^2 + k - 240$$

$$(k + 16)(k - 15) = 0$$

Ignoring the negative solution gives $k = 15$.

Q6 Subtract the sum of the first 15 natural numbers from the sum of the first 35:

$$S_{35} = \frac{1}{2} \times 35 \times 36 = 630$$

$$S_{15} = \frac{1}{2} \times 15 \times 16 = 120$$

So the sum of the series is $630 - 120 = 510$.

Q7 $S_n = \frac{1}{2}n(n + 1)$

$$\frac{1}{2}k(k + 1) > 1\,000\,000$$

$$k^2 + k > 2\,000\,000$$

$$k^2 + k - 2\,000\,000 > 0$$

Put the quadratic equal to zero and solve using the quadratic formula to get $k = 1413.7...$ or $-1414.7...$

It's a u-shaped quadratic, so the quadratic is positive when $k > 1413.7$ (ignoring the negative solution).

So the first natural number for which the sum exceeds $1\,000\,000$ is 1414.

5.4 Geometric Sequences and Series

Exercise 5.4.1 — Geometric sequences

Q1 E.g. $r = \dfrac{\text{second term}}{\text{first term}} = \dfrac{1875}{3125} = \dfrac{3}{5}$

Q2 Common ratio $r = \dfrac{\text{second term}}{\text{first term}} = \dfrac{3}{2} = 1.5$.

Then:

4th term = 3rd term $\times\ 1.5 = 4.5 \times 1.5 = 6.75$

5th term = 4th term $\times\ 1.5 = 6.75 \times 1.5 = 10.125$,

6th term = 5th term $\times\ 1.5 = 10.125 \times 1.5 = 15.1875$,

7th term = 6th term $\times\ 1.5 = 15.1875 \times 1.5 = 22.78125$.

This method isn't as slow as it looks because you can use a scientific calculator to get the terms of the series quickly: press '2 =' then '× 1.5 =' to get the second term. Pressing '=' repeatedly will give you the following terms. Even so, the method below is quicker, so unless you're asked to find the term after one you've already got, you're better off doing this:

Or: First term $a = 2$, common ratio $r = 1.5$

nth term $= ar^{n-1} = 2 \times (1.5)^{n-1}$

7th term $= 2 \times (1.5)^6 = 2 \times 11.390625 = 22.78125$

Q3 Common ratio $r = \dfrac{7\text{th term}}{6\text{th term}} = \dfrac{6561}{2187} = 3$.

The 6th term is $2187 = ar^5 = a \times 3^5 \Rightarrow a = \dfrac{2187}{3^5} = 9$.

So the 1st term is 9.

Q4 Common ratio: $r = \dfrac{\text{second term}}{\text{first term}} = \dfrac{12}{24} = 0.5$.

First term: $a = 24$.

nth term: $u_n = ar^{n-1} = 24 \times (0.5)^{n-1}$

9th term: $u_9 = ar^8 = 24 \times (0.5)^8 = 0.09375$

Q5 First term: $a = 1.125$

n^{th} term: $u_n = ar^{n-1} = 1.125r^{n-1}$

14th term: $9216 = u_{14} = 1.125r^{13}$

$9216 = 1.125r^{13} \Rightarrow r^{13} = \dfrac{9216}{1.125} = 8192$

$\Rightarrow r = \sqrt[13]{8192} = 2$

Q6 Common ratio: $r = \dfrac{1.1}{1} = 1.1$, first term: $a = 1$.

n^{th} term: $u_n = ar^{n-1} = 1 \times 1.1^{n-1} = 1.1^{n-1}$

So to find the number of terms in the sequence that are less than 4, solve: $u_n = 1.1^{n-1} < 4$

$\Rightarrow \log 1.1^{n-1} < \log 4$

Use the log law, $\log x^n = n(\log x)$:

$\Rightarrow (n-1)\log 1.1 < \log 4$

$\log 1.1 > 0$ so dividing through by $\log 1.1$ doesn't change the direction of the inequality:

$\Rightarrow n - 1 < \dfrac{\log 4}{\log 1.1} \Rightarrow n - 1 < 14.54 \Rightarrow n < 15.54$

so u_n is less than 4 when n is less than 15.54 (2 d.p.). Therefore u_{15} is the last term that's less than 4, so there are 15 terms that are less than 4.

You could solve this as an equation instead, finding the value of n such that $u_n = 4$ and rounding down.

Q7 $a = 5$, $r = 0.6$, n^{th} term: $u_n = ar^{n-1} = 5 \times (0.6)^{n-1}$

10th term: $u_{10} = 5 \times (0.6)^9 = 0.050388$ (6 d.p.)

15th term: $u_{15} = 5 \times (0.6)^{14} = 0.003918$ (6 d.p.)

Difference: $0.003918 - 0.050388 = -0.04647$ (5 d.p.)

You could also have:

Difference: $0.050388 - 0.003918 = 0.04647$ (5 d.p.)

Q8 $a = 25\,000$, $r = 0.8$

n^{th} term: $u_n = ar^{n-1} = 25\,000 \times (0.8)^{n-1}$

to find the first term in the sequence less than 1000, solve:

$u_n = 25\,000 \times (0.8)^{n-1} < 1000$

$25\,000 \times (0.8)^{n-1} < 1000 \Rightarrow (0.8)^{n-1} < \dfrac{1000}{25\,000} = 0.04$

$\Rightarrow \log(0.8)^{n-1} < \log 0.04 \Rightarrow (n-1)\log(0.8) < \log 0.04$

$\Rightarrow n - 1 > \dfrac{\log 0.04}{\log 0.8} \Rightarrow n - 1 > 14.425... \Rightarrow n > 15.425...$

so u_n is less than 1000 when n is greater than 15.425..., therefore u_{16} is the first term that's less than 1000.

$0.8 < 1$ so $\log 0.8 < 0$ and dividing through by $\log 0.8$ changes the direction of the inequality because $\log 0.8$ is negative. Again, you could solve this as an equation by finding n such that $u_n = 1000$ and rounding up.

Q9 Divide consecutive terms to find the common ratio r:

e.g. $r = \dfrac{\text{second term}}{\text{first term}} = \dfrac{-5}{5} = -1$

Q10 a) Common ratio $r = \dfrac{\text{second term}}{\text{first term}} = \dfrac{\frac{3}{16}}{\frac{1}{4}} = \dfrac{3}{4}$

b) First term: $a = \dfrac{1}{4}$

n^{th} term: $u_n = ar^{n-1} = \dfrac{1}{4} \times \left(\dfrac{3}{4}\right)^{n-1}$

8th term: $u_8 = \dfrac{1}{4} \times \left(\dfrac{3}{4}\right)^7 = \dfrac{1}{4} \times \dfrac{2187}{16\,384} = \dfrac{2187}{65\,536}$

Q11 $r = 0.8$, n^{th} term: $u_n = ar^{n-1} = a(0.8)^{n-1}$

7th term: $196.608 = u_7 = a(0.8)^6$

$196.608 = a(0.8)^6 \Rightarrow a = \dfrac{196.608}{0.8^6} = 750$

Q12 Common ratio: $r = \dfrac{6}{2} = 3$, first term: $a = 2$.

n^{th} term: $u_n = ar^{n-1} = 2 \times 3^{n-1}$

So to find the term which equals 1458, solve:

$u_n = 1458 = 2 \times 3^{n-1} \Rightarrow 3^{n-1} = \dfrac{1458}{2} = 729$

$\Rightarrow \log(3)^{n-1} = \log 729 \Rightarrow (n-1)\log 3 = \log 729$

$\Rightarrow n - 1 = \dfrac{\log 729}{\log 3} = 6 \Rightarrow n = 7$

So the 7th term of the progression is 1458.

Q13 a) Common ratio $r = \dfrac{\text{second term}}{\text{first term}} = \dfrac{-2.4}{3} = -0.8$

b) Continuing the sequence gives -1.536, 1.2288, -0.98304. So there are 5 terms in the series before a term has modulus less than 1.

You could also answer this part of the question by writing a new series where each term is the modulus of the old series, then using logs to find the first term less than 1. But in this case it's much easier to just find the next few terms.

Exercise 5.4.2 — Geometric series

Q1 The sum of the first n terms is $S_n = \dfrac{a(1-r^n)}{(1-r)}$, $a = 8$ and $r = 1.2$, so the sum of the first 15 terms is:

$S_{15} = \dfrac{a(1-r^{15})}{(1-r)} = \dfrac{8(1-(1.2)^{15})}{(1-1.2)} = 576.28$ to 2 d.p.

Q2 For a geometric series with first term a and common ratio r: $\displaystyle\sum_{k=0}^{n-1} ar^k = \dfrac{a(1-r^n)}{1-r}$,

$\displaystyle\sum_{k=0}^{9} ar^k = \sum_{k=0}^{9} 25(0.7)^k = \dfrac{25(1-(0.7)^{10})}{1-0.7} = 80.98$ (2 d.p.)

Q3 $a = 3$ and $r = 2$, the sum of the first n terms is:

$\dfrac{3(1-2^n)}{(1-2)} = -3(1-2^n)$

$196\,605 = S_n = -3(1-2^n) \Rightarrow -65\,535 = 1 - 2^n$

$\Rightarrow 65\,536 = 2^n \Rightarrow \log 65\,536 = \log 2^n$

$\Rightarrow \log 65\,536 = n\log 2 \Rightarrow n = \dfrac{\log 65\,536}{\log 2} = 16$

Q4 The first term is $a = 4$, the common ratio is $r = \dfrac{\text{second term}}{\text{first term}} = \dfrac{5}{4} = 1.25$

The sum of the first x terms is

$S_x = \dfrac{a(1-r^x)}{(1-r)} = \dfrac{4(1-(1.25)^x)}{(1-1.25)} = 16(1-(1.25)^x)$

So: $103.2 = -16(1-(1.25)^x) \Rightarrow -6.45 = 1 - (1.25)^x$

$\Rightarrow 7.45 = 1.25^x \Rightarrow \log 7.45 = x\log 1.25$

$\Rightarrow x = \dfrac{\log 7.45}{\log 1.25} = 9.00$ to 2 d.p.

Q5 a) 3rd term $= ar^2 = 6$, 8th term $= ar^7 = 192$.

Dividing the two equations gives:

$\dfrac{ar^7}{ar^2} = r^5 = \dfrac{192}{6} = 32 \Rightarrow r = \sqrt[5]{32} = 2$

b) 3rd term $= ar^2 = 6$ and $r = 2$, so $a = \dfrac{6}{r^2} = \dfrac{6}{2^2} = 1.5$

c) The sum of the first 15 terms is:

$S_{15} = \dfrac{a(1-r^{15})}{(1-r)} = \dfrac{1.5(1-2^{15})}{(1-2)} = 49\,150.5$

Q6 a) Common ratio: $\dfrac{\text{2nd term}}{\text{1st term}} = \dfrac{\text{3rd term}}{\text{2nd term}}$, so:

$\dfrac{m}{m+10} = \dfrac{2m-21}{m} \Rightarrow m^2 = (m+10)(2m-21)$

$\Rightarrow m^2 = 2m^2 - 21m + 20m - 210 \Rightarrow 0 = m^2 - m - 210$

b) Factorising $m^2 - m - 210 = 0$ gives:

$(m-15)(m+14) = 0$, so $m = 15$ or $m = -14$, since $m > 0$, $m = 15$.

c) $m = 15$ gives the first three terms 25, 15, 9.

Common ratio $= \dfrac{\text{second term}}{\text{first term}} = \dfrac{15}{25} = 0.6$

d) $a = 25$ and $r = 0.6$, so sum of first 10 terms is:

$S_{10} = \dfrac{a(1-r^{10})}{(1-r)} = \dfrac{25(1-0.6^{10})}{(1-0.6)} = 62.12$ to 2 d.p.

Q7 a) $1 + x + x^2 = 3 \Rightarrow x^2 + x - 2 = 0$

$\Rightarrow (x-1)(x+2) = 0 \Rightarrow x = 1$ or $x = -2$.

Since the terms are all different $x \neq 1$ (as 1 is the first term and $x = 1 \Rightarrow x^2 = 1^2 = 1$), hence $x = -2$.

b) $a = 1$ and $r = \dfrac{\text{second term}}{\text{first term}} = \dfrac{-2}{1} = -2$,

so the sum of the first 7 terms is:

$$S_7 = \frac{a(1-r^7)}{(1-r)} = \frac{1(1-(-2)^7)}{(1-(-2))} = 43$$

Q8 $a = 7.2$ and $r = 0.38$, so:

$$\sum_{k=0}^{9} ar^k = \frac{a(1-r^{10})}{(1-r)} = \frac{7.2(1-0.38^{10})}{(1-0.38)} = 11.61 \text{ to 2 d.p.}$$

Q9 $1.2 = S_8 = \dfrac{a(1-r^8)}{(1-r)} = \dfrac{a\left(1-\left(-\frac{1}{3}\right)^8\right)}{\left(1-\left(-\frac{1}{3}\right)\right)} = a(0.749...)$

$\Rightarrow a = 1.60$ to 2 d.p.

Q10 The geometric sequence $a, -2a, 4a, ...$ has first term a and
common ratio $r = -2$, so $\sum_{k=0}^{12} a(-2)^k$ is the sum of the first 13 terms
of the sequence. Therefore:

$$\sum_{k=0}^{12} a(-2)^k = -5735.1$$

$$\sum_{k=0}^{12} a(-2)^k = \frac{a(1-r^{13})}{(1-r)} = \frac{a(1-(-2)^{13})}{(1-(-2))} = 2731a$$

$\Rightarrow -5735.1 = 2731a \Rightarrow a = -2.1$

Exercise 5.4.3 — Convergent geometric series

Q1 a) $r = \dfrac{1.1}{1} = 1.1$, $|r| = |1.1| = 1.1 > 1$,
so the sequence does not converge.

b) $r = \dfrac{0.8^2}{0.8} = 0.8$, $|r| = |0.8| = 0.8 < 1$,
so the sequence converges.

c) $r = \dfrac{\frac{1}{4}}{1} = \dfrac{1}{4}$, $|r| = \left|\dfrac{1}{4}\right| = \dfrac{1}{4} < 1$, so the sequence converges.

d) $r = \dfrac{\frac{9}{2}}{3} = \dfrac{3}{2}$, $|r| = \left|\dfrac{3}{2}\right| = \dfrac{3}{2} > 1$,
so the sequence does not converge.

e) $r = \dfrac{-\frac{1}{2}}{1} = -\dfrac{1}{2}$, $|r| = \left|-\dfrac{1}{2}\right| = \dfrac{1}{2} < 1$,
so the sequence converges.

f) $r = \dfrac{5}{5} = 1$, $|r| = |1| = 1$ (and 1 is not less than 1),
so the sequence does not converge.

Q2 Find the common ratio: $r = \dfrac{2^{nd}\text{ term}}{1^{st}\text{ term}} = \dfrac{8.1}{9} = 0.9$.
The first term is $a = 9$.
The sum to infinity is:
$$S_\infty = \frac{a}{1-r} = \frac{9}{1-0.9} = \frac{9}{0.1} = 90$$

Q3 $\sum_{k=0}^{\infty} ar^k = S_\infty = \dfrac{a}{1-r} = \dfrac{33}{1-0.25} = \dfrac{33}{0.75} = 44$

Q4 $S_\infty = \dfrac{a}{1-r} = 2a \Rightarrow \dfrac{1}{1-r} = 2 \Rightarrow 1 = 2 - 2r \Rightarrow 2r = 1 \Rightarrow r = 0.5$

Q5 a) Sum to infinity is $13.5 = S_\infty = \dfrac{a}{1-r}$
Sum of the first three terms is $13 = S_3 = \dfrac{a(1-r^3)}{(1-r)}$
Divide S_3 by S_∞:
$$\frac{13}{13.5} = \frac{a(1-r^3)}{1-r} \div \frac{a}{1-r} = \frac{a(1-r^3)}{1-r} \times \frac{1-r}{a} = 1 - r^3$$
You can cancel the $1-r$ because r can't be 1
(as the series converges), so $1-r \neq 0$.
So $1 - r^3 = \dfrac{13}{13.5} = \dfrac{26}{27} \Rightarrow r^3 = \dfrac{1}{27} \Rightarrow r = \dfrac{1}{3}$.

b) $13.5 = S_\infty = \dfrac{a}{1-r} \Rightarrow a = 13.5(1-r) = 13.5 \times \dfrac{2}{3} = 9$

Q6 $ar = 3$, $12 = S_\infty = \dfrac{a}{1-r} \Rightarrow 12 - 12r = a$
The first equation gives $a = \dfrac{3}{r}$,
plugging this into the second equation gives:
$12 - 12r = \dfrac{3}{r} \Rightarrow 12r - 12r^2 = 3$
$\Rightarrow 12r^2 - 12r + 3 = 0$
$\Rightarrow 4r^2 - 4r + 1 = 0$
$4r^2 - 4r + 1 = 0$ factorises to $(2r-1)(2r-1) = 0$
Hence $2r - 1 = 0 \Rightarrow r = 0.5$
Then $a = \dfrac{3}{r} = \dfrac{3}{0.5} = 6$.

Q7 a) $a = 6$, $10 = S_\infty = \dfrac{a}{1-r} = \dfrac{6}{1-r}$
$\Rightarrow 1 - r = \dfrac{6}{10} = 0.6 \Rightarrow r = 0.4$

b) 5th term: $u_5 = ar^4 = 6 \times 0.4^4 = 0.1536$.

Q8 a) Second term $= ar = -48$, 5th term $= ar^4 = 0.75$.
Dividing gives: $r^3 = \dfrac{ar^4}{ar} = \dfrac{0.75}{-48} = -0.015625 \Rightarrow r = -0.25$

b) $ar = -48 \Rightarrow a = \dfrac{-48}{r} = \dfrac{-48}{-0.25} = 192$

c) $|r| < 1$ so you can find the sum to infinity:
$$S_\infty = \frac{a}{1-r} = \frac{192}{1-(-0.25)} = \frac{192}{1.25} = 153.6.$$

Q9 The sum of terms after the 10th is $S_\infty - S_{10}$.
So the question tells you that $S_\infty - S_{10} < \dfrac{1}{100} S_\infty$
$\Rightarrow \dfrac{99}{100} S_\infty - S_{10} < 0 \qquad \dfrac{99}{100} S_\infty < S_{10}$
Then: $0.99(S_\infty) = \dfrac{0.99a}{1-r} < \dfrac{a(1-r^{10})}{(1-r)} = S_{10}$
You can cancel and keep the inequality sign because the series is
convergent so $|r| < 1 \Rightarrow 1 - r > 0$,
and you know $a > 0$ from the question:
$\Rightarrow 0.99 < 1 - r^{10} \qquad \Rightarrow r^{10} < 0.01$
$\Rightarrow |r| < \sqrt[10]{0.01} \qquad \Rightarrow |r| < 0.631$ (to 3 s.f.)

Q10 Using the formulas for S_∞ and S_4
$$\frac{a}{1-r} = \frac{9}{8} \times \frac{a(1-r^4)}{1-r}$$
Cancelling $(1-r)$ and a gives
$$\frac{8}{9} = 1 - r^4 \Rightarrow r^4 = \frac{1}{9} \Rightarrow r = \sqrt[4]{\frac{1}{9}}$$
So, given that r is positive and real, $r = \dfrac{1}{\sqrt{3}} = \dfrac{\sqrt{3}}{3}$.

5.5 Modelling Problems

Exercise 5.5.1 — Real life problems

Q1 $a = 60$, $d = 3$
n^{th} term $= a + (n-1)d = 60 + (n-1)3 = 3n + 57$
12th term $= 3(12) + 57 = 93$
So she'll earn £93 in her 12th week.
With wordy problems, don't forget to check what
the units should be and include them.

Q2 The heights form a geometric sequence (starting from the smallest
doll), with $a = 3$, $r = 1.25$. The nth term is $ar^{n-1} = 3 \times 1.25^{n-1}$.
The first term is the height of the first doll, so the height of the 8th
doll is the 8th term. The 8th term is: $3 \times 1.25^7 = 14.3$ cm (1 d.p.)

Q3 $a = 40$, $d = 5$
n^{th} term $= a + (n-1)d = 40 + (n-1)5 = 5n + 35$
$80 = 5n + 35 \Rightarrow n = (80 - 35) \div 5 = 9$
So he'll sell 80 sandwiches on the 9th day.

Q4 $a = 300\,000$, $d = -30\,000$
n^{th} term $= a + (n-1)d = 300\,000 - 30\,000(n-1)$
$= 330\,000 - 30\,000n$
$330\,000 - 30\,000n < 50\,000$
$n > 280\,000 \div 30\,000 = 9.33...$
You want the smallest integer value of n that
satisfies the inequality, so round up. Sales will
have fallen below £50 000 after 10 months.
n = 9 doesn't satisfy the inequality.

Q5 The value decreases by 15% each year so multiply by
$1 - 0.15 = 0.85$ to get from one term to the next,
so the common ratio $r = 0.85$.
So the nth term $u_n = ar^{n-1} = a(0.85)^{n-1}$
The price when new is the first term in the series and the value
after 10 years is the 11th term.
11th term: $2362 = u_{11} = a(0.85)^{10}$
$2362 = a(0.85)^{10} \Rightarrow a = \frac{2362}{0.85^{10}} = 11\,997.496...$
$= 11\,997.50$ to 2 d.p.

When new, the car cost £11 997.50

Q6 a) The cost increases by 3% each year so multiply by
$1 + 0.03 = 1.03$ to get from one term to the next,
so 2006 cost $= 1.03 \times (2011\text{ cost}) = 1.03 \times £120 = £123.60$

b) The costs each year form a geometric sequence with
common ratio $r = 1.03$ and first term $a = 120$, so the total
cost between 2011 and 2016 (including 2011 and 2016) is
the sum of the first 6 terms:
$S_6 = \frac{a(1-r^6)}{(1-r)} = \frac{120(1-1.03^6)}{(1-1.03)} = 776.21$ to 2 d.p.

Nigel paid £776.21 (the cost to the nearest penny).

Q7 $a = 6000$, $d = 2000$, $n = 12$ (12 months in the year)
$S_n = \frac{n}{2}[2a + (n-1)d]$
$S_{12} = \frac{12}{2}[2(6000) + 11(2000)] = 204\,000$
204 000 copies will be sold.

Q8 4 weeks is 28 days. The claim is that the leeks' height
increases by 15% every 2 days.
$28 \div 2 = 14$, so there are 14 lots of 2 days in 28 days

In 28 days, the height should increase 14 times by 15%. So if
the claim is correct, the height of the leeks after 28 days will be
the 15th term of a geometric progression with first term 5 and
common ratio 1.15.

The first term is the initial height, the second term is the height
after one 15% increase and so on, so the 15th term is the height
after fourteen 15% increases.

The common ratio is 1.15 because multiplying something
by 1.15 is the same as increasing it by 15%.

So $a = 5$ and $r = 1.15$.

The nth term is: $u_n = ar^{n-1} = 5(1.15)^{n-1}$

So the 15th term is: $5 \times 1.15^{14} = 35.3785...$ cm.

So if the claim were true, the leeks would be 35.4 cm
tall (to 1 d.p.). Since the leeks only reach a height of
25 cm, the claim on the compost is not justified.

Q9 a) The gnome value goes up by 2% each year,
so the price after 1 year is 102% of £80 000:
$80\,000 \times 1.02 = 81\,600$
The value after 1 year is £ 81 600.

b) To get from one term to the next you multiply by 1.02 (to
increase by 2% each time), so the common ratio $r = 1.02$.

c) Price at start $= a = 80\,000$, $r = 1.02$
nth term $= u_n = ar^{n-1} = 80\,000 \times (1.02)^{n-1}$
The value at the start is the 1st term,
the value after 1 year is the 2nd term and so on,
so the value after 10 years is the 11th term:
11th term $= u_{11} = 80\,000 \times (1.02)^{10}$
$= 97\,519.55$ (2 d.p.)
The value after 10 years is £97 519.55 (to the nearest penny)

d) The value after k years is the $(k + 1)$th term:
$(k + 1)$th term $= u_{k+1} = ar^k = 80\,000 \times (1.02)^k$

After k years the value is more than 120 000, so:
$u_{k+1} = 80\,000 \times (1.02)^k > 120\,000$
$\Rightarrow (1.02)^k > \frac{120\,000}{80\,000} = 1.5$
$\Rightarrow \log(1.02)^k > \log 1.5$
$\Rightarrow k \log(1.02) > \log 1.5$
$\Rightarrow k > \frac{\log 1.5}{\log 1.02} = 20.475...$

So u_{k+1} (the value after k years) is more than 120 000
when $k > 20.475...$, therefore the value exceeds 120 000
after 21 years.

Q10 Frazer's series is the natural numbers up to 31.
$S_n = \frac{1}{2}n(n + 1)$
$S_{31} = \frac{1}{2} \times 31 \times 32 = 496$
So Frazer draws 496 dots.

Q11 The thickness of the paper doubles every time you fold it in half.
So the paper thickness forms a geometric progression:
After 1 fold, thickness $= 0.01 \times 2$ cm.
After 2 folds, thickness $= 0.01 \times 2^2$ cm
After n folds, thickness $= 0.01 \times 2^n$ cm
Distance to the moon:
$384\,000$ km $= 3.84 \times 10^5$ km
$= (3.84 \times 10^5 \times 1000)$ m
$= (3.84 \times 10^5 \times 1000 \times 100)$ cm
$= 3.84 \times 10^{10}$ cm
Therefore the paper reaches the moon when:
$0.01 \times 2^n = 3.84 \times 10^{10}$
$2^n = 3.84 \times 10^{12}$
Taking logs: $n \log 2 = \log(3.84 \times 10^{12})$
$\Rightarrow n = \log(3.84 \times 10^{12}) \div \log 2 = 41.80...$
So after approximately 42 folds the paper would reach the moon.

Q12 a) The distances she runs form a geometric sequence
with $a = 12$, $r = 1.03$.
The nth term is $ar^{n-1} = 12 \times 1.03^{n-1}$, so the 10th term is:
$12 \times 1.03^9 = 15.7$ miles (to 1 d.p.).

b) The total distance she runs in 20 days is the sum
of the first 20 terms of the sequence.
Using: $S_n = \frac{a(1-r^n)}{(1-r)}$, where $a = 12$, $r = 1.03$, $n = 20$,
$S_{20} = \frac{12(1-1.03^{20})}{(1-1.03)} = 322.44...$
In 20 days she runs a total of 322 miles (to the nearest mile).

Q13 Laura's series is the natural numbers. You need to find how many
are needed to exceed 1000 (£10 in pence).
$S_n = \frac{1}{2}n(n + 1)$
$\frac{1}{2}(n^2 + n) > 1000$
$n^2 + n > 2000 \Rightarrow n^2 + n - 2000 > 0$
Putting the quadratic equal to zero and solving using the
quadratic formula gives $n = 44.2$ (ignoring the negative solution),
which by looking at the shape of the quadratic graph gives
$n > 44.2$ as the solution to the inequality.
So on the 45th day she'll have over £10.

Q14 After 0 years, $u_1 = a$ and after 1 year, $u_2 = ar$.
So after 10 years, $u_{11} = ar^{10}$. She wants her investment
to double so $u_{11} = ar^{10} = 2a \Rightarrow r^{10} = 2$
$\Rightarrow |r| = \sqrt[10]{2} = 1.071773$.
So the interest rate needed is 7.17 % (3 s.f.).

Review Exercise — Chapter 5

Q1 $x_8 = 8^2 - 3 = 61$
It's increasing — each term is greater than the previous
one (e.g. it continues $x_9 = 78$, $x_{10} = 97...$)

Q2 $k^2 + 3k + 4 = 44 \Rightarrow k^2 + 3k - 40 = 0 \Rightarrow (k + 8)(k - 5) = 0$
k must be a positive integer, so $k = 5$.

Q3 $u_3 = a(3)^2 + b(3) = 18 \Rightarrow 9a + 3b = 18 \Rightarrow 3a + b = 6$ — eqn 1
$u_7 = a(7)^2 + b(7) = 70 \Rightarrow 49a + 7b = 70 \Rightarrow 7a + b = 10$ — eqn 2
Solving simultaneously:
Subtract eqn 1 from eqn 2: $4a = 4 \Rightarrow a = 1$
In eqn 1: $3 + b = 6 \Rightarrow b = 3$

Q4 **a)** $x_1 = 7$
$x_2 = 7 + 3 = 10$
$x_3 = 10 + 3 = 13$
$x_4 = 13 + 3 = 16$
$x_5 = 16 + 3 = 19$

b) $u_1 = 2$
$u_2 = 6 \div 2 = 3$
$u_3 = 6 \div 3 = 2$
$u_4 = 6 \div 2 = 3$
$u_5 = 6 \div 3 = 2$

Q5 **a)** Each term is the square root of the previous term,
so $u_{k+1} = \sqrt{u_k}$, $u_1 = 65\,536$.

b) The difference between the terms is:
$-2, -4, -6, -8...$ i.e. $-2k$, so $u_{k+1} = u_k - 2k$, $u_1 = 40$

c) Each term from u_3 is the sum of the previous two terms (it's a Fibonacci sequence), so $u_{k+2} = u_k + u_{k+1}$, $u_1 = 1$, $u_2 = 1$

Q6 $u_{n+1} = ku_n + 3 \Rightarrow 11 = 4k + 3 \Rightarrow k = 2$
$u_3 = 2(11) + 3 = 25$
$u_4 = 2(25) + 3 = 53$

Q7 $u_1 = 8$
$u_2 = 18 - 8 = 10$
$u_3 = 18 - 10 = 8$
$u_4 = 18 - 8 = 10$
$u_5 = 18 - 10 = 8$
The terms are alternating between 8 and 10,
i.e. each term is 9 ± 1, starting with $9 - 1$ for $n = 1$, so:
$u_n = 9 + (-1)^n$. The sequence is periodic.

Q8 There are 28 lots of d between the first term (-2) and the 29th term (19), so $d = [19 - (-2)] \div 28 = 0.75$.
You could also plug the values for a (-2), n (29) and u_n (19) into the formula for the nth term in an arithmetic sequence.

Q9 $u_n = a + (n - 1)d$
$u_7 = a + 6d = 8$ — eqn 1
$u_{11} = a + 10d = 10$ — eqn 2
eqn 2 − eqn 1:
$4d = 2 \Rightarrow d = 0.5$
In eqn 1: $a + (6 \times 0.5) = 8 \Rightarrow a = 5$
So $u_3 = 5 + 2 \times 0.5 = 6$

Q10 $u_n = a + (n - 1)d$
$u_7 = a + 6d = 36$ — eqn 1
$u_{10} = a + 9d = 30$ — eqn 2
eqn 2 − eqn 1:
$3d = -6 \Rightarrow d = -2$
In eqn 1: $a - 12 = 36 \Rightarrow a = 48$
So n^{th} term $= a + (n - 1)d = 48 + (-2)(n - 1) = -2n + 50$
$S_n = \frac{n}{2}[2a + (n - 1)d]$
$S_5 = \frac{5}{2}[2 \times 48 + (5 - 1) \times (-2)] = 220$

Q11 $a = 3(1) - 1 = 2$
$l = 3(20) - 1 = 59$
$S_n = \frac{1}{2}n(a + l)$
$S_{20} = \frac{1}{2} \times 20 \times (2 + 59) = 610$

Q12 **a)** $S_n = \frac{1}{2}n(n + 1)$
$S_{24} = \frac{1}{2} \times 24 \times 25 = 300$

b) $\sum_{n=13}^{24} n = S_{24} - S_{12}$
$S_{12} = \frac{1}{2} \times 12 \times 13 = 78$
So $S_{24} - S_{12} = 300 - 78 = 222$

c) $S_k = \frac{1}{2}k(k + 1) = 630$
$\Rightarrow k^2 + k = 1260 \Rightarrow k^2 + k - 1260 = 0$
$\Rightarrow (k + 36)(k - 35) = 0$
k must be a positive integer, so $k = 35$

Q13 First term $a = 3$, common ratio $r = \frac{-9}{3} = -3$
n^{th} term $= ar^{n-1} = 3(-3)^{n-1} = -(-3)^n$

Q14 **a)** First term $a = 2$, common ratio $r = \frac{-6}{2} = -3$
$u_n = ar^{n-1} = 2 \times (-3)^{n-1}$
$u_{10} = 2 \times (-3)^9 = -39\,366$

b) $S_n = \frac{a(1 - r^n)}{(1 - r)}$
$\Rightarrow S_{10} = \frac{2(1 - (-3)^{10})}{(1 - (-3))} = \frac{-118\,096}{4} = -29\,524$

Q15 $\sum_{k=0}^{5} 7(0.6)^k = \sum_{k=1}^{6} 7(0.6)^{k-1} = S_6$
$S_n = \frac{a(1 - r^n)}{(1 - r)} \Rightarrow S_6 = \frac{7(1 - 0.6^6)}{(1 - 0.6)} = 16.68$ (2 d.p.)

Q16 The sum of the first n terms of a geometric series is S_n:
$S_n = a + ar + ar^2 + ar^3 + ... + ar^{n-1}$
Then: $rS_n = ar + ar^2 + ar^3 + ar^4... + ar^n$
Subtracting rS_n from S_n gives:
$(1 - r)S_n = a - ar^n = a(1 - r^n) \Rightarrow S_n = \frac{a(1 - r^n)}{1 - r}$

Q17 **a)** $r = \frac{\text{second term}}{\text{first term}} = \frac{12}{24} = \frac{1}{2}$

b) First term $a = 24$, $r = \frac{1}{2}$
$u_n = ar^{n-1} = 24 \times \left(\frac{1}{2}\right)^{n-1}$
$u_7 = 24 \times \left(\frac{1}{2}\right)^6 = \frac{3}{8} = 0.375$

c) $S_n = \frac{a(1 - r^n)}{(1 - r)}$
$\Rightarrow S_{10} = \frac{24(1 - 0.5^{10})}{(1 - 0.5)} = 47.953$ (3 d.p.)

d) $S_\infty = \frac{a}{1 - r} = \frac{24}{1 - 0.5} = 48$

Q18 The takings can be modelled as an arithmetic sequence with $a = 300$ and $d = 15$.
$u_n = a + (n - 1)d$ so find n where:
$a + (n - 1)d > 500$
$\Rightarrow 300 + 15(n - 1) > 500$
$\Rightarrow 15n > 500 - 285$
$\Rightarrow n > 14.3333...$
So the shop will take over £500 on the 15th day.

Q19 The sequence of stones is the sequence of natural numbers (1, 2, 3...).
13 weeks × 5 days = 65
So the total number of stones is $S_n = \frac{1}{2}n(n + 1)$ with $n = 65$:
$S_{65} = \frac{1}{2} \times 65 \times 66 = 2145$ stones

Exam-Style Questions — Chapter 5

Q1 **a)** $u_{n+2} = \frac{u_{n+1} + 1}{u_n}$ and $u_1 = 3$ and $u_2 = 5$ so:
$u_3 = \frac{5 + 1}{3} = 2$
$u_4 = \frac{2 + 1}{5} = \frac{3}{5}$
$u_5 = \frac{\frac{3}{5} + 1}{2} = \frac{4}{5}$
$u_6 = \frac{\frac{4}{5} + 1}{\frac{3}{5}} = 3$
$u_7 = \frac{3 + 1}{\frac{4}{5}} = 5$

[2 marks available — 1 mark for substituting u_1 and u_2 into the recurrence relation, 1 mark for correct values of u_6 and u_7]

b) As $u_6 = u_1$ and $u_7 = u_2$ this series is periodic, so each block of 5 terms will have the same sum i.e. $3 + 5 + 2 + \frac{3}{5} + \frac{4}{5} = \frac{57}{5}$.

So the sum of the first 25 terms = $5 \times \frac{57}{5} = 57$.

[3 marks available — 1 mark for using fact that the series is periodic, 1 mark for correct working, 1 mark for correct final answer]

Q2 a) For an arithmetic sequence: $u_n = a + (n-1)d$.

$u_6 = a + 5d = p$ — eqn 1
$u_{12} = a + 11d = 4p$ — eqn 2

Subtract eqn 1 from eqn 2:
$6d = 3p \Rightarrow d = \frac{p}{2}$

[3 marks available — 1 mark for forming two simultaneous equations in a, d and p, 1 mark for eliminating a, 1 mark for correct final answer]

b) $S_n = \frac{n}{2}[2a + (n-1)d]$

$S_6 = 3[2a + 5\left(\frac{p}{2}\right)] = 6a + \frac{15}{2}p = 72$ — eqn 1

$S_{12} = 6[2a + 11\left(\frac{p}{2}\right)] = 12a + 33p = 288$ — eqn 2

Subtract 2 × eqn 1 from eqn 2:
$18p = 144 \Rightarrow p = 8$, so $d = 4$
Substitute $p = 8$ into eqn 2:
$12a + (33 \times 8) = 288 \Rightarrow a = 2$

So the series is:
$u_1 = a = 2$
$u_2 = a + d = 2 + 4 = 6$
$u_3 = a + 2d = 2 + 8 = 10$

[4 marks available — 1 mark for forming two simultaneous equations in a and p, 1 mark for solving for p, 1 mark for solving for a, 1 mark for finding u_2 and u_3]

Q3 a) The run times can be modelled by an arithmetic sequence with $a = 30$ and $d = 5$, where u_{Rn} is the nth term.
So $u_{R3} = 30 + (3-1) \times 5 = 40$ minutes
The cycling times can be modelled by a geometric sequence with $a = 15$ and $r = 1.12$, where u_{Cn} is the nth term.
So $u_{C3} = 15 \times 1.12^{(3-1)} = 18.816$ minutes
The swim times are always 60 minutes per day, so the total exercise time is $40 + 18.816 + 60$
$= 119$ minutes (to the nearest minute)

[3 marks available — 1 mark for correct run time, 1 mark for correct cycle time, 1 mark for correct final answer]

b) The run is longer than the swim when:
$30 + (n-1) \times 5 > 60 \Rightarrow n > 7$, i.e. from day 8.
The cycle is longer than the swim when:
$15 \times 1.12^{(n-1)} > 60 \Rightarrow 1.12^{(n-1)} > 4$
$\Rightarrow (n-1)\log 1.12 > \log 4$
$\Rightarrow n - 1 > \log 4 \div \log 1.12$
$\Rightarrow n > 13.232...$, i.e. from day 14.
So the first day when both the cycle and the run are longer than the swim is day 14.

[4 marks available — 1 mark for solving inequality for the run, 1 mark for forming inequality for the cycle, 1 mark for correctly using logs to solve the inequality for the cycle, 1 mark for correct final answer]

c) Find the sum of the geometric series from day 8 to day 14, i.e. $S_{C14} - S_{C7}$. $S_n = \frac{a(1-r^n)}{1-r}$, so:

$S_{C14} - S_{C7} = \frac{15(1-1.12^{14})}{1-1.12} - \frac{15(1-1.12^7)}{1-1.12}$

$= 485.889... - 151.335... = 334.553...$

$= 5$ hours 35 minutes (to the nearest minute)

[3 marks available — 1 mark for stating that the answer would be the difference between the sum to 14 terms and the sum to 7 terms, 1 mark for correct use of sum formulas, 1 mark for correct final answer in hours and minutes]

d) E.g. neither the arithmetic or geometric series models allow for the fact that there are a finite number of hours in a day that Samira could use for training.
[1 mark for correct explanation]

Q4 a) $S_\infty = \frac{a}{1-r} = 8k \Rightarrow a = 8k - 8kr$ — eqn 1
$u_2 = ar = 6$ — eqn 2
Substitute a from eqn 1 into eqn 2:
$(8k - 8kr)r = 6 \Rightarrow 8kr - 8kr^2 = 6$
$\Rightarrow 8kr^2 - 8kr + 6 = 0 \Rightarrow 4kr^2 - 4kr + 3 = 0$ — as required

[3 marks available — 1 mark for forming two simultaneous equations, 1 mark for correct working to solve, 1 mark for rearranging into the required final answer]

b) $4kr^2 - 4kr + 3 = 0$ has one real root, so the discriminant must be zero:
$(-4k)^2 - 4 \times 4k \times 3 = 0 \Rightarrow 16k^2 - 48k = 0$
$\Rightarrow k(k-3) = 0$, so $k = 0$ or 3, but $k \neq 0$ so $k = 3$.
Substitute into $4kr^2 - 4kr + 3 = 0$ to find r:
$12r^2 - 12r + 3 = 0 \Rightarrow 4r^2 - 4r + 1 = 0$
$\Rightarrow (2r - 1)^2 = 0 \Rightarrow r = \frac{1}{2}$
Using eqn 2 from part a):
$ar = 6 \Rightarrow a \times \frac{1}{2} = 6 \Rightarrow a = 12$.
So the first three terms are 12, 6 and $6 \times \frac{1}{2} = 3$.

[5 marks available — 1 mark for stating that the discriminant is zero, 1 mark for a correct value of k, 1 mark for a correct value of r, 1 mark for a correct value of a, 1 mark for correct third term]

Chapter 6: The Binomial Expansion

6.1 The Binomial Expansion

Exercise 6.1.1 — Expansions where n is a positive integer

Q1 $(1 + x)^3 = 1 + 3x + \frac{3(3-1)}{1 \times 2}x^2 + \frac{3(3-1)(3-2)}{1 \times 2 \times 3}x^3$
$= 1 + 3x + 3x^2 + x^3$

Q2 $(1 + x)^7 = 1 + 7x + \frac{7(7-1)}{1 \times 2}x^2 + \frac{7(7-1)(7-2)}{1 \times 2 \times 3}x^3 + ...$
$= 1 + 7x + 21x^2 + 35x^3 + ...$
This isn't the full expansion, so keep the dots at the end to show it carries on.

Q3 $(1 - x)^4 = 1 + 4(-x) + \frac{4(4-1)}{1 \times 2}(-x)^2 + \frac{4(4-1)(4-2)}{1 \times 2 \times 3}(-x)^3$
$+ \frac{4(4-1)(4-2)(4-3)}{1 \times 2 \times 3 \times 4}(-x)^4$
$= 1 - 4x + 6x^2 - 4x^3 + x^4$

Q4 $(1 + 3x)^6 = 1 + 6(3x) + \frac{6(6-1)}{1 \times 2}(3x)^2 + ...$
$= 1 + 6(3x) + 15(9x^2) + ... = 1 + 18x + 135x^2 + ...$

Q5 $(1 + 2x)^8 = 1 + 8(2x) + \frac{8(8-1)}{1 \times 2}(2x)^2 + \frac{8(8-1)(8-2)}{1 \times 2 \times 3}(2x)^3 + ...$
$= 1 + 8(2x) + 28(4x^2) + 56(8x^3) + ...$
$= 1 + 16x + 112x^2 + 448x^3 + ...$

Q6 $(1 - 5x)^5 = 1 + 5(-5x) + \frac{5(5-1)}{1 \times 2}(-5x)^2 + ...$
$= 1 + 5(-5x) + 10(25x^2) + ... = 1 - 25x + 250x^2 - ...$

Q7 $(1 - 4x)^3 = 1 + 3(-4x) + \frac{3(3-1)}{1 \times 2}(-4x)^2 + \frac{3(3-1)(3-2)}{1 \times 2 \times 3}(-4x)^3$
$= 1 + 3(-4x) + 3(16x^2) + (-64x^3) = 1 - 12x + 48x^2 - 64x^3$

Q8 $(1 + 6x)^6 = 1 + 6(6x) + \frac{6(6-1)}{1 \times 2}(6x)^2 + \frac{6(6-1)(6-2)}{1 \times 2 \times 3}(6x)^3 + ...$
$= 1 + 6(6x) + 15(36x^2) + 20(216x^3)$
$= 1 + 36x + 540x^2 + 4320x^3 + ...$

Exercise 6.1.2 — Expansions where n is negative or a fraction

Q1 $(1 + x)^{-4}$

$= 1 + (-4)x + \dfrac{-4(-4-1)}{1 \times 2} x^2 + \dfrac{-4(-4-1)(-4-2)}{1 \times 2 \times 3} x^3 + \dots$

$= 1 + (-4)x + \dfrac{-4 \times -5}{2} x^2 + \dfrac{-4 \times -5 \times -6}{6} x^3 + \dots$

$= 1 - 4x + 10x^2 - 20x^3 + \dots$

Q2 **a)** $(1 - 6x)^{-3} = 1 + (-3)(-6x) + \dfrac{-3(-3-1)}{1 \times 2} (-6x)^2$

$\qquad\qquad + \dfrac{-3(-3-1)(-3-2)}{1 \times 2 \times 3} (-6x)^3 + \dots$

$\qquad = 1 + 18x + \dfrac{-3 \times -4}{2} (36x^2)$

$\qquad\qquad + \dfrac{-3 \times -4 \times -5}{6} (-216x^3) + \dots$

$\qquad = 1 + 18x + 6(36x^2) + (-10)(-216x^3) + \dots$

$\qquad = 1 + 18x + 216x^2 + 2160x^3 + \dots$

b) The expansion is valid for $\left| \dfrac{-6x}{1} \right| < 1$, so $|x| < \dfrac{1}{6}$.

Q3 **a)** $(1 + 4x)^{\frac{1}{3}} = 1 + \dfrac{1}{3}(4x) + \dfrac{\frac{1}{3}\left(\frac{1}{3} - 1\right)}{1 \times 2}(4x)^2 + \dots$

$\qquad = 1 + \dfrac{1}{3}(4x) + \dfrac{\frac{1}{3} \times -\frac{2}{3}}{2}(16x^2) + \dots$

$\qquad = 1 + \dfrac{1}{3}(4x) + \left(-\dfrac{1}{9}\right)(16x^2) + \dots$

$\qquad = 1 + \dfrac{4x}{3} - \dfrac{16x^2}{9} + \dots$

b) $(1 + 4x)^{-\frac{1}{2}} = 1 + \left(-\dfrac{1}{2}\right)(4x) + \dfrac{-\frac{1}{2}\left(-\frac{1}{2} - 1\right)}{1 \times 2}(4x)^2 + \dots$

$\qquad = 1 - \dfrac{1}{2}(4x) + \dfrac{-\frac{1}{2} \times -\frac{3}{2}}{2}(16x^2) + \dots$

$\qquad = 1 - \dfrac{1}{2}(4x) + \left(\dfrac{3}{8}\right)(16x^2) + \dots = 1 - 2x + 6x^2 - \dots$

c) Both a) and b) are valid for $|x| < \dfrac{1}{4}$.

Q4 **a)** $\dfrac{1}{(1 - 4x)^2} = (1 - 4x)^{-2}$

$\qquad = 1 + (-2)(-4x) + \dfrac{-2(-2-1)}{1 \times 2}(-4x)^2$

$\qquad\qquad + \dfrac{-2(-2-1)(-2-2)}{1 \times 2 \times 3}(-4x)^3 + \dots$

$\qquad = 1 + (-2)(-4x) + \dfrac{-2 \times -3}{2}(16x^2)$

$\qquad\qquad + \dfrac{-2 \times -3 \times -4}{6}(-64x^3) + \dots$

$\qquad = 1 + 8x + 3(16x^2) + (-4)(-64x^3) + \dots$

$\qquad = 1 + 8x + 48x^2 + 256x^3 + \dots$

b) $\sqrt{1 + 6x} = (1 + 6x)^{\frac{1}{2}}$

$\qquad = 1 + \dfrac{1}{2}(6x) + \dfrac{\frac{1}{2}\left(\frac{1}{2} - 1\right)}{1 \times 2}(6x)^2$

$\qquad\qquad + \dfrac{\frac{1}{2}\left(\frac{1}{2} - 1\right)\left(\frac{1}{2} - 2\right)}{1 \times 2 \times 3}(6x)^3 + \dots$

$\qquad = 1 + \dfrac{1}{2}(6x) + \dfrac{\frac{1}{2} \times -\frac{1}{2}}{2}(36x^2)$

$\qquad\qquad + \dfrac{\frac{1}{2} \times -\frac{1}{2} \times -\frac{3}{2}}{6}(216x^3) + \dots$

$\qquad = 1 + \dfrac{1}{2}(6x) + \left(-\dfrac{1}{8}\right)(36x^2) + \dfrac{1}{16}(216x^3) + \dots$

$\qquad = 1 + 3x - \dfrac{9x^2}{2} + \dfrac{27x^3}{2} - \dots$

c) $\dfrac{1}{\sqrt{1 - 3x}} = (1 - 3x)^{-\frac{1}{2}}$

$\qquad = 1 + \left(-\dfrac{1}{2}\right)(-3x) + \dfrac{-\frac{1}{2}\left(-\frac{1}{2} - 1\right)}{1 \times 2}(-3x)^2$

$\qquad\qquad + \dfrac{-\frac{1}{2}\left(-\frac{1}{2} - 1\right)\left(-\frac{1}{2} - 2\right)}{1 \times 2 \times 3}(-3x)^3 + \dots$

$\qquad = 1 + \left(-\dfrac{1}{2}\right)(-3x) + \dfrac{-\frac{1}{2} \times -\frac{3}{2}}{2}(9x^2)$

$\qquad\qquad + \dfrac{-\frac{1}{2} \times -\frac{3}{2} \times -\frac{5}{2}}{6}(-27x^3) + \dots$

$\qquad = 1 + \dfrac{3x}{2} + \dfrac{3}{8}(9x^2) + \left(-\dfrac{5}{16}\right)(-27x^3) + \dots$

$\qquad = 1 + \dfrac{3x}{2} + \dfrac{27x^2}{8} + \dfrac{135x^3}{16} + \dots$

d) $\sqrt[3]{1 + \dfrac{x}{2}} = \left(1 + \dfrac{1}{2}x\right)^{\frac{1}{3}}$

$\qquad = 1 + \dfrac{1}{3}\left(\dfrac{x}{2}\right) + \dfrac{\frac{1}{3}\left(\frac{1}{3} - 1\right)}{1 \times 2}\left(\dfrac{x}{2}\right)^2$

$\qquad\qquad + \dfrac{\frac{1}{3}\left(\frac{1}{3} - 1\right)\left(\frac{1}{3} - 2\right)}{1 \times 2 \times 3}\left(\dfrac{x}{2}\right)^3 \dots$

$\qquad = 1 + \dfrac{1}{3}\left(\dfrac{x}{2}\right) + \dfrac{\frac{1}{3} \times -\frac{2}{3}}{2}\left(\dfrac{x}{2}\right)^2$

$\qquad\qquad + \dfrac{\frac{1}{3} \times -\frac{2}{3} \times -\frac{5}{3}}{6}\left(\dfrac{x}{2}\right)^3 \dots$

$\qquad = 1 + \dfrac{1}{3}\left(\dfrac{x}{2}\right) + \left(-\dfrac{1}{9}\right)\left(\dfrac{x}{2}\right)^2 + \dfrac{5}{81}\left(\dfrac{x}{2}\right)^3 \dots$

$\qquad = 1 + \dfrac{x}{6} - \dfrac{x^2}{36} + \dfrac{5x^3}{648} \dots$

Q5 **a)** $\dfrac{1}{(1 + 7x)^4} = (1 + 7x)^{-4}$

The x^3 term is $\dfrac{-4(-4-1)(-4-2)}{1 \times 2 \times 3}(7x)^3$

$\qquad = \dfrac{-4 \times -5 \times -6}{6}(343x^3) = -20(343x^3) = -6860x^3$

So the coefficient of the x^3 term is -6860.

b) The expansion is valid for $|x| < \dfrac{1}{7}$.

Q6 **a)** $\sqrt[4]{1 - 4x} = (1 - 4x)^{\frac{1}{4}}$

The x^5 term is:

$\dfrac{\frac{1}{4}\left(\frac{1}{4} - 1\right)\left(\frac{1}{4} - 2\right)\left(\frac{1}{4} - 3\right)\left(\frac{1}{4} - 4\right)}{1 \times 2 \times 3 \times 4 \times 5}(-4x)^5$

$= \dfrac{\frac{1}{4} \times -\frac{3}{4} \times -\frac{7}{4} \times -\frac{11}{4} \times -\frac{15}{4}}{120}(-4)^5 x^5$

$= \dfrac{1 \times -3 \times -7 \times -11 \times -15}{120} \times \left(\dfrac{-4}{4}\right)^5 \times x^5$

$= \dfrac{3465}{120} \times -1 \times x^5 = -\dfrac{231x^5}{8}$

So the coefficient of the x^5 term is $-\dfrac{231}{8}$.

b) The expansion is valid for $|x| < \dfrac{1}{4}$.

Q7 **a)** $(1 - 5x)^{\frac{1}{6}} = 1 + \dfrac{1}{6}(-5x) + \dfrac{\frac{1}{6}\left(\frac{1}{6} - 1\right)}{1 \times 2}(-5x)^2 + \dots$

$\qquad = 1 + \dfrac{1}{6}(-5x) + \dfrac{\frac{1}{6} \times -\frac{5}{6}}{2}(25x^2) + \dots$

$\qquad = 1 - \dfrac{5x}{6} + \left(-\dfrac{5}{72}\right)(25x^2) + \dots = 1 - \dfrac{5x}{6} - \dfrac{125x^2}{72} - \dots$

b) $(1 + 4x)^4 = 1 + 16x + 96x^2 + \dots$

So $(1 + 4x)^4 (1 - 5x)^{\frac{1}{6}}$

$= (1 + 16x + 96x^2 + \dots)(1 - \dfrac{5x}{6} - \dfrac{125x^2}{72} + \dots)$

$= 1(1 + 16x + 96x^2) - \dfrac{5x}{6}(1 + 16x) - \dfrac{125x^2}{72}(1) + \dots$

$= 1 + 16x + 96x^2 - \dfrac{5x}{6} - \dfrac{40x^2}{3} - \dfrac{125x^2}{72} + \dots$

$= 1 + \dfrac{91x}{6} + \dfrac{5827x^2}{72} + \dots$

c) The expansion of $(1 - 5x)^{\frac{1}{6}}$ is valid for $|x| < \frac{1}{5}$.
The expansion of $(1 + 4x)^4$ is valid for all values of x, since n is a positive integer.
So overall, the expansion of $(1 + 4x)^4 (1 - 5x)^{\frac{1}{6}}$ is valid for the narrower of these ranges, i.e. $|x| < \frac{1}{5}$.

Q8 a) $(1 + x)^2 = 1 + 2x + x^2$
$(1 - 2x)^{-2} = 1 + (-2)(-2x) + \dfrac{-2(-2-1)}{1 \times 2}(-2x)^2 + ...$
$\qquad = 1 + 4x + 12x^2 + ...$
So $(1 + x)^2(1 - 2x)^{-2}$
$= (1 + 2x + x^2)(1 + 4x + 12x^2 + ...)$
$= 1(1 + 4x + 12x^2) + 2x(1 + 4x) + x^2(1) + ...$
$= 1 + 4x + 12x^2 + 2x + 8x^2 + x^2 + ...$
$= 1 + 6x + 21x^2 + ...$
The expansion of $(1 + x)^2$ is valid for all values of x, since n is a positive integer.
The expansion of $(1 - 2x)^{-2}$ is valid for $|x| < \frac{1}{2}$.
So overall, the expansion of $(1 + x)^2(1 - 2x)^{-2}$ is valid for the narrower of these ranges, i.e. $|x| < \frac{1}{2}$.

b) $(1 + 2x)^2 = 1 + 4x + 4x^2$
$(1 + 3x)^{-3} = 1 + (-3)(3x) + \dfrac{-3(-3-1)}{1 \times 2}(3x)^2 + ...$
$\qquad = 1 - 9x + 54x^2 + ...$
So $(1 + 2x)^2(1 + 3x)^{-3} = (1 + 4x + 4x^2)(1 - 9x + 54x^2 + ...)$
$= 1(1 - 9x + 54x^2) + 4x(1 - 9x) + 4x^2(1) + ...$
$= 1 - 9x + 54x^2 + 4x - 36x^2 + 4x^2 + ...$
$= 1 - 5x + 22x^2 + ...$
The expansion of $(1 + 2x)^2$ is valid for all values of x, since n is a positive integer.
The expansion of $(1 + 3x)^{-3}$ is valid for $|x| < \frac{1}{3}$.
So overall, the expansion of $(1 + 2x)^2(1 + 3x)^{-3}$ is valid for the narrower of these ranges, i.e. $|x| < \frac{1}{3}$.

c) $(1 + 2x)^{\frac{1}{7}} = 1 + \dfrac{1}{7}(2x) + \dfrac{\frac{1}{7}\left(\frac{1}{7} - 1\right)}{1 \times 2}(2x)^2 + ...$
$= 1 + \dfrac{2}{7}x + \dfrac{\frac{1}{7} \times -\frac{6}{7}}{2}(4x^2) + ...$
$= 1 + \dfrac{2}{7}x - \dfrac{12}{49}x^2 + ...$
So $(1 - 7x)(1 + 2x)^{\frac{1}{7}} = (1 - 7x)(1 + \dfrac{2}{7}x - \dfrac{12}{49}x^2 + ...)$
$= 1(1 + \dfrac{2}{7}x - \dfrac{12}{49}x^2) - 7x(1 + \dfrac{2}{7}x) + ...$
$= 1 + \dfrac{2}{7}x - \dfrac{12}{49}x^2 - 7x - 2x^2 + ...$
$= 1 - \dfrac{47}{7}x - \dfrac{110}{49}x^2 + ...$
$(1 + 7x)$ is valid for all values of x.
The expansion of $(1 + 2x)^{\frac{1}{7}}$ is valid for $|x| < \frac{1}{2}$.
So the expansion of $(1 - 7x)(1 + 2x)^{\frac{1}{7}}$ is valid for the narrower of these ranges, i.e. $|x| < \frac{1}{2}$.

d) $(1 - x)^2 = 1 - 2x + x^2$
$(1 + 4x)^{-\frac{1}{3}} = 1 + \left(-\dfrac{1}{3}\right)(4x) + \dfrac{\left(-\frac{1}{3}\right)\left(-\frac{1}{3} - 1\right)}{1 \times 2}(4x)^2 + ...$
$= 1 - \dfrac{4}{3}x + \dfrac{-\frac{1}{3} \times -\frac{4}{3}}{2}(16x^2) + ...$
$= 1 - \dfrac{4}{3}x + \dfrac{32}{9}x^2 + ...$
So $(1 - x)^2(1 + 4x)^{-\frac{1}{3}} = (1 - 2x + x^2)(1 - \dfrac{4}{3}x + \dfrac{32}{9}x^2 + ...)$
$= 1(1 - \dfrac{4}{3}x + \dfrac{32}{9}x^2) - 2x(1 - \dfrac{4}{3}x) + x^2(1) + ...$
$= 1 - \dfrac{4}{3}x + \dfrac{32}{9}x^2 - 2x + \dfrac{8}{3}x^2 + x^2 + ...$
$= 1 - \dfrac{10}{3}x + \dfrac{65}{9}x^2 + ...$
The expansion of $(1 - x)^2$ is valid for all values of x, since n is a positive integer.
The expansion of $(1 + 4x)^{-\frac{1}{3}}$ is valid for $|x| < \frac{1}{4}$.
So the expansion of $(1 - x)^2(1 + 4x)^{-\frac{1}{3}}$ is valid for the narrower of these ranges, i.e. $|x| < \frac{1}{4}$.

Q9 a) $\dfrac{(1 + 3x)^4}{(1 + x)^3} = (1 + 3x)^4(1 + x)^{-3}$
$(1 + 3x)^4 = 1 + 12x + 54x^2 + ...$
$(1 + x)^{-3} = 1 - 3x + 6x^2 - ...$
So $(1 + 3x)^4(1 + x)^{-3} = 1 - 3x + 6x^2 + [12x(1 - 3x)] + 54x^2 + ...$
$= 1 - 3x + 6x^2 + 12x - 36x^2 + 54x^2 + ... = 1 + 9x + 24x^2 + ...$

b) The expansion of $(1 + 3x)^4$ is valid for all values of x, since n is a positive integer.
The expansion of $(1 + x)^{-3}$ is valid for $|x| < 1$.
So overall, the expansion of $\dfrac{(1 + 3x)^4}{(1 + x)^3}$ is valid for the narrower of these ranges, i.e. $|x| < 1$.

Q10 a) (i) $(1 + ax)^4 = 1 + 4ax + \dfrac{4 \times 3}{1 \times 2}(ax)^2 + \dfrac{4 \times 3 \times 2}{1 \times 2 \times 3}(ax)^3$
$\qquad + \dfrac{4 \times 3 \times 2 \times 1}{1 \times 2 \times 3 \times 4}(ax)^4$
$= 1 + 4ax + 6a^2x^2 + 4a^3x^3 + a^4x^4$

(ii) $(1 - bx)^{-3} = 1 + (-3)(-bx) + \dfrac{-3 \times -4}{1 \times 2}(-bx)^2 + ...$
$= 1 + 3bx + 6b^2x^2 + ...$

b) $\dfrac{(1 + ax)^4}{(1 - bx)^3} = (1 + ax)^4(1 - bx)^{-3}$
$= (1 + 4ax + 6a^2x^2 + ...)(1 + 3bx + 6b^2x^2 + ...)$
$= 1 + 3bx + 6b^2x^2 + 4ax + 12abx^2 + 6a^2x^2 + ...$
$= 1 + (4a + 3b)x + (6a^2 + 12ab + 6b^2)x^2 + ...$
You're only asked to expand up to the x^2 term, so you don't need to write down any x^3 or higher power terms here.

c) Equating coefficients — x^2 terms:
$6a^2 + 12ab + 6b^2 = 24 \implies 6(a + b)^2 = 24$
$\qquad\qquad\qquad\qquad \implies (a + b)^2 = 4 \implies a + b = \pm 2$
Equating coefficients — x terms:
$4a + 3b = 1 \implies a + 3(a + b) = 1$
So $a + b = 2 \implies a + 3 \times 2 = 1 \implies a = -5$
$\qquad\qquad \implies -5 + b = 2 \implies b = 7$
$a + b = -2 \implies a + 3 \times -2 = 1 \implies a = 7$
$\qquad\qquad \implies 7 + b = -2 \implies b = -9$
So the two pairs of values are: $a = -5$, $b = 7$ and $a = 7$, $b = -9$
You could also have rearranged to get either a or b in terms of the other, and then substituted that into the other equation. You would get the same answer, but the working is a bit longer.

Exercise 6.1.3 — Expanding $(p + qx)^n$

Q1 a) $(2 + 4x)^3 = 2^3(1 + 2x)^3 = 8(1 + 2x)^3$
$(1 + 2x)^3 = 1 + 3(2x) + \dfrac{3 \times 2}{1 \times 2}(2x)^2 + \dfrac{3 \times 2 \times 1}{1 \times 2 \times 3}(2x)^3$
$\qquad = 1 + 6x + 3(4x^2) + 8x^3 = 1 + 6x + 12x^2 + 8x^3$
So $(2 + 4x)^3 = 8(1 + 6x + 12x^2 + 8x^3) = 8 + 48x + 96x^2 + 64x^3$

b) $(3 + 4x)^5 = 3^5\left(1 + \dfrac{4}{3}x\right)^5 = 243\left(1 + \dfrac{4}{3}x\right)^5$
$\left(1 + \dfrac{4}{3}x\right)^5 = 1 + 5\left(\dfrac{4}{3}x\right) + \dfrac{5 \times 4}{1 \times 2}\left(\dfrac{4}{3}x\right)^2$
$\qquad\qquad\qquad + \dfrac{5 \times 4 \times 3}{1 \times 2 \times 3}\left(\dfrac{4}{3}x\right)^3 + ...$
$= 1 + \dfrac{20x}{3} + \dfrac{160x^2}{9} + \dfrac{640x^3}{27} + ...$
$(3 + 4x)^5 = 243(1 + \dfrac{20x}{3} + \dfrac{160x^2}{9} + \dfrac{640x^3}{27} + ...)$
$= 243 + 1620x + 4320x^2 + 5760x^3 + ...$

c) $(4 + x)^{\frac{1}{2}} = 4^{\frac{1}{2}}\left(1 + \dfrac{x}{4}\right)^{\frac{1}{2}} = 2\left(1 + \dfrac{x}{4}\right)^{\frac{1}{2}}$
$\left(1 + \dfrac{x}{4}\right)^{\frac{1}{2}} = 1 + \dfrac{1}{2}\left(\dfrac{x}{4}\right) + \dfrac{\frac{1}{2} \times -\frac{1}{2}}{1 \times 2}\left(\dfrac{x}{4}\right)^2$
$\qquad\qquad\qquad + \dfrac{\frac{1}{2} \times -\frac{1}{2} \times -\frac{3}{2}}{1 \times 2 \times 3}\left(\dfrac{x}{4}\right)^3 + ...$
$= 1 + \dfrac{x}{8} - \dfrac{x^2}{128} + \dfrac{x^3}{1024} - ...$
$(4 + x)^{\frac{1}{2}} = 2\left(1 + \dfrac{x}{4}\right)^{\frac{1}{2}}$
$= 2(1 + \dfrac{x}{8} - \dfrac{x^2}{128} + \dfrac{x^3}{1024} - ...)$
$= 2 + \dfrac{x}{4} - \dfrac{x^2}{64} + \dfrac{x^3}{512} - ...$

d) $(8 + 2x)^{-\frac{1}{3}} = 8^{-\frac{1}{3}}\left(1 + \frac{2x}{8}\right)^{-\frac{1}{3}} = \frac{1}{2}\left(1 + \frac{x}{4}\right)^{-\frac{1}{3}}$

$\left(1 + \frac{x}{4}\right)^{-\frac{1}{3}} = 1 + \left(-\frac{1}{3}\right)\left(\frac{x}{4}\right) + \frac{-\frac{1}{3}\times-\frac{4}{3}}{1\times2}\left(\frac{x}{4}\right)^2$

$\qquad\qquad + \frac{-\frac{1}{3}\times-\frac{4}{3}\times-\frac{7}{3}}{1\times2\times3}\left(\frac{x}{4}\right)^3 + ...$

$\qquad = 1 - \frac{x}{12} + \frac{x^2}{72} - \frac{7x^3}{2592} + ...$

$(8 + 2x)^{-\frac{1}{3}} = \frac{1}{2}\left(1 + \frac{x}{4}\right)^{-\frac{1}{3}}$

$\qquad = \frac{1}{2}\left(1 - \frac{x}{12} + \frac{x^2}{72} - \frac{7x^3}{2592} + ...\right)$

$\qquad = \frac{1}{2} - \frac{x}{24} + \frac{x^2}{144} - \frac{7x^3}{5184} + ...$

Q2 $(a + 5x)^5 = a^5\left(1 + \frac{5}{a}x\right)^5$

So the x^2 term is:

$a^5\left(\frac{5\times4}{1\times2}\right)\left(\frac{5}{a}x\right)^2 = 10a^5\left(\frac{25}{a^2}x^2\right) = \left(\frac{250a^5}{a^2}\right)x^2 = 250a^3x^2$

So $250a^3 = 2000 \Rightarrow a^3 = 8 \Rightarrow a = 2$

Q3 **a)** $(2 - 5x)^7 = 2^7\left(1 - \frac{5}{2}x\right)^7 = 128\left(1 - \frac{5}{2}x\right)^7$

$\left(1 - \frac{5}{2}x\right)^7 = 1 + 7\left(-\frac{5}{2}x\right) + \frac{7\times6}{1\times2}\left(-\frac{5}{2}x\right)^2 + ...$

$\qquad = 1 - \frac{35x}{2} + \frac{525x^2}{4} - ...$

$(2 - 5x)^7 = 128(1 - \frac{35x}{2} + \frac{525x^2}{4} - ...)$

$\qquad = 128 - 2240x + 16\,800x^2 - ...$

b) $(1 + 6x)^3 = 1 + 18x + 108x^2 + ...$

So $(1 + 6x)^3(2 - 5x)^7 =$

$128 - 2240x + 16\,800x^2 + 18x(128 - 2240x)$

$\qquad\qquad\qquad\qquad + 108x^2(128) + ...$

$\qquad = 128 + 64x - 9696x^2 + ...$

Q4 **a)** $\left(1 + \frac{6}{5}x\right)^{-\frac{1}{2}} = 1 + \left(-\frac{1}{2}\right)\left(\frac{6}{5}x\right) + \frac{\left(-\frac{1}{2}\right)\times\left(-\frac{3}{2}\right)}{1\times2}\left(\frac{6}{5}x\right)^2$

$\qquad\qquad + \frac{\left(-\frac{1}{2}\right)\times\left(-\frac{3}{2}\right)\times\left(-\frac{5}{2}\right)}{1\times2\times3}\left(\frac{6}{5}x\right)^3 + ...$

$\qquad = 1 - \frac{3x}{5} + \frac{27x^2}{50} - \frac{27x^3}{50} + ...$

The expansion is valid for $\left|\frac{6x}{5}\right| < 1$, so $|x| < \frac{5}{6}$.

b) $\sqrt{\frac{20}{5 + 6x}} = \frac{\sqrt{20}}{\sqrt{5 + 6x}} = 20^{\frac{1}{2}}(5 + 6x)^{-\frac{1}{2}}$

$\qquad = (20^{\frac{1}{2}})(5^{-\frac{1}{2}})\left(1 + \frac{6}{5}x\right)^{-\frac{1}{2}}$

$\qquad = \left(\frac{20^{\frac{1}{2}}}{5^{\frac{1}{2}}}\right)\left(1 + \frac{6}{5}x\right)^{-\frac{1}{2}} = \left(\frac{20}{5}\right)^{\frac{1}{2}}\left(1 + \frac{6}{5}x\right)^{-\frac{1}{2}}$

$\qquad = 4^{\frac{1}{2}}\left(1 + \frac{6}{5}x\right)^{-\frac{1}{2}} = 2\left(1 + \frac{6}{5}x\right)^{-\frac{1}{2}}$

So, using the expansion in part a):

$\sqrt{\frac{20}{5 + 6x}} = 2(1 - \frac{3x}{5} + \frac{27x^2}{50} - \frac{27x^3}{50} + ...)$

$\qquad = 2 - \frac{6x}{5} + \frac{27x^2}{25} - \frac{27x^3}{25} + ...$

Q5 **a)** $\frac{1}{\sqrt{5 - 2x}} = (5 - 2x)^{-\frac{1}{2}} = 5^{-\frac{1}{2}}\left(1 - \frac{2}{5}x\right)^{-\frac{1}{2}}$

$\left(1 - \frac{2}{5}x\right)^{-\frac{1}{2}} = 1 + \left(-\frac{1}{2}\right)\left(-\frac{2}{5}x\right) + \frac{\left(-\frac{1}{2}\right)\times\left(-\frac{3}{2}\right)}{1\times2}\left(-\frac{2}{5}x\right)^2 + ...$

$\qquad = 1 + \frac{x}{5} + \left(\frac{3}{8}\right)\left(\frac{4}{25}x^2\right) + ... = 1 + \frac{x}{5} + \frac{3x^2}{50} + ...$

So $\frac{1}{\sqrt{5 - 2x}} = 5^{-\frac{1}{2}}\left(1 - \frac{2}{5}x\right)^{-\frac{1}{2}} = \frac{1}{\sqrt{5}}(1 + \frac{x}{5} + \frac{3x^2}{50} ...)$

$\qquad = \frac{1}{\sqrt{5}} + \frac{x}{5\sqrt{5}} + \frac{3x^2}{50\sqrt{5}} + ...$

b) $\frac{3 + x}{\sqrt{5 - 2x}} \approx (3 + x)\left(\frac{1}{\sqrt{5}} + \frac{x}{5\sqrt{5}} + \frac{3x^2}{50\sqrt{5}}\right)$

$\qquad \approx 3\left(\frac{1}{\sqrt{5}} + \frac{x}{5\sqrt{5}} + \frac{3x^2}{50\sqrt{5}}\right) + x\left(\frac{1}{\sqrt{5}} + \frac{x}{5\sqrt{5}}\right)$

$\qquad = \frac{3}{\sqrt{5}} + \frac{3x}{5\sqrt{5}} + \frac{9x^2}{50\sqrt{5}} + \frac{x}{\sqrt{5}} + \frac{x^2}{5\sqrt{5}}$

$\qquad = \frac{3}{\sqrt{5}} + \frac{8x}{5\sqrt{5}} + \frac{19x^2}{50\sqrt{5}}$

Q6 **a)** $(9 + 4x)^{-\frac{1}{2}} = 9^{-\frac{1}{2}}\left(1 + \frac{4}{9}x\right)^{-\frac{1}{2}}$

$\left(1 + \frac{4}{9}x\right)^{-\frac{1}{2}} = 1 + \left(-\frac{1}{2}\right)\left(\frac{4}{9}x\right) + \frac{\left(-\frac{1}{2}\right)\times\left(-\frac{3}{2}\right)}{1\times2}\left(\frac{4}{9}x\right)^2 + ...$

$\qquad = 1 - \frac{2x}{9} + \frac{2x^2}{27} - ...$

So $(9 + 4x)^{-\frac{1}{2}} = \frac{1}{\sqrt{9}}\left(1 - \frac{2x}{9} + \frac{2x^2}{27} - ...\right) = \frac{1}{3} - \frac{2x}{27} + \frac{2x^2}{81} - ...$

b) $(1 + 6x)^4 = 1 + 24x + 216x^2 + ...$

So $\frac{(1 + 6x)^4}{\sqrt{9 + 4x}} = (1 + 6x)^4(9 + 4x)^{-\frac{1}{2}}$

$\qquad \approx (1 + 24x + 216x^2)\left(\frac{1}{3} - \frac{2x}{27} + \frac{2x^2}{81}\right)$

$\qquad \approx \frac{1}{3} - \frac{2x}{27} + \frac{2x^2}{81} + 24x\left(\frac{1}{3} - \frac{2x}{27}\right) + 216x^2\left(\frac{1}{3}\right)$

$\qquad = \frac{1}{3} - \frac{2x}{27} + \frac{2x^2}{81} + 8x - \frac{16x^2}{9} + 72x^2$

$\qquad = \frac{1}{3} + \frac{214x}{27} + \frac{5690x^2}{81}$

6.2 Using the Binomial Expansion as an Approximation

Exercise 6.2.1 — Approximating with binomial expansions

Q1 **a)** $(1 + 6x)^{-1} = 1 + (-1)(6x) + \frac{-1\times-2}{1\times2}(6x)^2 + ...$

$\qquad = 1 - 6x + 36x^2 - ...$

b) The expansion is valid if $|x| < \frac{1}{6}$.

c) $\frac{100}{106} = \frac{1}{1.06} = \frac{1}{1 + 0.06} = (1 + 0.06)^{-1}$

This is the same as $(1 + 6x)^{-1}$ with $x = 0.01$.

$0.01 < \frac{1}{6}$ so the approximation is valid.

$(1 + 6(0.01))^{-1} \approx 1 - 6(0.01) + 36(0.01^2)$

$\qquad = 1 - 0.06 + 0.0036 = 0.9436$

d) $\left|\frac{\left(\frac{100}{106}\right) - 0.9436}{\left(\frac{100}{106}\right)}\right| \times 100 = 0.02\%$ (1 s.f.)

In the answers that follow, the expansions will just be stated. Look back at the previous sections of this chapter to check how to set out the working if you need to.

Q2 **a)** $(1 + 3x)^{\frac{1}{4}} = 1 + \frac{3x}{4} - \frac{27x^2}{32} + \frac{189x^3}{128} - ...$

b) The expansion is valid if $|x| < \frac{1}{3}$.

c) $\sqrt[4]{1.9} = 1.9^{\frac{1}{4}} = (1 + 0.9)^{\frac{1}{4}}$

This is the same as $(1 + 3x)^{\frac{1}{4}}$ with $x = 0.3$.

$0.3 < \frac{1}{3}$ so the approximation is valid.

$(1 + 3(0.3))^{\frac{1}{4}} \approx 1 + \frac{3(0.3)}{4} - \frac{27(0.3^2)}{32} + \frac{189(0.3^3)}{128}$

$\qquad = 1.1889$ (4 d.p.)

d) $\left|\frac{(\sqrt[4]{1.9}) - 1.1889}{(\sqrt[4]{1.9})}\right| \times 100 = 1.26\%$ (3 s.f.)

Q3 **a)** $(1 - 2x)^{-\frac{1}{2}} = 1 + x + \frac{3x^2}{2} + \frac{5x^3}{2} + ...$

b) The expansion is valid if $|x| < \frac{1}{2}$.

c) Using $x = \frac{1}{10}$ gives:

$$\left(1 - \frac{2}{10}\right)^{-\frac{1}{2}} \approx 1 + \frac{1}{10} + \frac{3}{200} + \frac{5}{2000}$$

$$\left(\frac{4}{5}\right)^{-\frac{1}{2}} \approx 1 + 0.1 + 0.015 + 0.0025$$

$$\left(\frac{5}{4}\right)^{\frac{1}{2}} \approx 1.1175$$

$$\left(\frac{5}{4}\right)^{\frac{1}{2}} = \sqrt{\frac{5}{4}} = \frac{\sqrt{5}}{\sqrt{4}} = \frac{\sqrt{5}}{2}$$

So $\sqrt{5} \approx 2 \times 1.1175 = 2.235$

d) $\left|\dfrac{\sqrt{5} - 2.235}{\sqrt{5}}\right| \times 100 = 0.048\%$ (2 s.f.)

Q4 a) $(2 - 5x)^6 = 2^6\left(1 - \frac{5}{2}x\right)^6 = 64\left(1 - 15x + \frac{375x^2}{4} - \ldots\right)$
$$= 64 - 960x + 6000x^2 - \ldots$$

b) $1.95^6 = (2 - 0.05)^6$
This is the same as $(2 - 5x)^6$ with $x = 0.01$.
$(2 - 5(0.01))^6 \approx 64 - 960(0.01) + 6000(0.01)^2$
$$= 64 - 9.6 + 0.6 = 55$$

c) $\left|\dfrac{1.95^6 - 55}{1.95^6}\right| \times 100 = 0.036\%$ (2 s.f.)

Q5 a) $\sqrt{3 - 4x} = (3 - 4x)^{\frac{1}{2}} = \sqrt{3}\left(1 - \frac{4}{3}x\right)^{\frac{1}{2}}$
$$= \sqrt{3}\left(1 - \frac{2x}{3} - \frac{2x^2}{9} - \ldots\right) = \sqrt{3} - \frac{2\sqrt{3}x}{3} - \frac{2\sqrt{3}x^2}{9} - \ldots$$

Remember to factorise the original expression to get it in the form $(1 + ax)^n$.

b) The expansion is valid if $|x| < \frac{3}{4}$.

c) $\sqrt{3 - 4\left(\frac{3}{40}\right)} \approx \sqrt{3} - \frac{2\sqrt{3} \times 3}{3 \times 40} - \frac{2\sqrt{3} \times 9}{9 \times 1600}$

$$\sqrt{3 - \frac{3}{10}} \approx \sqrt{3} - \frac{\sqrt{3}}{20} - \frac{\sqrt{3}}{800}$$

$$\sqrt{\frac{27}{10}} \approx \frac{759\sqrt{3}}{800}$$

$$\frac{3\sqrt{3}}{\sqrt{10}} \approx \frac{759\sqrt{3}}{800} \implies \frac{3}{\sqrt{10}} \approx \frac{759}{800}$$

d) $\left|\dfrac{\left(\frac{3}{\sqrt{10}}\right) - \left(\frac{759}{800}\right)}{\left(\frac{3}{\sqrt{10}}\right)}\right| \times 100 = 0.007\%$ (1 s.f.)

Q6 a) $\dfrac{(1 - 5x)}{(1 + 3x)^{\frac{1}{3}}} = (1 - 5x)(1 + 3x)^{-\frac{1}{3}}$
$$= (1 - 5x)(1 - x + 2x^2 + \ldots) = 1 - 6x + 7x^2 + \ldots$$

b) The expansion is valid if $|x| < \frac{1}{3}$.

c) $\dfrac{(1 - 5(0.1))}{(1 + 3(0.1))^{\frac{1}{3}}} = \dfrac{0.5}{1.3^{\frac{1}{3}}} = \dfrac{1}{2\sqrt[3]{1.3}}$
$$\implies \frac{1}{2\sqrt[3]{1.3}} \approx 1 - 6(0.1) + 7(0.01) = 0.47$$

d) $\left|\dfrac{\left(\frac{1}{2\sqrt[3]{1.3}}\right) - 0.47}{\left(\frac{1}{2\sqrt[3]{1.3}}\right)}\right| \times 100 = 2.6\%$ (2 s.f.)

6.3 Binomial Expansion and Partial Fractions

Exercise 6.3.1 — Finding binomial expansions using partial fractions

Q1 a) $5 - 12x \equiv A(4 + 3x) + B(1 + 6x)$
Using the substitution method:
When $x = -\frac{4}{3}$, $5 + 16 = -7B \implies B = -3$.
When $x = -\frac{1}{6}$, $5 + 2 = \frac{7A}{2} \implies A = 2$.

You could also have used the 'equating coefficients' method.

b) (i) $(1 + 6x)^{-1} = 1 - 6x + 36x^2 - \ldots$

(ii) $(4 + 3x)^{-1} = 4^{-1}\left(1 + \frac{3}{4}x\right)^{-1}$
$$= \frac{1}{4}\left(1 - \frac{3x}{4} + \frac{9x^2}{16} - \ldots\right) = \frac{1}{4} - \frac{3x}{16} + \frac{9x^2}{64} - \ldots$$

c) From a): $\dfrac{5 - 12x}{(1 + 6x)(4 + 3x)} \equiv \dfrac{2}{(1 + 6x)} - \dfrac{3}{(4 + 3x)}$
$$\equiv 2(1 + 6x)^{-1} - 3(4 + 3x)^{-1}$$

$2(1 + 6x)^{-1} - 3(4 + 3x)^{-1}$
$$\approx 2(1 - 6x + 36x^2) - 3\left(\frac{1}{4} - \frac{3x}{16} + \frac{9x^2}{64}\right)$$
$$= 2 - 12x + 72x^2 - \frac{3}{4} + \frac{9x}{16} - \frac{27x^2}{64}$$
$$= \frac{5}{4} - \frac{183x}{16} + \frac{4581x^2}{64}$$

d) $(1 + 6x)^{-1}$ is valid if $|x| < \frac{1}{6}$.
$(4 + 3x)^{-1}$ is valid if $|x| < \frac{4}{3}$.
So the full expansion is valid if $|x| < \frac{1}{6}$.

Q2 a) $\dfrac{6}{(1 - x)(1 + x)(1 + 2x)} \equiv \dfrac{A}{(1 - x)} + \dfrac{B}{(1 + x)} + \dfrac{C}{(1 + 2x)}$
$6 \equiv A(1 + x)(1 + 2x) + B(1 - x)(1 + 2x) + C(1 - x)(1 + x)$
Using the substitution method:
When $x = 1$, $6 = 6A \implies A = 1$
When $x = -1$, $6 = -2B \implies B = -3$
When $x = -\frac{1}{2}$, $6 = \frac{3}{4}C \implies C = 8$
Putting these values back into the expression gives:
$$\frac{6}{(1 - x)(1 + x)(1 + 2x)} \equiv \frac{1}{(1 - x)} - \frac{3}{(1 + x)} + \frac{8}{(1 + 2x)}$$

b) $f(x)$ can also be expressed as:
$(1 - x)^{-1} - 3(1 + x)^{-1} + 8(1 + 2x)^{-1}$
Expanding these three parts separately:
$(1 - x)^{-1} = 1 + x + x^2 + \ldots$
$(1 + x)^{-1} = 1 - x + x^2 + \ldots$
$(1 + 2x)^{-1} = 1 - 2x + 4x^2 + \ldots$
So $f(x) \approx 1 + x + x^2 - 3(1 - x + x^2) + 8(1 - 2x + 4x^2)$
$$= 1 + x + x^2 - 3 + 3x - 3x^2 + 8 - 16x + 32x^2$$
$$= 6 - 12x + 30x^2$$

c) $f(0.01) = \dfrac{6}{(1 - 0.01)(1 + 0.01)(1 + 2(0.01))} = 5.8829\ldots$
From the expansion:
$f(0.01) \approx 6 - 12(0.01) + 30(0.01)^2$
$$= 6 - 0.12 + 0.003 = 5.883$$
So the % error is:
$\left|\dfrac{5.8829\ldots - 5.883}{5.8829\ldots}\right| \times 100 = 0.0010\%$ (2 s.f.)

Q3 a) $2x^3 + 5x^2 - 3x = x(2x - 1)(x + 3)$

b) $\dfrac{5x - 6}{2x^3 + 5x^2 - 3x} \equiv \dfrac{5x - 6}{x(2x - 1)(x + 3)} \equiv \dfrac{A}{x} + \dfrac{B}{(2x - 1)} + \dfrac{C}{(x + 3)}$
$5x - 6 \equiv A(2x - 1)(x + 3) + Bx(x + 3) + Cx(2x - 1)$
Using the substitution method:
When $x = 0$, $-6 = -3A \implies A = 2$
When $x = \frac{1}{2}$, $\frac{5}{2} - 6 = \frac{7}{4}B \implies B = -2$
When $x = -3$, $-15 - 6 = 21C \implies C = -1$
So $\dfrac{5x - 6}{2x^3 + 5x^2 - 3x} \equiv \dfrac{2}{x} - \dfrac{2}{(2x - 1)} - \dfrac{1}{(x + 3)}$

c) $(2x - 1)^{-1} = -(1 - 2x)^{-1} = -(1 + 2x + 4x^2 + \ldots)$
$(x + 3)^{-1} = \frac{1}{3}\left(1 + \frac{1}{3}x\right)^{-1} = \frac{1}{3}\left(1 - \frac{x}{3} + \frac{x^2}{9} + \ldots\right)$
$$= \frac{1}{3} - \frac{x}{9} + \frac{x^2}{27} + \ldots$$

$\dfrac{5x - 6}{2x^3 + 5x^2 - 3x} \equiv \dfrac{2}{x} - 2(2x - 1)^{-1} - (x + 3)^{-1}$
$$\approx \frac{2}{x} - 2[-(1 + 2x + 4x^2)] - \left(\frac{1}{3} - \frac{x}{9} + \frac{x^2}{27}\right)$$
$$= \frac{2}{x} + 2 + 4x + 8x^2 - \frac{1}{3} + \frac{x}{9} - \frac{x^2}{27}$$
$$= \frac{2}{x} + \frac{5}{3} + \frac{37x}{9} + \frac{215x^2}{27}$$

d) $(2x - 1)^{-1}$ is valid for $|x| < \frac{1}{2}$.

$(x + 3)^{-1}$ is valid for $|x| < 3$.

$\frac{2}{x}$ is valid for $x \neq 0$.

So the full expansion is valid for $|x| < \frac{1}{2}$, $x \neq 0$.

Make sure you don't get caught out here — the brackets are in the form $(qx + p)^n$, not $(p + qx)^n$.

Q4 a) $\frac{55x + 7}{(2x - 5)(3x + 1)^2} \equiv \frac{A}{(2x - 5)} + \frac{B}{(3x + 1)} + \frac{C}{(3x + 1)^2}$

$55x + 7 \equiv A(3x + 1)^2 + B(2x - 5)(3x + 1) + C(2x - 5)$

Using the substitution method:

When $x = \frac{5}{2}$, $\frac{275}{2} + 7 = A\left(\frac{17}{2}\right)^2$

$\Rightarrow \frac{289}{2} = \frac{289}{4}A \Rightarrow A = 2$

When $x = -\frac{1}{3}$, $-\frac{55}{3} + 7 = C\left(-\frac{2}{3} - 5\right)$

$-\frac{34}{3} = -\frac{17}{3}C \Rightarrow C = 2$

Equating coefficients of x^2:

$0 = 9A + 6B \Rightarrow 6B = -18 \Rightarrow B = -3$.

So: $\frac{55x + 7}{(2x - 5)(3x + 1)^2} \equiv \frac{2}{(2x - 5)} - \frac{3}{(3x + 1)} + \frac{2}{(3x + 1)^2}$

b) $(2x - 5)^{-1} = -\frac{1}{5}\left(1 - \frac{2}{5}x\right)^{-1} = -\frac{1}{5}\left(1 + \frac{2x}{5} + \frac{4x^2}{25} + ...\right)$

$= -\frac{1}{5} - \frac{2x}{25} - \frac{4x^2}{125} - ...$

$(3x + 1)^{-1} = 1 - 3x + 9x^2 + ...$

$(3x + 1)^{-2} = 1 - 6x + 27x^2 + ...$

$f(x) = 2(2x - 5)^{-1} - 3(3x + 1)^{-1} + 2(3x + 1)^{-2}$

$\approx 2\left(-\frac{1}{5} - \frac{2x}{25} - \frac{4x^2}{125}\right) - 3(1 - 3x + 9x^2) + 2(1 - 6x + 27x^2)$

$= -\frac{2}{5} - 3 + 2 - \frac{4x}{25} + 9x - 12x - \frac{8x^2}{125} - 27x^2 + 54x^2$

$= -\frac{7}{5} - \frac{79x}{25} - \frac{3367x^2}{125}$

Q5 a) Using the Factor Theorem, if $f(0.5) = 0$ then

$(x - 0.5)$ is a factor $\Rightarrow (2x - 1)$ is a factor.

Using e.g. algebraic long division:

$f(x) = (2x - 1)(6x^2 - x - 1) \Rightarrow f(x) = (2x - 1)(2x - 1)(3x + 1)$

$\Rightarrow f(x) = (3x + 1)(2x - 1)^2$

b) $\frac{8 - x}{12x^3 - 8x^2 - x + 1} \equiv \frac{8 - x}{(3x + 1)(2x - 1)^2}$

$\equiv \frac{A}{(3x + 1)} + \frac{B}{(2x - 1)} + \frac{C}{(2x - 1)^2}$

$8 - x \equiv A(2x - 1)^2 + B(3x + 1)(2x - 1) + C(3x + 1)$

Using the substitution method:

When $x = \frac{1}{2}$, $8 - \frac{1}{2} = \frac{5}{2}C \Rightarrow C = 3$

When $x = -\frac{1}{3}$, $8 + \frac{1}{3} = \frac{25}{9}A \Rightarrow A = 3$

Equating coefficients of x^2:

$0 = 4A + 6B \Rightarrow 0 = 12 + 6B \Rightarrow B = -2$

So $\frac{8 - x}{(3x + 1)(2x - 1)^2} \equiv \frac{3}{(3x + 1)} - \frac{2}{(2x - 1)} + \frac{3}{(2x - 1)^2}$

c) $(3x + 1)^{-1} = (1 + 3x)^{-1} = (1 - 3x + 9x^2 + ...)$

$(2x - 1)^{-1} = -(1 - 2x)^{-1} = -(1 + 2x + 4x^2 + ...)$

$(2x - 1)^{-2} = (-1)^{-2}(1 - 2x)^{-2} = (1 + 4x + 12x^2 + ...)$

$\frac{8 - x}{(3x + 1)(2x - 1)^2} \equiv 3(3x + 1)^{-1} - 2(2x - 1)^{-1} + 3(2x - 1)^{-2}$

$\approx 3[1 - 3x + 9x^2] - 2[-1 - 2x - 4x^2] + 3[1 + 4x + 12x^2]$

$= 3 - 9x + 27x^2 + 2 + 4x + 8x^2 + 3 + 12x + 36x^2$

$= 8 + 7x + 71x^2$

d) $(3x + 1)^{-1}$ is valid for $|x| < \frac{1}{3}$.

$(2x - 1)^{-1}$ and $(2x - 1)^{-2}$ are valid for $|x| < \frac{1}{2}$.

So the full expansion is valid for $|x| < \frac{1}{3}$.

---

e) $g(0.001) = \frac{8 - 0.001}{(0.003 + 1)(0.002 - 1)^2}$

$= 8.007071032... = 8.007071$ (6 d.p.)

From the expansion:

$g(0.001) \approx 8 + 7(0.001) + 71(0.001)^2$

$= 8 + 0.007 + 0.000071 = 8.007071$

So the estimate is correct to 6 decimal places.

Review Exercise — Chapter 6

Q1 a) $(1 + 2x)^3$

$= 1 + 3(2x) + \frac{3(3 - 1)}{1 \times 2}(2x)^2 + \frac{3(3 - 1)(3 - 2)}{1 \times 2 \times 3}(2x)^3$

$= 1 + 6x + 12x^2 + 8x^3$

b) $(1 - x)^5 = 1 + 5(-x) + \frac{5(5 - 1)}{1 \times 2}(-x)^2$

$+ \frac{5(5 - 1)(5 - 2)}{1 \times 2 \times 3}(-x)^3$

$+ \frac{5(5 - 1)(5 - 2)(5 - 3)}{1 \times 2 \times 3 \times 4}(-x)^4$

$+ \frac{5(5 - 1)(5 - 2)(5 - 3)(5 - 4)}{1 \times 2 \times 3 \times 4 \times 5}(-x)^5$

$= 1 - 5x + 10x^2 - 10x^3 + 5x^4 - x^5$

c) $(1 - 4x)^4 = 1 + 4(-4x) + \frac{4(4 - 1)}{1 \times 2}(-4x)^2$

$+ \frac{4(4 - 1)(4 - 2)}{1 \times 2 \times 3}(-4x)^3$

$+ \frac{4(4 - 1)(4 - 2)(4 - 3)}{1 \times 2 \times 3 \times 4}(-4x)^4$

$= 1 - 16x + 96x^2 - 256x^3 + 256x^4$

d) $\left(1 - \frac{2}{3}x\right)^4 = 1 + 4\left(-\frac{2x}{3}\right) + \frac{4(4 - 1)}{1 \times 2}\left(-\frac{2x}{3}\right)^2$

$+ \frac{4(4 - 1)(4 - 2)}{1 \times 2 \times 3}\left(-\frac{2x}{3}\right)^3$

$+ \frac{4(4 - 1)(4 - 2)(4 - 3)}{1 \times 2 \times 3 \times 4}\left(-\frac{2x}{3}\right)^4$

$= 1 - \frac{8x}{3} + \frac{8x^2}{3} - \frac{32x^3}{27} + \frac{16x^4}{81}$

Q2 For positive integer values (and zero).

Q3 a) $\frac{-2(-2 - 1)}{1 \times 2}a^2 = 48 \Rightarrow 3a^2 = 48 \Rightarrow a = 4$

You're told that a is a positive integer, so ignore the negative root.

b) $\frac{\left(\frac{1}{3}\right)\left(\frac{1}{3} - 1\right)\left(\frac{1}{3} - 2\right)\left(\frac{1}{3} - 3\right)}{1 \times 2 \times 3 \times 4}(-a)^4 = -\frac{10}{3}$

$\Rightarrow -\frac{10a^4}{243} = -\frac{10}{3} \Rightarrow a^4 = 81 \Rightarrow a = 3$

Again, you need to take the positive root.

Q4 The expansion is valid for $\left|\frac{dx}{c}\right| < 1$ or $|x| < \left|\frac{c}{d}\right|$.

Q5 a) $\frac{1}{(1 + x)^5} = (1 + x)^{-5}$

$= 1 + (-5)x + \frac{-5(-5 - 1)}{1 \times 2}x^2 + \frac{-5(-5 - 1)(-5 - 2)}{1 \times 2 \times 3}x^3 + ...$

$= 1 - 5x + 15x^2 - 35x^3 + ...$

The expansion is valid for $|x| < 1$.

b) $\frac{1}{(1 - 3x)^3} = (1 - 3x)^{-3}$

$= 1 + (-3)(-3x) + \frac{-3(-3 - 1)}{1 \times 2}(-3x)^2$

$+ \frac{-3(-3 - 1)(-3 - 2)}{1 \times 2 \times 3}(-3x)^3 + ...$

$= 1 + 9x + 54x^2 + 270x^3 + ...$

The expansion is valid for $|x| < \frac{1}{3}$.

c) $\sqrt{1 - 5x} = (1 - 5x)^{\frac{1}{2}}$

$= 1 + \frac{1}{2}(-5x) + \frac{\left(\frac{1}{2}\right)\left(\frac{1}{2} - 1\right)}{1 \times 2}(-5x)^2$

$+ \frac{\left(\frac{1}{2}\right)\left(\frac{1}{2} - 1\right)\left(\frac{1}{2} - 2\right)}{1 \times 2 \times 3}(-5x)^3 + ...$

$= 1 - \frac{5x}{2} - \frac{25x^2}{8} - \frac{125x^3}{16} + ...$

The expansion is valid for $|x| < \frac{1}{5}$.

d) $\dfrac{1}{\sqrt[3]{1+2x}} = (1+2x)^{-\frac{1}{3}}$

$\qquad = 1 + \left(-\dfrac{1}{3}\right)(2x) + \dfrac{\left(-\frac{1}{3}\right)\left(-\frac{1}{3}-1\right)}{1 \times 2}(2x)^2$

$\qquad\qquad + \dfrac{\left(-\frac{1}{3}\right)\left(-\frac{1}{3}-1\right)\left(-\frac{1}{3}-2\right)}{1 \times 2 \times 3}(2x)^3 + \dots$

$\qquad = 1 - \dfrac{2x}{3} + \dfrac{8x^2}{9} - \dfrac{112x^3}{81} + \dots$

The expansion is valid for $|x| < \dfrac{1}{2}$.

Q6 a) (i) $\dfrac{1}{(3+2x)^2} = 3^{-2}\left(1 + \dfrac{2}{3}x\right)^{-2} = \dfrac{1}{9}\left(1 + \dfrac{2}{3}x\right)^{-2}$

$\left(1 + \dfrac{2}{3}x\right)^{-2} = 1 + (-2)\left(\dfrac{2x}{3}\right)$

$\qquad\qquad\qquad + \dfrac{-2(-2-1)}{1 \times 2}\left(\dfrac{2x}{3}\right)^2 + \dots$

$\qquad\qquad = 1 - \dfrac{4x}{3} + \dfrac{4x^2}{3} - \dots$

$\dfrac{1}{(3+2x)^2} = \dfrac{1}{9}\left[1 - \dfrac{4x}{3} + \dfrac{4x^2}{3} - \dots\right]$

$\qquad\qquad = \dfrac{1}{9} - \dfrac{4}{27}x + \dfrac{4}{27}x^2 - \dots$

This is valid for $|x| < \dfrac{3}{2}$.

(ii) $\sqrt[3]{8-x} = 8^{\frac{1}{3}}\left(1 - \dfrac{1}{8}x\right)^{\frac{1}{3}} = 2\left(1 - \dfrac{1}{8}x\right)^{\frac{1}{3}}$

$\left(1 - \dfrac{1}{8}x\right)^{\frac{1}{3}} = 1 + \dfrac{1}{3}\left(-\dfrac{x}{8}\right) + \dfrac{\frac{1}{3}\left(\frac{1}{3}-1\right)}{1 \times 2}\left(-\dfrac{x}{8}\right)^2 + \dots$

$\qquad\qquad = 1 - \dfrac{x}{24} - \dfrac{x^2}{576} - \dots$

$\sqrt[3]{8-x} = 2\left[1 - \dfrac{x}{24} - \dfrac{x^2}{576} - \dots\right] = 2 - \dfrac{1}{12}x - \dfrac{1}{288}x^2 - \dots$

This is valid for $|x| < 8$.

b) $\dfrac{\sqrt[3]{8-x}}{(3+2x)^2} = \left[2 - \dfrac{1}{12}x - \dfrac{1}{288}x^2 - \dots\right] \times \left[\dfrac{1}{9} - \dfrac{4}{27}x + \dfrac{4}{27}x^2 - \dots\right]$

$= 2\left[\dfrac{1}{9} - \dfrac{4}{27}x + \dfrac{4}{27}x^2\right] - \dfrac{x}{12}\left[\dfrac{1}{9} - \dfrac{4}{27}x\right] - \dfrac{x^2}{288}\left[\dfrac{1}{9}\right] + \dots$

$= \dfrac{2}{9} - \dfrac{11x}{36} + \dfrac{799x^2}{2592} - \dots$

This is valid for the narrower of the two ranges, i.e. $|x| < \dfrac{3}{2}$.

c) (i) $\sqrt[3]{8-x} = \sqrt[3]{7}$ when $x = 1$.

$\sqrt[3]{7} \approx 2 - \dfrac{1}{12}(1) - \dfrac{1}{288}(1)^2 = \dfrac{551}{288}$

(ii) The % error is:

$\left| \dfrac{\sqrt[3]{7} - \left(\frac{551}{228}\right)}{\sqrt[3]{7}} \right| \times 100 = 0.014\%$ (to 2 s.f.)

Q7 a) Write as an identity:

$\dfrac{5-10x}{(1+2x)(2-x)} \equiv \dfrac{A}{(1+2x)} + \dfrac{B}{(2-x)}$

So $5 - 10x \equiv A(2-x) + B(1+2x)$
Using the substitution method:
$x = 2 \Rightarrow 5 - 20 = 5B \Rightarrow B = -3$
$x = -0.5 \Rightarrow 5 + 5 = 2.5A \Rightarrow A = 4$.
So: $\dfrac{5-10x}{(1+2x)(2-x)} \equiv \dfrac{4}{(1+2x)} - \dfrac{3}{(2-x)}$ as required

b) $\dfrac{4}{(1+2x)} = 4(1+2x)^{-1}$

$\dfrac{3}{(2-x)} = 3(2-x)^{-1} = 3 \times 2^{-1}\left(1 - \dfrac{1}{2}x\right)^{-1} = \dfrac{3}{2}\left(1 - \dfrac{1}{2}x\right)^{-1}$

$(1+2x)^{-1} = 1 - 2x + 4x^2 - \dots$

$\left(1 - \dfrac{1}{2}x\right)^{-1} = 1 + \dfrac{x}{2} + \dfrac{x^2}{4} + \dots$

So $\dfrac{5-10x}{(1+2x)(2-x)} = 4(1+2x)^{-1} - \dfrac{3}{2}\left(1 - \dfrac{1}{2}x\right)^{-1}$

$\approx 4[1 - 2x + 4x^2] - \dfrac{3}{2}\left[1 + \dfrac{x}{2} + \dfrac{x^2}{4}\right] + \dots$

$\approx \dfrac{5}{2} - \dfrac{35x}{4} + \dfrac{125x^2}{8}$

---

c) The expansion is valid for $|x| < \dfrac{1}{2}$, so using $x = 0.1$ is valid.

$\dfrac{4}{1.2 \times 1.9} = \dfrac{100}{57}$

Expansion gives an approximation of:

$\dfrac{5}{2} - \dfrac{35(0.1)}{4} + \dfrac{125(0.01)}{8} = \dfrac{57}{32}$

The % error is:

$\left| \dfrac{\left(\frac{100}{57}\right) - \left(\frac{52}{32}\right)}{\left(\frac{100}{57}\right)} \right| \times 100 = 1.5\%$ (to 2 s.f.)

Q8 a) $f(x) = \dfrac{1}{(a-2x)^2} = (a-2x)^{-2} = a^{-2}\left(1 - \dfrac{2}{a}x\right)^{-2}$

$\qquad = \dfrac{1}{a^2}\left(1 - \dfrac{2}{a}x\right)^{-2} = \dfrac{1}{a^2}\left[1 + \dfrac{4x}{a} + \dfrac{12x^2}{a^2} + \dots\right]$

$\qquad = \dfrac{1}{a^2} + \dfrac{4x}{a^3} + \dfrac{12x^2}{a^4} + \dots$

b) The expansion is valid for $|x| < \left|\dfrac{a}{2}\right|$.

c) $g(x) = \dfrac{1}{\sqrt{4-ax}} = (4-ax)^{-\frac{1}{2}} = 4^{-\frac{1}{2}}\left(1 - \dfrac{a}{4}x\right)^{-\frac{1}{2}}$

$\qquad = \dfrac{1}{2}\left(1 - \dfrac{a}{4}x\right)^{-\frac{1}{2}} = \dfrac{1}{2}\left[1 + \dfrac{ax}{8} + \dfrac{3a^2x^2}{128} + \dots\right]$

$\qquad = \dfrac{1}{2} + \dfrac{ax}{16} + \dfrac{3a^2x^2}{256} + \dots$

d) The expansion is valid for $|x| < \left|\dfrac{4}{a}\right|$.

e) $\left[\dfrac{1}{a^2} + \dfrac{4x}{a^3} + \dfrac{12x^2}{a^4} + \dots\right] \times \left[\dfrac{1}{2} + \dfrac{ax}{16} + \dfrac{3a^2x^2}{256} + \dots\right]$

$= \dfrac{1}{a^2}\left[\dfrac{1}{2} + \dfrac{ax}{16}\right] + \dfrac{4x}{a^3}\left[\dfrac{1}{2}\right] + \dots = \dfrac{1}{2a^2} + \dfrac{ax}{16a^2} + \dfrac{4x}{2a^3} + \dots$

$= \dfrac{1}{2a^2} + \dfrac{(a^2+32)x}{16a^3} + \dots$

f) When $a = 2$, $\dfrac{(a^2+32)}{16a^3} = \dfrac{(2^2+32)}{16(2)^3} = \dfrac{9}{32}$

Exam-Style Questions — Chapter 6

Q1 $\sqrt[3]{(1+2x)^2} = (1+2x)^{\frac{2}{3}} = 1 + \dfrac{2}{3}(2x) + \dfrac{\frac{2}{3}\left(\frac{2}{3}-1\right)}{1 \times 2}(2x)^2 + \dots$

$\qquad = 1 + \dfrac{4}{3}x + \dfrac{4}{9}x^2 + \dots$

[2 marks available — 1 mark for expansion, 1 mark for simplifying and writing correct coefficients of constant, x and x^2]

Q2 The coefficient of x^3 in the expansion of $(1+ax)^{-4}$ is:

$\dfrac{-4(-4-1)(-4-2)}{1 \times 2 \times 3}a^3 = -20a^3$

So: $-20a^3 = -160 \Rightarrow a^3 = 8 \Rightarrow a = 2$

[3 marks available — 1 mark for correct coefficient of x^3 in the expansion, 1 mark for equating to −160, 1 mark for correct value of a]

Q3 a) $(1-3x)^{\frac{1}{2}} = 1 + \dfrac{1}{2}(-3x) + \dfrac{\frac{1}{2}\left(\frac{1}{2}-1\right)}{1 \times 2}(-3x)^2 + \dots$

$\qquad = 1 - \dfrac{3}{2}x - \dfrac{9}{8}x^2 + \dots$

The expansion is valid for $|3x| < 1$ or $|x| < \dfrac{1}{3}$.

[3 marks available — 1 mark for expansion, 1 mark for simplifying and writing correct coefficients of constant, x and x^2, 1 mark for correct limit]

b) $1 - 3x = 0.97 \Rightarrow x = 0.01$
Using the expansion:

$\sqrt{0.97} \approx 1 - \dfrac{3}{2}(0.01) - \dfrac{9}{8}(0.01)^2 = 0.9848875$

[2 marks available — 1 mark for correct x value, 1 mark for substitution leading to correct answer]

Q4 **a)** $3x^2 + x + 2 \equiv$
$A(x-1)(2x+1) + B(x+1)(2x+1) + C(x+1)(x-1)$
Using the substitution method:
When $x = -1$, $3 - 1 + 2 = 2A \Rightarrow A = 2$
When $x = 1$, $3 + 1 + 2 = 6B \Rightarrow B = 1$
When $x = -\frac{1}{2}$, $\frac{3}{4} - \frac{1}{2} + 2 = -\frac{3}{4}C \Rightarrow C = -3$

[5 marks available — 1 mark for adding three fractions to give correct numerator (on right of identity), 1 mark for equating numerators, 1 mark for attempting a correct method to find the unknowns (either substitution or equating coefficients), 1 mark for two correct values, 1 mark for third correct value]

b) $\dfrac{3x^2 + x + 2}{(x+1)(x-1)(2x+1)} \equiv \dfrac{2}{(x+1)} + \dfrac{1}{(x-1)} - \dfrac{3}{(2x+1)}$

$\equiv 2(x+1)^{-1} + (x-1)^{-1} - 3(2x+1)^{-1}$
$(x+1)^{-1} = (1+x)^{-1} = (1 - x + x^2 + \ldots)$
$(x-1)^{-1} = -(1-x)^{-1} = -(1 + x + x^2 + \ldots)$
$(2x+1)^{-1} = (1+2x)^{-1} = (1 - 2x + 4x^2 + \ldots)$

So $\dfrac{3x^2 + x + 2}{(x+1)(x-1)(2x+1)}$
$\approx 2[1 - x + x^2] - [1 + x + x^2] - 3[1 - 2x + 4x^2]$
$= 2 - 2x + 2x^2 - 1 - x - x^2 - 3 + 6x - 12x^2 = -2 + 3x - 11x^2$

[6 marks available — 1 mark for each correct expansion of the denominators, 1 mark for multiplying the denominator expansions by the correct values, 1 mark for attempting to add the three expansions, 1 mark for correct simplified final answer]

c) $(x+1)^{-1}$ and $(x-1)^{-1}$ are valid for $|x| < 1$.
$(2x+1)^{-1}$ is valid for $|x| < \frac{1}{2}$.
So the whole expansion is valid for $|x| < \frac{1}{2}$.
[1 mark]

Q5 $(1 + ax)^n = 1 + nax + \dfrac{n(n-1)}{1 \times 2}(ax)^2 + \ldots$
Compare coefficients of x: $na = -6 \Rightarrow a = -\dfrac{6}{n}$

Compare coefficients of x^2:
$\dfrac{n(n-1)a^2}{2} = \dfrac{45}{2} \Rightarrow (n^2 - n)\left(-\dfrac{6}{n}\right)^2 = 45$
$\Rightarrow 36(n^2 - n) = 45n^2 \Rightarrow 0 = 9n^2 + 36n$
$\Rightarrow 0 = 9n(n+4) \Rightarrow n = 0$ or -4, but $n \neq 0$, so $n = -4$
$a = \dfrac{-6}{-4} = \dfrac{3}{2}$
[6 marks available — 1 mark for correct expansion, 1 mark for equating the coefficients of x, 1 mark for equating the coefficients of x^2, 1 mark for attempt to solve simultaneously, 1 mark for correct value of n, 1 mark for correct value of a]

Q6 **a)** $\sqrt{\dfrac{1+x}{1-x}} = (1+x)^{\frac{1}{2}}(1-x)^{-\frac{1}{2}}$

$(1+x)^{\frac{1}{2}} = 1 + \frac{1}{2}x + \dfrac{\frac{1}{2}\left(\frac{1}{2} - 1\right)}{1 \times 2}x^2 + \dfrac{\frac{1}{2}\left(\frac{1}{2} - 1\right)\left(\frac{1}{2} - 2\right)}{1 \times 2 \times 3}x^3 + \ldots$

$= 1 + \frac{1}{2}x - \frac{1}{8}x^2 + \frac{1}{16}x^3 + \ldots$

$(1-x)^{-\frac{1}{2}} = 1 + \left(-\frac{1}{2}\right)(-x) + \dfrac{-\frac{1}{2}\left(-\frac{1}{2} - 1\right)}{1 \times 2}(-x)^2$
$\qquad + \dfrac{-\frac{1}{2}\left(-\frac{1}{2} - 1\right)\left(-\frac{1}{2} - 2\right)}{1 \times 2 \times 3}(-x)^3 + \ldots$

$= 1 + \frac{1}{2}x + \frac{3}{8}x^2 + \frac{5}{16}x^3 + \ldots$

So $\sqrt{\dfrac{1+x}{1-x}} = [1 + \frac{1}{2}x - \frac{1}{8}x^2 + \frac{1}{16}x^3 + \ldots]$
$\qquad \times [1 + \frac{1}{2}x + \frac{3}{8}x^2 + \frac{5}{16}x^3 + \ldots]$

$= 1[1 + \frac{1}{2}x + \frac{3}{8}x^2 + \frac{5}{16}x^3]$
$\quad + \frac{1}{2}x[1 + \frac{1}{2}x + \frac{3}{8}x^2]$
$\quad - \frac{1}{8}x^2[1 + \frac{1}{2}x] + \frac{1}{16}x^3 + \ldots$

$= 1 + \frac{1}{2}x + \frac{3}{8}x^2 + \frac{5}{16}x^3 + \frac{1}{2}x + \frac{1}{4}x^2$
$\quad + \frac{3}{16}x^3 - \frac{1}{8}x^2 - \frac{1}{16}x^3 + \frac{1}{16}x^3 + \ldots$

$= 1 + x + \frac{1}{2}x^2 + \frac{1}{2}x^3 + \ldots$

Both $(1+x)^{\frac{1}{2}}$ and $(1-x)^{-\frac{1}{2}}$ are valid for $|x| < 1$, so the expansion is valid for $|x| < 1$.

[8 marks available — 1 mark for writing as the product of two expressions, 1 mark for correct use of formula for each expansion, 1 mark for each correct and simplified expansion, 1 mark for correct working to multiply the expansions, 1 mark for correct simplified final answer, 1 mark for correct limit]

b) $\dfrac{1+x}{1-x} = 3 \Rightarrow 1 + x = 3 - 3x \Rightarrow 4x = 2 \Rightarrow x = \frac{1}{2}$
Using the expansion:
$\sqrt{3} \approx 1 + \frac{1}{2} + \frac{1}{2}\left(\frac{1}{2}\right)^2 + \frac{1}{2}\left(\frac{1}{2}\right)^3$
$= 1 + \frac{1}{2} + \frac{1}{8} + \frac{1}{16} = \frac{27}{16}$

[2 marks available — 1 mark for correct value of x, 1 mark for correct final answer]

Chapter 7: Differentiation
7.1 Points of Inflection
Exercise 7.1.1 — Points of inflection

Q1 **a)** $y = \frac{1}{6}x^3 - \frac{5}{2}x^2 + \frac{1}{4}x + \frac{1}{9}$
$\Rightarrow \dfrac{dy}{dx} = \frac{1}{2}x^2 - 5x + \frac{1}{4} \Rightarrow \dfrac{d^2y}{dx^2} = x - 5$
The graph is concave when $\dfrac{d^2y}{dx^2} < 0 \Rightarrow x - 5 < 0 \Rightarrow x < 5$

b) $y = 4x^2 - x^4 \Rightarrow \dfrac{dy}{dx} = 8x - 4x^3 \Rightarrow \dfrac{d^2y}{dx^2} = 8 - 12x^2$
The graph is concave when $\dfrac{d^2y}{dx^2} < 0 \Rightarrow 8 - 12x^2 < 0$
$\Rightarrow 8 < 12x^2 \Rightarrow \frac{2}{3} < x^2 \Rightarrow x < -\sqrt{\frac{2}{3}}$ or $x > \sqrt{\frac{2}{3}}$

Q2 $y = \frac{3}{2}x^4 - x^2 - 3x \Rightarrow \dfrac{dy}{dx} = 6x^3 - 2x - 3 \Rightarrow \dfrac{d^2y}{dx^2} = 18x^2 - 2$
At the points of inflection, $\dfrac{d^2y}{dx^2} = 0$
$\Rightarrow 18x^2 - 2 = 0 \Rightarrow x^2 = \frac{1}{9} \Rightarrow x = \pm\frac{1}{3}$

Q3 $f(x) = \frac{1}{16}x^4 + \frac{3}{4}x^3 - \frac{21}{8}x^2 - 6x + 20$
$\Rightarrow f'(x) = \frac{1}{4}x^3 + \frac{9}{4}x^2 - \frac{21}{4}x - 6 \Rightarrow f''(x) = \frac{3}{4}x^2 + \frac{9}{2}x - \frac{21}{4}$
So $f(x)$ is convex when $f''(x) > 0 \Rightarrow \frac{3}{4}x^2 + \frac{9}{2}x - \frac{21}{4} > 0$
$\Rightarrow 3x^2 + 18x - 21 > 0 \Rightarrow x^2 + 6x - 7 > 0$
$\Rightarrow (x + 7)(x - 1) > 0 \Rightarrow x < -7$ or $x > 1$
So $f(x)$ is convex for $x < -7$ and $x > 1$, and concave for $-7 < x < 1$.
Sketch the graph of $f''(x)$ if you're not sure which way the inequalities should go.

Q4 $y = x^2 - \frac{1}{x} \Rightarrow \dfrac{dy}{dx} = 2x + \frac{1}{x^2} \Rightarrow \dfrac{d^2y}{dx^2} = 2 - \frac{2}{x^3}$
At a point of inflection, $\dfrac{d^2y}{dx^2} = 0 \Rightarrow 2 - \frac{2}{x^3} = 0$
$\Rightarrow 2 = \frac{2}{x^3} \Rightarrow x^3 = 1 \Rightarrow x = 1$
If $x < 1$, $x^3 < 1$, so $\frac{2}{x^3} > 2$, so $\dfrac{d^2y}{dx^2}$ is negative.
If $x > 1$, $x^3 > 1$, so $\frac{2}{x^3} < 2$, so $\dfrac{d^2y}{dx^2}$ is positive.
So at $x = 1$, $\dfrac{d^2y}{dx^2} = 0$ and the sign of $\dfrac{d^2y}{dx^2}$ changes, so this is a point of inflection.
When $x = 1$, $y = 1^2 - \frac{1}{1} = 0$,
so $(1, 0)$ is a point of inflection of $y = x^2 - \frac{1}{x}$.

Q5 **a)** $f(x) = x^3 + 2x^2 + 3x + 3 \Rightarrow f'(x) = 3x^2 + 4x + 3$
$\Rightarrow f''(x) = 6x + 4$
At a point of inflection, $f''(x) = 0 \Rightarrow 6x + 4 = 0 \Rightarrow x = -\frac{2}{3}$
When $x > -\frac{2}{3}$, $6x + 4 > 0$ and when $x < -\frac{2}{3}$, $6x + 4 < 0$
So the graph of $y = f(x)$ has one point of inflection, at $x = -\frac{2}{3}$.

b) $f'(x) = 3x^2 + 4x + 3$, so at $x = -\frac{2}{3}$,

$f'(x) = 3\left(-\frac{2}{3}\right)^2 + 4\left(-\frac{2}{3}\right) + 3 = \frac{4}{3} - \frac{8}{3} + 3 = \frac{5}{3}$

$f'(x) \neq 0$ at the point of inflection, so it is not a stationary point.

Q6 $y = \frac{1}{10}x^5 - \frac{1}{3}x^3 + \frac{1}{2}x + 4$

$\Rightarrow \frac{dy}{dx} = \frac{1}{2}x^4 - x^2 + \frac{1}{2} \Rightarrow \frac{d^2y}{dx^2} = 2x^3 - 2x$

At a stationary point, $\frac{dy}{dx} = 0$

$\Rightarrow \frac{1}{2}x^4 - x^2 + \frac{1}{2} = 0 \Rightarrow x^4 - 2x^2 + 1 = 0$

$\Rightarrow (x^2 - 1)^2 = 0 \Rightarrow [(x + 1)(x - 1)]^2 = 0 \Rightarrow x = \pm 1$

When $x = 1$, $y = \frac{1}{10} - \frac{1}{3} + \frac{1}{2} + 4 = \frac{64}{15}$ and $\frac{d^2y}{dx^2} = 2 - 2 = 0$.

When $x = -1$, $y = -\frac{1}{10} + \frac{1}{3} - \frac{1}{2} + 4 = \frac{56}{15}$ and $\frac{d^2y}{dx^2} = -2 + 2 = 0$.

$\frac{d^2y}{dx^2} = 0$ at both stationary points,

so check what happens to $\frac{d^2y}{dx^2}$ around $x = 1$ and $x = -1$.

$\frac{d^2y}{dx^2} = 2x^3 - 2x = 2x(x^2 - 1) = 2x(x + 1)(x - 1)$

When $x < -1$, $2x$ is negative, $x + 1$ is negative

and $x - 1$ is negative, so $\frac{d^2y}{dx^2}$ is negative for $x < -1$.

When $-1 < x < 0$, $2x$ is negative, $x + 1$ is positive and $x - 1$ is negative, so $\frac{d^2y}{dx^2}$ is positive for $-1 < x < 0$.

So $\frac{d^2y}{dx^2}$ changes sign at $x = -1$.

When $0 < x < 1$, $2x$ is positive, $x + 1$ is positive and $x - 1$ is negative, so $\frac{d^2y}{dx^2}$ is negative for $0 < x < 1$.

When $1 < x$, $2x$ is positive, $x + 1$ is positive and $x - 1$ is positive, so $\frac{d^2y}{dx^2}$ is positive for $1 < x$. So $\frac{d^2y}{dx^2}$ changes sign at $x = 1$.

The graph of $y = \frac{1}{10}x^5 - \frac{1}{3}x^3 + \frac{1}{2}x + 4$ has stationary points at $\left(-1, \frac{56}{15}\right)$ and $\left(1, \frac{64}{15}\right)$, and both stationary points are points of inflection.

Again, it might help to sketch the graph of $\frac{d^2y}{dx^2}$. You could also use the fact that $\frac{dy}{dx} = \frac{1}{2}(x^2 - 1)^2$ to show that the gradient is always ≥ 0, which means that any stationary points must be points of inflection.

7.2 Chain Rule

Exercise 7.2.1 — The chain rule

Q1

a) $y = (x + 7)^2$, so let $y = u^2$ where $u = x + 7$

$\Rightarrow \frac{dy}{du} = 2u = 2(x + 7)$, $\frac{du}{dx} = 1$

$\frac{dy}{dx} = \frac{dy}{du} \times \frac{du}{dx} = 2(x + 7) \times 1 = 2(x + 7)$

b) $y = (2x - 1)^5$, so let $y = u^5$ where $u = 2x - 1$

$\Rightarrow \frac{dy}{du} = 5u^4 = 5(2x - 1)^4$, $\frac{du}{dx} = 2$

$\frac{dy}{dx} = \frac{dy}{du} \times \frac{du}{dx} = 5(2x - 1)^4 \times 2 = 10(2x - 1)^4$

c) $y = 3(4 - x)^8$, so let $y = 3u^8$ where $u = 4 - x$

$\Rightarrow \frac{dy}{du} = 24u^7 = 24(4 - x)^7$, $\frac{du}{dx} = -1$

$\frac{dy}{dx} = \frac{dy}{du} \times \frac{du}{dx} = 24(4 - x)^7 \times (-1) = -24(4 - x)^7$

d) $y = (3 - 2x)^7$, so let $y = u^7$ where $u = 3 - 2x$

$\Rightarrow \frac{dy}{du} = 7u^6 = 7(3 - 2x)^6$, $\frac{du}{dx} = -2$

$\frac{dy}{dx} = \frac{dy}{du} \times \frac{du}{dx} = 7(3 - 2x)^6 \times (-2) = -14(3 - 2x)^6$

e) $y = (x^2 + 3)^5$, so let $y = u^5$ where $u = x^2 + 3$

$\Rightarrow \frac{dy}{du} = 5u^4 = 5(x^2 + 3)^4$, $\frac{du}{dx} = 2x$

$\frac{dy}{dx} = \frac{dy}{du} \times \frac{du}{dx} = 5(x^2 + 3)^4 \times 2x = 10x(x^2 + 3)^4$

f) $y = (5x^2 + 3)^2$, so let $y = u^2$ where $u = 5x^2 + 3$

$\Rightarrow \frac{dy}{du} = 2u = 2(5x^2 + 3)$, $\frac{du}{dx} = 10x$

$\frac{dy}{dx} = \frac{dy}{du} \times \frac{du}{dx} = 2(5x^2 + 3) \times 10x = 20x(5x^2 + 3)$

Q2

a) $f(x) = (4x^3 - 9)^8$, so let $y = u^8$ where $u = 4x^3 - 9$

$\Rightarrow \frac{dy}{du} = 8u^7 = 8(4x^3 - 9)^7$, $\frac{du}{dx} = 12x^2$

$f'(x) = \frac{dy}{du} \times \frac{du}{dx} = 8(4x^3 - 9)^7 \times 12x^2 = 96x^2(4x^3 - 9)^7$

b) $f(x) = (6 - 7x^2)^4$, so let $y = u^4$ where $u = 6 - 7x^2$

$\Rightarrow \frac{dy}{du} = 4u^3 = 4(6 - 7x^2)^3$, $\frac{du}{dx} = -14x$

$f'(x) = \frac{dy}{du} \times \frac{du}{dx} = 4(6 - 7x^2)^3 \times (-14x) = -56x(6 - 7x^2)^3$

c) $f(x) = (x^2 + 5x + 7)^6$, so let $y = u^6$

where $u = x^2 + 5x + 7$

$\Rightarrow \frac{dy}{du} = 6u^5 = 6(x^2 + 5x + 7)^5$, $\frac{du}{dx} = 2x + 5$

$f'(x) = \frac{dy}{du} \times \frac{du}{dx} = 6(x^2 + 5x + 7)^5 \times (2x + 5)$
$= (x^2 + 5x + 7)^5 (12x + 30)$

d) $f(x) = (x + 4)^{-3}$, so let $y = u^{-3}$ where $u = x + 4$

$\Rightarrow \frac{dy}{du} = -3u^{-4} = -3(x + 4)^{-4}$, $\frac{du}{dx} = 1$

$f'(x) = \frac{dy}{du} \times \frac{du}{dx} = -3(x + 4)^{-4} \times 1 = -3(x + 4)^{-4}$

e) $f(x) = (5 - 3x)^{-2}$, so let $y = u^{-2}$ where $u = 5 - 3x$

$\Rightarrow \frac{dy}{du} = -2u^{-3} = -2(5 - 3x)^{-3}$, $\frac{du}{dx} = -3$

$f'(x) = \frac{dy}{du} \times \frac{du}{dx} = -2(5 - 3x)^{-3} \times (-3) = 6(5 - 3x)^{-3}$

f) $f(x) = \frac{1}{(5 - 3x)^4} = (5 - 3x)^{-4}$, so let $y = u^{-4}$ where $u = 5 - 3x$

$\Rightarrow \frac{dy}{du} = -4u^{-5} = -4(5 - 3x)^{-5}$, $\frac{du}{dx} = -3$

$f'(x) = \frac{dy}{du} \times \frac{du}{dx} = -4(5 - 3x)^{-5} \times (-3) = \frac{12}{(5 - 3x)^5}$

g) $f(x) = (3x^2 + 4)^{\frac{3}{2}}$, so let $y = u^{\frac{3}{2}}$ where $u = 3x^2 + 4$

$\Rightarrow \frac{dy}{du} = \frac{3}{2}u^{\frac{1}{2}} = \frac{3}{2}(3x^2 + 4)^{\frac{1}{2}}$, $\frac{du}{dx} = 6x$

$f'(x) = \frac{dy}{du} \times \frac{du}{dx} = \frac{3}{2}(3x^2 + 4)^{\frac{1}{2}} \times 6x = 9x(3x^2 + 4)^{\frac{1}{2}}$

h) $f(x) = \frac{1}{\sqrt{5 - 3x}} = (5 - 3x)^{-\frac{1}{2}}$, so let $y = u^{-\frac{1}{2}}$ where $u = 5 - 3x$

$\Rightarrow \frac{dy}{du} = -\frac{1}{2}u^{-\frac{3}{2}} = -\frac{1}{2}(5 - 3x)^{-\frac{3}{2}}$, $\frac{du}{dx} = -3$

$f'(x) = \frac{dy}{du} \times \frac{du}{dx} = -\frac{1}{2}(5 - 3x)^{-\frac{3}{2}} \times (-3) = \frac{3}{2(\sqrt{5 - 3x})^3}$

i) $f(x) = \frac{1}{\sqrt{x^3 + 2x^2}} = (x^3 + 2x^2)^{-\frac{1}{2}}$, so let $y = u^{-\frac{1}{2}}$ where $u = x^3 + 2x^2$

$\Rightarrow \frac{dy}{du} = -\frac{1}{2}u^{-\frac{3}{2}} = -\frac{1}{2}(x^3 + 2x^2)^{-\frac{3}{2}}$, $\frac{du}{dx} = 3x^2 + 4x$

$f'(x) = \frac{dy}{du} \times \frac{du}{dx} = -\frac{1}{2}(x^3 + 2x^2)^{-\frac{3}{2}} \times (3x^2 + 4x)$
$= -\frac{3x^2 + 4x}{2(\sqrt{x^3 + 2x^2})^3}$

Q3

a) $y = (5x - 3x^2)^{-\frac{1}{2}}$, so let $y = u^{-\frac{1}{2}}$ where $u = 5x - 3x^2$

$\Rightarrow \frac{dy}{du} = -\frac{1}{2}u^{-\frac{3}{2}} = -\frac{1}{2}(5x - 3x^2)^{-\frac{3}{2}}$, $\frac{du}{dx} = 5 - 6x$

$\frac{dy}{dx} = \frac{dy}{du} \times \frac{du}{dx} = -\frac{1}{2}(5x - 3x^2)^{-\frac{3}{2}} \times (5 - 6x)$
$= -\frac{5 - 6x}{2(\sqrt{5x - 3x^2})^3}$

When $x = 1$, $\frac{dy}{dx} = -\frac{5 - (6 \times 1)}{2(\sqrt{(5 \times 1) - (3 \times 1^2)})^3} = \frac{1}{4\sqrt{2}}$

b) $y = \frac{12}{\sqrt[3]{x + 6}} = 12(x + 6)^{-\frac{1}{3}}$,

so let $y = 12u^{-\frac{1}{3}}$ where $u = x + 6$

$\Rightarrow \frac{dy}{du} = -4u^{-\frac{4}{3}} = -4(x + 6)^{-\frac{4}{3}}$, $\frac{du}{dx} = 1$

$\frac{dy}{dx} = \frac{dy}{du} \times \frac{du}{dx} = -4(x + 6)^{-\frac{4}{3}} \times 1 = -\frac{4}{\sqrt[3]{(x + 6)^4}}$

When $x = 1$, $\frac{dy}{dx} = -\frac{4}{\sqrt[3]{(1 + 6)^4}} = -\frac{4}{7(\sqrt[3]{7})}$

Q4 **a)** $\left(\sqrt{x} + \dfrac{1}{\sqrt{x}}\right)^2 = \sqrt{x}\sqrt{x} + 2\sqrt{x}\dfrac{1}{\sqrt{x}} + \dfrac{1}{\sqrt{x}}\dfrac{1}{\sqrt{x}} = x + \dfrac{1}{x} + 2$

$\dfrac{d}{dx}(x + \dfrac{1}{x} + 2) = 1 - \dfrac{1}{x^2}$

Remember $\dfrac{1}{x} = x^{-1}$.

b) $y = \left(\sqrt{x} + \dfrac{1}{\sqrt{x}}\right)^2$, so let $y = u^2$ where $u = \sqrt{x} + \dfrac{1}{\sqrt{x}}$

$\Rightarrow \dfrac{dy}{du} = 2u = 2\left(\sqrt{x} + \dfrac{1}{\sqrt{x}}\right)$,

$\dfrac{du}{dx} = \dfrac{1}{2}x^{-\frac{1}{2}} - \dfrac{1}{2}x^{-\frac{3}{2}} = \dfrac{1}{2\sqrt{x}} - \dfrac{1}{2(\sqrt{x})^3}$

$\dfrac{dy}{dx} = \dfrac{dy}{du} \times \dfrac{du}{dx} = 2\left(\sqrt{x} + \dfrac{1}{\sqrt{x}}\right) \times \left(\dfrac{1}{2\sqrt{x}} - \dfrac{1}{2(\sqrt{x})^3}\right)$

$= 2\left(\dfrac{1}{2} + \dfrac{1}{2x} - \dfrac{1}{2x} - \dfrac{1}{2x^2}\right) = 1 - \dfrac{1}{x^2}$

Using powers notation makes this question easier to handle.

Q5 $y = (x - 3)^5$, so let $y = u^5$ where $u = x - 3$

$\Rightarrow \dfrac{dy}{du} = 5u^4 = 5(x - 3)^4$, $\dfrac{du}{dx} = 1$

$\dfrac{dy}{dx} = \dfrac{dy}{du} \times \dfrac{du}{dx} = 5(x - 3)^4 \times 1 = 5(x - 3)^4$

At the point $(1, -32)$, gradient $= 5(1 - 3)^4 = 80$
The equation of a straight line is $y = mx + c$
$\Rightarrow -32 = (80 \times 1) + c \Rightarrow c = -112$
So the equation of the tangent is $y = 80x - 112$.

Q6 $y = \dfrac{1}{4}(x - 7)^4$, so let $y = \dfrac{1}{4}u^4$ where $u = x - 7$

$\Rightarrow \dfrac{dy}{du} = u^3 = (x - 7)^3$, $\dfrac{du}{dx} = 1$

$\dfrac{dy}{dx} = \dfrac{dy}{du} \times \dfrac{du}{dx} = (x - 7)^3 \times 1 = (x - 7)^3$

When $x = 6$, $y = \dfrac{1}{4}(6 - 7)^4 = \dfrac{1}{4}$ and $\dfrac{dy}{dx} = (6 - 7)^3 = -1$

The gradient of the normal is $-1 \div -1 = 1$.
The equation of a straight line is $y = mx + c$
$\Rightarrow \dfrac{1}{4} = (1 \times 6) + c \Rightarrow c = -\dfrac{23}{4}$
So the equation of the normal is $y = x - \dfrac{23}{4}$

Q7 $y = (7x^2 - 3)^{-4}$, so let $y = u^{-4}$ where $u = 7x^2 - 3$

$\Rightarrow \dfrac{dy}{du} = -4u^{-5} = -4(7x^2 - 3)^{-5}$, $\dfrac{du}{dx} = 14x$

$\dfrac{dy}{dx} = \dfrac{dy}{du} \times \dfrac{du}{dx} = -4(7x^2 - 3)^{-5} \times 14x = -56x(7x^2 - 3)^{-5}$

When $x = 1$, $\dfrac{dy}{dx} = -56(1)(7(1)^2 - 3)^{-5} = -56(4^{-5}) = -\dfrac{7}{128}$

Q8 $y = \dfrac{7}{\sqrt[3]{3 - 2x}}$, so let $y = 7u^{-\frac{1}{3}}$ where $u = 3 - 2x$

$\Rightarrow \dfrac{dy}{du} = -\dfrac{7}{3}u^{-\frac{4}{3}} = -\dfrac{7}{3(\sqrt[3]{3 - 2x})^4}$, $\dfrac{du}{dx} = -2$

$f'(x) = \dfrac{dy}{du} \times \dfrac{du}{dx} = -\dfrac{7}{3(\sqrt[3]{3 - 2x})^4} \times -2 = \dfrac{14}{3(\sqrt[3]{3 - 2x})^4}$

$f'(x)$ could also be written as $\dfrac{14}{3}(3 - 2x)^{-\frac{4}{3}}$.

Q9 $y = \sqrt{5x - 1}$, so let $y = u^{\frac{1}{2}}$ where $u = 5x - 1$

$\Rightarrow \dfrac{dy}{du} = \dfrac{1}{2}u^{-\frac{1}{2}} = \dfrac{1}{2}\dfrac{1}{\sqrt{5x - 1}}$, $\dfrac{du}{dx} = 5$

$\dfrac{dy}{dx} = \dfrac{dy}{du} \times \dfrac{du}{dx} = \dfrac{1}{2}\dfrac{1}{\sqrt{5x - 1}} \times 5 = \dfrac{5}{2\sqrt{5x - 1}}$

when $x = 2$, $\dfrac{dy}{dx} = \dfrac{5}{2\sqrt{10 - 1}} = \dfrac{5}{6}$

and $y = \sqrt{10 - 1} = 3$

$y = mx + c \Rightarrow 3 = (\dfrac{5}{6} \times 2) + c \Rightarrow c = \dfrac{4}{3}$

So the equation of the tangent is $y = \dfrac{5}{6}x + \dfrac{4}{3}$.

In the form $ax + by + c = 0$, $5x - 6y + 8 = 0$.

Q10 $y = \sqrt[3]{3x - 7}$, so let $y = u^{\frac{1}{3}}$ where $u = 3x - 7$

$\Rightarrow \dfrac{dy}{du} = \dfrac{1}{3}u^{-\frac{2}{3}} = \dfrac{1}{3(\sqrt[3]{3x - 7})^2}$, $\dfrac{du}{dx} = 3$

$\dfrac{dy}{dx} = \dfrac{dy}{du} \times \dfrac{du}{dx} = \dfrac{1}{3(\sqrt[3]{3x - 7})^2} \times 3 = \dfrac{1}{(\sqrt[3]{3x - 7})^2}$

When $x = 5$, $\dfrac{dy}{dx} = \dfrac{1}{(\sqrt[3]{(3 \times 5) - 7})^2} = \dfrac{1}{4}$,

$y = \sqrt[3]{15 - 7} = 2$

Gradient of normal $= \dfrac{-1}{\frac{1}{4}} = -4$

$y = mx + c \Rightarrow 2 = (-4 \times 5) + c \Rightarrow c = 22$
So the equation of the normal is $y = 22 - 4x$.

Q11 $y = (x^4 + x^3 + x^2)^2$, so let $y = u^2$ where $u = x^4 + x^3 + x^2$

$\Rightarrow \dfrac{dy}{du} = 2u = 2(x^4 + x^3 + x^2)$, $\dfrac{du}{dx} = 4x^3 + 3x^2 + 2x$

$\dfrac{dy}{dx} = \dfrac{dy}{du} \times \dfrac{du}{dx} = 2(x^4 + x^3 + x^2) \times (4x^3 + 3x^2 + 2x)$

At $x = -1$, $\dfrac{dy}{dx} = 2(1 - 1 + 1) \times (-4 + 3 + -2) = -6$

$y = ((-1)^4 + (-1)^3 + (-1)^2)^2 = 1$
$y = mx + c \Rightarrow 1 = (-6 \times -1) + c \Rightarrow c = -5$
So the equation of the tangent is $y = -6x - 5$.

Q12 $y = (2x - 3)^7$, so let $y = u^7$ where $u = 2x - 3$

$\Rightarrow \dfrac{dy}{du} = 7u^6 = 7(2x - 3)^6$, $\dfrac{du}{dx} = 2$

$\dfrac{dy}{dx} = \dfrac{dy}{du} \times \dfrac{du}{dx} = 7(2x - 3)^6 \times 2 = 14(2x - 3)^6$

Use the chain rule again to find $\dfrac{d^2y}{dx^2}$:

$\dfrac{dy}{dx} = 14(2x - 3)^6$, so let $\dfrac{dy}{dx} = 14u^6$ where $u = 2x - 3$

$\Rightarrow \dfrac{d}{du}\left(\dfrac{dy}{dx}\right) = 84u^5 = 84(2x - 3)^5$, $\dfrac{du}{dx} = 2$

$\dfrac{d^2y}{dx^2} = \dfrac{d}{dx}\left(\dfrac{dy}{dx}\right) = \dfrac{d}{du}\left(\dfrac{dy}{dx}\right) \times \dfrac{du}{dx} = 84(2x - 3)^5 \times 2$
$\qquad = 168(2x - 3)^5$

At a point of inflection, $\dfrac{d^2y}{dx^2} = 0 \Rightarrow 2x - 3 = 0 \Rightarrow x = \dfrac{3}{2}$

When $x < \dfrac{3}{2}$, $(2x - 3) < 0 \Rightarrow \dfrac{d^2y}{dx^2} < 0$

When $x > \dfrac{3}{2}$, $(2x - 3) > 0 \Rightarrow \dfrac{d^2y}{dx^2} > 0$

So the sign of $\dfrac{d^2y}{dx^2}$ changes at $x = \dfrac{3}{2}$, so this is a point of inflection.

$x = \dfrac{3}{2} \Rightarrow y = (2 \times \dfrac{3}{2} - 3)^7 = 0$

So the coordinates of the point of inflection are $\left(\dfrac{3}{2}, 0\right)$.

Q13 $y = (\dfrac{x}{4} - 2)^3$, so let $y = u^3$ where $u = \dfrac{x}{4} - 2$

$\Rightarrow \dfrac{dy}{du} = 3u^2 = 3(\dfrac{x}{4} - 2)^2$, $\dfrac{du}{dx} = \dfrac{1}{4}$

$\dfrac{dy}{dx} = \dfrac{dy}{du} \times \dfrac{du}{dx} = 3(\dfrac{x}{4} - 2)^2 \times \dfrac{1}{4} = \dfrac{3}{4}(\dfrac{x}{4} - 2)^2$

Use the chain rule again to find $\dfrac{d^2y}{dx^2}$:

$\dfrac{dy}{dx} = \dfrac{3}{4}(\dfrac{x}{4} - 2)^2$, so let $\dfrac{dy}{dx} = \dfrac{3}{4}u^2$ where $u = \dfrac{x}{4} - 2$

$\Rightarrow \dfrac{d}{du}\left(\dfrac{dy}{dx}\right) = \dfrac{3}{2}u = \dfrac{3}{2}(\dfrac{x}{4} - 2) = \dfrac{3}{8}x - 3$, $\dfrac{du}{dx} = \dfrac{1}{4}$

$\dfrac{d^2y}{dx^2} = \dfrac{d}{dx}\left(\dfrac{dy}{dx}\right) = \dfrac{d}{du}\left(\dfrac{dy}{dx}\right) \times \dfrac{du}{dx} = \left(\dfrac{3}{8}x - 3\right) \times \dfrac{1}{4} = \dfrac{3}{32}x - \dfrac{3}{4}$

The curve is convex when $\dfrac{d^2y}{dx^2} > 0 \Rightarrow \dfrac{3}{32}x - \dfrac{3}{4} > 0$
$\Rightarrow \dfrac{3}{32}x > \dfrac{3}{4} \Rightarrow x > 8$

The curve is concave when $\dfrac{d^2y}{dx^2} < 0 \Rightarrow \dfrac{3}{32}x - \dfrac{3}{4} < 0$
$\Rightarrow \dfrac{3}{32}x < \dfrac{3}{4} \Rightarrow x < 8$

So the curve is convex for $x > 8$ and concave for $x < 8$.

Exercise 7.2.2 — Finding $\dfrac{dy}{dx}$ when $x = f(y)$

Q1 **a)** $\dfrac{dx}{dy} = 6y + 5 \Rightarrow \dfrac{dy}{dx} = \dfrac{1}{6y + 5}$

At $(5, -1)$, $y = -1$ so $\dfrac{dy}{dx} = \dfrac{1}{-1} = -1$

b) $\dfrac{dx}{dy} = 3y^2 - 2 \Rightarrow \dfrac{dy}{dx} = \dfrac{1}{3y^2 - 2}$

At $(-4, -2)$, $y = -2$ so $\dfrac{dy}{dx} = \dfrac{1}{10} = 0.1$

c) $x = (2y + 1)(y - 2) = 2y^2 - 3y - 2$

$\dfrac{dx}{dy} = 4y - 3 \Rightarrow \dfrac{dy}{dx} = \dfrac{1}{4y - 3}$

At $(3, -1)$ $y = -1$ so $\dfrac{dy}{dx} = -\dfrac{1}{7}$.

d) $x = \dfrac{4+y^2}{y} = 4y^{-1} + y$

$\dfrac{dx}{dy} = -4y^{-2} + 1 \Rightarrow \dfrac{dy}{dx} = \dfrac{1}{1 - \frac{4}{y^2}} = \dfrac{y^2}{y^2 - 4}$

At $(5, 4)$, $y = 4$ so $\dfrac{dy}{dx} = \dfrac{4}{3}$.

Q2 $x = (2y^3 - 5)^3$, so let $x = u^3$ where $u = 2y^3 - 5$

$\Rightarrow \dfrac{dx}{du} = 3u^2 = 3(2y^3 - 5)^2, \quad \dfrac{du}{dy} = 6y^2$

$\dfrac{dx}{dy} = \dfrac{dx}{du} \times \dfrac{du}{dy} = 3(2y^3 - 5)^2 \times 6y^2 = 18y^2(2y^3 - 5)^2$

$\dfrac{dy}{dx} = \dfrac{1}{18y^2(2y^3 - 5)^2}$

Q3 a) $x = \sqrt{4+y} \Rightarrow x = u^{\frac{1}{2}}, u = 4 + y$

$\Rightarrow \dfrac{dx}{du} = \dfrac{1}{2}u^{-\frac{1}{2}} = \dfrac{1}{2}\dfrac{1}{\sqrt{4+y}}, \quad \dfrac{du}{dy} = 1$

$\dfrac{dx}{dy} = \dfrac{dx}{du} \times \dfrac{du}{dy} = \dfrac{1}{2}\dfrac{1}{\sqrt{4+y}} \times 1 = \dfrac{1}{2\sqrt{4+y}} = \dfrac{1}{2x}$

$\Rightarrow \dfrac{dy}{dx} = 2x$

Use $x = \sqrt{4+y}$ from the question to get dx/dy in terms of x.

b) $x = \sqrt{4+y} \Rightarrow x^2 = 4 + y \Rightarrow y = x^2 - 4 \Rightarrow \dfrac{dy}{dx} = 2x$

Q4 $x = \dfrac{1}{\sqrt{2y-3}} = (2y-3)^{-\frac{1}{2}} \Rightarrow x = u^{-\frac{1}{2}}, u = 2y - 3$

$\Rightarrow \dfrac{dx}{du} = -\dfrac{1}{2}u^{-\frac{3}{2}} = -\dfrac{1}{2(\sqrt{2y-3})^3}, \quad \dfrac{du}{dy} = 2$

$\dfrac{dx}{dy} = \dfrac{dx}{du} \times \dfrac{du}{dy} = -\dfrac{1}{2(\sqrt{2y-3})^3} \times 2 = -\dfrac{1}{(\sqrt{2y-3})^3} = -x^3$

$\Rightarrow \dfrac{dy}{dx} = -\dfrac{1}{x^3}$

7.3 Differentiation of e^x, ln x and a^x
Exercise 7.3.1 — Differentiating e^x

Q1 a) $y = e^{f(x)}$, where $f(x) = 3x$, so $f'(x) = 3$

$\dfrac{dy}{dx} = f'(x)e^{f(x)} = 3 \times e^{3x} = 3e^{3x}$

b) $\dfrac{dy}{dx} = f'(x)e^{f(x)} = 2 \times e^{2x-5} = 2e^{2x-5}$

c) $\dfrac{dy}{dx} = f'(x)e^{f(x)} = 1 \times e^{x+7} = e^{x+7}$

d) $\dfrac{dy}{dx} = f'(x)e^{f(x)} = 3 \times e^{3x+9} = 3e^{3x+9}$

e) $\dfrac{dy}{dx} = f'(x)e^{f(x)} = (-2) \times e^{7-2x} = -2e^{7-2x}$

f) $\dfrac{dy}{dx} = f'(x)e^{f(x)} = 3x^2 \times e^{x^3} = 3x^2 e^{x^3}$

Q2 a) $f'(x) = g'(x)e^{g(x)} = (3x^2 + 3) e^{x^3+3x}$

b) $f'(x) = g'(x)e^{g(x)} = (3x^2 - 3) e^{x^3-3x-5}$

c) $f(x) = e^{2x^2+x}$, so:

$f'(x) = g'(x)e^{g(x)} = (4x + 1) \times e^{2x^2+x} = (4x + 1)e^{x(2x+1)}$

Q3 a) e^x differentiates to e^x and e^{-x} differentiates to $-e^{-x}$

so $f'(x) = \dfrac{1}{2} \times (e^x - (-e^{-x})) = \dfrac{1}{2}(e^x + e^{-x})$

b) $f(x) = e^{x^2+7x+12}$

$f'(x) = g'(x)e^{g(x)} = (2x + 7) e^{x^2+7x+12}$

c) $\dfrac{d}{dx}(e^{x^4+3x^2}) = (4x^3 + 6x)e^{x^4+3x^2}$ and $\dfrac{d}{dx}(2e^{2x}) = 4e^{2x}$

So $f'(x) = (4x^3 + 6x) e^{x^4+3x^2} + 4e^{2x}$

Q4 $\dfrac{dy}{dx} = f'(x)e^{f(x)} = 2 \times e^{2x} = 2e^{2x}$

At $x = 0$, $\dfrac{dy}{dx} = 2 \times e^{2 \times 0} = 2 \times 1 = 2$

$y = mx + c \Rightarrow 1 = (2 \times 0) + c \Rightarrow c = 1$

So the equation of the tangent is $y = 2x + 1$.

There's no real need to use the $y = mx + c$ formula here as we already know the place it crosses the y-axis is (0, 1) (it's given in the question), but it's good to be safe.

Q5 $\dfrac{dy}{dx} = x - f'(x)e^{f(x)} = x - 2e^{2x-6}$

$\dfrac{d^2y}{dx^2} = 1 - 2 \times f'(x)e^{f(x)} = 1 - 4e^{2x-6}$

At the point of inflection, $\dfrac{d^2y}{dx^2} = 0$

$\Rightarrow 1 - 4e^{2x-6} = 0 \Rightarrow 1 = 4e^{2x-6} \Rightarrow \ln(1) = \ln(4e^{2x-6})$

$\Rightarrow 0 = \ln 4 + \ln(e^{2x-6}) = \ln 4 + 2x - 6 \Rightarrow 2x = 6 - \ln 4$

$\Rightarrow x = 3 - \dfrac{1}{2}\ln 4 = 3 - \ln 2$

Remember from laws of logs that $\frac{1}{2}\ln 4 = \ln 4^{\frac{1}{2}} = \ln 2$. There are other ways you could have used the log laws in this question — you should get the same answer.

Q6 $\dfrac{dy}{dx} = f'(x)e^{f(x)} = 4x\, e^{2x^2}$

At $x = 1$, $\dfrac{dy}{dx} = 4 \times 1 \times e^2 = 4e^2$ and $y = e^2$

$y = mx + c \Rightarrow e^2 = (4e^2 \times 1) + c \Rightarrow c = -3e^2$

So the equation of the tangent is $y = 4e^2 x - 3e^2$.

Q7 $f(x) = \sqrt{e^x + e^{2x}}$ so let $y = \sqrt{u} = u^{\frac{1}{2}}$ where $u = e^x + e^{2x}$

$\Rightarrow \dfrac{dy}{du} = \dfrac{1}{2}u^{-\frac{1}{2}} = \dfrac{1}{2\sqrt{u}} = \dfrac{1}{2\sqrt{e^x + e^{2x}}}$,

$\dfrac{du}{dx} = e^x + e^{2x} = e^x + 2e^{2x}$

$\Rightarrow \dfrac{dy}{dx} = \dfrac{dy}{du} \times \dfrac{du}{dx} = \dfrac{1}{2\sqrt{e^x + e^{2x}}} \times (e^x + 2e^{2x}) = \dfrac{e^x + 2e^{2x}}{2\sqrt{e^x + e^{2x}}}$

At $x = 0$, $\dfrac{dy}{dx} = \dfrac{e^0 + 2e^{2(0)}}{2\sqrt{e^0 + e^{2(0)}}} = \dfrac{3}{2\sqrt{2}} = \dfrac{3\sqrt{2}}{4}$

Q8 $\dfrac{dy}{dx} = f'(x)e^{f(x)} - 1 = 2e^{2x-4} - 1$,

$\dfrac{d^2y}{dx^2} = 2 \times f'(x)e^{f(x)} = 4e^{2x-4}$

$4e^{2x-4} > 0$ for all values of x, so $\dfrac{d^2y}{dx^2}$ is always positive, which means the graph of $y = e^{2x-4} - x$ is always convex.

Q9 $\dfrac{dy}{dx} = f'(x)e^{f(x)} = (3 \times e^{3x}) = 3e^{3x}$

When it crosses the y-axis, $x = 0$, so $y = e^{3 \times 0} + 3 = 4$

$\dfrac{dy}{dx} = (3 \times e^{3 \times 0}) = (3 \times 1) = 3 \Rightarrow$ Gradient of the normal $= -\dfrac{1}{3}$

$y = mx + c \Rightarrow 4 = (-\dfrac{1}{3} \times 0) + c \Rightarrow c = 4$

So the equation of the normal is $y = -\dfrac{1}{3}x + 4$.

Q10 Let $f(x) = 2x$ and $g(x) = 3 - 4x$, then

$\dfrac{dy}{dx} = 2 \times f'(x)e^{f(x)} - \dfrac{1}{2} \times g'(x)e^{g(x)} = 2 \times 2e^{2x} - \dfrac{1}{2} \times -4e^{3-4x}$

$= 4e^{2x} + 2e^{3-4x}$

$\dfrac{d^2y}{dx^2} = 4 \times f'(x)e^{f(x)} + 2 \times g'(x)e^{g(x)} = 4 \times 2e^{2x} + 2 \times -4e^{3-4x}$

$= 8e^{2x} - 8e^{3-4x}$

At a point of inflection, $\dfrac{d^2y}{dx^2} = 0$

$\Rightarrow 8e^{2x} - 8e^{3-4x} = 0 \Rightarrow e^{2x} = e^{3-4x}$

$\Rightarrow 2x = 3 - 4x \Rightarrow 6x = 3 \Rightarrow x = \dfrac{1}{2}$

$\dfrac{d^2y}{dx^2} > 0$ if $x > \dfrac{1}{2}$ and $\dfrac{d^2y}{dx^2} < 0$ if $x < \dfrac{1}{2}$

$\dfrac{d^2y}{dx^2}$ changes sign from negative to positive at $x = \dfrac{1}{2}$.

So $x = \dfrac{1}{2}$ is a point of inflection.

At $x = \dfrac{1}{2}$, $y = 2e^{2x} - \dfrac{1}{2}e^{3-4x} = 2e^1 - \dfrac{1}{2}e^1 = \dfrac{3}{2}e$.

The graph has one point of inflection, at $\left(\dfrac{1}{2}, \dfrac{3}{2}e\right)$.

Q11 If y has a stationary point, the gradient $\dfrac{dy}{dx}$ will be 0.

$\dfrac{dy}{dx} = f'(x)e^{f(x)} = (3x^2 - 3) e^{x^3-3x-5}$

So if $\dfrac{dy}{dx} = 0$, either $3x^2 - 3 = 0$ or $e^{x^3-3x-5} = 0$.

If $3x^2 - 3 = 0 \Rightarrow 3(x^2 - 1) = 0 \Rightarrow x^2 = 1 \Rightarrow x = \pm 1$ and if $e^{x^3-3x-5} = 0$, there are no solutions.

So the gradient is 0 when $x = \pm 1$

$\Rightarrow$ the curve has stationary points at $x = \pm 1$.

Q12 Stationary points occur when the gradient is 0.

$\dfrac{dy}{dx} = f'(x)e^{f(x)} - 6 = 3e^{3x} - 6$

$3e^{3x} - 6 = 0 \Rightarrow e^{3x} = 2 \Rightarrow 3x = \ln 2 \Rightarrow x = \frac{1}{3}\ln 2$

Take ln of both sides to get rid of the exponential.

To find the nature of the stationary point, calculate $\dfrac{d^2y}{dx^2}$

$\dfrac{d^2y}{dx^2} = 3f'(x)e^{f(x)} = 9e^{3x}$

When $x = \frac{1}{3}\ln 2$, $\dfrac{d^2y}{dx^2} = 9e^{\ln 2} = 9 \times 2 = 18$

$\dfrac{d^2y}{dx^2}$ is positive, so it's a minimum point.

You could also use the fact that $9e^{3x}$ is always positive to show that it's a minimum without needing to substitute.

Exercise 7.3.2 — Differentiating ln x

Q1 **a)** $y = \ln (3x) = \ln 3 + \ln x \Rightarrow \dfrac{dy}{dx} = \dfrac{1}{x}$

You could use that the derivative of ln (f(x)) is $\dfrac{f'(x)}{f(x)}$ — it'd give the same answer.

b) $\dfrac{dy}{dx} = \dfrac{f'(x)}{f(x)} = \dfrac{1}{1+x}$

The coefficient of x is 1 so it's a 1 on top of the fraction.

c) $\dfrac{dy}{dx} = \dfrac{f'(x)}{f(x)} = \dfrac{2}{3+2x}$

d) $\dfrac{dy}{dx} = \dfrac{f'(x)}{f(x)} = \dfrac{5}{1+5x}$

e) $\dfrac{dy}{dx} = 4 \times \dfrac{f'(x)}{f(x)} = 4 \times \dfrac{4}{4x-2} = \dfrac{16}{4x-2} = \dfrac{8}{2x-1}$

Don't forget to simplify your answers if you can.

f) $\dfrac{dy}{dx} = 9 \times \dfrac{f'(x)}{f(x)} = 9 \times \dfrac{3}{3x-3} = \dfrac{9}{x-1}$

Q2 **a)** $\dfrac{dy}{dx} = \dfrac{f'(x)}{f(x)} = \dfrac{2x}{1+x^2}$

b) $y = \ln (2+x)^2 = 2\ln (2+x)$

$\dfrac{dy}{dx} = 2 \times \dfrac{f'(x)}{f(x)} = 2 \times \dfrac{1}{2+x} = \dfrac{2}{2+x}$

c) $y = \ln (2x-8)^3 = 3\ln (2x-8)$

$\dfrac{dy}{dx} = 3 \times \dfrac{f'(x)}{f(x)} = 3 \times \dfrac{2}{2x-8} = \dfrac{3}{x-4}$

d) $3\ln x^3 = 9\ln x \Rightarrow \dfrac{dy}{dx} = \dfrac{9}{x}$

e) $\dfrac{dy}{dx} = \dfrac{f'(x)}{f(x)} = \dfrac{3x^2+2x}{x^3+x^2} = \dfrac{3x+2}{x^2+x}$

f) $y = \ln \sqrt{2x^2-4} = \ln (2x^2-4)^{\frac{1}{2}} = \frac{1}{2}\ln (2x^2-4)$

$\dfrac{dy}{dx} = \frac{1}{2} \times \dfrac{f'(x)}{f(x)} = \frac{1}{2} \times \dfrac{4x}{2x^2-4} = \dfrac{4x}{4x^2-8} = \dfrac{x}{x^2-2}$

Q3 **a)** $f(x) = \ln \dfrac{1}{x} = \ln x^{-1} = -\ln x \Rightarrow f'(x) = -\dfrac{1}{x}$

b) $f(x) = \ln \sqrt{x} = \ln x^{\frac{1}{2}} = \frac{1}{2}\ln x \Rightarrow f'(x) = \dfrac{1}{2x}$

Q4 $\ln ((2x+1)^2 \sqrt{x-4}) = \ln (2x+1)^2 + \ln \sqrt{x-4}$

$\qquad = 2 \ln (2x+1) + \frac{1}{2}\ln (x-4)$

First part: $f'(x) = 2 \times \dfrac{2}{2x+1} = \dfrac{4}{2x+1}$

Second part: $f'(x) = \frac{1}{2} \times \dfrac{1}{x-4} = \dfrac{1}{2(x-4)}$

Putting it all together:

$f'(x) = \dfrac{4}{2x+1} + \dfrac{1}{2(x-4)} = \dfrac{8(x-4)+2x+1}{2(2x+1)(x-4)}$

$\qquad = \dfrac{10x-31}{2(2x+1)(x-4)}$

Q5 $g(x) = x - \sqrt{x-4} \Rightarrow g'(x) = 1 - \left(\dfrac{dy}{du} \times \dfrac{du}{dx}\right) = 1 - \dfrac{1}{2\sqrt{x-4}}$

$f'(x) = \dfrac{g'(x)}{g(x)} = \dfrac{1 - \dfrac{1}{2\sqrt{x-4}}}{x - \sqrt{x-4}} = \dfrac{2\sqrt{x-4}-1}{2(x\sqrt{x-4}-x+4)}$

Q6 $\ln \left(\dfrac{(3x+1)^2}{\sqrt{2x+1}}\right) = \ln (3x+1)^2 - \ln \sqrt{2x+1}$

$\qquad = 2\ln (3x+1) - \frac{1}{2}\ln (2x+1)$

First part: $f'(x) = 2 \times \dfrac{3}{3x+1} = \dfrac{6}{3x+1}$

Second part: $f'(x) = \frac{1}{2} \times \dfrac{2}{2x+1} = \dfrac{1}{2x+1}$

Putting it all together:

$f'(x) = \dfrac{6}{3x+1} - \dfrac{1}{2x+1} = \dfrac{6(2x+1)-3x-1}{(3x+1)(2x+1)} = \dfrac{9x+5}{(3x+1)(2x+1)}$

You could have left your answer as 2 fractions.

Q7 **a)** $y = \ln (3x)^2 = 2 \ln (3x) = 2 \ln 3 + 2 \ln x \Rightarrow \dfrac{dy}{dx} = \dfrac{2}{x}$

When $x = -2$, $\dfrac{dy}{dx} = -1$ and $y = \ln 36$

$y = mx + c \Rightarrow \ln 36 = [(-1) \times (-2)] + c \Rightarrow c = \ln 36 - 2$

So the equation of the tangent is $y = -x + \ln 36 - 2$

b) When $x = 2$, $\dfrac{dy}{dx} = 1$ and $y = \ln 36$

$y = mx + c \Rightarrow \ln 36 = [1 \times 2] + c \Rightarrow c = \ln 36 - 2$

So the equation of the tangent is $y = x + \ln 36 - 2$

Q8 **a)** $y = \ln (x+6)^2 = 2 \ln (x+6)$

$\Rightarrow \dfrac{dy}{dx} = 2\dfrac{f'(x)}{f(x)} = \dfrac{2}{x+6}$

When $x = -3$, $\dfrac{dy}{dx} = \frac{2}{3}$ and $y = \ln 9$

So the gradient of the normal $= -\dfrac{1}{\left(\frac{2}{3}\right)} = -\dfrac{3}{2}$

$y = mx + c \Rightarrow \ln 9 = (-\frac{3}{2} \times -3) + c \Rightarrow c = \ln 9 - \frac{9}{2}$

so the equation of the normal is $y = -\frac{3}{2}x + \ln 9 - \frac{9}{2}$.

b) When $x = 0$, $\dfrac{dy}{dx} = \frac{2}{6} = \frac{1}{3}$ and $y = \ln 36$

So the gradient of the normal $= -\dfrac{1}{\left(\frac{1}{3}\right)} = -3$

$y = mx + c \Rightarrow \ln 36 = (-3 \times 0) + c \Rightarrow c = \ln 36$

So the equation of the normal is $y = -3x + \ln 36$

Q9 Stationary points occur when the gradient is 0.

$\dfrac{dy}{dx} = \dfrac{f'(x)}{f(x)} = \dfrac{3x^2-6x+3}{x^3-3x^2+3x}$

so $3x^2 - 6x + 3 = 0 \Rightarrow 3(x-1)(x-1) = 0$

You can ignore the denominator here, as it's only the top part that affects when it's equal to 0.

So the gradient is 0 when $x = 1$.

When $x = 1$, $y = 0$ so the stationary point is at (1, 0).

Exercise 7.3.3 — Differentiating a^x

Q1 **a)** $\dfrac{dy}{dx} = 5^x \ln 5$

b) Let $u = 2x$ and $y = 3^u$, then

$\dfrac{dy}{du} = 3^u \ln 3 = 3^{2x} \ln 3$ and $\dfrac{du}{dx} = 2$

So $\dfrac{dy}{dx} = \dfrac{dy}{du} \times \dfrac{du}{dx} = 3^{2x} \ln 3 \times 2 = (2 \ln 3)3^{2x}$

c) Let $u = -x$ and $y = 10^u$, then

$\dfrac{dy}{du} = 10^u \ln 10 = 10^{-x} \ln 10$ and $\dfrac{du}{dx} = -1$

So $\dfrac{dy}{dx} = 10^{-x} \ln 10 \times (-1) = -(10^{-x} \ln 10)$

d) Let $u = qx$ and $y = p^u$, then

$\dfrac{dy}{du} = p^u \ln p = p^{qx} \ln p$ and $\dfrac{du}{dx} = q$

So $\dfrac{dy}{dx} = p^{qx} \ln p \times q = (q \ln p)p^{qx}$

Q2 **a)** Let $u = 4x$, then $y = 2^u$ and

$\dfrac{dy}{dx} = \dfrac{d}{du}(2^u) \times \dfrac{d}{dx}(4x) = 4(2^{4x} \ln 2)$

b) When $x = 2$, $\dfrac{dy}{dx} = 4(2^8 \ln 2) = 1024 \ln 2$

$y = 2^8 = 256$

Putting this into $y = mx + c$ gives:

$256 = 2048 \ln 2 + c \Rightarrow c = 256 - 2048 \ln 2$.

So the equation of the tangent is:

$y = (1024 \ln 2) x + 256 - 2048 \ln 2$

or $y = (1024 \ln 2) x + 256(1 - 8 \ln 2)$

Q3 **a)** When $x = 1$, $2^p = 32$, so $p = 5$.

You should just know this result, but if not you can take logs (p ln 2 = ln 32, so p = ln 32 ÷ ln 2 = 5).

b) $\dfrac{dy}{dx} = 5(2^{5x} \ln 2)$

When $x = 1$, $\dfrac{dy}{dx} = 5(32 \ln 2) = 160 \ln 2$

Q4 a) Let $u = x^3$, then $y = p^u$, and so

$\dfrac{dy}{dx} = \dfrac{d}{du}(p^u) \times \dfrac{d}{dx}(x^3) = 3x^2(p^{x^3} \ln p)$

b) When $x = 2$, $y = p^8 = 6561$.
So $p = \sqrt[8]{6561} = 3$.
You can also work this out by taking logs.
8 ln p = ln 6561, so $p = \exp\left(\dfrac{\ln 6561}{8}\right) = 3$.

c) When $x = 1$, $y = 3^1 = 3$.
The gradient at $x = 1$ is $3(3 \ln 3) = 9 \ln 3$.
Putting this into $y = mx + c$ gives:
$3 = 9 \ln 3 + c \Rightarrow c = 3 - 9 \ln 3$
So the equation of the tangent at $(1, 3)$ is
$y = (9 \ln 3)x + (3 - 9 \ln 3)$

Q5 When $x = 25$, $y = 4^5 = 1024$, so a = 1024.
Let $u = x^{\frac{1}{2}}$ and $y = 4^u$, so
$\dfrac{dy}{dx} = \dfrac{d}{du}(4^u)\dfrac{d}{dx}(x^{\frac{1}{2}}) = \dfrac{1}{2}x^{-\frac{1}{2}}(4^{\sqrt{x}} \ln 4)$
The gradient of the tangent when $x = 25$ is
$\dfrac{1}{10}(1024 \ln 4) = 102.4 \ln 4$

Putting this into $y = mx + c$ gives:
$1024 = 2560 \ln 4 + c \Rightarrow c = 1024 - 2560 \ln 4$.

So the equation of the tangent is
$y = (102.4 \ln 4)x + (1024 - 2560 \ln 4)$
$\Rightarrow y = 142x - 2520$ to 3 s.f.

Q6 a) Let $u = -3x$, then $y = 2^u$, so
$\dfrac{du}{dx} = -3$ and $\dfrac{dy}{du} = 2^u \ln 2 = 2^{-3x} \ln 2 \Rightarrow \dfrac{dy}{dx} = -3(2^{-3x} \ln 2)$

b) When $x = 2$, $y = b = 2^{-6} = \dfrac{1}{64}$ and $\dfrac{dy}{dx} = -\dfrac{3}{64} \ln 2$

c) At $\left(2, \dfrac{1}{64}\right)$, the gradient of the tangent is $-\dfrac{3}{64} \ln 2$.

Putting this into $y = mx + c$ gives:

$\dfrac{1}{64} = -\dfrac{6}{64} \ln 2 + c \Rightarrow c = \dfrac{1}{64} + \dfrac{6}{64} \ln 2$.
So the equation of the tangent is
$y = \dfrac{1 + 6\ln 2}{64} - \left(\dfrac{3\ln 2}{64}\right)x \Rightarrow 64y = 1 + 6 \ln 2 - (3 \ln 2)x$.

Q7 a) Let $u = x^2$, then $y = 3^u$, so
$\dfrac{du}{dx} = 2x$ and $\dfrac{dy}{du} = 3^u \ln 3 = 3^{x^2} \ln 3 \Rightarrow \dfrac{dy}{dx} = 2x(3^{x^2} \ln 3)$

b) When $x = 2$, $y = p = 3^4 = 81$ and $\dfrac{dy}{dx} = 4(81 \ln 3) = 324 \ln 3$

c) At $(2, 81)$, the gradient of the tangent is $324 \ln 3$, so the
gradient of the normal is $-\dfrac{1}{324 \ln 3}$.
Putting this into $y = mx + c$ gives:
$81 = -\dfrac{1}{324 \ln 3} \times 2 + c \Rightarrow c = 81 + \dfrac{2}{324 \ln 3}$.

So the equation of the normal is
$y = 81 + \dfrac{2}{324 \ln 3} - \dfrac{1}{324 \ln 3}x = 81 + \dfrac{2 - x}{324 \ln 3}$

7.4 Differentiating Trig Functions
Exercise 7.4.1 — Differentiating sin, cos and tan

Q1 a) $y = \sin (3x)$, so let $y = \sin u$ where $u = 3x$
$\Rightarrow \dfrac{dy}{du} = \cos u = \cos (3x)$, $\dfrac{du}{dx} = 3$
$\dfrac{dy}{dx} = \dfrac{dy}{du} \times \dfrac{du}{dx} = 3 \cos (3x)$

b) $y = \cos (-2x)$, so let $y = \cos u$ where $u = -2x$
$\Rightarrow \dfrac{dy}{du} = -\sin (u) = -\sin (-2x)$, $\dfrac{du}{dx} = -2$
$\dfrac{dy}{dx} = \dfrac{dy}{du} \times \dfrac{du}{dx} = (-\sin (-2x)) \times (-2) = 2 \sin (-2x)$
As you can see, the number you multiply by is always just the coefficient of x inside the trig function — but check whether it should be positive or negative.

c) $\dfrac{dy}{dx} = \dfrac{dy}{du} \times \dfrac{du}{dx} = \dfrac{1}{2} \times -\sin \dfrac{x}{2} = -\dfrac{1}{2} \sin \dfrac{x}{2}$

d) $\dfrac{dy}{dx} = \dfrac{dy}{du} \times \dfrac{du}{dx} = \cos (x + \dfrac{\pi}{4}) \times 1 = \cos (x + \dfrac{\pi}{4})$

e) $\dfrac{dy}{dx} = \dfrac{dy}{du} \times \dfrac{du}{dx} = 6 \times \sec^2 \dfrac{x}{2} \times \dfrac{1}{2} = 3 \sec^2 \dfrac{x}{2}$

f) $\dfrac{dy}{dx} = \dfrac{dy}{du} \times \dfrac{du}{dx} = 3 \times \sec^2 (5x) \times 5 = 15 \sec^2 (5x)$

Q2 $f'(x) = \dfrac{dy}{du} \times \dfrac{du}{dx} = 3 \times \sec^2 (2x - 1) \times 2 = 6 \sec^2 (2x - 1)$

Q3 First part: $\dfrac{dy}{dx} = 3 \sec^2 x$
Second part: $\dfrac{dy}{dx} = \dfrac{dy}{du} \times \dfrac{du}{dx} = 3 \sec^2 (3x)$
Putting it all together: $f'(x) = 3(\sec^2 x + \sec^2 (3x))$

Q4 $f'(x) = \dfrac{dy}{du} \times \dfrac{du}{dx} = 2x \cos (x^2 + \dfrac{\pi}{3})$

Q5 $f(x) = \sin^2 x$, so let $y = u^2$ where $u = \sin x$
$f'(x) = \dfrac{dy}{du} \times \dfrac{du}{dx} = (2 \sin x) \times \cos x = 2 \sin x \cos x$

Q6 $f(x) = 2 \sin^3 x$, so let $y = 2u^3$ where $u = \sin x$
$f'(x) = \dfrac{dy}{du} \times \dfrac{du}{dx} = 6 \sin^2 x \cos x$

Q7 a) $f'(x) = 3 \cos x - 2 \sin x$

b) $f'(x) = 0 \Rightarrow 3 \cos x - 2 \sin x = 0 \Rightarrow 3 \cos x = 2 \sin x$
$\Rightarrow \dfrac{3}{2} = \tan x \Rightarrow x = \tan^{-1} \dfrac{3}{2} = 0.983$ (3 s.f.)
Remember that $\tan x = \dfrac{\sin x}{\cos x}$.

Q8 $y = \dfrac{1}{\cos x} = (\cos x)^{-1}$, so let $y = u^{-1}$ where $u = \cos x$
$\Rightarrow \dfrac{dy}{du} = -u^{-2} = -\dfrac{1}{\cos^2 x}$, $\dfrac{du}{dx} = -\sin x$
$\dfrac{dy}{dx} = \dfrac{dy}{du} \times \dfrac{du}{dx} = -\dfrac{1}{\cos^2 x} \times -\sin x = \dfrac{\sin x}{\cos^2 x} = \sec x \tan x$
Remember that $\dfrac{1}{\cos x} = \sec x$.

Q9 Let $y = f(x)$, where $f(x) = \cos x$.
Then $\dfrac{dy}{dx} = \lim_{h \to 0}\left[\dfrac{f(x+h) - f(x)}{(x+h) - x}\right] = \lim_{h \to 0}\left[\dfrac{\cos(x+h) - \cos x}{(x+h) - x}\right]$
Using the cos addition formula:
$\dfrac{dy}{dx} = \lim_{h \to 0}\left[\dfrac{\cos x \cos h - \sin x \sin h - \cos x}{(x+h) - x}\right]$
$= \lim_{h \to 0}\left[\dfrac{\cos x (\cos h - 1) - \sin x \sin h}{h}\right]$
$= \lim_{h \to 0}\left[\dfrac{\cos x (\cos h - 1)}{h} - \dfrac{\sin x \sin h}{h}\right]$
Using small angle approximations,
$\cos h \approx 1 - \dfrac{1}{2}h^2$ and $\sin h \approx h$, so:
$\dfrac{dy}{dx} = \lim_{h \to 0}\left[\dfrac{\cos x \times \left(-\dfrac{1}{2}h^2\right)}{h} - \dfrac{\sin x \times h}{h}\right]$
$= \lim_{h \to 0}\left[-\dfrac{h \cos x}{2} - \sin x\right] = -\sin x$

Q10 a) $y = \cos^2 x$, so let $y = u^2$ where $u = \cos x$.
$\dfrac{dy}{dx} = \dfrac{dy}{du} \times \dfrac{du}{dx} = (2 \cos x) \times (-\sin x) = -2 \sin x \cos x$

b) Using the double angle formula:
$\cos (2x) \equiv 2 \cos^2 x - 1 \Rightarrow \cos^2 x = \dfrac{1}{2}(\cos (2x) + 1)$
$\dfrac{dy}{dx} = \dfrac{1}{2} \times 2 \times (-\sin (2x)) = -\sin (2x)$
As the original function was in terms of cos x rather than cos (2x), it would be better to rearrange this.

From the double angle formula for sin:
$-\sin (2x) \equiv -2 \sin x \cos x$

Q11 First part:

$y = 6 \cos^2 x = 6(\cos x)^2$, so let $y = 6u^2$ where $u = \cos x$

$\Rightarrow \dfrac{dy}{du} = 12u = 12 \cos x$, $\dfrac{du}{dx} = -\sin x$

$\dfrac{dy}{dx} = \dfrac{dy}{du} \times \dfrac{du}{dx} = -12 \sin x \cos x$

Second part:

$y = 2 \sin (2x)$, so let $y = 2 \sin u$ where $u = 2x$

$\Rightarrow \dfrac{dy}{du} = 2 \cos u = 2 \cos (2x)$, $\dfrac{du}{dx} = 2$

$\dfrac{dy}{dx} = \dfrac{dy}{du} \times \dfrac{du}{dx} = 4 \cos (2x)$

Putting it all together:

$\dfrac{dy}{dx} = -12 \sin x \cos x - 4 \cos (2x)$

Double angle formula: $2 \sin x \cos x \equiv \sin (2x)$

$\Rightarrow -12 \sin x \cos x - 4 \cos (2x) = -6 \sin (2x) - 4 \cos (2x)$

Q12 $\dfrac{dy}{dx} = \cos x$. When $x = \dfrac{\pi}{4}$, $\dfrac{dy}{dx} = \dfrac{1}{\sqrt{2}}$

Q13 $\dfrac{dy}{dx} = -2 \sin (2x)$

When $x = \dfrac{\pi}{4}$, $y = 0$ and $\dfrac{dy}{dx} = -2$

So the gradient of the normal is $\dfrac{-1}{-2} = \dfrac{1}{2}$.

$y = mx + c \Rightarrow 0 = \left(\dfrac{1}{2} \times \dfrac{\pi}{4}\right) + c \Rightarrow c = -\dfrac{\pi}{8}$

So the equation of the normal is $y = \dfrac{1}{2}x - \dfrac{\pi}{8}$ (or $4x - 8y - \pi = 0$)

Q14 a) $\dfrac{dx}{dy} = 2 \cos (2y)$, $\dfrac{dy}{dx} = \dfrac{1}{2 \cos(2y)} = \dfrac{1}{2} \sec (2y)$

At the point $\left(\dfrac{\sqrt{3}}{2}, \dfrac{\pi}{6}\right)$, $\dfrac{dy}{dx} = \dfrac{1}{2 \cos \frac{\pi}{3}} = 1$

$y = mx + c \Rightarrow \dfrac{\pi}{6} = \dfrac{\sqrt{3}}{2} + c \Rightarrow c = \dfrac{\pi}{6} - \dfrac{\sqrt{3}}{2}$

So the equation of the tangent is $y = x + \dfrac{\pi}{6} - \dfrac{\sqrt{3}}{2}$.

b) From part a), $\dfrac{dy}{dx} = 1$, so the normal gradient is -1.

$y = mx + c \Rightarrow \dfrac{\pi}{6} = -\dfrac{\sqrt{3}}{2} + c \Rightarrow c = \dfrac{\pi}{6} + \dfrac{\sqrt{3}}{2}$

So the equation of the normal is $y = -x + \dfrac{\pi}{6} + \dfrac{\sqrt{3}}{2}$.

Q15 a) $y = 2 \sin (2x) \cos x \Rightarrow y = 4 \sin x \cos^2 x$

(from double angle formula $\sin (2x) \equiv 2 \sin x \cos x$)

$\Rightarrow y = 4 \sin x (1 - \sin^2 x)$ *(from $\sin^2 x + \cos^2 x \equiv 1$)*

$\Rightarrow y = 4 \sin x - 4 \sin^3 x$

b) First part: $\dfrac{dy}{dx} = 4 \cos x$

Second part: $y = 4 \sin^3 x = 4 (\sin x)^3$,

so let $y = 4u^3$ where $u = \sin x$

$\dfrac{dy}{dx} = \dfrac{dy}{du} \times \dfrac{du}{dx} = 12 \sin^2 x \cos x$

Putting it all together: $\dfrac{dy}{dx} = 4 \cos x - 12 \sin^2 x \cos x$

Exercise 7.4.2 — Differentiating by using the chain rule twice

Q1 a) $y = \sin^2 (x + 2)$, so let $y = u^2$ where $u = \sin (x + 2)$

$\dfrac{dy}{du} = 2u = 2 \sin (x + 2)$

$u = \sin (x + 2)$, so let $u = \sin v$ where $v = x + 2$

$\Rightarrow \dfrac{du}{dv} = \cos v = \cos (x + 2)$ and $\dfrac{dv}{dx} = 1$

$\Rightarrow \dfrac{du}{dx} = \dfrac{du}{dv} \times \dfrac{dv}{dx} = \cos (x + 2)$

So $\dfrac{dy}{dx} = \dfrac{dy}{du} \times \dfrac{du}{dx} = 2 \sin (x + 2) \times \cos (x + 2)$
$= 2 \sin (x + 2) \cos (x + 2)$

b) $y = \cos^2 (x^2)$, so let $y = u^2$ where $u = \cos (x^2)$

$\dfrac{dy}{du} = 2u = 2 \cos (x^2)$

$u = \cos (x^2)$, so let $u = \cos v$ where $v = x^2$

$\Rightarrow \dfrac{du}{dv} = -\sin v = -\sin (x^2)$ and $\dfrac{dv}{dx} = 2x$

$\Rightarrow \dfrac{du}{dx} = \dfrac{du}{dv} \times \dfrac{dv}{dx} = -\sin (x^2) \times 2x = -2x \sin (x^2)$

So $\dfrac{dy}{dx} = \dfrac{dy}{du} \times \dfrac{du}{dx} = 2 \cos (x^2) \times -2x \sin (x^2)$
$= -4x \sin (x^2) \cos (x^2)$

c) $y = \sqrt{\tan(4x)}$, so let $y = \sqrt{u} = u^{\frac{1}{2}}$ where $u = \tan (4x)$

$\dfrac{dy}{du} = \dfrac{u^{-\frac{1}{2}}}{2} = \dfrac{1}{2\sqrt{u}} = \dfrac{1}{2\sqrt{\tan(4x)}}$

$u = \tan (4x)$, so let $u = \tan v$ where $v = 4x$

$\Rightarrow \dfrac{du}{dv} = \sec^2 v = \sec^2 (4x)$ and $\dfrac{dv}{dx} = 4$

$\Rightarrow \dfrac{du}{dx} = \dfrac{du}{dv} \times \dfrac{dv}{dx} = 4 \sec^2 (4x)$

So $\dfrac{dy}{dx} = \dfrac{dy}{du} \times \dfrac{du}{dx} = \dfrac{1}{2\sqrt{\tan(4x)}} \times 4 \sec^2 (4x) = \dfrac{2 \sec^2(4x)}{\sqrt{\tan(4x)}}$

Q2 a) $y = \sin (\cos (2x))$, so let $y = \sin u$ where $u = \cos (2x)$

$\dfrac{dy}{du} = \cos u = \cos (\cos (2x))$

Using the chain rule again on $\dfrac{du}{dx}$ gives:

$u = \cos (2x) \Rightarrow \dfrac{du}{dx} = -2 \sin (2x)$

Putting it all together:

$\dfrac{dy}{dx} = \dfrac{dy}{du} \times \dfrac{du}{dx} = -2 \sin (2x) \cos (\cos (2x))$

b) $y = 2 \ln f(x) \Rightarrow \dfrac{dy}{dx} = 2 \dfrac{f'(x)}{f(x)}$

$f(x) = \cos (3x) \Rightarrow f'(x) = -3 \sin (3x)$

$\dfrac{dy}{dx} = 2 \dfrac{-3 \sin (3x)}{\cos(3x)} = -6 \tan (3x)$

c) $y = \ln (\tan^2 x) = \ln (f(x)) \Rightarrow \dfrac{dy}{dx} = \dfrac{f'(x)}{f(x)}$

$f(x) = (\tan x)^2$, so let $f(x) = v = u^2$ where $u = \tan x$

$\dfrac{dv}{du} = 2u = 2 \tan x$, $\dfrac{du}{dx} = \sec^2 x$

$f'(x) = \dfrac{dv}{dx} = \dfrac{dv}{du} \times \dfrac{du}{dx} = 2 \tan x \sec^2 x$

Putting it all together:

$\dfrac{dy}{dx} = \dfrac{2 \tan x \sec^2 x}{\tan^2 x} = 2 \sec x \operatorname{cosec} x$

You could've written $\ln (\tan^2 x)$ as $2 \ln (\tan x)$ using the laws of logs and then differentiated — you'd end up with the same answer.

d) $y = e^{f(x)} \Rightarrow \dfrac{dy}{dx} = f'(x)e^{f(x)}$

$f(x) = \tan (2x)$, so let $f(x) = v = \tan u$ where $u = 2x$

$\dfrac{dv}{du} = \sec^2 u = \sec^2 (2x)$, $\dfrac{du}{dx} = 2$

$\Rightarrow f'(x) = \dfrac{dv}{dx} = \dfrac{dv}{du} \times \dfrac{du}{dx} = 2 \sec^2 (2x)$

$\Rightarrow \dfrac{dy}{dx} = 2 \sec^2 (2x) e^{\tan (2x)}$

Q3 a) $\dfrac{dy}{dx} = \sin^4 x^2 = (\sin x^2)^4$, so let $y = u^4$ where $u = \sin x^2$

$\dfrac{dy}{du} = 4u^3 = 4 \sin^3 x^2$

For $\dfrac{du}{dx}$, set up another chain rule:

$u = \sin x^2$ so let $u = \sin v$, $v = x^2$

$\dfrac{du}{dv} = \cos v = \cos x^2$, $\dfrac{dv}{dx} = 2x$

$\dfrac{du}{dx} = \dfrac{du}{dv} \times \dfrac{dv}{dx} = 2x \cos x^2$

Putting it all together:

$\dfrac{dy}{dx} = \dfrac{dy}{du} \times \dfrac{du}{dx} = 8x \sin^3 x^2 \cos x^2$

b) $\dfrac{dy}{dx} = f'(x)e^{f(x)}$

$f(x) = \sin^2 x = (\sin x)^2$, so let $y = u^2$ where $u = \sin x$

$f'(x) = \dfrac{dy}{du} \times \dfrac{du}{dx} = (2 \sin x) \times (\cos x) = 2 \sin x \cos x$

$\Rightarrow \dfrac{dy}{dx} = 2 e^{\sin^2 x} \sin x \cos x$

c) First part:

$y = \tan^2(3x) = (\tan(3x))^2$, so let $y = u^2$ where $u = \tan(3x)$

$\dfrac{dy}{du} = 2u = 2\tan(3x)$

For $\dfrac{du}{dx}$ set up the chain rule again:

$u = \tan(3x)$, so let $u = \tan v$ where $v = 3x$

$\dfrac{du}{dv} = \sec^2 v = \sec^2(3x)$, $\dfrac{dv}{dx} = 3$

$\Rightarrow \dfrac{du}{dx} = \dfrac{du}{dv} \times \dfrac{dv}{dx} = 3\sec^2(3x)$

$\Rightarrow \dfrac{dy}{dx} = \dfrac{dy}{du} \times \dfrac{du}{dx} = 6\tan(3x)\sec^2(3x)$

Second part:

$\dfrac{dy}{dx} = \cos x$

Putting it all together:

$\dfrac{dy}{dx} = 6\tan(3x)\sec^2(3x) + \cos x$

With practice, you should be able to do some of the simpler chain rule calculations in your head, e.g. $\dfrac{d}{dx}\tan^2(3x) = 6\tan(3x)\sec^2(3x)$, which will make these questions much quicker.

d) First part: $y = e^{f(x)}$, $f(x) = 2\cos(2x) \Rightarrow \dfrac{dy}{dx} = f'(x)e^{f(x)}$

$f(x) = 2\cos(2x) \Rightarrow f'(x) = -4\sin(2x)$

So $\dfrac{dy}{dx} = -4\sin(2x)e^{2\cos(2x)}$

Second part: $y = \cos^2(2x) = (\cos(2x))^2$,

so let $y = u^2$ where $u = \cos(2x)$

$\dfrac{dy}{du} = 2u = 2\cos(2x)$

For $\dfrac{du}{dx}$, set up the chain rule again:

$u = \cos(2x) \Rightarrow \dfrac{du}{dx}\ -2\sin(2x)$

$\Rightarrow \dfrac{dy}{dx} = \dfrac{dy}{du} \times \dfrac{du}{dx} = -4\sin(2x)\cos(2x)$

Putting it all together:

$\dfrac{dy}{dx} = -4\sin(2x)\,e^{2\cos(2x)} - 4\sin(2x)\cos(2x)$

7.5 Product Rule

Exercise 7.5.1 — Differentiating functions multiplied together

Q1 **a)** $y = x(x + 2) = x^2 + 2x$

$\dfrac{dy}{dx} = 2x + 2$

b) $u = x, v = x + 2 \Rightarrow \dfrac{du}{dx} = 1, \dfrac{dv}{dx} = 1$

$\dfrac{dy}{dx} = u\dfrac{dv}{dx} + v\dfrac{du}{dx} = x + (x + 2) = 2x + 2$

Q2 **a)** $u = x^2, v = (x + 6)^3 \Rightarrow \dfrac{du}{dx} = 2x, \dfrac{dv}{dx} = 3(x + 6)^2$

$\dfrac{dy}{dx} = u\dfrac{dv}{dx} + v\dfrac{du}{dx} = [x^2 \times 3(x + 6)^2] + [(x + 6)^3 \times 2x]$

$= 3x^2(x + 6)^2 + 2x(x + 6)^3$

$= x(x + 6)^2[3x + 2(x + 6)] = x(x + 6)^2(5x + 12)$

Here the chain rule was used to find $\dfrac{dv}{dx}$ — write out all the steps if you're struggling.

b) $u = x^3, v = (5x + 2)^4 \Rightarrow \dfrac{du}{dx} = 3x^2, \dfrac{dv}{dx} = 20(5x + 2)^3$

$\dfrac{dy}{dx} = u\dfrac{dv}{dx} + v\dfrac{du}{dx} = [x^3 \times 20(5x + 2)^3] + [(5x + 2)^4 \times 3x^2]$

$= 20x^3(5x + 2)^3 + 3x^2(5x + 2)^4$

$= x^2(5x + 2)^3[20x + 3(5x + 2)]$

$= x^2(5x + 2)^3(35x + 6)$

c) $u = x^3, v = e^x \Rightarrow \dfrac{du}{dx} = 3x^2, \dfrac{dv}{dx} = e^x$

$\dfrac{dy}{dx} = u\dfrac{dv}{dx} + v\dfrac{du}{dx} = x^3e^x + e^x 3x^2 = x^2e^x(x + 3)$

d) $u = x, v = e^{4x} \Rightarrow \dfrac{du}{dx} = 1, \dfrac{dv}{dx} = 4e^{4x}$

$\dfrac{dy}{dx} = u\dfrac{dv}{dx} + v\dfrac{du}{dx} = 4xe^{4x} + e^{4x} = e^{4x}(4x + 1)$

e) $u = x, v = e^{x^2} \Rightarrow \dfrac{du}{dx} = 1, \dfrac{dv}{dx} = 2xe^{x^2}$

$\dfrac{dy}{dx} = u\dfrac{dv}{dx} + v\dfrac{du}{dx} = x \times 2xe^{x^2} + e^{x^2} = e^{x^2}(2x^2 + 1)$

f) $u = e^{2x}, v = \sin x \Rightarrow \dfrac{du}{dx} = 2e^{2x}, \dfrac{dv}{dx} = \cos x$

$\dfrac{dy}{dx} = u\dfrac{dv}{dx} + v\dfrac{du}{dx} = e^{2x} \times \cos x + \sin x \times 2e^{2x}$

$= e^{2x}(\cos x + 2\sin x)$

Q3 **a)** $u = x^3, v = (x + 3)^{\frac{1}{2}} \Rightarrow \dfrac{du}{dx} = 3x^2, \dfrac{dv}{dx} = \dfrac{1}{2}(x + 3)^{-\frac{1}{2}}$

$f'(x) = u\dfrac{dv}{dx} + v\dfrac{du}{dx} = \left[x^3 \times \dfrac{1}{2}(x + 3)^{-\frac{1}{2}}\right] + \left[(x + 3)^{\frac{1}{2}} \times 3x^2\right]$

$= \dfrac{x^3}{2(x + 3)^{\frac{1}{2}}} + 3x^2(x + 3)^{\frac{1}{2}}$

b) $u = x^2, v = (x - 7)^{-\frac{1}{2}} \Rightarrow \dfrac{du}{dx} = 2x, \dfrac{dv}{dx} = -\dfrac{1}{2}(x - 7)^{-\frac{3}{2}}$

$f'(x) = u\dfrac{dv}{dx} + v\dfrac{du}{dx} = \left[x^2 \times \left(-\dfrac{1}{2}\right) \times (x - 7)^{-\frac{3}{2}}\right] + \left[(x - 7)^{-\frac{1}{2}} \times 2x\right]$

$= -\dfrac{x^2}{2(\sqrt{x - 7})^3} + \dfrac{2x}{\sqrt{x - 7}}$

c) $u = x^4, v = \ln x \Rightarrow \dfrac{du}{dx} = 4x^3, \dfrac{dv}{dx} = \dfrac{1}{x}$

$f'(x) = u\dfrac{dv}{dx} + v\dfrac{du}{dx} = \left[x^4 \times \dfrac{1}{x}\right] + [\ln x \times 4x^3]$

$= x^3 + 4x^3 \ln x = x^3(1 + 4\ln x)$

d) $u = 4x, v = \ln x^2 = 2\ln x \Rightarrow \dfrac{du}{dx} = 4, \dfrac{dv}{dx} = \dfrac{2}{x}$

$f'(x) = u\dfrac{dv}{dx} + v\dfrac{du}{dx} = \left[4x \times \dfrac{2}{x}\right] + [\ln x^2 \times 4] = 8 + 4\ln x^2$

e) $u = 2x^3, v = \cos x \Rightarrow \dfrac{du}{dx} = 6x^2, \dfrac{dv}{dx} = -\sin x$

$f'(x) = u\dfrac{dv}{dx} + v\dfrac{du}{dx} = (-2x^3 \times \sin x) + (\cos x \times 6x^2)$

$= 2x^2(3\cos x - x\sin x)$

f) $u = x^2, v = \cos(2x) \Rightarrow \dfrac{du}{dx} = 2x, \dfrac{dv}{dx} = -2\sin(2x)$

$f'(x) = u\dfrac{dv}{dx} + v\dfrac{du}{dx} = [x^2 \times -2\sin(2x)] + [\cos(2x) \times 2x]$

$= 2x\cos(2x) - 2x^2\sin(2x) = 2x(\cos(2x) - x\sin(2x))$

Q4 **a)** $u = (x + 1)^2, v = x^2 - 1 \Rightarrow \dfrac{du}{dx} = 2(x + 1), \dfrac{dv}{dx} = 2x$

$\dfrac{dy}{dx} = u\dfrac{dv}{dx} + v\dfrac{du}{dx} = [(x + 1)^2 \times 2x] + [(x^2 - 1) \times 2(x + 1)]$

$= 2x(x + 1)^2 + 2(x^2 - 1)(x + 1)$

$= 2x^3 + 4x^2 + 2x + 2x^3 + 2x^2 - 2x - 2 = 4x^3 + 6x^2 - 2$

b) $u = (x + 1)^3, v = x - 1 \Rightarrow \dfrac{du}{dx} = 3(x + 1)^2, \dfrac{dv}{dx} = 1$

$\dfrac{dy}{dx} = u\dfrac{dv}{dx} + v\dfrac{du}{dx} = [(x + 1)^3 \times 1] + [(x - 1) \times 3(x + 1)^2]$

$= (x + 1)^3 + 3(x - 1)(x + 1)^2$

$= (x^3 + 3x^2 + 3x + 1) + (3x^3 + 6x^2 + 3x - 3x^2 - 6x - 3)$

$= 4x^3 + 6x^2 - 2$

Use the binomial formula to expand $(x + 1)^3$ — you'll get the coefficients 1, 3, 3, 1.

c) $y = (x + 1)^2(x^2 - 1) = (x + 1)^2(x + 1)(x - 1) = (x + 1)^3(x - 1)$

$x^2 - 1$ is the difference of two squares.

Q5 When $y = xe^x$ is concave, $\dfrac{d^2y}{dx^2}$ is negative.

$u = x, v = e^x \Rightarrow \dfrac{du}{dx} = 1, \dfrac{dv}{dx} = e^x$

$\dfrac{dy}{dx} = u\dfrac{dv}{dx} + v\dfrac{du}{dx} = xe^x + e^x$

$\dfrac{d^2y}{dx^2} = \dfrac{d}{dx}(xe^x) + \dfrac{d}{dx}(e^x) = [xe^x + e^x] + [e^x] = xe^x + 2e^x$

$\dfrac{d^2y}{dx^2} < 0 \Rightarrow xe^x + 2e^x < 0 \Rightarrow e^x(x + 2) < 0$

Since $e^x > 0$ for all x, this means that $(x + 2) < 0 \Rightarrow x < -2$

So the curve $y = xe^x$ is concave when $x < -2$.

Q6 $u = \sqrt{x+2}$, $v = \sqrt{x+7}$ $\Rightarrow$ $\dfrac{du}{dx} = \dfrac{1}{2\sqrt{x+2}}$, $\dfrac{dv}{dx} = \dfrac{1}{2\sqrt{x+7}}$

$\dfrac{dy}{dx} = u\dfrac{dv}{dx} + v\dfrac{du}{dx} = \dfrac{\sqrt{x+2}}{2\sqrt{x+7}} + \dfrac{\sqrt{x+7}}{2\sqrt{x+2}}$

At the point (2, 6), $\dfrac{dy}{dx} = \dfrac{\sqrt{4}}{2\sqrt{9}} + \dfrac{\sqrt{9}}{2\sqrt{4}} = \dfrac{13}{12}$

$y = mx + c \Rightarrow 6 = \left(2 \times \dfrac{13}{12}\right) + c \Rightarrow c = \dfrac{23}{6}$

So the equation of the tangent is $y = \dfrac{13}{12}x + \dfrac{23}{6}$.

To write this in the form $ax + by + c = 0$ where a, b and c are integers, multiply by 12 and rearrange.

$y = \dfrac{13}{12}x + \dfrac{23}{6} \Rightarrow 12y = 13x + 46 \Rightarrow 13x - 12y + 46 = 0$

Q7   **a)** $u = (x-1)^{\frac{1}{2}}$, $v = (x+4)^{-\frac{1}{2}}$

$\Rightarrow \dfrac{du}{dx} = \dfrac{1}{2\sqrt{x-1}}$, $\dfrac{dv}{dx} = -\dfrac{1}{2(\sqrt{x+4})^3}$

$\dfrac{dy}{dx} = u\dfrac{dv}{dx} + v\dfrac{du}{dx} = \dfrac{1}{2\sqrt{x-1}\sqrt{x+4}} - \dfrac{\sqrt{x-1}}{2(\sqrt{x+4})^3}$

When $x = 5$, $\dfrac{dy}{dx} = \dfrac{1}{2\sqrt{4}\sqrt{9}} - \dfrac{\sqrt{4}}{2(\sqrt{9})^3} = \dfrac{5}{108}$

and $y = \dfrac{\sqrt{4}}{\sqrt{9}} = \dfrac{2}{3}$

$y = mx + c \Rightarrow \dfrac{2}{3} = \left(5 \times \dfrac{5}{108}\right) + c \Rightarrow c = \dfrac{47}{108}$

So the equation of the tangent is $y = \dfrac{5}{108}x + \dfrac{47}{108}$

To write this in the form $ax + by + c = 0$ where a, b and c are integers, multiply by 108 and rearrange.

$y = \dfrac{5}{108}x + \dfrac{47}{108} \Rightarrow 108y = 5x + 47 \Rightarrow 5x - 108y + 47 = 0$

b)   Gradient of the normal $= -\dfrac{1}{\left(\dfrac{5}{108}\right)} = -\dfrac{108}{5}$

$y = mx + c \Rightarrow \dfrac{2}{3} = \left(5 \times \left(-\dfrac{108}{5}\right)\right) + c \Rightarrow c = \dfrac{326}{3}$

So the equation of the normal is $y = -\dfrac{108}{5}x + \dfrac{326}{3}$.

To write this in the form $ax + by + c = 0$ where a, b and c are integers, multiply by 15 and rearrange.

$y = -\dfrac{108}{5}x + \dfrac{326}{3} \Rightarrow 15y = -324x + 1630$
$\Rightarrow 324x + 15y - 1630 = 0$

Q8   First use the chain rule:

$\dfrac{dy}{dx} = f'(x)e^{f(x)}$ where $f(x) = x^2\sqrt{x+3}$.

Then use the product rule to find $f'(x)$:

$u = x^2, v = \sqrt{x+3} \Rightarrow \dfrac{du}{dx} = 2x, \dfrac{dv}{dx} = \dfrac{1}{2\sqrt{x+3}}$

$\dfrac{dy}{dx} = u\dfrac{dv}{dx} + v\dfrac{du}{dx} = \left[x^2 \times \dfrac{1}{2\sqrt{x+3}}\right] + \left[\sqrt{x+3} \times 2x\right]$

$= \dfrac{x^2 + 4x(x+3)}{2\sqrt{x+3}} = \dfrac{5x^2 + 12x}{2\sqrt{x+3}}$

Now putting it all together:

$\dfrac{dy}{dx} = \dfrac{5x^2 + 12x}{2\sqrt{x+3}}\, e^{x^2\sqrt{x+3}}$

Q9   Stationary points occur when the gradient is 0.
Differentiate with the product rule:

$u = x, v = e^{x-x^2} \Rightarrow \dfrac{du}{dx} = 1, \dfrac{dv}{dx} = (1-2x)e^{x-x^2}$

$\dfrac{dy}{dx} = u\dfrac{dv}{dx} + v\dfrac{du}{dx} = \left[x(1-2x)e^{x-x^2}\right] + \left[e^{x-x^2} \times 1\right]$

$= e^{x-x^2}(x - 2x^2 + 1)$

e^{x-x^2} cannot be 0, so the stationary points occur when $-2x^2 + x + 1 = 0$

$\Rightarrow (2x+1)(-x+1) = 0 \Rightarrow x = 1 \text{ or } x = -\dfrac{1}{2}$

When $x = 1$, $y = 1 \times e^0 = 1$.

When $x = -\dfrac{1}{2}$, $y = -\dfrac{1}{2} \times e^{-\frac{3}{4}} = -\dfrac{e^{-\frac{3}{4}}}{2}$.

So the stationary points are (1, 1) and $\left(-\dfrac{1}{2}, -\dfrac{e^{-\frac{3}{4}}}{2}\right)$.

Q10   **a)**   Stationary points occur when the gradient is 0.

$u = (x-2)^2, v = (x+4)^3 \Rightarrow \dfrac{du}{dx} = 2(x-2), \dfrac{dv}{dx} = 3(x+4)^2$

$\dfrac{dy}{dx} = u\dfrac{dv}{dx} + v\dfrac{du}{dx}$
$= [(x-2)^2 \times 3(x+4)^2] + [(x+4)^3 \times 2(x-2)]$
$= 3(x-2)^2(x+4)^2 + 2(x-2)(x+4)^3$
$= (x-2)(x+4)^2[3x - 6 + 2x + 8] = (x-2)(x+4)^2(5x+2)$

So the stationary points occur when:

$x - 2 = 0 \Rightarrow x = 2$
and $x + 4 = 0 \Rightarrow x = -4$
and $5x + 2 = 0 \Rightarrow x = -\dfrac{2}{5} = -0.4$

When $x = 2$, $y = 0 \times 6^3 = 0$
When $x = -4$, $y = (-6)^2 \times 0 = 0$
When $x = -0.4$, $y = (-2.4)^2(3.6)^3 = 268.74$ (2 d.p.)
So the stationary points are (2, 0), (−4, 0) and (−0.4, 268.74).

b)   To write $\dfrac{dy}{dx}$ in the form $(Ax^2 + Bx + C)(x+D)^n$,
multiply out the brackets $(x-2)$ and $(5x+2)$, which will give you the quadratic bracket:

$\dfrac{dy}{dx} = (x-2)(x+4)^2(5x+2) = [5x^2 - 10x + 2x - 4](x+4)^2$
$= (5x^2 - 8x - 4)(x+4)^2$

Now you can differentiate this using the product rule:

$u = (5x^2 - 8x - 4), v = (x+4)^2$

$\Rightarrow \dfrac{du}{dx} = (10x - 8), \dfrac{dv}{dx} = 2(x+4)$

$\dfrac{d^2y}{dx^2} = u\dfrac{dv}{dx} + v\dfrac{du}{dx}$
$= [(5x^2 - 8x - 4) \times 2(x+4)] + [(x+4)^2 \times (10x - 8)]$
$= (x+4)(10x^2 - 16x - 8) + (x+4)(10x^2 + 32x - 32)$
$= (x+4)(20x^2 + 16x - 40) = 4(x+4)(5x^2 + 4x - 10)$

When $x = 2$, $\dfrac{d^2y}{dx^2} = 4(2+4)(5(2)^2 + 4(2) - 10)$
$= 4(6)(20 + 8 - 10) = 432\ (> 0)$

So (2, 0) is a minimum point.

When $x = -4$, $\dfrac{d^2y}{dx^2} = 4(-4+4)(5(-4)^2 + 4(-4) - 10)$
$= 4(0)(80 - 16 - 10) = 0$

Check $\dfrac{d^2y}{dx^2}$ either side of $x = -4$:
When $x > -4$, $(x+4) > 0$ and $(5x^2 + 4x - 10) > 0$
$\Rightarrow \dfrac{d^2y}{dx^2} > 0$
When $x < -4$, $(x+4) < 0$ and $(5x^2 + 4x - 10) > 0$
$\Rightarrow \dfrac{d^2y}{dx^2} < 0$

So (−4, 0) is a point of inflection.

When $x = -0.4$, $\dfrac{d^2y}{dx^2} = 4(-0.4+4)(5(-0.4)^2 + 4(-0.4) - 10)$
$= 4(3.6)(0.8 - 1.6 - 10) = -155.52\ (< 0)$

So (−0.4, 268.74) is a maximum point.

7.6 Quotient Rule

Exercise 7.6.1 — Differentiating a function divided by a function

Q1   **a)** $u = x + 5, v = x - 3 \Rightarrow \dfrac{du}{dx} = 1, \dfrac{dv}{dx} = 1$

$\dfrac{dy}{dx} = \dfrac{v\dfrac{du}{dx} - u\dfrac{dv}{dx}}{v^2} = \dfrac{((x-3) \times 1) - ((x+5) \times 1)}{(x-3)^2} = -\dfrac{8}{(x-3)^2}$

b) $u = (x-7)^4, v = (5-x)^3$

$\Rightarrow \dfrac{du}{dx} = 4(x-7)^3, \dfrac{dv}{dx} = -3(5-x)^2$

$\dfrac{dy}{dx} = \dfrac{v\dfrac{du}{dx} - u\dfrac{dv}{dx}}{v^2}$

$= \dfrac{[(5-x)^3 \times 4(x-7)^3] - [(x-7)^4 \times (-3)(5-x)^2]}{(5-x)^6}$

$= \dfrac{(5-x)^2(x-7)^3[4(5-x) + 3(x-7)]}{(5-x)^6} = \dfrac{(x-7)^3(-x-1)}{(5-x)^4}$

c) $u = e^x, v = x^2 \Rightarrow \dfrac{du}{dx} = e^x, \dfrac{dv}{dx} = 2x$

$\dfrac{dy}{dx} = \dfrac{v\dfrac{du}{dx} - u\dfrac{dv}{dx}}{v^2} = \dfrac{x^2e^x - e^x 2x}{x^4} = \dfrac{xe^x(x-2)}{x^4} = \dfrac{e^x(x-2)}{x^3}$

d) $u = 3x$, $v = (x-1)^2 \Rightarrow \dfrac{du}{dx} = 3$, $\dfrac{dv}{dx} = 2(x-1)$

$\dfrac{dy}{dx} = \dfrac{v\frac{du}{dx} - u\frac{dv}{dx}}{v^2} = \dfrac{[(x-1)^2 \times 3] - [3x \times 2(x-1)]}{(x-1)^4}$

$= \dfrac{(x-1)[3(x-1) - 6x]}{(x-1)^4} = \dfrac{-3x-3}{(x-1)^3}$

e) $u = \ln x^2 = 2\ln x$, $v = 5x \Rightarrow \dfrac{du}{dx} = \dfrac{2}{x}$, $\dfrac{dv}{dx} = 5$

$\dfrac{dy}{dx} = \dfrac{v\frac{du}{dx} - u\frac{dv}{dx}}{v^2} = \dfrac{\left[5x \times \frac{2}{x}\right] - [\ln x^2 \times 5]}{25x^2}$

$= \dfrac{10 - 5\ln x^2}{25x^2} = \dfrac{2 - \ln x^2}{5x^2}$

f) $u = 4x^3$, $v = e^x \Rightarrow \dfrac{du}{dx} = 12x^2$, $\dfrac{dv}{dx} = e^x$

$\dfrac{dy}{dx} = \dfrac{v\frac{du}{dx} - u\frac{dv}{dx}}{v^2} = \dfrac{12x^2 e^x - 4x^3 e^x}{(e^x)^2} = \dfrac{12x^2 - 4x^3}{e^x}$

Q2 a) $u = x^3$, $v = (x+3)^3 \Rightarrow \dfrac{du}{dx} = 3x^2$, $\dfrac{dv}{dx} = 3(x+3)^2$

$f'(x) = \dfrac{v\frac{du}{dx} - u\frac{dv}{dx}}{v^2} = \dfrac{[(x+3)^3 \times 3x^2] - [x^3 \times 3(x+3)^2]}{(x+3)^6}$

$= \dfrac{3x^2(x+3) - 3x^3}{(x+3)^4} = \dfrac{9x^2}{(x+3)^4}$

b) $u = x^2$, $v = \sqrt{x-7} \Rightarrow \dfrac{du}{dx} = 2x$, $\dfrac{dv}{dx} = \dfrac{1}{2\sqrt{x-7}}$

$f'(x) = \dfrac{v\frac{du}{dx} - u\frac{dv}{dx}}{v^2} = \dfrac{[\sqrt{x-7} \times 2x] - \left[x^2 \frac{1}{2\sqrt{x-7}}\right]}{x-7}$

$= \dfrac{4x(x-7) - x^2}{2(\sqrt{x-7})^3} = \dfrac{3x^2 - 28x}{2(\sqrt{x-7})^3}$

c) $u = e^{2x}$, $v = e^{2x} + e^{-2x} \Rightarrow \dfrac{du}{dx} = 2e^{2x}$, $\dfrac{dv}{dx} = 2e^{2x} - 2e^{-2x}$

$f'(x) = \dfrac{v\frac{du}{dx} - u\frac{dv}{dx}}{v^2} = \dfrac{[(e^{2x} + e^{-2x})2e^{2x}] - [e^{2x}(2e^{2x} - 2e^{-2x})]}{(e^{2x} + e^{-2x})^2}$

$= \dfrac{2e^{4x} + 2 - 2e^{4x} + 2}{e^{4x} + e^{-4x} + 2} = \dfrac{4}{e^{4x} + e^{-4x} + 2}$

d) $u = x$, $v = \sin x \Rightarrow \dfrac{du}{dx} = 1$, $\dfrac{dv}{dx} = \cos x$

$f'(x) = \dfrac{v\frac{du}{dx} - u\frac{dv}{dx}}{v^2} = \dfrac{\sin x - x\cos x}{\sin^2 x}$

e) $u = \sin x$, $v = x \Rightarrow \dfrac{du}{dx} = \cos x$, $\dfrac{dv}{dx} = 1$

$f'(x) = \dfrac{v\frac{du}{dx} - u\frac{dv}{dx}}{v^2} = \dfrac{x\cos x - \sin x}{x^2}$

f) $u = \cos x$, $v = 3x \Rightarrow \dfrac{du}{dx} = -\sin x$, $\dfrac{dv}{dx} = 3$

$f'(x) = \dfrac{v\frac{du}{dx} - u\frac{dv}{dx}}{v^2} = \dfrac{-3x\sin x - 3\cos x}{9x^2} = \dfrac{-x\sin x - \cos x}{3x^2}$

Q3 $u = x^2$, $v = \tan x \Rightarrow \dfrac{du}{dx} = 2x$, $\dfrac{dv}{dx} = \sec^2 x$

$f'(x) = \dfrac{v\frac{du}{dx} - u\frac{dv}{dx}}{v^2} = \dfrac{[\tan x \times 2x] - [x^2 \times \sec^2 x]}{\tan^2 x}$

$= \dfrac{2x\tan x - x^2\sec^2 x}{\tan^2 x} = \dfrac{2x}{\tan x} - x^2 \dfrac{\frac{1}{\cos^2 x}}{\frac{\sin^2 x}{\cos^2 x}} = 2x\cot x - x^2\operatorname{cosec}^2 x$

Q4 $u = 5x - 4$, $v = 2x^2 \Rightarrow \dfrac{du}{dx} = 5$, $\dfrac{dv}{dx} = 4x$

$\dfrac{dy}{dx} = \dfrac{v\frac{du}{dx} - u\frac{dv}{dx}}{v^2} = \dfrac{[2x^2 \times 5] - [(5x-4) \times 4x]}{(2x^2)^2}$

$= \dfrac{10x^2 - (20x^2 - 16x)}{4x^4} = \dfrac{16x - 10x^2}{4x^4} = \dfrac{8 - 5x}{2x^3}$

There is a stationary point when $\dfrac{dy}{dx} = 0$:

$\dfrac{dy}{dx} = 0 \Rightarrow 8 - 5x = 0 \Rightarrow 5x = 8 \Rightarrow x = \dfrac{8}{5}$

When $x = \dfrac{8}{5}$, $y = \dfrac{5\left(\frac{8}{5}\right) - 4}{2\left(\frac{8}{5}\right)^2} = \dfrac{8-4}{2\left(\frac{64}{25}\right)} = \dfrac{25}{32}$

So the coordinates of the stationary point are $\left(\dfrac{8}{5}, \dfrac{25}{32}\right)$.

To determine the nature of the stationary point, differentiate again to find $\dfrac{d^2y}{dx^2}$: $\dfrac{dy}{dx} = \dfrac{8 - 5x}{2x^3}$

$u = 8 - 5x$, $v = 2x^3 \Rightarrow \dfrac{du}{dx} = -5$, $\dfrac{dv}{dx} = 6x^2$

$\dfrac{d^2y}{dx^2} = \dfrac{v\frac{du}{dx} - u\frac{dv}{dx}}{v^2} = \dfrac{[2x^3 \times (-5)] - [(8 - 5x) \times 6x^2]}{(2x^3)^2}$

$= \dfrac{-10x^3 - (48x^2 - 30x^3)}{4x^6} = \dfrac{20x^3 - 48x^2}{4x^6} = \dfrac{5x - 12}{x^4}$

When $x = \dfrac{8}{5}$, $\dfrac{d^2y}{dx^2} = \dfrac{5\left(\frac{8}{5}\right) - 12}{\left(\frac{8}{5}\right)^4} = \dfrac{8 - 12}{\left(\frac{8}{5}\right)^4} = \dfrac{-4}{\left(\frac{8}{5}\right)^4}$

Since the denominator is positive, $\dfrac{d^2y}{dx^2}$ is negative, and so the stationary point must be a maximum.

Q5 $u = x$, $v = e^x \Rightarrow \dfrac{du}{dx} = 1$, $\dfrac{dv}{dx} = e^x$

$\dfrac{dy}{dx} = \dfrac{v\frac{du}{dx} - u\frac{dv}{dx}}{v^2} = \dfrac{[e^x \times 1] - [x \times e^x]}{(e^x)^2} = \dfrac{e^x - xe^x}{(e^x)^2} = \dfrac{1 - x}{e^x}$

Use the quotient rule again to find $\dfrac{d^2y}{dx^2}$:

$u = 1 - x$, $v = e^x \Rightarrow \dfrac{du}{dx} = -1$, $\dfrac{dv}{dx} = e^x$

$\dfrac{d^2y}{dx^2} = \dfrac{v\frac{du}{dx} - u\frac{dv}{dx}}{v^2} = \dfrac{[e^x \times -1] - [(1 - x) \times e^x]}{(e^x)^2}$

$= \dfrac{-e^x - e^x + xe^x}{(e^x)^2} = \dfrac{-1 - 1 + x}{e^x} = \dfrac{x - 2}{e^x}$

$\dfrac{d^2y}{dx^2} = 0$ when $x - 2 = 0 \Rightarrow x = 2$

Check $\dfrac{d^2y}{dx^2}$ either side of $x = 2$:

When $x > 2$, $(x - 2) > 0 \Rightarrow \dfrac{d^2y}{dx^2} > 0$

When $x < 2$, $(x - 2) < 0 \Rightarrow \dfrac{d^2y}{dx^2} < 0$

$\dfrac{d^2y}{dx^2}$ changes sign at $x = 2$, so it's a point of inflection.

When $x = 2$, $y = \dfrac{2}{e^2}$, so the only point of inflection of the graph $y = \dfrac{x}{e^x}$ occurs at the point $\left(2, \dfrac{2}{e^2}\right)$.

Q6 a) $u = x$, $v = \cos(2x) \Rightarrow \dfrac{du}{dx} = 1$, $\dfrac{dv}{dx} = -2\sin(2x)$

$\dfrac{dy}{dx} = \dfrac{v\frac{du}{dx} - u\frac{dv}{dx}}{v^2} = \dfrac{\cos(2x) - [x \times -2\sin(2x)]}{\cos^2(2x)}$

$= \dfrac{\cos(2x) + 2x\sin(2x)}{\cos^2(2x)}$

b) $\dfrac{dy}{dx} = 0$ if $\cos(2x) + 2x\sin(2x) = 0 \Rightarrow -\cos(2x) = 2x\sin(2x)$

$\Rightarrow 2x = -\dfrac{\cos(2x)}{\sin(2x)} = -\cot(2x) \Rightarrow x = -\dfrac{1}{2}\cot(2x)$

Remember $\cos x/\sin x = 1/\tan x = \cot x$.

Q7 a) $u = 1$, $v = 1 + 4\cos x \Rightarrow \dfrac{du}{dx} = 0$, $\dfrac{dv}{dx} = -4\sin x$

$\dfrac{dy}{dx} = \dfrac{v\frac{du}{dx} - u\frac{dv}{dx}}{v^2} = \dfrac{[(1 + 4\cos x) \times 0] - [1 \times (-4\sin x)]}{(1 + 4\cos x)^2}$

$= \dfrac{4\sin x}{(1 + 4\cos x)^2}$

When $x = \dfrac{\pi}{2}$, $\dfrac{dy}{dx} = \dfrac{4}{(1)^2} = 4$ and $y = \dfrac{1}{1} = 1$

$y = mx + c \Rightarrow 1 = 4\dfrac{\pi}{2} + c \Rightarrow c = 1 - 2\pi$

So the equation of the tangent is $y = 4x + 1 - 2\pi$.

b) From part a), the gradient of the normal must be $-\dfrac{1}{4}$. Equation of a straight line:

$y = mx + c \Rightarrow 1 = -\dfrac{1}{4}\dfrac{\pi}{2} + c \Rightarrow c = 1 + \dfrac{\pi}{8}$

So the equation of the normal is $y = -\dfrac{1}{4}x + 1 + \dfrac{\pi}{8}$

You could also do the differentiation here by writing y as $(1 + 4\cos x)^{-1}$, and then using the chain rule. In general, you don't have to use the quotient rule when the numerator is just a number.

Q8 $u = 2x$, $v = \cos x \Rightarrow \dfrac{du}{dx} = 2$, $\dfrac{dv}{dx} = -\sin x$

$\dfrac{dy}{dx} = \dfrac{v\frac{du}{dx} - u\frac{dv}{dx}}{v^2} = \dfrac{[\cos x \times 2] - [2x \times (-\sin x)]}{\cos^2 x}$

$= \dfrac{2\cos x + 2x\sin x}{\cos^2 x}$

When $x = \dfrac{\pi}{3}$, $\dfrac{dy}{dx} = \dfrac{1 + \frac{\pi\sqrt{3}}{3}}{\left(\frac{1}{2}\right)^2} = 4 + \dfrac{4\pi\sqrt{3}}{3}$

Q9 $u = x - \sin x$, $v = 1 + \cos x$

$\Rightarrow \dfrac{du}{dx} = 1 - \cos x$, $\dfrac{dv}{dx} = -\sin x$

$\dfrac{dy}{dx} = \dfrac{v\frac{du}{dx} - u\frac{dv}{dx}}{v^2} = \dfrac{[(1 + \cos x)(1 - \cos x)] - [(x - \sin x)(-\sin x)]}{(1 + \cos x)^2}$

$= \dfrac{1 - \cos^2 x - \sin^2 x + x\sin x}{(1 + \cos x)^2} = \dfrac{1 - 1 + x\sin x}{(1 + \cos x)^2} = \dfrac{x\sin x}{(1 + \cos x)^2}$

Use the identity $\sin^2 x + \cos^2 x \equiv 1$ to simplify the expression.

Q10 Stationary points occur when the gradient is 0.

$u = \cos x$, $v = 4 - 3\cos x$, $\Rightarrow \dfrac{du}{dx} = -\sin x$, $\dfrac{dv}{dx} = 3\sin x$

$\dfrac{dy}{dx} = \dfrac{v\frac{du}{dx} - u\frac{dv}{dx}}{v^2} = \dfrac{[(4 - 3\cos x)(-\sin x)] - [\cos x(3\sin x)]}{(4 - 3\cos x)^2}$

$= \dfrac{-4\sin x}{(4 - 3\cos x)^2}$

$\dfrac{dy}{dx} = 0 \Rightarrow -4\sin x = 0 \Rightarrow x = \sin^{-1} 0 = 0$, π and 2π.

When $x = 0$, $y = \dfrac{1}{4 - 3} = 1$

When $x = \pi$, $y = \dfrac{-1}{4 - (-3)} = -\dfrac{1}{7}$

When $x = 2\pi$, $y = \dfrac{1}{4 - 3} = 1$

So the stationary points are (0, 1), $\left(\pi, -\dfrac{1}{7}\right)$ and $(2\pi, 1)$.

Q11 First use the chain rule: $y = e^{f(x)} \Rightarrow \dfrac{dy}{dx} = f'(x)e^{f(x)}$

Then use the quotient rule to find $f'(x)$:

$u = 1 + x$, $v = 1 - x \Rightarrow \dfrac{du}{dx} = 1$, $\dfrac{dv}{dx} = -1$

$\dfrac{dy}{dx} = \dfrac{v\frac{du}{dx} - u\frac{dv}{dx}}{v^2} = \dfrac{[(1 - x)(1)] - [(1 + x)(-1)]}{(1 - x)^2} = \dfrac{2}{(1 - x)^2}$

So $\dfrac{dy}{dx} = f'(x)e^{f(x)} = \dfrac{2e^{\frac{1+x}{1-x}}}{(1 - x)^2}$

Q12 $y = \dfrac{2 + 3x^2}{3x - 1}$ is increasing when $\dfrac{dy}{dx} > 0$.

$u = 2 + 3x^2$, $v = 3x - 1 \Rightarrow \dfrac{du}{dx} = 6x$, $\dfrac{dv}{dx} = 3$

$\dfrac{dy}{dx} = \dfrac{v\frac{du}{dx} - u\frac{dv}{dx}}{v^2} = \dfrac{[(3x - 1) \times 6x] - [(2 + 3x^2) \times 3]}{(3x - 1)^2}$

$= \dfrac{(18x^2 - 6x) - (6 + 9x^2)}{(3x - 1)^2} = \dfrac{9x^2 - 6x - 6}{(3x - 1)^2}$

Since the denominator is squared, it is always positive.

So $\dfrac{dy}{dx} > 0$ when $9x^2 - 6x - 6 > 0 \Rightarrow 3x^2 - 2x - 2 > 0$

Use the quadratic formula to solve $\dfrac{dy}{dx} = 0$:

$x = \dfrac{2 \pm \sqrt{4 - (4 \times 3 \times -2)}}{6} = \dfrac{2 \pm \sqrt{28}}{6} = \dfrac{1 \pm \sqrt{7}}{3}$

Since the coefficient of x^2 in $9x^2 - 6x - 6$ is positive,

the graph of $\dfrac{dy}{dx}$ is u-shaped. So the values of x where $\dfrac{dy}{dx} > 0$

and where $\dfrac{2 + 3x^2}{3x - 1}$ is increasing are $x < \dfrac{1 - \sqrt{7}}{3}$ and $x > \dfrac{1 + \sqrt{7}}{3}$.

*The function y is undefined when $3x - 1 = 0$, i.e. $x = \dfrac{1}{3}$
(the graph has an asymptote), but this isn't in the range
where the function is increasing, so it doesn't affect the answer.*

7.7 More Differentiation

Exercise 7.7.1 — Differentiating cosec, sec and cot

Q1 **a)** $\dfrac{dy}{dx} = -2\cosec (2x)\cot (2x)$

b) $\dfrac{dy}{dx} = \dfrac{dy}{du} \times \dfrac{du}{dx} = (2\cosec x)(-\cosec x\cot x)$

$= -2\cosec^2 x\cot x$

c) $\dfrac{dy}{dx} = \dfrac{dy}{du} \times \dfrac{du}{dx} = -7\cosec^2 (7x)$

d) $\dfrac{dy}{dx} = \dfrac{dy}{du} \times \dfrac{du}{dx} = (7\cot^6 x)(-\cosec^2 x) = -7\cot^6 x\cosec^2 x$

e) $\dfrac{dy}{dx} = u\dfrac{dv}{dx} + v\dfrac{du}{dx} = [x^4 \times (-\cosec^2 x)] + [\cot x \times 4x^3]$

$= 4x^3\cot x - x^4\cosec^2 x$

$= x^3(4\cot x - x\cosec^2 x)$

f) $\dfrac{dy}{dx} = \dfrac{dy}{du} \times \dfrac{du}{dx} = 2(x + \sec x)(1 + \sec x\tan x)$

g) $\dfrac{dy}{dx} = \dfrac{dy}{du} \times \dfrac{du}{dx} = [-\cosec (x^2 + 5)\cot (x^2 + 5)] \times 2x$

$= -2x\cosec (x^2 + 5)\cot (x^2 + 5)$

h) $\dfrac{dy}{dx} = u\dfrac{dv}{dx} + v\dfrac{du}{dx} = [e^{3x} \times \sec x\tan x] + [\sec x \times 3e^{3x}]$

$= e^{3x}\sec x (\tan x + 3)$

i) $\dfrac{dy}{dx} = \dfrac{dy}{du} \times \dfrac{du}{dx} = 3(2x + \cot x)^2(2 - \cosec^2 x)$

Q2 **a)** $f'(x) = \dfrac{v\frac{du}{dx} - u\frac{dv}{dx}}{v^2} = \dfrac{(x + 3)\sec x\tan x - \sec x}{(x + 3)^2}$

b) $f'(x) = \dfrac{dy}{du} \times \dfrac{du}{dx} = \left(\sec \dfrac{1}{x}\tan \dfrac{1}{x}\right)\left(-\dfrac{1}{x^2}\right) = -\dfrac{\sec \frac{1}{x}\tan \frac{1}{x}}{x^2}$

c) $f'(x) = \dfrac{dy}{du} \times \dfrac{du}{dx} = (\sec \sqrt{x}\tan \sqrt{x})\left(\dfrac{1}{2} \times \dfrac{1}{\sqrt{x}}\right)$

$= \dfrac{\sec \sqrt{x}\tan \sqrt{x}}{2\sqrt{x}} = \dfrac{\tan \sqrt{x}}{2\sqrt{x}\cos \sqrt{x}}$

Q3 $f'(x) = \dfrac{dy}{du} \times \dfrac{du}{dx} = 2(\sec x + \cosec x)(\sec x\tan x - \cosec x\cot x)$

Q4 $f(x) = \dfrac{1}{x\cot x} = \dfrac{\tan x}{x}$

$f'(x) = \dfrac{v\frac{du}{dx} - u\frac{dv}{dx}}{v^2} = \dfrac{x\sec^2 x - \tan x}{x^2}$

Q5 $f'(x) = u\dfrac{dv}{dx} + v\dfrac{du}{dx}$

$= [e^x \times (-\cosec x\cot x)] + [\cosec x \times e^x] = e^x\cosec x (1 - \cot x)$

Q6 $f'(x) = u\dfrac{dv}{dx} + v\dfrac{du}{dx} = [e^{3x} \times (-4\cosec^2 4x)] + [\cot 4x \times 3e^{3x}]$

$= e^{3x}(3\cot 4x - 4\cosec^2 4x)$

*The chain rule was used here to differentiate $\cot 4x$
— use $y = \cot u$ and $u = 4x$.*

Q7 $f'(x) = u\dfrac{dv}{dx} + v\dfrac{du}{dx}$

$= [e^{-2x} \times (-4\cosec 4x\cot 4x)] + [\cosec 4x \times (-2)e^{-2x}]$

$= -2e^{-2x}\cosec 4x [2\cot 4x + 1]$

Q8 $f'(x) = u\dfrac{dv}{dx} + v\dfrac{du}{dx} = [\ln x \times (-\cosec x\cot x)] + \left[\cosec x \times \dfrac{1}{x}\right]$

$= \cosec x\left(\dfrac{1}{x} - \ln x\cot x\right)$

Q9 $f'(x) = \dfrac{dy}{du} \times \dfrac{du}{dx} = \left(\dfrac{1}{2} \times \dfrac{1}{\sqrt{\sec x}}\right) \times \sec x\tan x$

$= \dfrac{\sec x\tan x}{2\sqrt{\sec x}} = \dfrac{1}{2}\tan x\sqrt{\sec x}$

Q10 $f'(x) = g'(x)e^{g(x)} = e^{\sec x}\sec x\tan x$

Q11 **a)** $f'(x) = \dfrac{g'(x)}{g(x)} = \dfrac{-\cosec x\cot x}{\cosec x} = -\cot x$

b) $\ln (\cosec x) = \ln \left(\dfrac{1}{\sin x}\right) = \ln 1 - \ln (\sin x)$

$= -\ln (\sin x)$ (as $\ln 1 = 0$)

*Here you could also rearrange by saying
$\ln (1/\sin x) = \ln (\sin x)^{-1} = -\ln (\sin x)$.*

$f'(x) = \dfrac{g'(x)}{g(x)} = -\dfrac{\cos x}{\sin x} = -\dfrac{1}{\tan x} = -\cot x$

Q12 $f'(x) = \dfrac{g'(x)}{g(x)} = \dfrac{1 + \sec x\tan x}{x + \sec x}$

Q13 $\dfrac{dy}{dx} = \dfrac{dy}{du} \times \dfrac{du}{dx} = \sec \sqrt{x^2 + 5}\tan \sqrt{x^2 + 5} \times \dfrac{2x}{2\sqrt{x^2 + 5}}$

$= \dfrac{x\sec \sqrt{x^2 + 5}\tan \sqrt{x^2 + 5}}{\sqrt{x^2 + 5}}$

7.8 Connected Rates of Change

Exercise 7.8.1 — Connected rates of change

Q1 $\dfrac{dx}{dt} = -0.1$ (it's negative as the cube is shrinking),

and $V = x^3$, so $\dfrac{dV}{dx} = 3x^2$

$\dfrac{dV}{dt} = \dfrac{dV}{dx} \times \dfrac{dx}{dt} = -0.3x^2$ cm^3 min^{-1}

Q2 $V = 30x^3$ so $\dfrac{dV}{dx} = 90x^2$, and $\dfrac{dx}{d\theta} = 0.15$.

$\dfrac{dV}{d\theta} = \dfrac{dV}{dx} \times \dfrac{dx}{d\theta} = 13.5x^2$ cm^3 °C^{-1}

When $x = 3$, $\dfrac{dV}{d\theta} = 121.5$ cm^3 °C^{-1}

Q3 $A = 4\pi r^2$ so $\dfrac{dA}{dr} = 8\pi r$, and $\dfrac{dr}{dt} = -1.6$.

$\dfrac{dA}{dt} = \dfrac{dA}{dr} \times \dfrac{dr}{dt} = -12.8\pi r$ cm^2 h^{-1}

When $r = 5.5$ cm, $\dfrac{dA}{dt} = -221.17$ cm^2 h^{-1} (2 d.p.)

Q4 $\dfrac{dr}{d\theta} = 2 \times 10^{-2}$ mm °C$^{-1} = 2 \times 10^{-5}$ m °C^{-1},

and $V = \dfrac{4}{3}\pi r^3$ m^3, so $\dfrac{dV}{dr} = 4\pi r^2$ m^3 m^{-1}.

$\dfrac{dV}{d\theta} = \dfrac{dV}{dr} \times \dfrac{dr}{d\theta} = 8 \times 10^{-5}\pi r^2$ m^3 °C^{-1}

You could have converted to mm instead,
and given your answer in mm^3 °C^{-1}.

Q5 The surface area of the tank, $A = 2(\pi r^2) + 3r(2\pi r) = 8\pi r^2$,

so $\dfrac{dA}{dr} = 16\pi r$, and $\dfrac{dH}{dA} = -2$ (it's negative as heat is lost).

$\dfrac{dH}{dr} = \dfrac{dH}{dA} \times \dfrac{dA}{dr} = -32\pi r$ J cm^{-1}

When $r = 12.3$, $\dfrac{dH}{dr} = -1236.53$ J cm^{-1} (2 d.p.)

Q6 $\dfrac{dH}{dt} = -0.5$ mm h$^{-1} = -0.05$ cm h^{-1} (length is decreasing).

$V = \pi r^2 H$, so $\dfrac{dV}{dH} = \pi r^2$.

$\dfrac{dV}{dt} = \dfrac{dV}{dH} \times \dfrac{dH}{dt} = -0.05\pi r^2$ cm^3 h^{-1}

Q7 **a)** Using Pythagoras, the height of the triangle is

$\sqrt{x^2 - \left(\dfrac{x}{2}\right)^2} = \dfrac{\sqrt{3}x}{2}$, so the area of the end is

$A = \dfrac{1}{2}\left(\dfrac{\sqrt{3}x}{2}\right)x = \dfrac{\sqrt{3}x^2}{4}$.

b) $V = A \times 20 = 5\sqrt{3}\,x^2$, so $\dfrac{dV}{dx} = 10\sqrt{3}\,x$.

$\dfrac{dx}{dt} = 0.6$.

$\dfrac{dV}{dt} = \dfrac{dV}{dx} \times \dfrac{dx}{dt} = 6\sqrt{3}\,x$ mm^3 per day

c) $x = 0.5 \Rightarrow \dfrac{dV}{dt} = 3\sqrt{3} = 5.20$ mm^3 per day (2 d.p.)

Q8 **a)** n is directly proportional to D, so you can write this as
$n = kD$, where k is a constant.
Use the condition that when $D = 2$, $n = 208$:
$208 = 2k \Rightarrow k = 104$

$n = 104D \Rightarrow \dfrac{dn}{dD} = 104$

$D = 1 + 2^{\lambda t}$, so $\dfrac{dD}{dt} = \lambda 2^{\lambda t} \ln 2$.

Use the rule for differentiating a^x from earlier in the chapter.

So $\dfrac{dn}{dt} = \dfrac{dn}{dD} \times \dfrac{dD}{dt} = 104\lambda 2^{\lambda t} \ln 2$ per day.

b) If $t = 1$ day and $\lambda = 5$,

$\dfrac{dn}{dt} = 104 \times 5 \times 2^5 \times \ln 2 = 16640 \ln 2$
$= 1.15 \times 10^4$ per day (3 s.f.)

Q9 **a)** Volume of water $V = \pi r^2 h$, so $\dfrac{dV}{dh} = \pi r^2$.

$\dfrac{dV}{dt} = -0.3$.

It's negative because the volume of water remaining
is decreasing with time.

$\dfrac{dh}{dt} = \dfrac{dh}{dV} \times \dfrac{dV}{dt}$

$= \dfrac{1}{\dfrac{dV}{dh}} \times \dfrac{dV}{dt} = \dfrac{1}{\pi r^2} \times -0.3 = -\dfrac{3}{10\pi r^2}$ cm s^{-1}

b) $r = 6$, so $\dfrac{dh}{dt} = -\dfrac{1}{120\pi}$ cm s^{-1}.

So the water level falls at a constant rate
of $\dfrac{1}{120\pi}$ cm s^{-1} and $\dfrac{1}{2\pi} = 0.159$ cm min^{-1} (3 s.f.)

You don't actually need to use h in the calculation.

Q10 **a)** $\dfrac{dV}{d\theta} = k$, $V = \dfrac{2}{3}\pi r^3$, so $\dfrac{dV}{dr} = 2\pi r^2$.

$\dfrac{dr}{d\theta} = \dfrac{dr}{dV} \times \dfrac{dV}{d\theta} = \dfrac{1}{\dfrac{dV}{dr}} \times \dfrac{dV}{d\theta} = \dfrac{1}{2\pi r^2} \times k = \dfrac{k}{2\pi r^2}$ cm °C^{-1}

b) $V = 4$, so $r = \sqrt[3]{\dfrac{6}{\pi}} = 1.240...$, and $k = 1.5$.

So $\dfrac{dr}{d\theta} = \dfrac{1.5}{2\pi(1.240...)^2} = 0.155$ cm °C^{-1} (3 s.f.)

7.9 Differentiation with Parametric Equations

Exercise 7.9.1 — Differentiating parametric equations

Q1 **a)** $\dfrac{dx}{dt} = 2t$, $\dfrac{dy}{dt} = 3t^2 - 1$.
Using the chain rule, $\dfrac{dy}{dx} = \dfrac{dy}{dt} \div \dfrac{dx}{dt}$ so $\dfrac{dy}{dx} = \dfrac{3t^2 - 1}{2t}$

b) $\dfrac{dx}{dt} = 3t^2 + 1$, $\dfrac{dy}{dt} = 4t$, so $\dfrac{dy}{dx} = \dfrac{4t}{3t^2 + 1}$

c) $\dfrac{dx}{dt} = 4t^2$, $\dfrac{dy}{dt} = 3t^2 - 2t$, so $\dfrac{dy}{dx} = \dfrac{3t^2 - 2t}{4t^3} = \dfrac{3t - 2}{4t^2}$

d) $\dfrac{dx}{dt} = -\sin t$, $\dfrac{dy}{dt} = 4 - 2t$, so $\dfrac{dy}{dx} = \dfrac{2t - 4}{\sin t}$

Q2 **a)** $\dfrac{dx}{dt} = 2t$, $\dfrac{dy}{dt} = 2e^{2t}$, so $\dfrac{dy}{dx} = \dfrac{e^{2t}}{t}$

b) When $t = 1$, $\dfrac{dy}{dx} = e^2$.

Q3 **a)** $\dfrac{dy}{dt} = 12t^2 - 4t$, $\dfrac{dx}{dt} = 3e^{3t}$, so $\dfrac{dy}{dx} = \dfrac{12t^2 - 4t}{3e^{3t}}$

b) When $t = 0$, $\dfrac{dy}{dx} = 0$.

Q4 **a)** $\dfrac{dx}{dt} = 3t^2$, $\dfrac{dy}{dt} = 2t\cos t - t^2\sin t$,

so $\dfrac{dy}{dx} = \dfrac{2t\cos t - t^2\sin t}{3t^2} = \dfrac{2\cos t - t\sin t}{3t}$

b) When $t = \pi$, $\dfrac{dy}{dx} = -\dfrac{2}{3\pi}$

Q5 **a)** $\dfrac{dx}{dt} = 2t\sin t + t^2\cos t$,

$\dfrac{dy}{dt} = t^3\cos t + 3t^2\sin t - \sin t$,

so $\dfrac{dy}{dx} = \dfrac{t^3\cos t + (3t^2 - 1)\sin t}{2t\sin t + t^2\cos t}$

b) When $t = \pi$, $\dfrac{dy}{dx} = \pi$.

Q6 **a)** $\dfrac{dx}{dt} = \dfrac{1}{t}$, $\dfrac{dy}{dt} = 6t - 3t^3$, so $\dfrac{dy}{dx} = 6t^2 - 3t^3$

b) When $t = -1$, $\dfrac{dy}{dx} = 9$.

c) At the stationary points $6t^2 - 3t^3 = 3t^2(2 - t) = 0$,
so the stationary points occur at $t = 0$ and $t = 2$.
At $t = 0$, x is not defined.
At $t = 2$, the coordinates are ($\ln 2$, 4).

Q7 a) $\frac{dx}{dt} = 2t$, $\frac{dy}{dt} = 9t^2 - 4$, so $\frac{dy}{dx} = \frac{9t^2 - 4}{2t}$

b) At the stationary points $\frac{9t^2 - 4}{2t} = 0$

$\Rightarrow 9t^2 - 4 = 0 \Rightarrow t^2 = \frac{4}{9} \Rightarrow t = -\frac{2}{3}$ or $\frac{2}{3}$

$x = t^2 = \frac{4}{9}$

At $t = -\frac{2}{3}$, $y = 3\left(-\frac{2}{3}\right)^3 - 4\left(-\frac{2}{3}\right) = \frac{16}{9}$

At $t = \frac{2}{3}$, $y = 3\left(\frac{2}{3}\right)^3 - 4\left(\frac{2}{3}\right) = -\frac{16}{9}$

The stationary points are $\left(\frac{4}{9}, -\frac{16}{9}\right)$ and $\left(\frac{4}{9}, \frac{16}{9}\right)$.

Exercise 7.9.2 — Finding tangents and normals

Q1 $\frac{dx}{dt} = 2t$, $\frac{dy}{dt} = 3t^2 - 6$.

Using the chain rule, $\frac{dy}{dx} = \frac{dy}{dt} \div \frac{dx}{dt}$, so $\frac{dy}{dx} = \frac{3t^2 - 6}{2t}$.

When $t = 3$: $\frac{dy}{dx} = \frac{21}{6} = \frac{7}{2}$, $x = 3^2 = 9$ and $y = 3^3 - 6(3) = 9$.

Putting this into $y = mx + c$ gives: $9 = \frac{7}{2}(9) + c \Rightarrow c = -\frac{45}{2}$

So the equation of the tangent is:

$y = \frac{7}{2}x - \frac{45}{2} \Rightarrow 7x - 2y - 45 = 0$.

Q2 $\frac{dy}{dx} = \frac{3t^2 - 2t + 5}{3t^2 - 4t}$

When $t = -1$: $\frac{dy}{dx} = \frac{10}{7}$, $x = -3$ and $y = -7$.

Putting this into $y = mx + c$ gives: $-7 = \frac{10}{7}(-3) + c \Rightarrow c = -\frac{19}{7}$

So the equation of the tangent is $10x - 7y - 19 = 0$.

Q3 $\frac{dy}{dx} = \frac{3\cos t - t \sin t}{2 \cos 2t}$

When $t = \pi$: $\frac{dy}{dx} = -\frac{3}{2}$, $x = 0$ and $y = -\pi$.

The gradient of the normal is $\frac{2}{3}$.

Putting this into $y = mx + c$ gives: $-\pi = \frac{2}{3}(0) + c \Rightarrow c = -\pi$

So the equation of the normal is $y = \frac{2}{3}x - \pi$.

Q4 $\frac{dy}{dx} = \frac{3t^2 - 2t}{1 + \ln t}$

When $t = 1$: $\frac{dy}{dx} = \frac{3 - 2}{1 + 0} = 1$, $x = 0$ and $y = 3$.

Putting this into $y = mx + c$ gives: $3 = 0 + c \Rightarrow c = 3$

So the equation of the tangent is: $y = x + 3$

Q5 $\frac{dy}{dx} = \frac{2\theta + \cos \theta - \theta \sin \theta}{\sin 2\theta + 2\theta \cos 2\theta}$

When $\theta = \frac{\pi}{2}$: $\frac{dy}{dx} = -\frac{1}{2}$, $x = 0$ and $y = \frac{\pi^2}{4}$.

The gradient of the normal is 2.

Putting this into $y = mx + c$ gives: $\frac{\pi^2}{4} = 2(0) + c \Rightarrow c = \frac{\pi^2}{4}$

So the equation of the normal is $y = 2x + \frac{\pi^2}{4}$.

Q6 a) $\frac{dy}{dx} = \frac{3 - 3t^2}{2t - 1}$

When $t = 2$, $\frac{dy}{dx} = -3$, $x = 2$ and $y = -2$.

Putting this into $y = mx + c$ gives: $-2 = -3(2) + c \Rightarrow c = 4$

So the equation of the tangent is $y = 4 - 3x$.

b) The gradient of the normal at $t = 2$ is $\frac{1}{3}$.

Putting this into $y = mx + c$ gives: $-2 = \frac{1}{3}(2) + c \Rightarrow c = -\frac{8}{3}$

So the equation of the normal is $3y = x - 8$.

This crosses the x-axis at $y = 0$, so $0 = x - 8$

$\Rightarrow x = 8$ and so the coordinates are $(8, 0)$.

Q7 a) $\frac{dy}{dx} = \frac{\theta \cos \theta + \sin \theta}{2 \cos 2\theta - 2 \sin \theta}$

b) When $\theta = \frac{\pi}{2}$: $\frac{dy}{dx} = -\frac{1}{4}$, $x = 0$ and $y = \frac{\pi}{2}$.

Putting this into $y = mx + c$ gives: $\frac{\pi}{2} = -\frac{1}{4}(0) + c \Rightarrow c = \frac{\pi}{2}$

So the equation of the tangent is $y = \frac{\pi}{2} - \frac{1}{4}x$.

The gradient of the normal is 4. The normal also goes

through the point $\left(0, \frac{\pi}{2}\right)$, so again $c = \frac{\pi}{2}$.

So the equation of the normal is $y = 4x + \frac{\pi}{2}$.

Q8 a) The path cuts the y-axis when $x = 0$, so $s^3 \ln s = 0$. Since $\ln 0$ is undefined, $s = 0$ cannot be a solution, so the only solution is $s = 1$ (i.e. when $\ln s = 0$).

b) $\frac{dy}{dx} = \frac{3s^2 - s - 2s \ln s}{s^2 + 3s^2 \ln s} = \frac{3s - 1 - 2 \ln s}{s + 3s \ln s}$.

From a), when $x = 0$, $s = 1$.

When $s = 1$: $\frac{dy}{dx} = 2$, $x = 0$ and $y = 1$.

Putting this into $y = mx + c$ gives: $1 = 2(0) + c \Rightarrow c = 1$.

So the equation of the tangent is $y = 2x + 1$.

Q9 a) Using the quotient rule, $\frac{dy}{d\theta} = \frac{-\theta^3 \sin \theta - 3\theta^2 \cos \theta}{\theta^6}$

$= \frac{-\theta \sin \theta - 3 \cos \theta}{\theta^4}$

$\frac{dx}{d\theta} = \theta^2 \cos \theta + 2\theta \sin \theta$

Hence $\frac{dy}{dx} = \frac{-\theta \sin \theta - 3 \cos \theta}{\theta^6 \cos \theta + 2\theta^5 \sin \theta}$

This looks a bit complicated but leave it as it is — you'll find the cos and sin terms usually disappear when you substitute.

When $\theta = \pi$, $\frac{dy}{dx} = \frac{-\pi(0) - 3(-1)}{\pi^6(-1) + 2\pi^5(0)} = -\frac{3}{\pi^6}$.

b) The gradient of the normal when $\theta = \pi$ is $\frac{\pi^6}{3}$,

and $y = -\frac{1}{\pi^3}$, $x = 0$.

Putting this into $y = mx + c$ gives:

$-\frac{1}{\pi^3} = \frac{\pi^6}{3}(0) + c \Rightarrow c = -\frac{1}{\pi^3}$

So the equation of the normal is $y = \frac{\pi^6}{3}x - \frac{1}{\pi^3}$.

Q10 a) Use the quotient rule to find $\frac{dx}{d\theta}$:

$\frac{dx}{d\theta} = \frac{\theta^2 \cos \theta - 2\theta \sin \theta}{\theta^4} = \frac{\theta \cos \theta - 2 \sin \theta}{\theta^3}$

And $\frac{dy}{d\theta} = -2\theta \sin 2\theta + \cos 2\theta$

So $\frac{dy}{dx} = \frac{dy}{d\theta} \times \frac{1}{\left(\frac{dx}{d\theta}\right)}$

$= (-2\theta \sin 2\theta + \cos 2\theta) \times \frac{\theta^3}{\theta \cos \theta - 2 \sin \theta}$

$= \frac{\theta^3(-2\theta \sin 2\theta + \cos 2\theta)}{\theta \cos \theta - 2 \sin \theta}$

When $\theta = \frac{\pi}{2}$, $\frac{dy}{dx} = \frac{\left(\frac{\pi}{2}\right)^3 \left(-2\left(\frac{\pi}{2}\right)(0) - 1\right)}{\left(\frac{\pi}{2}\right)(0) - 2(1)} = \frac{\pi^3}{16}$

b) When $\theta = \frac{\pi}{2}$, $x = \frac{4}{\pi^2}$ and $y = -\frac{\pi}{2}$

The tangent to the curve has a gradient of $\frac{\pi^3}{16}$ and an equation in the form $y = mx + c$.

So substitute in the values of x, y and m to find c:

$-\frac{\pi}{2} = \frac{\pi^3}{16} \times \frac{4}{\pi^2} + c = \frac{\pi}{4} + c \Rightarrow c = -\frac{3\pi}{4}$

So the tangent has the equation

$y = \frac{\pi^3}{16}x - \frac{3\pi}{4}$.

c) At the x-axis, $y = 0$, so $0 = \theta \cos 2\theta$

$\Rightarrow \theta = 0$ (ignore this result, since $\theta > 0$), or

$\cos 2\theta = 0 \Rightarrow \theta = \frac{\pi}{4}, \frac{3\pi}{4}, \frac{5\pi}{4}$... etc.

The solution with $0 < \theta \le \frac{\pi}{2}$ is $\theta = \frac{\pi}{4}$.

When $\theta = \frac{\pi}{4}$, $x = \frac{\sqrt{2}}{2} \div \frac{\pi^2}{16} = \frac{8\sqrt{2}}{\pi^2}$, so the coordinates of the

first point where the curve cuts the x-axis are $\left(\frac{8\sqrt{2}}{\pi^2}, 0\right)$.

7.10 Implicit Differentiation

Exercise 7.10.1 — Implicit differentiation

Q1 a) $\frac{d}{dx}(y) + \frac{d}{dx}(y^3) = \frac{d}{dx}(x^2) + \frac{d}{dx}(4)$

$\frac{dy}{dx} + 3y^2 \frac{dy}{dx} = 2x + 0$

$(1 + 3y^2)\frac{dy}{dx} = 2x \Rightarrow \frac{dy}{dx} = \frac{2x}{1 + 3y^2}$

b) $2x + 2y\frac{dy}{dx} = 2 + 2\frac{dy}{dx}$

$(2y - 2)\frac{dy}{dx} = 2 - 2x \Rightarrow \frac{dy}{dx} = \frac{2 - 2x}{2y - 2} = \frac{1 - x}{y - 1}$

c) $9x^2 - 4\frac{dy}{dx} = 2y\frac{dy}{dx} + 1$

$9x^2 - 1 = (2y + 4)\frac{dy}{dx} \Rightarrow \frac{dy}{dx} = \frac{9x^2 - 1}{2y + 4}$

d) $5 - 2y\frac{dy}{dx} = 5x^4 - 6\frac{dy}{dx}$

$5 - 5x^4 = (2y - 6)\frac{dy}{dx} \Rightarrow \frac{dy}{dx} = \frac{5 - 5x^4}{2y - 6}$

e) $-\sin x + \cos y\frac{dy}{dx} = 2x + 3y^2\frac{dy}{dx}$

$(\cos y - 3y^2)\frac{dy}{dx} = 2x + \sin x \Rightarrow \frac{dy}{dx} = \frac{2x + \sin x}{\cos y - 3y^2}$

f) $3x^2y^2 + 2x^3y\frac{dy}{dx} - \sin x = 4y + 4x\frac{dy}{dx}$

$(2x^3y - 4x)\frac{dy}{dx} = 4y - 3x^2y^2 + \sin x$

$\Rightarrow \frac{dy}{dx} = \frac{4y - 3x^2y^2 + \sin x}{2x^3y - 4x}$

g) $e^x + e^y\frac{dy}{dx} = 3x^2 - \frac{dy}{dx}$

$(e^y + 1)\frac{dy}{dx} = 3x^2 - e^x \Rightarrow \frac{dy}{dx} = \frac{3x^2 - e^x}{e^y + 1}$

h) $3y^2 + 6xy\frac{dy}{dx} + 4xy + 2x^2\frac{dy}{dx} = 3x^2 + 4$

$(6xy + 2x^2)\frac{dy}{dx} = 3x^2 + 4 - 3y^2 - 4xy$

$\Rightarrow \frac{dy}{dx} = \frac{3x^2 + 4 - 3y^2 - 4xy}{6xy + 2x^2}$

i) $12x^2y^2 + 8x^3y\frac{dy}{dx} + 6xy + 3x^2\frac{dy}{dx} = 2\cos x - 4x^3$

$\frac{dy}{dx}(8x^3y + 3x^2) = 2\cos x - 4x^3 - 12x^2y^2 - 6xy$

$\Rightarrow \frac{dy}{dx} = \frac{2\cos x - 4x^3 - 12x^2y^2 - 6xy}{8x^3y + 3x^2}$

Q2 a) $3x^2 + 2y + 2x\frac{dy}{dx} = 4y^3\frac{dy}{dx}$

$(4y^3 - 2x)\frac{dy}{dx} = 3x^2 + 2y \Rightarrow \frac{dy}{dx} = \frac{3x^2 + 2y}{4y^3 - 2x}$

b) $2xy + x^2\frac{dy}{dx} + 2y\frac{dy}{dx} = 3x^2$

$(x^2 + 2y)\frac{dy}{dx} = 3x^2 - 2xy \Rightarrow \frac{dy}{dx} = \frac{3x^2 - 2xy}{x^2 + 2y}$

c) $y^3 + 3xy^2\frac{dy}{dx} + \frac{dy}{dx} = \cos x$

$(3xy^2 + 1)\frac{dy}{dx} = \cos x - y^3 \Rightarrow \frac{dy}{dx} = \frac{\cos x - y^3}{3xy^2 + 1}$

d) $-y\sin x + \cos x\frac{dy}{dx} + \sin y + x\cos y\frac{dy}{dx} = y + x\frac{dy}{dx}$

$(\cos x + x\cos y - x)\frac{dy}{dx} = y + y\sin x - \sin y$

$\Rightarrow \frac{dy}{dx} = \frac{y + y\sin x - \sin y}{\cos x + x\cos y - x}$

e) $e^x + e^y\frac{dy}{dx} = y + x\frac{dy}{dx}$

$(e^y - x)\frac{dy}{dx} = y - e^x \Rightarrow \frac{dy}{dx} = \frac{y - e^x}{e^y - x}$

f) $\frac{1}{x} + 2x = 3y^2\frac{dy}{dx} + \frac{dy}{dx}$

$(3y^2 + 1)\frac{dy}{dx} = \frac{1}{x} + 2x \Rightarrow \frac{dy}{dx} = \frac{\frac{1}{x} + 2x}{3y^2 + 1} = \frac{1 + 2x^2}{3xy^2 + x}$

g) $2e^{2x} + 3e^{3y}\frac{dy}{dx} = 6xy^2 + 6x^2y\frac{dy}{dx}$

$(3e^{3y} - 6x^2y)\frac{dy}{dx} = 6xy^2 - 2e^{2x} \Rightarrow \frac{dy}{dx} = \frac{6xy^2 - 2e^{2x}}{3e^{3y} - 6x^2y}$

h) $\ln x + 1 + \frac{y}{x} + \ln x\frac{dy}{dx} = 5x^4 + 3y^2\frac{dy}{dx}$

$(\ln x - 3y^2)\frac{dy}{dx} = 5x^4 - \ln x - 1 - \frac{y}{x}$

$\Rightarrow \frac{dy}{dx} = \frac{5x^4 - \ln x - 1 - \frac{y}{x}}{\ln x - 3y^2} = \frac{5x^5 - x\ln x - x - y}{x\ln x - 3xy^2}$

Q3 a) At $(0, 1)$: LHS: $e^0 + 2\ln 1 = 1$
RHS: $1^3 = 1$
So $(0, 1)$ is a point on the curve.

b) $e^x + \frac{2}{y}\frac{dy}{dx} = 3y^2\frac{dy}{dx} \Rightarrow \frac{dy}{dx} = \frac{e^x}{3y^2 - \frac{2}{y}} = \frac{ye^x}{3y^3 - 2}$.

At $(0, 1)$ the gradient is $\frac{1e^0}{3(1^3) - 2} = 1$

Q4 a) $3x^2 + 2y\frac{dy}{dx} - 2y - 2x\frac{dy}{dx} = 0 \Rightarrow \frac{dy}{dx} = \frac{2y - 3x^2}{2y - 2x}$

b) Putting $x = -2$ into the equation gives: $-8 + y^2 + 4y = 0$
Complete the square to solve...
$(y + 2)^2 - 4 - 8 = 0 \Rightarrow y + 2 = \pm\sqrt{12} = \pm2\sqrt{3}$
so $y = -2 \pm 2\sqrt{3}$

c) At $(-2, -2 + 2\sqrt{3})$:

$\frac{dy}{dx} = \frac{(-4 + 4\sqrt{3}) - 3(-2)^2}{(-4 + 4\sqrt{3}) - 2(-2)} = \frac{-16 + 4\sqrt{3}}{4\sqrt{3}} = \frac{\sqrt{3} - 4}{\sqrt{3}}$

Rationalise the denominator: $= \frac{3 - 4\sqrt{3}}{3} = 1 - \frac{4}{3}\sqrt{3}$

Q5 a) Putting $x = 1$ into the equation gives:
$1 - y = 2y^2 \Rightarrow 2y^2 + y - 1 = 0 \Rightarrow (2y - 1)(y + 1) = 0$
So $y = -1$ (given as the other point) and $y = \frac{1}{2}$. So $a = \frac{1}{2}$.

b) $3x^2 - y - x\frac{dy}{dx} = 4y\frac{dy}{dx}$

$\frac{dy}{dx} = \frac{3x^2 - y}{4y + x}$

At $(1, -1)$, $\frac{dy}{dx} = \frac{3(1^2) - (-1)}{4(-1) + 1} = -\frac{4}{3}$

At $\left(1, \frac{1}{2}\right)$, $\frac{dy}{dx} = \frac{3(1^2) - \left(\frac{1}{2}\right)}{4\left(\frac{1}{2}\right) + 1} = \frac{5}{6}$

Q6 a) Putting $x = 1$ into the equation gives:
$y + y^2 - y - 4 = 0 \Rightarrow y^2 - 4 = 0$
so it cuts the curve at $y = 2$ and $y = -2$.

b) $2xy + x^2\frac{dy}{dx} + y^2 + 2xy\frac{dy}{dx} = y + x\frac{dy}{dx} + 0$

$(x^2 + 2xy - x)\frac{dy}{dx} = y - 2xy - y^2$

$\frac{dy}{dx} = \frac{y - 2xy - y^2}{x^2 + 2xy - x}$

At $(1, 2)$, $\frac{dy}{dx} = \frac{2 - 2(1)(2) - 2^2}{1^2 + 2(1)(2) - 1} = -\frac{3}{2}$

At $(1, -2)$, $\frac{dy}{dx} = \frac{(-2) - 2(1)(-2) - (-2)^2}{1^2 + 2(1)(-2) - 1} = \frac{1}{2}$

Exercise 7.10.2 — Applications of implicit differentiation

Q1 a) Differentiating:
$2x + 2 + 3\frac{dy}{dx} - 2y\frac{dy}{dx} = 0 \Rightarrow \frac{dy}{dx} = \frac{2x + 2}{2y - 3}$.
At the stationary points, $\frac{dy}{dx} = 0$, so:
$2x + 2 = 0 \Rightarrow x = -1$
When $x = -1$, $y^2 - 3y + 1 = 0$
$\Rightarrow y = \frac{3 \pm \sqrt{5}}{2} = 2.62$ or 0.38 (2 d.p.)
So there are 2 stationary points with coordinates
$(-1, 2.62)$ and $(-1, 0.38)$.

b) Putting $x = 0$ into the equation gives:
$3y - y^2 = 0 \Rightarrow y(3 - y) = 0 \Rightarrow y = 0$ and $y = 3$
At $(0, 0)$, $\frac{dy}{dx} = \frac{2(0) + 2}{2(0) - 3} = -\frac{2}{3}$
The y-intercept is 0 (as it goes through $(0, 0)$).
So the equation of the tangent is $y = -\frac{2}{3}x$ or $3y = -2x$.
At $(0, 3)$, $\frac{dy}{dx} = \frac{2(0) + 2}{2(3) - 3} = \frac{2}{3}$
The y-intercept is 3 (as it goes through $(0, 3)$).
Putting this into $y = mx + c$ gives
the equation of the tangent as $y = \frac{2}{3}x + 3$.

Q2 **a)** Differentiating:

$3x^2 + 2x + \dfrac{dy}{dx} = 2y\dfrac{dy}{dx} \implies \dfrac{dy}{dx} = \dfrac{3x^2 + 2x}{2y - 1}$.

At the stationary points, $\dfrac{dy}{dx} = 0$, so:

$3x^2 + 2x = 0 \implies x(3x + 2) = 0 \implies x = 0$ and $x = -\dfrac{2}{3}$

When $x = 0$, $y = y^2 \implies y(y - 1) = 0 \implies y = 0$ and $y = 1$.

When $x = -\dfrac{2}{3}$, $-\dfrac{8}{27} + \dfrac{4}{9} + y = y^2$

$\implies \dfrac{4}{27} + y = y^2 \implies 27y^2 - 27y - 4 = 0$

This has solutions $y = 1.13$ and -0.13 (2 d.p.)
So there are 4 stationary points with coordinates
$(0, 0)$, $(0, 1)$, $\left(-\dfrac{2}{3}, 1.13\right)$ and $\left(-\dfrac{2}{3}, -0.13\right)$.

b) Putting $x = 2$ into the equation gives:
$8 + 4 + y = y^2 \implies y^2 - y - 12 = 0$
$\implies (y - 4)(y + 3) = 0 \implies y = 4$ and $y = -3$

At $(2, 4)$, $\dfrac{dy}{dx} = \dfrac{3(2^2) + 2(2)}{2(4) - 1} = \dfrac{16}{7}$

Putting this into $y = mx + c$ gives:
$4 = \dfrac{16}{7}(2) + c \implies c = -\dfrac{4}{7}$

So the equation of the tangent is
$y = \dfrac{16}{7}x - \dfrac{4}{7}$ or $16x - 7y - 4 = 0$.

At $(2, -3)$, $\dfrac{dy}{dx} = \dfrac{3(2^2) + 2(2)}{2(-3) - 1} = -\dfrac{16}{7}$

Putting this into $y = mx + c$ gives:
$-3 = -\dfrac{16}{7}(2) + c \implies c = \dfrac{11}{7}$

So the equation of the tangent is $y = \dfrac{11}{7} - \dfrac{16}{7}x$
or $16x + 7y - 11 = 0$.

Q3 **a)** Putting $y = 1$ into the equation gives:
$x^2 + 1 = x + 7 \implies x^2 - x - 6 = 0$
$\implies (x - 3)(x + 2) = 0 \implies x = 3$ and $x = -2$.
Differentiating:

$2xy + x^2\dfrac{dy}{dx} + 3y^2\dfrac{dy}{dx} = 1 \implies \dfrac{dy}{dx} = \dfrac{1 - 2xy}{x^2 + 3y^2}$

At $(-2, 1)$, $\dfrac{dy}{dx} = \dfrac{1 - 2(-2)(1)}{(-2)^2 + 3(1^2)} = \dfrac{5}{7}$

so the gradient of the normal is $-\dfrac{7}{5}$.
Putting this into $y = mx + c$ gives:
$1 = -\dfrac{7}{5}(-2) + c \implies c = -\dfrac{9}{5}$

and so the equation of the normal is $y = -\dfrac{7}{5}x - \dfrac{9}{5}$
or $7x + 5y + 9 = 0$.

At $(3, 1)$, $\dfrac{dy}{dx} = \dfrac{1 - 2(3)(1)}{(3)^2 + 3(1^2)} = -\dfrac{5}{12}$

so the gradient of the normal is $\dfrac{12}{5}$.
Putting this into $y = mx + c$ gives:
$1 = \dfrac{12}{5}(3) + c \implies c = -\dfrac{31}{5}$

so the equation of the normal is $y = \dfrac{12}{5}x - \dfrac{31}{5}$
or $12x - 5y - 31 = 0$.

b) The normals intersect when:
$-7x - 9 = 12x - 31 \implies 22 = 19x \implies x = \dfrac{22}{19}$

And so $5y = \dfrac{264}{19} - 31 = -\dfrac{325}{19} \implies y = -\dfrac{65}{19}$

So they intersect at $\left(\dfrac{22}{19}, -\dfrac{65}{19}\right)$.

Q4 **a)** Putting $x = 0$ into the equation gives:
$1 + y^2 = 5 - 3y \implies y^2 + 3y - 4 = 0$
$\implies (y + 4)(y - 1) = 0 \implies y = -4$ and $y = 1$.
So $a = -4$ and $b = 1$ ($a < b$).
Differentiating:

$e^x + 2y\dfrac{dy}{dx} - y - x\dfrac{dy}{dx} = -3\dfrac{dy}{dx} \implies \dfrac{dy}{dx} = \dfrac{y - e^x}{2y - x + 3}$

At $(0, 1)$, $\dfrac{dy}{dx} = \dfrac{1 - e^0}{2(1) - 0 + 3} = 0$ so this is a stationary point.

b) At $(0, -4)$, $\dfrac{dy}{dx} = \dfrac{(-4) - e^0}{2(-4) - 0 + 3} = 1$.

So the gradient of the tangent is 1 and the gradient of the normal is -1.
$-4 = 0 + c$ (so $c = -4$) for both, since $x = 0$,
so the equation of the tangent is $y = x - 4$
and the equation of the normal is $y = -x - 4$.

Q5 $y = \arccos x \implies \cos y = x$
Differentiating:

$-\sin y\dfrac{dy}{dx} = 1 \implies \dfrac{dy}{dx} = -\dfrac{1}{\sin y} = -\dfrac{1}{\sqrt{\sin^2 y}} = -\dfrac{1}{\sqrt{1 - \cos^2 y}}$

Using $\cos y = x$: $\dfrac{dy}{dx} = -\dfrac{1}{\sqrt{1 - x^2}}$

Q6 $y = \arctan x \implies \tan y = x$
Differentiating:

$\sec^2 y\dfrac{dy}{dx} = 1 \implies \dfrac{dy}{dx} = \dfrac{1}{\sec^2 y}$

Using the identity $\sec^2 y \equiv 1 + \tan^2 y$:
$\dfrac{dy}{dx} = \dfrac{1}{1 + \tan^2 y}$

Using $\tan y = x$: $\dfrac{dy}{dx} = \dfrac{1}{1 + x^2}$ as required.

Q7 **a)** When $x = 1$:
$0 + y^2 = y + 6 \implies y^2 - y - 6 = 0$
$\implies (y - 3)(y + 2) = 0 \implies y = 3$ and $y = -2$.
So the curve passes through $(1, 3)$ and $(1, -2)$.

b) Differentiating:

$\dfrac{1}{x} + 2y\dfrac{dy}{dx} = 2xy + x^2\dfrac{dy}{dx}$

$\dfrac{dy}{dx} = \dfrac{2xy - \dfrac{1}{x}}{2y - x^2} = \dfrac{2x^2 y - 1}{2xy - x^3}$

At $(1, 3)$, $\dfrac{dy}{dx} = \dfrac{2(1^2)(3) - 1}{2(1)(3) - (1)^3} = 1$

so the gradient of the normal is -1.
Putting this into $y = mx + c$ gives:
$3 = -1(1) + c \implies c = 4$
so the equation of the normal is $y = 4 - x$.

At $(1, -2)$, $\dfrac{dy}{dx} = \dfrac{2(1^2)(-2) - 1}{2(1)(-2) - (1)^3} = 1$,

so the gradient of the normal is also -1.
$-2 = -1(1) + c \implies c = -1$
so the equation of the normal is $y = -x - 1$.
Because the gradients are the same,
these lines are parallel and can never intersect.

Q8 When $y = 0$:
$1 + x^2 = 0 + 4x \implies x^2 - 4x + 1 = 0$
Complete the square to solve...
$(x - 2)^2 - 4 + 1 = 0 \implies x - 2 = \pm\sqrt{3} \implies x = 2 \pm \sqrt{3}$
So $a = 2 + \sqrt{3}$ and $b = 2 - \sqrt{3}$.
Differentiating:

$e^y\dfrac{dy}{dx} + 2x = 3y^2\dfrac{dy}{dx} + 4 \implies \dfrac{dy}{dx} = \dfrac{2x - 4}{3y^2 - e^y}$

At $(2 + \sqrt{3}, 0)$, $\dfrac{dy}{dx} = \dfrac{4 + 2\sqrt{3} - 4}{3(0) - e^0} = -2\sqrt{3}$

$0 = -2\sqrt{3}(2 + \sqrt{3}) + c \implies c = 4\sqrt{3} + 6$
So the tangent at this point is $y = 4\sqrt{3} + 6 - 2\sqrt{3}x$.

At $(2 - \sqrt{3}, 0)$, $\dfrac{dy}{dx} = \dfrac{4 - 2\sqrt{3} - 4}{3(0) - e^0} = 2\sqrt{3}$

$0 = 2\sqrt{3}(2 - \sqrt{3}) + c \implies c = 6 - 4\sqrt{3}$
So the tangent at this point is $y = 2\sqrt{3}x + 6 - 4\sqrt{3}$.

Q9 Differentiating:

$\ln x\dfrac{dy}{dx} + \dfrac{y}{x} + 2x = 2y\dfrac{dy}{dx} - \dfrac{dy}{dx}$

$\dfrac{dy}{dx} = \dfrac{\dfrac{y}{x} + 2x}{2y - \ln x - 1} = \dfrac{y + 2x^2}{2xy - x\ln x - x}$

$y + 2x^2 = 0 \implies \dfrac{dy}{dx} = \dfrac{y + 2x^2}{2xy - x\ln x - x} = 0$

So if a point on the curve satisfies $y + 2x^2 = 0$,
then it's a stationary point.

Q10 Use the chain rule to find $f'(x)$:
$y = \arccos u$, $u = x^2$

$\dfrac{dy}{dx} = \dfrac{dy}{du} \times \dfrac{du}{dx} = -\dfrac{1}{\sqrt{1 - u^2}} \times 2x = -\dfrac{2x}{\sqrt{1 - x^4}}$

When $x = \dfrac{1}{\sqrt{2}}$, $y = \arccos x^2 = \arccos\dfrac{1}{2} = \dfrac{\pi}{3}$
This is the only solution for y in the given interval.

$$\frac{dy}{dx} = -\frac{2\left(\frac{1}{\sqrt{2}}\right)}{\sqrt{1-\left(\frac{1}{\sqrt{2}}\right)^4}} = -\frac{\frac{2}{\sqrt{2}}}{\sqrt{1-\frac{1}{(\sqrt{2})^4}}} = -\frac{\sqrt{2}}{\sqrt{1-\frac{1}{4}}}$$

$$= -\frac{\sqrt{2}}{\sqrt{\frac{3}{4}}} = -\frac{\sqrt{2}}{\frac{\sqrt{3}}{2}} = -\frac{2\sqrt{2}}{\sqrt{3}}$$

Rationalising the denominator:

$$= -\frac{2\sqrt{2} \times \sqrt{3}}{\sqrt{3} \times \sqrt{3}} = -\frac{2\sqrt{6}}{3}$$

So the tangent has a gradient of $-\frac{2\sqrt{6}}{3}$ and passes through the point $\left(\frac{1}{\sqrt{2}}, \frac{\pi}{3}\right)$.

$$y = mx + c \implies \frac{\pi}{3} = -\frac{2\sqrt{6}}{3} \times \frac{1}{\sqrt{2}} + c$$

$$c = \frac{\pi}{3} + \frac{2\sqrt{3}}{3} = \frac{\pi + 2\sqrt{3}}{3}$$

So the equation of the tangent is

$$y = -\frac{2\sqrt{6}}{3}x + \frac{\pi + 2\sqrt{3}}{3}$$

Q11 a) Differentiating:

$$2e^{2y}\frac{dy}{dx} + e^x = 2x\frac{dy}{dx} + 2y$$

$$\frac{dy}{dx} = \frac{2y - e^x}{2e^{2y} - 2x}$$

When $y = 0$:

$$1 + e^x - e^4 = 1 \implies e^x = e^4 \implies x = 4$$

$$\frac{dy}{dx} = \frac{2(0) - e^4}{2e^0 - 2(4)} = \frac{e^4}{6} \text{ (gradient of the tangent)}$$

$$0 = \frac{e^4}{6}(4) + c \implies c = -\frac{2e^4}{3}.$$

So the equation of the tangent is $y = \frac{e^4}{6}(x - 4)$.

b) The gradient of the normal is $-6e^{-4}$.

$$0 = -6e^{-4}(4) + c \implies c = 24e^{-4}$$

So the normal is $y = 6e^{-4}(4 - x)$.

c) The lines intersect when

$$\frac{e^4}{6}(x - 4) = 6e^{-4}(4 - x) \implies e^8(x - 4) = 36(4 - x)$$

$$\implies e^8x + 36x = 4e^8 + 144 \implies x(e^8 + 36) = 4e^8 + 144$$

$$\implies x = \frac{4e^8 + 144}{e^8 + 36}$$

Q12 When $x = 2$:

$$2y^2 + 4y - 24 = 4 + 2 \implies 2y^2 + 4y - 30 = 0$$

$$\implies y^2 + 2y - 15 = 0 \implies (y + 5)(y - 3) = 0$$

$$\implies y = -5 \text{ and } y = 3.$$

Differentiating:

$$y^2 + 2yx\frac{dy}{dx} + 2y + 2x\frac{dy}{dx} - 9x^2 = 2x$$

$$\frac{dy}{dx} = \frac{2x - y^2 - 2y + 9x^2}{2yx + 2x}$$

At $(2, -5)$, $\frac{dy}{dx} = \frac{4 - 25 + 10 + 36}{-20 + 4} = -\frac{25}{16}$

This is the gradient of the tangent at $(2, -5)$, so:

$$-5 = -\frac{25}{16}(2) + c \implies c = -\frac{15}{8}$$

So the equation of the tangent at $(2, -5)$ is:

$$y = -\frac{25}{16}x - \frac{15}{8} \text{ or } 16y = -25x - 30$$

At $(2, 3)$, $\frac{dy}{dx} = \frac{4 - 9 - 6 + 36}{12 + 4} = \frac{25}{16}$

This is the gradient of the tangent at $(2, 3)$, so:

$$3 = \frac{25}{16}(2) + c \implies c = -\frac{1}{8}$$

So the equation of the tangent at $(2, 3)$ is:

$$y = \frac{25}{16}x - \frac{1}{8} \text{ or } 16y = 25x - 2$$

The two tangents intersect when:

$$-25x - 30 = 25x - 2 \implies 50x = -28$$

$$\implies x = -\frac{14}{25}$$

And $16y = 25\left(-\frac{14}{25}\right) - 2 \implies 16y = -16 \implies y = -1$.

So they intersect at $\left(-\frac{14}{25}, -1\right)$.

Q13 a) When $x = \frac{\pi}{2}$:

$$\cos y \cos \frac{\pi}{2} + \cos y \sin \frac{\pi}{2} = \frac{1}{2},$$

$$0 + \cos y = \frac{1}{2} \implies y = \frac{\pi}{3}$$

This is the only solution for y in the given interval.

When $x = \pi$:

$$\cos y \cos \pi + \cos y \sin \pi = \frac{1}{2},$$

$$-\cos y + 0 = \frac{1}{2} \implies y = \frac{2\pi}{3}$$

You can use the CAST diagram or the graph of cos x to find this solution.

b) Differentiating:

$$-\cos y \sin x - \sin y \cos x\frac{dy}{dx} + \cos y \cos x - \sin y \sin x\frac{dy}{dx} = 0$$

$$\frac{dy}{dx} = \frac{\cos y \cos x - \cos y \sin x}{\sin y \cos x + \sin y \sin x}$$

At $\left(\frac{\pi}{2}, \frac{\pi}{3}\right)$, $\frac{dy}{dx} = \frac{\cos\frac{\pi}{3}\cos\frac{\pi}{2} - \cos\frac{\pi}{3}\sin\frac{\pi}{2}}{\sin\frac{\pi}{3}\cos\frac{\pi}{2} + \sin\frac{\pi}{3}\sin\frac{\pi}{2}} = \frac{0 - \frac{1}{2}}{0 + \frac{\sqrt{3}}{2}} = -\frac{1}{\sqrt{3}}$

This is the gradient of the tangent, so:

$$\frac{\pi}{3} = -\frac{1}{\sqrt{3}}\left(\frac{\pi}{2}\right) + c \implies c = \frac{(2 + \sqrt{3})\pi}{6}$$

So the equation of the tangent at $\left(\frac{\pi}{2}, \frac{\pi}{3}\right)$ is

$$y = -\frac{1}{\sqrt{3}}x + \frac{(2 + \sqrt{3})\pi}{6}.$$

At $\left(\pi, \frac{2\pi}{3}\right)$,

$$\frac{dy}{dx} = \frac{\cos\frac{2\pi}{3}\cos\pi - \cos\frac{2\pi}{3}\sin\pi}{\sin\frac{2\pi}{3}\cos\pi + \sin\frac{2\pi}{3}\sin\pi} = \frac{\frac{1}{2} - 0}{-\frac{\sqrt{3}}{2} + 0} = -\frac{1}{\sqrt{3}}$$

This is the gradient of the tangent, so:

$$\frac{2\pi}{3} = -\frac{1}{\sqrt{3}}(\pi) + c \implies c = \frac{(2 + \sqrt{3})\pi}{3}$$

So the equation of the tangent at $\left(\pi, \frac{2\pi}{3}\right)$ is

$$y = -\frac{1}{\sqrt{3}}x + \frac{(2 + \sqrt{3})\pi}{3}.$$

Q14 Differentiating: $\left(\frac{2}{3}y\right)\frac{dy}{dx} = 18x^2 - \left(2y + 2x\frac{dy}{dx}\right)$

$$\left(\frac{2}{3}y + 2x\right)\frac{dy}{dx} = 18x^2 - 2y$$

$$\frac{dy}{dx} = \frac{18x^2 - 2y}{\frac{2}{3}y + 2x} = \frac{9x^2 - y}{\frac{1}{3}y + x} = \frac{27x^2 - 3y}{y + 3x}$$

When $\frac{dy}{dx} = 0$, $27x^2 - 3y = 0 \implies 3y = 27x^2 \implies y = 9x^2$

Substitute $y = 9x^2$ back into the original equation:

$$\frac{1}{3}(9x^2)^2 = 6x^3 - 2x(9x^2) \implies 27x^4 = 6x^3 - 18x^3$$

$$\implies 27x^4 + 12x^3 = 0 \implies 3x^3(9x + 4) = 0$$

So the stationary points occur when $x = 0$ and $x = -\frac{4}{9}$.

When $x = 0$, $y = 9(0)^2 = 0$

When $x = -\frac{4}{9}$, $y = 9\left(-\frac{4}{9}\right)^2 = \frac{16}{9}$

So the stationary points are at $(0, 0)$ and $\left(-\frac{4}{9}, \frac{16}{9}\right)$.

Review Exercise — Chapter 7

Q1 a) (i) $\frac{dy}{dx} = 6x^2 - 24x + 18 \implies \frac{d^2y}{dx^2} = 12x - 24$

The graph is concave when $\frac{d^2y}{dx^2} < 0$

$$\implies 12x - 24 < 0 \implies x < 2$$

(ii) The graph is convex when $\frac{d^2y}{dx^2} > 0$

$$\implies 12x - 24 > 0 \implies x > 2$$

b) (i) Point of inflection occurs when $\frac{d^2y}{dx^2} = 0$:

$$\implies 12x - 24 = 0 \implies x = 2$$

$$y = 2(2)^3 - 12(2)^2 + 18(2) + 2 = 16 - 48 + 36 + 2 = 6$$

So the point of inflection is at $(2, 6)$.

(ii) Substitute $x = 2$ into $\frac{dy}{dx}$:

$$\frac{dy}{dx} = 6(2)^2 - 24(2) + 18 = 24 - 48 + 18 = -6 \neq 0,$$

So this is not a stationary point of inflection.

Q2 **a)** $y = (x^3 + 2x^2)^{\frac{1}{2}}$, so let $y = u^{\frac{1}{2}}$ where $u = x^3 + 2x^2$

$\Rightarrow \dfrac{dy}{du} = \dfrac{1}{2}u^{-\frac{1}{2}} = \dfrac{1}{2\sqrt{x^3 + 2x^2}}, \quad \dfrac{du}{dx} = 3x^2 + 4x$

$\dfrac{dy}{dx} = \dfrac{dy}{du} \times \dfrac{du}{dx} = \dfrac{3x^2 + 4x}{2\sqrt{x^3 + 2x^2}}$

b) $y = e^{f(x)}$, where $f(x) = 5x^2$, so $f'(x) = 10x$

$\dfrac{dy}{dx} = f'(x)e^{f(x)} = 10xe^{5x^2}$

c) $y = \ln f(x)$, where $f(x) = 6 - x^2$, so $f'(x) = -2x$

$\dfrac{dy}{dx} = \dfrac{f'(x)}{f(x)} = \dfrac{-2x}{6 - x^2}$

Q3 **a)** $y = (x^2 - 1)^3$, so let $y = u^3$ where $u = x^2 - 1$

$\Rightarrow \dfrac{dy}{du} = 3u^2 = 3(x^2 - 1)^2, \quad \dfrac{du}{dx} = 2x$

$\dfrac{dy}{dx} = \dfrac{dy}{du} \times \dfrac{du}{dx} = 3(x^2 - 1)^2 \times 2x = 6x(x^2 - 1)^2$

b) At $x = 2$, $y = (2^2 - 1)^3 = 27$

Gradient of C at $x = 2$, $\dfrac{dy}{dx} = 6 \times 2(2^2 - 1)^2 = 108$

So the normal at $x = 2$ has a gradient of $-\dfrac{1}{108}$ and an equation in the form $y = mx + c$.

Substitute in x, y and m to find c:

$27 = -\dfrac{1}{108} \times 2 + c \Rightarrow c = \dfrac{1459}{54}$

So $y = -\dfrac{1}{108}x + \dfrac{1459}{54}$,

which rearranges to $x + 108y - 2918 = 0$.

Q4 **a)** Differentiate each term separately:

$y = 3e^{2x+1} - \ln(1 - x^2) + 2x^3$

$\dfrac{dy}{dx} = 2(3e^{2x+1}) - \dfrac{(-2)x}{1 - x^2} + 6x^2 = 6e^{2x+1} + \dfrac{2x}{1 - x^2} + 6x^2$

b) Differentiate each term separately:

$y = 16x + e^{\sqrt{x}} + \ln(\cos x)$

$\dfrac{dy}{dx} = 16 + \dfrac{1}{2\sqrt{x}} \times e^{\sqrt{x}} - \dfrac{\sin x}{\cos x} = 16 + \dfrac{e^{\sqrt{x}}}{2\sqrt{x}} - \tan x$

Q5 **a)** **(i)** $x = 2e^{2y} \Rightarrow \dfrac{dx}{dy} = 4e^{2y} = 2x \Rightarrow \dfrac{dy}{dx} = \dfrac{1}{2x}$

(ii) $x = \ln(2y + 3) \Rightarrow \dfrac{dx}{dy} = \dfrac{2}{2y + 3} = \dfrac{2}{e^x} \Rightarrow \dfrac{dy}{dx} = \dfrac{e^x}{2}$

b) $x = \tan y \Rightarrow \dfrac{dx}{dy} = \sec^2 y = \dfrac{1}{\cos^2 y} \Rightarrow \dfrac{dy}{dx} = \cos^2 y$

Q6 **a)** $f(x) = 2\cos(3x)$, so let $y = 2\cos u$, where $u = 3x$

$\Rightarrow \dfrac{dy}{du} = -2\sin u = -2\sin(3x), \quad \dfrac{du}{dx} = 3$

$f'(x) = \dfrac{dy}{du} \times \dfrac{du}{dx} = -2\sin(3x) \times 3 = -6\sin(3x)$

b) $f(x) = \sqrt{\tan x} = (\tan x)^{\frac{1}{2}}$, so let $y = u^{\frac{1}{2}}$, where $u = \tan x$

$\Rightarrow \dfrac{dy}{du} = \dfrac{1}{2}u^{-\frac{1}{2}} = \dfrac{1}{2\sqrt{\tan x}}, \quad \dfrac{du}{dx} = \sec^2 x$

$f'(x) = \dfrac{dy}{du} \times \dfrac{du}{dx} = \dfrac{1}{2\sqrt{\tan x}} \times \sec^2 x = \dfrac{\sec^2 x}{2\sqrt{\tan x}}$

c) $f(x) = e^{\cos(3x)}$, so let $y = e^u$, where $u = \cos(3x)$

$\Rightarrow \dfrac{dy}{du} = e^u = e^{\cos(3x)}$

$u = \cos(3x)$, so let $u = \cos v$, where $v = 3x$

$\Rightarrow \dfrac{du}{dv} = -\sin v = -\sin(3x), \quad \dfrac{dv}{dx} = 3$

$\dfrac{du}{dx} = \dfrac{du}{dv} \times \dfrac{dv}{dx} = -3\sin(3x)$

$f'(x) = \dfrac{dy}{du} \times \dfrac{du}{dx} = e^{\cos(3x)} \times -3\sin(3x) = -3e^{\cos(3x)}\sin(3x)$

You don't need to use the chain rule twice if you can remember the rules of differentiating $e^{f(x)}$ and trig functions.

d) $f(x) = \sin(4x)\tan(x^3)$,

so let $y = uv$, where $u = \sin(4x)$ and $v = \tan(x^3)$

$\Rightarrow \dfrac{du}{dx} = 4\cos(4x), \quad \dfrac{dv}{dx} = 3x^2\sec^2(x^3)$

$f'(x) = \dfrac{dy}{dx} = u\dfrac{dv}{dx} + v\dfrac{du}{dx}$

$= \sin(4x) \times 3x^2\sec^2(x^3) + \tan(x^3) \times 4\cos(4x)$

$= 3x^2\sin(4x)\sec^2(x^3) + 4\cos(4x)\tan(x^3)$

Q7 **a)** $y = e^{2x}(x^2 - 3)$, so let $y = uv$, where $u = e^{2x}$ and $v = x^2 - 3$

$\Rightarrow \dfrac{du}{dx} = 2e^{2x}, \quad \dfrac{dv}{dx} = 2x$

$\dfrac{dy}{dx} = u\dfrac{dv}{dx} + v\dfrac{du}{dx} = e^{2x} \times 2x + (x^2 - 3)2e^{2x}$

$= 2xe^{2x} + 2x^2e^{2x} - 6e^{2x}$

When $x = 0$, $\dfrac{dy}{dx} = 2(0)e^{2(0)} + 2(0)^2e^{2(0)} - 6e^{2(0)} = -6$

b) $y = (\ln x)(\sin x)$, so let $y = uv$, where $u = \ln x$ and $v = \sin x$

$\Rightarrow \dfrac{du}{dx} = \dfrac{1}{x}, \quad \dfrac{dv}{dx} = \cos x$

$\dfrac{dy}{dx} = u\dfrac{dv}{dx} + v\dfrac{du}{dx} = \ln x \times \cos x + \sin x \times \dfrac{1}{x}$

$= \ln x \cos x + \dfrac{\sin x}{x}$

When $x = 1$, $\dfrac{dy}{dx} = \ln(1)\cos(1) + \dfrac{\sin(1)}{(1)} = 0.841$ (3 s.f.)

If you got a different answer, check your calculator is set to radians and not degrees.

Q8 $y = e^{x^2}\sqrt{x + 1}$, so let $y = uv$,

where $u = e^{x^2}$ and $v = (x + 1)^{\frac{1}{2}} = \sqrt{x + 1}$

$\Rightarrow \dfrac{du}{dx} = 2xe^{x^2}, \quad \dfrac{dv}{dx} = \dfrac{1}{2}(x + 1)^{-\frac{1}{2}} = \dfrac{1}{2\sqrt{x + 1}}$

$\dfrac{dy}{dx} = u\dfrac{dv}{dx} + v\dfrac{du}{dx} = e^{x^2} \times \dfrac{1}{2\sqrt{x + 1}} + \sqrt{x + 1} \times 2xe^{x^2}$

$= \dfrac{e^{x^2}}{2\sqrt{x + 1}} + 2xe^{x^2}\sqrt{x + 1}$

When $x = 1$, $\dfrac{dy}{dx} = \dfrac{e^{(1)^2}}{2\sqrt{(1) + 1}} + 2(1)e^{(1)^2}\sqrt{(1) + 1}$

$= \dfrac{e}{2\sqrt{2}} + 2\sqrt{2}e = \dfrac{9e}{2\sqrt{2}} = \dfrac{9\sqrt{2}e}{4}$

Q9 $y = \dfrac{\sqrt{x^2 + 3}}{\cos(3x)}$, so let $y = \dfrac{u}{v}$, where $u = \sqrt{x^2 + 3}$ and $v = \cos(3x)$

$\Rightarrow \dfrac{du}{dx} = \dfrac{2x}{2\sqrt{x^2 + 3}}, \quad \dfrac{dv}{dx} = -3\sin(3x)$

$\dfrac{dy}{dx} = \dfrac{v\dfrac{du}{dx} - u\dfrac{dv}{dx}}{v^2} = \dfrac{\cos(3x) \times \dfrac{2x}{2\sqrt{x^2 + 3}} - \sqrt{x^2 + 3} \times -3\sin(3x)}{\cos^2(3x)}$

$= \dfrac{\dfrac{2x\cos(3x)}{2\sqrt{x^2 + 3}} + 3\sqrt{x^2 + 3}\sin(3x)}{\cos^2(3x)} = \dfrac{\dfrac{2x}{2\sqrt{x^2 + 3}} + 3\sqrt{x^2 + 3}\tan(3x)}{\cos(3x)}$

$= \dfrac{\dfrac{x}{\sqrt{x^2 + 3}} + 3\sqrt{x^2 + 3}\tan(3x)}{\cos(3x)} = \dfrac{x + 3(x^2 + 3)\tan(3x)}{\sqrt{x^2 + 3}\cos(3x)}$

Here, you have to use the quotient rule — but you have to use the chain rule to differentiate both u and v before you can put them in the quotient rule formula. Finally, you have to do a bit of rearranging to tidy up the fraction.

Q10 **a)** $y = \cos x \ln x^2$, so let $y = uv$,

where $u = \cos x$ and $v = \ln x^2 = 2\ln x$

$\Rightarrow \dfrac{du}{dx} = -\sin x, \quad \dfrac{dv}{dx} = \dfrac{2}{x}$

$\dfrac{dy}{dx} = u\dfrac{dv}{dx} + v\dfrac{du}{dx} = \cos x \times \dfrac{2}{x} + \ln x^2 \times -\sin x$

$= \dfrac{2\cos x}{x} - \ln x^2 \sin x$

b) $y = \dfrac{e^{x^2 - x}}{(x + 2)^4}$, so let $y = \dfrac{u}{v}$,

where $u = e^{x^2 - x}$ and $v = (x + 2)^4$

$\Rightarrow \dfrac{du}{dx} = (2x - 1)e^{x^2 - x}, \quad \dfrac{dv}{dx} = 4(x + 2)^3$

$\dfrac{dy}{dx} = \dfrac{v\dfrac{du}{dx} - u\dfrac{dv}{dx}}{v^2} = \dfrac{(x + 2)^4(2x - 1)e^{x^2 - x} - 4e^{x^2 - x}(x + 2)^3}{(x + 2)^8}$

$= \dfrac{(x + 2)(2x - 1)e^{x^2 - x} - 4e^{x^2 - x}}{(x + 2)^5} = \dfrac{(2x^2 + 3x - 6)e^{x^2 - x}}{(x + 2)^5}$

Q11 $y = \frac{e^x}{\sqrt{x}}$, so let $y = \frac{u}{v}$, where $u = e^x$ and $v = \sqrt{x}$

$\Rightarrow \frac{du}{dx} = e^x, \frac{dv}{dx} = \frac{1}{2}x^{-\frac{1}{2}} = \frac{1}{2\sqrt{x}}$

$\frac{dy}{dx} = \frac{v\frac{du}{dx} - u\frac{dv}{dx}}{v^2} = \frac{\sqrt{x}e^x - \frac{e^x}{2\sqrt{x}}}{x} = \frac{2xe^x - e^x}{2\sqrt{x^3}} = \frac{(2x-1)e^x}{2\sqrt{x^3}}$

When $\frac{dy}{dx} = 0, \frac{(2x-1)e^x}{2\sqrt{x^3}} = 0$

$e^x \neq 0$ for all real x, so $2x - 1 = 0 \Rightarrow x = \frac{1}{2}$

When $x = \frac{1}{2}, y = \frac{e^{\frac{1}{2}}}{\sqrt{\frac{1}{2}}} = \frac{e^{\frac{1}{2}}}{\frac{\sqrt{2}}{2}} = \sqrt{2}e^{\frac{1}{2}}$

So the coordinates of the stationary point are $\left(\frac{1}{2}, \sqrt{2}e^{\frac{1}{2}}\right)$.

Q12 $y = \frac{6x^2 + 3}{4x^2 - 1}$, so let $y = \frac{u}{v}$, where $u = 6x^2 + 3$ and $v = 4x^2 - 1$

$\Rightarrow \frac{du}{dx} = 12x, \frac{dv}{dx} = 8x$

$\frac{dy}{dx} = \frac{v\frac{du}{dx} - u\frac{dv}{dx}}{v^2} = \frac{12x(4x^2 - 1) - 8x(6x^2 + 3)}{(4x^2 - 1)^2}$

$= \frac{48x^3 - 12x - 48x^3 - 24x}{(4x^2 - 1)^2} = \frac{-36x}{(4x^2 - 1)^2}$

At (1, 3), $x = 1$ so $\frac{dy}{dx} = -\frac{36}{(4 - 1)^2} = -4$

The tangent to the curve at (1, 3) has a gradient of –4 and an equation in the form $y = mx + c$.
Substitute in the values of x, y and m to find c:
$3 = -4(1) + c \Rightarrow c = 7$
So the tangent to the curve at (1, 3) has the equation
$y = -4x + 7$, which can be rearranged to $y = 7 - 4x$.

Q13 $y = 3 \cosec \frac{x}{4}$, so let $y = 3 \cosec u$, where $u = \frac{x}{4}$

$\Rightarrow \frac{dy}{du} = -3 \cosec u \cot u = -3 \cosec \frac{x}{4} \cot \frac{x}{4}$

$\frac{du}{dx} = \frac{1}{4}$

$\frac{dy}{dx} = \frac{dy}{du} \times \frac{du}{dx} = -3 \cosec \frac{x}{4} \cot \frac{x}{4} \times \frac{1}{4} = -\frac{3}{4} \cosec \frac{x}{4} \cot \frac{x}{4}$

At $x = \pi$, $y = 3 \cosec \frac{\pi}{4} = 3\sqrt{2}$

$\frac{dy}{dx} = -\frac{3}{4} \cosec \frac{\pi}{4} \cot \frac{\pi}{4} = -\frac{3\sqrt{2}}{4}$

The normal to the curve at $x = \pi$ has a gradient of

$-1 \div \frac{3\sqrt{2}}{4} = \frac{2\sqrt{2}}{3}$ and an equation in the form $y = mx + c$.

Substitute in the values of x, y and m to find c:

$3\sqrt{2} = \frac{2\sqrt{2}\pi}{3} + c \Rightarrow c = 3\sqrt{2} - \frac{2\sqrt{2}\pi}{3}$

So the normal to the curve at $x = \pi$ has the equation

$y = \frac{2\sqrt{2}}{3}x + 3\sqrt{2} - \frac{2\sqrt{2}\pi}{3}$

Q14 $y = \sec(3x - 2)$, so let $y = \sec u$, where $u = 3x - 2$

$\Rightarrow \frac{dy}{du} = \tan u \sec u = \tan(3x - 2) \sec(3x - 2)$,

$\frac{du}{dx} = 3$

$\frac{dy}{dx} = \frac{dy}{du} \times \frac{du}{dx} = 3 \tan(3x - 2) \sec(3x - 2)$

At $x = 0$, $\frac{dy}{dx} = 3 \tan(3(0) - 2) \sec(3(0) - 2) = -15.8$ (3 s.f.)

Q15 a) $y = \sqrt{\cosec x}$, so let $y = \sqrt{u}$, where $u = \cosec x$

$\Rightarrow \frac{dy}{du} = \frac{1}{2}u^{-\frac{1}{2}} = \frac{1}{2\sqrt{\cosec x}}, \frac{du}{dx} = -\cosec x \cot x$

$\frac{dy}{dx} = \frac{dy}{du} \times \frac{du}{dx} = \frac{-\cosec x \cot x}{2\sqrt{\cosec x}} = \frac{-\cot x \sqrt{\cosec x}}{2}$

b) $y = \frac{\sec x}{x^2}$, so let $y = \frac{u}{v}$, where $u = \sec x$ and $v = x^2$

$\Rightarrow \frac{du}{dx} = \sec x \tan x, \frac{dv}{dx} = 2x$

$\frac{dy}{dx} = \frac{v\frac{du}{dx} - u\frac{dv}{dx}}{v^2} = \frac{x^2 \sec x \tan x - 2x \sec x}{x^4} = \frac{\sec x(x \tan x - 2)}{x^3}$

c) $y = \cot(x^2 + 5)$, so let $y = \cot u$, where $u = x^2 + 5$

$\Rightarrow \frac{dy}{du} = -\cosec^2 u = -\cosec^2(x^2 + 5), \frac{du}{dx} = 2x$

$\frac{dy}{dx} = \frac{dy}{du} \times \frac{du}{dx} = -2x \cosec^2(x^2 + 5)$

d) $y = e^{2x} \cosec(5x)$, so let $y = uv$,
where $u = e^{2x}$ and $v = \cosec(5x)$

$\Rightarrow \frac{du}{dx} = 2e^{2x}, \frac{dv}{dx} = -5 \cosec(5x) \cot(5x)$

$\frac{dy}{dx} = u\frac{dv}{dx} + v\frac{du}{dx}$

$= -5e^{2x} \cosec(5x) \cot(5x) + 2e^{2x} \cosec(5x)$

$= e^{2x} \cosec(5x)(2 - 5 \cot(5x))$

Q16 a) $V = \frac{4}{3}\pi r^3 \Rightarrow \frac{dV}{dr} = 4\pi r^2$

$\frac{dV}{d\theta} = \frac{dV}{dr} \times \frac{dr}{d\theta} = 4\pi r^2 \times -2500 = -10\,000\,\pi r^2$ km³ K⁻¹

b) Density $(\rho) = \frac{m}{V} = \frac{m}{kD^3} = \frac{m}{k}D^{-3} \Rightarrow \frac{d\rho}{dD} = -3\frac{m}{k}D^{-4} = -\frac{3m}{kD^4}$

From the question $\frac{dD}{d\theta} = -215$ km K⁻¹,

so $\frac{d\rho}{d\theta} = \frac{d\rho}{dD} \times \frac{dD}{d\theta} = -\frac{3m}{kD^4} \times -215$ km K⁻¹ $= \frac{645m}{kD^4}$ kg km⁻³ K⁻¹

Q17 a) $\frac{dx}{dt} = 2t - 6, \frac{dy}{dt} = 6t^2 - 12t - 18$.

Using the chain rule, $\frac{dy}{dx} = \frac{dy}{dt} \div \frac{dx}{dt}$

$= \frac{6t^2 - 12t - 18}{2t - 6} = \frac{(2t - 6)(3t + 3)}{2t - 6} = 3(t + 1)$

b) When $\frac{dy}{dx} = 0$, $3(t + 1) = 0 \Rightarrow t = -1$

When $t = -1$, $x = (-1)^2 - 6(-1) = 7$ and
$y = 2(-1)^3 - 6(-1)^2 - 18(-1) = 10$
So the particle has a stationary point at (7, 10).

Q18 a) $x = 3se^s$, so let $x = uv$, where $u = 3s$ and $v = e^s$

$\Rightarrow \frac{du}{ds} = 3, \frac{dv}{ds} = e^s$,

$\frac{dx}{ds} = u\frac{dv}{ds} + v\frac{du}{ds} = 3se^s + 3e^s = 3e^s(s + 1)$

$y = e^{2s} + se^{2s} \Rightarrow \frac{dy}{ds} = 2e^{2s} + 2se^{2s} + e^{2s}$

$= 3e^{2s} + 2se^{2s} = e^{2s}(3 + 2s)$

$\frac{dy}{dx} = \frac{dy}{ds} \div \frac{dx}{ds} = \frac{e^{2s}(3 + 2s)}{3e^s(s + 1)} = \frac{e^s(3 + 2s)}{3(s + 1)}$

When $s = 0$, $x = 3(0)e^{(0)} = 0$, $y = e^{2(0)} + (0)e^{2(0)} = 1$,

$\frac{dy}{dx} = \frac{e^{(0)}(3 + 2(0))}{3((0) + 1)} = 1$

The tangent to the curve at $s = 0$ has an equation in the form $y = mx + c$. Substitute in the values of x, y and m to find c:
$1 = 1 \times 0 + c \Rightarrow c = 1$
So the tangent to the curve at $s = 0$
has the equation $y = x + 1$.

When $s = 2$, $x = 3(2)e^{(2)} = 6e^2$,
$y = e^{2(2)} + (2)e^{2(2)} = e^4 + 2e^4 = 3e^4$

$\frac{dy}{dx} = \frac{e^{(2)}(3 + 2(2))}{3((2) + 1)} = \frac{7e^2}{9}$

The tangent to the curve at $s = 2$ has an equation in the form $y = mx + c$. Substitute in the values of x, y and m to find c:
$3e^4 = \frac{7e^2}{9} \times 6e^2 + c = \frac{42e^4}{9} + c \Rightarrow c = -\frac{5e^4}{3}$
So the tangent to the curve at $s = 0$ has
the equation $y = \left(\frac{7e^2}{9}\right)x - \frac{5e^4}{3}$.

b) The tangents intersect where:
$x + 1 = \left(\frac{7e^2}{9}\right)x - \frac{5e^4}{3} \Rightarrow 1 + \frac{5e^4}{3} = \left(\frac{7e^2}{9}\right)x - x$

$\Rightarrow 9 + 15e^4 = x(7e^2 - 9) \Rightarrow x = \frac{9 + 15e^4}{7e^2 - 9}$

$y = x + 1 = \frac{9 + 15e^4}{7e^2 - 9} + 1$

So the tangents intersect at the point $\left(\frac{9 + 15e^4}{7e^2 - 9}, \frac{9 + 15e^4}{7e^2 - 9} + 1\right)$

Q19 At $x = 2$, $4y + (2)^2y^2 = 4(2) \Rightarrow 4y + 4y^2 = 8$
$\Rightarrow y^2 + y - 2 = 0 \Rightarrow (y + 2)(y - 1) = 0$
$\Rightarrow y = -2$ or $y = 1$, so $a = 1$ and $b = -2$
Differentiate $4y + x^2y^2 = 4x$: $\frac{d}{dx}4y + \frac{d}{dx}x^2y^2 = \frac{d}{dx}4x$

$\Rightarrow 4\frac{dy}{dx} + 2x^2y\frac{dy}{dx} + 2xy^2 = 4 \Rightarrow \frac{dy}{dx}(4 + 2x^2y) = 4 - 2xy^2$

$\Rightarrow \frac{dy}{dx} = \frac{4 - 2xy^2}{4 + 2x^2y} = \frac{2 - xy^2}{2 + x^2y}$

At $(2, 1)$, $\frac{dy}{dx} = \frac{2 - (2)(1)^2}{2 + (2)^2(1)} = 0$, so $(2, 1)$ is a stationary point and
the equation of the tangent is $y = 1$.
At $(2, -2)$, $\frac{dy}{dx} = \frac{2 - (2)(-2)^2}{2 + (2)^2(-2)} = 1$ and the tangent has an equation
in the form $y = mx + c$. Substitute in the values of x, y and m to
find c: $-2 = 2 + c \Rightarrow c = -4$
So the tangent at $(2, -2)$ has the equation $y = x - 4$.
The tangents intersect where $x - 4 = 1 \Rightarrow x = 5$
So the tangents intersect at the point $(5, 1)$.

Q20 **a)** $x \ln x + x^2y = y^2x - 6x \Rightarrow (1)\ln(1) + (1)^2y = y^2(1) - 6(1)$
$\Rightarrow 0 + y = y^2 - 6 \Rightarrow 0 = y^2 - y - 6 \Rightarrow (y + 2)(y - 3) = 0$
$\Rightarrow y = -2$ or $y = 3$, so $a = 3$ and $b = -2$

b) Differentiate $x \ln x + x^2y = y^2x - 6x$:
$\frac{d}{dx}x \ln x + \frac{d}{dx}x^2y = \frac{d}{dx}y^2x - \frac{d}{dx}6x$

$\Rightarrow 1 + \ln x + x^2\frac{dy}{dx} + 2xy = y^2 + 2xy\frac{dy}{dx} - 6$

$\Rightarrow \frac{dy}{dx}(x^2 - 2xy) = y^2 - 2xy - \ln x - 7$

$\Rightarrow \frac{dy}{dx} = \frac{y^2 - 2xy - \ln x - 7}{x^2 - 2xy}$

At $(1, 3)$, $\frac{dy}{dx} = \frac{(3)^2 - 2(1)(3) - \ln(1) - 7}{(1)^2 - 2(1)(3)} = \frac{4}{5}$

The normal to the curve at $(1, 3)$ has a gradient of
$-1 \div \frac{4}{5} = -\frac{5}{4}$ and an equation in the form $y = mx + c$.
Substitute in the values of x, y and m to find c:
$3 = -\frac{5}{4}(1) + c \Rightarrow c = \frac{17}{4}$. So the normal to the curve
at $(1, 3)$ has the equation $y = -\frac{5}{4}x + \frac{17}{4}$.

At $(1, -2)$, $\frac{dy}{dx} = \frac{(-2)^2 - 2(1)(-2) - \ln(1) - 7}{(1)^2 - 2(1)(-2)} = \frac{1}{5}$
The normal to the curve at $(1, -2)$ has a gradient of
$-1 \div \frac{1}{5} = -5$ and an equation in the form $y = mx + c$.
Substitute in the values of x, y and m to find c:
$-2 = -5(1) + c \Rightarrow c = 3$. So the normal to the curve
at $(1, -2)$ has the equation $y = -5x + 3$.

c) The normals intersect where:
$-\frac{5}{4}x + \frac{17}{4} = -5x + 3 \Rightarrow \frac{15}{4}x = -\frac{5}{4} \Rightarrow x = -\frac{1}{3}$
At $x = -\frac{1}{3}$, $y = -5\left(-\frac{1}{3}\right) + 3 = \frac{14}{3}$
So the normals intersect at the point $\left(-\frac{1}{3}, \frac{14}{3}\right)$.

Exam-Style Questions — Chapter 7

Q1 **a)** $f(x) = (3x + 1)^5$, so let $f(x) = y = u^5$, where $u = 3x + 1$

$\Rightarrow \frac{dy}{du} = 5u^4 = 5(3x + 1)^4$, $\frac{du}{dx} = 3$

$f'(x) = \frac{dy}{dx} = \frac{dy}{du} \times \frac{du}{dx} = 15(3x + 1)^4$

*[2 marks available — 1 mark for correct method,
1 mark for correct answer]*

b) Use the chain rule on $f'(x)$ to find $f''(x)$:
$f'(x) = 15(3x + 1)^4$, so let $f'(x) = z = 15u^4$,
where $u = 3x + 1$

$\Rightarrow \frac{dz}{du} = 15 \times 4u^3 = 60(3x + 1)^3$, $\frac{du}{dx} = 3$

$f''(x) = \frac{dz}{dx} = \frac{dz}{du} \times \frac{du}{dx} = 180(3x + 1)^3$

At a point of inflection, $f''(x) = 0$
$\Rightarrow 180(3x + 1)^3 = 0 \Rightarrow 3x + 1 = 0 \Rightarrow x = -\frac{1}{3}$
When $x < -\frac{1}{3}$, $3x + 1 < 0 \Rightarrow f''(x) < 0$

When $x > -\frac{1}{3}$, $3x + 1 > 0 \Rightarrow f''(x) > 0$
So the sign of $f''(x)$ changes at $x = -\frac{1}{3}$,
so this is the point of inflection.
And $x = -\frac{1}{3}$ is the only real solution to $f''(x) = 0$, so it's the
only point of inflection.
$x = -\frac{1}{3} \Rightarrow y = f(x) = \left(3\left(-\frac{1}{3}\right) + 1\right)^5 = 0$
So the point of inflection of $f(x)$ has the coordinates $\left(-\frac{1}{3}, 0\right)$.
*[3 marks available — 1 mark for correct differentiation of
answer to part a) (allow errors carried forward), 1 mark for
clearly showing f(x) has one point of inflection, 1 mark for
correct coordinates]*

c) $f(x)$ is concave where $f''(x) < 0$, so is concave where $x < -\frac{1}{3}$.
[1 mark for correct answer]

Q2 **a)** $y = \frac{\cos x^2}{\ln(2x)}$, so let $y = \frac{u}{v}$, where $u = \cos x^2$ and $v = \ln(2x)$

$\Rightarrow \frac{du}{dx} = 2x \times -\sin x^2 = -2x \sin x^2$, $\frac{dv}{dx} = 2 \times \frac{1}{2x} = \frac{1}{x}$

$\frac{dy}{dx} = \frac{v\frac{du}{dx} - u\frac{dv}{dx}}{v^2} = \frac{\ln(2x) \times -2x \sin x^2 - \cos x^2 \times \frac{1}{x}}{(\ln(2x))^2}$

$= -\frac{2x \sin x^2}{\ln(2x)} - \frac{\cos x^2}{x(\ln(2x))^2}$

*[4 marks available — 1 mark for attempting to use quotient
(or product) rule, 1 mark for finding $\frac{du}{dx}$, 1 mark for finding
$\frac{dv}{dx}$, 1 mark for correct answer in any form]*

b) At $x = 2$, $\frac{dy}{dx} = -\frac{2(2)\sin(2^2)}{\ln(2 \times 2)} - \frac{\cos(2^2)}{2(\ln(2 \times 2))^2}$
$= 2.35$ (3 s.f.)
[1 mark for correct answer]

Q3 **a)** Differentiate $4x^2 - 2y^2 = 7x^2y$:

$\frac{d}{dx}4x^2 - \frac{d}{dx}2y^2 = \frac{d}{dx}7x^2y \Rightarrow 8x - 4y\frac{dy}{dx} = 7x^2\frac{dy}{dx} + 14xy$

$\Rightarrow 8x - 14xy = 7x^2\frac{dy}{dx} + 4y\frac{dy}{dx} \Rightarrow \frac{dy}{dx} = \frac{8x - 14xy}{7x^2 + 4y}$

*[3 marks available — 1 mark for one term correctly
differentiated, 1 mark for other two terms correctly
differentiated, 1 mark for terms rearranged to give expression
for $\frac{dy}{dx}$ (allow for incorrectly differentiated terms)]*

b) **(i)** At $(1, -4)$, $\frac{dy}{dx} = \frac{8(1) - 14(1)(-4)}{7(1)^2 + 4(-4)} = -\frac{64}{9}$
So the gradient of the tangent to C at $(1, -4)$ is $-\frac{64}{9}$.
[1 mark for correct answer]

(ii) From part b)(i) you know that the gradient
of the tangent at $(1, -4)$ is $-\frac{64}{9}$, so the gradient
of the normal (m) is $-1 \div -\frac{64}{9} = \frac{9}{64}$.
Substitute x, y and m into the equation for the normal to
find c: $y = mx + c \Rightarrow -4 + \frac{9}{64}(1) + c \Rightarrow c = -\frac{265}{64}$
So the equation of the normal to C at $(1, -4)$
is $y = \frac{9}{64}x - \frac{265}{64}$, which can be rearranged as
$9x - 64y - 265 = 0$.
*[3 marks available — 1 mark for correct value
of m, 1 mark for correct value of c, 1 mark for
correct equation for normal in correct form]*

Q4 a) $x = t \ln t \Rightarrow \dfrac{dx}{dt} = t \times \dfrac{1}{t} + 1 \times \ln t = 1 + \ln t$

$y = 2t^3 - t^2 \Rightarrow \dfrac{dy}{dt} = 6t^2 - 2t$

$\dfrac{dy}{dx} = \dfrac{dy}{dt} \div \dfrac{dx}{dt} = \dfrac{6t^2 - 2t}{1 + \ln t}$

[3 marks available — 1 mark for $\dfrac{dx}{dt}$, 1 mark for $\dfrac{dy}{dt}$, 1 mark for correct answer]

b) At $(0, 1)$, $x = 0$, so $t \ln t = 0$.

t cannot be 0 because $\ln 0$ is undefined $\Rightarrow \ln t = 0 \Rightarrow t = 1$

So $\dfrac{dy}{dx} = \dfrac{6(1)^2 - 2(1)}{1 + \ln(1)} = 4$

So the tangent to the curve at $(0, 1)$ has a gradient of 4 and an equation in the form $y = mx + c$. Substitute in the values of x, y and m to find c: $1 = 4(0) + c \Rightarrow c = 1$

So the tangent to the curve at $(0, 1)$ has the equation $y = 4x + 1$.

[3 marks available — 1 mark for finding $t = 1$, 1 mark for substituting $t = 1$ into $\dfrac{dy}{dx}$, 1 mark for correct equation for tangent]

Q5 a) (i) $A = 2(x)(2x) + 2(x)(3x) + 2(2x)(3x) = 4x^2 + 6x^2 + 12x^2 = 22x^2$

$\Rightarrow \dfrac{dA}{dx} = 44x$

(ii) $V = (x)(2x)(3x) = 6x^3 \Rightarrow \dfrac{dV}{dx} = 18x^2$

[2 marks available — 1 mark for each correct answer]

b) $\dfrac{dx}{d\theta} = \dfrac{dx}{dV} \times \dfrac{dV}{d\theta} = \dfrac{1}{\left(\dfrac{dV}{dx}\right)} \times \dfrac{dV}{d\theta} = \dfrac{1}{18x^2} \times 3 = \dfrac{1}{6x^2}$

So $\dfrac{dA}{d\theta} = \dfrac{dA}{dx} \times \dfrac{dx}{d\theta} = 44x \times \dfrac{1}{6x^2} = \dfrac{22}{3x}$

[2 marks available — 1 mark for using connected rates of change, 1 mark for clearly showing $\dfrac{dA}{d\theta} = \dfrac{22}{3x}$]

There are several different ways you could have solved this question.

Q6 a) $x = t^3 - t^2 \Rightarrow \dfrac{dx}{dt} = 3t^2 - 2t$

$y = t^3 + 3t^2 - 9t \Rightarrow \dfrac{dy}{dt} = 3t^2 + 6t - 9$

$\Rightarrow \dfrac{dy}{dx} = \dfrac{dy}{dt} \div \dfrac{dx}{dt} = \dfrac{3t^2 + 6t - 9}{3t^2 - 2t}$

At turning points, $\dfrac{dy}{dx} = 0 \Rightarrow \dfrac{3t^2 + 6t - 9}{3t^2 - 2t} = 0$

$\Rightarrow t^2 + 2t - 3 = 0 \Rightarrow (t + 3)(t - 1) = 0 \Rightarrow t = -3 \text{ or } t = 1$

When $t = -3$, $x = (-3)^3 - (-3)^2 = -36$

and $y = (-3)^3 + 3(-3)^2 - 9(-3) = 27$

When $t = 1$, $x = (1)^3 - (1)^2 = 0$ and $y = (1)^3 + 3(1)^2 - 9(1) = -5$

So the coordinates of the turning points are $(-36, 27)$ and $(0, -5)$.

[4 marks available — 1 mark for using $\dfrac{dy}{dx} = \dfrac{dy}{dt} \div \dfrac{dx}{dt}$, 1 mark for correct $\dfrac{dy}{dx}$, 1 mark for setting $\dfrac{dy}{dx} = 0$ and using it to find values of t, 1 mark for correct coordinates using values of t]

b) $y = 0$ at the x-axis, so $t^3 + 3t^2 - 9t = 0 \Rightarrow t(t^2 + 3t - 9) = 0$

$\Rightarrow t = 0 \text{ or } t = \dfrac{-3 \pm \sqrt{3^2 - 4 \times 1 \times (-9)}}{2 \times 1} = \dfrac{-3 \pm 3\sqrt{5}}{2}$

The quadratic formula was used here to find two of the values of t.

When $t = 0$, $x = (0)^3 - (0)^2 = 0$ and $y = (0)^3 + 3(0)^2 - 9(0)$, so C passes through the origin.

[2 marks available — 1 mark for values of t, 1 mark for clearly showing C passes through the origin]

c) At $t = 2$, $x = (2)^3 - (2)^2 = 4$, $y = (2)^3 + 3(2)^2 - 9(2) = 2$

$\dfrac{dy}{dx} = \dfrac{3(2)^2 + 6(2) - 9}{3(2)^2 - 2(2)} = \dfrac{15}{8}$

The tangent to C at $t = 2$ has the gradient $\dfrac{15}{8}$ and an equation in the form $y = mx + c$. Substitute in the values of x, y and m to find c:

$2 = \dfrac{15}{8}(4) + c \Rightarrow c = -\dfrac{11}{2}$

So the tangent to C at $t = 2$ has the equation $y = \dfrac{15}{8}x - \dfrac{11}{2}$, which can be rearranged as $15x - 8y - 44 = 0$.

[2 marks available — 1 mark for substituting $t = 2$ to find x, y and $\dfrac{dy}{dx}$, 1 mark for correct equation for tangent in any form]

Q7 a) Differentiate $x^2y + y^2 = x^2 + 1$:

$\dfrac{d}{dx}x^2y + \dfrac{d}{dx}y^2 = \dfrac{d}{dx}x^2 + \dfrac{d}{dx}1 \Rightarrow x^2\dfrac{dy}{dx} + 2xy + 2y\dfrac{dy}{dx} = 2x$

The product rule has been used to differentiate x^2y.

$\Rightarrow \dfrac{dy}{dx}(x^2 + 2y) = 2x - 2xy \Rightarrow \dfrac{dy}{dx} = \dfrac{2x - 2xy}{x^2 + 2y}$

At $(1, -2)$, $\dfrac{dy}{dx} = \dfrac{2(1) - 2(1)(-2)}{(1)^2 + 2(-2)} = -2$

[4 marks available — 1 mark for two terms correctly differentiated, 1 mark for other two terms correctly differentiated, 1 mark for terms rearranged to give expression for $\dfrac{dy}{dx}$, 1 mark for correct gradient]

b) At $(1, a)$, $x = 1 \Rightarrow (1)^2y + y^2 = (1)^2 + 1 \Rightarrow y + y^2 = 2$

$\Rightarrow y^2 + y - 2 = 0 \Rightarrow (y + 2)(y - 1) = 0 \Rightarrow y = -2 \text{ or } y = 1$

The point $(1, -2)$ is already given in the question, so $a = 1$.

At $(1, 1)$, $\dfrac{dy}{dx} = \dfrac{2(1) - 2(1)(1)}{(1)^2 + 2(1)} = 0$, so it is a turning point.

[2 marks available — 1 mark for correct value of a, 1 mark for showing $\dfrac{dy}{dx} = 0$ at $(1, a)$]

Q8 a) Differentiate $x \cos x + y \sin x = y^3$:

$\dfrac{d}{dx}x \cos x + \dfrac{d}{dx}y \sin x = \dfrac{d}{dx}y^3$

$\Rightarrow -x \sin x + \cos x + y \cos x + \left(\dfrac{dy}{dx}\right)\sin x = 3y^2\dfrac{dy}{dx}$

Use the product rule to differentiate $x \cos x$ and $y \sin x$.

$\Rightarrow \cos x - x \sin x + y \cos x = 3y^2\dfrac{dy}{dx} - \left(\dfrac{dy}{dx}\right)\sin x$

$\Rightarrow \dfrac{dy}{dx} = \dfrac{\cos x - x \sin x + y \cos x}{3y^2 - \sin x}$

At stationary points $\dfrac{dy}{dx} = 0$, so $\dfrac{\cos x - x \sin x + y \cos x}{3y^2 - \sin x} = 0$

$\Rightarrow \cos x - x \sin x + y \cos x = 0 \Rightarrow y \cos x = x \sin x - \cos x$

$\Rightarrow y = \dfrac{x \sin x - \cos x}{\cos x} \Rightarrow y = x \tan x - 1$

[5 marks available — 1 mark for one term correctly differentiated, 1 mark for other two terms correctly differentiated, 1 mark for terms rearranged to give expression for $\dfrac{dy}{dx}$, 1 mark for setting $\dfrac{dy}{dx} = 0$, 1 mark for clearly showing $y = x \tan x - 1$ at stationary points]

b) When $x = \dfrac{\pi}{2}$, $\left(\dfrac{\pi}{2}\right)\cos\left(\dfrac{\pi}{2}\right) + y \sin\left(\dfrac{\pi}{2}\right) = y^3$

$\Rightarrow \left(\dfrac{\pi}{2}\right)(0) + y(1) = y^3 \Rightarrow 0 = y^3 - y = y(y + 1)(y - 1)$

$\Rightarrow y = 0 \text{ or } y = -1 \text{ or } y = 1$

So the three points have the coordinates $\left(\dfrac{\pi}{2}, 0\right)$, $\left(\dfrac{\pi}{2}, -1\right)$ and $\left(\dfrac{\pi}{2}, 1\right)$.

[3 marks available — 1 mark for substituting in $x = \dfrac{\pi}{2}$, 1 mark for simplifying and factorising equation, 1 mark for correct three y-coordinates]

c) At $\left(\dfrac{\pi}{2}, 0\right)$, $\dfrac{dy}{dx} = \dfrac{\cos x - x \sin x + y \cos x}{3y^2 - \sin x} = \dfrac{0 - \dfrac{\pi}{2} + 0}{0 - 1} = \dfrac{\pi}{2}$

At $\left(\dfrac{\pi}{2}, -1\right)$, $\dfrac{dy}{dx} = \dfrac{0 - \dfrac{\pi}{2} + 0}{3 - 1} = -\dfrac{\pi}{4}$

At $\left(\dfrac{\pi}{2}, 1\right)$, $\dfrac{dy}{dx} = \dfrac{0 - \dfrac{\pi}{2} + 0}{3 - 1} = -\dfrac{\pi}{4}$

The tangents at $\left(\dfrac{\pi}{2}, -1\right)$ and $\left(\dfrac{\pi}{2}, 1\right)$ are both $-\dfrac{\pi}{4}$, so they are parallel and will never intersect.

[2 marks available — 1 mark for at least two correct tangent gradients, 1 mark for clearly showing the correct two tangents will not intersect]

Chapter 8: Integration

8.1 Integration of $(ax + b)^n$

Exercise 8.1.1 — Integrating $(ax + b)^n$, $n \neq -1$

Q1 **a)** $\int (x+10)^{10}\, dx = \frac{1}{1\times 11}(x+10)^{11} + C = \frac{1}{11}(x+10)^{11} + C$

b) $\int (5x)^7\, dx = \frac{1}{5\times 8}(5x)^8 + C = \frac{1}{40}(5x)^8 + C$

$= \frac{1}{40}5^8 x^8 + C = \frac{5^8}{40}x^8 + C = \frac{78125 x^8}{8} + C$

c) $\int (3-5x)^{-2}\, dx = \frac{1}{-5\times -1}(3-5x)^{-1} + C$

$= \frac{1}{5}(3-5x)^{-1} + C = \frac{1}{5(3-5x)} + C$

d) $\int (3x-4)^{-\frac{4}{3}}\, dx = \frac{1}{3\times\left(-\frac{1}{3}\right)}(3x-4)^{-\frac{1}{3}} + C$

$= \frac{1}{-1}(3x-4)^{-\frac{1}{3}} + C = -(3x-4)^{-\frac{1}{3}} + C = \frac{-1}{\sqrt[3]{3x-4}} + C$

Q2 **a)** Begin by taking the constant of 8 outside of the integration and then integrate $\int (2x-4)^4\, dx$ as usual.

$\int 8(2x-4)^4\, dx = 8\int (2x-4)^4\, dx$

$= 8\times\left(\frac{1}{2\times 5}(2x-4)^5 + c\right) = \frac{8}{10}(2x-4)^5 + C$

$= \frac{4}{5}(2x-4)^5 + C = \frac{4(2x-4)^5}{5} + C$

b) Use your answer to part a). The integral you found will be the same but without the constant of integration — it'll have limits instead.

$\int_{\frac{3}{2}}^{\frac{5}{2}} 8(2x-4)^4\, dx = \frac{4}{5}[(2x-4)^5]_{\frac{3}{2}}^{\frac{5}{2}}$

$= \frac{4}{5}\left(\left[\left(2\left(\frac{5}{2}\right)-4\right)^5\right] - \left[\left(2\left(\frac{3}{2}\right)-4\right)^5\right]\right)$

$= \frac{4}{5}([(1)^5] - [(-1)^5]) = \frac{4}{5}([1] - [-1]) = \frac{8}{5}$

Q3 $\int_0^1 (6x+1)^{-3}\, dx = \left[\frac{1}{6\times(-2)}(6x+1)^{-2}\right]_0^1$

$= -\frac{1}{12}[(6x+1)^{-2}]_0^1$

$= -\frac{1}{12}([(7)^{-2}] - [(1)^{-2}])$

$= -\frac{1}{12}\left(\frac{1}{49} - 1\right) = \frac{4}{49}$

Q4 You've been given that $f'(x) = (8 - 7x)^4$ and you need to find $f(x)$, so integrate with respect to x.

$f(x) = \int f'(x)\, dx = \int (8-7x)^4\, dx$

$= \frac{1}{-7\times 5}(8-7x)^5 + C = -\frac{1}{35}(8-7x)^5 + C$

Substitute in the values of x and y at the point given to find the value of C.

$\frac{3}{35} = -\frac{1}{35}(8 - (7\times 1))^5 + C \Rightarrow \frac{3}{35} = -\frac{1}{35}(1)^5 + C \Rightarrow C = \frac{4}{35}$

So $f(x) = -\frac{1}{35}(8-7x)^5 + \frac{4}{35}$

8.2 Integration of e^x and $\frac{1}{x}$

Exercise 8.2.1 — Integrating e^x and e^{ax+b}

Q1 **a)** $\int 2e^x\, dx = 2\int e^x\, dx = 2e^x + C$

b) $\int 4x + 7e^x\, dx = \int 4x\, dx + \int 7e^x\, dx$

$= \int 4x\, dx + 7\int e^x\, dx = 2x^2 + 7e^x + C$

c) $\int e^{10x}\, dx = \frac{1}{10}e^{10x} + C$

d) $\int e^{-3x} + x\, dx = \int e^{-3x}\, dx + \int x\, dx$

$= -\frac{1}{3}e^{-3x} + \frac{1}{2}x^2 + C$

e) $\int e^{\frac{7}{2}x}\, dx = \frac{1}{\left(\frac{7}{2}\right)}e^{\frac{7}{2}x} + C = \frac{2}{7}e^{\frac{7}{2}x} + C$

f) $\int e^{4x-2}\, dx = \frac{1}{4}e^{4x-2} + C$

g) $\int \frac{1}{2}e^{2-\frac{3}{2}x}\, dx = \frac{1}{2}\int e^{2-\frac{3}{2}x}\, dx$

$= \frac{1}{2}\left(\frac{1}{\left(-\frac{3}{2}\right)}e^{2-\frac{3}{2}x} + c\right) = \left(\frac{1}{2}\times -\frac{2}{3}e^{2-\frac{3}{2}x}\right) + C$

$= -\frac{1}{3}e^{2-\frac{3}{2}x} + C$

h) $\int e^{4\left(\frac{4}{3}x+1\right)}\, dx = \int e^{\frac{4}{3}x+4}\, dx$

$= \frac{1}{\left(\frac{4}{3}\right)}e^{\frac{4}{3}x+4} + C = \frac{3}{4}e^{4\left(\frac{4}{3}x+1\right)} + C$

Q2 You've been given the derivative of the curve, so integrate it to get the equation of the curve.

$y = \int \frac{dy}{dx}\, dx = \int 10e^{-5x-1}\, dx = 10\int e^{-5x-1}\, dx$

$= 10\left(\frac{1}{-5}e^{-5x-1} + c\right) = -2e^{-5x-1} + C$

To find C, use the fact that the curve goes through the origin (0, 0). The equation of the curve is $y = -2e^{-5x-1} + C$ and substituting in $x = 0$ and $y = 0$ gives:

$0 = -2e^{-(5\times 0)-1} + C = -2e^{-1} + C = -\frac{2}{e} + C$ so $C = \frac{2}{e}$.

So the curve has equation $y = -2e^{-5x-1} + \frac{2}{e}$.

Q3 $\int e^{8y+5}\, dy = \frac{1}{8}e^{8y+5} + C$

Q4 **a)** $\int_2^3 e^{2x}\, dx = \frac{1}{2}[e^{2x}]_2^3 = \frac{1}{2}([e^6] - [e^4])$

$= \frac{1}{2}(e^6 - e^4)$

b) $\int_{-1}^0 12e^{12x+12}\, dx = \left[12\times\frac{1}{12}e^{12x+12}\right]_{-1}^0$

$= [e^{12x+12}]_{-1}^0 = e^{12} - e^0 = e^{12} - 1$

c) $\int_{-\frac{\pi}{2}}^{\frac{\pi}{2}} e^{\pi-2x}\, dx = \left[-\frac{1}{2}e^{\pi-2x}\right]_{-\frac{\pi}{2}}^{\frac{\pi}{2}}$

$= -\frac{1}{2}[e^{\pi-2x}]_{-\frac{\pi}{2}}^{\frac{\pi}{2}}$

$= -\frac{1}{2}([e^{\pi-\pi}] - [e^{\pi+\pi}])$

$= -\frac{1}{2}(e^0 - e^{2\pi}) = \frac{1}{2}(e^{2\pi} - 1)$

d) $\int_3^6 \sqrt[6]{e^x} + \frac{1}{\sqrt[3]{e^x}}\, dx = \int_3^6 (e^x)^{\frac{1}{6}} + (e^x)^{-\frac{1}{3}}\, dx$

$= \int_3^6 e^{\frac{x}{6}} + e^{-\frac{x}{3}}\, dx = \left[\frac{1}{\left(\frac{1}{6}\right)}e^{\frac{x}{6}} + \frac{1}{\left(-\frac{1}{3}\right)}e^{-\frac{x}{3}}\right]_3^6$

$= [6e^{\frac{x}{6}} - 3e^{-\frac{x}{3}}]_3^6$

$= [6e^1 - 3e^{-2}] - [6e^{\frac{1}{2}} - 3e^{-1}]$

$= 6e - \frac{3}{e^2} - 6\sqrt{e} + \frac{3}{e}$

Exercise 8.2.2 — Integrating $\frac{1}{x}$ and $\frac{1}{ax+b}$

Q1 **a)** $\int \frac{19}{x}\, dx = 19\int \frac{1}{x}\, dx = 19\ln|x| + C$

b) $\int \frac{1}{7x}\, dx = \frac{1}{7}\int \frac{1}{x}\, dx = \frac{1}{7}\ln|x| + C$

An equivalent answer to b) would be $\frac{1}{7}\ln|7x| + C$ if you used the general formula for integrating $\frac{1}{ax+b}$ instead.

c) There is no constant term to take out here, so use the general formula:

$\int \frac{1}{7x+2}\, dx = \frac{1}{7}\ln|7x+2| + C$

d) $\int \frac{4}{1-3x}\, dx = 4\left(\frac{1}{-3}\ln|1-3x| + c\right) = -\frac{4}{3}\ln|1-3x| + C$

Q2 $\int \frac{1}{8x} - \frac{20}{x}\, dx = \frac{1}{8}\int \frac{1}{x}\, dx - 20\int \frac{1}{x}\, dx$

$= \frac{1}{8}\ln|x| - 20\ln|x| + C = -\frac{159}{8}\ln|x| + C$

You could also notice that $\frac{1}{8x} - \frac{20}{x} = \frac{1-160}{8x} = \frac{-159}{8x}$ and integrate $\frac{-159}{8x}$ using the method for $\frac{1}{x}$.

Q3 **a)** $\int \frac{6}{x} - \frac{3}{x}\,dx = \int \frac{3}{x}\,dx = 3\ln|x| + C = \ln|x|^3 + C = \ln|x^3| + C$

b) $\int_4^5 \frac{6}{x} - \frac{3}{x}\,dx = [\ln|x^3|]_4^5$

$= [\ln 5^3] - [\ln 4^3] = 3\ln 5 - 3\ln 4$

$= 3(\ln 5 - \ln 4) = 3\ln\left(\frac{5}{4}\right)$

You could also have written your answer as $\ln\frac{125}{64}$.

Q4 $\int_b^a 15(5+3x)^{-1}\,dx = \int_b^a \frac{15}{(5+3x)}\,dx$

$= \left[15 \times \frac{1}{3}\ln|5+3x|\right]_b^a = 5[\ln|5+3x|]_b^a = 5(\ln|5+3a| - \ln|5+3b|)$

$= 5\ln\left(\frac{|5+3a|}{|5+3b|}\right) = 5\ln\left|\frac{5+3a}{5+3b}\right| = \ln\left|\frac{5+3a}{5+3b}\right|^5$

Q5 Integrate the derivative to find f(x).

$f(x) = \int f'(x)\,dx = \int \frac{4}{10-9x}\,dx$

$= 4 \times \frac{1}{-9}\ln|10-9x| + C = -\frac{4}{9}\ln|10-9x| + C$

The curve passes through the point (1, 2),
so substitute these values to find C.

$2 = -\frac{4}{9}\ln|10-(9\times 1)| + C \Rightarrow 2 = -\frac{4}{9}\ln|1| + C \Rightarrow 2 = 0 + C$

So C = 2 and the equation of f(x) is $f(x) = -\frac{4}{9}\ln|10-9x| + 2$.

Q6 **a)** The area required is the shaded area below:

This is found by integrating the curve with respect to x
between the limits $x = -3$ and $x = 0$.
So the area is expressed by the integral $\int_{-3}^0 \frac{-7}{16-2x}\,dx$

b) $\int_{-3}^0 \frac{-7}{16-2x} = \left[-7 \times \frac{1}{-2}\ln|16-2x|\right]_{-3}^0$

$= \frac{7}{2}[\ln|16-2x|]_{-3}^0 = \frac{7}{2}(\ln 16 - \ln 22)$

$= \frac{7}{2}\ln\frac{16}{22} = \frac{7}{2}\ln\frac{8}{11} = \ln\left[\left(\frac{8}{11}\right)^{\frac{7}{2}}\right]$

Q7 Work out the integral and put in the limits to find A.

$\int_1^A \frac{4}{6x-5}\,dx = 10 \Rightarrow \left[4 \times \frac{1}{6}\ln|6x-5|\right]_1^A = 10 \Rightarrow \frac{2}{3}[\ln|6x-5|]_1^A = 10$

$\Rightarrow \frac{2}{3}(\ln|6A-5| - \ln|1|) = 10 \Rightarrow \frac{2}{3}(\ln|6A-5| - 0) = 10$

$\Rightarrow \frac{2}{3}\ln|6A-5| = 10 \Rightarrow \ln|6A-5| = \frac{10}{\left(\frac{2}{3}\right)} = 15$

Take the exponential of both sides to get rid of the ln.

$|6A-5| = e^{15} \Rightarrow A = \frac{e^{15}+5}{6}$

As $A \geq 1$, then $6A - 5$ must be greater than $6 - 5 = 1$,
so the modulus can be removed as it'll always be positive.

8.3 Integration of Trigonometric Functions

Exercise 8.3.1 — Integration of sin x and cos x

Q1 **a)** $\int \frac{1}{7}\cos x\,dx = \frac{1}{7}\int \cos x\,dx = \frac{1}{7}\sin x + C$

b) $\int -3\sin x\,dx = -3\int \sin x\,dx = -3(-\cos x) + C = 3\cos x + C$

c) $\int -3\cos x - 3\sin x\,dx = -3\int \cos x + \sin x\,dx$

$= -3(\sin x - \cos x + c) = -3\sin x + 3\cos x + C$

d) $\int \sin 5x\,dx = -\frac{1}{5}\cos 5x + C$

e) $\int \cos\left(\frac{x}{7}\right)dx = \frac{1}{\left(\frac{1}{7}\right)}\sin\left(\frac{x}{7}\right) + C = 7\sin\left(\frac{x}{7}\right) + C$

f) $\int 2\sin(-3x)\,dx = 2\int \sin(-3x)\,dx$

$= 2\left(-\left(-\frac{1}{3}\right)\cos(-3x) + c\right) = \frac{2}{3}\cos(-3x) + C$

An alternative solution would be $\frac{2}{3}\cos(3x) + C$ since $\cos(x) = \cos(-x)$.

g) $\int 5\cos\left(3x + \frac{\pi}{5}\right)dx = 5\left(\frac{1}{3}\sin\left(3x + \frac{\pi}{5}\right) + c\right)$

$= \frac{5}{3}\sin\left(3x + \frac{\pi}{5}\right) + C$

h) $\int -4\sin\left(4x - \frac{\pi}{3}\right)dx = -4\left(-\frac{1}{4}\cos\left(4x - \frac{\pi}{3}\right) + c\right)$

$= \cos\left(4x - \frac{\pi}{3}\right) + C$

i) $\int \cos(4x+3) + \sin(3-4x)\,dx$

$= \frac{1}{4}\sin(4x+3) + \frac{1}{-4}(-\cos(3-4x)) + C$

$= \frac{1}{4}\sin(4x+3) + \frac{1}{4}\cos(3-4x) + C$

Q2 $\int \frac{1}{2}\cos 3\theta - \sin\theta\,d\theta = \frac{1}{2}\left(\frac{1}{3}\sin 3\theta\right) - (-\cos\theta) + C$

$= \frac{1}{6}\sin 3\theta + \cos\theta + C$

Q3 **a)** $\int_0^{\frac{\pi}{2}}\sin x\,dx = [-\cos x]_0^{\frac{\pi}{2}} = -\cos\frac{\pi}{2} + \cos 0 = 0 + 1 = 1$

b) $\int_{\frac{\pi}{6}}^{\frac{\pi}{3}}\sin 3x\,dx = -\frac{1}{3}[\cos 3x]_{\frac{\pi}{6}}^{\frac{\pi}{3}} = -\frac{1}{3}\left(\left[\cos\left(3 \times \frac{\pi}{3}\right)\right] - \left[\cos\left(3 \times \frac{\pi}{6}\right)\right]\right)$

$= -\frac{1}{3}\left(\cos\pi - \cos\frac{\pi}{2}\right) = -\frac{1}{3}(-1-0) = \frac{1}{3}$

c) $\int_{-1}^2 3\sin(\pi x + \pi)\,dx = -\frac{3}{\pi}[\cos(\pi x + \pi)]_{-1}^2$

$= -\frac{3}{\pi}(\cos 3\pi - \cos 0) = -\frac{3}{\pi}(-1-1) = \frac{6}{\pi}$

Q4 **a)** Integrate the function with respect to x
within the limits 1 and 2:

$\int_1^2 2\pi\cos\left(\frac{\pi x}{2}\right)dx = \frac{2\pi}{\left(\frac{\pi}{2}\right)}\left[\sin\left(\frac{\pi x}{2}\right)\right]_1^2 = 4\left[\sin\left(\frac{\pi x}{2}\right)\right]_1^2$

$= 4\left(\sin(\pi) - \sin\left(\frac{\pi}{2}\right)\right) = 4(0-1) = -4$

b) Since the function doesn't cross the x-axis for $1 < x < 2$,
the described area has to be either entirely above the x-axis
or entirely below it. The integral gives a negative value,
so all of the area is below the x-axis.

Q5 $\int_{\frac{\pi}{3}}^{\frac{\pi}{2}}\sin(-x) + \cos(-x)\,dx = \int_{\frac{\pi}{3}}^{\frac{\pi}{2}} -\sin x + \cos x\,dx$

$= [-(-\cos x) + \sin x]_{\frac{\pi}{3}}^{\frac{\pi}{2}} = [\cos x + \sin x]_{\frac{\pi}{3}}^{\frac{\pi}{2}}$

$= \left[\cos\left(\frac{\pi}{2}\right) + \sin\left(\frac{\pi}{2}\right)\right] - \left[\cos\left(\frac{\pi}{3}\right) + \sin\left(\frac{\pi}{3}\right)\right]$

$= [0 + 1] - \left[\frac{1}{2} + \frac{\sqrt{3}}{2}\right] = 1 - \frac{1}{2} - \frac{\sqrt{3}}{2} = \frac{1}{2} - \frac{\sqrt{3}}{2} = \frac{1-\sqrt{3}}{2}$

$\sin(-x) = -\sin x$ and $\cos(-x) = \cos x$ are used in the first step of this solution.

Q6 $\int_{-\frac{\pi}{3}}^{\frac{\pi}{3}}\sin(3x+2) - \cos x\,dx = \left[-\frac{1}{3}\cos(3x+2) - \sin x\right]_{-\frac{\pi}{3}}^{\frac{\pi}{3}}$

$= \left[-\frac{1}{3}\cos\left(3\left(\frac{\pi}{3}\right) + 2\right) - \sin\frac{\pi}{3}\right] - \left[-\frac{1}{3}\cos\left(3\left(-\frac{\pi}{3}\right) + 2\right) - \sin\left(-\frac{\pi}{3}\right)\right]$

$= \left[-\frac{1}{3}\cos(\pi + 2) - \frac{\sqrt{3}}{2}\right] - \left[-\frac{1}{3}\cos(-\pi + 2) - \left(-\frac{\sqrt{3}}{2}\right)\right] = -\sqrt{3}$

Q7 Integrate the function between -2π and π:

$\int_{-2\pi}^\pi 5\cos\frac{x}{6}\,dx = \left[\frac{5}{\left(\frac{1}{6}\right)}\sin\left(\frac{x}{6}\right)\right]_{-2\pi}^\pi = 30\left[\sin\left(\frac{x}{6}\right)\right]_{-2\pi}^\pi$

$= 30\left(\sin\left(\frac{\pi}{6}\right) - \sin\left(-\frac{\pi}{3}\right)\right) = 30\left(\frac{1}{2} - \left(-\frac{\sqrt{3}}{2}\right)\right) = 30\left(\frac{1+\sqrt{3}}{2}\right)$

$= 15(1+\sqrt{3})$

Exercise 8.3.2 — Integration of sec² x

Q1 **a)** $\int 2\sec^2 x + 1\,dx = 2\tan x + x + C$

b) $\int \sec^2 9x\,dx = \frac{1}{9}\tan 9x + C$

c) $\int 20\sec^2 3y\,dy = 20 \times \frac{1}{3}\tan 3y + C = \frac{20}{3}\tan 3y + C$

d) $\int \sec^2 \frac{x}{7}\,dx = \frac{1}{\left(\frac{1}{7}\right)}\tan\left(\frac{x}{7}\right) + C = 7\tan\left(\frac{x}{7}\right) + C$

e) $\int_0^{\frac{\pi}{3}} -\frac{1}{\cos^2\theta}\,d\theta = \int_0^{\frac{\pi}{3}} -\sec^2\theta\,d\theta = [-\tan\theta]_0^{\frac{\pi}{3}} = -\sqrt{3} + 0 = -\sqrt{3}$

f) $\int_0^{\frac{\pi}{4}} 3\sec^2(-3x)\,dx = \left[\frac{3}{-3}\tan(-3x)\right]_0^{\frac{\pi}{4}}$

$= [-\tan(-3x)]_0^{\frac{\pi}{4}} = \left[-\tan\left(-3 \times \frac{\pi}{4}\right)\right] - [-\tan(0)] = -1 + 0 = -1$

Q2 Integrate the function between the limits:

$\int_{\frac{4\pi}{3}}^{\pi}\sec^2 x\,dx = [\tan x]_{\frac{4\pi}{3}}^{\pi} = \tan\pi - \tan\frac{2\pi}{3} = 0 - (-\sqrt{3}) = \sqrt{3}$

Q3 The constants α and β do not affect the integration. You only need to worry about the coefficients of x.

$\int \sec^2(x + \alpha) + \sec^2(3x + \beta)\,dx = \tan(x + \alpha) + \frac{1}{3}\tan(3x + \beta) + C$

Q4 $\int_{\frac{\pi}{12}}^{\frac{\pi}{6}} 5A\sec^2\left(\frac{\pi}{3} - 2\theta\right)d\theta = \left[-\frac{5A}{2}\tan\left(\frac{\pi}{3} - 2\theta\right)\right]_{\frac{\pi}{12}}^{\frac{\pi}{6}}$

$= -\frac{5A}{2}\left[\tan\left(\frac{\pi}{3} - 2\theta\right)\right]_{\frac{\pi}{12}}^{\frac{\pi}{6}} = -\frac{5A}{2}\left(\left[\tan\left(\frac{\pi}{3} - \frac{\pi}{3}\right)\right] - \left[\tan\left(\frac{\pi}{3} - \frac{\pi}{6}\right)\right]\right)$

$= -\frac{5A}{2}\left(\tan(0) - \tan\left(\frac{\pi}{6}\right)\right) = -\frac{5A}{2}\left(0 - \frac{\sqrt{3}}{3}\right) = \frac{5\sqrt{3}A}{6}$

Exercise 8.3.3 — Integration of other trigonometric functions

Q1 a) $\int \csc^2 11x\,dx = -\frac{1}{11}\cot 11x + C$

b) $\int 5\sec 10\theta\tan 10\theta\,d\theta = 5 \times \frac{1}{10}\sec 10\theta + C = \frac{1}{2}\sec 10\theta + C$

c) $\int -\csc(x + 17)\cot(x + 17)\,dx$

$= -(-\csc(x + 17)) + C = \csc(x + 17) + C$

d) $\int -3\csc 3x\cot 3x\,dx = -3\left(-\frac{1}{3}\csc 3x\right) + C = \csc 3x + C$

e) $\int 13\sec\left(\frac{\pi}{4} - x\right)\tan\left(\frac{\pi}{4} - x\right)dx = 13\left(\frac{1}{-1}\sec\left(\frac{\pi}{4} - x\right)\right) + C$

$= -13\sec\left(\frac{\pi}{4} - x\right) + C$

f) $\int 4\csc^2(5x + 3)\,dx = 4\left(-\frac{1}{5}\cot(5x + 3)\right) + C$

$= -\frac{4}{5}\cot(5x + 3) + C$

Q2 $\int 10\csc^2\left(\alpha - \frac{x}{2}\right) - 60\sec(\alpha - 6x)\tan(\alpha - 6x)\,dx$

$= -\frac{10}{\left(-\frac{1}{2}\right)}\cot\left(\alpha - \frac{x}{2}\right) - \frac{60}{-6}\sec(\alpha - 6x) + C$

$= 20\cot\left(\alpha - \frac{x}{2}\right) + 10\sec(\alpha - 6x) + C$

Q3 $\int_{\frac{\pi}{12}}^{\frac{\pi}{8}} 6\sec 2x\tan 2x + 6\csc 2x\cot 2x\,dx = \left[\frac{6}{2}\sec 2x - \frac{6}{2}\csc 2x\right]_{\frac{\pi}{12}}^{\frac{\pi}{8}}$

$= 3[\sec 2x - \csc 2x]_{\frac{\pi}{12}}^{\frac{\pi}{8}} = 3\left(\left[\sec\frac{\pi}{4} - \csc\frac{\pi}{4}\right] - \left[\sec\frac{\pi}{6} - \csc\frac{\pi}{6}\right]\right)$

$= 3\left(\sqrt{2} - \sqrt{2} - \frac{2}{\sqrt{3}} + 2\right) = 3\left(2 - \frac{2}{\sqrt{3}}\right) = 6 - 2\sqrt{3}$

Q4 $\int_{\frac{\pi}{12}}^{\frac{\pi}{6}}\csc^2(3x)\,dx = \left[-\frac{1}{3}\cot(3x)\right]_{\frac{\pi}{12}}^{\frac{\pi}{6}}$

$= -\frac{1}{3}\left(\cot\left(\frac{\pi}{2}\right) - \cot\left(\frac{\pi}{4}\right)\right) = -\frac{1}{3}(0 - 1) = \frac{1}{3}$

If you know the tan values for the common angles, you can work out the cot values using cot x = 1/tan x.

8.4 Integration of $\frac{f'(x)}{f(x)}$

Exercise 8.4.1 — Integrating $\frac{f'(x)}{f(x)}$

Q1 a) Differentiating the denominator:

$\frac{d}{dx}(x^4 - 1) = 4x^3 = \text{numerator}$

$\int \frac{4x^3}{x^4 - 1}\,dx = \ln|x^4 - 1| + C$

b) $\frac{d}{dx}(x^2 - x) = 2x - 1 = \text{numerator}$

$\int \frac{2x - 1}{x^2 - x}\,dx = \ln|x^2 - x| + C$

c) $\frac{d}{dx}(3x^5 + 6) = 15x^4$

$\int \frac{x^4}{3x^5 + 6}\,dx = \frac{1}{15}\int \frac{15x^4}{3x^5 + 6}\,dx = \frac{1}{15}\ln|3x^5 + 6| + C$

d) $\frac{d}{dx}(x^4 + 2x^3 - x) = 4x^3 + 6x^2 - 1$

$\int \frac{12x^3 + 18x^2 - 3}{x^4 + 2x^3 - x}\,dx = \int \frac{3(4x^3 + 6x^2 - 1)}{x^4 + 2x^3 - x}\,dx$

$= 3\int \frac{4x^3 + 6x^2 - 1}{x^4 + 2x^3 - x}\,dx = 3\ln|x^4 + 2x^3 - x| + C$

e) $\frac{d}{dx}(x - 2)(2x + 3) = \frac{d}{dx}(2x^2 - x - 6) = 4x - 1$

$\int \frac{8x - 2}{(x - 2)(2x + 3)}\,dx = 2\int \frac{4x - 1}{2x^2 - x - 3}\,dx$

$= 2\ln|(x - 2)(2x + 3)| + C$

f) $\frac{d}{dx}(2x^3 - 9x + 7) = 6x^2 - 9$

$\int \frac{6 - 4x^2}{2x^3 - 9x + 7}\,dx = -\frac{2}{3}\int \frac{6x^2 - 9}{2x^3 - 9x + 7}\,dx$

$= -\frac{2}{3}\ln|2x^3 - 9x + 7| + C$

Q2 a) $\frac{d}{dx}(e^x + 6) = e^x$

$\int \frac{e^x}{e^x + 6}\,dx = \ln|e^x + 6| + C$

b) $\frac{d}{dx}(e^{2x} + 6e^x) = 2e^{2x} + 6e^x = 2(e^{2x} + 3e^x)$

$\int \frac{2(e^{2x} + 3e^x)}{e^{2x} + 6e^x}\,dx = \ln|e^{2x} + 6e^x| + C$

c) $\frac{d}{dx}(e^x + 3) = e^x$

$\int \frac{e^x}{3(e^x + 3)}\,dx = \frac{1}{3}\int \frac{e^x}{(e^x + 3)}\,dx = \frac{1}{3}\ln|e^x + 3| + C$

d) $\frac{d}{dx}(5e^{4x} + 10x) = 20e^{4x} + 10$

$\int \frac{10e^{4x} + 5}{5e^{4x} + 10x}\,dx = \frac{1}{2}\int \frac{20e^{4x} + 10}{5e^{4x} + 10x}\,dx = \frac{1}{2}\ln|5e^{4x} + 10x| + C$

Q3 a) $\frac{d}{dx}(1 + \sin 2x) = 2\cos 2x$

$\int \frac{2\cos 2x}{1 + \sin 2x}\,dx = \ln|1 + \sin 2x| + C$

b) $\frac{d}{dx}(\cos 3x - 1) = -3\sin 3x$

$\int \frac{\sin 3x}{\cos 3x - 1}\,dx = -\frac{1}{3}\int \frac{-3\sin 3x}{\cos 3x - 1}\,dx$

$= -\frac{1}{3}\ln|\cos 3x - 1| + C$

c) $\frac{d}{dx}(\csc x - x^2 + 4) = -\csc x\cot x - 2x$

$\int \frac{3\csc x\cot x + 6x}{\csc x - x^2 + 4}\,dx = \int \frac{-3(-\csc x\cot x - 2x)}{\csc x - x^2 + 4}\,dx$

$= -3\int \frac{-\csc x\cot x - 2x}{\csc x - x^2 + 4}\,dx = -3\ln|\csc x - x^2 + 4| + C$

d) $\frac{d}{dx}(\tan x) = \sec^2 x$

$\int \frac{\sec^2 x}{\tan x}\,dx = \ln|\tan x| + C$

e) $\frac{d}{dx}(\sec x + 5) = \sec x\tan x$

$\int \frac{\sec x\tan x}{\sec x + 5}\,dx = \ln|\sec x + 5| + C$

f) $\frac{d}{dx}(2\cot x - 1) = -2\csc^2 x$

$\int \frac{\csc^2 x}{2\cot x - 1}\,dx = -\frac{1}{2}\int \frac{2\csc^2 x}{2\cot x - 1}\,dx = -\frac{1}{2}\ln|2\cot x - 1| + C$

Q4 $\frac{d}{dx}(\sin(2x + 7)) = 2\cos(2x + 7)$

$\int \frac{4\cos(2x + 7)}{\sin(2x + 7)}\,dx = 2\int \frac{2\cos(2x + 7)}{\sin(2x + 7)}\,dx = 2(\ln|\sin(2x + 7)| + C)$

$= 2(\ln|\sin(2x + 7)| + \ln k) = 2\ln|k\sin(2x + 7)|$

Q5 **a)** Using the hint, multiply the inside of the integral by a fraction which is the same on the top and bottom (it's equal to 1, so it'll make no difference).

$$\int \sec x \, dx = \int \sec x \left(\frac{\sec x + \tan x}{\sec x + \tan x}\right) dx$$

$$= \int \frac{\sec^2 x + \sec x \tan x}{\sec x + \tan x} \, dx$$

Now differentiating the denominator of this integral gives:

$$\frac{d}{dx}(\sec x + \tan x) = \sec x \tan x + \sec^2 x$$

So the numerator is the derivative of the denominator, so use the result:

$$\int \sec x \, dx = \int \frac{\sec^2 x + \sec x \tan x}{\sec x + \tan x} \, dx = \ln|\sec x + \tan x| + C$$

b) Use the same method as part a), this time using $\frac{\operatorname{cosec} x + \cot x}{\operatorname{cosec} x + \cot x}$:

$$\int \operatorname{cosec} x \, dx = \int \operatorname{cosec} x \left(\frac{\operatorname{cosec} x + \cot x}{\operatorname{cosec} x + \cot x}\right) dx$$

$$= \int \frac{\operatorname{cosec}^2 x + \operatorname{cosec} x \cot x}{\operatorname{cosec} x + \cot x} \, dx$$

Differentiating the denominator of this integral:

$$\frac{d}{dx}(\operatorname{cosec} x + \cot x) = -\operatorname{cosec} x \cot x - \operatorname{cosec}^2 x$$
$$= -(\operatorname{cosec} x \cot x + \operatorname{cosec}^2 x)$$

So the numerator is $-1 \times$ the derivative of the denominator, so use the result:

$$\int \operatorname{cosec} x \, dx = \int \frac{\operatorname{cosec}^2 x + \operatorname{cosec} x \cot x}{\operatorname{cosec} x + \cot x} \, dx$$

$$= -\int \frac{-\operatorname{cosec}^2 x - \operatorname{cosec} x \cot x}{\operatorname{cosec} x + \cot x} \, dx = -\ln|\operatorname{cosec} x + \cot x| + C$$

Q6 **a)** $\int 2 \tan x \, dx = 2 \int \frac{\sin x}{\cos x} \, dx = -2 \int \frac{-\sin x}{\cos x} = -2 \ln|\cos x| + C$

b) $\int \tan 2x \, dx = \int \frac{\sin 2x}{\cos 2x} \, dx = -\frac{1}{2} \int \frac{-2 \sin 2x}{\cos 2x} \, dx$

$$= -\frac{1}{2} \ln|\cos 2x| + C$$

c) $\int 4 \operatorname{cosec} x \, dx = 4 \int \operatorname{cosec} x \, dx = -4 \ln|\operatorname{cosec} x + \cot x| + C$

d) $\int \cot 3x \, dx = \frac{1}{3} \ln|\sin 3x| + C$

e) $\int \frac{1}{2} \sec 2x \, dx = \frac{1}{2}\left(\frac{1}{2} \ln|\sec 2x + \tan 2x| + C\right)$

$$= \frac{1}{4} \ln|\sec 2x + \tan 2x| + C$$

f) $\int 3 \operatorname{cosec} 6x \, dx = 3\left(-\frac{1}{6} \ln|\operatorname{cosec} 6x + \cot 6x| + C\right)$

$$= -\frac{1}{2} \ln|\operatorname{cosec} 6x + \cot 6x| + C$$

The next two look pretty complicated, but if you split them into parts and use some standard results they're actually pretty simple.

Q7 $\int \frac{4 \sin(3 - 2x)}{3 + \cos(3 - 2x)} + \frac{x^2}{6x^3 - 5} \, dx$

$$= 2 \int \frac{2 \sin(3 - 2x)}{3 + \cos(3 - 2x)} \, dx + \frac{1}{18} \int \frac{x^2}{6x^3 - 5} \, dx$$

$$= 2 \ln|3 + \cos(3 - 2x)| + \frac{1}{18} \ln|6x^3 - 5| + C$$

Q8 $\int \frac{\sec^2 x}{2 \tan x} - 4 \sec 2x \tan 2x + \frac{\operatorname{cosec} 2x \cot 2x - 1}{\operatorname{cosec} 2x + 2x} \, dx$

$$= \int \frac{\sec^2 x}{2 \tan x} \, dx - \int 4 \sec 2x \tan 2x \, dx + \int \frac{\operatorname{cosec} 2x \cot 2x - 1}{\operatorname{cosec} 2x + 2x} \, dx$$

$$= \frac{1}{2} \int \frac{\sec^2 x}{\tan x} \, dx - 2 \int 2 \sec 2x \tan 2x \, dx$$

$$- \frac{1}{2} \int \frac{-2 \operatorname{cosec} 2x \cot 2x + 2}{\operatorname{cosec} 2x + 2x} \, dx$$

$$= \frac{1}{2} \ln|\tan x| - 2 \sec 2x - \frac{1}{2} \ln|\operatorname{cosec} 2x + 2x| + C$$

The first and third integrals were put in the form $\int \frac{f'(x)}{f(x)} \, dx$, and the second one you can tackle by reversing the result $\frac{d}{dx}(\sec 2x) = 2 \sec 2x \tan 2x$.

8.5 Integrating $\frac{du}{dx} f'(u)$

Exercise 8.5.1 — Integrating using the reverse of the chain rule

Q1 Let $u = x^2$ so $\frac{du}{dx} = 2x$ and $f'(u) = e^u$ so $f(u) = e^u$.
Using the formula: $\int 2xe^{x^2} \, dx = e^{x^2} + C$

Q2 Let $u = 2x^3$ so $\frac{du}{dx} = 6x^2$ and $f'(u) = e^u$ so $f(u) = e^u$.
Using the formula: $\int 6x^2 e^{2x^3} \, dx = e^{2x^3} + C$

Q3 Let $u = \sqrt{x}$ so $\frac{du}{dx} = \frac{1}{2\sqrt{x}}$, and $f'(u) = e^u$ so $f(u) = e^u$.
Using the formula: $\int \frac{1}{2\sqrt{x}} e^{\sqrt{x}} \, dx = e^{\sqrt{x}} + C$

Q4 Let $u = x^4$ so $\frac{du}{dx} = 4x^3$, and $f'(u) = e^u$ so $f(u) = e^u$.
Use the formula: $\int 4x^3 e^{x^4} \, dx = e^{x^4} + C$
So divide by 4 to get the original integral:
$\int x^3 e^{x^4} \, dx = \frac{1}{4} \int 4x^3 e^{x^4} \, dx = \frac{1}{4} e^{x^4} + C$

Q5 Let $u = x^2 - \frac{1}{2}x$ so $\frac{du}{dx} = 2x - \frac{1}{2} = \frac{1}{2}(4x - 1)$,
and $f'(u) = e^u$ so $f(u) = e^u$.
Use the formula: $\int \left(2x - \frac{1}{2}\right) e^{\left(x^2 - \frac{1}{2}x\right)} \, dx = e^{\left(x^2 - \frac{1}{2}x\right)} + C$
Multiply by 2 to get the original integral:
$\int (4x - 1) e^{\left(x^2 - \frac{1}{2}x\right)} \, dx = \int 2\left(2x - \frac{1}{2}\right) e^{\left(x^2 - \frac{1}{2}x\right)} \, dx$
$= 2 \int \left(2x - \frac{1}{2}\right) e^{\left(x^2 - \frac{1}{2}x\right)} \, dx = 2e^{\left(x^2 - \frac{1}{2}x\right)} + C$

Q6 Let $u = x^2 + 1$ so $\frac{du}{dx} = 2x$, and $f'(u) = \sin u$ so $f(u) = -\cos u$.
Use the formula: $\int 2x \sin(x^2 + 1) \, dx = -\cos(x^2 + 1) + C$

Q7 Let $u = x^4$ so $\frac{du}{dx} = 4x^3$, and $f'(u) = \cos u$ so $f(u) = \sin u$.
Use the formula: $\int 4x^3 \cos(x^4) \, dx = \sin(x^4) + C$
Now divide by 4 to get the original integral:
$\int x^3 \cos(x^4) \, dx = \frac{1}{4} \int 4x^3 \cos(x^4) \, dx = \frac{1}{4} \sin(x^4) + C$

Q8 Let $u = x^2$ so $\frac{du}{dx} = 2x$, and $f'(u) = \sec^2 u$ so $f(u) = \tan u$.
Use the formula: $\int 2x \sec^2(x^2) \, dx = \tan(x^2) + C$
Now divide by 2 to get the original integral:
$\int x \sec^2(x^2) \, dx = \frac{1}{2} \int 2x \sec^2(x^2) \, dx = \frac{1}{2} \tan(x^2) + C$

Q9 *It's less obvious which function to choose as u in this one — keep looking out for a function and its derivative. Here we have cos x and sin x. Remember to make u the one which is within another function, i.e. cos x.*
Let $u = \cos x$ so $\frac{du}{dx} = -\sin x$, and $f'(u) = e^u$ so $f(u) = e^u$.
Use the formula: $\int -\sin x \, e^{\cos x} \, dx = e^{\cos x} + C$
Multiply by -1 to get the original integral:
$\int \sin x \, e^{\cos x} \, dx = -\int -\sin x \, e^{\cos x} \, dx = -e^{\cos x} + C$

Q10 Let $u = \sin 2x$ so $\frac{du}{dx} = 2\cos 2x$, and $f'(u) = e^u$ so $f(u) = e^u$.
Use the formula: $\int 2 \cos 2x \, e^{\sin 2x} \, dx = e^{\sin 2x} + C$
Divide by 2 to get the original integral:
$\int \cos 2x \, e^{\sin 2x} \, dx = \frac{1}{2} \int 2 \cos 2x \, e^{\sin 2x} \, dx = \frac{1}{2} e^{\sin 2x} + C$

Q11 Let $u = \tan x$ then $\frac{du}{dx} = \sec^2 x$, and $f'(u) = e^u$ so $f(u) = e^u$.
Use the formula: $\int \sec^2 x \, e^{\tan x} \, dx = e^{\tan x} + C$

Q12 Let $u = \sec x$ then $\frac{du}{dx} = \sec x \tan x$, and $f'(u) = e^u$ so $f(u) = e^u$.
Use the formula: $\int \sec x \tan x \, e^{\sec x} \, dx = e^{\sec x} + C$

Q13 Let $u = \cot x$ then $\frac{du}{dx} = -\operatorname{cosec}^2 x$, and $f'(u) = e^u$, so $f(u) = e^u$.
Use the formula: $\int -\operatorname{cosec}^2 x \, e^{\cot x} \, dx = e^{\cot x} + C$
Now multiply by -2 to get the original integral:
$-2 \int -\operatorname{cosec}^2 x \, e^{\cot x} \, dx = -2e^{\cot x} + C$

Q14 Let $u = \text{cosec } 3x$ then $\dfrac{du}{dx} = -3 \text{ cosec } 3x \cot 3x$,

and $f'(u) = e^u$, so $f(u) = e^u$.

Use the formula: $\int -3 \text{ cosec } 3x \cot 3x \, e^{\text{cosec } 3x} \, dx = e^{\text{cosec } 3x} + C$

Divide by –3 to get the original integral:

$-\dfrac{1}{3}\int 3\text{cosec } 3x \cot 3x \, e^{\text{cosec } 3x} \, dx = -\dfrac{1}{3} e^{\text{cosec } 3x} + C$

Q15 a) Let $u = \cos(2 - 5x)$ then $\dfrac{du}{dx} = 5\sin(2 - 5x)$,

and $f'(u) = e^u$, so $f(u) = e^u$.

Use the formula: $\int 5 \sin(2 - 5x) \, e^{\cos(2-5x)} \, dx = e^{\cos(2-5x)} + C$

b) $\int_{0}^{1} 5\sin(2 - 5x) \, e^{\cos(2-5x)} \, dx = [e^{\cos(2-5x)}]_{0}^{1}$

$= [e^{\cos(2-5(1))}] - [e^{\cos(2-5(0))}] = [e^{\cos(-3)}] - [e^{\cos(2)}] = e^{\cos(-3)} - e^{\cos(2)}$
$= -0.288$ (3 s.f.)

You could also have $e^{\cos 3} - e^{\cos 2}$, because $\cos(-x) = \cos(x)$ for all x.

Q16 a) Let $u = \sin(4x^2 - x)$ then $\dfrac{du}{dx} = (8x - 1)\cos(4x^2 - x)$,

and $f'(u) = e^u$, so $f(u) = e^u$.

Use the formula:

$\int (8x - 1)\cos(4x^2 - x) \, e^{\sin(4x^2-x)} \, dx = e^{\sin(4x^2-x)} + C$

b) $\int_{0}^{\pi} (8x - 1)\cos(4x^2 - x) \, e^{\sin(4x^2-x)} \, dx$

$= [e^{\sin(4x^2-x)}]_{0}^{\pi} = [e^{\sin(4\pi^2-\pi)}] - [e^{\sin(4(0)^2-0)}] = -0.624$ (3 s.f.)

Exercise 8.5.2 — Integrating f'(x) × [f(x)]ⁿ

Q1 a) Let $f(x) = x^2 + 5$ so $f'(x) = 2x$. $n = 2$ so $n + 1 = 3$.
Using the formula: $\int 3 \times 2x(x^2 + 5)^2 \, dx = (x^2 + 5)^3 + C$
So $\int 6x(x^2 + 5)^2 \, dx = (x^2 + 5)^3 + C$

b) Let $f(x) = x^2 + 7x$ so $f'(x) = 2x + 7$. $n = 4$ so $n + 1 = 5$.
Using the formula: $\int 5(2x + 7)(x^2 + 7x)^4 \, dx = (x^2 + 7x)^5 + C$
Divide by 5 to get the original integral:
$\int (2x + 7)(x^2 + 7x)^4 \, dx = \dfrac{1}{5}(x^2 + 7x)^5 + C$

c) Let $f(x) = x^4 + 4x^2$ so $f'(x) = 4x^3 + 8x$. $n = 3$ so $n + 1 = 4$.
Using the formula: $\int 4(4x^3 + 8x)(x^4 + 4x^2)^3 \, dx = (x^4 + 4x^2)^4 + C$
Divide by 16 to get the original integral:
$\int (x^3 + 2x)(x^4 + 4x^2)^3 \, dx$
$= \dfrac{1}{16}\int 4(4x^3 + 8x)(x^4 + 4x^2)^3 \, dx = \dfrac{1}{16}(x^4 + 4x^2)^4 + C$

d) Let $f(x) = x^2 - 1$, so $f'(x) = 2x$. $n = -3$ so $n + 1 = -2$.
Using the formula: $\int -2(2x)(x^2 - 1)^{-3} \, dx = (x^2 - 1)^{-2} + C$
Divide by –2 to get the original integral:
$\int \dfrac{2x}{(x^2-1)^3} \, dx = \int (2x)(x^2 - 1)^{-3} \, dx$
$= -\dfrac{1}{2}(x^2 - 1)^{-2} + C = -\dfrac{1}{2(x^2-1)^2} + C$

e) Let $f(x) = e^{3x} - 5$, so $f'(x) = 3e^{3x}$. $n = -2$ so $n + 1 = -1$.
Using the formula: $\int -1(3e^{3x})(e^{3x} - 5)^{-2} \, dx = (e^{3x} - 5)^{-1} + C$
Multiply by –2 to get the original integral:
$\int \dfrac{6e^{3x}}{(e^{3x}-5)^2} \, dx = \int 6e^{3x}(e^{3x} - 5)^{-2} \, dx$
$= -2\int -3e^{3x}(e^{3x} - 5)^{-2} \, dx = -2(e^{3x} - 5)^{-1} + C$

f) $\sin x \cos^5 x = \sin x (\cos x)^5$
Let $f(x) = \cos x$ so $f'(x) = -\sin x$. $n = 5$ so $n + 1 = 6$.
Using the formula:
$\int 6(-\sin x)(\cos x)^5 \, dx = (\cos x)^6 + C = \cos^6 x + C$
Divide by –6 to get the original integral:
$\int \sin x \cos^5 x \, dx = \dfrac{1}{-6}\int 6(-\sin x)(\cos x)^5 \, dx = -\dfrac{1}{6}\cos^6 x + C$

g) It's a bit more difficult to tell which is the derivative and which is the function here — both functions are to a power. Remember that the derivative of $\tan x$ is $\sec^2 x$.
$2 \sec^2 x \tan^3 x = 2 \sec^2 x (\tan x)^3$
Let $f(x) = \tan x$ so $f'(x) = \sec^2 x$. $n = 3$ so $n + 1 = 4$.
Using the formula:
$\int 4 \sec^2 x (\tan x)^3 \, dx = (\tan x)^4 + C = \tan^4 x + C$
Divide by 2 to get the original integral:
$\int 2 \sec^2 x \tan^3 x \, dx = \dfrac{1}{2}\int 4 \sec^2 x (\tan x)^3 \, dx = \dfrac{1}{2}\tan^4 x + C$

h) Let $f(x) = e^x + 4$ so $f'(x) = e^x$. $n = 2$ so $n + 1 = 3$.
Using the formula: $\int 3e^x(e^x + 4)^2 \, dx = (e^x + 4)^3 + C$

i) Let $f(x) = e^{4x} - 3x^2$ so $f'(x) = 4e^{4x} - 6x$. $n = 7$ so $n + 1 = 8$.
Using the formula:
$\int 8(4e^{4x} - 6x)(e^{4x} - 3x^2)^7 \, dx = (e^{4x} - 3x^2)^8 + C$
So $\int 16(2e^{4x} - 3x)(e^{4x} - 3x^2)^7 \, dx = (e^{4x} - 3x^2)^8 + C$
Multiply by 2 to get the original integral:
$\int 32(2e^{4x} - 3x)(e^{4x} - 3x^2)^7 \, dx$
$= 2\int 16(2e^{4x} - 3x)(e^{4x} - 3x^2)^7 \, dx = 2(e^{4x} - 3x^2)^8 + C$

j) Let $f(x) = 2 + \sin x$, so $f'(x) = \cos x$. $n = -4$, so $n + 1 = -3$.
Using the formula:
$\int -3(\cos x)(2 + \sin x)^{-4} \, dx = (2 + \sin x)^{-3} + C$
Divide by –3 to get the original integral:
$\int \dfrac{\cos x}{(2+\sin x)^4} \, dx = \int \cos x(2 + \sin x)^{-4} \, dx$
$= -\dfrac{1}{3}(2 + \sin x)^{-3} + C = -\dfrac{1}{3(2+\sin x)^3} + C$

k) Using the hint, you know the derivative of $\text{cosec } x$ is $-\text{cosec } x \cot x$.
Let $f(x) = \text{cosec } x$ so $f'(x) = -\text{cosec } x \cot x$. $n = 4$ so $n + 1 = 5$.
Using the formula:
$\int 5(-\text{cosec } x \cot x)(\text{cosec } x)^4 \, dx = (\text{cosec } x)^5 + C$
Multiply by –1: $\int 5 \text{ cosec } x \cot x \, \text{cosec}^4 x \, dx = -\text{cosec}^5 x + C$

l) Using the hint, $\cot x$ differentiates to $-\text{cosec}^2 x$.
Let $f(x) = \cot x$ so $f'(x) = -\text{cosec}^2 x$. $n = 3$ so $n + 1 = 4$.
Using the formula: $\int 4(-\text{cosec}^2 x) \cot^3 x \, dx = \cot^4 x + C$
Divide by –2 to get the original integral:
$\int 2 \text{ cosec}^2 x \cot^3 x \, dx = \dfrac{1}{-2}\int -4 \text{ cosec}^2 x \cot^3 x \, dx$
$= -\dfrac{1}{2}\cot^4 x + C$

Q2 a) $\sec x$ differentiates to $\sec x \tan x$, so try to write the function as a product of $\sec x \tan x$ and $\sec x$ to a power.
$6 \tan x \sec^6 x = 6 \tan x \sec x \sec^5 x$
Let $f(x) = \sec x$ so $f'(x) = \sec x \tan x$. $n = 5$ so $n + 1 = 6$.
Using the formula: $\int 6(\tan x \sec x)(\sec^5 x) \, dx = \sec^6 x + C$
So $\int 6 \tan x \sec^6 x \, dx = \sec^6 x + C$

b) $\text{cosec } x$ differentiates to $-\cot x \text{ cosec } x$ so do the same as you did in part a).
$\cot x \text{ cosec}^3 x = \cot x \text{ cosec } x \text{ cosec}^2 x$
Let $f(x) = \text{cosec } x$ so $f'(x) = -\cot x \text{ cosec } x$. $n = 2$ so $n + 1 = 3$.
Using the formula:
$\int 3(-\cot x \text{ cosec } x)(\text{cosec}^2 x) \, dx = \text{cosec}^3 x + C$
So $\int -3 \cot x \text{ cosec}^3 x \, dx = \text{cosec}^3 x + C$
Divide by –3 to get the original integral.
$\int \cot x \text{ cosec}^3 x \, dx = \dfrac{1}{-3}\int -3 \cot x \text{ cosec}^3 x \, dx = -\dfrac{1}{3}\text{cosec}^3 x + C$

Q3 a) This one looks really complicated, but if you differentiate the bracket $(e^{\sin x} - 5)$ using the chain rule, you'll get the function at the front.
Let $f(x) = e^{\sin x} - 5$ so $f'(x) = \cos x \, e^{\sin x}$. $n = 3$ so $n + 1 = 4$.
Using the formula:
$\int 4(\cos x \, e^{\sin x})(e^{\sin x} - 5)^3 \, dx = (e^{\sin x} - 5)^4 + C$

b) Let $f(x) = e^{\cos x} + 4x$ so $f'(x) = -\sin x \, e^{\cos x} + 4$.
$n = 6$ so $n + 1 = 7$. Using the formula:
$\int 7(-\sin x \, e^{\cos x} + 4)(e^{\cos x} + 4x)^6 \, dx = (e^{\cos x} + 4x)^7 + C$
So divide by -7 to get the original integral:
$\int (\sin x \, e^{\cos x} - 4)(e^{\cos x} + 4x)^6 \, dx$
$= -\frac{1}{7}\int 7(-\sin x \, e^{\cos x} + 4)(e^{\cos x} + 4x)^6 \, dx = -\frac{1}{7}(e^{\cos x} + 4x)^7 + C$

Q4 a) Start by writing the function as $\sec^2 x \tan^{-4} x$.
Let $f(x) = \tan x$ so $f'(x) = \sec^2 x$. $n = -4$ so $n + 1 = -3$.
Using the formula: $\int -3 \sec^2 x \tan^{-4} x \, dx = \tan^{-3} x + C$
Divide by -3 to get the original integral:
$\int \frac{\sec^2 x}{\tan^4 x} \, dx = -\frac{1}{3}\tan^{-3} x + C = -\frac{1}{3 \tan^3 x} + C$

b) Start by writing the function as $\cot x \, \mathrm{cosec}\, x \, (\mathrm{cosec}\, x)^{\frac{1}{2}}$.
Let $f(x) = \mathrm{cosec}\, x$ so $f'(x) = -\cot x \, \mathrm{cosec}\, x$.
$n = \frac{1}{2}$ so $n + 1 = \frac{3}{2}$. Using the formula:
$\int \frac{3}{2}(-\cot x \, \mathrm{cosec}\, x)(\mathrm{cosec}\, x)^{\frac{1}{2}} \, dx = (\mathrm{cosec}\, x)^{\frac{3}{2}} + C$
Divide by $-\frac{3}{2}$ to get the original integral:
$\int \cot x \, \mathrm{cosec}\, x \sqrt{\mathrm{cosec}\, x} \, dx = -\frac{2}{3}(\mathrm{cosec}\, x)^{\frac{3}{2}} + C$
$= -\frac{2}{3}(\sqrt{\mathrm{cosec}\, x})^3 + C$

Q5 a) Start by writing the function as $e^{\cot 2x} \mathrm{cosec}^2 2x \, (e^{\cot 2x})^3$.
Let $f(x) = e^{\cot 2x}$ so $f'(x) = -2 e^{\cot 2x} \mathrm{cosec}^2 2x$.
$n = 3$ so $n + 1 = 4$. Using the formula:
$\int 4(-2 e^{\cot 2x} \mathrm{cosec}^2 2x) e^{\cot 2x} = (e^{\cot 2x})^4 + c$
Divide by -8 to get the original integral:
$\int e^{\cot 2x} \mathrm{cosec}^2 2x \, e^{\cot 2x} = -\frac{1}{8}e^{4\cot 2x} + C$, as required.

b) $\int_{\frac{1}{2}}^{1} e^{\cot 2x} \mathrm{cosec}^2 2x \, e^{\cot 2x} = -\frac{1}{8}\left[e^{4\cot 2x}\right]_{\frac{1}{2}}^{1}$
$= -\frac{1}{8}\left[e^{4\cot 2(1)}\right] - -\frac{1}{8}\left[e^{4\cot 2(\frac{1}{2})}\right] = \frac{1}{8}(e^{4\cot 1} - e^{4\cot 2}) = 1.61 \text{ (3.s.f)}$

8.6 Using Trigonometric Identities in Integration

Exercise 8.6.1 — Integrating using trig identities

Q1 a) Using the cos double angle formula: $\cos^2 x = \frac{1}{2}(\cos 2x + 1)$
So the integral is:
$\int \cos^2 x \, dx = \int \frac{1}{2}(\cos 2x + 1) \, dx = \frac{1}{2}\left(\frac{1}{2}\sin 2x + x\right) + C$
$= \frac{1}{4}\sin 2x + \frac{1}{2}x + C$

b) $6 \sin x \cos x = 3(2 \sin x \cos x) = 3 \sin 2x$
So the integral is:
$\int 6 \sin x \cos x \, dx = \int 3 \sin 2x \, dx = -\frac{3}{2}\cos 2x + C$

c) $\sin^2 6x = \frac{1}{2}(1 - \cos(2 \times 6x)) = \frac{1}{2}(1 - \cos 12x)$
So the integral is:
$\int \sin^2 6x \, dx = \int \frac{1}{2}(1 - \cos 12x) \, dx$
$= \frac{1}{2}\left(x - \frac{1}{12}\sin 12x\right) + C = \frac{1}{2}x - \frac{1}{24}\sin 12x + C$

d) Using the tan double angle formula: $\frac{2 \tan 2x}{1 - \tan^2 2x} = \tan 4x$
So the integral is:
$\int \frac{2 \tan 2x}{1 - \tan^2 2x} \, dx = \int \tan 4x \, dx$
$= -\frac{1}{4}\ln|\cos 4x| + C \left(\text{or} = \frac{1}{4}\ln|\sec 4x| + C\right)$

e) $2 \sin 4x \cos 4x = \sin 8x$
So the integral is:
$\int 2 \sin 4x \cos 4x \, dx = \int \sin 8x \, dx = -\frac{1}{8}\cos 8x + C$

f) $2 \cos^2 4x = 2\left(\frac{1}{2}(\cos 8x + 1)\right) = \cos 8x + 1$
So the integral is:
$\int 2 \cos^2 4x \, dx = \int \cos 8x + 1 \, dx = \frac{1}{8}\sin 8x + x + C$

g) $\cos x \sin x = \frac{1}{2}(2 \cos x \sin x) = \frac{1}{2}\sin 2x$
So the integral is:
$\int \cos x \sin x \, dx = \int \frac{1}{2}\sin 2x \, dx$
$= \frac{1}{2}\left(-\frac{1}{2}\cos 2x\right) + C = -\frac{1}{4}\cos 2x + C$

h) $\sin 3x \cos 3x = \frac{1}{2}(2 \sin 3x \cos 3x) = \frac{1}{2}\sin 6x$
So the integral is:
$\int \sin 3x \cos 3x \, dx = \int \frac{1}{2}\sin 6x \, dx$
$= \frac{1}{2}\left(-\frac{1}{6}\cos 6x\right) + C = -\frac{1}{12}\cos 6x + C$

i) $\frac{6 \tan 3x}{1 - \tan^2 3x} = 3\left(\frac{2 \tan 3x}{1 - \tan^2 3x}\right) = 3 \tan 6x$
So the integral is:
$\int \frac{6 \tan 3x}{1 - \tan^2 3x} \, dx = \int 3 \tan 6x \, dx = 3\left(-\frac{1}{6}\ln|\cos 6x|\right) + C$
$= -\frac{1}{2}\ln|\cos 6x| + C \left(\text{or} = \frac{1}{2}\ln|\sec 6x| + C\right)$

j) $5 \sin 2x \cos 2x = \frac{5}{2}(2 \sin 2x \cos 2x) = \frac{5}{2}\sin 4x$
So the integral is:
$\int 5 \sin 2x \cos 2x \, dx = \int \frac{5}{2}\sin 4x \, dx$
$= \frac{5}{2}\left(-\frac{1}{4}\cos 4x\right) + C = -\frac{5}{8}\cos 4x + C$

k) $(\sin x + \cos x)^2 = \sin^2 x + 2 \sin x \cos x + \cos^2 x$
$= \sin^2 x + \cos^2 x + 2 \sin x \cos x = 1 + 2 \sin x \cos x = 1 + \sin 2x$
$\sin^2 x + \cos^2 x \equiv 1$ has been used to simplify here.
So the integral is:
$\int (\sin x + \cos x)^2 \, dx = \int 1 + \sin 2x \, dx = x - \frac{1}{2}\cos 2x + C$

l) $4 \sin x \cos x \cos 2x = 2(2 \sin x \cos x) \cos 2x$
$= 2 \sin 2x \cos 2x = \sin 4x$
So the integral is:
$\int 4 \sin x \cos x \cos 2x \, dx = \int \sin 4x \, dx = -\frac{1}{4}\cos 4x + C$

m) $(\cos x + \sin x)(\cos x - \sin x)$
$= \cos^2 x - \cos x \sin x + \sin x \cos x - \sin^2 x$
$= \cos^2 x - \sin^2 x = \cos 2x$
So the integral is:
$\int (\cos x + \sin x)(\cos x - \sin x) \, dx = \int \cos 2x \, dx = \frac{1}{2}\sin 2x + C$

n) $\sin^2 x \cot x = \sin^2 x \, \frac{1}{\tan x} = \sin^2 x \, \frac{\cos x}{\sin x}$
$= \sin x \cos x = \frac{1}{2}\sin 2x$
So the integral is:
$\int \sin^2 x \cot x \, dx = \int \frac{1}{2}\sin 2x \, dx$
$= \frac{1}{2}\left(-\frac{1}{2}\cos 2x\right) + C = -\frac{1}{4}\cos 2x + C$

Q2 a) $\sin^2 x = \frac{1}{2}(1 - \cos 2x)$
So the integral is:
$\int_0^{\frac{\pi}{4}} \sin^2 x \, dx = \int_0^{\frac{\pi}{4}} \frac{1}{2}(1 - \cos 2x) \, dx$
$= \frac{1}{2}\left[\left(x - \frac{1}{2}\sin 2x\right)\right]_0^{\frac{\pi}{4}} = \frac{1}{2}\left(\left(\frac{\pi}{4} - \frac{1}{2}\sin \frac{\pi}{2}\right) - \left(-\frac{1}{2}\sin 0\right)\right)$
$= \frac{1}{2}\left(\left(\frac{\pi}{4} - \left(\frac{1}{2} \times 1\right)\right) - \left(-\frac{1}{2} \times 0\right)\right) = \frac{1}{2}\left(\frac{\pi}{4} - \frac{1}{2}\right) = \frac{\pi}{8} - \frac{1}{4}$

b) $\cos^2 2x = \frac{1}{2}(\cos 4x + 1)$
So the integral is:
$\int_0^{\pi} \frac{1}{2}(\cos 4x + 1) \, dx = \left[\frac{1}{2}\left(\frac{1}{4}\sin 4x + x\right)\right]_0^{\pi} = \left[\left(\frac{1}{8}\sin 4x + \frac{x}{2}\right)\right]_0^{\pi}$
$= \left(\frac{1}{8}\sin 4\pi + \frac{\pi}{2}\right) - \left(\frac{1}{8}\sin 0 + \frac{0}{2}\right) = \left(\frac{1}{8} \times 0 + \frac{\pi}{2}\right) - (0 + 0) = \frac{\pi}{2}$

c) $\sin\frac{x}{2}\cos\frac{x}{2} = \frac{1}{2}\left(2\sin\frac{x}{2}\cos\frac{x}{2}\right) = \frac{1}{2}\sin x$

So the integral is:

$\int_0^\pi \sin\frac{x}{2}\cos\frac{x}{2}\,dx = \int_0^\pi \frac{1}{2}\sin x\,dx = -\frac{1}{2}[\cos x]_0^\pi$

$= -\frac{1}{2}(\cos\pi - \cos 0) = -\frac{1}{2}(-1-1) = 1$

d) $\sin^2 2x = \frac{1}{2}(1-\cos 4x)$

So the integral is:

$\int_{\frac{\pi}{4}}^{\frac{\pi}{2}} \sin^2 2x\,dx = \int_{\frac{\pi}{4}}^{\frac{\pi}{2}} \frac{1}{2}(1-\cos 4x)\,dx$

$= \frac{1}{2}\left[x - \frac{1}{4}\sin 4x\right]_{\frac{\pi}{4}}^{\frac{\pi}{2}} = \frac{1}{2}\left(\left[\frac{\pi}{2} - \frac{1}{4}\sin 2\pi\right] - \left[\frac{\pi}{4} - \frac{1}{4}\sin\pi\right]\right)$

$= \frac{1}{2}\left(\left[\frac{\pi}{2} - 0\right] - \left[\frac{\pi}{4} - 0\right]\right) = \frac{\pi}{8}$

e) $\cos 2x \sin 2x = \frac{1}{2}(2\sin 2x\cos 2x) = \frac{1}{2}\sin 4x$

So the integral is:

$\int_0^{\frac{\pi}{4}} \cos 2x\sin 2x\,dx = \int_0^{\frac{\pi}{4}} \frac{1}{2}\sin 4x\,dx$

$= \frac{1}{2}\left[\left(-\frac{1}{4}\cos 4x\right)\right]_0^{\frac{\pi}{4}} = -\frac{1}{8}[\cos 4x]_0^{\frac{\pi}{4}}$

$= -\frac{1}{8}(\cos\pi - \cos 0) = -\frac{1}{8}(-1-1) = \frac{1}{4}$

f) $\sin^2 x - \cos^2 x = -(\cos^2 x - \sin^2 x) = -\cos 2x$

So the integral is:

$\int_{\frac{\pi}{4}}^{\frac{\pi}{2}} \sin^2 x - \cos^2 x\,dx = \int_{\frac{\pi}{4}}^{\frac{\pi}{2}} -\cos 2x\,dx = -\frac{1}{2}[\sin 2x]_{\frac{\pi}{4}}^{\frac{\pi}{2}}$

$= -\frac{1}{2}\left(\sin\pi - \sin\frac{\pi}{2}\right) = -\frac{1}{2}(0-1) = \frac{1}{2}$

Q3 Using the tan addition formula:

$\int_0^{\frac{\pi}{6}} \frac{\tan 7x - \tan 5x}{1 + \tan 7x\tan 5x}\,dx = \int_0^{\frac{\pi}{6}} \tan(7x-5x)\,dx$

$= \int_0^{\frac{\pi}{6}} \tan 2x\,dx = \left[\frac{1}{2}\ln|\sec 2x|\right]_0^{\frac{\pi}{6}} = \frac{1}{2}\ln 2 - 0 = \frac{\ln 2}{2}$

Q4 a) $\cot^2 x - 4 = (\mathrm{cosec}^2 x - 1) - 4 = \mathrm{cosec}^2 x - 5$

So the integral is:

$\int \cot^2 x - 4\,dx = \int \mathrm{cosec}^2 x - 5\,dx = -\cot x - 5x + C$

b) $\tan^2 x = \sec^2 x - 1$

So the integral is:

$\int \tan^2 x\,dx = \int \sec^2 x - 1\,dx = \tan x - x + C$

c) $3\cot^2 x = 3(\mathrm{cosec}^2 x - 1) = 3\,\mathrm{cosec}^2 x - 3$

So the integral is:

$\int 3\cot^2 x\,dx = \int 3\,\mathrm{cosec}^2 x - 3\,dx = -3\cot x - 3x + C$

d) $\tan^2 4x = \sec^2 4x - 1$

So the integral is:

$\int \tan^2 4x\,dx = \int \sec^2 4x - 1\,dx = \frac{1}{4}\tan 4x - x + C$

Q5 $\tan^2 x + \cos^2 x - \sin^2 x = (\sec^2 x - 1) + \cos 2x$

So the integral is:

$\int_0^{\frac{\pi}{4}} \tan^2 x + \cos^2 x - \sin^2 x\,dx = \int_0^{\frac{\pi}{4}} \sec^2 x - 1 + \cos 2x\,dx$

$= \left[\tan x - x + \frac{1}{2}\sin 2x\right]_0^{\frac{\pi}{4}} = \left[\tan\frac{\pi}{4} - \frac{\pi}{4} + \frac{1}{2}\sin\frac{2\pi}{4}\right] - \left[\tan 0 - 0 + \frac{1}{2}\sin 0\right]$

$= \left[1 - \frac{\pi}{4} + \frac{1}{2}\right] - [0 - 0 + 0] = \frac{3}{2} - \frac{\pi}{4}$

Q6 $(\sec x + \tan x)^2 = \sec^2 x + 2\tan x\sec x + \tan^2 x$

$= \sec^2 x + 2\tan x\sec x + (\sec^2 x - 1) = 2\sec^2 x + 2\tan x\sec x - 1$

Remember that the derivative of sec x is sec x tan x.

So the integral is:

$\int (\sec x + \tan x)^2\,dx = \int 2\sec^2 x + 2\tan x\sec x - 1\,dx$

$= 2\tan x + 2\sec x - x + C$

Q7 $(\cot x + \mathrm{cosec}\,x)^2 = \cot^2 x + 2\cot x\,\mathrm{cosec}\,x + \mathrm{cosec}^2 x$

$= (\mathrm{cosec}^2 x - 1) + 2\cot x\,\mathrm{cosec}\,x + \mathrm{cosec}^2 x$

$= 2\,\mathrm{cosec}^2 x + 2\cot x\,\mathrm{cosec}\,x - 1$

Just keep using the identities that you know until you get to something that you know how to integrate.

So the integral is:

$\int (\cot x + \mathrm{cosec}\,x)^2\,dx = \int 2\,\mathrm{cosec}^2 x + 2\cot x\,\mathrm{cosec}\,x - 1\,dx$

$= -2\cot x - 2\,\mathrm{cosec}\,x - x + C$

Q8 $4 + \cot^2 3x = 4 + (\mathrm{cosec}^2 3x - 1) = 3 + \mathrm{cosec}^2 3x$

So the integral is:

$\int 4 + \cot^2 3x\,dx = \int 3 + \mathrm{cosec}^2 3x\,dx = 3x - \frac{1}{3}\cot 3x + C$

Q9 $\cos^2 4x + \cot^2 4x = \frac{1}{2}(\cos 8x + 1) + (\mathrm{cosec}^2 4x - 1)$

$= \frac{1}{2}\cos 8x + \mathrm{cosec}^2 4x - \frac{1}{2}$

So the integral is:

$\int \cos^2 4x + \cot^2 4x\,dx = \int \frac{1}{2}\cos 8x + \mathrm{cosec}^2 4x - \frac{1}{2}\,dx$

$= \frac{1}{2}\left(\frac{1}{8}\sin 8x\right) - \frac{1}{4}\cot 4x - \frac{1}{2}x + C = \frac{1}{16}\sin 8x - \frac{1}{4}\cot 4x - \frac{1}{2}x + C$

Q10 a) $\tan^3 x + \tan^5 x = \tan^3 x(1 + \tan^2 x) = \tan^3 x\sec^2 x = \sec^2 x\tan^3 x$

This is a product containing tan x to a power, and its derivative sec^2 x. Using the formula with f(x) = tan x, f'(x) = sec^2 x, n = 3 and n + 1 = 4 gives:

$\int 4\sec^2 x\tan^3 x\,dx = \tan^4 x + C$

So the integral is:

$\int \tan^3 x + \tan^5 x\,dx = \int \sec^2 x\tan^3 x\,dx$

$= \frac{1}{4}\int 4\sec^2 x\tan^3 x\,dx = \frac{1}{4}\tan^4 x + C$

b) $\cot^5 x + \cot^3 x = \cot^3 x(\cot^2 x + 1) = \cot^3 x\,\mathrm{cosec}^2 x$

Again, this is a product of a function to a power and its derivative so use the formula with f(x) = cot x, f'(x) = −cosec^{2}x, n = 3 and n + 1 = 4.

$\int -4\,\mathrm{cosec}^2 x\cot^3 x\,dx = \cot^4 x + C$

So the integral is:

$\int \cot^5 x + \cot^3 x\,dx = \int \mathrm{cosec}^2 x\cot^3 x\,dx$

$= -\frac{1}{4}\int -4\,\mathrm{cosec}^2 x\cot^3 x\,dx = -\frac{1}{4}\cot^4 x + C$

c) $\sin^3 x = \sin x\sin^2 x = \sin x(1 - \cos^2 x) = \sin x - \sin x\cos^2 x$

The second term of this function is a product of a function to a power and its derivative. Using the result with f(x) = cos x, f'(x) = −sin x, n = 2 and n + 1 = 3 gives:

$\int -3\sin x\cos^2 x\,dx = \cos^3 x + c$

So the integral is:

$\int \sin^3 x\,dx = \int \sin x - \sin x\cos^2 x\,dx$

$= \int \sin x\,dx + \int -\sin x\cos^2 x\,dx = -\cos x + \frac{1}{3}\cos^3 x + C$

Q11 You want to find A and B, where $\frac{A+B}{2} = 4x$, and $\frac{A-B}{2} = x$.

Solve simultaneously:

$\frac{A+B}{2} + \frac{A-B}{2} = 4x + x \Rightarrow A = 5x.$ So $B = 3x.$ Then

$2\sin 4x\cos x \equiv 2\sin\left(\frac{5x+3x}{2}\right)\cos\left(\frac{5x-3x}{2}\right) \equiv \sin 5x + \sin 3x$

So $\int 2\sin 4x\cos x\,dx = \int \sin 5x + \sin 3x\,dx$

$= -\frac{1}{5}\cos 5x - \frac{1}{3}\cos 3x + C$

8.7 Finding Area using Integration
Exercise 8.7.1 — Finding enclosed areas

Q1 a) Start by finding the points where the curve and the line intersect. Solve $3x^2 + 4 = 16$:

$\Rightarrow 3x^2 = 12 \Rightarrow x^2 = 4 \Rightarrow x = -2$ or 2.

So they intersect at x = −2 and x = 2.

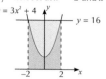

$y = 3x^2 + 4$, $y = 16$

So the area is found by subtracting the integral of $3x^2 + 4$ between −2 and 2 from the integral of 16 between −2 and 2. The area under the line is just a rectangle which is 16 by 4 so the area is 16 × 4 = 64.

$\int_{-2}^{2} (3x^2 + 4)\,dx = [x^3 + 4x]_{-2}^{2} = (2^3 + 4(2)) - ((-2)^3 + 4(-2))$

$= (8 + 8) - (-8 - 8) = 16 + 16 = 32$

So the area is 64 − 32 = 32.

b) Solving to find the point of intersection of $x = 2$ and $y = x^3 + 4$: $y = 2^3 + 4 = 12$

Draw a diagram:

So the required area is the area under $y = 12$ between $x = 0$ and $x = 2$, minus the area under $y = x^3 + 4$ between $x = 0$ and $x = 2$.

The first area is a rectangle which is $12 \times 2 = 24$.

$$\int_0^2 x^3 + 4 \, dx = \left[\frac{x^4}{4} + 4x\right]_0^2$$
$$= \left(\frac{2^4}{4} + 8\right) - \left(\frac{0^4}{4} + 0\right) = 12$$

So the shaded area is $24 - 12 = 12$.

c) Solving to find the point of intersection of $y = 4$ and $y = \frac{1}{x^2}$:

$$4 = \frac{1}{x^2} \Rightarrow 4x^2 = 1 \Rightarrow x^2 = \frac{1}{4} \Rightarrow x = \pm\frac{1}{2}$$

so the intersection in the diagram is $x = \frac{1}{2}$:

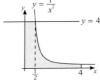

So required area is the area under the line $y = 4$ from $x = 0$ and $x = \frac{1}{2}$ added to the area under the curve $y = \frac{1}{x^2}$ from $x = \frac{1}{2}$ and $x = 4$.

The first area is just a rectangle which is $\frac{1}{2}$ by 4 so the area is $\frac{1}{2} \times 4 = 2$.

Area under curve $= \int_{\frac{1}{2}}^4 \frac{1}{x^2} \, dx = \int_{\frac{1}{2}}^4 x^{-2} \, dx = \left[\frac{x^{-1}}{-1}\right]_{\frac{1}{2}}^4 = \left[-\frac{1}{x}\right]_{\frac{1}{2}}^4$

$= \left(-\frac{1}{4}\right) - \left(-\frac{1}{\left(\frac{1}{2}\right)}\right) = -\frac{1}{4} + 2 = \frac{7}{4}$

So the area is $2 + \frac{7}{4} = \frac{15}{4}$.

d) Solve $-1 - (x - 3)^2 = -5 \Rightarrow 4 = (x - 3)^2$
$\Rightarrow x - 3 = \pm 2 \Rightarrow x = 1$ and $x = 5$.

Be careful — this area is below the x-axis so the integrals will give negative areas.

So the area you want is the area above the line between 1 and 5 minus the area between the curve and the x-axis between 1 and 5.

The first area is just a rectangle which is 5 by 4 so the area is $5 \times 4 = 20$. So the area between the line and the x-axis between 0 and 5 is 20.

Area between curve and x-axis

$= \int_1^5 (-1 - (x-3)^2) \, dx = \int_1^5 (-1 - (x^2 - 6x + 9)) \, dx$

$= \int_1^5 (6x - x^2 - 10) \, dx = \left[\frac{6x^2}{2} - \frac{x^3}{3} - 10x\right]_1^5 = \left[3x^2 - \frac{x^3}{3} - 10x\right]_1^5$

$= \left((3 \times 5^2) - \frac{5^3}{3} - (10 \times 5)\right) - \left((3 \times 1^2) - \frac{1^3}{3} - (10 \times 1)\right)$

$= \left(75 - \frac{125}{3} - 50\right) - \left(3 - \frac{1}{3} - 10\right) = -\frac{28}{3}$

So the area between the curve and the x-axis between 1 and 5 is $\frac{28}{3}$. So the area is $20 - \frac{28}{3} = \frac{32}{3}$.

e) Solve $x^2 = 2x \Rightarrow x^2 - 2x = 0 \Rightarrow x(x - 2) = 0$
$\Rightarrow x = 0$ and $x = 2$.

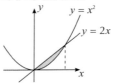

The shaded area is the area under $y = 2x$ from $x = 0$ and $x = 2$, minus the area under $y = x^2$ from $x = 0$ to $x = 2$.

$\int_0^2 2x \, dx = [x^2]_0^2 = 2^2 - 0^2 = 4$

$\int_0^2 x^2 \, dx = \left[\frac{x^3}{3}\right]_0^2 = \frac{2^3}{3} - \frac{0^3}{3} = \frac{8}{3}$

So the shaded area is $4 - \frac{8}{3} = \frac{4}{3}$.

f) Solve $x^3 = 4x \Rightarrow x^3 - 4x = 0 \Rightarrow x(x^2 - 4) = 0$
$\Rightarrow x(x + 2)(x - 2) = 0 \Rightarrow x = 0$ and $x = \pm 2$.

The area above the x-axis is the same as the area below the x-axis (from the symmetry of the graph).

For the area above the x-axis, find the area under the line from $x = 0$ to $x = 2$, minus the area under the curve from $x = 0$ to $x = 2$.

$\int_0^2 4x \, dx = [2x^2]_0^2 = (2 \times 2^2) - (2 \times 0^2) = 8$

$\int_0^2 x^3 \, dx = \left[\frac{x^4}{4}\right]_0^2 = \left(\frac{2^4}{4}\right) - \left(\frac{0^2}{4}\right) = 4$

So the area above the axis is $8 - 4 = 4$.
So the area below the x-axis is also 4.
The total area is $4 + 4 = 8$.

For parts e) and f) you could have used the formula for finding the area of a triangle rather than integrating.

Q2 **a)** Solve $x^2 + 4 = x + 4 \Rightarrow x^2 - x = 0 \Rightarrow x(x - 1) = 0$
$\Rightarrow x = 0$ and $x = 1$. Draw a diagram:

So the area you want is the area under the line minus the area under the curve, between $x = 0$ and $x = 1$.

$\int_0^1 (x + 4) \, dx = \left[\frac{x^2}{2} + 4x\right]_0^1$
$= \left(\frac{1^2}{2} + (4 \times 1)\right) - \left(\frac{0^2}{2} + (4 \times 0)\right) = \frac{1}{2} + 4 = \frac{9}{2}$

$\int_0^1 (x^2 + 4) \, dx = \left[\frac{x^3}{3} + 4x\right]_0^1$
$= \left(\frac{1^3}{3} + (4 \times 1)\right) - \left(\frac{0^3}{3} + (4 \times 0)\right) = \frac{1}{3} + 4 = \frac{13}{3}$

So the area is $\frac{9}{2} - \frac{13}{3} = \frac{1}{6}$.

b) Solve $x^2 + 2x - 3 = 4x \Rightarrow x^2 - 2x - 3 = 0$
$\Rightarrow (x - 3)(x + 1) = 0 \Rightarrow x = -1$ and $x = 3$.
It'll also help to find where the curve meets the x-axis by
solving $x^2 + 2x - 3 = 0 \Rightarrow (x + 3)(x - 1) \Rightarrow x = 1$ and $x = -3$.
Draw a diagram:

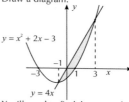

You'll need to find the areas above and below the x-axis
separately.
For the area above the x-axis, integrate $4x$ from $x = 0$ to $x = 3$
and subtract the integral of $x^2 + 2x - 3$ from $x = 1$ to $x = 3$.
$\int_0^3 4x \, dx = [2x^2]_0^3 = (2(3)^2) - (2(0)^2) = 18$

$\int_1^3 (x^2 + 2x - 3) \, dx = \left[\frac{x^3}{3} + x^2 - 3x\right]_1^3$
$= \left(\frac{(3)^3}{3} + (3)^2 - 3(3)\right) - \left(\frac{(1)^3}{3} + (1)^2 - 3(1)\right)$
$= \left(\frac{27}{3} + 9 - 9\right) - \left(\frac{1}{3} + 1 - 3\right) = \frac{32}{3}$

So the area above the x-axis is $18 - \frac{32}{3} = \frac{22}{3}$
To find the area below the x-axis you need to find the
positive area between the curve and the axis between -1
and 1 minus the positive area between the line and the axis
between -1 and 0.
$\int_{-1}^1 (x^2 + 2x - 3) \, dx = \left[\frac{x^3}{3} + x^2 - 3x\right]_{-1}^1$
$= \left(\frac{(1)^3}{3} + (1)^2 - 3(1)\right) - \left(\frac{(-1)^3}{3} + (-1)^2 - 3(-1)\right)$
$= \left(\frac{1}{3} + 1 - 3\right) - \left(\frac{-1}{3} + 1 + 3\right) = -\frac{16}{3}$
So the area between the curve and the axis
between -1 and 1 is $\frac{16}{3}$.
$\int_{-1}^0 4x \, dx = [2x^2]_{-1}^0 = (2(0)^2) - (2(-1)^2) = -2$
So the area between the line and the
axis between -1 and 1 is 2.
So the area under the x-axis is $\frac{16}{3} - 2 = \frac{10}{3}$
So the total area enclosed by the curve and the line is
$\frac{22}{3} + \frac{10}{3} = \frac{32}{3}$

Q3 Solve $\cos x = 0.5 \Rightarrow x = \cos^{-1} 0.5 = \frac{\pi}{3}$ and $\frac{5\pi}{3}$.

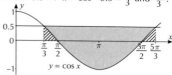

The area above the x-axis is the area of the rectangle
between $\frac{\pi}{3}$ and $\frac{5\pi}{3}$, minus the striped areas.
Rectangle $= (\frac{5\pi}{3} - \frac{\pi}{3}) \times 0.5 = \frac{2\pi}{3}$
One striped area $= \int_{\frac{\pi}{3}}^{\frac{\pi}{2}} \cos x \, dx = [\sin x]_{\frac{\pi}{3}}^{\frac{\pi}{2}}$
$= \sin\left(\frac{\pi}{2}\right) - \sin\left(\frac{\pi}{3}\right) = 1 - \frac{\sqrt{3}}{2}$.
The two striped areas are the same (because of the
symmetry of the cosine curve). So the area above
the x-axis is: $\frac{2\pi}{3} - 2\left(1 - \frac{\sqrt{3}}{2}\right) = \frac{2\pi}{3} - 2 + \sqrt{3}$
Integrate to find the area below the x-axis:
$\int_{\frac{\pi}{2}}^{\frac{3\pi}{2}} \cos x \, dx = [\sin x]_{\frac{\pi}{2}}^{\frac{3\pi}{2}} = \sin\left(\frac{3\pi}{2}\right) - \sin\left(\frac{\pi}{2}\right) = -1 - 1 = -2$
So the area below the x-axis is 2.
The shaded area is $\frac{2\pi}{3} - 2 + \sqrt{3} + 2 = \frac{2\pi}{3} + \sqrt{3}$

Q4 The area of each grey section is the integral of the upper function
minus the integral of the lower function. So the total grey area is:
$$\left(\int_0^\pi 5\sin x \, dx - \int_0^\pi 4\sin x \, dx\right)$$
$$+ \left(\int_0^\pi 3\sin x \, dx - \int_0^\pi 2\sin x \, dx\right) + \left(\int_0^\pi \sin x \, dx\right)$$
$$= 5\int_0^\pi \sin x \, dx - 4\int_0^\pi \sin x \, dx$$
$$+ 3\int_0^\pi \sin x \, dx - 2\int_0^\pi \sin x \, dx + \int_0^\pi \sin x \, dx$$
$$= (5 - 4 + 3 - 2 + 1)\int_0^\pi \sin x \, dx = 3\int_0^\pi \sin x \, dx = 3[-\cos x]_0^\pi$$
$$= 3[(-\cos \pi) - (-\cos 0)] = 3[(-(-1)) - (-1)] = 3(1 + 1) = 6$$

Exercise 8.7.2 — Parametric integration

Q1 **a)** $x = 3t^{-1} \Rightarrow \frac{dx}{dt} = -3t^{-2} = -\frac{3}{t^2}$
$y = 4t^2$

$\int y \, dx = \int y \frac{dx}{dt} \, dt = \int (4t^2) \times \left(-\frac{3}{t^2}\right) dt = \int -12 \, dt$

You could take the constant outside the integral
— i.e. this could be written as $-12\int 1 \, dt$.

b) $x = \tan 5\theta \Rightarrow \frac{dx}{d\theta} = 5\sec^2 5\theta$
$y = \sec^2 5\theta$

$\int y \, dx = \int y \frac{dx}{d\theta} \, d\theta = \int (\sec^2 5\theta)(5\sec^2 5\theta) \, d\theta$

$= \int 5\sec^4 5\theta \, d\theta$

Q2 **a)** $x = (4t - 5)^2 \Rightarrow \frac{dx}{dt} = 2(4t - 5) \times 4 = 32t - 40$
$y = t^2 - 3t$

$\int y \, dx = \int y \frac{dx}{dt} \, dt = \int (t^2 - 3t) \times (32t - 40) \, dt$

$= \int (32t^3 - 136t^2 + 120t) \, dt = 8t^4 - \frac{136}{3}t^3 + 60t^2 + C$

b) $x = t^2 + 3 \Rightarrow \frac{dx}{dt} = 2t$
$y = 4t - 1$

$\int y \, dx = \int y \frac{dx}{dt} \, dt = \int (4t - 1) \times (2t) \, dt$

$= \int (8t^2 - 2t) \, dt = \frac{8}{3}t^3 - t^2 + C$

Q3 $x = 3t^2 \Rightarrow \frac{dx}{dt} = 6t$
$y = \frac{5}{t}$
So $y \frac{dx}{dt} = \frac{5}{t} \times 6t = 30$
When $x = 75$, $3t^2 = 75 \Rightarrow t = 5$ (since $t > 0$).
When $x = 3$, $3t^2 = 3 \Rightarrow t = 1$ (since $t > 0$).
$\int_3^{75} y \, dx = \int_1^5 y \frac{dx}{dt} \, dt = \int_1^5 30 \, dt = 30\int_1^5 1 \, dt$
$= 30[t]_1^5 = 30(5 - 1) = 120$

Q4 **a)** When $x = 8$:
$4t(t + 1) = 8 \Rightarrow t(t + 1) = 2 \Rightarrow t^2 + t - 2 = 0$
$(t - 1)(t + 2) = 0 \Rightarrow t = 1 \; (t > 0)$.
When $x = 120$:
$4t(t + 1) = 120 \Rightarrow t(t + 1) = 30 \Rightarrow t^2 + t - 30 = 0$
$(t - 5)(t + 6) = 0 \Rightarrow t = 5 \; (t > 0)$.

b) $x = 4t^2 + 4t \Rightarrow \frac{dx}{dt} = 8t + 4$
$y = 3t^3$
So $y \frac{dx}{dt} = 24t^4 + 12t^3$
$\int_8^{120} y \, dx = \int_1^5 y \frac{dx}{dt} \, dt$
$= \int_1^5 24t^4 + 12t^3 \, dt = \left[\frac{24t^5}{5} + 3t^4\right]_1^5$
$= (15\,000 + 1875) - \left(\frac{24}{5} + 3\right) = \frac{84\,336}{5} = 16\,867.2$

8.8 Integration by Substitution

Exercise 8.8.1 — Integration by substitution

Q1 **a)** $u = x + 3 \Rightarrow \frac{du}{dx} = 1 \Rightarrow dx = du$

So $\int 12(x + 3)^5 \, dx = \int 12u^5 \, du = 2u^6 + C = 2(x + 3)^6 + C$

You could also have solved this by using the rule given on p.200, as it's of the form $(ax + b)^n$.

b) $u = 11 - x \Rightarrow \frac{du}{dx} = -1 \Rightarrow dx = -du$

So $\int (11 - x)^4 \, dx = -\int u^4 \, du = -\frac{1}{5} u^5 + C = -\frac{1}{5}(11 - x)^5 + C$

c) $u = x^2 + 4 \Rightarrow \frac{du}{dx} = 2x \Rightarrow dx = \frac{1}{2x} \, du$

So $\int 24x(x^2 + 4)^3 \, dx = \int 24x \times u^3 \times \frac{1}{2x} \, du$

$= \int 12u^3 \, du = 3u^4 + C = 3(x^2 + 4)^4 + C$

d) $u = \sin x \Rightarrow \frac{du}{dx} = \cos x \Rightarrow dx = \frac{1}{\cos x} \, du$

So $\int \sin^5 x \cos x \, dx = \int u^5 \cos x \times \frac{1}{\cos x} \, du$

$= \int u^5 \, du = \frac{1}{6} u^6 + C = \frac{1}{6} \sin^6 x + C$

e) $u = x - 1 \Rightarrow \frac{du}{dx} = 1 \Rightarrow dx = du$

and $u = x - 1 \Rightarrow x = u + 1$

So $\int x(x - 1)^5 \, dx = \int (u + 1)u^5 \, du = \int u^6 + u^5 \, du$

$= \frac{1}{7} u^7 + \frac{1}{6} u^6 + C = \frac{1}{7}(x - 1)^7 + \frac{1}{6}(x - 1)^6 + C$

f) $u = x^2 - 3 \Rightarrow \frac{du}{dx} = 2x \Rightarrow dx = \frac{1}{2x} \, du$

and $u = x^2 - 3 \Rightarrow x^2 = u + 3$

So $\int 4x^3(x^2 - 3)^6 \, dx = \int 4x^3 u^6 \times \frac{1}{2x} \, du = \int 2x^2 u^6 \, du$

$= \int 2(u + 3)u^6 \, du = \int 2u^7 + 6u^6 \, du = \frac{2}{8} u^8 + \frac{6}{7} u^7 + C$

$= \frac{1}{4}(x^2 - 3)^8 + \frac{6}{7}(x^2 - 3)^7 + C$

Q2 **a)** Let $u = x + 2 \Rightarrow \frac{du}{dx} = 1 \Rightarrow dx = du$

So $\int 21(x + 2)^6 \, dx = \int 21u^6 \, du = 3u^7 + C = 3(x + 2)^7 + C$

b) Let $u = 5x + 4 \Rightarrow \frac{du}{dx} = 5 \Rightarrow dx = \frac{1}{5} \, du$

So $\int (5x + 4)^3 \, dx = \int \frac{1}{5} u^3 \, du = \frac{1}{20} u^4 + C = \frac{1}{20}(5x + 4)^4 + C$

c) Let $u = 2x + 3 \Rightarrow \frac{du}{dx} = 2 \Rightarrow dx = \frac{1}{2} \, du$

and $u = 2x + 3 \Rightarrow x = \frac{u - 3}{2}$

So $\int x(2x + 3)^3 \, dx = \int \frac{u - 3}{2} \times u^3 \times \frac{1}{2} \, du$

$= \frac{1}{4} \int u^4 - 3u^3 \, du = \frac{1}{4} \left(\frac{1}{5} u^5 - \frac{3}{4} u^4 \right) + C$

$= \frac{1}{20} u^5 - \frac{3}{16} u^4 + C = \frac{1}{20}(2x + 3)^5 - \frac{3}{16}(2x + 3)^4 + C$

d) Let $u = x^2 - 5 \Rightarrow \frac{du}{dx} = 2x \Rightarrow dx = \frac{1}{2x} \, du$

So $\int 24x(x^2 - 5)^7 \, dx = \int 24x \times u^7 \times \frac{1}{2x} \, du = \int 12u^7 \, du$

$= \frac{3}{2} u^8 + C = \frac{3}{2}(x^2 - 5)^8 + C$

Q3 **a)** $u = \sqrt{x + 1} \Rightarrow \frac{du}{dx} = \frac{1}{2\sqrt{x + 1}} = \frac{1}{2u} \Rightarrow dx = 2u \, du$

$u = \sqrt{x + 1} \Rightarrow x = u^2 - 1$

So $\int 6x \sqrt{x + 1} \, dx = \int 6(u^2 - 1) \times u \times 2u \, du$

$= \int 12u^4 - 12u^2 \, du = \frac{12}{5} u^5 - 4u^3 + C$

$= \frac{12}{5} (\sqrt{x + 1})^5 - 4(\sqrt{x + 1})^3 + C$

b) $u = \sqrt{4 - x} \Rightarrow \frac{du}{dx} = -\frac{1}{2\sqrt{4 - x}} = -\frac{1}{2u} \Rightarrow dx = -2u \, du$

$u = \sqrt{4 - x} \Rightarrow x = 4 - u^2$

So $\int \frac{x}{\sqrt{4 - x}} \, dx = \int \frac{4 - u^2}{u} \times -2u \, du$

$= \int -2(4 - u^2) \, du = \int 2u^2 - 8 \, du$

$= \frac{2}{3} u^3 - 8u + C = \frac{2}{3} (\sqrt{4 - x})^3 - 8(\sqrt{4 - x}) + C$

c) $u = \ln x \Rightarrow \frac{du}{dx} = \frac{1}{x} \Rightarrow dx = x \, du$

So $\int \frac{15(\ln x)^4}{x} \, dx = \int \frac{15u^4}{x} \times x \, du = \int 15u^4 \, du$

$= 3u^5 + C = 3(\ln x)^5 + C$

d) $u = \ln (x^2) \Rightarrow \frac{du}{dx} = \frac{2}{x} \Rightarrow dx = \frac{x}{2} \, du$

So $\int \frac{3}{x(\ln (x^2))^3} \, dx = \int \frac{3}{xu^3} \times \frac{x}{2} \, du$

$= \int \frac{3}{2} u^{-3} \, du = -\frac{3}{4} u^{-2} + C = -\frac{3}{4(\ln (x^2))^2} + C$

Q4 *You might use different substitutions to the ones shown below, but as long as your substitution is valid and you get the same final answer then it's okay.*

a) Let $u = \sqrt{2x - 1} \Rightarrow \frac{du}{dx} = \frac{1}{\sqrt{2x - 1}} = \frac{1}{u} \Rightarrow dx = u \, du$

and $u = \sqrt{2x - 1} \Rightarrow x = \frac{u^2 + 1}{2}$

So $\int \frac{4x}{\sqrt{(2x - 1)}} \, dx = \int 4\left(\frac{u^2 + 1}{2} \right) \times \frac{1}{u} \times u \, du$

$= \int 2u^2 + 2 \, du = \frac{2}{3} u^3 + 2u + C$

$= \frac{2}{3} (\sqrt{2x - 1})^3 + 2(\sqrt{2x - 1}) + C$

b) Let $u = 4 - \sqrt{x} \Rightarrow \frac{du}{dx} = -\frac{1}{2\sqrt{x}} \Rightarrow -2\sqrt{x} \, du = dx$

and $u = 4 - \sqrt{x} \Rightarrow x = (4 - u)^2$

$\Rightarrow dx$ can be written $-2(4 - u) \, du = (2u - 8) du$

So $\int \frac{1}{4 - \sqrt{x}} \, dx = \int \frac{1}{u}(2u - 8) \, du$

$= \int 2 - \frac{8}{u} \, du = 2u - 8\ln|u| + C$

$= 2(4 - \sqrt{x}) - 8\ln|4 - \sqrt{x}| + C = -2\sqrt{x} - 8\ln|4 - \sqrt{x}| + C$

You can leave out any constant terms that appear after you integrate (like the 8 you get out of the term $2(4 - \sqrt{x})$ here) — they just get absorbed into the constant of integration, C.

c) Let $u = 1 + e^x \Rightarrow \frac{du}{dx} = e^x \Rightarrow dx = \frac{1}{e^x} \, du$

and $u = 1 + e^x \Rightarrow e^x = u - 1$

So $\int \frac{e^{2x}}{1 + e^x} \, dx = \int \frac{e^{2x}}{u} \times \frac{1}{e^x} \, du = \int \frac{e^x}{u} \, du = \int \frac{u - 1}{u} \, du$

$= \int 1 - \frac{1}{u} \, du = u - \ln|u| + c = 1 + e^x - \ln|1 + e^x| + c$

$= e^x - \ln(1 + e^x) + C$

You can remove the modulus as e^x is always positive, so $1 + e^x > 1$.

Q5 Let $u = f(x) \Rightarrow \frac{du}{dx} = f'(x) \Rightarrow dx = \frac{1}{f'(x)} \, du$

So $\int (n + 1)f'(x)[f(x)]^n \, dx = \int (n + 1)f'(x)u^n \times \frac{1}{f'(x)} \, du$

$= \int (n + 1)u^n \, du = u^{n + 1} + C = [f(x)]^{n + 1} + C$, as required

Exercise 8.8.2 — Definite integrals

Q1 **a)** $u = 3x - 2 \Rightarrow \frac{du}{dx} = 3 \Rightarrow dx = \frac{1}{3} \, du$

$x = \frac{2}{3} \Rightarrow u = 2 - 2 = 0$

$x = 1 \Rightarrow u = 3 - 2 = 1$

So $\int_{\frac{2}{3}}^{1} (3x - 2)^4 \, dx = \int_0^1 \frac{1}{3} u^4 \, du = \left[\frac{1}{15} u^5 \right]_0^1 = \frac{1}{15}$

b) $u = x + 3 \Rightarrow \frac{du}{dx} = 1 \Rightarrow dx = 1 \, du$

$u = x + 3 \Rightarrow x = u - 3$

$x = -2 \Rightarrow u = -2 + 3 = 1$

$x = 1 \Rightarrow u = 1 + 3 = 4$

So $\int_{-2}^{1} 2x(x + 3)^4 \, dx = \int_1^4 2(u - 3) \times u^4 \times 1 \, du$

$= \int_1^4 (2u - 6)u^4 \, du = \int_1^4 (2u^5 - 6u^4) \, du$

$= \left[\frac{u^6}{3} - \frac{6u^5}{5} \right]_1^4 = \left(\frac{4^6}{3} - \frac{6(4)^5}{5} \right) - \left(\frac{1^6}{3} - \frac{6(1)^5}{5} \right) = \frac{687}{5} \ (= 137.4)$

c) $u = \sin x \Rightarrow \dfrac{du}{dx} = \cos x \Rightarrow dx = \dfrac{1}{\cos x}\, du$

$x = 0 \Rightarrow u = \sin(0) = 0$

$x = \dfrac{\pi}{6} \Rightarrow u = \sin \dfrac{\pi}{6} = \dfrac{1}{2}$

So $\displaystyle\int_0^{\frac{\pi}{6}} 8 \sin^3 x \cos x\, dx = \int_0^{\frac{1}{2}} 8u^3 \cos x \times \dfrac{1}{\cos x}\, du$

$= \displaystyle\int_0^{\frac{1}{2}} 8u^3\, du = \left[2u^4\right]_0^{\frac{1}{2}} = 2\left(\dfrac{1}{2}\right)^4 - 0 = \dfrac{1}{8}$

d) $u = \sqrt{x+1} \Rightarrow \dfrac{du}{dx} = \dfrac{1}{2\sqrt{x+1}} = \dfrac{1}{2u} \Rightarrow dx = 2u\, du$

$u = \sqrt{x+1} \Rightarrow x = u^2 - 1$

$x = 0 \Rightarrow u = \sqrt{x+1} = \sqrt{1} = 1$

$x = 3 \Rightarrow u = \sqrt{4} = 2$

So $\displaystyle\int_0^3 x\sqrt{x+1}\, dx = \int_1^2 (u^2 - 1) \times u \times 2u\, du$

$= \displaystyle\int_1^2 2u^4 - 2u^2\, du = \left[\dfrac{2}{5}u^5 - \dfrac{2}{3}u^3\right]_1^2$

$= \left[\left(\dfrac{64}{5} - \dfrac{16}{3}\right) - \left(\dfrac{2}{5} - \dfrac{2}{3}\right)\right] = \dfrac{116}{15}$

In Q2, 3 and 5 below, there are different substitutions you could use — again, if you get the final answer right and you use a valid substitution, then your method is fine.

Q2 a) Let $u = x^2 - 3 \Rightarrow \dfrac{du}{dx} = 2x \Rightarrow dx = \dfrac{1}{2x}\, du$

$x = 2 \Rightarrow u = 4 - 3 = 1$

$x = \sqrt{5} \Rightarrow u = 5 - 3 = 2$

So $\displaystyle\int_2^{\sqrt{5}} x(x^2 - 3)^4\, dx = \int_1^2 x \times u^4 \times \dfrac{1}{2x}\, du$

$= \displaystyle\int_1^2 \dfrac{1}{2}u^4\, du = \left[\dfrac{1}{10}u^5\right]_1^2 = \dfrac{32}{10} - \dfrac{1}{10} = \dfrac{31}{10}$ (= 3.1)

b) Let $u = 3x - 4 \Rightarrow \dfrac{du}{dx} = 3 \Rightarrow dx = \dfrac{1}{3}\, du$

and $u = 3x - 4 \Rightarrow x = \dfrac{u+4}{3}$

$x = 1 \Rightarrow u = 3 - 4 = -1$

$x = 2 \Rightarrow u = 6 - 4 = 2$

So $\displaystyle\int_1^2 x(3x-4)^3\, dx = \int_{-1}^2 \dfrac{u+4}{3} \times u^3 \times \dfrac{1}{3}\, du$

$= \dfrac{1}{9}\displaystyle\int_{-1}^2 u^4 + 4u^3\, du = \dfrac{1}{9}\left[\dfrac{u^5}{5} + u^4\right]_{-1}^2$

$= \dfrac{1}{9}\left[\left(\dfrac{32}{5} + 16\right) - \left(\dfrac{-1}{5} + 1\right)\right] = \dfrac{1}{9}\left[\dfrac{108}{5}\right] = \dfrac{12}{5}$ (= 2.4)

c) Let $u = \sqrt{x-1} \Rightarrow \dfrac{du}{dx} = \dfrac{1}{2\sqrt{x-1}} = \dfrac{1}{2u} \Rightarrow dx = 2u\, du$

and $u = \sqrt{x-1} \Rightarrow x = u^2 + 1$

Using $u = \sqrt{x-1}$, $x = 2 \Rightarrow u = \sqrt{1} = 1$

and $x = 10 \Rightarrow u = \sqrt{9} = 3$

So $\displaystyle\int_2^{10} \dfrac{x}{\sqrt{x-1}}\, dx = \int_1^3 \dfrac{u^2 + 1}{u} \times 2u\, du = \int_1^3 2u^2 + 2\, du$

$= \left[\dfrac{2}{3}u^3 + 2u\right]_1^3 = \left[(18 + 6) - \left(\dfrac{2}{3} + 2\right)\right] = \dfrac{64}{3}$

Q3 Let $u = 3 - \sqrt{x} \Rightarrow \dfrac{du}{dx} = -\dfrac{1}{2\sqrt{x}} \Rightarrow dx = -2\sqrt{x}\, du$

$u = 3 - \sqrt{x} \Rightarrow x = (3 - u)^2 \Rightarrow dx = (2u - 6)\, du$

So $x = 1 \Rightarrow u = 3 - 1 = 2$ and $x = 4 \Rightarrow u = 3 - 2 = 1$

So $\displaystyle\int_1^4 \dfrac{1}{3 - \sqrt{x}}\, dx = \int_2^1 \dfrac{1}{u} \times (2u - 6)\, du = \int_2^1 2 - \dfrac{6}{u}\, du$

$= \left[2u - 6 \ln|u|\right]_2^1 = (2 - 6 \ln 1) - (4 - 6 \ln 2)$

$= 2 - 0 - 4 + 6 \ln 2 = -2 + 6 \ln 2$

You could have put 2 as the upper limit and 1 as the lower limit in the integral with respect to u, and put a minus sign in front. Both methods give the right answer, but whichever you use, be careful not to lose any minus signs.

Q4 $u = 1 + e^x \Rightarrow \dfrac{du}{dx} = e^x \Rightarrow dx = \dfrac{1}{e^x}\, du$

$x = 0 \Rightarrow u = 1 + e^0 = 2$

$x = 1 \Rightarrow u = 1 + e$

So $\displaystyle\int_0^1 2e^x(1 + e^x)^3\, dx = \int_2^{1+e} 2e^x u^3 \times \dfrac{1}{e^x}\, du$

$= \displaystyle\int_2^{1+e} 2u^3\, du = \left[\dfrac{u^4}{2}\right]_2^{1+e} = \dfrac{(1+e)^4}{2} - 8 = 87.6$ (1 d.p.)

Q5 Let $u = \sqrt{3x+1} \Rightarrow \dfrac{du}{dx} = \dfrac{3}{2\sqrt{3x+1}} = \dfrac{3}{2u} \Rightarrow dx = \dfrac{2}{3}u\, du$

and $u = \sqrt{3x+1} \Rightarrow x = \dfrac{u^2 - 1}{3}$

$x = 1 \Rightarrow u = \sqrt{4} = 2$

$x = 5 \Rightarrow u = \sqrt{16} = 4$

So $\displaystyle\int_1^5 \dfrac{x}{\sqrt{3x+1}}\, dx = \int_2^4 \dfrac{u^2 - 1}{3u} \times \dfrac{2}{3}u\, du = \dfrac{2}{9}\int_2^4 u^2 - 1\, du$

$= \dfrac{2}{9}\left[\dfrac{1}{3}u^3 - u\right]_2^4 = \dfrac{2}{9}\left[\left(\dfrac{64}{3} - 4\right) - \left(\dfrac{8}{3} - 2\right)\right] = \dfrac{2}{9}\left[\dfrac{50}{3}\right] = \dfrac{100}{27}$

Exercise 8.8.3 — Trig identities

Q1 $x = \tan \theta \Rightarrow \dfrac{dx}{d\theta} = \sec^2 \theta \Rightarrow dx = \sec^2 \theta\, d\theta$

$x = 0 \Rightarrow \tan \theta = 0 \Rightarrow \theta = 0$

$x = 1 \Rightarrow \tan \theta = 1 \Rightarrow \theta = \dfrac{\pi}{4}$

So, using the identity $\sec^2 \theta \equiv 1 + \tan^2 \theta$:

$\displaystyle\int_0^1 \dfrac{1}{1 + x^2}\, dx = \int_0^{\frac{\pi}{4}} \dfrac{1}{1 + \tan^2 \theta} \times \sec^2 \theta\, d\theta$

$= \displaystyle\int_0^{\frac{\pi}{4}} \dfrac{\sec^2 \theta}{\sec^2 \theta}\, d\theta = \int_0^{\frac{\pi}{4}} 1\, d\theta = \left[\theta\right]_0^{\frac{\pi}{4}} = \dfrac{\pi}{4}$

Q2 $u = \sin x \Rightarrow \dfrac{du}{dx} = \cos x \Rightarrow dx = \dfrac{1}{\cos x}\, du$

$x = 0 \Rightarrow u = \sin 0 = 0$

$x = \dfrac{\pi}{6} \Rightarrow u = \sin \dfrac{\pi}{6} = \dfrac{1}{2}$

So, using the identity $\sin 2x \equiv 2\sin x \cos x$:

$\displaystyle\int_0^{\frac{\pi}{6}} 3 \sin x \sin 2x\, dx \equiv \int_0^{\frac{\pi}{6}} 6 \sin^2 x \cos x\, dx$

$= \displaystyle\int_0^{\frac{1}{2}} 6u^2 \cos x \times \dfrac{1}{\cos x}\, du = \int_0^{\frac{1}{2}} 6u^2\, du = \left[2u^3\right]_0^{\frac{1}{2}} = \dfrac{1}{4}$

Q3 $x = 2 \sin \theta \Rightarrow \dfrac{dx}{d\theta} = 2 \cos \theta \Rightarrow dx = 2 \cos \theta\, d\theta$

$x = 1 \Rightarrow \sin \theta = \dfrac{1}{2} \Rightarrow \theta = \dfrac{\pi}{6}$

$x = \sqrt{3} \Rightarrow \sin \theta = \dfrac{\sqrt{3}}{2} \Rightarrow \theta = \dfrac{\pi}{3}$

So, using the identity $\sin^2 \theta + \cos^2 \theta \equiv 1$:

$\displaystyle\int_1^{\sqrt{3}} \dfrac{1}{(4 - x^2)^{\frac{3}{2}}}\, dx = \int_{\frac{\pi}{6}}^{\frac{\pi}{3}} \dfrac{1}{(4 - 4\sin^2 \theta)^{\frac{3}{2}}} \times 2 \cos \theta\, d\theta$

$= \displaystyle\int_{\frac{\pi}{6}}^{\frac{\pi}{3}} \dfrac{2 \cos \theta}{(4 - 4 + 4\cos^2 \theta)^{\frac{3}{2}}}\, d\theta = \int_{\frac{\pi}{6}}^{\frac{\pi}{3}} \dfrac{2 \cos \theta}{8 \cos^3 \theta}\, d\theta$

$= \displaystyle\int_{\frac{\pi}{6}}^{\frac{\pi}{3}} \dfrac{1}{4}\sec^2 \theta\, d\theta = \dfrac{1}{4}\left[\tan \theta\right]_{\frac{\pi}{6}}^{\frac{\pi}{3}} = \dfrac{1}{4}\left(\sqrt{3} - \dfrac{1}{\sqrt{3}}\right) = \dfrac{\sqrt{3}}{6}$

Q4 $x = \cos \theta \Rightarrow \dfrac{dx}{d\theta} = -\sin \theta \Rightarrow dx = -\sin \theta\, d\theta$

$x = \dfrac{1}{2} \Rightarrow \cos \theta = \dfrac{1}{2} \Rightarrow \theta = \dfrac{\pi}{3}$

$x = 1 \Rightarrow \cos \theta = 1 \Rightarrow \theta = 0$

So, using the identity $\sin^2 \theta + \cos^2 \theta \equiv 1$:

$\displaystyle\int_{\frac{1}{2}}^1 \dfrac{1}{x^2 \sqrt{1 - x^2}}\, dx = \int_{\frac{\pi}{3}}^0 \dfrac{1}{\cos^2 \theta \sqrt{1 - \cos^2 \theta}} \times -\sin \theta\, d\theta$

$= \displaystyle\int_{\frac{\pi}{3}}^0 -\dfrac{\sin \theta}{\cos^2 \theta \sin \theta}\, d\theta = \int_0^{\frac{\pi}{3}} \dfrac{\sin \theta}{\cos^2 \theta \sin \theta}\, d\theta$

$= \displaystyle\int_0^{\frac{\pi}{3}} \dfrac{1}{\cos^2 \theta}\, d\theta = \int_0^{\frac{\pi}{3}} \sec^2 \theta\, d\theta = \left[\tan \theta\right]_0^{\frac{\pi}{3}} = \sqrt{3} - 0 = \sqrt{3}$

Q5 $u = \sec^2 x \Rightarrow \dfrac{du}{dx} = 2\sec^2 x \tan x$

$\Rightarrow dx = \dfrac{1}{2 \sec^2 x \tan x}\, du = \dfrac{1}{2u \tan x}\, du$

And using the identity

$\sec^2 x \equiv 1 + \tan^2 x \Rightarrow \tan^2 x \equiv \sec^2 x - 1 = u - 1$

$\displaystyle\int 2 \tan^3 x\, dx = \int 2 \tan x(u - 1) \times \dfrac{1}{2u \tan x}\, du = \int \dfrac{u - 1}{u}\, du$

$= \displaystyle\int 1 - \dfrac{1}{u}\, du = u - \ln|u| + C = \sec^2 x - \ln(\sec^2 x) + C$

Q6 a) $u = \cos\theta \Rightarrow du = -\sin\theta\,d\theta \Rightarrow d\theta = -\dfrac{1}{\sin\theta}\,du$

$\theta = \dfrac{\pi}{2} \Rightarrow u = \cos\dfrac{\pi}{2} \Rightarrow u = 0$

$\theta = -\pi \Rightarrow u = \cos -\pi \Rightarrow u = -1$

$\displaystyle\int_{-\pi}^{\frac{\pi}{2}} 3\sin\theta\cos^4\theta\,d\theta = \int_{-1}^{0} 3\sin\theta\,u^4 \times -\dfrac{1}{\sin\theta}\,du$

$\displaystyle = \int_{-1}^{0} -3u^4\,du = \left[-\dfrac{3u^5}{5}\right]_{-1}^{0} = 0 - \dfrac{3}{5} = -\dfrac{3}{5}$

b) $u = \sec x \Rightarrow du = \sec x\tan x\,dx$

$\Rightarrow dx = \dfrac{1}{\sec x\tan x}\,du = \dfrac{1}{u\tan x}\,du$

$x = \dfrac{\pi}{3} \Rightarrow u = \sec\dfrac{\pi}{3} \Rightarrow u = 2$

$x = \dfrac{\pi}{4} \Rightarrow u = \sec\dfrac{\pi}{4} \Rightarrow u = \sqrt{2}$

$\displaystyle\int_{\frac{\pi}{4}}^{\frac{\pi}{3}} \sec^4 x\tan x\,dx = \int_{\sqrt{2}}^{2} u^4\tan x\,\dfrac{1}{u\tan x}\,du$

$\displaystyle = \int_{\sqrt{2}}^{2} u^3\,du = \left[\dfrac{u^4}{4}\right]_{\sqrt{2}}^{2} = \dfrac{2^4}{4} - \dfrac{\sqrt{2}^4}{4} = 4 - 1 = 3$

Q7 $x = \cot\theta \Rightarrow dx = -\operatorname{cosec}^2\theta\,d\theta$

$x = 1 \Rightarrow \tan\theta = 1 \Rightarrow \theta = \dfrac{\pi}{4}$

$x = \sqrt{3} \Rightarrow \tan\theta = \dfrac{1}{\sqrt{3}} \Rightarrow \theta = \dfrac{\pi}{6}$

$\displaystyle\int_{1}^{\sqrt{3}} \dfrac{4x}{\sqrt{1+x^2}}\,dx = \int_{\frac{\pi}{4}}^{\frac{\pi}{6}} \dfrac{4\cot\theta}{\sqrt{1+\cot^2\theta}} \times -\operatorname{cosec}^2\theta\,d\theta$

$\displaystyle = \int_{\frac{\pi}{6}}^{\frac{\pi}{4}} 4\cot\theta\operatorname{cosec}\theta\,d\theta = [-4\operatorname{cosec}\theta]_{\frac{\pi}{6}}^{\frac{\pi}{4}} = -4(\sqrt{2}-2) = 8 - 4\sqrt{2}$

8.9 Integration by Parts

Exercise 8.9.1 — Integration by parts

Q1 a) Let $u = x$ and $\dfrac{dv}{dx} = e^x$.

Then $\dfrac{du}{dx} = 1$ and $v = e^x$.

So $\displaystyle\int xe^x\,dx = xe^x - \int e^x\,dx = xe^x - e^x + C$

b) Let $u = x$ and $\dfrac{dv}{dx} = e^{-x}$. Then $\dfrac{du}{dx} = 1$ and $v = -e^{-x}$.

So $\displaystyle\int xe^{-x}\,dx = -xe^{-x} - \int -e^{-x}\,dx = -xe^{-x} - e^{-x} + C$

c) Let $u = x$ and $\dfrac{dv}{dx} = e^{-\frac{x}{3}}$. Then $\dfrac{du}{dx} = 1$ and $v = -3\,e^{-\frac{x}{3}}$.

So $\displaystyle\int xe^{-\frac{x}{3}}\,dx = -3x\,e^{-\frac{x}{3}} - \int -3\,e^{-\frac{x}{3}}\,dx = -3x\,e^{-\frac{x}{3}} - 9\,e^{-\frac{x}{3}} + C$

d) Let $u = x$ and $\dfrac{dv}{dx} = e^x + 1$. Then $\dfrac{du}{dx} = 1$ and $v = e^x + x$.

So $\displaystyle\int x(e^x + 1)\,dx = x(e^x + x) - \int e^x + x\,dx$

$= xe^x + x^2 - e^x - \dfrac{1}{2}x^2 + C = xe^x - e^x + \dfrac{1}{2}x^2 + C$

You could also have solved this one by expanding the brackets and integrating xe^x + x separately.

You might have spotted a pattern here — all the parts of this question had u = x and $\dfrac{dv}{dx}$ as a function involving e.

Your answers might look a bit different if you factorised them.

Q2 a) Let $u = x$ and $\dfrac{dv}{dx} = \sin x$. Then $\dfrac{du}{dx} = 1$ and $v = -\cos x$.

So $\displaystyle\int_{0}^{\pi} x\sin x\,dx = [-x\cos x]_{0}^{\pi} - \int_{0}^{\pi} -\cos x\,dx$

$= [-x\cos x]_{0}^{\pi} + [\sin x]_{0}^{\pi} = (\pi - 0) + (0 - 0) = \pi$

b) Let $u = 2x$ and $\dfrac{dv}{dx} = \cos x$. Then $\dfrac{du}{dx} = 2$ and $v = \sin x$.

So $\displaystyle\int 2x\cos x\,dx = 2x\sin x - \int 2\sin x\,dx$

$= 2x\sin x + 2\cos x + C$

c) Let $u = 3x$ and $\dfrac{dv}{dx} = \cos\dfrac{1}{2}x$.

Then $\dfrac{du}{dx} = 3$ and $v = 2\sin\dfrac{1}{2}x$.

So $\displaystyle\int 3x\cos\dfrac{1}{2}x\,dx = 6x\sin\dfrac{1}{2}x - \int 6\sin\dfrac{1}{2}x\,dx$

$= 6x\sin\dfrac{1}{2}x + 12\cos\dfrac{1}{2}x + C$

d) Let $u = 2x$ and $\dfrac{dv}{dx} = 1 - \sin x$. Then $\dfrac{du}{dx} = 2$ and $v = x + \cos x$.

So $\displaystyle\int_{-\frac{\pi}{2}}^{\frac{\pi}{2}} 2x(1 - \sin x)\,dx = [2x(x + \cos x)]_{-\frac{\pi}{2}}^{\frac{\pi}{2}} - \int_{-\frac{\pi}{2}}^{\frac{\pi}{2}} 2(x + \cos x)\,dx$

$= [2x(x + \cos x)]_{-\frac{\pi}{2}}^{\frac{\pi}{2}} - [x^2 + 2\sin x]_{-\frac{\pi}{2}}^{\frac{\pi}{2}}$

$= \left[\pi\left(\dfrac{\pi}{2} + 0\right) - (-\pi)\left(-\dfrac{\pi}{2} + 0\right)\right] - \left[\left(\dfrac{\pi^2}{4} + 2\right) - \left(\dfrac{\pi^2}{4} - 2\right)\right] = -4$

Q3 a) Let $u = \ln x$ and $\dfrac{dv}{dx} = 2$. Then $\dfrac{du}{dx} = \dfrac{1}{x}$ and $v = 2x$.

So $\displaystyle\int 2\ln x\,dx = 2x\ln x - \int 2\,dx = 2x\ln x - 2x + C$

b) Let $u = \ln x$ and $\dfrac{dv}{dx} = x^4$. Then $\dfrac{du}{dx} = \dfrac{1}{x}$ and $v = \dfrac{1}{5}x^5$.

So $\displaystyle\int x^4\ln x\,dx = \dfrac{1}{5}x^5\ln x - \int \dfrac{1}{5}x^4\,dx = \dfrac{1}{5}x^5\ln x - \dfrac{1}{25}x^5 + C$

c) Let $u = \ln 4x$ and $\dfrac{dv}{dx} = 1$. Then $\dfrac{du}{dx} = \dfrac{1}{x}$ and $v = x$.

So $\displaystyle\int \ln 4x\,dx = x\ln 4x - \int 1\,dx = x\ln 4x - x + C$

d) Let $u = \ln x^3$ and $\dfrac{dv}{dx} = 1$. Then $\dfrac{du}{dx} = \dfrac{3}{x}$ and $v = x$.

So $\displaystyle\int \ln x^3\,dx = x\ln x^3 - \int 3\,dx = x\ln x^3 - 3x + C$

For parts a), c) and d), if the question hadn't told you to use integration by parts, you could have just used the result for integrating ln x shown on p.236 (you'd need to rewrite the logs in parts c) and d) as ln 4 + ln x and 3 ln x).

Q4 a) Let $u = 20x$ and $\dfrac{dv}{dx} = (x + 1)^3$.

Then $\dfrac{du}{dx} = 20$ and $v = \dfrac{1}{4}(x + 1)^4$.

So $\displaystyle\int_{-1}^{1} 20x(x + 1)^3\,dx = [5x(x + 1)^4]_{-1}^{1} - \int_{-1}^{1} 5(x + 1)^4\,dx$

$= [5x(x + 1)^4]_{-1}^{1} - [(x + 1)^5]_{-1}^{1} = [5(2^4) - 0] - [(2^5) - 0]$

$= 80 - 32 = 48$

b) Let $u = 30x$ and $\dfrac{dv}{dx} = (2x + 1)^{\frac{1}{2}}$.

Then $\dfrac{du}{dx} = 30$ and $v = \dfrac{1}{3}(2x + 1)^{\frac{3}{2}}$.

So $\displaystyle\int_{0}^{1.5} 30x\sqrt{2x + 1}\,dx = [10x(2x + 1)^{\frac{3}{2}}]_{0}^{1.5} - \int_{0}^{1.5} 10(2x + 1)^{\frac{3}{2}}\,dx$

$= [10x(2x + 1)^{\frac{3}{2}}]_{0}^{1.5} - [2(2x + 1)^{\frac{5}{2}}]_{0}^{1.5}$

$= [15(4)^{\frac{3}{2}} - 0] - [2(4)^{\frac{5}{2}} - 2(1)^{\frac{5}{2}}] = 120 - 62 = 58$

Q5 a) Let $u = x$ and $\dfrac{dv}{dx} = 12e^{2x}$. Then $\dfrac{du}{dx} = 1$ and $v = 6e^{2x}$.

So $\displaystyle\int_{0}^{1} 12xe^{2x}\,dx = [6xe^{2x}]_{0}^{1} - \int_{0}^{1} 6e^{2x}\,dx$

$= 6e^2 - [3e^{2x}]_{0}^{1} = 6e^2 - (3e^2 - 3e^0) = 3e^2 + 3$

b) Let $u = x$ and $\dfrac{dv}{dx} = 18\sin 3x$.

Then $\dfrac{du}{dx} = 1$ and $v = -6\cos 3x$.

$\displaystyle\int_{0}^{\frac{\pi}{3}} 18x\sin 3x\,dx = [-6x\cos 3x]_{0}^{\frac{\pi}{3}} - \int_{0}^{\frac{\pi}{3}} -6\cos 3x\,dx$

$= -2\pi\cos\pi + [2\sin 3x]_{0}^{\frac{\pi}{3}} = 2\pi + [2\sin\pi - 2\sin 0] = 2\pi$

c) Let $u = \ln x$ and $\dfrac{dv}{dx} = \dfrac{1}{x^2}$. Then $\dfrac{du}{dx} = \dfrac{1}{x}$ and $v = -\dfrac{1}{x}$.

So $\displaystyle\int_{1}^{2} \dfrac{1}{x^2}\ln x\,dx = \left[-\dfrac{1}{x}\ln x\right]_{1}^{2} - \int_{1}^{2} -\dfrac{1}{x^2}\,dx$

$= -\dfrac{1}{2}\ln 2 + \ln 1 - \left[\dfrac{1}{x}\right]_{1}^{2} = -\dfrac{1}{2}\ln 2 - \dfrac{1}{2} + 1 = \dfrac{1}{2} - \dfrac{1}{2}\ln 2$

Q6 a) Let $u = x$ and $\dfrac{dv}{dx} = e^{-2x}$. Then $\dfrac{du}{dx} = 1$ and $v = -\dfrac{1}{2}e^{-2x}$.

So $\displaystyle\int \dfrac{x}{e^{2x}}\,dx = -\dfrac{x}{2}e^{-2x} - \int -\dfrac{1}{2}e^{-2x}\,dx = -\dfrac{x}{2e^{2x}} - \dfrac{1}{4e^{2x}} + C$

b) Let $u = x + 1$ and $\dfrac{dv}{dx} = (x + 2)^{\frac{1}{2}}$.

Then $\dfrac{du}{dx} = 1$ and $v = \dfrac{2}{3}(x + 2)^{\frac{3}{2}}$.

So $\displaystyle\int (x + 1)\sqrt{x + 2}\,dx = \dfrac{2}{3}(x + 1)(x + 2)^{\frac{3}{2}} - \int \dfrac{2}{3}(x + 2)^{\frac{3}{2}}\,dx$

$= \dfrac{2}{3}(x + 1)(x + 2)^{\frac{3}{2}} - \dfrac{4}{15}(x + 2)^{\frac{5}{2}} + C$

c) Let $u = \ln(x+1)$ and $\dfrac{dv}{dx} = 1$. Then $\dfrac{du}{dx} = \dfrac{1}{x+1}$ and $v = x$.

So $\displaystyle\int \ln(x+1)\, dx = x\ln(x+1) - \int \dfrac{x}{x+1}\, dx$

$= x\ln(x+1) - \displaystyle\int \dfrac{x+1-1}{x+1}\, dx = x\ln(x+1) - \int 1 - \dfrac{1}{x+1}\, dx$

$= x\ln|x+1| - x + \ln|x+1| + C = (x+1)\ln|x+1| - x + C$

Exercise 8.9.2 — Repeated use of integration by parts

Q1 a) Let $u = x^2$ and $\dfrac{dv}{dx} = e^x$. Then $\dfrac{du}{dx} = 2x$ and $v = e^x$.

So $\displaystyle\int x^2 e^x\, dx = x^2 e^x - \int 2xe^x\, dx$

Integrate by parts again to find $\displaystyle\int 2xe^x\, dx$:

Let $u = 2x$ and $\dfrac{dv}{dx} = e^x$. Then $\dfrac{du}{dx} = 2$ and $v = e^x$.

So $\displaystyle\int 2xe^x\, dx = 2xe^x - \int 2e^x\, dx = 2xe^x - 2e^x + c$

So $\displaystyle\int x^2 e^x\, dx = x^2 e^x - \int 2xe^x\, dx = x^2 e^x - (2xe^x - 2e^x + c)$

$= x^2 e^x - 2xe^x + 2e^x + C$

b) Let $u = x^2$ and $\dfrac{dv}{dx} = \cos x$. Then $\dfrac{du}{dx} = 2x$ and $v = \sin x$.

So $\displaystyle\int x^2 \cos x\, dx = x^2 \sin x - \int 2x \sin x\, dx$

Integrate by parts again to find $\displaystyle\int 2x \sin x\, dx$:

Let $u = 2x$ and $\dfrac{dv}{dx} = \sin x$. Then $\dfrac{du}{dx} = 2$ and $v = -\cos x$.

So $\displaystyle\int 2x \sin x\, dx = -2x\cos x - \int -2\cos x\, dx$

$= -2x\cos x + 2\sin x + c$

So $\displaystyle\int x^2 \cos x\, dx = x^2 \sin x - \int 2x \sin x\, dx$

$= x^2 \sin x - (-2x\cos x + 2\sin x + c)$

$= x^2 \sin x + 2x\cos x - 2\sin x + C$

c) Let $u = x^2$ and $\dfrac{dv}{dx} = 4\sin 2x$.

Then $\dfrac{du}{dx} = 2x$ and $v = -2\cos 2x$.

So $\displaystyle\int 4x^2 \sin 2x\, dx = -2x^2 \cos 2x + \int 4x \cos 2x\, dx$

Integrate by parts again to find $\displaystyle\int 4x \cos 2x\, dx$:

Let $u = x$ and $\dfrac{dv}{dx} = 4\cos 2x$. Then $\dfrac{du}{dx} = 1$ and $v = 2\sin 2x$.

So $\displaystyle\int 4x \cos 2x\, dx = 2x\sin 2x - \int 2\sin 2x\, dx$

$= 2x\sin 2x + \cos 2x + C$

So $\displaystyle\int 4x^2 \sin 2x\, dx = -2x^2 \cos 2x + \int 4x \cos 2x\, dx$

$= -2x^2 \cos 2x + 2x\sin 2x + \cos 2x + C$

d) Let $u = 40x^2$ and $\dfrac{dv}{dx} = (2x-1)^4$.

Then $\dfrac{du}{dx} = 80x$ and $v = \dfrac{1}{10}(2x-1)^5$.

$\displaystyle\int 40x^2(2x-1)^4\, dx = 4x^2(2x-1)^5 - \int 8x(2x-1)^5\, dx$

Integrate by parts again to find $\displaystyle\int 8x(2x-1)^5\, dx$:

Let $u = 8x$ and $\dfrac{dv}{dx} = (2x-1)^5$.

Then $\dfrac{du}{dx} = 8$ and $v = \dfrac{1}{12}(2x-1)^6$

$\displaystyle\int 8x(2x-1)^5\, dx = \dfrac{2x}{3}(2x-1)^6 - \int \dfrac{2}{3}(2x-1)^6\, dx$

$= \dfrac{2x}{3}(2x-1)^6 - \dfrac{1}{21}(2x-1)^7 + C$

So $\displaystyle\int 40x^2(2x-1)^4\, dx$

$= 4x^2(2x-1)^5 - \dfrac{2x}{3}(2x-1)^6 + \dfrac{1}{21}(2x-1)^7 + C$

Q2 Let $u = x^2$ and $\dfrac{dv}{dx} = (x+1)^4$. Then $\dfrac{du}{dx} = 2x$ and $v = \dfrac{1}{5}(x+1)^5$.

So $\displaystyle\int_{-1}^{0} x^2(x+1)^4\, dx = \left[\dfrac{x^2}{5}(x+1)^5\right]_{-1}^{0} - \int_{-1}^{0} \dfrac{2}{5}x(x+1)^5\, dx$

$= 0 - \displaystyle\int_{-1}^{0} \dfrac{2}{5}x(x+1)^5\, dx$

Integrate by parts again to find $\displaystyle\int_{-1}^{0} \dfrac{2}{5}x(x+1)^5\, dx$:

Let $u = x$ and $\dfrac{dv}{dx} = \dfrac{2}{5}(x+1)^5$. Then $\dfrac{du}{dx} = 1$ and $v = \dfrac{1}{15}(x+1)^6$.

$\displaystyle\int_{-1}^{0} \dfrac{2}{5}x(x+1)^5\, dx = \left[\dfrac{x}{15}(x+1)^6\right]_{-1}^{0} - \int_{-1}^{0} \dfrac{1}{15}(x+1)^6\, dx$

$= 0 - \left[\dfrac{1}{105}(x+1)^7\right]_{-1}^{0} = -\dfrac{1}{105}$

So $\displaystyle\int_{-1}^{0} x^2(x+1)^4\, dx = 0 - \int_{-1}^{0} \dfrac{2}{5}x(x+1)^5\, dx = -\left(-\dfrac{1}{105}\right) = \dfrac{1}{105}$

Q3 Let $u = x^2$ and $\dfrac{dv}{dx} = e^{-2x}$. Then $\dfrac{du}{dx} = 2x$ and $v = -\dfrac{1}{2}e^{-2x}$.

So area $= \displaystyle\int_{0}^{1} x^2 e^{-2x}\, dx = \left[-\dfrac{x^2}{2}e^{-2x}\right]_{0}^{1} + \int_{0}^{1} xe^{-2x}\, dx$

Integrate by parts again to find $\displaystyle\int_{0}^{1} xe^{-2x}\, dx$:

Let $u = x$ and $\dfrac{dv}{dx} = e^{-2x}$. Then $\dfrac{du}{dx} = 1$ and $v = -\dfrac{1}{2}e^{-2x}$.

So $\displaystyle\int_{0}^{1} xe^{-2x}\, dx = \left[-\dfrac{x}{2}e^{-2x}\right]_{0}^{1} + \int_{0}^{1} \dfrac{1}{2}e^{-2x}\, dx$

$= \left[-\dfrac{x}{2}e^{-2x}\right]_{0}^{1} + \left[-\dfrac{1}{4}e^{-2x}\right]_{0}^{1}$

So area $= \left[-\dfrac{x^2}{2}e^{-2x}\right]_{0}^{1} + \left[-\dfrac{x}{2}e^{-2x}\right]_{0}^{1} + \left[-\dfrac{1}{4}e^{-2x}\right]_{0}^{1}$

$= -\dfrac{1}{2}e^{-2} - \dfrac{1}{2}e^{-2} - \dfrac{1}{4}e^{-2} + \dfrac{1}{4} = \dfrac{1}{4} - \dfrac{5}{4}e^{-2}$

8.10 Integrating Using Partial Fractions

Exercise 8.10.1 — Use of partial fractions

Q1 a) First write the function as partial fractions. Factorise the denominator and write as an identity:

$\dfrac{24(x-1)}{9-4x^2} \equiv \dfrac{24(x-1)}{(3-2x)(3+2x)} \equiv \dfrac{A}{(3-2x)} + \dfrac{B}{(3+2x)}$

Add the fractions and cancel denominators:

$\dfrac{24(x-1)}{(3-2x)(3+2x)} \equiv \dfrac{A(3+2x) + B(3-2x)}{(3-2x)(3+2x)}$

$\Rightarrow 24(x-1) \equiv A(3+2x) + B(3-2x)$

Substituting $x = -\dfrac{3}{2}$ gives: $-60 = 6B \Rightarrow B = -10$.

Substituting $x = \dfrac{3}{2}$ gives: $12 = 6A \Rightarrow A = 2$.

So $\dfrac{24(x-1)}{9-4x^2} \equiv \dfrac{2}{(3-2x)} - \dfrac{10}{(3+2x)}$.

So the integral can be expressed:

$\displaystyle\int \dfrac{24(x-1)}{9-4x^2}\, dx = \int \dfrac{2}{(3-2x)} - \dfrac{10}{(3+2x)}\, dx$

$= \dfrac{2}{-2}\ln|3-2x| - \dfrac{10}{2}\ln|3+2x| + C$

$= -\ln|3-2x| - 5\ln|3+2x| + C$

b) $\dfrac{21x-82}{(x-2)(x-3)(x-4)} \equiv \dfrac{A}{x-2} + \dfrac{B}{x-3} + \dfrac{C}{x-4}$

$\equiv \dfrac{A(x-3)(x-4) + B(x-2)(x-4) + C(x-2)(x-3)}{(x-2)(x-3)(x-4)}$

$21x - 82 \equiv A(x-3)(x-4) + B(x-2)(x-4) + C(x-2)(x-3)$

Substituting $x = 2$ gives: $-40 = 2A \Rightarrow A = -20$

Substituting $x = 3$ gives: $-19 = -B \Rightarrow B = 19$

Substituting $x = 4$ gives: $2 = 2C \Rightarrow C = 1$

So $\dfrac{21x-82}{(x-2)(x-3)(x-4)} \equiv -\dfrac{20}{x-2} + \dfrac{19}{x-3} + \dfrac{1}{x-4}$

$\equiv \dfrac{1}{x-4} + \dfrac{19}{x-3} - \dfrac{20}{x-2}$

So the integral can be expressed as:

$\displaystyle\int \dfrac{21x-82}{(x-2)(x-3)(x-4)}\, dx = \int \dfrac{1}{x-4} + \dfrac{19}{x-3} - \dfrac{20}{x-2}\, dx$

$= \ln|x-4| + 19\ln|x-3| - 20\ln|x-2| + C$

Q2 First write the function as partial fractions:

$$\frac{x}{(x-2)(x-3)} \equiv \frac{A}{x-2} + \frac{B}{x-3} \equiv \frac{A(x-3)+B(x-2)}{(x-2)(x-3)}$$

$$\Rightarrow x \equiv A(x-3) + B(x-2)$$

Substituting $x = 3$: $B = 3$
Substituting $x = 2$: $-A = 2 \Rightarrow A = -2$

So $\dfrac{x}{(x-2)(x-3)} \equiv \dfrac{-2}{x-2} + \dfrac{3}{x-3} \equiv \dfrac{3}{x-3} - \dfrac{2}{x-2}$

$$\Rightarrow \int_0^1 \frac{x}{(x-2)(x-3)}\, dx = \int_0^1 \frac{3}{x-3} - \frac{2}{x-2}\, dx$$

$$= \left[3\ln|x-3| - 2\ln|x-2| \right]_0^1$$

$$= \left[3\ln|1-3| - 2\ln|1-2| \right] - \left[3\ln|0-3| - 2\ln|0-2| \right]$$

$$= 3\ln 2 - 2\ln 1 - 3\ln 3 + 2\ln 2 = 0 + 5\ln 2 - 3\ln 3$$

$$= \ln 2^5 - \ln 3^3 = \ln \frac{32}{27}$$

Note that the modulus is important in this question, for example $|1 - 2| = |-1| = 1$.

Q3 **a)** Factorise the denominator, then write as an identity:

$$\frac{6}{2x^2-5x+2} = \frac{6}{(2x-1)(x-2)} \equiv \frac{A}{2x-1} + \frac{B}{x-2}$$

$$\Rightarrow 6 \equiv A(x-2) + B(2x-1)$$

Substituting $x = 2$ gives $6 = 3B$ so $B = 2$.
Substituting $x = \frac{1}{2}$ gives $6 = -\frac{3}{2}A$ so $A = -4$.

So $\dfrac{6}{2x^2-5x+2} \equiv \dfrac{-4}{2x-1} + \dfrac{2}{x-2} = \dfrac{2}{x-2} - \dfrac{4}{2x-1}$

b) Using part a)

$$\int \frac{6}{2x^2-5x+2}\, dx = \int \frac{2}{x-2} - \frac{4}{2x-1}\, dx$$

$$= 2\ln|x-2| - \frac{4}{2}\ln|2x-1| + C = 2\ln|x-2| - 2\ln|2x-1| + C$$

$x > 2$ so $x - 2 > 0$ and $2x - 1 > 3 > 0$ so the modulus signs can be removed. So:

$$\int \frac{6}{2x^2-5x+2}\, dx = 2\ln(x-2) - 2\ln(2x-1) + C$$

$$= 2\ln\left(\frac{x-2}{2x-1}\right) + C = \ln\left[\left(\frac{x-2}{2x-1}\right)^2\right] + C$$

c) Using part b)

$$\int_3^5 \frac{6}{2x^2-5x+2}\, dx = \left[\ln\left[\left(\frac{x-2}{2x-1}\right)^2\right] \right]_3^5$$

$$= \ln\left[\left(\frac{5-2}{10-1}\right)^2\right] - \ln\left[\left(\frac{3-2}{6-1}\right)^2\right]$$

$$= \ln\frac{1}{9} - \ln\frac{1}{25} = \ln\frac{25}{9}$$

Q4 First express the fraction as an identity:

$$\frac{f(x)}{g(x)} = \frac{3x+5}{x(x+10)} \equiv \frac{A}{x} + \frac{B}{x+10} \Rightarrow 3x + 5 \equiv A(x+10) + Bx$$

Now use the equating coefficients method:
Equating constant terms: $10A = 5 \Rightarrow A = \frac{1}{2}$
Equating x coefficients: $A + B = 3 \Rightarrow \frac{1}{2} + B = 3 \Rightarrow B = \frac{5}{2}$

So $\dfrac{3x+5}{x(x+10)} \equiv \dfrac{1}{2x} + \dfrac{5}{2(x+10)}$

Now the integration can be expressed:

$$\int_1^2 \frac{f(x)}{g(x)}\, dx = \int_1^2 \frac{3x+5}{x(x+10)}\, dx = \int_1^2 \frac{1}{2x} + \frac{5}{2(x+10)}\, dx$$

$$= \left[\frac{1}{2}\ln|x| + \frac{5}{2}\ln|x+10| \right]_1^2$$

$$= \left[\frac{1}{2}\ln|2| + \frac{5}{2}\ln|2+10| \right] - \left[\frac{1}{2}\ln|1| + \frac{5}{2}\ln|1+10| \right]$$

$$= \left[\frac{1}{2}\ln 2 + \frac{5}{2}\ln 12 \right] - \left[0 + \frac{5}{2}\ln 11 \right]$$

$$= \frac{1}{2}\ln 2 + \frac{5}{2}\ln 12 - \frac{5}{2}\ln 11 = \frac{1}{2}\left(\ln 2 + 5\ln\frac{12}{11} \right)$$

$$= \frac{1}{2}\left(\ln 2 + \ln\left(\frac{12}{11}\right)^5 \right) = 0.564 \text{ (3 d.p.)}$$

Q5 Begin by writing the function as partial fractions.

$$\frac{-(t+3)}{(3t+2)(t+1)} \equiv \frac{A}{(3t+2)} + \frac{B}{(t+1)}$$

$$\Rightarrow -(t+3) \equiv A(t+1) + B(3t+2)$$

Substituting $t = -1$ gives: $-2 = -B \Rightarrow B = 2$
Equating coefficients of t gives
$A + 3B = -1 \Rightarrow A + 6 = -1 \Rightarrow A = -7$

So $\dfrac{-(t+3)}{(3t+2)(t+1)} \equiv \dfrac{2}{(t+1)} - \dfrac{7}{(3t+2)}$

The integral can be expressed:

$$\int_0^{\frac{2}{3}} \frac{-(t+3)}{(3t+2)(t+1)}\, dt = \int_0^{\frac{2}{3}} \frac{2}{(t+1)} - \frac{7}{(3t+2)}\, dt$$

$$= \left[2\ln|t+1| - \frac{7}{3}\ln|3t+2| \right]_0^{\frac{2}{3}} = \left[2\ln\left|\frac{5}{3}\right| - \frac{7}{3}\ln|4| \right] - \left[2\ln|1| - \frac{7}{3}\ln|2| \right]$$

$$= \left[2\ln\left(\frac{5}{3}\right) - \frac{7}{3}\ln(4) \right] - \left[0 - \frac{7}{3}\ln(2) \right] = 2\ln\left(\frac{5}{3}\right) - \frac{7}{3}\ln(4) + \frac{7}{3}\ln(2)$$

$$= 2\ln\left(\frac{5}{3}\right) - \frac{7}{3}(\ln(4) - \ln(2)) = 2\ln\left(\frac{5}{3}\right) - \frac{7}{3}\ln\left(\frac{4}{2}\right) = 2\ln\frac{5}{3} - \frac{7}{3}\ln 2$$

Q6 $u = \sqrt{x} \Rightarrow \dfrac{du}{dx} = \dfrac{1}{2\sqrt{x}} \Rightarrow dx = 2\sqrt{x}\, du = 2u\, du$

and $u = \sqrt{x} \Rightarrow x = u^2$.
Using $u = \sqrt{x}$, $x = 9 \Rightarrow u = \sqrt{9} = 3$
$x = 16 \Rightarrow u = \sqrt{16} = 4$

So $\displaystyle\int_9^{16} \frac{4}{\sqrt{x}(9x-4)}\, dx = \int_3^4 \frac{4}{u(9u^2-4)}\, 2u\, dx = \int_3^4 \frac{8}{(9u^2-4)}\, dx$

This function still needs some work before it can be integrated. The next step is to write it as partial fractions.

$$\frac{8}{(9u^2-4)} \equiv \frac{8}{(3u+2)(3u-2)} \equiv \frac{A}{(3u+2)} + \frac{B}{(3u-2)}$$

So $8 = A(3u-2) + B(3u+2)$
Using substitution:

$$u = \frac{2}{3} \Rightarrow 8 = 4B \Rightarrow 2 = B$$

$$u = -\frac{2}{3} \Rightarrow 8 = -4A \Rightarrow -2 = A$$

So $\dfrac{8}{(9u^2-4)} \equiv \dfrac{-2}{(3u+2)} + \dfrac{2}{(3u-2)} \equiv \dfrac{2}{(3u-2)} - \dfrac{2}{(3u+2)}$

So the integral can be expressed:

$$\int_3^4 \frac{8}{(9u^2-4)}\, dx = \int_3^4 \frac{2}{(3u-2)} - \frac{2}{(3u+2)}\, dx$$

$$= \left[\frac{2}{3}\ln|3u-2| - \frac{2}{3}\ln|3u+2| \right]_3^4$$

$$= \left[\frac{2}{3}\ln\left|\frac{3u-2}{3u+2}\right| \right]_3^4 = \frac{2}{3}\ln\frac{10}{14} - \frac{2}{3}\ln\frac{7}{11} = \frac{2}{3}\ln\frac{55}{49}$$

8.11 Differential Equations

Exercise 8.11.1 — Differential equations

Q1 The rate of change of N with respect to t is $\dfrac{dN}{dt}$.
So $\dfrac{dN}{dt} \propto N \Rightarrow \dfrac{dN}{dt} = kN$, for some $k > 0$.

Q2 The rate of change of x with respect to t is $\dfrac{dx}{dt}$.
So $\dfrac{dx}{dt} \propto \dfrac{1}{x^2} \Rightarrow \dfrac{dx}{dt} = \dfrac{k}{x^2}$, for some $k > 0$.

Q3 Let the variable t represent time.
Then the rate of change of A with respect to t is $\dfrac{dA}{dt}$.
So $\dfrac{dA}{dt} \propto \sqrt{A} \Rightarrow \dfrac{dA}{dt} = -k\sqrt{A}$, for some $k > 0$.
Don't forget to include a minus sign when the situation involves a rate of decrease.

Q4 Let the variable t represent time.
Then the rate of change of y with respect to t is $\dfrac{dy}{dt}$.
So $\dfrac{dy}{dt} \propto (y - \lambda) \Rightarrow \dfrac{dy}{dt} = -k(y - \lambda)$, for some $k > 0$.

Q5 Let the variable t represent time. V is the volume in the container and it is equal to $V_{in} - V_{out}$.
Then the rate of change of V with respect to t is $\dfrac{dV}{dt} = \dfrac{dV_{in}}{dt} - \dfrac{dV_{out}}{dt}$. $\dfrac{dV_{in}}{dt}$ is directly proportional to V,
so $\dfrac{dV_{in}}{dt} = kV$ for some constant k, $k > 0$ and $\dfrac{dV_{out}}{dt} = 20$.
So the overall rate of change of V is $\dfrac{dV}{dt} = kV - 20$, for some $k > 0$.

Exercise 8.11.2 — Solving differential equations

Q1 **a)** $\frac{dy}{dx} = 8x^3 \Rightarrow dy = 8x^3\,dx$

$\Rightarrow \int 1\,dy = \int 8x^3\,dx \Rightarrow y = 2x^4 + C$

b) $\frac{dy}{dx} = 5y \Rightarrow \frac{1}{y}\,dy = 5\,dx \Rightarrow \int \frac{1}{y}\,dy = \int 5\,dx$

$\Rightarrow \ln |y| = 5x + \ln k \Rightarrow y = e^{5x + \ln k} = ke^{5x}$

c) $\frac{dy}{dx} = 6x^2y \Rightarrow \frac{1}{y}\,dy = 6x^2 dx \Rightarrow \int \frac{1}{y}\,dy = \int 6x^2\,dx$

$\Rightarrow \ln|y| = 2x^3 + \ln k \Rightarrow y = e^{2x^3 + \ln k} = ke^{2x^3}$

d) $\frac{dy}{dx} = \frac{y}{x} \Rightarrow \frac{1}{y}\,dy = \frac{1}{x}\,dx \Rightarrow \int \frac{1}{y}\,dy = \int \frac{1}{x}\,dx$

$\Rightarrow \ln|y| = \ln|x| + \ln k = \ln|kx| \Rightarrow y = kx$

e) $\frac{dy}{dx} = (y + 1)\cos x \Rightarrow \frac{1}{y+1}\,dy = \cos x\,dx$

$\Rightarrow \int \frac{1}{y+1}\,dy = \int \cos x\,dx \Rightarrow \ln|y + 1| = \sin x + \ln k$

$\Rightarrow y + 1 = e^{\sin x + \ln k} \Rightarrow y = ke^{\sin x} - 1$

f) $\frac{dy}{dx} = \frac{3xy - 6y}{(x-4)(2x-5)} = \frac{(3x-6)y}{(x-4)(2x-5)}$

$\Rightarrow \frac{1}{y}\,dy = \frac{(3x-6)}{(x-4)(2x-5)}\,dx$

$\Rightarrow \int \frac{1}{y}\,dy = \int \frac{(3x-6)}{(x-4)(2x-5)}\,dx$

The integration on the right hand side needs to be split into partial fractions before you can integrate.

$\frac{(3x-6)}{(x-4)(2x-5)} \equiv \frac{A}{(x-4)} + \frac{B}{(2x-5)}$

$\Rightarrow (3x - 6) \equiv A(2x - 5) + B(x - 4)$

Substitution: $x = 4$: $6 = 3A \Rightarrow A = 2$

$\qquad\qquad x = \frac{5}{2}$: $\frac{3}{2} = -\frac{3}{2}B \Rightarrow B = -1$

So $\int \frac{(3x-6)}{(x-4)(2x-5)}\,dx \equiv \int \frac{2}{(x-4)} - \frac{1}{(2x-5)}\,dx$

So $\int \frac{1}{y}\,dy = \int \frac{2}{(x-4)} - \frac{1}{(2x-5)}\,dx$

$\Rightarrow \ln|y| = 2 \ln|x - 4| - \frac{1}{2} \ln|2x - 5| + \ln k$

$\Rightarrow \ln|y| = \ln|(x-4)^2| - \ln|\sqrt{2x-5}| + \ln k$

$\Rightarrow \ln|y| = \ln \left| \frac{k(x-4)^2}{\sqrt{2x-5}} \right| \Rightarrow y = \frac{k(x-4)^2}{\sqrt{2x-5}}$

Q2 **a)** $\frac{dy}{dx} = -\frac{x}{y} \Rightarrow y\,dy = -x\,dx \Rightarrow \int y\,dy = \int -x\,dx$

$\Rightarrow \frac{1}{2}y^2 = -\frac{1}{2}x^2 + c \Rightarrow y^2 = -x^2 + C$

So when $x = 0$ and $y = 2$, $C = 4 \Rightarrow y^2 + x^2 = 4$

b) $\frac{dx}{dt} = \frac{2}{\sqrt{x}} \Rightarrow \sqrt{x}\,dx = 2\,dt \Rightarrow \int x^{\frac{1}{2}}\,dx = \int 2\,dt$

$\Rightarrow \frac{2}{3}x^{\frac{3}{2}} = 2t + C$

So when $t = 5$ and $x = 9$,

$\frac{2}{3}(27) = 10 + C \Rightarrow 18 = 10 + C \qquad \Rightarrow C = 8$

$\Rightarrow \frac{2}{3}x^{\frac{3}{2}} = 2t + 8 \Rightarrow x^{\frac{3}{2}} = 3t + 12 \Rightarrow x^3 = (3t + 12)^2$

You could have left out the last couple of steps here, as the question didn't specify the form of the answer.

c) $\frac{dV}{dt} = 3(V - 1) \Rightarrow \frac{1}{V-1}\,dV = 3\,dt$

$\Rightarrow \int \frac{1}{V-1}\,dV = \int 3\,dt \Rightarrow \ln|V - 1| = 3t + \ln k$

$\Rightarrow V = ke^{3t} + 1$

So when $t = 0$ and $V = 5$, $5 = k + 1 \Rightarrow k = 4$

$\Rightarrow V = 4e^{3t} + 1$

d) $\frac{dy}{dx} = \frac{\tan y}{x} \Rightarrow \frac{1}{\tan y}\,dy = \frac{1}{x}\,dx \Rightarrow \int \cot y\,dy = \int \frac{1}{x}\,dx$

$\Rightarrow \ln|\sin y| = \ln|x| + \ln k \Rightarrow \sin y = kx$

So when $x = 2$ and $y = \frac{\pi}{2}$,

$1 = 2k \Rightarrow k = \frac{1}{2} \Rightarrow \sin y = \frac{x}{2}$

e) $\frac{dx}{dt} = 10x(x + 1) \Rightarrow \frac{1}{x(x+1)}\,dx = 10\,dt$

Using partial fractions, $\frac{1}{x(x+1)} \equiv \frac{1}{x} - \frac{1}{x+1}$, so

$\int \frac{1}{x} - \frac{1}{x+1}\,dx = \int 10\,dt \Rightarrow \ln|x| - \ln|x + 1| = 10t + \ln k$

$\Rightarrow \ln \left| \frac{x}{x+1} \right| = 10t + \ln k \Rightarrow \frac{x}{x+1} = ke^{10t}$

So when $t = 0$ and $x = 1$, $\frac{1}{2} = k \Rightarrow \frac{x}{x+1} = \frac{1}{2}e^{10t}$

Q3 **a)** $\frac{dx}{d\theta} = \cos^2 x \cot \theta \Rightarrow \int \frac{1}{\cos^2 x}\,dx = \int \cot \theta\,d\theta$

$\Rightarrow \int \sec^2 x\,dx = \int \cot \theta\,d\theta \Rightarrow \tan x = \ln|\sin \theta| + C$

b) $x = \frac{\pi}{4}$ when $\theta = \frac{\pi}{2}$, so:

$\tan \frac{\pi}{4} = \ln \left| \sin \frac{\pi}{2} \right| + C \Rightarrow 1 = \ln 1 + C \Rightarrow C = 1$

So $\tan x = \ln|\sin \theta| + 1$

c) $x = \tan^{-1}(\ln|\sin \theta| + 1)$, so when $\theta = \frac{\pi}{6}$,

$x = \tan^{-1}(\ln|\sin \frac{\pi}{6}| + 1) = 0.298$ (3 s.f.)

Q4 **a)** $\frac{dV}{dt} = a - bV \Rightarrow \frac{1}{a - bV}\,dV = dt$

$\Rightarrow \int \frac{1}{a-bV}\,dV = \int 1\,dt \Rightarrow -\frac{1}{b} \ln|a - bV| = t + C$

$\Rightarrow \ln|a - bV| = -bt - bC$

b and C are both constants, so let $-bC = \ln k$:

$\Rightarrow \ln|a - bV| = -bt + \ln k \Rightarrow a - bV = ke^{-bt}$

$\Rightarrow bV = a - ke^{-bt} \Rightarrow V = \frac{a}{b} - Ae^{-bt}$ (letting $A = k \div b$)

b) When $t = 0$ and $V = \frac{a}{4b}$,

$\frac{a}{4b} = \frac{a}{b} - A \Rightarrow A = \frac{a}{b} - \frac{a}{4b} = \frac{4a - a}{4b} = \frac{3a}{4b}$

c) As t gets very large, e^{-bt} gets very close to zero, so V approaches $\frac{a}{b}$.

Exercise 8.11.3 — Applying differential equations to real-life problems

Q1 **a)** $\frac{dN}{dt} = kN \Rightarrow \frac{1}{N}\,dN = k\,dt \Rightarrow \int \frac{1}{N}\,dN = \int k\,dt$

$\Rightarrow \ln N = kt + \ln A \Rightarrow N = e^{kt + \ln A} = Ae^{kt}$

Note that you don't need to put modulus signs in ln N here, as N can't be negative — you can't have a negative number of germs in your body. The same principle will apply to a lot of real-life differential equations questions.

b) $t = 0, N = 200 \Rightarrow 200 = Ae^0 = A \Rightarrow N = 200e^{kt}$

$t = 8, N = 400 \Rightarrow 400 = 200e^{8k} \Rightarrow \ln 2 = 8k$

$\Rightarrow k = \frac{1}{8} \ln 2 \Rightarrow N = 200\,e^{\frac{t}{8}\ln 2}$

So $t = 24 \Rightarrow N = 200e^{3 \ln 2} = 1600$

c) Some possible answers are:
- The number of germs doubles every 8 hours, so over a long time the model becomes unrealistic because the total number of germs will become very large.
- The number of germs is a discrete variable (you can't have half of a germ) but the model is a continuous function.
- The model does not account for the differences between patients or other conditions such as the presence of other germs or chemicals.

Q2 **a)** $\frac{dV}{dt} \propto V \Rightarrow \frac{dV}{dt} = -kV$, for some $k > 0$

$\Rightarrow \frac{1}{V}\,dV = -k\,dt \Rightarrow \int \frac{1}{V}\,dV = \int -k\,dt$

$\Rightarrow \ln V = -kt + \ln A \Rightarrow V = Ae^{-kt}$

$t = 0, V = V_0 \Rightarrow V_0 = Ae^0 = A \Rightarrow V = V_0e^{-kt}$

b) Using years as the unit of time:

$t = 1$, $V = \frac{1}{2}V_0 \Rightarrow \frac{1}{2}V_0 = V_0 e^{-k} \Rightarrow \frac{1}{2} = e^{-k}$

$\Rightarrow \ln \frac{1}{2} = -k \Rightarrow k = \ln 2 \Rightarrow V = V_0 e^{-t \ln 2}$

So $V = 0.05V_0 \Rightarrow 0.05V_0 = V_0 e^{-t \ln 2} \Rightarrow 0.05 = e^{-t \ln 2}$

$\Rightarrow \ln 0.05 = -t \ln 2 \Rightarrow t = \ln 0.05 \div -\ln 2 = 4.322...$

$\Rightarrow t = 4$ years, 4 months (or 52 months)

You could have used months as the units of time instead, and started with $t = 12$. You'd get the same answer.

Q3 a) The rate of change is proportional to S,

so $\frac{dS}{dt} \propto S \Rightarrow \frac{dS}{dt} = kS$.

b) Initially, $\frac{dS}{dt} = 6$ and $S = 30$, so $6 = 30k \Rightarrow k = 0.2$.

Solve the differential equation:

$\frac{dS}{dt} = 0.2S \Rightarrow \int \frac{1}{S} \, dS = \int 0.2 \, dt$

$\Rightarrow \ln S = 0.2t + C \Rightarrow S = e^{0.2t + C} = Ae^{0.2t}$

Initially, $t = 0$ and $S = 30$: $30 = Ae^0 \Rightarrow A = 30$, so $S = 30e^{0.2t}$.
Then $150 = 30e^{0.2t} \Rightarrow e^{0.2t} = 5 \Rightarrow 0.2t = \ln 5$

$\Rightarrow t = 5 \ln 5 = 8.047...$

So it will take 8 weeks (to the nearest week) for the squirrels to take over.

Q4 a) $\frac{dN}{dt} \propto N \Rightarrow \frac{dN}{dt} = kN$

b) $\frac{dN}{dt} = kN \Rightarrow \int \frac{1}{N} \, dN = \int k \, dt$

$\Rightarrow \ln N = kt + \ln A \Rightarrow N = e^{kt + \ln A} = Ae^{kt}$

$N = 20$ at $t = 0 \Rightarrow 20 = Ae^0 = A \Rightarrow N = 20e^{kt}$

$N = 30$ at $t = 4 \Rightarrow 30 = 20e^{4k}$

$\Rightarrow k = 0.25 \ln 1.5 \Rightarrow N = 20e^{0.25t \ln 1.5}$

So $N = 1000 \Rightarrow 1000 = 20e^{0.25t \ln 1.5}$

$\Rightarrow \ln 50 = 0.25t \ln 1.5 \Rightarrow t = 4 \ln 50 \div \ln 1.5 = 38.59$

So the field will be over-run in 39 weeks.

c) $\frac{dN}{dt} \propto \sqrt{N} \Rightarrow \frac{dN}{dt} = k\sqrt{N}$

$\Rightarrow \int \frac{1}{\sqrt{N}} \, dN = \int k \, dt \Rightarrow 2\sqrt{N} = kt + C$

$N = 20$ at $t = 0 \Rightarrow 2\sqrt{20} = 4\sqrt{5} = C \Rightarrow 2\sqrt{N} = kt + 4\sqrt{5}$

$N = 30$ at $t = 4 \Rightarrow 2\sqrt{30} = 4k + 4\sqrt{5} \Rightarrow k = \frac{\sqrt{30} - 2\sqrt{5}}{2}$

$\Rightarrow 2\sqrt{N} = \frac{\sqrt{30} - 2\sqrt{5}}{2}t + 4\sqrt{5}$

So $N = 1000 \Rightarrow 2\sqrt{1000} = \frac{\sqrt{30} - 2\sqrt{5}}{2}t + 4\sqrt{5}$

$\Rightarrow t = \frac{4\sqrt{1000} - 8\sqrt{5}}{\sqrt{30} - 2\sqrt{5}} = 108.05$

So the field will be over-run in 108 weeks.

Be careful with all these square roots knocking about — it's easy to make a mistake.

d) Some possible answers are:
- The model could be adjusted to use a discrete-valued function, since the number of mice is a discrete variable.
- When there is only 1 mouse (i.e. $N = 1$), the population still increases, which is unrealistic. The model could be adjusted to be more accurate for very low values of N.
- As t increases, N gets larger without any limit. Introducing an upper limit on t or N would show at which point the model stops being accurate.

Q5 a) $\frac{dx}{dt} = \frac{1}{x^2(t+1)}$

$V = x^3 \Rightarrow \frac{dV}{dx} = 3x^2$

So $\frac{dV}{dt} = \frac{dV}{dx} \times \frac{dx}{dt} = \frac{3x^2}{x^2(t+1)} = \frac{3}{t+1}$

b) $\frac{dV}{dt} = \frac{3}{t+1} \Rightarrow \int 1 \, dV = \int \frac{3}{t+1} \, dt$

$\Rightarrow V = 3 \ln (t+1) + C$

$V = 15$ at $t = 0 \Rightarrow 15 = 3 \ln (1) + C \Rightarrow C = 15$

$\Rightarrow V = 3 \ln (t+1) + 15$

So $V = 18 \Rightarrow 18 = 3 \ln (t+1) + 15$

$\Rightarrow \frac{3}{3} = \ln (t+1)$

$\Rightarrow t = e^1 - 1 = 1.72$ seconds (3 s.f.)

Q6 a) $\frac{dy}{dt} = k(p-y) \Rightarrow \int \frac{1}{p-y} \, dy = \int k \, dt$

$\Rightarrow -\ln (p-y) = kt + \ln a \Rightarrow \ln (p-y) = -kt - \ln a$

$\Rightarrow p - y = e^{-kt - \ln a} = e^{-kt} e^{-\ln a} = e^{-kt} e^{\ln \frac{1}{a}} = \frac{1}{a}e^{-kt} = Ae^{-kt}$

$\Rightarrow y = p - Ae^{-kt}$

b) If $p = 30\,000$ and $y = 10\,000$ at $t = 0$, then:

$10\,000 = 30\,000 - Ae^0 = 30\,000 - A$

$\Rightarrow A = 20\,000 \Rightarrow y = 30\,000 - 20\,000e^{-kt}$

$t = 5$, $y = 12\,000 \Rightarrow 12\,000 = 30\,000 - 20\,000e^{-5k}$

$\Rightarrow e^{-5k} = 18\,000 \div 20\,000 = 0.9 \Rightarrow -5k = \ln 0.9$

$\Rightarrow k = -0.2 \ln 0.9 \Rightarrow y = 30\,000 - 20\,000e^{0.2t \ln 0.9}$

So $y = 25\,000 \Rightarrow 20\,000e^{0.2t \ln 0.9} = 5000$

$\Rightarrow e^{0.2t \ln 0.9} = 0.25 \Rightarrow 0.2t \ln 0.9 = \ln 0.25$

$\Rightarrow t = 5 \ln 0.25 \div \ln 0.9 = 65.79 = 66$ days

c)

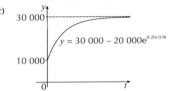

Remember that (0.2 ln 0.9) is negative when sketching the graph.

d) $t = 92$

$\Rightarrow y = 30\,000 - 20\,000e^{18.4 \ln 0.9} = 30\,000 - 20\,000e^{-1.939}$

$= 30\,000 - 20\,000(0.1439) = 27\,122$ signatures

So no, the target will not be achieved.

Don't forget, you'll often need to relate your answer back to the question when you've finished calculating.

e) Some possible answers are:
- The model suggests that the number of signatures eventually reaches the entire population of 30 000 (if you round to the nearest whole number). It may be more accurate to assume that there are some people who will never sign the petition, no matter how much time elapses, and allow for this in the model.
- The number of signatures is a discrete variable, and the model uses a continuous function. Adjusting the function to only allow integer values of y would fix this.
- The model does not account for people entering or leaving the town. Adjusting the function so that p varies with time may make the model more accurate.

Review Exercise — Chapter 8

Q1 a) $\int \frac{1}{\sqrt[3]{(2-11x)}} \, dx = \int (2-11x)^{-\frac{1}{3}} \, dx = -\frac{3}{22}(2-11x)^{\frac{2}{3}} + C$

b) Integrate the curve between the two limits:

$\int_{-\frac{123}{11}}^{-\frac{62}{11}} \frac{1}{\sqrt[3]{(2-11x)}} \, dx = -\frac{3}{22}[(\sqrt[3]{2-11x})^2]_{-\frac{123}{11}}^{-\frac{62}{11}}$

$= -\frac{3}{22}([(\sqrt[3]{2+62})^2] - [(\sqrt[3]{2+123})^2])$

$= -\frac{3}{22}((\sqrt[3]{64})^2 - (\sqrt[3]{125})^2) = -\frac{3}{22}(16-25) = \frac{27}{22}$

Q2 $y = \int (1-7x)^{\frac{1}{2}} \, dx = -\frac{2}{21}(1-7x)^{\frac{3}{2}} + C$

y goes through the point $(0, 1)$, so:

$1 = -\frac{2}{21}(1)^{\frac{3}{2}} + C \Rightarrow C = 1 + \frac{2}{21} \Rightarrow C = \frac{23}{21}$

$\Rightarrow y = -\frac{2}{21}(1-7x)^{\frac{3}{2}} + \frac{23}{21}$

Q3 **a)** $\int 4e^{2x}\,dx = 4\int e^{2x}\,dx = 4\left(\frac{1}{2}e^{2x}\right)+C = 2e^{2x}+C$

b) $\int e^{3x-5}\,dx = \frac{1}{3}e^{3x-5}+C$

c) $\int \frac{2}{3x}\,dx = \frac{2}{3}\int \frac{1}{x}\,dx = \frac{2}{3}\ln|x|+C$

d) $\int \frac{2}{2x+1}\,dx = \ln|2x+1|+C$

Q4 $\int \frac{8}{2-x}-\frac{8}{x}\,dx = -8\ln|2-x|-8\ln|x|+C$
$= -8(\ln|2-x|+\ln|x|)+C$
$= -8\ln|2x-x^2|+C = \ln|(2x-x^2)^{-8}|+C$

So $P = (2x-x^2)^{-8}$.

Q5 **a)** $\int \cos(x+A)\,dx = \sin(x+A)+C$

b) $\int \csc^2((A+B)t+A+B)\,dt$
$= -\frac{1}{A+B}\cot((A+B)t+A+B)+C$

Q6 **a)** $\int \cos 4x - \sec^2 7x\,dx = \frac{1}{4}\sin 4x - \frac{1}{7}\tan 7x + C$

b) $\int 6\sec 3x\tan 3x - \csc^2\frac{x}{5}\,dx$
$= 2\sec 3x + 5\cot\frac{x}{5}+C$

Q7 **a)** Differentiate the denominator: $\frac{d}{dx}\sin x = \cos x =$ numerator
So $\int \frac{\cos x}{\sin x}\,dx = \ln|\sin x| + C$
You could also write $\frac{\cos x}{\sin x}$ as cot x and use the standard result.

b) Differentiate the denominator: $\frac{d}{dx}(x^5+x^3-3x)=5x^4+3x^2-3$

Numerator = 4 × derivative of the denominator:
$\int \frac{20x^4+12x^2-12}{x^5+x^3-3x}\,dx = 4\int \frac{5x^4+3x^2-3}{x^5+x^3-3x}\,dx$
$= 4\ln|x^5+x^3-3x| + C$

Q8 **a)** Let $u = x^3$ so $\frac{du}{dx}=3x^2$ and f'(u) = e^u, so f(u) = e^u.
Using the formula: $\int 3x^2 e^{x^3}\,dx = e^{x^3}+C$

b) Let $u = \sin(x^2)$ so $\frac{du}{dx}=2x\cos(x^2)$ and f'(u) = e^u, so f(u) = e^u.
Using the formula: $\int 2x\cos(x^2)e^{\sin(x^2)}\,dx = e^{\sin(x^2)}+C$

c) Let $u = \sec 4x$ so $\frac{du}{dx}=4\sec 4x\tan 4x$

and f'(u) = e^u, so f(u) = e^u.

Using the formula: $\int 4\sec 4x\tan 4x\,e^{\sec 4x}\,dx = e^{\sec 4x}+C$
Divide by 4 to get the original integral:
$\frac{1}{4}\int 4\sec 4x\tan 4x\,e^{\sec 4x}\,dx = \frac{1}{4}e^{\sec 4x}+C$

Q9 Using the tan double angle formula:
$\int \frac{2\tan 3x}{1-\tan^2 3x}\,dx = \int \tan 6x\,dx = \frac{1}{6}\ln|\sec 6x|+C$
You could also have $-\frac{1}{6}\ln|\cos 6x| + C$ instead.

Q10 **a)** Using the cos double angle formula:
$\int 2\sin^2 x\,dx = 2\int \frac{1}{2}(1-\cos 2x)\,dx$
$= \int 1-\cos 2x\,dx = x-\frac{1}{2}\sin 2x+C$

b) Using the sin double angle formula:
$\int \sin 2x\cos 2x\,dx = \int \frac{1}{2}\sin 4x\,dx$
$= \frac{1}{2}x-\frac{1}{4}\cos 4x+C = -\frac{1}{8}\cos 4x+C$

c) Using the identity $\sec^2 x = \tan^2 x + 1$:
$\int \tan^2 x + 1\,dx = \int \sec^2 x\,dx = \tan x + C$

Q11 **a)** Find the points of intersection between the curves:
$6+2x-x^2 = \frac{x^2}{2}-x+\frac{3}{2} \Rightarrow 12+4x-2x^2=x^2-2x+3$
$\Rightarrow 9+6x-3x^2=0 \Rightarrow x^2-2x-3=0 \Rightarrow (x-3)(x+1)=0$
The curves intersect at $x=-1$ and $x=3$.

The shaded area is the area under $y=6+2x-x^2$
between $x=-1$ and $x=3$ minus the area under
$y=\frac{x^2}{2}-x+\frac{3}{2}$ between $x=-1$ and $x=3$.

$\int_{-1}^{3} 6+2x-x^2\,dx = \left[6x+x^2-\frac{x^3}{3}\right]_{-1}^{3}$
$= \left(6\times 3+3^2-\frac{3^3}{3}\right)-\left(6\times-1+(-1)^2-\frac{(-1)^3}{3}\right)$
$= (18+9-9)-\left(-6+1+\frac{1}{3}\right)=18-\left(-\frac{14}{3}\right)=\frac{68}{3}$

$\int_{-1}^{3}\frac{x^2}{2}-x+\frac{3}{2}\,dx = \left[\frac{x^3}{6}-\frac{x^2}{2}+\frac{3x}{2}\right]_{-1}^{3}$
$= \left(\frac{3^3}{6}-\frac{3^2}{2}+\frac{3\times 3}{2}\right)-\left(\frac{(-1)^3}{6}-\frac{(-1)^2}{2}+\frac{3\times(-1)}{2}\right)$
$= \left(\frac{9}{2}-\frac{9}{2}+\frac{9}{2}\right)-\left(-\frac{1}{6}-\frac{1}{2}-\frac{3}{2}\right)=\frac{9}{2}-\left(-\frac{13}{6}\right)=\frac{20}{3}$

Total area under the curve $= \frac{68}{3}-\frac{20}{3}=\frac{48}{3}=16$

b) Find the points of intersection between
the curve and the line:
$\frac{2}{x}=5-2x \Rightarrow 2=5x-2x^2 \Rightarrow 2x^2-5x+2=0$
$\Rightarrow (x-2)(2x-1)=0$
The curve and the line intersect at $x=\frac{1}{2}$ and $x=2$.
The shaded area is the area under $y=5-2x$
between $x=\frac{1}{2}$ and $x=2$ minus the area under
$y=\frac{2}{x}$ between $x=\frac{1}{2}$ and $x=2$.
$\int_{\frac{1}{2}}^{2}5-2x\,dx = [5x-x^2]_{\frac{1}{2}}^{2}$
$= (5\times 2-2^2)-\left(5\times\frac{1}{2}-\frac{1}{2}^2\right)$
$= (10-4)-\left(\frac{5}{2}-\frac{1}{4}\right)=6-\frac{9}{4}=\frac{15}{4}$

$\int_{\frac{1}{2}}^{2}\frac{2}{x}\,dx = [2\ln x]_{\frac{1}{2}}^{2}=2\ln 2-2\ln\frac{1}{2}$
$= \ln\left(\left(2\div\frac{1}{2}\right)^2\right)=\ln(4^2)=\ln 16$

So the total area is $\frac{15}{4}-\ln 16$.
You could have found the area under $y=5-2x$ using the formula for the area of the trapezium instead of integrating.

Q12 **a)** $y=\arctan x \Rightarrow x=\tan y$, so integrate x with respect to y:
$\int_{\frac{\pi}{6}}^{\frac{\pi}{4}}\tan y\,dy = [\ln|\sec y|]_{\frac{\pi}{6}}^{\frac{\pi}{4}}=\ln\left|\sec\frac{\pi}{4}\right|-\ln\left|\sec\frac{\pi}{6}\right|$
$= \ln\sqrt{2}-\ln\left(\frac{2}{\sqrt{3}}\right)=\ln\left(\sqrt{2}\div\frac{2}{\sqrt{3}}\right)=\ln\left(\frac{\sqrt{6}}{2}\right)$

b) $y=\frac{1}{x^2} \Rightarrow x=\frac{1}{\sqrt{y}}$, so integrate with respect to x:
$\int_{4}^{16}y^{-\frac{1}{2}}\,dy=\left[2y^{\frac{1}{2}}\right]_{4}^{16}=2(4-2)=4$

Q13 **a)** $4=t^2+3 \Rightarrow t^2=1 \Rightarrow t=1$
$12=t^2+3 \Rightarrow t^2=9 \Rightarrow t=3$

b) $\int y\,dx = \int y\frac{dx}{dt}\,dt$, so
$\int_{1}^{3}(4t-1)2t\,dt = \int_{1}^{3}8t^2-2t\,dt=\left[\frac{8t^3}{3}-t^2\right]_{1}^{3}$
$= \left(\frac{8(3)^3}{3}-3^2\right)-\left(\frac{8(1)^3}{3}-1^2\right)$
$= (72-9)-\left(\frac{8}{3}-1\right)=\frac{184}{3}$

Q14 **a)** $u=5-x^2 \Rightarrow \frac{du}{dx}=-2x \Rightarrow dx=-\frac{1}{2x}\,du$
So $\int 16x(5-x^2)^5\,dx = \int 16x\,u^5\times-\frac{1}{2x}\,du$
$= \int 8u^5\,du=\frac{4}{3}u^6+C=\frac{4}{3}(5-x^2)^6+C$

b) $u = e^x - 1 \Rightarrow \dfrac{du}{dx} = e^x \Rightarrow dx = \dfrac{1}{e^x}\,du = \dfrac{1}{u+1}\,du$

So $\displaystyle\int e^x(e^x + 1)(e^x - 1)^2\,dx = \int (u+1)(u+2)u^2 \times \dfrac{1}{u+1}\,du$

$= \displaystyle\int u^3 + 2u^2\,du = \dfrac{u^4}{4} - \dfrac{2u^3}{3} + C = \dfrac{1}{4}(e^x - 1)^4 + \dfrac{2}{3}(e^x - 1)^3 + C$

c) $u = x^2 - 4 \Rightarrow \dfrac{du}{dx} = 2x \Rightarrow dx = \dfrac{1}{2x}\,du$

$x = 2 \Rightarrow u = 2^2 - 4 = 0$
$x = 4 \Rightarrow u = 4^2 - 4 = 12$

So $\displaystyle\int_2^4 x(x^2 - 4)^3\,dx = \int_0^{12} x u^3 \times \dfrac{1}{2x}\,du = \int_0^{12} \dfrac{1}{2}u^3\,du$

$= \left[\dfrac{1}{8}u^4\right]_0^{12} = \dfrac{1}{8}[12^4 - 0^4] = 2592$

d) $u = \sqrt{3x - 8} \Rightarrow \dfrac{du}{dx} = \dfrac{3}{2\sqrt{3x-8}}$

$\Rightarrow dx = \dfrac{2\sqrt{3x-8}}{3}\,du = \dfrac{2u}{3}\,du$

$u = \sqrt{3x-8} \Rightarrow u^2 = 3x - 8 \Rightarrow x = \dfrac{u^2 + 8}{3}$

$x = 3 \Rightarrow u = \sqrt{3(3) - 8} = 1$
$x = 11 \Rightarrow u = \sqrt{3(11) - 8} = 5$

So $\displaystyle\int_3^{11} \dfrac{2x}{\sqrt{3x-8}}\,dx = \int_1^5 \dfrac{2x}{u} \times \dfrac{2u}{3}\,du = \int_1^5 \dfrac{4x}{3}\,du$

$= \displaystyle\int_1^5 \dfrac{4}{3} \times \dfrac{u^2 + 8}{3}\,du = \int_1^5 \dfrac{4}{9}(u^2 + 8)\,du = \dfrac{4}{9}\left[\dfrac{u^3}{3} + 8u\right]_1^5$

$= \dfrac{4}{9}\left[\left(\dfrac{125}{3} + 40\right) - \left(\dfrac{1}{3} + 8\right)\right] = \dfrac{4}{9}\left(\dfrac{220}{3}\right) = \dfrac{880}{27}$

Q15 $u = \cos x \Rightarrow \dfrac{du}{dx} = -\sin x \Rightarrow dx = -\dfrac{1}{\sin x}\,du$

$x = 0 \Rightarrow u = \cos 0 = 1$

$x = \dfrac{\pi}{2} \Rightarrow u = \cos\dfrac{\pi}{2} = 0$

Using the sin double angle formula:

$\displaystyle\int_0^{\frac{\pi}{2}} \dfrac{1}{4}\cos x \sin 2x\,dx = \int_0^{\frac{\pi}{2}} \dfrac{1}{2}\cos^2 x \sin x\,dx$

So $\displaystyle\int_0^{\frac{\pi}{2}} \dfrac{1}{4}\cos x \sin 2x\,dx = \int_1^0 \dfrac{1}{2}u^2 \sin x \times -\dfrac{1}{\sin x}\,du$

$= \displaystyle\int_0^1 \dfrac{1}{2}u^2\,du = \left[\dfrac{u^3}{6}\right]_0^1 = \dfrac{1}{6}$

Q16 a) Let $u = \ln x$ and $\dfrac{dv}{dx} = 3x^2$. Then $\dfrac{du}{dx} = \dfrac{1}{x}$ and $v = x^3$.

So $\displaystyle\int 3x^2 \ln x\,dx = x^3 \ln x - \int x^3 \times \dfrac{1}{x}\,dx$

$= x^3 \ln x - \displaystyle\int x^2\,dx = x^3 \ln x - \dfrac{x^3}{3} + C$

b) Let $u = 4x$ and $\dfrac{dv}{dx} = \cos 4x$. Then $\dfrac{du}{dx} = 4$ and $v = \dfrac{1}{4}\sin 4x$.

So $\displaystyle\int 4x \cos 4x\,dx = x \sin 4x - \int 4 \times \dfrac{1}{4}\sin 4x\,dx$

$= x \sin 4x - \displaystyle\int \sin 4x\,dx = x \sin 4x + \dfrac{1}{4}\cos 4x + C$

c) Let $u = x^2$ and $\dfrac{dv}{dx} = e^{\frac{x}{2}}$. Then $\dfrac{du}{dx} = 2x$ and $v = 2e^{\frac{x}{2}}$.

So $\displaystyle\int_0^4 e^{\frac{x}{2}}x^2\,dx = \left[2x^2 e^{\frac{x}{2}}\right]_0^4 - \int_0^4 4x e^{\frac{x}{2}}\,dx = 32e^2 - \int_0^4 4x e^{\frac{x}{2}}\,dx$

Integrate by parts again to find $\displaystyle\int_0^4 4x e^{\frac{x}{2}}\,dx$:

Let $u_1 = 4x$ and $\dfrac{dv_1}{dx} = e^{\frac{x}{2}}$. Then $\dfrac{du_1}{dx} = 4$ and $v_1 = 2e^{\frac{x}{2}}$.

So $\displaystyle\int_0^4 4x e^{\frac{x}{2}}\,dx = \left[8x e^{\frac{x}{2}}\right]_0^4 - \int_0^4 8e^{\frac{x}{2}}\,dx = \left[8x e^{\frac{x}{2}}\right]_0^4 - 8\left[2e^{\frac{x}{2}}\right]_0^4$

$= 32e^2 - (16e^2 - 16e^0) = 16e^2 + 16$

So $\displaystyle\int_0^4 e^{\frac{x}{2}}x^2\,dx = 32e^2 - (16e^2 + 16) = 16e^2 - 16$

Q17 Let $u = 10x^2$ and $\dfrac{dv}{dx} = e^{5x}$. Then $\dfrac{du}{dx} = 20x$ and $v = \dfrac{1}{5}e^{5x}$.

So $\displaystyle\int 10x^2 e^{5x}\,dx = 2x^2 e^{5x} - \int 4x e^{5x}\,dx$

Integrate by parts again to find $\displaystyle\int 4x e^{5x}\,dx$:

Let $u_1 = 4x$ and $\dfrac{dv_1}{dx} = e^{5x}$. Then $\dfrac{du_1}{dx} = 4$ and $v_1 = \dfrac{1}{5}e^{5x}$.

So $\displaystyle\int 4x e^{5x}\,dx = \dfrac{4}{5}x e^{5x} - \int \dfrac{4}{5}e^{5x}\,dx = \dfrac{4}{5}x e^{5x} - \dfrac{4}{25}e^{5x} + C$

$\displaystyle\int 10x^2 e^{5x}\,dx = 2x^2 e^{5x} - \int 4x e^{5x}\,dx = 2x^2 e^{5x} - \dfrac{4}{5}x e^{5x} + \dfrac{4}{25}e^{5x} + C$

Q18 Write the function as partial fractions:

$\dfrac{3x + 10}{(2x+3)(x-4)} \equiv \dfrac{A}{2x+3} + \dfrac{B}{x-4} \Rightarrow 3x + 10 \equiv A(x-4) + B(2x+3)$

Substituting $x = 4$ gives: $22 = 11B \Rightarrow B = 2$

Substituting $x = -\dfrac{3}{2}$ gives: $\dfrac{11}{2} = -\dfrac{11}{2}A \Rightarrow A = -1$

So $\dfrac{3x+10}{(2x+3)(x-4)} \equiv \dfrac{-1}{2x+3} + \dfrac{2}{x-4}$

So the integral can be expressed:

$\displaystyle\int \dfrac{3x+10}{(2x+3)(x-4)}\,dx = \int \dfrac{-1}{2x+3} + \dfrac{2}{x-4}\,dx$

$= -\dfrac{1}{2}\ln|2x+3| + 2\ln|x-4| + C$

Q19 $\dfrac{13x - 18}{(x-3)^2(2x+1)} \equiv \dfrac{A}{(x-3)^2} + \dfrac{B}{(x-3)} + \dfrac{C}{(2x+1)}$

$\Rightarrow 13x - 18 \equiv A(2x+1) + B(2x+1)(x-3) + C(x-3)^2$

Substituting $x = 3$ gives: $21 = 7A \Rightarrow A = 3$

Substituting $x = -\dfrac{1}{2}$ gives: $-\dfrac{49}{2} = \dfrac{49}{4}C \Rightarrow C = -2$

Substituting $x = 0$ gives:
$-18 = A - 3B + 9C \Rightarrow -18 = 3 - 3B - 18 \Rightarrow 3 = 3B \Rightarrow B = 1$

So $\dfrac{13x - 18}{(x-3)^2(2x+1)} \equiv \dfrac{3}{(x-3)^2} + \dfrac{1}{(x-3)} - \dfrac{2}{(2x+1)}$

So the integral can be expressed:

$\displaystyle\int_4^9 \dfrac{3}{(x-3)^2} + \dfrac{1}{(x-3)} - \dfrac{2}{(2x+1)}\,dx = \left[-\dfrac{3}{x-3} + \ln|x-3| - \ln|2x+1|\right]_4^9$

$= \left(-\dfrac{1}{2} + \ln 6 - \ln 19\right) - (-3 + \ln 1 - \ln 9) = \dfrac{5}{2} + \ln\left(\dfrac{6 \times 9}{19}\right) = \dfrac{5}{2} + \ln\left(\dfrac{54}{19}\right)$

Q20 $\dfrac{dy}{dx} = \dfrac{1}{y}\cos x \Rightarrow \displaystyle\int y\,dy = \int \cos x\,dx$

$\Rightarrow \dfrac{y^2}{2} = \sin x + C \Rightarrow y^2 = 2\sin x + C$

Q21 $\dfrac{dx}{dt} = kte^t\,dt \Rightarrow x = \displaystyle\int kte^t\,dt.$

Using integration by parts:

Let $u = kt$ and $\dfrac{dv}{dt} = e^t$. Then $\dfrac{du}{dt} = k$ and $v = e^t$.

So $x = \displaystyle\int kte^t\,dt = kte^t - \int ke^t\,dt = kte^t - ke^t + C = ke^t(t - 1) + C$

$x = 0$ when $t = 1 \Rightarrow 0 = ke(0) + C \Rightarrow C = 0$

$x = -3$ when $t = 0 \Rightarrow -3 = ke^0(0 - 1) \Rightarrow k = 3$

So the particular solution is $x = 3e^t(t - 1)$.

Q22 a) $\dfrac{dT}{dt} = -k(T - 21) \Rightarrow \displaystyle\int \dfrac{1}{T - 21}\,dT = \int -k\,dt$

$\Rightarrow \ln|T - 21| = -kt + C$

$\Rightarrow T - 21 = e^{-kt+C} = Ae^{-kt} \Rightarrow T = Ae^{-kt} + 21$

When $t = 0$, $T = 90$: $90 = Ae^0 + 21 \Rightarrow A = 69$

When $t = 5$, $T = 80$:

$80 = 69e^{-5k} + 21 \Rightarrow 59 = 69e^{-5k} \Rightarrow \ln\dfrac{59}{69} = -5k$

$\Rightarrow k = -\dfrac{1}{5}\ln\dfrac{59}{69} = 0.0313$ (3 s.f.)

So the particular solution is $T = 69e^{-0.0313t} + 21$

b) (i) When $t = 15$, $T = 69e^{-0.0313 \times 15} + 21 = 64.1\ °C$

(ii) $40 = 69e^{-0.0313t} + 21 \Rightarrow \dfrac{19}{69} = e^{-0.0313t}$

$\Rightarrow \ln\dfrac{19}{69} = -0.0313t \Rightarrow t = \ln\dfrac{19}{69} \div -0.0313$

$= 41.2$ minutes

c)

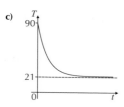

Exam-Style Questions — Chapter 8

Q1 $\int_{\frac{\pi}{6}}^{\frac{\pi}{2}} \sin(3x - \pi)\,dx = \left[-\frac{1}{3}\cos(3x - \pi)\right]_{\frac{\pi}{6}}^{\frac{\pi}{2}}$

$= -\frac{1}{3}\left[\cos\left(3\frac{\pi}{2} - \pi\right) - \cos\left(3\frac{\pi}{6} - \pi\right)\right] = -\frac{1}{3}\left(\cos\frac{\pi}{2} - \cos 0\right)$

$= -\frac{1}{3}(0 - 1) = \frac{1}{3}$

[3 marks available — 1 mark for integrating sin correctly, 1 mark for substituting limits, 1 mark for correct final value]

Q2 Differentiate the denominator: $\frac{d}{dx}(4x - 3) = 4$

So $\int_{2}^{7} \frac{8}{4x - 3}\,dx = 2\int_{2}^{7} \frac{4}{4x - 3}\,dx = 2[\ln|4x - 3|]_{2}^{7}$

$= 2[\ln 25 - \ln 5] = 2\ln 5 = \ln 25$

[4 marks available — 1 mark for differentiating the denominator, 1 mark for integrating the fraction, 1 mark for substituting limits, 1 mark for correct answer]

Q3 $\int_{0}^{A} e^{5x}\,dx = \left[\frac{1}{5}e^{5x}\right]_{0}^{A} = \frac{1}{5}[e^{5A} - e^{0}] = \frac{31}{5}$

$\Rightarrow e^{5A} - 1 = 31 \Rightarrow e^{5A} = 32$

$\Rightarrow \ln e^{5A} = \ln 32 = \ln 2^5 = 5\ln 2 \Rightarrow 5A = 5\ln 2 \Rightarrow A = \ln 2$

[4 marks available — 1 mark for integrating the exponential, 1 mark for substituting limits, 1 mark for attempting to solve the equation, 1 mark for the correct value of A]

Q4 Let $u = \cot(x^2)$ so $\frac{du}{dx} = -2x\,\text{cosec}^2(x^2)$ and $f'(u) = e^u$ so $f(u) = e^u$.

Using the formula: $\int -2x\,\text{cosec}^2(x^2)\,e^{\cot(x^2)}\,dx = e^{\cot(x^2)} + C$

Multiply by -2 to get the original integral:

$-2\int -2x\,\text{cosec}^2(x^2)\,e^{\cot(x^2)}\,dx = -2e^{\cot(x^2)} + C$

[4 marks available — 1 mark for identifying u, 1 mark for differentiating u, 1 mark for attempting to use the formula, 1 mark for the correct answer]

Q5 $\int_{0}^{\frac{\pi}{4}} 3\sin 2x \cos 2x\,dx = 3\int_{0}^{\frac{\pi}{4}} \frac{1}{2}\sin 4x\,dx = \frac{3}{2}\left[-\frac{1}{4}\cos 4x\right]_{0}^{\frac{\pi}{4}}$

$= -\frac{3}{8}(\cos \pi - \cos 0) = -\frac{3}{8}((-1) - (1)) = \frac{3}{4}$

[4 marks available — 1 mark for using the sin double angle formula, 1 mark for integrating sin 4x, 1 mark for substituting limits, 1 mark for correct answer]

Q6 First find the points where the line $y = \frac{3}{2}x - 1$ intersects the coordinate axes:

$y = \frac{3}{2}(0) - 1 \Rightarrow y$-intercept $= -1$

and $0 = \frac{3}{2}x - 1 \Rightarrow x$-intercept $= \frac{2}{3}$.

At $x = 2$, $y = \frac{3}{2}(2) - 1 = 2$.

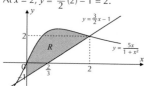

R can be found using the areas:

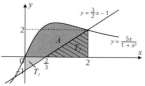

(A is the entire dark grey area, T_1 is the light grey area and T_2 is the hatched area. So $R = A + T_1 - T_2$.)

$A = \int_{0}^{2} \frac{5x}{1 + x^2}\,dx = \frac{5}{2}[\ln|1 + x^2|]_{0}^{2} = \frac{5}{2}[\ln 5 - \ln 1] = \frac{5}{2}\ln 5$

$T_1 = \frac{1}{2} \times \frac{2}{3} \times 1 = \frac{1}{3}$

$T_2 = \frac{1}{2} \times (2 - \frac{2}{3}) \times 2 = \frac{4}{3}$

So $R = A + T_1 - T_2 = \frac{5}{2}\ln 5 + \frac{1}{3} - \frac{4}{3} = \frac{5}{2}\ln 5 - 1$

[7 marks available — 1 mark for finding the axis intercepts, 1 mark for integrating the curve, 1 mark for substituting the limits, 1 mark for the correct value, 1 mark for finding the area of the triangle above the x-axis, 1 mark for finding the area of the triangle below the x-axis, 1 mark for the total area of the shaded region]

Q7 Alter the limits from x-values into t-values:

$x = 2 \Rightarrow 2 = 2t^3 \Rightarrow t^3 = 1 \Rightarrow t = 1$

$x = 54 \Rightarrow 54 = 2t^3 \Rightarrow t^3 = 27 \Rightarrow t = 3$

$\int y\,dx = \int y\frac{dx}{dt}\,dt$ and $\frac{dx}{dt} = 6t^2$, so:

$\int_{2}^{54} y\,dx = \int_{1}^{3} \frac{2}{t} \times 6t^2\,dt = \int_{1}^{3} 12t\,dt = [6t^2]_{1}^{3} = 6(3^2 - 1^2) = 48$

[6 marks available — 1 mark for altering the limits, 1 mark for finding $\frac{dx}{dt}$, 1 mark for using the formula for integrating parametric equations, 1 mark for integrating, 1 mark for substituting the limits, 1 mark for the correct answer]

Q8 Let $u = x + 1 \Rightarrow \frac{du}{dx} = 1 \Rightarrow dx = du$ and $u = x + 1 \Rightarrow x = u - 1$

So $\int x(x + 1)^3\,dx = \int (u - 1)u^3\,du = \int u^4 - u^3\,du$

$= \frac{u^5}{5} - \frac{u^4}{4} + C = \frac{(x + 1)^5}{5} - \frac{(x + 1)^4}{4} + C$

[3 marks available — 1 mark for choosing an appropriate substitution, 1 mark for integrating the function in terms of u, 1 mark for the correct integral in terms of x]

Q9 $x = 3\tan u \Rightarrow \frac{dx}{du} = 3\sec^2 u \Rightarrow dx = 3\sec^2 u\,du$

So $\int \frac{1}{9 + x^2}\,dx = \int \frac{1}{9 + 9\tan^2 u} 3\sec^2 u\,du$

$= \int \frac{1}{9(1 + \tan^2 u)} 3\sec^2 u\,du = \frac{1}{3}\int \frac{\sec^2 u}{\sec^2 u}\,du = \frac{1}{3}u + C$

But $x = 3\tan u \Rightarrow u = \tan^{-1}\frac{x}{3}$, so $\int \frac{1}{9 + x^2}\,dx = \frac{1}{3}\tan^{-1}\frac{x}{3} + C$

You could also write this as $\frac{1}{3}\arctan\frac{x}{3} + C$.

[6 marks available — 1 mark for differentiating 3 tan u, 1 mark for substituting x = 3 tan u into the function, 1 mark for simplifying the integral, 1 mark for using $\sec^2 u \equiv 1 + \tan^2 u$, 1 mark for integrating, 1 mark for the correct integral in terms of x]

Q10 Integrate by parts:

Let $u = 2x^2$ and $\dfrac{dv}{dx} = e^{3x}$. Then $\dfrac{du}{dx} = 4x$ and $v = \dfrac{1}{3}e^{3x}$.

So $\displaystyle\int_0^1 2x^2 e^{3x}\,dx = \left[\dfrac{2}{3}x^2 e^{3x}\right]_0^1 - \int_0^1 \dfrac{4}{3}x e^{3x}\,dx = \dfrac{2}{3}e^3 - \int_0^1 \dfrac{4}{3}x e^{3x}\,dx$

Integrate by parts again to find $\displaystyle\int_0^1 \dfrac{4}{3}x e^{3x}\,dx$:

Let $u_1 = \dfrac{4}{3}x$ and $\dfrac{dv_1}{dx} = e^{3x}$. Then $\dfrac{du_1}{dx} = \dfrac{4}{3}$ and $v_1 = \dfrac{1}{3}e^{3x}$.

So $\displaystyle\int_0^1 \dfrac{4}{3}x e^{3x}\,dx = \left[\dfrac{4}{9}x e^{3x}\right]_0^1 - \int_0^1 \dfrac{4}{9}e^{3x}\,dx = \left[\dfrac{4}{9}x e^{3x}\right]_0^1 - \dfrac{4}{9}\left[\dfrac{1}{3}e^{3x}\right]_0^1$

$\qquad = \dfrac{4}{9}e^3 - \left(\dfrac{4}{27}e^3 - \dfrac{4}{27}\right) = \dfrac{8}{27}e^3 + \dfrac{4}{27}$

So $\displaystyle\int_0^1 2x^2 e^{3x}\,dx = \dfrac{2}{3}e^3 - \left(\dfrac{8}{27}e^3 + \dfrac{4}{27}\right)$

$\qquad = \dfrac{10}{27}e^3 - \dfrac{4}{27} = \dfrac{2}{27}(5e^3 - 2)$

[7 marks available — 1 mark for identifying u and $\dfrac{dv}{dx}$, 1 mark for finding v and $\dfrac{du}{dx}$, 1 mark for using the integration by parts formula, 1 mark for using integration by parts again on the integral, 1 mark for the correct integral, 1 mark for substituting the limits, 1 mark for the correct final answer]

Q11 Factorise the denominator: $x^2 + 2x - 3 = (x + 3)(x - 1)$

Then express $\dfrac{5x + 7}{x^2 + 2x - 3}$ as partial fractions:

$\dfrac{5x + 7}{x^2 + 2x - 3} \equiv \dfrac{5x + 7}{(x + 3)(x - 1)} \equiv \dfrac{A}{x + 3} + \dfrac{B}{x - 1}$

$\Rightarrow 5x + 7 \equiv A(x - 1) + B(x + 3)$

Substituting $x = 1$ gives: $12 = 4B \Rightarrow B = 3$
Substituting $x = -3$ gives: $-8 = -4A \Rightarrow A = 2$

So $\dfrac{5x + 7}{x^2 + 2x - 3} \equiv \dfrac{2}{x + 3} + \dfrac{3}{x - 1}$.

Then $\displaystyle\int \dfrac{5x + 7}{x^2 + 2x - 3}\,dx = \int \dfrac{2}{x + 3} + \dfrac{3}{x - 1}\,dx$

$\qquad = 2\ln|x + 3| + 3\ln|x - 1| + C$

[6 marks available — 1 mark for factorising the denominator, 1 mark for expressing as partial fractions, 1 mark for finding A, 1 mark for finding B, 1 mark for integrating one term correctly, 1 mark for integrating the second term correctly]

Q12 a) The rate of change of the population is proportional to the population, i.e. $\dfrac{dP}{dt} \propto P$, and the population is decreasing, so $\dfrac{dP}{dt} = -kP$ where k is a constant, $k > 0$.

Then by separating the variables:

$\displaystyle\int \dfrac{1}{P}\,dP = \int -k\,dt \Rightarrow \ln P = -kt + C \Rightarrow P = e^{-kt + C} = Ae^{-kt}$
When $t = 0$, $P = 75$: $75 = Ae^0 \Rightarrow A = 75$
When $t = 3$, $P = 58$:
$58 = 75e^{-3k} \Rightarrow -3k = \ln\dfrac{58}{75}$

$\qquad \Rightarrow k = -\dfrac{1}{3}\ln\dfrac{58}{75} = 0.0857$ (3 s.f.)

So $P = 75e^{-0.0857t}$

[5 marks available — 1 mark for finding an expression for $\dfrac{dP}{dt}$, 1 mark for integrating, 1 mark for finding A, 1 mark for finding k, 1 mark for the correct equation for P]

b) $30 = 75e^{-0.0857t} \Rightarrow -0.0857t = \ln\dfrac{30}{75}$

$\qquad \Rightarrow t = \ln\dfrac{30}{75} \div -0.0857 = 10.69...$

So it will take 11 weeks (to the nearest week) for the population to reach 30 birds.
[3 marks available — 1 mark for substituting P = 30 into the equation, 1 mark for finding t, 1 mark for the correct answer]

Chapter 9: Numerical Methods

9.1 Location of Roots

Exercise 9.1.1 — Locating roots by changes of sign

Q1 $f(2) = 2^3 - 5 \times 2 + 1 = -1$
$f(3) = 3^3 - 5 \times 3 + 1 = 13$
There is a sign change (and the function is continuous in this interval) so there is a root in this interval.
They wouldn't ask you if there's a root if the function wasn't continuous in this interval, but it's worth saying anyway just to keep your answer 'strictly true'.

Q2 $f(0.9) = \sin(1.8) - 0.9 = 0.0738...$
$f(1.0) = \sin(2.0) - 1.0 = -0.0907...$
There is a sign change (and the function is continuous in this interval) so there is a root in this interval.

Q3 $f(1.2) = 1.2^3 + \ln 1.2 - 2 = -0.089...$
$f(1.3) = 1.3^3 + \ln 1.3 - 2 = 0.459...$
There is a sign change (and the function is continuous in this interval) so there is a root in this interval.

Q4 $x^2 + 4x + 4 = 0 \Rightarrow (x + 2)^2 = 0$
$\Rightarrow$ there is a single repeated root $x = -2$, so the graph touches the x-axis at $x = -2$ but doesn't cross it.
$f(x)$ is never negative and there is no change of sign.

Q5 $f(1.2) = (2 \times 1.2^2) - (8 \times 1.2) + 7 = 0.28$
$f(1.3) = (2 \times 1.3^2) - (8 \times 1.3) + 7 = -0.02$
There is a sign change (and the function is continuous in this interval) so there is a root in this interval — i.e. the bird hits water between 1.2 and 1.3 seconds.

Q6 $f(1.6) = (3 \times 1.6) - 1.6^4 + 3 = 1.24...$
$f(1.7) = (3 \times 1.7) - 1.7^4 + 3 = -0.25...$
There is a sign change (and the function is continuous in this interval) so there is a root in this interval.
$f(-1) = (3 \times (-1)) - (-1)^4 + 3 = -1$
$f(0) = (3 \times 0) - 0^4 + 3 = 3$
There is a sign change (and the function is continuous in this interval) so there is a root in this interval.

Q7 $f(0.01) = e^{0.01 - 2} - \sqrt{0.01} = 0.0366...$
$f(0.02) = e^{0.02 - 2} - \sqrt{0.02} = -0.0033...$
There is a sign change (and the function is continuous in this interval) so there is a root in this interval.
$f(2.4) = e^{2.4 - 2} - \sqrt{2.4} = -0.057...$
$f(2.5) = e^{2.5 - 2} - \sqrt{2.5} = 0.067...$
There is a sign change (and the function is continuous in this interval) so there is a root in this interval.

Q8 The upper and lower bounds are 2.75 and 2.85.
$f(2.75) = 2.75^3 - (7 \times 2.75) - 2 = -0.45...$
$f(2.85) = 2.85^3 - (7 \times 2.85) - 2 = 1.19...$
There is a sign change between the upper and lower bounds (and the function is continuous in this interval), so a solution to 1 d.p. is $x = 2.8$.

Q9 Upper and lower bounds are 0.65 and 0.75
$f(0.65) = (2 \times 0.65) - \dfrac{1}{0.65} = -0.23...$
$f(0.75) = (2 \times 0.75) - \dfrac{1}{0.75} = 0.16...$
There is a sign change between the upper and lower bounds (and the function is continuous in this interval), so a solution to 1 d.p. is $x = 0.7$.

Q10 Upper and lower bound are 0.245 and 0.255
$f(0.245) = e^{0.245} - 0.245^3 - (5 \times 0.245) = 0.037...$
$f(0.255) = e^{0.255} - 0.255^3 - (5 \times 0.255) = -0.001...$
There is a sign change between the upper and lower bounds (and the function is continuous in this interval), so a solution to 2 d.p. is $x = 0.25$.

Q11 Rearrange the equation to get $f(x) = 4x - 2x^3 - 15 = 0$
$f(-2.3) = (4 \times -2.3) - (2 \times (-2.3)^3) - 15 = 0.134$
$f(-2.2) = (4 \times -2.2) - (2 \times (-2.2)^3) - 15 = -2.504$
There is a sign change (and the function is continuous in this interval) so there is a root in this interval.

Q12 Rearrange the equation to get $f(x) = \ln(x + 3) - 5x = 0$
$f(0.23) = \ln(0.23 + 3) - (5 \times 0.23) = 0.022...$
$f(0.24) = \ln(0.24 + 3) - (5 \times 0.24) = -0.024...$
There is a sign change (and the function is continuous in this interval) so there is a root in this interval.

Q13 Rearrange the equation to get $f(x) = e^{3x}\sin x - 5 = 0$
$f(0) = e^{3 \times 0} \sin 0 - 5 = -5$
$f(1) = e^{3 \times 1} \sin 1 - 5 = 11.9...$
There is a sign change (and the function is continuous in this interval) so there is a root in this interval.

In Q11-13, it's not actually strictly necessary to rearrange to $f(x) = 0$. It's enough to show that the left-hand side of the original equation is greater than the right-hand side for one of the values of x (x_1 or x_2), and less than the right-hand side for the other.

Exercise 9.1.2 — Sketching graphs to find approximate roots

Q1 a)

b) The graphs cross twice, so the equation has 2 roots.

c) Rearranging, $f(x) = x - \dfrac{1}{x} - 2$, and the roots are at $f(x) = 0$
$f(2.4) = 2.4 - \dfrac{1}{2.4} - 2 = -0.016...$
$f(2.5) = 2.5 - \dfrac{1}{2.5} - 2 = 0.1$
There is a sign change (and the function is continuous in this interval) so there is a root in this interval.

Q2 a)

b) The graphs cross 3 times, so the equation has 3 roots.

c) $f(-2) = (2 \times (-2)^3) - (-2)^2 - (7 \times -2) = -6$
$f(-1) = (2 \times (-1)^3) - (-1)^2 - (7 \times -1) = 4$
There is a sign change (and the function is continuous in this interval) so there is a root in this interval.

Q3 a)
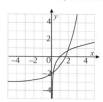

b) The graphs cross twice so the equation has 2 roots.

c) $f(1.8) = \ln(1.8) - 2^{1.8} + 3 = 0.105...$
$f(2.2) = \ln(2.2) - 2^{2.2} + 3 = -0.806...$
There is a sign change (and the function is continuous in this interval), so there is a root in this interval.
$f(2.0) = \ln(2.0) - 2^{2.0} + 3 = -0.306...$
So the root is between 1.8 and 2.0
$f(1.9) = \ln(1.9) - 2^{1.9} + 3 = -0.090...$
So the root is between 1.8 and 1.9
$f(1.85) = \ln(1.85) - 2^{1.85} + 3 = 0.010...$
There is a sign change (and the function is continuous) between 1.85 and 1.9, so the root is at $x = 1.9$ (to 1 d.p.).

Q4 a)
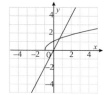

b) The graphs cross once so the equation has 1 root.

c) The roots are at $f(x) = \sqrt{x + 1} - 2x = 0$
$f(0.6) = \sqrt{0.6 + 1} - (2 \times 0.6) = 0.064...$
$f(0.7) = \sqrt{0.7 + 1} - (2 \times 0.7) = -0.096...$
There is a sign change (and the function is continuous in this interval), so there is a root in this interval.

d) $\sqrt{x + 1} = 2x \Rightarrow x + 1 = 4x^2 \Rightarrow 4x^2 - x - 1 = 0$
From quadratic formula root is $x = 0.640$ to 3 s.f.
You can ignore the other solution to this quadratic equation — you want the root between 0.6 and 0.7.

Q5 a)

b) If the two functions are set equal to each other they can be rearranged to make $e^{2x} + x^2 = 3$. The graphs cross twice, so the equation has 2 roots.

c) Rearrange to $f(x) = 0$ so $e^{2x} + x^2 - 3 = 0$
$f(-2) = e^{(2 \times -2)} + (-2)^2 - 3 = 1.01...$
$f(-1) = e^{(2 \times -1)} + (-1)^2 - 3 = -1.86...$
There is a sign change (and the function is continuous in this interval) so there is a root in this interval.
$f(-1.5) = e^{(2 \times -1.5)} + (-1.5)^2 - 3 = -0.70...$
So the root is between -1.5 and -2
$f(-1.7) = e^{(2 \times -1.7)} + (-1.7)^2 - 3 = -0.07...$
So the root is between -1.7 and -2
$f(-1.8) = e^{(2 \times -1.8)} + (-1.8)^2 - 3 = 0.26...$
So the root is between -1.7 and -1.8
$f(-1.75) = e^{(2 \times -1.75)} + (-1.75)^2 - 3 = 0.09...$
So the root is between -1.7 and -1.75, so the value to 1 decimal place is $x = -1.7$.

9.2 Iterative Methods
Exercise 9.2.1 — Using iteration formulas

Q1 a) $f(1) = 1^3 + 3 \times 1^2 - 7 = -3$
$f(2) = 2^3 + 3 \times 2^2 - 7 = 13$
There is a sign change (and the function is continuous in this interval) so there is a root in this interval.

b) $x_1 = \sqrt{\dfrac{7 - x_0^3}{3}} = \sqrt{\dfrac{7 - 1^3}{3}} = 1.414,$
$x_2 = 1.179,$ $x_3 = 1.337,$ $x_4 = 1.240$

Q2 a) $x_1 = 2 + \ln x_0 = 2 + \ln 3.1 = 3.1314,$
$x_2 = 3.1415,$ $x_3 = 3.1447,$ $x_4 = 3.1457,$
$x_5 = 3.1460$

b) $\alpha = 3.146$

Q3 a) $f(1.4) = 1.4^4 - (5 \times 1.4) + 3 = -0.1584$
$f(1.5) = 1.5^4 - (5 \times 1.5) + 3 = 0.5625$
There is a sign change (and the function is continuous in this interval) so there is a root in this interval.

b) $x_1 = \sqrt[3]{5 - \dfrac{3}{x_0}} = \sqrt[3]{5 - \dfrac{3}{1.4}} = 1.419,$
$x_2 = 1.424,$ $x_3 = 1.425,$ $x_4 = 1.425,$
$x_5 = 1.425,$ $x_6 = 1.425$

c) The last 4 iterations round to the same answer, so to 2 d.p. $x = 1.43$

Q4 a) $f(5) = 5^2 - (5 \times 5) - 2 = -2$
$f(6) = 6^2 - (5 \times 6) - 2 = 4$
There is a sign change (and the function is continuous in this interval) so there is a root in this interval.

b) $x_1 = \frac{2}{x_0} + 5 = \frac{2}{5} + 5 = 5.4$,
$x_2 = 5.370$, $x_3 = 5.372$, $x_4 = 5.372$

Q5 $x_1 = 2 - \ln x_0 = 2 - \ln 1.5 = 1.595$, $x_2 = 1.533$,
$x_3 = 1.573$, $x_4 = 1.547$, $x_5 = 1.563$, $x_6 = 1.553$,
$x_7 = 1.560$, $x_8 = 1.555$, $x_9 = 1.558$ (all 4 s.f.)
The iterative sequence is bouncing up and down but closing in on the correct answer.
The last three iterations round to the same answer to 2 d.p., so to 2 d.p. $x = 1.56$

Q6 a) $f(3) = e^3 - (10 \times 3) = -9.914...$
$f(4) = e^4 - (10 \times 4) = 14.598...$
There is a sign change (and the function is continuous in this interval) so there is a root in this interval.

b) Using starting value $x_0 = 3$:
$x_1 = \ln(10x_0) = \ln(10 \times 3) = 3.401$
$x_2 = 3.527$, $x_3 = 3.563$, $x_4 = 3.573$
You could have started with x_0 as anything between 3 and 4, in which case you'd get different values for $x_1 - x_4$.

c) The upper and lower bounds are 3.5765 and 3.5775.
$f(3.5765) = e^{3.5765} - (10 \times 3.5765) = -0.016...$
$f(3.5775) = e^{3.5775} - (10 \times 3.5775) = 0.0089...$
There is a sign change between the upper and lower bounds (and the function is continuous in this interval), so the root to 3 d.p. is $x = 3.577$.

d) Using the new iterative formula with $x_0 = 3$
$x_1 = 2.00855...$, $x_2 = 0.74525..$, $x_3 = 0.21069...$,
$x_4 = 0.12345...$, $x_5 = 0.11313...$, $x_6 = 0.11197...$,
$x_7 = 0.11184...$, $x_8 = 0.11183...$
The formula appears to converge to another root at $x = 0.112$ (3 d.p.)

Q7 a) $x_1 = \frac{x_0^2 - 3x_0}{2} - 5 = \frac{(-1)^2 - (3 \times (-1))}{2} - 5 = -3$
$x_2 = 4$, $x_3 = -3$, $x_4 = 4$
The sequence is alternating between -3 and 4.

b) Using the iterative formula given:
$x_1 = 6.32455...$, $x_2 = 6.45157...$, $x_3 = 6.50060...$,
$x_4 = 6.51943...$, $x_5 = 6.52665...$, $x_6 = 6.52941...$,
$x_7 = 6.53047...$, $x_8 = 6.53087...$
The last 4 iterations all round to 6.53, so the value of the root is $x = 6.53$ to 3 s.f. To verify this, check it's between the upper and lower bounds of 6.53:
$f(6.525) = 6.525^2 - (5 \times 6.525) - 10 = -0.049...$
$f(6.535) = 6.535^2 - (5 \times 6.535) - 10 = 0.031...$
There is a sign change between the upper and lower bounds (and the function is continuous in this interval) so this value is correct to 3 s.f.

Exercise 9.2.2 — Finding iteration formulas

Q1 a) $x^4 + 7x - 3 = 0 \Rightarrow x^4 = 3 - 7x \Rightarrow x = \sqrt[4]{3 - 7x}$
b) $x^4 + 7x - 3 = 0 \Rightarrow x^4 + 5x + 2x - 3 = 0$
$\Rightarrow 2x = 3 - 5x - x^4 \Rightarrow x = \frac{3 - 5x - x^4}{2}$
c) $x^4 + 7x - 3 = 0 \Rightarrow x^4 = 3 - 7x$
$\Rightarrow x^2 = \sqrt{3 - 7x} \Rightarrow x = \frac{\sqrt{3 - 7x}}{x}$

Q2 a) $x^3 - 2x^2 - 5 = 0 \Rightarrow x^3 = 2x^2 + 5 \Rightarrow x = 2 + \frac{5}{x^2}$
b) $x_1 = 2 + \frac{5}{2^2} = 3.25$
$x_2 = 2.473...$, $x_3 = 2.817...$,
$x_4 = 2.629...$, $x_5 = 2.722...$,
So $x_5 = 2.7$ to 1 d.p.

c) $f(2.65) = 2.65^3 - (2 \times 2.65^2) - 5 = -0.43...$
$f(2.75) = 2.75^3 - (2 \times 2.75^2) - 5 = 0.67...$
There is a sign change between the upper and lower bounds (and the function is continuous in this interval) so this value is correct to 1 d.p.

Q3 a) $x^2 + 3x - 8 = 0 \Rightarrow x^2 = 8 - 3x \Rightarrow x = \frac{8}{x} - 3$
b) $f(-5) = (-5)^2 + (3 \times -5) - 8 = 2$
$f(-4) = (-4)^2 + (3 \times -4) - 8 = -4$
There is a sign change (and the function is continuous in this interval) so there is a root in this interval.

c) $x_1 = \frac{a}{x_0} + b = \frac{8}{-5} - 3 = -4.6$
$x_2 = -4.739$, $x_3 = -4.688$, $x_4 = -4.706$,
$x_5 = -4.700$, $x_6 = -4.702$
So $x = -4.70$ to 2 d.p.

Q4 a) $2^{x-1} = 4\sqrt{x} \Rightarrow 2^{x-1} = 2^2 x^{\frac{1}{2}}$
$\Rightarrow 2^{x-1} \times 2^{-2} = x^{\frac{1}{2}} \Rightarrow 2^{x-3} = x^{\frac{1}{2}}$
$\Rightarrow (2^{x-3})^2 = x \Rightarrow x = 2^{2x-6}$

b) Using the iterative formula given:
$x_1 = 0.0625$, $x_2 = 0.0170$, $x_3 = 0.0160$,
$x_4 = 0.0160$

c) $f(0.01595) = 2^{0.01595 - 1} - 4\sqrt{0.01595} = 0.00038...$
$f(0.01605) = 2^{0.01605 - 1} - 4\sqrt{0.01605} = -0.00116...$
There is a sign change between the upper and lower bounds (and the function is continuous in this interval) so $x = 0.0160$ is correct to 4 d.p.

Q5 a) $f(0.4) = \ln(2 \times 0.4) + 0.4^3 = -0.159...$
$f(0.5) = \ln(2 \times 0.5) + 0.5^3 = 0.125$
There is a sign change (and the function is continuous in this interval) so there is a root in this interval.

b) $\ln 2x + x^3 = 0 \Rightarrow \ln 2x = -x^3$
$\Rightarrow 2x = e^{-x^3} \Rightarrow x = \frac{e^{-x^3}}{2}$

c) Using iterative formula $x_{n+1} = \frac{e^{-x_n^3}}{2}$
with starting value $x_0 = 0.4$:
You know the root is between 0.4 and 0.5, so it's a good idea to use one of these as your starting value.
$x_1 = \frac{e^{-x_0^3}}{2} = \frac{e^{-0.4^3}}{2} = 0.4690...$,
$x_2 = 0.4509...$, $x_3 = 0.4561...$, $x_4 = 0.4547...$,
$x_5 = 0.4551...$, $x_6 = 0.4550...$
So the value of the root is $x = 0.455$ to 3 d.p.

Q6 a) $x^2 - 9x - 20 = 0 \Rightarrow x^2 = 9x + 20 \Rightarrow x = \sqrt{9x + 20}$
So an iterative formula is $x_{n+1} = \sqrt{9x_n + 20}$

b) $x_1 = \sqrt{9x_0 + 20} = \sqrt{(9 \times 10) + 20} = 10.488...$,
$x_2 = 10.695...$, $x_3 = 10.782...$, $x_4 = 10.818...$,
$x_5 = 10.833...$, $x_6 = 10.839...$
The last 4 iterations round to 10.8, so the value of the root is $x = 10.8$ to 3 s.f.

c) $x^2 - 9x - 20 = 0 \Rightarrow x^2 - 5x - 4x - 20 = 0$
$\Rightarrow 5x = x^2 - 4x - 20 \Rightarrow x = \frac{x^2 - 4x}{5} - 4$
So an iterative formula is $x_{n+1} = \frac{x_n^2 - 4x_n}{5} - 4$

d) $x_1 = \frac{x_0^2 - 4x_0}{5} - 4 = \frac{1^2 - (4 \times 1)}{5} - 4 = -4.6$,
$x_2 = 3.912$, $x_3 = -4.0688...$, $x_4 = 2.5661...$,
$x_5 = -4.7358...$, $x_6 = 4.2744...$, $x_7 = -3.7653...$,
$x_8 = 1.8479...$

e) The iterations seem to be bouncing up and down without converging to any particular root.

9.3 Sketching Iterations

Exercise 9.3.1 — Cobweb and staircase diagrams

Q1

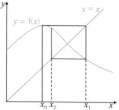

Q2 **a)**

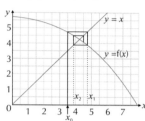

A convergent cobweb diagram.

b)

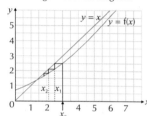

A convergent staircase diagram.

c)

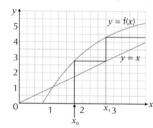

A divergent staircase diagram.
x_2 goes off the scale of the graph so you can't label it.

d)

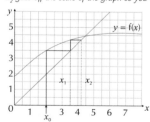

A convergent staircase diagram.

e)

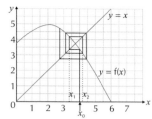

A divergent cobweb diagram.

f)

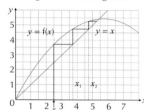

A convergent staircase diagram.

9.4 The Newton-Raphson Method

Exercise 9.4.1 — The Newton-Raphson method

Q1 **a)** Differentiating f(x) gives f'(x) = 10x.
Putting this into the Newton-Raphson formula gives:
$$x_{n+1} = x_n - \frac{f(x_n)}{f'(x_n)} = x_n - \frac{5x_n^2 - 6}{10x_n}$$

b) Differentiating g(x) gives g'(x) = 3e^{3x} – 8x.
Putting this into the Newton-Raphson formula gives:
$$x_{n+1} = x_n - \frac{g(x_n)}{g'(x_n)} = x_n - \frac{e^{3x_n} - 4x_n^2 - 1}{3e^{3x_n} - 8x_n}$$

c) Differentiating h(x) gives h'(x) = cos x + 3x².
Putting this into the Newton-Raphson formula gives:
$$x_{n+1} = x_n - \frac{h(x_n)}{h'(x_n)} = x_n - \frac{\sin(x_n) + x_n^3 - 1}{\cos(x_n) + 3x_n^2}$$

Q2 Differentiating f(x) gives f'(x) = 4x³ – 6x².
Putting this into the Newton-Raphson formula gives:
$$x_{n+1} = x_n - \frac{x_n^4 - 2x_n^3 - 5}{4x_n^3 - 6x_n^2}.$$
Starting with $x_0 = 2.5$,
$$x_1 = 2.5 - \frac{2.5^4 - 2(2.5)^3 - 5}{4(2.5)^3 - 6(2.5)^2} = 2.3875$$
$x_2 = 2.373982...$, $x_3 = 2.373799...$, $x_4 = 2.373799...$
so x = 2.3738 (5 s.f.)

Q3 Differentiating f(x) gives f'(x) = 2x – 5.
Putting this into the Newton-Raphson formula gives:
$$x_{n+1} = x_n - \frac{x_n^2 - 5x_n - 12}{2x_n - 5}$$
Starting with $x_0 = -1$,
$$x_1 = -1 - \frac{(-1)^2 - 5(-1) - 12}{2(-1) - 5} = -1.857142...$$
$x_2 = -1.772833...$, $x_3 = -1.772001...$,
$x_4 = -1.772001...$
so x = –1.7720 (5 s.f.)
In this situation, you could easily find the roots in an exact form using the quadratic formula.

Q4 Differentiating the function gives cos x – 1.
Putting this into the Newton-Raphson formula gives:
$$x_{n+1} = x_n - \frac{\sin x_n - x_n + 1}{\cos x_n - 1}$$
Starting with $x_0 = 1$, $x_1 = 1 - \frac{\sin(1) - 1 + 1}{\cos(1) - 1} = 2.830487...$
$x_2 = 2.049555...$, $x_3 = 1.938656...$, $x_4 = 1.934568...$,
$x_5 = 1.934563...$, so x = 1.9346 (5 s.f.)

Q5 Rearrange the equation to get $x^2 \ln x - 5 = 0$.
Differentiating using the product rule gives $x(1 + 2 \ln x)$.
Putting this into the Newton-Raphson formula gives:
$$x_{n+1} = x_n - \frac{x_n^2 \ln x_n - 5}{x_n(1 + 2\ln x_n)}$$
Starting with $x_0 = 2$, $x_1 = 2 - \frac{2^2 \ln 2 - 5}{2(1 + 2\ln 2)} = 2.466709...$
$x_2 = 2.395369...$, $x_3 = 2.393518...$, $x_4 = 2.393517...$
so $x = 2.3935$ (5 s.f.)

Q6 Differentiating the function gives $-e^{-x} + \sin\frac{1}{2}x$.
Putting this into the Newton-Raphson formula:
$$x_{n+1} = x_n - \frac{e^{-x_n} - 2\cos\frac{1}{2}x_n}{-e^{-x_n} + \sin\frac{1}{2}x_n}$$
Starting with $x_0 = 1$, $x_1 = 1 - \frac{e^{-1} - 2\cos\frac{1}{2}(1)}{-e^{-1} + \sin\frac{1}{2}(1)} = 13.43688...$
$x_2 = 17.73798...$, $x_3 = 14.51784...$, $x_4 = 15.87165...$,
$x_5 = 15.70759...$ $x_6 = 15.70796...$, so $x = 15.708$ (5 s.f.)

Q7 Differentiating the function gives $6x^2 - 30x$.
Putting this into the Newton-Raphson formula:
$$x_{n+1} = x_n - \frac{2x_n^3 - 15x_n^2 + 109}{6x_n^2 - 30x_n}$$
Starting with $x_0 = 1$:
$x_1 = 1 - \frac{2(1)^3 - 15(1)^2 + 109}{6(1)^2 - 30(1)} = 1 - \frac{96}{-24} = 1 + 4 = 5$
$x_2 = 5 - \frac{2(5)^3 - 15(5)^2 + 109}{6(5)^2 - 30(5)} = 5 - \frac{-16}{0}$
Since this involves dividing by 0, the method fails,
so $x_0 = 1$ cannot be used to find a root.
$f'(5) = 0$, which means that the tangent line at x_1 is
horizontal, and it won't intercept the x-axis.

Exercise 9.4.2 — Combining the methods

Q1 **a)** $(x + 2)g(x) = (x + 2)(x^3 - 4x + 1)$
$= x^4 - 4x^2 + x + 2x^3 - 8x + 2 = x^4 + 2x^3 - 4x^2 - 7x + 2 = f(x)$
So $x = -2$ is a root of f(x).

b) $g(1) = 1^3 - 4(1) + 1 = 1 - 4 + 1 = -2$
$g(2) = 2^3 - 4(2) + 1 = 8 - 8 + 1 = 1$
There is a sign change (and the function is continuous in this interval) so there is a root in this interval.

c) $x^3 - 4x + 1 = 0 \Rightarrow x^3 = 4x - 1 \Rightarrow x = \sqrt[3]{4x - 1}$

d) $x_1 = \sqrt[3]{4x_0 - 1} = \sqrt[3]{4(2) - 1} = 1.91293...$
$x_2 = 1.88066...$, $x_3 = 1.86842...$, $x_4 = 1.86373...$,
$x_5 = 1.86193...$, so $\alpha = 1.86$ (3 s.f.)

e) Differentiating g(x) gives $g'(x) = 3x^2 - 4$.
Putting this into the Newton-Raphson formula gives:
$$x_{n+1} = x_n - \frac{x_n^3 - 4x_n + 1}{3x_n^2 - 4}$$
$x_1 = -2 - \frac{(-2)^3 - 4(-2) + 1}{3(-2)^2 - 4} = -2.125$
$x_2 = -2.114975...$, $x_3 = -2.114907...$
so $\beta = -2.115$ (4 s.f.)

f) The Newton-Raphson method fails when $g'(x_n) = 0$ because it involves dividing by zero in the formula. Graphically, it means that the tangent at x_n is horizontal, and so it won't cut the x-axis to find the next iteration.
When $x_n = \frac{2\sqrt{3}}{3}$,
$g'\left(\frac{2\sqrt{3}}{3}\right) = 3\left(\frac{2\sqrt{3}}{3}\right)^2 - 4 = 3\left(\frac{12}{9}\right) - 4 = 4 - 4 = 0$

9.5 The Trapezium Rule

Exercise 9.5.1 — The trapezium rule

Q1 **a)** $h = (2 - 0) \div 2 = 1$, so the x-values are 0, 1, 2.
$\int_0^2 \sqrt{x + 2}\, dx \approx \frac{h}{2}[y_0 + 2y_1 + y_2] = \frac{1}{2}[\sqrt{2} + 2\sqrt{3} + \sqrt{4}]$
$= \frac{1}{2}[1.4142 + 3.4641 + 2] = 3.44$ (3 s.f.)

b) $h = (3 - 1) \div 4 = 0.5$,
so the x-values are 1, 1.5, 2, 2.5, 3.
$\int_1^3 2(\ln x)^2\, dx \approx \frac{h}{2}[y_0 + 2(y_1 + y_2 + y_3) + y_4]$
$= \frac{1}{4}[2(\ln 1)^2 + 2(2(\ln 1.5)^2 + 2(\ln 2)^2 + 2(\ln 2.5)^2) + 2(\ln 3)^2]$
$= \frac{1}{4}[0 + 2(0.3288 + 0.9609 + 1.6792) + 2.4139]$
$= 2.09$ (3 s.f.)

c) $h = (0.4 - 0) \div 2 = 0.2$, so the x-values are 0, 0.2, 0.4.
$\int_0^{0.4} e^{x^2}\, dx \approx \frac{h}{2}[y_0 + 2y_1 + y_2] = \frac{0.2}{2}[e^0 + 2e^{0.04} + e^{0.16}]$
$= 0.1[1 + 2.0816 + 1.1735] = 0.426$ (3 s.f.)

d) $h = \left(\frac{\pi}{4} - \frac{\pi}{4}\right) \div 4 = \frac{\pi}{8}$, so the x-values are $-\frac{\pi}{4}, -\frac{\pi}{8}, 0, \frac{\pi}{8}, \frac{\pi}{4}$.
$\int_{-\frac{\pi}{4}}^{\frac{\pi}{4}} 4x\tan x\, dx \approx \frac{h}{2}[y_0 + 2(y_1 + y_2 + y_3) + y_4]$
$= \frac{\pi}{16}\left[-\pi\tan\left(-\frac{\pi}{4}\right) + 2\left(-\frac{\pi}{2}\tan\left(-\frac{\pi}{8}\right) + 0 + \frac{\pi}{2}\tan\left(\frac{\pi}{8}\right)\right) + \pi\tan\left(\frac{\pi}{4}\right)\right]$
$= \frac{\pi}{16}[\pi + 2(0.6506 + 0.6506) + \pi] = 1.74$ (3 s.f.)

e) $h = (0.3 - 0) \div 6 = 0.05$, so the x-values are
0, 0.05, 0.1, 0.15, 0.2, 0.25, 0.3.
$\int_0^{0.3} \sqrt{e^x + 1}\, dx \approx \frac{h}{2}[y_0 + 2(y_1 + y_2 + y_3 + y_4 + y_5) + y_6]$
$= \frac{0.05}{2}[\sqrt{e^0 + 1} + 2(\sqrt{e^{0.05} + 1} + \sqrt{e^{0.1} + 1}$
$+ \sqrt{e^{0.15} + 1} + \sqrt{e^{0.2} + 1} + \sqrt{e^{0.25} + 1}) + \sqrt{e^{0.3} + 1}]$
$= 0.025[\sqrt{2} + 2(\sqrt{2.0513} + \sqrt{2.1052} + \sqrt{2.1618}$
$+ \sqrt{2.2214} + \sqrt{2.2840}) + \sqrt{2.3499}]$
$= 0.025[1.4142 + 2(1.4322 + 1.4509 + 1.4703$
$+ 1.4904 + 1.5113) + 1.5329]$
$= 0.441$ (3 s.f.)

f) $h = (\pi - 0) \div 6 = \frac{\pi}{6}$,
so the x-values are $0, \frac{\pi}{6}, \frac{\pi}{3}, \frac{\pi}{2}, \frac{2\pi}{3}, \frac{5\pi}{6}, \pi$.
$\int_0^\pi \ln(2 + \sin x)\, dx \approx \frac{h}{2}[y_0 + 2(y_1 + y_2 + y_3 + y_4 + y_5) + y_6]$
$= \frac{\pi}{12}[\ln(2 + \sin 0) + 2(\ln(2 + \sin\frac{\pi}{6}) + \ln(2 + \sin\frac{\pi}{3})$
$+ \ln(2 + \sin\frac{\pi}{2}) + \ln(2 + \sin\frac{2\pi}{3})$
$+ \ln(2 + \sin\frac{5\pi}{6})) + \ln(2 + \sin\pi)]$
$= \frac{\pi}{12}[0.6931 + 2(0.9163 + 1.0529 + 1.0986$
$+ 1.0529 + 0.9163) + 0.6931]$
$= 3.00$ (3 s.f.)

Q2 **a)** $h = 1$, so the x-values are 0, 1, 2 and the y-values are:
$y_0 = \sqrt{2}$, $y_1 = \sqrt{3}$, $y_2 = \sqrt{4}$
Use the simplified versions of the trapezium rule.
The lower bound is found using:
$\int_0^2 \sqrt{x + 2}\, dx \approx h[y_0 + y_1] = 1[\sqrt{2} + \sqrt{3}] = 3.146$ (4 s.f.)
The upper bound is found using:
$\int_0^2 \sqrt{x + 2}\, dx \approx h[y_1 + y_2] = 1[\sqrt{3} + \sqrt{4}] = 3.732$ (4 s.f.)

b) $h = 0.5$, so the *x*-values are 1, 1.5, 2, 2.5, 3
Substitute these into the function to get *y*-values:
$y_0 = 0$, $y_1 = 0.3288...$, $y_2 = 0.9609...$,
$y_3 = 1.6791...$, $y_4 = 2.4138...$

Use the simplified versions of the trapezium rule.
The lower bound is found using:
$\int_1^3 2(\ln x)^2\, dx \approx h[y_0 + y_1 + y_2 + y_3]$
$= 0.5[0 + 0.3288... + 0.9609... + 1.6791...] = 1.484$ (4 s.f.)
The upper bound is found using:
$\int_1^3 2(\ln x)^2\, dx \approx h[y_1 + y_2 + y_3 + y_4]$
$= 0.5[0.3288... + 0.9609... + 1.6791... + 2.4138...]$
$= 2.691$ (4 s.f.)
The corresponding trapezium rule answers from Q1 lie inside the lower and upper bounds.

Q3 $h = \frac{\pi}{2} \div 3 = \frac{\pi}{6}$, so the *x*-values are 0, $\frac{\pi}{6}, \frac{\pi}{3}, \frac{\pi}{2}$.
$\int_0^{\frac{\pi}{2}} \sin^3\theta\, d\theta \approx \frac{h}{2}[y_0 + 2(y_1 + y_2) + y_3]$
$= \frac{\pi}{12}\left[\sin^3 0 + 2\left(\sin^3\frac{\pi}{6} + \sin^3\frac{\pi}{3}\right) + \sin^3\frac{\pi}{2}\right]$
$= \frac{\pi}{12}[0 + 2(0.125 + 0.6495) + 1] = 0.667$ (3 d.p.)

Q4 $h = (7 - 2) \div 5 = 1$, so the *x*-values are 2, 3, 4, 5, 6, 7.
$\int_2^7 \sqrt{\ln x}\, dx \approx \frac{h}{2}[y_0 + 2(y_1 + y_2 + y_3 + y_4) + y_5]$
$= \frac{1}{2}[\sqrt{\ln 2} + 2(\sqrt{\ln 3} + \sqrt{\ln 4} + \sqrt{\ln 5} + \sqrt{\ln 6}) + \sqrt{\ln 7}]$
$= \frac{1}{2}[0.8326 + 2(1.0481 + 1.1774 + 1.2686 + 1.3386) + 1.3950]$
$= 5.947$ m² (3 d.p.)

Q5 a)

x	0	$\frac{\pi}{8}$	$\frac{\pi}{4}$	$\frac{3\pi}{8}$	$\frac{\pi}{2}$
y	1	1.466	2.028	2.519	2.718

b) (i) $\int_0^{\frac{\pi}{2}} e^{\sin x}\, dx \approx \frac{\pi}{8}[1 + 2(2.028) + 2.718] = 3.05$ (2 d.p.)

(ii) $\int_0^{\frac{\pi}{2}} e^{\sin x}\, dx \approx \frac{\pi}{16}[1 + 2(1.466 + 2.028 + 2.519) + 2.718]$
$= 3.09$ (2 d.p.)

c) 3.09 is the better estimate as more intervals have been used in the calculation.

Q6 a) $h = (4 - 2) \div 4 = 0.5$, so the *x*-values are 2, 2.5, 3, 3.5, 4.
$\int_2^4 \frac{3}{\ln x}\, dx \approx \frac{1}{4}\left[\frac{3}{\ln 2} + 2\left(\frac{3}{\ln 2.5} + \frac{3}{\ln 3} + \frac{3}{\ln 3.5}\right) + \frac{3}{\ln 4}\right]$
$= 0.25[4.3281 + 2(3.2741 + 2.7307 + 2.3947) + 2.1640]$
$= 5.82$ (2 d.p.)

b) It is an over-estimate as the top of each trapezium lies above the curve.

Q7 a) There are 6 intervals of $h = \frac{\pi}{6}$ between $-\frac{\pi}{2}$ and $\frac{\pi}{2}$.

x	$-\frac{\pi}{2}$	$-\frac{\pi}{3}$	$-\frac{\pi}{6}$	0	$\frac{\pi}{6}$	$\frac{\pi}{3}$	$\frac{\pi}{2}$
$y = \cos x$	0	0.5	$\frac{\sqrt{3}}{2}$	1	$\frac{\sqrt{3}}{2}$	0.5	0

$\int_{-\frac{\pi}{2}}^{\frac{\pi}{2}} \cos x\, dx \approx \frac{h}{2}[y_0 + 2(y_1 + y_2 + y_3 + y_4 + y_5) + y_6]$
$= \frac{\left(\frac{\pi}{6}\right)}{2}\left[0 + 2\left(0.5 + \frac{\sqrt{3}}{2} + 1 + \frac{\sqrt{3}}{2} + 0.5\right) + 0\right]$
$= \frac{\pi}{12}[0 + 2(2 + \sqrt{3}) + 0] = \pi\left(\frac{2(2 + \sqrt{3})}{12}\right)$
$= \frac{\pi(2 + \sqrt{3})}{6}$ as required

b) It's an under-estimate because between $-\frac{\pi}{2}$ and $\frac{\pi}{2}$ the curve of the graph $y = \cos x$ is concave, and so the top of each trapezium lies below the curve.

Review Exercise — Chapter 9

Q1 a) $f(3) = \sin(2 \times 3) = -0.279...$
$f(4) = \sin(2 \times 4) = 0.989...$
There is a sign change (and the function is continuous in this interval) so there is a root in this interval.

b) $f(2.1) = \ln(2.1 - 2) + 2 = -0.302...$
$f(2.2) = \ln(2.2 - 2) + 2 = 0.390...$
There is a sign change (and the function is continuous in this interval) so there is a root in this interval.

c) Rearrange to get $f(x) = x^3 - 4x^2 - 7 = 0$
$f(4.3) = (4.3)^3 - 4(4.3)^2 - 7 = -1.453$
$f(4.5) = (4.5)^3 - 4(4.5)^2 - 7 = 3.125$
There is a sign change (and the function is continuous in this interval) so there is a root in this interval.

d) Rearrange to get $f(x) = e^{2x} + 2e^x - 4 = 0$
$f(0) = e^{2(0)} + 2e^{(0)} - 4 = -1$
$f(0.5) = e^{2(0.5)} + 2e^{(0.5)} - 4 = 2.015...$
There is a sign change (and the function is continuous in this interval) so there is a root in this interval.

Q2 Pick two numbers close to and either side of 1.2, e.g. 1.15 and 1.25
$f(1.15) = (1.15)^3 + 1.15 - 3 = -0.329...$
$f(1.25) = (1.25)^3 + 1.25 - 3 = 0.203...$
There is a sign change in the interval $1.15 < x < 1.25$ (where the function is continuous) so $x = 1.2$ to 1 d.p.

Q3 a)

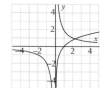

The graphs cross once, so the equation has 1 root.

b) $f(2) = \ln 2 - \frac{2}{2} = -0.306...$

$f(3) = \ln 3 - \frac{2}{3} = 0.431...$

There is a sign change (and the function is continuous in this interval) so there is a root in this interval.

Q4 a)

b) $f(-1.4) = \frac{1}{(-1.4) + 1} - (-1.4) + 2 = 0.9$

$f(-1.3) = \frac{1}{(-1.3) + 1} - (-1.3) + 2 = -0.033...$

There is a sign change (and the function is continuous in this interval) so there is a root in this interval.

c) $\frac{1}{x + 1} - x + 2 = 0 \Rightarrow 1 - x(x + 1) + 2(x + 1) = 0$
$\Rightarrow 1 - x^2 - x + 2x + 2 = 0$
$\Rightarrow -x^2 + x + 3 = 0 \Rightarrow x^2 - x - 3 = 0$

Q5 $x_1 = \sqrt{\ln x_0 + 4} = \sqrt{\ln(2) + 4} = 2.1663...$
$x_2 = 2.1847...$, $x_3 = 2.1866...$, $x_4 = 2.1868...$
So the root is $x = 2.187$ to 3 d.p.

Q6 a) Rearrange to get $f(x) = x^x - 3 = 0$
$f(1.5) = (1.5)^{1.5} - 3 = -1.162...$
$f(2) = 2^2 - 3 = 1$
There is a sign change (and the function is continuous in this interval) so there is a root in this interval.

b) Start with $x_0 = 2$:
$x_1 = 3^{\frac{1}{x_0}} = 3^{\frac{1}{2}} = 1.732...$, $x_2 = 1.886...$,
$x_3 = 1.790...$, $x_4 = 1.846...$
So the root is $x = 1.8$ to 1 d.p.

Q7 a) $f(1.1) = 2(1.1) - 5 \cos{(1.1)} = -0.067...$
$f(1.2) = 2(1.2) - 5 \cos{(1.2)} = 0.588...$
There is a sign change (and the function is continuous in this interval) so there is a root in this interval.

b) $2x - 5\cos x = 0 \implies 2x = 5\cos x$
$\implies x = \frac{5}{2}\cos x \implies p = \frac{5}{2}$

c) Using the iterative formula $x_{n+1} = \frac{5}{2}\cos x_n$:
$x_1 = \frac{5}{2}\cos{(1.1)} = 1.1340$, $x_2 = 1.0576$,
$x_3 = 1.2274$, $x_4 = 0.8418$, $x_5 = 1.6653$,
$x_6 = -0.2360$, $x_7 = 2.4307$, $x_8 = -1.8945$
The sequence at first looks like it might converge to the root in part a) but then it continues to jump up and down and diverges.

Q8 a) $f'(x) = 2x + 9$
Put this into the Newton-Raphson formula:
$x_{n+1} = x_n - \dfrac{x_n^2 + 9x_n - 4}{2x_n + 9}$
Starting with $x_0 = 1$,
$x_1 = 0.4545...$, $x_2 = 0.4245...$, $x_3 = 0.4244...$, $x_4 = 0.4244$
So $x = 0.424$ to 3 d.p.

b) $f'(x) = 3x^2 + 6x + 5$
Put this into the Newton-Raphson formula:
$x_{n+1} = x_n - \dfrac{x_n^3 + 3x_n^2 + 5x_n + 7}{3x_n^2 + 6x_n + 5}$
Starting with $x_0 = 1$,
$x_1 = -0.1428...$, $x_2 = -1.6518...$, $x_3 = -2.3906...$,
$x_4 = -2.2021...$, $x_5 = 2.1797...$, $x_6 = -2.1795...$
So $x = 2.180$ to 3 d.p.

c) $f'(x) = e^x - 4x^3$
Put this into the Newton-Raphson formula:
$x_{n+1} = x_n - \dfrac{e^{x_n} - x_n^4}{e^{x_n} - 4x_n^3}$
Starting with $x_0 = 1$,
$x_1 = 2.3406...$, $x_2 = 1.8608...$, $x_3 = 1.5733...$,
$x_4 = 1.4520...$, $x_5 = 1.4302...$, $x_6 = 1.4296...$
So $x = 1.430$ to 3 d.p.

d) $f'(x) = -\sin^2 x + \cos^2 x$
Put this into the Newton-Raphson formula:
$x_{n+1} = x_n - \dfrac{\sin x_n \cos x_n}{-\sin^2 x_n + \cos^2 x_n}$
Starting with $x_0 = 1$
$x_1 = 2.0925...$, $x_2 = 1.2339...$, $x_3 = 1.6330...$,
$x_4 = 1.5704...$, $x_5 = 1.5707...$, $x_6 = 1.5707...$
So $x = 1.571$ to 3 d.p.

Q9 a) $h = (3 - 0) \div 3 = 1$, so the x-values are 0, 1, 2, 3.
$\int_0^3 \sqrt{9 - x^2}\,dx \approx \frac{h}{2}[y_0 + 2y_1 + 2y_2 + y_3]$
$= \frac{1}{2}[3 + 4\sqrt{2} + 2\sqrt{5} + 0] = 6.56$ (3 s.f.)

b) $h = (1.2 - 0.2) \div 5 = 0.2$,
so the x-values are 0.2, 0.4, 0.6, 0.8, 1.0, 1.2.
$\int_{0.2}^{1.2} x^{x^2}\,dx \approx \frac{h}{2}[y_0 + 2y_1 + 2y_2 + 2y_3 + 2y_4 + y_5]$
$= \frac{1}{10}[0.937... + 1.727... + 1.664... + 1.733... + 2 + 1.300...]$
$= 0.936$ (3 s.f.)

c) $h = (3 - 1) \div 5 = 0.4$,
so the x-values are 1, 1.4, 1.8, 2.2, 2.6, 3.
$\int_1^3 2^{x^3}\,dx \approx \frac{h}{2}[y_0 + 2y_1 + 2y_2 + 2y_3 + 2y_4 + y_5]$
$= \frac{1}{5}[2 + 7.78... + 18.8... + 57.2... + 216.7... + 512]$
$= 163$ (3 s.f.)

Q10 Using 4 strips:
$h = (6 - 0) \div 4 = 1.5$, so the x-values are 0, 1.5, 3, 4.5, 6
$\int_0^6 (6x - 12)(x^2 - 4x + 3)^2\,dx \approx \frac{h}{2}[y_0 + 2y_1 + 2y_2 + 2y_3 + y_4]$
$= \frac{3}{4}[-108 - 3.375 + 0 + 826.875 + 5400] = 4586.625$
Using 6 strips:
$h = (6 - 0) \div 6 = 1$, so the x-values are 0, 1, 2, 3, 4, 5, 6
$\int_0^6 (6x - 12)(x^2 - 4x + 3)^2\,dx$
$\approx \frac{h}{2}[y_0 + 2y_1 + 2y_2 + 2y_3 + 2y_4 + 2y_5 + y_6]$
$= \frac{1}{2}[-108 + 0 + 0 + 0 + 216 + 2304 + 5400] = 3906$
Evaluate the integral:
$\int_0^6 (6x - 12)(x^2 - 4x + 3)^2\,dx$
$= \int_0^6 3(2x - 4)(x^2 - 4x + 3)^2\,dx = [(x^2 - 4x + 3)^3]_0^6$
$= ((6)^2 - 4(6) + 3)^3 - ((0)^2 - 4(0) + 3)^3 = 3375 - 27 = 3348$
The rule $\int (n + 1)f'(x)[f(x)]^n\,dx = [f(x)]^{n+1} + C$ was used here but you could have expanded the brackets instead.
% error using 4 strips $= \dfrac{4586.625 - 3348}{3348} \times 100 = 37.0\%$ (3 s.f.)
% error using 6 strips $= \dfrac{3906 - 3348}{3348} \times 100 = 16.7\%$ (3 s.f.)

Exam-Style Questions — Chapter 9

Q1 a) $\cos x + 2x = 0 \implies \cos x = -2x \implies x = -\frac{1}{2}\cos x$
[1 mark for correctly rearranging formula]

b) In part a) you found an iteration formula, so use it to find the root here:
$x_{n+1} = -\frac{1}{2}\cos x_n \implies x_1 = -\frac{1}{2}\cos{(-1)} = -0.270...$,
$x_2 = -0.481...$, $x_3 = -0.443...$, $x_4 = -0.451...$, $x_5 = 0.449...$
So the root is $x = -0.45$ to 2 d.p.
[2 marks available — 1 mark for using formula from part a), 1 mark for correct answer]

c)

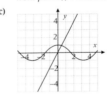

The graphs of $y = 2x$ and $y = \cos x$ intersect at only one point, therefore $y = \cos x + 2x$ has only one root.
[2 marks available — 1 mark for correctly drawn graphs, 1 mark for correct explanation]

Q2 a) $f(1.4) = 5 - 2(1.4) - (1.4)^2 = 0.24$
$f(1.5) = 5 - 2(1.5) - (1.5)^2 = -0.25$
There is a sign change (and the function is continuous in this interval) so there is a root in this interval.
[2 marks available — 1 mark for correct $f(1.4)$ and $f(1.5)$, 1 mark for identifying sign change]

b) Start with $x_0 = 1.5$:
$x_1 = \sqrt{5 - 2x_0} = \sqrt{5 - 2(1.5)} = 1.414...$,
$x_2 = 1.473...$, $x_3 = 1.432...$, $x_4 = 1.460...$,
$x_5 = 1.441...$, $x_6 = 1.454...$, $x_7 = 1.445...$
So the root is $\alpha = 1.45$ to 3 s.f.
The root is in the interval $1.4 < x < 1.5$ so it makes sense to use 1.4 or 1.5 as the starting value x_0.
[2 marks available — 1 mark for correctly substituting a value between 1.4 and 1.5 into the iteration formula to get at least one correct value, 1 mark for correct answer]

c) $f'(x) = -2 - 2x$

So $x_{n+1} = x_n - \dfrac{5 - 2x_n - x_n^2}{-2 - 2x_n}$

$x_1 = -4 - \dfrac{5 - 2(-4) - (-4)^2}{-2 - 2(-4)} = -3.5$

$x_2 = -3.45$, $x_3 = -3.449...$, so $\beta = -3.45$ (3 s.f.)

[3 marks available — 1 mark for correct iteration formula, 1 mark for using formula to get at least one correct value, 1 mark for correct answer]

Q3 a) $h = (7 - 1) \div 4 = 1.5$,

so the x-values are 1, 2.5, 4, 5.5, 7

$\int_1^7 \dfrac{5}{x^2}\,dx \approx \dfrac{h}{2}[y_0 + 2y_1 + 2y_2 + 2y_3 + y_4]$

$= \dfrac{3}{4}[5 + 1.6 + 0.625 + 0.330... + 0.102...] = 5.74$ (2 d.p.)

[3 marks available — 1 mark for using 4 strips, 1 mark for using trapezium rule correctly, 1 mark for correct answer]

b) E.g. It is an over-estimate as the top of each trapezium lies above the curve.
[1 mark for correct answer with explanation]

c) $\int_1^7 \dfrac{5}{x^2}\,dx = \int_1^7 5x^{-2}\,dx = [-5x^{-1}]_1^7 = \left[-\dfrac{5}{x}\right]_1^7$

$= -\dfrac{5}{7} - (-5) = 4.29$ (2 d.p.)

[3 marks available — 1 mark for correct integration, 1 mark for substituting in limits, 1 mark for correct answer]

d) Percentage error $= \dfrac{5.74 - 4.29...}{4.29...} \times 100 = 34\%$ (2 s.f.)
[1 mark for correct answer]

Chapter 10: Vectors

10.1 Vectors in Three Dimensions

Exercise 10.1.1 — Three-dimensional position vectors

Q1 a) $\overrightarrow{OR} = \begin{pmatrix} 4 \\ -5 \\ 1 \end{pmatrix}$ $\qquad$ $\overrightarrow{OS} = \begin{pmatrix} -3 \\ 0 \\ -1 \end{pmatrix}$

b) $\overrightarrow{OR} = 4\mathbf{i} - 5\mathbf{j} + \mathbf{k}$ $\qquad$ $\overrightarrow{OS} = -3\mathbf{i} - \mathbf{k}$

There's no j component written for $\overrightarrow{OS}$ because its j component is zero (you don't write $-3\mathbf{i} + 0\mathbf{j} - \mathbf{k}$).

Q2 $\overrightarrow{GH} = \overrightarrow{OH} - \overrightarrow{OG} = \begin{pmatrix} -1 \\ 4 \\ 9 \end{pmatrix} - \begin{pmatrix} 2 \\ -3 \\ 4 \end{pmatrix} = \begin{pmatrix} -3 \\ 7 \\ 5 \end{pmatrix}$

$\overrightarrow{HG} = -\overrightarrow{GH} = -\begin{pmatrix} -3 \\ 7 \\ 5 \end{pmatrix} = \begin{pmatrix} 3 \\ -7 \\ -5 \end{pmatrix}$

Q3 a) Point B is twice the distance of A from the origin in each direction, so $\overrightarrow{OB} = 2\overrightarrow{OA}$.
The position vector of B can also be described as:
$\overrightarrow{OB} = \overrightarrow{AB} + \overrightarrow{OA}$
Substituting for $\overrightarrow{OB}$: $2\overrightarrow{OA} = \overrightarrow{AB} + \overrightarrow{OA}$
$\Rightarrow 2\overrightarrow{OA} - \overrightarrow{OA} = \overrightarrow{AB}$
So $\overrightarrow{AB} = \overrightarrow{OA}$ — as required.

b) $\overrightarrow{OB} = 2\overrightarrow{OA} = 2(3\mathbf{i} + \mathbf{j} + 2\mathbf{k}) = 6\mathbf{i} + 2\mathbf{j} + 4\mathbf{k}$

Q4 $\overrightarrow{OJ} = 4\mathbf{i} - 3\mathbf{k}$, $\overrightarrow{OK} = -\mathbf{i} + 3\mathbf{j}$, and $\overrightarrow{OL} = 2\mathbf{i} + 2\mathbf{j} + 7\mathbf{k}$

$\overrightarrow{JK} = \overrightarrow{OK} - \overrightarrow{OJ} = -\mathbf{i} + 3\mathbf{j} - (4\mathbf{i} - 3\mathbf{k}) = -5\mathbf{i} + 3\mathbf{j} + 3\mathbf{k}$

$\overrightarrow{KL} = \overrightarrow{OL} - \overrightarrow{OK} = 2\mathbf{i} + 2\mathbf{j} + 7\mathbf{k} - (-\mathbf{i} + 3\mathbf{j}) = 3\mathbf{i} - \mathbf{j} + 7\mathbf{k}$

$\overrightarrow{LJ} = \overrightarrow{OJ} - \overrightarrow{OL} = 4\mathbf{i} - 3\mathbf{k} - (2\mathbf{i} + 2\mathbf{j} + 7\mathbf{k}) = 2\mathbf{i} - 2\mathbf{j} - 10\mathbf{k}$

Q5 The position vector of the midpoint of CD is at

$\overrightarrow{OC} + \dfrac{1}{2}\overrightarrow{CD} = \begin{pmatrix} -1 \\ 3 \\ -5 \end{pmatrix} + \dfrac{1}{2}\begin{pmatrix} 4 \\ -4 \\ 6 \end{pmatrix} = \begin{pmatrix} -1 \\ 3 \\ -5 \end{pmatrix} + \begin{pmatrix} 2 \\ -2 \\ 3 \end{pmatrix} = \begin{pmatrix} 1 \\ 1 \\ -2 \end{pmatrix} = \overrightarrow{OM}$

So M is the midpoint of CD.

Q6 A vector is parallel to another if it is multiplied by the same scalar in each direction.
$\mathbf{a} = \left(3 \times \dfrac{1}{4}\right)\mathbf{i} + \left(\dfrac{1}{3} \times 1\right)\mathbf{j} + \left(3 \times -\dfrac{2}{3}\right)\mathbf{k}$
$\mathbf{a} = 3\mathbf{b}$ in the i and k directions, but $\dfrac{1}{3}\mathbf{b}$ in the j direction, so they are not parallel.

Q7 Model the counters as points A, B and C, with position vectors
$\overrightarrow{OA} = \mathbf{i} + 3\mathbf{k}$, $\overrightarrow{OB} = 3\mathbf{i} + \mathbf{j} + 2\mathbf{k}$, and $\overrightarrow{OC} = 7\mathbf{i} + 3\mathbf{j}$.
$\overrightarrow{AB} = \overrightarrow{OB} - \overrightarrow{OA} = 2\mathbf{i} + \mathbf{j} - \mathbf{k}$
$\overrightarrow{BC} = \overrightarrow{OC} - \overrightarrow{OB} = 4\mathbf{i} + 2\mathbf{j} - 2\mathbf{k} = 2 \times (2\mathbf{i} + \mathbf{j} - \mathbf{k}) = 2\overrightarrow{AB}$
$\overrightarrow{BC}$ is a scalar multiple of $\overrightarrow{AB}$, therefore the vectors are parallel. They also share a point (B), so they must be collinear. So the counters must lie in a straight line.

Q8 Since the points are collinear, the vectors $\overrightarrow{PQ}$ and $\overrightarrow{QR}$ will be parallel, i.e. scalar multiples of one another.

$\overrightarrow{PQ} = \begin{pmatrix} 1 \\ b \\ -4 \end{pmatrix} - \begin{pmatrix} -2 \\ a \\ -8 \end{pmatrix} = \begin{pmatrix} 3 \\ b-a \\ 4 \end{pmatrix}$ and $\overrightarrow{QR} = \begin{pmatrix} -5 \\ 6 \\ 3b \end{pmatrix} - \begin{pmatrix} 1 \\ b \\ -4 \end{pmatrix} = \begin{pmatrix} -6 \\ 6-b \\ 3b+4 \end{pmatrix}$

Consider the i components of the two vectors:
$-2 \times 3 = -6$, so $-2\overrightarrow{PQ} = \overrightarrow{QR}$.
For the k components: $-2(4) = 3b + 4 \Rightarrow -12 = 3b \Rightarrow b = -4$
For the j components: $-2(b - a) = 6 - b \Rightarrow -2(-4 - a) = 6 - (-4)$
$\Rightarrow 8 + 2a = 10 \Rightarrow a = 1$

10.2 Calculating with Vectors

Exercise 10.2.1 — Calculating with 3D vectors

Q1 a) $\sqrt{1^2 + 4^2 + 8^2} = \sqrt{1 + 16 + 64} = \sqrt{81} = 9$

b) $\sqrt{4^2 + 2^2 + 4^2} = \sqrt{36} = 6$

c) $\sqrt{(-4)^2 + (-5)^2 + 20^2} = \sqrt{441} = 21$

d) $\sqrt{7^2 + 1^2 + (-7)^2} = \sqrt{99} = 3\sqrt{11}$

Q2 a) The resultant is: $(\mathbf{i} + \mathbf{j} + 2\mathbf{k}) + (\mathbf{i} + 2\mathbf{j} + 4\mathbf{k}) = 2\mathbf{i} + 3\mathbf{j} + 6\mathbf{k}$
Its magnitude is: $\sqrt{2^2 + 3^2 + 6^2} = \sqrt{49} = 7$

b) resultant: $2\mathbf{i} + 14\mathbf{j} + 23\mathbf{k}$
magnitude: $\sqrt{2^2 + 14^2 + 23^2} = \sqrt{729} = 27$

c) resultant: $\begin{pmatrix} 2 \\ 6 \\ 9 \end{pmatrix}$, magnitude: $\sqrt{2^2 + 6^2 + 9^2} = 11$

d) resultant: $\begin{pmatrix} 2 \\ 5 \\ 14 \end{pmatrix}$, magnitude: $\sqrt{2^2 + 5^2 + 14^2} = 15$

Q3 $\mathbf{a} + \mathbf{b} = \begin{pmatrix} 10 \\ 2 \\ 14 \end{pmatrix}$. $|\mathbf{a} + \mathbf{b}| = \sqrt{10^2 + 2^2 + 14^2} = 10\sqrt{3}$

Q4 a) $\sqrt{(5-3)^2 + (6-4)^2 + (6-5)^2}$
$= \sqrt{2^2 + 2^2 + 1^2} = \sqrt{4 + 4 + 1} = \sqrt{9} = 3$

b) $\sqrt{(-11-7)^2 + (1-2)^2 + (15-9)^2}$
$= \sqrt{324 + 1 + 36} = \sqrt{361} = 19$

c) $\sqrt{(6-10)^2 + (10-(-2))^2 + (-4-(-1))^2}$
$= \sqrt{16 + 144 + 9} = \sqrt{169} = 13$

d) $\sqrt{(7-0)^2 + (0-(-4))^2 + (14-10)^2}$
$= \sqrt{49 + 16 + 16} = \sqrt{81} = 9$

e) $\sqrt{(2-(-4))^2 + (4-7)^2 + (-12-10)^2}$
$= \sqrt{36 + 9 + 484} = \sqrt{529} = 23$

f) $\sqrt{(30-7)^2 + (9-(-1))^2 + (-6-4)^2}$
$= \sqrt{529 + 100 + 100} = \sqrt{729} = 27$

Q5 $|2\mathbf{m} - \mathbf{n}| = |-6\mathbf{i} - 5\mathbf{j} + 10\mathbf{k}| = \sqrt{(-6)^2 + (-5)^2 + 10^2}$
$= 12.68857... = 12.7$ m (1 d.p.)

Q6 $|\overrightarrow{AO}| = |\overrightarrow{OA}| = \sqrt{1^2 + (-4)^2 + 3^2} = \sqrt{26}$

$|\overrightarrow{BO}| = |\overrightarrow{OB}| = \sqrt{(-1)^2 + (-3)^2 + 5^2} = \sqrt{35}$

It's pretty clear that the magnitude of $\overrightarrow{AO}$ is going to be the same as $\overrightarrow{OA}$ so there's no need to find $\overrightarrow{AO}$.

$\overrightarrow{BA} = \overrightarrow{OA} - \overrightarrow{OB} = (\mathbf{i} - 4\mathbf{j} + 3\mathbf{k}) - (-\mathbf{i} - 3\mathbf{j} + 5\mathbf{k}) = 2\mathbf{i} - \mathbf{j} - 2\mathbf{k}$

$|\overrightarrow{BA}| = \sqrt{2^2 + (-1)^2 + (-2)^2} = 3$

Triangle AOB is right-angled because:

$|\overrightarrow{AO}|^2 + |\overrightarrow{BA}|^2 = (\sqrt{26})^2 + 3^2 = 26 + 9 = 35 = (\sqrt{35})^2 = |\overrightarrow{BO}|^2$

Q7 **a)** $|\mathbf{t}| = \sqrt{4^2 + (-4)^2 + (-7)^2} = 9$

so the unit vector is $\dfrac{\mathbf{t}}{|\mathbf{t}|} = \dfrac{1}{9}\mathbf{t} = \dfrac{4}{9}\mathbf{i} - \dfrac{4}{9}\mathbf{j} - \dfrac{7}{9}\mathbf{k}$

b) $|\mathbf{u}| = \sqrt{(-1)^2 + 2^2 + (-2)^2} = 3$

so the unit vector is $\dfrac{\mathbf{u}}{|\mathbf{u}|} = \dfrac{1}{3}\mathbf{u} = -\dfrac{1}{3}\mathbf{i} + \dfrac{2}{3}\mathbf{j} - \dfrac{2}{3}\mathbf{k}$

c) $|\mathbf{v}| = \sqrt{2^2 + 3^2 + (-1)^2} = \sqrt{14}$

so the unit vector is

$\dfrac{\mathbf{v}}{|\mathbf{v}|} = \dfrac{1}{\sqrt{14}}\mathbf{v} = \dfrac{\sqrt{14}}{14}\mathbf{v} = \dfrac{\sqrt{14}}{7}\mathbf{i} + \dfrac{3\sqrt{14}}{14}\mathbf{j} - \dfrac{\sqrt{14}}{14}\mathbf{k}$

Q8 $|\overrightarrow{PQ}| = \sqrt{(q-4)^2 + 6^2 + (2q-3)^2}$

So: $\sqrt{(q-4)^2 + 6^2 + (2q-3)^2} = 11$

$\Rightarrow q^2 - 8q + 16 + 36 + 4q^2 - 12q + 9 = 121$

$\Rightarrow 5q^2 - 20q - 60 = 0 \Rightarrow q^2 - 4q - 12 = 0 \Rightarrow (q-6)(q+2) = 0$

Either $q = 6$, then Q is (4, 5, 13),

or $q = -2$, then Q is (-4, 5, -3).

Q9 **a)** Form a triangle between the two vectors (call them **a** and **b**) with angle θ between them. The triangle has side lengths $|\mathbf{a}|$, $|\mathbf{b}|$ and $|\mathbf{b} - \mathbf{a}|$.

$\mathbf{a} = \begin{pmatrix} 1 \\ 3 \\ 2 \end{pmatrix}$, $|\mathbf{a}| = \sqrt{1^2 + 3^2 + 2^2} = \sqrt{14}$

$\mathbf{b} = \begin{pmatrix} 3 \\ 2 \\ 1 \end{pmatrix}$, $|\mathbf{b}| = \sqrt{3^2 + 2^2 + 1^2} = \sqrt{14}$

$\mathbf{b} - \mathbf{a} = \begin{pmatrix} 2 \\ -1 \\ -1 \end{pmatrix}$, $|\mathbf{b} - \mathbf{a}| = \sqrt{2^2 + (-1)^2 + (-1)^2} = \sqrt{6}$

Using the cosine rule,

$\cos\theta = \dfrac{(\sqrt{14})^2 + (\sqrt{14})^2 - (\sqrt{6})^2}{2 \times \sqrt{14} \times \sqrt{14}} = \dfrac{22}{28} = \dfrac{11}{14}$

$\theta = \cos^{-1}\left(\dfrac{11}{14}\right) = 38.2132... = 38.2°$ (1 d.p.)

b) $|\mathbf{a}| = \sqrt{14}$ as before

$\mathbf{b} = \begin{pmatrix} 0 \\ 1 \\ 0 \end{pmatrix}$, $|\mathbf{b}| = 1$

$\mathbf{b} - \mathbf{a} = \begin{pmatrix} -1 \\ -2 \\ -2 \end{pmatrix}$, $|\mathbf{b} - \mathbf{a}| = \sqrt{(-1)^2 + (-2)^2 + (-2)^2} = 3$

Using the cosine rule,

$\cos\theta = \dfrac{(\sqrt{14})^2 + 1^2 - 3^2}{2 \times \sqrt{14} \times 1} = \dfrac{6}{2\sqrt{14}} = \dfrac{3}{\sqrt{14}}$

$\theta = \cos^{-1}\left(\dfrac{3}{\sqrt{14}}\right) = 36.6992... = 36.7°$ (1 d.p.)

c) $|\mathbf{a}| = \sqrt{14}$ as before

$\mathbf{b} = \begin{pmatrix} -3 \\ 1 \\ -2 \end{pmatrix}$, $|\mathbf{b}| = \sqrt{(-3)^2 + 1^2 + (-2)^2} = \sqrt{14}$

$\mathbf{b} - \mathbf{a} = \begin{pmatrix} -4 \\ -2 \\ -4 \end{pmatrix}$, $|\mathbf{b} - \mathbf{a}| = \sqrt{(-4)^2 + (-2)^2 + (-4)^2} = 6$

Using the cosine rule,

$\cos\theta = \dfrac{(\sqrt{14})^2 + (\sqrt{14})^2 - 6^2}{2 \times \sqrt{14} \times \sqrt{14}} = \dfrac{-8}{28} = -\dfrac{2}{7}$

$\theta = \cos^{-1}\left(-\dfrac{2}{7}\right) = 106.6°$ (1 d.p.)

d) $|\mathbf{a}| = \sqrt{14}$ as before

$\mathbf{b} = \begin{pmatrix} 2 \\ 2 \\ 2 \end{pmatrix}$, $|\mathbf{b}| = \sqrt{2^2 + 2^2 + 2^2} = 2\sqrt{3}$

$\mathbf{b} - \mathbf{a} = \begin{pmatrix} 1 \\ -1 \\ 0 \end{pmatrix}$, $|\mathbf{b} - \mathbf{a}| = \sqrt{1^2 + (-1)^2 + 0^2} = \sqrt{2}$

Using the cosine rule,

$\cos\theta = \dfrac{(\sqrt{14})^2 + (2\sqrt{3})^2 - (\sqrt{2})^2}{2 \times \sqrt{14} \times 2\sqrt{3}} = \dfrac{24}{4\sqrt{42}} = \dfrac{6}{\sqrt{42}}$

$\theta = \cos^{-1}\left(\dfrac{6}{\sqrt{42}}\right) = 22.2°$ (1 d.p.)

Q10 Speed is the magnitude of velocity, so you want to find $|\mathbf{v}|$. Form a triangle between vector **v** and a vector $\mathbf{p} = \mathbf{i}$, with an angle of 60° between them. The triangle has side lengths $|\mathbf{v}|$, $|\mathbf{p}|$ and $|\mathbf{p} - \mathbf{v}|$.

$|\mathbf{v}| = \sqrt{1^2 + a^2 + 1^2} = \sqrt{2 + a^2}$

$|\mathbf{p}| = 1$

$\mathbf{p} - \mathbf{v} = -a\mathbf{j} - \mathbf{k}$, $|\mathbf{p} - \mathbf{v}| = \sqrt{0^2 + (-a)^2 + (-1)^2} = \sqrt{a^2 + 1}$

Using the cosine rule,

$\cos 60° = \dfrac{(\sqrt{2 + a^2})^2 + 1^2 - (\sqrt{a^2 + 1})^2}{2 \times \sqrt{2 + a^2}}$

$\dfrac{1}{2} = \dfrac{2 + a^2 + 1 - a^2 - 1}{2\sqrt{2 + a^2}} \Rightarrow \dfrac{1}{2} = \dfrac{2}{2\sqrt{2 + a^2}}$

$\Rightarrow \sqrt{2 + a^2} = 2 \Rightarrow 2 + a^2 = 4 \Rightarrow a = \pm\sqrt{2}$

Therefore the launch speed $|\mathbf{v}| = \sqrt{2 + (\pm\sqrt{2})^2} = 2$ ms^{-1}

Q11 Here, the displacement is just the distance, which is

$\sqrt{(15t \cos 36°)^2 + (15t \sin 36°)^2 + (8t)^2}$

$= \sqrt{(15t)^2 \cos^2 36° + (15t)^2 \sin^2 36° + 64t^2}$

$= \sqrt{225t^2(\cos^2 36° + \sin^2 36°) + 64t^2} = \sqrt{289t^2} = 17t$

Review Exercise — Chapter 10

Q1 $2\mathbf{i} - 4\mathbf{j} + 5\mathbf{k}$

Q2 $\overrightarrow{XO} = -6\mathbf{i} + \mathbf{j} = \begin{pmatrix} -6 \\ 1 \\ 0 \end{pmatrix}$, $\overrightarrow{YO} = -4\mathbf{i} + 4\mathbf{j} - 7\mathbf{k} = \begin{pmatrix} -4 \\ 4 \\ -7 \end{pmatrix}$

Q3 **a)** E.g. **a** and 4**a**

b) E.g. $6\mathbf{i} + 8\mathbf{j} - 4\mathbf{k}$ and $9\mathbf{i} + 12\mathbf{j} - 6\mathbf{k}$

c) E.g. $\begin{pmatrix} 2 \\ 4 \\ -2 \end{pmatrix}$ and $\begin{pmatrix} 4 \\ 8 \\ -4 \end{pmatrix}$

You could give any answer that is a scalar multiple of each vector.

Q4 $2\mathbf{a} + \mathbf{b} = 3\mathbf{i} - 2\mathbf{j} - 5\mathbf{k} = -\dfrac{1}{2}\mathbf{c}$.

They're scalar multiples, therefore they must be parallel.

Q5 $\overrightarrow{AB} = \begin{pmatrix} -1 \\ 4 \\ 4 \end{pmatrix}$, $\overrightarrow{BC} = \begin{pmatrix} -3 \\ 12 \\ 12 \end{pmatrix} = 3\,\overrightarrow{AB}$.

This shows $\overrightarrow{AB}$ and $\overrightarrow{BC}$ are parallel, and they share a point (B) so A, B and C must be collinear.

Q6 a) $\sqrt{3^2 + 4^2 + (-2)^2} = \sqrt{29}$

b) $\sqrt{1^2 + 2^2 + (-1)^2} = \sqrt{6}$

Q7 a) $|\overrightarrow{OA}| = \sqrt{1^2 + 2^2 + 3^2} = \sqrt{14}$

b) $|\overrightarrow{OB}| = \sqrt{3^2 + (-1)^2 + (-2)^2} = \sqrt{14}$

c) $\overrightarrow{AB} = \overrightarrow{OB} - \overrightarrow{OA} = (2, -3, -5)$
$|\overrightarrow{AB}| = \sqrt{2^2 + (-3)^2 + (-5)^2} = \sqrt{38}$

Q8 a) $|\mathbf{i} - 3\mathbf{k}| = \sqrt{1^2 + (-3)^2} = \sqrt{10} \Rightarrow \frac{1}{\sqrt{10}}\mathbf{i} - \frac{3}{\sqrt{10}}\mathbf{k}$

b) $|-2\mathbf{i} + 2\mathbf{j} + 5\mathbf{k}| = \sqrt{(-2)^2 + 2^2 + 5^2} = \sqrt{33}$
$\Rightarrow -\frac{2}{\sqrt{33}}\mathbf{i} + \frac{2}{\sqrt{33}}\mathbf{j} + \frac{5}{\sqrt{33}}\mathbf{k}$

c) $\left| \begin{pmatrix} -1 \\ -3 \\ 3 \end{pmatrix} \right| = \sqrt{(-1)^2 + (-3)^2 + 3^2} = \sqrt{19} \Rightarrow \begin{pmatrix} -\frac{\sqrt{19}}{19} \\ -\frac{3\sqrt{19}}{19} \\ \frac{3\sqrt{19}}{19} \end{pmatrix}$

d) $\left| \begin{pmatrix} 7 \\ -1 \\ 12 \end{pmatrix} \right| = \sqrt{7^2 + (-1)^2 + 12^2} = \sqrt{194} \Rightarrow \begin{pmatrix} \frac{7\sqrt{194}}{194} \\ -\frac{\sqrt{194}}{194} \\ \frac{12\sqrt{194}}{194} \end{pmatrix}$

Q9 $\overrightarrow{PQ} = \overrightarrow{OQ} - \overrightarrow{OP} = 3\mathbf{i} - 4\mathbf{j} + \mathbf{k}$
$|\overrightarrow{PQ}| = \sqrt{3^2 + (-4)^2 + 1^2} = \sqrt{26}$

Q10 $\overrightarrow{OY} = \overrightarrow{OX} + 6\frac{\overrightarrow{XY}}{|\overrightarrow{XY}|} = \begin{pmatrix} -2 \\ 1 \\ 0 \end{pmatrix} + 6\begin{pmatrix} \frac{2}{3} \\ \frac{2}{3} \\ -\frac{1}{3} \end{pmatrix} = \begin{pmatrix} 2 \\ 5 \\ -2 \end{pmatrix}$

So the coordinates of Y are (2, 5, −2).

Q11 $|\overrightarrow{OA}| = \sqrt{4^2 + 3^2 + (-3)^2} = \sqrt{34}$
$|\overrightarrow{OB}| = \sqrt{(-1)^2 + 2^2 + (-4)^2} = \sqrt{21}$

$\overrightarrow{AB} = \begin{pmatrix} -5 \\ -1 \\ -1 \end{pmatrix} \Rightarrow |\overrightarrow{AB}| = \sqrt{(-5)^2 + (-1)^2 + (-1)^2} = \sqrt{27}$

So you have a triangle:

Use the cosine rule:
$\cos\theta = \frac{(\sqrt{27})^2 + (\sqrt{21})^2 - (\sqrt{34})^2}{2 \times \sqrt{27} \times \sqrt{21}} = \frac{14}{18\sqrt{7}} = \frac{\sqrt{7}}{9}$

$\Rightarrow \theta = \cos^{-1}\left(\frac{\sqrt{7}}{9}\right) = 72.9°$ (1 d.p.)

Q12 a) R has speed $\sqrt{5^2 + 3^2 + (-1)^2} = \sqrt{35}$ ms⁻¹,
S has speed $\sqrt{(-2)^2 + (-2)^2 + 7^2} = \sqrt{57}$ ms⁻¹.

b) Distance = speed × time = $(\sqrt{57} - \sqrt{35}) \times 5$
= 8 m (to the nearest metre)

c) $\mathbf{s} - \mathbf{r} = -7\mathbf{i} - 5\mathbf{j} + 8\mathbf{k}$
$\Rightarrow |\mathbf{s} - \mathbf{r}| = \sqrt{(-7)^2 + (-5)^2 + 8^2} = \sqrt{138}$
$\cos\theta = \frac{(\sqrt{57})^2 + (\sqrt{35})^2 - (\sqrt{138})^2}{2 \times \sqrt{57} \times \sqrt{35}} = \frac{-23}{\sqrt{1995}}$

$\theta = \cos^{-1}\left(\frac{-23}{\sqrt{1995}}\right) = 121°$ (to the nearest degree)

d) E.g. This is a suitable model, as there are no resistance forces in space. This model could be improved by including the effect of gravity exerted on the asteroids by other astronomical bodies e.g. planets or moons.

Exam-Style Questions — Chapter 10

Q1 The vector $\overrightarrow{LN} = \frac{5}{2} \times \overrightarrow{LM}$.

$\frac{5}{2} \times \overrightarrow{LM} = \frac{5}{2}(2\mathbf{i} - \mathbf{j} - 2\mathbf{k}) = 5\mathbf{i} - \frac{5}{2}\mathbf{j} - 5\mathbf{k}$

To find N, add $\overrightarrow{LN}$ to the position vector of L:

$N = (3\mathbf{i} + \mathbf{j} + 8\mathbf{k}) + (5\mathbf{i} - \frac{5}{2}\mathbf{j} - 5\mathbf{k}) = 8\mathbf{i} - \frac{3}{2}\mathbf{j} + 3\mathbf{k}$

[3 marks available — 1 mark for attempting to find $\overrightarrow{LN}$, 1 mark for correct $\overrightarrow{LN}$, 1 mark for correct answer]

Q2 a) $\overrightarrow{AC} = \overrightarrow{AB} + \overrightarrow{BC} = \overrightarrow{AB} + \overrightarrow{AD} = \begin{pmatrix} 5 \\ -3 \\ 2 \end{pmatrix} + \begin{pmatrix} -1 \\ 6 \\ -5 \end{pmatrix} = \begin{pmatrix} 4 \\ 3 \\ -3 \end{pmatrix}$

[2 marks available — 1 mark for correctly identifying that $\overrightarrow{BC} = \overrightarrow{AD}$, 1 mark for correct answer]

b) Length of $\overrightarrow{AC} = \left| \begin{pmatrix} 4 \\ 3 \\ -3 \end{pmatrix} \right| = \sqrt{4^2 + 3^2 + (-3)^2} = \sqrt{34}$

[2 marks available — 1 mark for correct attempt at finding length, 1 mark for correct answer]

Q3 a) $|\overrightarrow{YZ}| = \left| \begin{pmatrix} -7 \\ 5 \\ -4 \end{pmatrix} \right| = \sqrt{(-7)^2 + 5^2 + (-4)^2} = \sqrt{90} = 3\sqrt{10}$

$|\overrightarrow{XZ}| = \frac{\sqrt{10}}{5}|\overrightarrow{YZ}| = \frac{\sqrt{10}}{5} \times 3\sqrt{10} = \frac{30}{5} = 6$

The unit vector in the direction $\overrightarrow{XZ}$ is $\begin{pmatrix} \frac{2}{3} \\ \frac{1}{2} \\ -\frac{\sqrt{11}}{6} \end{pmatrix}$, and $|\overrightarrow{XZ}| = 6$,

so $\overrightarrow{XZ} = \begin{pmatrix} \frac{2}{3} \\ \frac{1}{2} \\ -\frac{\sqrt{11}}{6} \end{pmatrix} \times 6 = \begin{pmatrix} 4 \\ 3 \\ -\sqrt{11} \end{pmatrix}$, as required.

[4 marks available — 1 mark for attempt at finding $|\overrightarrow{YZ}|$, 1 mark for finding $|\overrightarrow{XZ}|$, 1 mark for multiplying the unit vector by the length to give the required result]

b) $\overrightarrow{XY} = \begin{pmatrix} 7 \\ -5 \\ 4 \end{pmatrix} + \begin{pmatrix} 4 \\ 3 \\ -\sqrt{11} \end{pmatrix} = \begin{pmatrix} 11 \\ -2 \\ 4-\sqrt{11} \end{pmatrix}$,

so $|\overrightarrow{XY}|^2 = 11^2 + (-2)^2 + (4-\sqrt{11})^2 = 152 - 8\sqrt{11}$
From part a), $|\overrightarrow{XZ}| = 6$ and $|\overrightarrow{YZ}| = 3\sqrt{10}$
Using the cosine rule:
$\cos Z = \frac{(3\sqrt{10})^2 + 6^2 - (152 - 8\sqrt{11})}{2 \times 3\sqrt{10} \times 6} = 0.00468...$

$Z = \cos^{-1}(0.00468...) = 89.7°$ (1 d.p.)
[5 marks available — 1 mark for finding $\overrightarrow{XY}$, 1 mark for attempting to find $|\overrightarrow{XY}|$ or $|\overrightarrow{XY}|^2$, 1 mark for correctly finding $|\overrightarrow{XY}|$ or $|\overrightarrow{XY}|^2$, 1 mark for attempting to use the cosine rule, 1 mark for correct answer]

Practice Paper

Q1 $\cot^2\theta + \sin^2\theta \equiv (\csc^2\theta - 1) + (1 - \cos^2\theta) \equiv \csc^2\theta - \cos^2\theta$

[2 marks available — 1 mark for using $\csc^2\theta \equiv 1 + \cot^2\theta$, 1 mark for using $\sin^2\theta + \cos^2\theta \equiv 1$ and simplifying]

Q2 Suppose that $\pi + 1$ is a rational number, so $\pi + 1 = \dfrac{a}{b}$, where a and b are integers and b is non-zero.

So $\pi + 1 = \dfrac{a}{b} \Rightarrow \pi = \dfrac{a}{b} - 1 = \dfrac{a-b}{b}$

From the question, you know π is irrational and cannot be written as a quotient of two integers, where the denominator is non-zero, so $\pi + 1$ is irrational. You've reached a contradiction and so your initial assumption must have been wrong.

You don't have to use a and b — any two letters are fine.
[3 marks available — 1 mark for setting $\pi + 1$ equal to $\dfrac{a}{b}$, 1 mark for expressing π in terms of a and b, 1 mark for correct interpretation]

Q3 **a)** $Y_1 = 20\,000 = a$ and the common ratio (r) is 108%, which is 1.08. So $Y_n = 20\,000(1.08)^{n-1}$
[1 mark for correct expression]

b) Find the sum of the geometric series from Y_1 to Y_5:
$S_5 = \dfrac{a(1-r^n)}{1-r} = \dfrac{20\,000(1-1.08^5)}{1-1.08} = 117\,332.0192$
Find the sum of the geometric series from Y_6 to Y_{10}:
$S_{10} - S_5 = \dfrac{20\,000(1-1.08^{10})}{1-1.08} - 117\,332.0192$
$= 289\,731.2493 - 117\,332.0192$
$= \pounds172\,399.23$ (to nearest pence)

[3 marks available — 1 mark for understanding answer is difference between sum to 10 terms and sum to 5 terms, 1 mark for correct use of sum of geometric series formula, 1 mark for correct final answer to nearest pence]

Q4 **a)** $f(4.7) = (4.7)^3 - 4(4.7)^2 - 5(4.7) + 6 = -2.037$
$f(4.8) = (4.8)^3 - 4(4.8)^2 - 5(4.8) + 6 = 0.432$
There is a sign change (and the function is continuous in this interval) so there is a root in this interval.
[2 marks available — 1 mark for correct f(4.7) and f(4.8), 1 mark for identifying sign change]

b) $f(x) = 0$, so $x^3 - 4x^2 - 5x + 6 = 0$
$\Rightarrow x^3 = 4x^2 + 5x - 6 \Rightarrow x = \sqrt[3]{4x^2 + 5x - 6}$
[1 mark for correct answer]

c) $x_1 = \sqrt[3]{4x_0^2 + 5x_0 - 6} = 4.730...$, $x_2 = 4.749...$, $x_3 = 4.762...$, $x_4 = 4.769...$, $x_5 = 4.774...$
So the root $\alpha = 4.77$ (3 s.f)
[2 marks available — 1 mark for correctly substituting 4.7 into the iteration formula to get at least one correct value, 1 mark for correct answer]

d) $f'(x) = 3x^2 - 8x - 5$
So $x_{n+1} = x_n - \dfrac{x_n^3 - 4x_n^2 - 5x_n + 6}{3x_n^2 - 8x_n - 5}$
$x_1 = -1.5 - \dfrac{(-1.5)^3 - 4(-1.5)^2 - 5(-1.5) + 6}{3(-1.5)^2 - 8(-1.5) - 5} = -1.581...$
$x_2 = -1.578...$, so the root $\beta = -1.58$ (3 s.f.)

[3 marks available — 1 mark for correct iteration formula, 1 mark for using formula to get at least one correct value, 1 mark for correct answer]

Q5 Let $y = 5^x - 3 \Rightarrow y + 3 = 5^x \Rightarrow \log_5(y+3) = \log_5 5^x = x$
Replace x with $g^{-1}(x)$ and y with x: $g^{-1}(x) = \log_5(x+3)$
You could also have taken the natural log (ln) of both sides to get the equivalent solution $g^{-1}(x) = \dfrac{\ln(x+3)}{\ln 5}$.

[3 marks available — 1 mark for substituting g(x) for y and rearranging equation, 1 mark for taking logs of both sides, 1 mark for correct answer in correct form]

Q6 **a)** $x = t^3 + t^2 \Rightarrow \dfrac{dx}{dt} = 3t^2 + 2t$
$y = \dfrac{1}{2}t^2 - 6t \Rightarrow \dfrac{dy}{dt} = t - 6$
$\Rightarrow \dfrac{dy}{dx} = \dfrac{dy}{dt} \div \dfrac{dx}{dt} = \dfrac{t-6}{3t^2 + 2t}$
[2 marks available — 1 mark for using $\dfrac{dy}{dx} = \dfrac{dy}{dt} \div \dfrac{dx}{dt}$, 1 mark for correct $\dfrac{dy}{dx}$]

b) At turning points, $\dfrac{dy}{dx} = 0 \Rightarrow \dfrac{t-6}{3t^2 + 2t} = 0 \Rightarrow t - 6 = 0$
$\Rightarrow t = 6$
When $t = 6$, $x = 6^3 + 6^2 = 252$
and $y = \dfrac{1}{2} \times 6^2 - 6 \times 6 = -18$
So the coordinates of the turning point are $(252, -18)$.
[2 marks available — 1 mark for setting $\dfrac{dy}{dx} = 0$ and using it to find value of t, 1 mark for correct coordinates using t]

c) When $t = 12$, $x = 12^3 + 12^2 = 1872$, $y = \dfrac{1}{2}(12)^2 - 6(12) = 0$
and $\dfrac{dy}{dx} = \dfrac{12-6}{3(12)^2 + 2(12)} = \dfrac{1}{76}$
So the tangent to the trajectory when $t = 12$ has a gradient of $\dfrac{1}{76}$ and an equation in the form $y = mx + c$. Substitute in the values of x, y and m to find c:
$0 = \dfrac{1}{76} \times 1872 + c \Rightarrow c = -\dfrac{468}{19}$
So the tangent has the equation $y = \dfrac{1}{76}x - \dfrac{468}{19}$.
[3 marks available — 1 mark for finding correct x and y, 1 mark for correct $\dfrac{dy}{dx}$, 1 mark for correct equation for tangent]

Q7 **a)** $\overrightarrow{AC} = \overrightarrow{AB} + \overrightarrow{BC} = \begin{pmatrix} 2 \\ 6 \\ -8 \end{pmatrix} + \begin{pmatrix} -8 \\ 2 \\ 9 \end{pmatrix} = \begin{pmatrix} -6 \\ 8 \\ 1 \end{pmatrix}$
[1 mark for correct answer]

b) $\overrightarrow{AD} = \dfrac{5}{2}\begin{pmatrix} 2 \\ 6 \\ -8 \end{pmatrix} = \begin{pmatrix} 5 \\ 15 \\ -20 \end{pmatrix}$

$\overrightarrow{CD} = \overrightarrow{AD} - \overrightarrow{AC} = \begin{pmatrix} 5 \\ 15 \\ -20 \end{pmatrix} - \begin{pmatrix} -6 \\ 8 \\ 1 \end{pmatrix} = \begin{pmatrix} 11 \\ 7 \\ -21 \end{pmatrix}$

$|\overrightarrow{AC}| = \sqrt{(-6)^2 + 8^2 + 1^2} = \sqrt{101}$
$|\overrightarrow{AD}| = \sqrt{5^2 + 15^2 + (-20)^2} = \sqrt{650} = 5\sqrt{26}$
$|\overrightarrow{CD}| = \sqrt{11^2 + 7^2 + (-21)^2} = \sqrt{611}$

Using the cosine rule:
$\cos ACD = \dfrac{(\sqrt{101})^2 + (\sqrt{611})^2 - (5\sqrt{26})^2}{2 \times \sqrt{101} \times \sqrt{611}} = 0.124...$

$ACD = \cos^{-1}(0.124...) = 82.8°$ (1 d.p.)

[5 marks available — 1 mark for $\overrightarrow{AD}$, 1 mark for $\overrightarrow{CD}$, 1 mark for correct magnitudes, 1 mark for attempting to use cosine rule, 1 mark for correct answer]

Q8 Differentiate $x^4 - 3x^2y^2 = y^3$:

$\frac{d}{dx}x^4 - \frac{d}{dx}3x^2y^2 = \frac{d}{dx}y^3 \Rightarrow 4x^3 - 6x^2y\frac{dy}{dx} - 6xy^2 = 3y^2\frac{dy}{dx}$

The product rule was used to differentiate $3x^2y^2$.

$\Rightarrow 4x^3 - 6xy^2 = 6x^2y\frac{dy}{dx} + 3y^2\frac{dy}{dx} \Rightarrow \frac{dy}{dx} = \frac{4x^3 - 6xy^2}{6x^2y + 3y^2}$

At (4, 4), $\frac{dy}{dx} = \frac{4(4)^3 - 6(4)(4)^2}{6(4)^2(4) + 3(4)^2} = -\frac{8}{27}$

So the tangent to C at point (4, 4) has a gradient of $-\frac{8}{27}$ and an equation in the form $y = mx + c$.

Substitute in the values of x, y and m to find c:

$4 = -\frac{8}{27}(4) + c \Rightarrow c = \frac{140}{27}$

So the tangent has the equation $y = -\frac{8}{27}x + \frac{140}{27}$.

[5 marks available — 1 mark for two terms correctly differentiated, 1 mark for other two terms correctly differentiated, 1 mark for correct gradient, 1 mark for correct value of c, 1 mark for correct equation for tangent]

Q9 a) $a = 1^{st}$ term $= -3$, $d = 4$,
$\Rightarrow n^{th}$ term $= -3 + (n-1)4 = 4n - 7$
$\Rightarrow k = 4$ and $m = -7$
[2 marks available — 1 mark for using n^{th} term formula for an arithmetic sequence with correct values of a and d, 1 mark for k and m]

b) $u_n = 4n - 7 \Rightarrow u_{20} = 4 \times 20 - 7 = 73$
[1 mark for correct answer (allow errors carried forward)]

c) From previous parts $a = -3$ and $l = 73$.
$S_n = \frac{1}{2}n(a + l) = \frac{1}{2} \times 20 \times (-3 + 73) = 700$
[2 marks available — 1 mark for correct method, 1 mark for correct answer]

Q10 a)

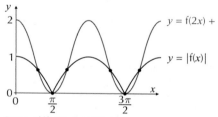

Range of $|f(x)|$ is $0 \le |f(x)| \le 1$
Range of $f(2x) + 1$ is $0 \le f(2x) + 1 \le 2$
[4 marks available — 1 mark for correct shape and position of $|f(x)|$, 1 mark for correct shape and position of $f(2x) + 1$, 1 mark for correct range of $|f(x)|$, 1 mark for correct range of $f(2x) + 1$]

b) $|f(x)| = f(2x) + 1$
On the graph above, you can see there are six solutions.
To find all the solutions, you need to solve $f(x) = f(2x) + 1$ and $-f(x) = f(2x) + 1$.
$f(x) = f(2x) + 1 \Rightarrow \cos x = \cos 2x + 1$
$\Rightarrow \cos x = 2\cos^2 x - 1 + 1 \Rightarrow 2\cos^2 x - \cos x = 0$
$\Rightarrow \cos x(2\cos x - 1) = 0 \Rightarrow \cos x = 0$ or $\cos x = \frac{1}{2}$
If $\cos x = 0$, $x = \frac{\pi}{2}$ and $\frac{3\pi}{2}$, where $0 \le x \le 2\pi$.
If $\cos x = \frac{1}{2}$, $x = \frac{\pi}{3}$ and $\frac{5\pi}{3}$, where $0 \le x \le 2\pi$.
$-f(x) = f(2x) + 1 \Rightarrow -\cos x = \cos 2x + 1$
$\Rightarrow -\cos x = 2\cos^2 x - 1 + 1 \Rightarrow 2\cos^2 x + \cos x = 0$
$\Rightarrow \cos x(2\cos x + 1) = 0 \Rightarrow \cos x = 0$ or $\cos x = -\frac{1}{2}$
The solutions for $\cos x = 0$ are given above.
If $\cos x = -\frac{1}{2}$, $x = \frac{2\pi}{3}$ and $\frac{4\pi}{3}$, where $0 \le x \le 2\pi$.
So the solutions for $|f(x)| = f(2x) + 1$ in the interval $0 \le x \le 2\pi$ are $x = \frac{\pi}{3}, \frac{\pi}{2}, \frac{2\pi}{3}, \frac{4\pi}{3}, \frac{3\pi}{2}$ and $\frac{5\pi}{3}$.
[5 marks available — 1 mark for setting $\cos x = \cos 2x + 1$, 1 mark for setting $-\cos x = \cos 2x + 1$, 1 mark for using double angle formula on $\cos 2x$, 1 mark for three correct solutions, 1 mark for all other correct solutions]

Q11 a) Use a double angle formula to write $y = \frac{\cos\theta \sin 2\theta}{2\sin\theta}$ in terms of $\cos\theta$:

$y = \frac{\cos\theta\sin 2\theta}{2\sin\theta} = \frac{\cos\theta(2\sin\theta\cos\theta)}{2\sin\theta} = \cos^2\theta$

Rearrange the equation for x to get $\cos\theta$:
$x = \frac{1 - \cos\theta}{3} \Rightarrow \cos\theta = 1 - 3x$
So $y = \cos^2\theta = (1 - 3x)^2 = 9x^2 - 6x + 1$
[3 marks available — 1 mark for correct use of double angle formula, 1 mark for writing y in terms of $\cos\theta$ only, 1 mark for correct Cartesian equation]

b) $y + 3 = 2x \Rightarrow y = 2x - 3$
Substitute this into the Cartesian equation:
$2x - 3 = 9x^2 - 6x + 1 \Rightarrow 0 = 9x^2 - 8x + 4$
Using the discriminant:
$b^2 - 4ac = (-8)^2 - 4 \times 9 \times 4 = -80 < 0$,
so there are no solutions to the quadratic equation and hence the curve does not intersect the line.
[2 marks available — 1 mark for correctly substituting y into Cartesian equation, 1 mark for using discriminant to show no intersection]

Q12 a) $\frac{\cos x}{(\cos x + 1)(\cos x - 1)} \equiv \frac{\cos x}{\cos^2 x - 1} \equiv \frac{-\cos x}{1 - \cos^2 x}$

$\equiv \frac{-\cos x}{\sin^2 x} \equiv \frac{1}{\sin x} \cdot \frac{-\cos x}{\sin x} \equiv -\text{cosec } x \cot x$
[3 marks available — 1 mark for expanding brackets, 1 mark for using $1 - \cos^2 x \equiv \sin^2 x$, 1 mark for splitting fraction and simplifying to $-\text{cosec } x \cot x$]

b) $\int \frac{\cos x \, e^{\frac{1}{\sin x}}}{(\cos x + 1)(\cos x - 1)} \, dx = \int -\text{cosec } x \cot x \times e^{\text{cosec } x} \, dx$

Let $u = \text{cosec } x$, so $\frac{du}{dx} = -\text{cosec } x \cot x$ and $f'(u) = e^u$.

Use the formula $\int \frac{du}{dx} f'(u) \, dx = f(u) + C$:
$\int -\text{cosec } x \cot x \times e^{\text{cosec } x} \, dx = e^{\text{cosec } x} + C$
[4 marks available — 1 mark for using part a) to simplify, 1 mark for u, 1 mark for $\frac{du}{dx}$ and $f'(u)$, 1 mark for correct answer]

Q13 a) $V = \sqrt{h^4 + 2} = (h^4 + 2)^{\frac{1}{2}}$, so let $V = u^{\frac{1}{2}}$, where $u = h^4 + 2$

$\Rightarrow \frac{dV}{du} = \frac{1}{2}u^{-\frac{1}{2}} = \frac{1}{2\sqrt{h^4 + 2}}, \frac{du}{dh} = 4h^3$

$\frac{dV}{dh} = \frac{dV}{du} \times \frac{du}{dh} = \frac{1}{2\sqrt{h^4 + 2}} \times 4h^3 = \frac{2h^3}{\sqrt{h^4 + 2}}$

When $h = 0.4$, $\frac{dV}{dh} = \frac{2(0.4)^3}{\sqrt{(0.4)^4 + 2}} = 0.08993...$
$= 0.0899$ (3 s.f.)
[3 marks available — 1 mark for attempting to use the chain rule, 1 mark for correct $\frac{dV}{dh}$, 1 mark for correct final answer]

b) From the question you know that $\frac{dV}{dt} = 0.15$ m^3 per hour.
You're looking for $\frac{dh}{dt}$:
$\frac{dV}{dt} = \frac{dV}{dh} \times \frac{dh}{dt}$, so $\frac{dh}{dt} = \frac{dV}{dt} \div \frac{dV}{dh} = 0.15 \div 0.0899$
$= 1.67$ (3 s.f.)
[2 marks available — 1 mark for correct method, 1 mark for correct answer (allow for errors carried forward from a))]

Q14 a) At $x = 1.3$, $y = \frac{3(1.3)^2}{(1.3)^3 + 4} = 0.818$ (3 d.p.)
At $x = 1.5$, $y = \frac{3(1.5)^2}{(1.5)^3 + 4} = 0.915$ (3 d.p.)
[1 mark for correct y-values]

b) Using the y-values from the table and part a), use the trapezium with 5 strips and $h = 0.1$.
$\int_1^{1.5} \frac{3x^2}{x^3 + 4} \, dx \approx \frac{h}{2}[y_0 + 2y_1 + 2y_2 + 2y_3 + 2y_4 + y_5]$
$= 0.05[0.6 + 1.362 + 1.508 + 1.636 + 1.744 + 0.915]$
$= 0.39$ (2 d.p.)
[3 marks available — 1 mark for using 5 strips with width of 0.1, 1 mark for using trapezium rule correctly, 1 mark for correct answer]

c) **(i)** Differentiating the denominator:

$\frac{d}{dx} x^3 + 4 = 3x^2 = $ numerator

So $\int_1^{1.5} \frac{3x^2}{x^3 + 4} dx = [\ln|x^3 + 4|]_1^{1.5}$

$= \ln \frac{59}{8} - \ln 5 = \ln \frac{59}{40}$

[3 marks available — 1 mark for integrating the fraction, 1 mark for substituting limits, 1 mark for correct final value]

(ii) Percentage error $= \frac{0.39 - \ln \frac{59}{40}}{\ln \frac{59}{40}} \times 100 = 0.35\%$ (2 d.p.)

[1 mark for correct answer]

Q15 a) E.g. by using algebraic division:

$$
\begin{array}{r}
x^2 + \ x \ - 12 \ r \ 0 \\
x + 4 \overline{) x^3 + 5x^2 - 8x - 48} \\
\underline{- (x^3 + 4x^2)} \\
x^2 - 8x \\
\underline{- (x^2 + 4x)} \\
-12x - 48 \\
\underline{- (-12x - 48)} \\
0
\end{array}
$$

So $f(x) = (x + 4)(x^2 + x - 12) = (x + 4)(x + 4)(x - 3)$
$= (x + 4)^2(x - 3)$

[3 marks available — 1 mark for a suitable method to find quadratic factor, 1 mark for correct quadratic, 1 mark for correct answer fully factorised]

b) $g(x) \equiv \frac{3x + 40}{(x + 4)^2(x - 3)} \equiv \frac{A}{x + 4} + \frac{B}{(x + 4)^2} + \frac{C}{x - 3}$

$\Rightarrow 3x + 40 \equiv A(x + 4)(x - 3) + B(x - 3) + C(x + 4)^2$
Substitution: $x = -4$: $28 = -7B \Rightarrow B = -4$
$x = 3$: $49 = 49C \Rightarrow C = 1$

Equating x coefficients: $3 = A + B + 8C = A - 4 + 8$
$\Rightarrow A = -1$

So $\frac{3x + 40}{(x + 4)^2(x - 3)} \equiv -\frac{1}{x + 4} - \frac{4}{(x + 4)^2} + \frac{1}{x - 3}$

[4 marks available — 1 mark for writing the expression as the sum of three fractions, 1 mark for finding one unknown, 1 mark for finding the other two unknowns, 1 mark for the correct answer]

c) $g(x) \equiv -\frac{1}{x + 4} - \frac{4}{(x + 4)^2} + \frac{1}{x - 3}$

$\equiv -(x + 4)^{-1} - 4(x + 4)^{-2} + (x - 3)^{-1}$

$(x + 4)^{-1} = (4 + x)^{-1} = \frac{1}{4}(1 + \frac{x}{4})^{-1}$

$= \frac{1}{4}(1 - \frac{x}{4} + \frac{x^2}{16} + ...) = (\frac{1}{4} - \frac{x}{16} + \frac{x^2}{64} - ...)$

$(x + 4)^{-2} = (4 + x)^{-2} = \frac{1}{16}(1 + \frac{x}{4})^{-2} = \frac{1}{16}(1 - \frac{x}{2} + \frac{3x^2}{16} - ...)$

$= (\frac{1}{16} - \frac{x}{32} + \frac{3x^2}{256} + ...)$

$(x - 3)^{-1} = -(3 - x)^{-1} = -\frac{1}{3}(1 - \frac{x}{3})^{-1} = -\frac{1}{3}(1 + \frac{x}{3} + \frac{x^2}{9} + ...)$

$= (-\frac{1}{3} - \frac{x}{9} - \frac{x^2}{27} - ...)$

So $g(x) \approx -[\frac{1}{4} - \frac{x}{16} + \frac{x^2}{64}] - 4[\frac{1}{16} - \frac{x}{32} + \frac{3x^2}{256}]$
$+ [-\frac{1}{3} - \frac{x}{9} - \frac{x^2}{27}]$

$= -\frac{1}{4} + \frac{x}{16} - \frac{x^2}{64} - \frac{1}{4} + \frac{x}{8} - \frac{3x^2}{64} - \frac{1}{3} - \frac{x}{9} - \frac{x^2}{27}$

$= -\frac{5}{6} + \frac{11x}{144} - \frac{43x^2}{432}$

[6 marks available — 1 mark for each correct expansion of the denominators, 1 mark for multiplying the denominator expansions by the correct values, 1 mark for attempting to add the three expansions, 1 mark for correct simplified final answer]

Q16 $y = 2\frac{dy}{dx}$, so at $(1, e)$, $\frac{dy}{dx} = \frac{e}{2}$

So the gradient of the tangent at P is $\frac{e}{2}$ and the gradient of the normal at P is $-\frac{2}{e}$.

The normal has equation in the form $y = mx + c$, so substitute in the values of x, y and m to find c:

$e = -\frac{2}{e}(1) + c \Rightarrow c = e + \frac{2}{e}$

So the equation for the normal is $y = -\frac{2}{e}x + e + \frac{2}{e}$.

Split the area into A_1 and A_2 at $x = 1$:

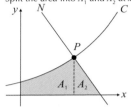

Find where the normal intersects the x-axis:

$y = 0 \Rightarrow 0 = -\frac{2}{e}x + e + \frac{2}{e} \Rightarrow \frac{2}{e}x = e + \frac{2}{e}$

$\Rightarrow 2x = e^2 + 2 \Rightarrow x = \frac{e^2}{2} + 1$

So $A_2 = \frac{1}{2} \times e \times (\frac{e^2}{2} + 1 - 1) = \frac{1}{2} \times e \times \frac{e^2}{2} = \frac{e^3}{4}$

The area of a triangle formula was used to find A_2.

Using differential equations:

$y = 2\frac{dy}{dx} \Rightarrow \int dx = \int \frac{2}{y} dy \Rightarrow x = 2 \ln|y| + C$

From the sketch you know y is positive so you don't need the modulus signs.

$\Rightarrow \frac{x - C}{2} = \ln y \Rightarrow y = e^{\frac{x - C}{2}} = ke^{\frac{x}{2}}$

When $x = 1$, $y = e$, so $e = ke^{\frac{1}{2}} \Rightarrow k = e^{\frac{1}{2}} \Rightarrow y = e^{\frac{x}{2} + \frac{1}{2}}$

For A_1, integrate y with limits $x = 0$ and $x = 1$:

$\int_0^1 y \, dx = \int_0^1 e^{\frac{x}{2} + \frac{1}{2}} dx = [2e^{\frac{x}{2} + \frac{1}{2}}]_0^1 = 2e - 2e^{\frac{1}{2}}$

Add the areas together for A: $A = A_1 + A_2 = 2e - 2e^{\frac{1}{2}} + \frac{e^3}{4}$

[10 marks available — 1 mark for correct gradient of tangent at P, 1 mark for correct gradient of normal at P, 1 mark for equation of normal at P, 1 mark for finding where normal intersect x-axis, 1 mark for correct A_2, 1 mark for correct method for finding y in terms of x, 1 mark for correct equation for y in terms of x, 1 mark for attempting to integrate for A_1, 1 mark for correct A_1, 1 mark for correct total area]

Formulas

These are the formulas you'll be given in the exam, but make sure you know exactly **when you need them** and **how to use them**.

Trigonometric Identities

$$\sin (A \pm B) \equiv \sin A \cos B \pm \cos A \sin B$$

$$\cos (A \pm B) \equiv \cos A \cos B \mp \sin A \sin B$$

$$\tan (A \pm B) \equiv \frac{\tan A \pm \tan B}{1 \mp \tan A \tan B} \quad (A \pm B \neq (k + \tfrac{1}{2})\pi)$$

$$\sin A + \sin B = 2 \sin \frac{A+B}{2} \cos \frac{A-B}{2}$$

$$\sin A - \sin B = 2 \cos \frac{A+B}{2} \sin \frac{A-B}{2}$$

$$\cos A + \cos B = 2 \cos \frac{A+B}{2} \cos \frac{A-B}{2}$$

$$\cos A - \cos B = -2 \sin \frac{A+B}{2} \sin \frac{A-B}{2}$$

Small Angle Approximations

$$\sin \theta \approx \theta \qquad \cos \theta \approx 1 - \tfrac{1}{2}\theta^2 \qquad \tan \theta \approx \theta \qquad \text{where } \theta \text{ is measured in radians}$$

Exponentials and Logarithms

$$\log_a x = \frac{\log_b x}{\log_b a}$$

$$e^{x \ln a} = a^x$$

Mensuration

Surface area of sphere $= 4\pi r^2$

Area of curved surface of cone $= \pi r \times$ slant height

Binomial Series

$$(a + b)^n = a^n + \binom{n}{1}a^{n-1}b + \binom{n}{2}a^{n-2}b^2 + \dots + \binom{n}{r}a^{n-r}b^r + \dots + b^n \quad (n \in \mathbb{N})$$

$$\text{where } \binom{n}{r} = {}^nC_r = \frac{n!}{r!(n-r)!}$$

$$(1 + x)^n = 1 + nx + \frac{n(n-1)}{2!}x^2 + \dots + \frac{n(n-1)\dots(n-r+1)}{r!}x^r + \dots \quad (|x| < 1, n \in \mathbb{R})$$

Arithmetic Series

$$S_n = \frac{1}{2}n(a + l) = \frac{1}{2}n[2a + (n-1)d]$$

Geometric Series

$$S_n = \frac{a(1 - r^n)}{1 - r}$$

$$S_\infty = \frac{a}{1 - r} \text{ for } |r| < 1$$

Differentiation From First Principles

$$f'(x) = \lim_{h \to 0} \frac{f(x + h) - f(x)}{h}$$

Differentiation

f(x)	f'(x)
$\tan kx$	$k\sec^2 kx$
$\sec kx$	$k\sec kx \tan kx$
$\cot kx$	$-k\operatorname{cosec}^2 kx$
$\operatorname{cosec} kx$	$-k\operatorname{cosec} kx \cot kx$

Quotient rule:

for $y = \dfrac{f(x)}{g(x)}$,

$$\frac{dy}{dx} = \frac{f'(x)g(x) - f(x)g'(x)}{(g(x))^2}$$

Integration (+ a constant)

f(x)	$\int f(x)\,dx$
$\sec^2 kx$	$\dfrac{1}{k}\tan kx$
$\tan kx$	$\dfrac{1}{k}\ln|\sec kx|$
$\cot kx$	$\dfrac{1}{k}\ln|\sin kx|$

f(x)	$\int f(x)\,dx$
$\operatorname{cosec} kx$	$-\dfrac{1}{k}\ln|\operatorname{cosec} kx + \cot kx|$, $\dfrac{1}{k}\ln\left|\tan\left(\dfrac{1}{2}kx\right)\right|$
$\sec kx$	$\dfrac{1}{k}\ln|\sec kx + \tan kx|$, $\dfrac{1}{k}\ln\left|\tan\left(\dfrac{1}{2}kx + \dfrac{\pi}{4}\right)\right|$

Integration by parts: $\displaystyle\int u\frac{dv}{dx}\,dx = uv - \int v\frac{du}{dx}\,dx$

Numerical Methods

Trapezium rule: $\displaystyle\int_a^b y\,dx \approx \frac{1}{2}h[y_0 + 2(y_1 + y_2 + \ldots + y_{n-1}) + y_n]$, where $h = \dfrac{b - a}{n}$

The Newton-Raphson formula: $x_{n+1} = x_n - \dfrac{f(x_n)}{f'(x_n)}$

Glossary

Absolute value
Another name for the **modulus**.

Algebraic division
Dividing one algebraic expression by another.

Algebraic fraction
A fraction made up of algebraic expressions.

Arc
The curved edge of a **sector** of a circle.

Arccos
The **inverse** of the cosine **function**, also written as arccosine or $\cos^{-1}$.

Arcsin
The **inverse** of the sine **function**, also written as arcsine or $\sin^{-1}$.

Arctan
The **inverse** of the tangent **function**, also written as arctangent or $\tan^{-1}$.

Arithmetic sequence/series
A **sequence** or **series** where successive terms have a common difference.

Binomial coefficient
The coefficients of terms of a **binomial expansion** $(1 + x)^r$. The coefficient of x^r is $\dfrac{n!}{r!(n-r)!}$.

Binomial expansion
A method of expanding **functions** of the form $(q + px)^n$. Can be used to give a finite expansion or to find an approximation of a value.

Cartesian equation
An equation relating the perpendicular axes x and y in 2D (or x, y and z in 3D). Cartesian coordinates are given in the form (x, y) in 2D (or (x, y, z) in 3D).

Chain rule
A method for **differentiating** a **function** of a function.

Collinear points
Three or more points are collinear if they all lie on the same straight line.

Component
The effect of a **vector** in a given direction.

Composite function
A combination of two or more **functions** acting on a value or set of values.

Concave curve
A curve with a negative **second derivative** — i.e. $f''(x) \leq 0$ for all x.

Constant of integration
A constant term coming from an **indefinite integration** representing any number.

Convergence
A **sequence** converges if the terms get closer and closer to a single value.

Convergent sequence/series
A **sequence/series** that tends towards a **limit**.

Convex curve
A curve with a positive **second derivative** — i.e. $f''(x) \geq 0$ for all x.

Cosec
The reciprocal of the sine **function**, sometimes written as cosecant.

Cot
The reciprocal of the tangent **function**, sometimes written as cotangent.

Definite integral
An **integral** that is evaluated over an interval given by two **limits**, representing the area under the curve between those limits.

Degree
The highest power of x in a **polynomial**.

Derivative
The result after **differentiating** a **function**.

Differential equation
An equation connecting variables with their rates of change.

Differentiation
A method for finding the rate of change of a **function** with respect to a variable — the opposite of **integration**.

Divergence
A sequence diverges if the terms get further and further apart.

Divergent sequence/series
A **sequence/series** that does not have a **limit**.

Divisor
The number or expression that you're dividing by in a division.

Domain
The set of values that can be input into a **mapping** or **function**. Usually given as the set of values that x can take.

e
An **irrational number** for which the gradient of $y = e^x$ is equal to e^x.

Equating coefficients
Making the coefficients of equivalent terms on each side of an **identity** equal in order to calculate the value of unknowns in the identity.

Exponential function
A **function** of the form $y = a^x$. $y = e^x$ is known as 'the' exponential function.

Function
A type of **mapping** which maps every number in the **domain** to only one number in the **range**.

Geometric sequence/series
A **sequence** or **series** in which you multiply by a **common ratio** to get from one term to the next.

i unit vector
The standard horizontal **unit vector** (i.e. along the x-axis).

Identity
An equation that is true for all values of a variable, usually denoted by the '$\equiv$' sign.

Implicit differentiation
A method of differentiating an **implicit relation**.

Implicit relation
An equation in x and y written in the form $f(x, y) = g(x, y)$, instead of $y = f(x)$.

Indefinite integral
An **integral** which contains a **constant of integration** that comes from integrating without **limits**.

Integer
A whole number, including 0 and negative numbers. The set of integers has the notation $\mathbb{Z}$.

Integral
The result you get when you **integrate** something.

Integration
Process for finding the equation of a **function**, given its **derivative** — the opposite of **differentiation**.

Integration by parts
A method for **integrating** a product of two **functions**. The reverse process of the **product rule**.

Integration by substitution
A method for **integrating** a **function** of a function. The reverse process of the **chain rule**.

Inverse function
An inverse **function**, e.g. $f^{-1}(x)$, reverses the effect of the function $f(x)$.

Irrational number
A number that can't be expressed as the **quotient** (division) of two **integers**. Examples include surds and π.

Iteration
A numerical method for solving equations that allows you to find the approximate value of a **root** by repeatedly using an iteration formula.

Iteration sequence
The list of results $x_1, x_2...$ etc. found with an iteration formula.

j unit vector
The standard vertical **unit vector** (i.e. along the y-axis).

k unit vector
The standard **unit vector** used in 3D to represent movement along the z-axis.

Limit (sequences and series)
The value that the individual terms in a **sequence**, or the sum of the terms in a **series**, tends towards.

Limits (integration)
The numbers between which you integrate to find a **definite integral**.

Logarithm
The logarithm to the base a of a number x (written $\log_a x$) is the power to which a must be raised to give that number.

Lower bound
The lowest value a number could take and still be rounded up to the correct answer.

Magnitude
The size of a **vector**.

Many-to-one function
A **function** where some values in the **range** correspond to more than one value in the **domain**.

Mapping
An operation that takes one number and transforms it into another.

Model
A mathematical approximation of a real-life situation, in which certain assumptions are made about the situation.

Modulus
The modulus of a number is its positive numerical value. The modulus of a **function**, $f(x)$, makes every value of $f(x)$ positive by removing any minus signs. The modulus of a **vector** is the same as its **magnitude**.

Natural logarithm
The **inverse function** of e^x, written as $\ln x$ or $\log_e x$.

Natural number
A positive integer, not including 0. The set of natural numbers has the notation $\mathbb{N}$.

$^n C_r$
The **binomial coefficient** of x^r in the **binomial expansion** of $(1 + x)^n$. Also written $\binom{n}{r}$.

Newton-Raphson Method
An **iterative** method for finding a root of an equation, using the formula:
$$x_{n+1} = x_n - \frac{f(x_n)}{f'(x_n)}$$

One-to-one function
A **function** where each value in the **range** corresponds to one and only one value in the **domain**.

Parameter
The variable linking a set of **parametric equations** (usually t or θ).

Parametric equations
A set of equations defining x and y in terms of another variable, called the **parameter**.

Partial fractions
A way of writing an **algebraic fraction** with several linear factors in its denominator as a sum of fractions with linear denominators.

Particular solution
A solution to a **differential equation** where known values have been used to find the constant term.

Percentage error
The difference between a value and its approximation, as a percentage of the real value.

Point of inflection
A **stationary point** on a graph where the **gradient** doesn't change sign on either side of the point.

Polynomial
An algebraic expression made up of the sum of constant terms and variables raised to positive **integer** powers.

Product rule
A method for **differentiating** a product of two **functions**.

Progression
Another word for **sequence**.

Proof
Using mathematical arguments to show that a statement is true or false.

Proof by contradiction
Assuming that a statement is false, then showing that this assumption is impossible, to prove that the statement is true.

Q

Quotient
The result when you divide one thing by another, not including the **remainder**.

Quotient rule
A method of **differentiating** one **function** divided by another.

R

Radian
A unit of measurement for angles. 1 radian is the angle in a **sector** of a circle with radius r that has an **arc** of length r.

Range
The set of values output by a **mapping** or **function**. Usually given as a set of values that y or $f(x)$ can take.

Rational expression
A **function** that can be written as a fraction where the numerator and denominator are both **polynomials**.

Rational number
A number that can be written as the **quotient** (division) of two **integers**, where the denominator is non-zero. The set of rational numbers has the notation $\mathbb{Q}$.

Real number
Any positive or negative number (or 0) including all **rational** and **irrational** **numbers**, e.g. fractions, decimals, integers and surds. The set of real numbers has the notation $\mathbb{R}$.

Remainder (algebraic division)
The expression left over following an **algebraic division** that has a **degree** lower than the **divisor**.

Resultant vector
The single **vector** which has the same effect as two or more vectors added together.

Root
A value of x at which a **function** is equal to 0.

S

Sec
The reciprocal of the cosine **function**, sometimes written as secant.

Second order derivative
The result of **differentiating** a **function** twice.

Sector
A section of a circle formed by two radii and part of the circumference.

Separating variables
A method for solving **differential equations** by first rewriting in the form $\frac{1}{g(y)}\,dy = f(x)\,dx$ in order to **integrate**.

Sequence
An ordered list of numbers (referred to as terms) that follow a set pattern. E.g. 2, 6, 10, ... or –4, 1, –4, 1, ...

Series
An ordered list of numbers, just like a **sequence**, but where the terms are being added together (to find a sum).

Sigma notation
Used for the sum of **series**. E.g. $\sum_{n=1}^{15}(2n+3)$ is the sum of the first 15 terms of the series with n^{th} term $2n+3$.

Small angle approximations
Functions that approximate $\sin x$, $\cos x$ and $\tan x$ for small values of x.

Stationary point
A point on a curve where the gradient is 0.

Sum to infinity
The sum to infinity of a **series** is the value that the sum tends towards as more and more terms are added. Also known as the **limit** of a series.

T

Trapezium rule
A way of estimating the area under a curve by dividing it up into trapezium-shaped strips.

Turning point
A **stationary point** that is a (local) maximum or minimum point of a curve.

U

Unit vector
A **vector** of **magnitude** one unit.

Upper bound
The upper limit of the values that a number could take and still be rounded down to the correct answer.

V

Vector
A quantity which has both a **magnitude** and a direction.

Index

N

natural logarithms
  differentiation 161, 162
  integration 236
Newton-Raphson method 265, 266

P

parametric equations 98-104
  differentiation 185-187
  integration 226, 227
partial fractions 41-45
  and integration 239, 240
  and the binomial expansion
      146, 147
points of inflection 151-154
product rule 170-172
  proof 170
proof 1, 2
  by contradiction 1, 2

Q

quotient rule 174-176
  proof 174

R

R addition formulas 87-90
radians 50, 51
range 13-29
recurrence relations 110-112

S

sectors 50-53
sequences 108-114, 120,
      121, 125, 129, 130
  arithmetic sequences 113, 114
  convergent sequences 125
  geometric sequences 120, 121
  increasing and decreasing
      sequences 109
  modelling problems 129, 130
  n^{th} term 108, 113
  periodic sequences 109
  recurrence relations 110-112

series 115-119, 123-130
  arithmetic series 115-119
  convergent series 126-128
  geometric series 123, 124
  modelling problems 129, 130
sigma notation 117, 124
sketching iterations 262, 263
small angle approximations 55, 56
staircase diagrams 263

T

transformations of graphs 35-38
  combinations of transformations
      36-38
trapezium rule 269-272
trigonometry 50-93
  addition formulas 74-79
  arcs 50-53
  arcsin, arccos and arctan 57-60
  cosec, sec and cot 61-73
  differentiation 165-167, 178-180
  double angle formulas 81-84
  half angle formulas 85
  identities 69-85
  integration
      206-210, 220-222, 232, 233
  modelling 92, 93
  R addition formulas 87-90
  radians 50, 51
  sectors 50-53
  small angle approximations 55, 56

U

upper bounds 254, 255

V

validity (of binomial expansions)
      135, 137, 138
vectors 277-282
  angle between two vectors 282
  distance between two points
      281, 282
  magnitude 281

MEPMT61